The American Institute of Physics (AIP) is a 501(c)(3) not-for-profit corporation, working to *advance, promote, and serve the physical sciences for the benefit of humanity.* As a federation of physical science societies, AIP offers programs, products, and services that

• advance and distribute the knowledge of the physical sciences and its applications;
• enhance and cultivate the physical sciences disciplines;
• enable and foster collaborative efforts among stakeholders in the physical sciences; and
• promote the physical sciences to the public, leaders, government officials, agencies, and the media.

AIP Member Societies cover a broad range of fields in the physical sciences and collectively represent more than 120,000 scientists, engineers, educators, and students in the global physical sciences community.

AIP offers authoritative information, services, and expertise in physics education and student programs, science communication, government relations, career services for science and engineering professionals, statistical research in physics employment and education, industrial outreach, and the history of physics and allied fields. AIP also publishes the flagship magazine *Physics Today* and is home to the Society of Physics Students and the Niels Bohr Library and Archives. AIP owns AIP Publishing LLC, a scholarly publisher in the physical and related sciences.

www.aip.org

Contact Information

Paolo Sian
Product Coordinator, GradSchoolShopper
info@gradschoolshopper.com
301-209-3026

Brad R. Conrad, PhD
Director, Society of Physics Students and Sigma Pi Sigma
sps@aip.org
301-209-3007

Kerry Kidwell-Slak
Associate Director, Education Programs
kkidwell@aip.org

David Reinbold
Manager, Marketing and Communication
dreinbold@aip.org

AIP Member Societies

Acoustical Society of America • American Association of Physicists in Medicine

American Association of Physics Teachers • American Astronomical Society American

Crystallographic Association • American Meteorological Society

American Physical Society • AVS: Science & Technology of Materials, Interfaces, and Processing

The Optical Society • The Society of Rheology

2019

Graduate Programs in Physics, Astronomy, and Related Fields

American Institute of Physics

Copyright 2018 by American Institute of Physics
One Physics Ellipse
College Park, MD 20740-3843
Tel. (301) 209-3026
Email: info@gradschoolshopper.com
www.aip.org

To request additional free copies of this book, contact info@gradschoolshopper.com. Have a question or concern about
this book? Let us know how we're doing. Contact us at 301-209-3026 or info@gradschoolshopper.com.

Cover Image: Cassini's orbit insertion around Saturn, Cassini | NASA

International Standards Book Number: 978-0-7354-1686-4
International Standards Serial Number: 2638-4078

Printed in the United States of America

CONTENTS

Part I
United States: Geographic Listing of Graduate Programs

Part II
International: Geographic Listing of Graduate Programs

Introduction

2019 GradSchoolShopper: Graduate Programs in Physics, Astronomy, and Related Fields is designed to provide easily accessible, comprehensive information on graduate programs in physics, astronomy, and the physical sciences. Students planning on graduate study, faculty advisors, and others interested in comparative information on graduate programs will find the information contained in this book valuable.

The content and format of this edition have remained largely the same as the previous edition but also include a few new fields. The information in this book is displayed, as much as possible, in tabular format to make it easier to compare data points and to make the department profiles more robust. The data presented here, dynamic search features, and additional department information can be accessed and downloaded online at www.GradSchoolShopper.com.

The information presented is collected directly from departments, giving them control over their information. As a result, the book and accompanying website are the most comprehensive and up-to-date source of information about graduate programs in physics, astronomy, and related fields.

Sources of Funding
It should be noted that the same approach was used to fund the preparation and distribution of this edition as for the previous edition. Listed graduate departments paid a listing charge to cover the cost of preparing the book, maintaining the website, and distributing information about the resource widely, including copies of this guide to all listed departments and to each chapter of the Society of Physics Students (SPS). The majority of all physics and astronomy doctoral programs in the United States and many Master's programs are included.

Organization of the Book
Each entry in the book describes the graduate program offered by an academic department at an institution of higher learning. Entries are organized alphabetically by state or province and, within each state or province, alphabetically by institution name.

Finding Departments
There are two mechanisms by which a user can locate the listing of a department at a particular institution. First, if the country, state, or province in which the institution is located is known, the entry can be found relatively quickly from Appendix I. Appendix II provides an alphabetical listing of institutions and departments.

Online
The information presented here is freely available at www.GradSchoolShopper.com and can be used to locate particular departments within various parameters. A search based on criteria such as the availability of a Master's degree, specific research specialties, and research budgets will produce a list of relevant departments and point to their data. The departmental profiles can then be viewed online or in the book.

Please share this directory with others by displaying copies in multiple locations:
• student lounges
• department offices
• student advisor offices
• SPS chapters
• libraries

Contact Paolo Sian at psian@aip.org or 301-209-3026 for additional free copies.

A Guide to Choosing the *Right* Grad Program

by Brad R. Conrad, Director of SPS and Sigma Pi Sigma

Choosing the right graduate school and program can be daunting, but it is also a wonderful opportunity for taking a step along your career pathway. While there are many strategies, the key to determining the right graduate program for *you* is to understand where you are likely to succeed, your personal preferences for community, and where each program can take you. I stressed the word *you* because your preferences really matter. The overall goal is not to get a degree from a specific institution or even to get a job in a specific field, but to achieve your career and life goals. There are many pathways to your specific goal, and often many programs—sometimes wildly different programs—can help you achieve your goals.

So, before you begin, realize that you are choosing between great opportunities, not good or bad options. The more honest you are with yourself, the easier it'll be to choose the program that's right for you.

When developing your list of schools, consider:

1 THE PHYSICAL LOCATION
- City vs. Suburban vs. Rural
- Large vs. Small School
- Warmer vs. Colder Climate
- Coastal vs. Midwestern vs. Mountain
- Are there other centers of science nearby?

2 FINANCIALS ARE IMPORTANT: WHAT IS YOUR MOST LIKELY LIVING SITUATION?
- Stipend amount vs. cost of living in that city
  > Is there a stipend?
  > Is it a research, teaching, or fellowship position?
  > Do you need to pay tuition or semester fees?
- Does the program provide health care?
- Does the stipend allow you to live comfortably?

3 LIFE OUTSIDE THE LAB
- House vs. shared apartment vs. campus housing
- Driving vs. biking vs. walking to work
- What is there to do in the area besides school work?
- What do current students do for fun?
- Do students live together? Do they have a social life?
- How many first-year graduate students will be there?
- Are there graduate student organizations you can be a part of?

42

4 CONSIDER DEPARTMENT CULTURE

- Large, diverse incoming class vs. small, personal
- Collaborative or competitive student culture
- Are interdepartmental projects normal?
- Can you work outside the university with national labs and researchers?
- Who teaches the courses?
- Who teaches the labs?
- Do you need to take any labs as a graduate student?
- Is there a foreign language requirement?
- Are there closely related departments: e.g., astrophysics, applied physics, chemical physics, etc.?
- Is there a graduate student group?
- Are graduate students unionized?
- How inclusive and diverse is the department?

5 CONSIDER POTENTIAL ADVISERS

- How many people are there with whom you could be excited to work?
- Do potential advisers have compatible work styles?
- Are there multiple potential advisers you'd be excited to work with?
- Does your potential adviser have research funding?
- Would you need to be a teaching assistant in your later years?
- How is funding within each department?
- What percentage of students who start finish the program?

6 QUESTIONS TO ASK CURRENT STUDENTS

- Are you happy?
- What's it like being a student here?
- Would you come here again if you could do it over?
- What's the worst part of being a student here?
- What's the best part of being a student here?
- What did they not tell you about in orientation?
- Is the stipend enough?
- Are students involved in community events?
- Do you like the department? Is it cohesive and supportive?

This list of questions is far from exhaustive. It's meant to get you thinking about the things that are important to you in graduate school.

While courses and the broader department matter most for your first two years, your adviser and research group matter most for the remaining years in graduate school. So, don't skip out on researching both aspects: classes and department culture versus individual advisers and research groups. Use this book and the online companion, GradSchoolShopper.com, to help you develop a list of 8-12 places to apply.

One item which is often overlooked is that your social and emotional well-being is just as important as your academic life. If you choose the perfect school for your career but you aren't happy there, it can be very difficult to succeed. Correspondingly, if you are at a school that matches your style but you aren't happy with your academic options, this can be an issue as well. Many students do not consider life issues and personal preferences when choosing their graduate programs, and this can alter their chances of success.

Above all else, realize that there is most likely not just one school that is the perfect school but many schools that can work for you. So do your grad school research well and ask the hard questions. If you do, you'll likely end up in the place best for you. Good luck!

Adapted from The SPS Observer Winter 2018

Thinking About Graduate School

A how-to guide to choosing good options

As you begin the process of selecting a graduate school, it is important to keep one piece of information in mind: there are most likely **many** schools you will succeed in. The experience you could have depends on the discipline, environment, classes, preparation, and your graduate advisor. The absolute best thing you can do for yourself is to research your options. GradSchoolShopper can help you get many of the facts you need to make a well-informed decision.

Things to keep in mind during the grad school selection process

- **Do your homework**: Critically consider what you are looking for in a graduate program. Keep track of what schools offer and how well these offerings match your needs.
- **Masters versus PhD:** There is a huge difference between the two in terms of applications and disciplines. Many programs only admit a limited number of master's students. Some programs only offer master's programs. Investigate options on a program by program basis.
- **Make sure it's a good fit:** Don't just apply to a program because it is rated well. Seek out and apply to the programs that are the best fit for you. Programs want students who will succeed. Don't blindly apply to programs or send generic applications.
- **Physics and Astronomy stipend/salary:** Often, PhD programs offer stipends or salaries to students who are enrolled full time. Amounts do vary so evaluate on a location by location basis.
- **PhD advisors are extremely important:** Choosing the right graduate advisor, or set of possible advisors, is one of the most important decisions you can make. A PhD advisor sets the tone, goals, and style of your graduate education. Be sure to talk to a potential advisor's current students individually about their experiences.
- **Research areas:** A program's research areas change over the years and so does availability in professor's labs. It is important to select a school where there are several people you'd want to work with.
- **Don't just apply to one school:** It's common to apply to several programs if you are serious about attending.
- **Consider a variety of research areas:** Consider other fields, research areas, and advisors. Many students end up in labs that are vastly different than the one they were initially aiming for. Sometimes your dream advisor is full that year, or they retire or move. Having several options is key to setting yourself up for success.
- **Don't plan on part-time jobs or side hustles:** Graduate school will be your full-time job and you often have to formally agree that you won't get another or part time job. Plan your time and finances accordingly.
- **Ask about tuition:** For many programs, you don't have to pay for tuition in addition to being paid for your work.
- **Ask grad students about their experiences:** The best advice comes from people who are at your potential school or have recently searched.
- **Visit your top choices:** Schedule a visit with your top graduate program choices. Meet the graduate program advisor (or appropriate person) and potential research advisors.

- **University environment:** Diversity and inclusion initiatives can vary between schools and programs. Investigate differences on a program-by-program basis.

How the GSS book and website can also help you:

- **Unbiased**: GradSchoolShopper provides unbiased, factual information so you can directly compare programs side-by-side. You won't find rankings, but you will find all the information necessary for you to find schools that match your goals.
- **FREE for students!** Create a free user account on the website GradSchoolShopper.com or request a free copy of this book.
- **Browse by geographic location:** Use the table of contents or the appendix in the back of the book to find schools by geographic region
- **Comprehensive department information:** Each program lists research areas, program funding, equipment, number of graduate students, first year student numbers, faculty members, stipend and tuition information, location, contact information, and general university info.
- **Direct comparison data**: On GradSchoolShopper.com, you can create an account, select and save your school list, and then compare your options.
- **Download your data**: After you have saved & you're ready to compare your schools, you can download a subset of information in an Excel sheet to give you an organized look at what each school offers. Admission deadlines, GRE requirements, # of full-time faculty, # of full-time grad students, acceptance rates, and average stipend per academic year are all available.
- **In-depth faculty data:** Each department provides a full list of the full-time department faculty. You can look at their research fields, where and when they graduated, and their areas of expertise. When coupled with equipment, you can get a sense of a department's strengths.
- **Understand incoming degree requirements:** Review this section to see what coursework is recommended before arriving.
- **Special equipment, facilities, or programs:** In this section, students can learn about special programs and equipment that make a department stand out.
- **Advanced search option:** On the GradSchoolShopper.com website you can do an advanced search to filter for degree specialty, degree type, and/or location.
- **Department size and acceptance rate:** On the website you can also sort by acceptance rates. Additionally, you can examine the number of students who have applied, been admitted, and are enrolled.
- **Culture & Diversity:** Also on the web prospective students can learn about the department culture & diversity. What is the environment like for students? Is there a weekly social time? What kind of graduate student groups are there? You can also quickly look up information on student and faculty demographics.
- **"Why choose us?":** This is where departments can highlight what they feel sets them apart from other institutions. Many programs focus on their department culture and some include social media networks.

Additional resource

AIP Statistical Research Center: The AIP Statistical Research Center (SRC) collects information about graduate students, their careers, and departments. Data can be used to understand national trends and averages. Details can be found at www.aip.org/statistics.

Grad School Application Timeline

As with any goal, the key to securing an acceptance offer into a graduate program that is a good fit for you is planning. Consider this timeline as you plan.

Freshman - Sophomore year

• Engage in research

Many graduate admissions committees will look for applicants to have undergraduate research experience. Explore the website at your school to find professors who are doing work that you find interesting and reach out to them to see if they have availability in their labs. Seek opportunities for REUs, independent study, sustained research, and research credits as possible avenues to gain this experience. Prolonged research with one professor allows for that person to write you a stronger letter of recommendation. Research experiences outside your home institution can assist you in exploring new geographic areas and academic settings.

• Explore a wide variety of career interests

The most common outcome for an undergraduate with an undergraduate degree in physics is to immediately enter the workforce. Speak with alumni and professors about where graduates from your department have gone. Job shadow with people that you meet who have positions you find interesting. Attend career fairs and department talks to speak with potential employers and industrial physicists. Take on an internship one summer rather than research to see what that experience is like. Don't be afraid to explore options you've not seriously considered. Now is the time to investigate as many options as possible.

Junior year
Spring

• Research graduate programs

Identify programs that you find interesting. The goal is to make a list of potential programs to *consider* applying to. You should only apply to programs you actually want to attend. Use the road map on the previous pages to think about various factors that will influence your decision. It's perfectly fine if you are unsure about what subfield within physics you want; it might be helpful to pick a top three and base decisions on that. It's important to consider program size, geography, program culture, and even proximity to research/cultural centers. Within physics, most of programs suggest/require the same courses but if you are looking at specialty fields (such as medical physics or engineering) prerequisites can vary.

• Prepare for the GRE and Physics subject test

While it might not be the most important element of your application, many physics and astronomy departments use the GRE as a criterion for admittance. Consider taking these tests this Spring, even if you've not had all the material that will be on the exam. Studying for the exams can improve how you do! The exam does require a fee.

• Plan your finances

Most PhD programs in physics and astronomy in the US have financial aid options that cover most, if not all, tuition costs. Additionally, the majority (~98%) of recent self-reported Bachelors enrolled in PhD programs one year after degree for the years 2013-2014 are financially supported by their program. A smaller percentage, but more than half, of self-reported Bachelors enrolled in Masters programs one year after degree for the years 2013-2014 are financially supported by their program. Specific program information for financial aid, teaching assistantships, and research assistant positions on www.GradSchoolShopper.com . The statistics reported here can be looked up: www.aip.org/statistics/reports/physics-bachelorsone-year-after-degree.

Additionally, applications are usually not free. Application fees can be in excess of $100 at some locations. Be sure to budget accordingly, as it is common to submit applications to 6 or even 10 programs.

Summer

• Craft your personal statement

Your personal statement is one of the most important parts of your application. A personal statement should be tailored to the prompt asked by the institution. Often, specific questions are posed but in general, you will be asked to explain why you want to attend that specific institution. Take the time to personalize it and receive critical feedback from those you trust: professors, advisors, and trusted friends.

• Apply to take the Subject GRE and General GRE if you haven't done so already

Identify the test location you prefer and schedule a testing day and time. Don't forget to prepare for the exam. The exam does require a fee.

Senior year

September

• Work on your personal statement

Continue to work on your personal statements. Each program should have a separate, tailored statement for their prompt. Be sure to include any information specific to that institution.

• Review the application requirements for each school

Create a spreadsheet to track deadlines, requirements (e.g., transcripts, GREs, recommendations, etc), and other information about potential applications.

• Ask for recommendations

Most programs require written recommendations, either through the physical mail or online. Ask professors, research advisers, and/or employers for their recommendation letters. This is best done in person, so that questions can be asked. Give potential recommenders a copy of your C.V. so they can speak to everything you have done. Provide them with ample time to write and submit their recommendation.

October

• Take the Subject GRE and General GRE

This is the ideal time to take your exams, if you didn't do so already or if you wish to improve your score. Remember, October is usually the last date the Subject GRE is offered before grad school applications are due.

• Prepare to pay the application fees

Applying to each program can cost in excess of $100 at some locations, so plan accordingly. Many schools offer application fee waivers for students with financial need. Be sure to ask about this option.

November

• Send professors/employers a friendly reminder about recommendation letters

It is your responsibility to make sure letters are submitted on your behalf. It is best to confirm with letter writers that letters and recommendations are completed on time.

• Get your transcripts

Make sure they are sent directly to the departments you're applying to. It is often a good idea to order an extra copy for yourself.

• Update your C.V.
Consult the SPS Career Toolbox https://www.spsnational.org/sites/all/careerstoolbox/ for a detailed guide on how to craft your C.V. and resume.

December
• Finalize your application packets
Use your tracking spreadsheet to keep track of application components and make sure deadlines are met.

• Send your applications
Many graduate programs process applications as they come, which means that the sooner you send yours in, the sooner it's processed.

January
• Verify receipt of application
After submitting, if you haven't received an electronic confirmation, contact the program administrator to verify that your application and all letters of recommendation were received.

• Prepare for your interviews
Some departments have department visits or pre-selection interviews. Start preparing for these by reading about the department's offered programs, professors, and research specialties on www.GradSchoolShopper.com. Interview tips and advice can be found at www.spsnational.org/sites/all/careerstoolbox/ .

• Focus on financial aid or options for financing
If you are a U.S. citizen, you're eligible for Free Application for Federal Student Aid (FAFSA) and should fill out the forms as early as possible (federalstudentaid.ed.gov/). There are also many scholarships and fellowships you may be eligible for, even as an international student.

February-March
• Learn about graduate school life
Speak with current graduate students who can share their experiences and offer free advice on what it takes to succeed. Sigma Pi Sigma alumni can be a great resource. Take advantage of these opportunities!

April
• Go over the results
Statistically, there will be some rejection notices, but celebrate acceptances and, provided you have a choice, take the time to review your options and weigh the pros & cons of each. If you have not received any acceptance letters, don't be discouraged: you can always try again in the future. Once you've accepted a program, notify other institutions of your decision.

• Thank your professors/employers
Update anyone who helped you along the way and send thank you notes to the people who took the time to write recommendation letters for you.

PART I

UNITED STATES

Geographic Listing of Graduate Programs

ALABAMA AGRICULTURAL & MECHANICAL UNIVERSITY

DEPARTMENT OF PHYSICS, CHEMISTRY & MATHEMATICS

Normal, Alabama 35762
http://www.physics.aamu.edu

General University Information
President: Dr. Andrew Hugine, Jr.
Dean of Graduate School: Dr. Derrek Dunn, Dean
University website: http://www.aamu.edu/physics
School Type: Public
Setting: Urban
Total Faculty: 348
Total Graduate Faculty: 149
Total number of Students: 5,814
Total number of Graduate Students: 874

Department Information
Department Chairman: Prof. Dr. M. D. Aggarwal, Chair
Department Contact: Dr. M. D. Aggarwal, Professor,
  Chairman of Physics, Chemistry & Mathematics
Total full-time faculty: 12
Total number of full-time equivalent positions: 10
Full-Time Graduate Students: 21
Female Full-Time Graduate Students: 2
First-Year Graduate Students: 8
Female First-Year Students: 3
Total Post Doctorates: 2

Department Address
4900 North Meridian Street
Normal, AL 35762
Phone: (256) 372-8132
E-mail: mohan.aggarwal@aamu.edu
Website: http://www.physics.aamu.edu

ADMISSIONS

Admission Contact Information
Address admission inquiries to: Dean, School of Graduate Studies, Alabama A&M University, P. O. Box 998, Normal, AL 35762
Phone: (256) 372-5266
E-mail: gradschool@aamu.edu
Admissions website: http://www.aamu.edu/academics/gradstudies/Pages/default.aspx

Application deadlines
Fall admission:
U.S. students: July 15   *Int'l. students*: July 15
Spring admission:
U.S. students: November 1   *Int'l. students*: November 1

Application fee
U.S. students: $45   *Int'l. students*: $45

Admissions information
For Fall of 2017:
  Number of applicants: 8
  Number admitted: 5
  Number enrolled: 4

Admission requirements
Bachelor's degree requirements: Bachelor's degree in Physical Science/Electrical Engineering Materials Science/Optics is required.

Minimum undergraduate GPA: 3.0

GRE requirements
The GRE is required.
  Quantitative score: 140
  Verbal score: 146
No analytical writing or Mean GRE score required.

Subjective GRE requirements
The Subjective GRE is not required.
No Physics GRE Exam.

TOEFL requirements
The TOEFL exam is required for students from non-English-speaking countries.
  iBT score: 61

Other admissions information
Undergraduate preparation assumed: Physics: Halliday, Resnick, and Krane, Physics Part I & II; Modern Physics: Beiser, Concepts of Modern Physics; Mechanics: Arya, Introduction to Classical Mechanics; Methods in Mathematical Physics: Boas, Mathematical Methods in the Physical Sciences; Electricity and Magnetism: Lorrain, Corson, and Lorrain, Electric Fields and Waves.

TUITION

Tuition year 2018–19:
Tuition for in-state residents
  Full-time students: $393 per credit
Tuition for out-of-state residents
  Full-time students: $786 per credit
Credit hours per semester to be considered full-time: 9
Deferred tuition plan: No $76.00 for Domestics Student, $816.00 for International Student
Other academic fees: $635.00
Academic term: Semester
Number of first-year students who received full tuition waivers: 3

Teaching Assistants, Research Assistants, and Fellowships
Number of first-year
  Teaching Assistants: 1
  Research Assistants: 8
  Fellowship students: 8
Average stipend per academic year
  Teaching Assistant: $12,000
  Research Assistant: $15,000
  Fellowship student: $18,000

FINANCIAL AID

Application deadlines
Fall admission:
U.S. students: September 1   *Int'l. students*: September 1
Spring admission:
U.S. students: September 1   *Int'l. students*: September 1

Loans

Loans are available for U.S. students.
Loans are not available for international students.
GAPSFAS application required: Yes
FAFSA application required: No

For further information

Address financial aid inquiries to: Dean, School of Graduate Studies, Alabama A&M University, Normal, AL 35762.
Phone: (256) 372-5266
E-mail: financialaid@aamu.edu
Financial aid website: http://www.aamu.edu/admissions/fincialaid/pages/default.aspx

HOUSING

Availability of on-campus housing

Single students: Yes
Married students: Yes

For further information

Address housing inquiries to: Residential Life & Housing Office, P. O. Box 630, Alabama A&M University, Normal, AL 35762.
Phone: (256) 372-5797
E-mail: housing@aamu.edu
Housing aid website: http://www.aamu.edu/campuslife/living-on-campus/residentiallife/pages/default.aspx

Table A—Faculty, Enrollments, and Degrees Granted

Research Specialty	2017–18 Faculty	Enrollment Fall 2018 Master's	Enrollment Fall 2018 Doctorate	Number of Degrees Granted 2017–18 (2013–18) Master's	Number of Degrees Granted 2017–18 (2013–18) Terminal Master's	Number of Degrees Granted 2017–18 (2013–18) Doctorate
Materials Science, Metallurgy	5	3	8	2	–	2
Optics	3	5	4	2	–	1
Other	2	–	1	–	–	–
Total	10	8	13	4(10)	–	3(9)
Full-time Grad. Stud.	–	5	10	–	–	–
First-year Grad. Stud.	–	3	2	–	–	–

GRADUATE DEGREE REQUIREMENTS

Master's: For admission to the program, applicants must: 1. Have a bachelor's degree from a regionally accredited university with a major in physics, chemistry, physical science, astronomy or engineering; 2. Have an overall GPA of 3.00 (based on a 4.00 system); 3. Submit a minimum score of 146 on the verbal and 140 on the quantitative portions of GRE; Students from non-English speaking countries are required to have a minimum score of 61 (internet-based test) on the Test for English as a Foreign Language (TOEFL). Students with bachelor's degrees in optical, materials, or space sciences will be eligible for admission into the graduate program with optics/lasers and materials science and space science concentrations. Students with a degree in an area other than physics may be required to take prerequisite undergraduate physics courses. Thesis Option: The students must complete at least 24 semester hours of course work with a minimum of 12 hours in area of concentration, and write a thesis (6 semester hours credit) on an approved topic under the supervision of a thesis advisor, and satisfactorily defend the finding of the thesis before a committee of faculty appointed by the department and appointed by the Dean of Graduate Studies. Non-Thesis Option: The students must complete at least 30 semester hours

of course work with at least 18 of these being in the area of concentration and pass a comprehensive examination given by the Department.

Doctorate: Admission to the doctoral program requires a Master's degree in physics, chemistry, physical science, astronomy, or engineering. Applicants must have a GPA of 3.05 on a scale of 4.0. A Graduate Record Examination (GRE) score of at least 600 in the quantitative section of the general area is also required (The GRE Advanced in Physics is strongly urged). Students from non-English speaking countries are required to have a minimum score of 61 (internet-based test) on the Test for English as a Foreign Language (TOEFL). Persons seeking the Ph.D. in Physics must complete a total of at least 48 semester hours of credit including 15 semester hours in the area of general physics. In addition to this requirement, students must pass the departmental qualifying examination (A person who has been admitted on the basis of a master's degree may take the qualifying examination after the first semester in the program). Students also must pass the candidacy examination. The departmental qualifying exam must be taken after the completion of 18 credit hours. Candidacy examinations must be passed at least nine months before the expected graduation date (Students are not considered Ph.D. candidates until they pass the departmental candidacy examination). Student also must prepare an acceptable dissertation with a minimum of 12 semester hours. No student is allowed to register for more than six hours of dissertation credits in any given semester. There is no foreign language requirement for the degree. Ph.D. candidates must make an oral presentation on the dissertation and must defend the findings before a committee of examiners as stated earlier. The presentation of the dissertation must be completed at least six weeks before the intended graduation date.

Thesis: Theses may be written in absentia.

SPECIAL EQUIPMENT, FACILITIES, OR PROGRAMS

The Department houses 20 laboratories, a Center for the Irradiation of Materials, Center for Nonlinear Optics and Materials, a Departmental Library, a glass shop, a Learning Resource Center, machine shop, graduate student office to 15 graduate students. Argon laser (6 W, 15 W C.W. and Ring dye laser)

High pressure CO_2 Laser (Continuously tunable)

Nd:YAG Nanosecond Laser (second and third harmonics)

244 nm and 365 nm UV Lasers

Nd:YAG Laser pumped Optical Parametric Oscillator

Keithley 2400 Photovoltaic Solar Cell's Testing Station

Quad Tech 7600 LCR Meter, Czochralski Crystal Pullers with automatic diameter control, Bridgman Growth Furnaces for Organic and Inorganic Crystals, Joel-6200 Scanning Electron Microscope, NEC Pelletron Ion Beam Accelerator (2X2.0 MeV) Leitz Microscope with heating stage up to 1400C, Optical and Metallurgical Microscopes, Automatic C-V Data Acquisition Station, DTA-1700 Differential Thermal Analyzer, GenRad 1620 Capacitance Measuring Assembly, Ferroelectric Materials Characterization set-up, Automatic C-V Data Acquisition Station, Furnaces and Temperature Controllers, X-Band Electron Spin Resonance, Solution Crystal Growth System, X-Ray Diffraction Unit (Norelco), Excimer Laser and a tunable dye laser, Perkin Elmer 5100 Atomic Absorption Spectrometer, Varian-Cary 3E Spectrophotometer, Nd:YAG Laser pumped Optical Parametric Oscillator, 0.5 m Monochromator fitted with a CCD Detector, PDA1 Dye Amplifier (Spectra Physics), Bomem DA8 FT-IR Spectrophotometer, Hamamatsu Streak Camera,PDA1 Dye Amplifier (Spectra Physics), Heterodyne Optical Profilometer.

Table B—Separately Budgeted Research Expenditures by Source of Support

Source of Support	Departmental Research	Physics-related Research Outside Department
Federal government	$3,150,000	
State/local government		
Non-profit organizations	$12,000	
Business and industry		
Other		$150,000
Total	**$3,162,000**	**$150,000**

Table C—Separately Budgeted Research Expenditures by Research Specialty

Research Specialty	No. of Grants	Expenditures ($)
Materials Science, Metallurgy	4	$800,000
Optics	4	$600,000
Other	2	$550,000
Total	**10**	**$1,950,000**

FACULTY

Professor

Aggarwal, M. D., Ph.D., University of Calcutta, 1974. Chairman of Department. *Applied Physics, Materials Science, Metallurgy, Optics*. Crystal growth and characterization.

Edwards, Matthew E., Ph.D., Howard University, 1977. *Applied Physics, Optics*. Materials science/condensed matter, laser optics.

Reddy, B. R., Ph.D., Indian Institute of Technology, Kanpur, 1981. *Applied Physics, Optics*. Laser spectroscopy.

Sharma, A., Ph.D., Columbia University, 1982. *Applied Physics, Optics*. Optics.

Zhang, T. X., Ph.D., Nagoya University, 1995. *Applied Physics, Astrophysics, Materials Science, Metallurgy*. Space science, physics.

Associate Professor

Batra, A. K ., Ph.D., Indian Institute of Technology, Delhi, 1981. *Applied Physics, Materials Science, Metallurgy*. Materials science, physics.

Guggilla, Padmaja, Ph.D., Alabama A&M University, 2007. *Applied Physics, Materials Science, Metallurgy*. Applied physics.

Assistant Professor

Babalola, O. Stephen S., Ph.D., Vanderbilt University, 2010. *Applied Physics, Materials Science, Metallurgy, Other*.

Edwards, Vernessa, Ph.D., Alabama A&M University, 2004. *Applied Physics, Optics*. Applied physics.

Schamschula, M., Ph.D., University of Alabama, Huntsville, 1994. *Applied Physics, Optics*. Optics.

Sirohi, Rajpal S., Ph.D., Indian Institute of Technology, 1970. *Applied Physics*. Optics.

Emeritus

Lal, R. B., Ph.D., Agra University, 1963. Emeritus Professor. *Applied Physics*. Solid-state physics; materials science; crystal growth.

Tan, A., Ph.D., University of Alabama, Huntsville, 1979. Emeritus Professor. *Applied Physics, Theoretical Physics*. Space science.

Research Professor

Curley, Michael, Ph.D., Alabama A&M University, 1997. *Applied Physics, Optics*. Applied physics.

Kukhtarev, N., Ph.D., Institute of Physics, Kiev, Ukraine, 1973. *Applied Physics, Optics*. Optics.

Research Associate Professor

Hathaway, David H., Ph.D., University of Colorado, 1979. Astrophysics.

Kukhtareva, Tanya, Ph.D., Kiev University, Ukraine, 1972. *Applied Physics, Optics*.

Adjunct Professor

Johnson, R. Barry, Ph.D., Southeastern Institute of Technology. *Applied Physics, Optics*. Optical systems.

Koshak, William J., Ph.D., University of Arizona. Atmospheric physics.

Nash-Stevenson, Dr. Shelia, Ph.D., Alabama A&M University, 1993. Applied physics.

Phanord, Diendonne D., Ph.D., University of Illinois, 1988. *Optics*. Mathematical physics.

Ruffin, Dr. Paul, Ph.D., University of Alabama, 1986. Optics, physics.

DEPARTMENTAL RESEARCH SPECIALTIES AND STAFF

Theoretical

Atmosphere, Space Physics, Cosmic Rays. Hathaway, Tan, Zhang.

Materials Science, Metallurgy. Melt single crystal growth of nonlinear optical materials, Czochralski crystal pulling, Bridgman-Stockbarger crystal growth, Ni-based superalloys, solid state devices, Organic and inorganic Nonlinear optical materials, Ion Implantation, microgravity research, solution crystal growth of IR materials Infrared window and dome materials, soil moisture sensors, Bulk growth of piezoelectric materials, scintillator materials. Aggarwal, Babalola, Batra, Matthew Edwards, Guggilla, Lal.

Optics. Curley, Matthew Edwards, Vernessa Edwards, Johnson, Kukhtarev, Kukhtareva, Reddy, Ruffin, Schamschula, Sharma.

Other.

Experimental

Atmosphere, Space Physics, Cosmic Rays. Hathaway, Tan, Zhang.

Materials Science, Metallurgy. Aggarwal, Babalola, Batra, Matthew Edwards, Guggilla, Lal.

Optics. Curley, Matthew Edwards, Vernessa Edwards, Johnson, Kukhtarev, Kukhtareva, Nash-Stevenson, Reddy, Ruffin, Schamschula, Sharma, Sirohi.

View additional information about this department at www.gradschoolshopper.com. Check out the "Why Choose Us?" section, find out more about the department's culture and get links to social media networks.

AUBURN UNIVERSITY

DEPARTMENT OF PHYSICS

Auburn, Alabama 36849

http://www.auburn.edu/academic/cosam/departments/physics/

General University Information
President: Steven Leath
Dean of Graduate School: George Flowers
University website: http://www.auburn.edu/
School Type: Public
Setting: Rural
Total Faculty: 1,555
Total Graduate Faculty: 1,368
Total number of Students: 28,290
Total number of Graduate Students: 4,313

Department Information
Department Chairman: Prof. James D. Hanson, Chair
Department Contact: James D. Hanson, Chair
  Total full-time faculty: 22
  Total number of full-time equivalent positions: 24
  Full-Time Graduate Students: 50
  Female Full-Time Graduate Students: 6
  First-Year Graduate Students: 9
  Total Post Doctorates: 2

Department Address
206 Allison Lab
Auburn, AL 36849
Phone: (334) 844-4264
Fax: (334) 844-4613
E-mail: jdhanson@auburn.edu
Website: http://www.auburn.edu/academic/cosam/departments/physics/

ADMISSIONS

Admission Contact Information
Address admission inquiries to: Dr. Allen L. Landers, Chairman, Physics Graduate Admissions Committee, 206 Allison Lab, Auburn University, AL 36849
Phone: (334) 844-4264
E-mail: landeal@auburn.edu
Admissions website: http://www.auburn.edu/academic/cosam/departments/physics/grad/applying.htm

Application deadlines
Fall admission:
U.S. students: March 15   *Int'l. students*: January 15

Application fee
U.S. students: $60   *Int'l. students*: $70

Admissions information
For Fall of 2017:
  Number of applicants: 58
  Number admitted: 9
  Number enrolled: 12

Admission requirements
Bachelor's degree requirements: Bachelor's degree in Physics or related major is required.
Minimum undergraduate GPA: 3.0

GRE requirements
The GRE is required.

Subjective GRE requirements
The Subjective GRE is not required.

TOEFL requirements
The TOEFL exam is required for students from non-English-speaking countries.
  PBT score: 550
Minimum accepted computer-based exam (CBT) score: 213.

Other admissions information
Additional requirements: A combined total greater than 1,200 is desired.
Undergraduate preparation assumed: Upper division mechanics, electricity and magnetism, quantum mechanics, and thermal physics. Students sometimes take these courses during their first year as graduate students.

TUITION

Tuition year 2017–18:
Tuition for in-state residents
  Full-time students: $535 per credit
Tuition for out-of-state residents
  Full-time students: $1,605 per credit
Students with assistantships pay no tuition.
Credit hours per semester to be considered full-time: 9
Deferred tuition plan: No
Health insurance: Available at the cost of $1,930 per year.
Other academic fees: GTA/GRA enrollment fee $615
Academic term: Semester
Number of first-year students who received full tuition waivers: 12

Teaching Assistants, Research Assistants, and Fellowships
Number of first-year
  Teaching Assistants: 9
Average stipend per academic year
  Teaching Assistant: $23,270
  Research Assistant: $23,270

FINANCIAL AID

Application deadlines
Fall admission:
U.S. students: March 15   *Int'l. students*: January 15

Loans
Loans are not available for U.S. students.
Loans are not available for international students.
GAPSFAS application required: No
FAFSA application required: No

For further information
Address financial aid inquiries to: Chairman, Physics Graduate Admissions Committee.
Phone: (334) 844-4264
E-mail: landeal@auburn.edu
Financial aid website: http://www.auburn.edu/academic/cosam/departments/physics/grad/graduate-application.htm

HOUSING

Availability of on-campus housing
Single students: No
Married students: No

For further information
Address housing inquiries to: Director of Housing, Burton Hall.
  Kim Trupp.
Phone: (334) 844-4580
E-mail: truppki@auburn.edu

Table A—Faculty, Enrollments, and Degrees Granted

Research Specialty	2016–17 Faculty	Enrollment Fall 2016		Number of Degrees Granted 2016–17 (2010–17)		
		Mas-ter's	Doc-torate	Mas-ter's	Terminal Master's	Doc-torate
Atomic, Molecular, & Optical Physics	5	–	2	–	–	2(6)
Condensed Matter Physics	4	–	–	–	–	–(10)
Plasma and Fusion	11	–	1	–	–	1(11)
Solid State Physics	1	–	–	–	–	–(1)
Total	21	–	3	–(40)	–(19)	3(28)
Full-time Grad. Stud.	–	–	49	–	–	–
First-year Grad. Stud.	–	–	12	–	–	–

GRADUATE DEGREE REQUIREMENTS

Master's: Each student must complete 30 hours of course work with a minimum grade average of 3.0/4.0. No specific residency period is stipulated. A thesis option and nonthesis option are available.

Doctorate: Each student must complete 60 hours of course work including dissertation and research hours. Each candidate must maintain a grade point average of 3.0/4.0 or better. Passage of a general doctoral examination is required of all students. A dissertation based on original research must be completed and defended in a final oral examination.

SPECIAL EQUIPMENT, FACILITIES, OR PROGRAMS

Materials characterization facilities including low-energy ion accelerator; surface science laboratory; magnetic fusion laboratory with Compact Toroidal Hybrid device; laboratory plasma devices; dusty plasma laboratory; atomic physics laboratory; High-performance computing capabilities

Table B—Separately Budgeted Research Expenditures by Source of Support

Source of Support	Departmental Research	Physics-related Research Outside Department
Federal government	$3,915,819	
State/local government	$80,807	
Non-profit organizations	$74,533	
Business and industry		
Other		
Total	$4,071,159	

FACULTY

Professor
Dong, Jianjun, Ph.D., Ohio University, 1998. Condensed matter theory; computational physics.
Giordano, Nicholas J., Ph.D., Yale University, 1977. Dean. The physics of nanostructures and mesoscopic systems; musical acoustics and the physics of the piano; computational neuroscience; computational physics.
Hanson, James D., Ph.D., University of Maryland, 1982. Plasma physics.
Landers, Allen, Ph.D., Kansas State University, 1999. Atomic and molecular physics.
Lin, Yu, Ph.D., University of Alaska, 1993. Space Plasma Physics.
Loch, Stuart, Ph.D., University of Strathclyde, 2001. Atomic and molecular physics.
Maurer, David A., Ph.D., Columbia University, 2000. Plasma physics.
Park, Minseo, Ph.D., North Carolina State University, 1998. Experimental Condensed Matter.
Perez, Joseph D., Ph.D., University of Maryland, 1968. Space and plasma physics.
Pindzola, Michael S., Ph.D., University of Virginia, 1975. Atomic and molecular physics.
Thomas, Edward, Ph.D., Auburn University, 1996. Experimental plasma physics.

Associate Professor
Dhar, Sarit, Ph.D., Vanderbilt University, 2005. *Condensed Matter Physics*. Experimental Condensed Matter Physics.
Fogle, Michael R., Ph.D., University of Stockholm, 2004. Experimental atomic physics.
Guazzotto, Luca, Ph.D., University of Rochester, 2005. Theoretical Plasma Physics.
Konopka, Uwe, Ph.D., Ruhr-University of Bochum, 2000. Plasma physics.
Laurent, Guillaume M., Ph.D., University of Caen Lower Normandy, 2007. Experimental Atomic, Molecular and Optics Physics.

Assistant Professor
Comes, Ryan, Ph.D., University of Virginia, 2013. Experimental Condensed Matter Physics.
Ennis, David A., Ph.D., University of Wisconsin-Madison, 2008. Plasma Physics.
Kuroda, Marcelo A., Ph.D., University of Illinois, 2009. Condensed matter of Physics.
Liu, Kaijun, Ph.D., Cornell University, 2007. Plasma physics.

Lecturer
Kolarkar, Ameya S., Ph.D., University of Kentucky, 2008.
Merrill, Daniel A., Ph.D., Purdue University, 2016.

DEPARTMENTAL RESEARCH SPECIALTIES AND STAFF

Theoretical
Atomic, Molecular, & Optical Physics. Photon interactions with atoms; electron scattering by atoms and molecules. Stark Broadening; line-shape analysis. Loch, Pindzola.
Condensed Matter Physics. Electronic structure; charge transport; dielectric breakdown. Surface dynamics. Dong, Kuroda.
Other. Magnetospheric plasma physics. Lin, Liu, Perez.
Plasma and Fusion. MHD equilibrium and equilibrium reconstruction; magnetic field configurations; particle dynamics. Guazzotto, Hanson.

Experimental

Atomic, Molecular, & Optical Physics. Synchotron studies using imaging techniques; electron spectroscopy; momentum imaging. Fogle, Landers, Laurent.

Condensed Matter Physics. Surface kinetics; gas-surface interactions; thermal desorption; electron-stimulated desorption; low-work function surfaces; wetting and adhesion; corrosion phenomena. Comes, Dhar, Park.

Condensed Matter Physics. Wide-bandgap semiconductors; epitaxy; solid state switches; surface properties of solids.

Plasma and Fusion. Magnetic confinement of fusion plasma, plasma diagnostics; plasma spectroscopy;low temperature plasmas, dusty plasmas. Ennis, Konopka, Maurer, Thomas.

View additional information about this department at www.gradschoolshopper.com. Check out the "Why Choose Us?" section, find out more about the department's culture and get links to social media networks.

THE UNIVERSITY OF ALABAMA

DEPARTMENT OF PHYSICS AND ASTRONOMY

Tuscaloosa, Alabama 35487-0324
http://physics.ua.edu

General University Information
President: Stuart Bell
Dean of Graduate School: Susan Carvalho
University website: http://www.ua.edu
School Type: Public
Setting: Suburban
Total Faculty: 1,435
Total Graduate Faculty: 1,005
Total number of Students: 38,563
Total number of Graduate Students: 5,258

Department Information
Department Chairman: Prof. Patrick R. LeClair, Chair
Department Contact: Nancy Pekera, Administrative Secretary
   Total full-time faculty: 30
   Total number of full-time equivalent positions: 30
   Full-Time Graduate Students: 59
   Female Full-Time Graduate Students: 13
   First-Year Graduate Students: 16
   Female First-Year Students: 7
   Total Post Doctorates: 12

Department Address
514 University Boulevard
Tuscaloosa, AL 35487-0324
Phone: (205) 348-5050
Fax: (205) 348-5051
E-mail: npekera@ua.edu
Website: http://physics.ua.edu

ADMISSIONS

Admission Contact Information
Address admission inquiries to: Graduate School Office, Box 870118, Tuscaloosa, AL 35487-0118
Phone: (877) 824-7237
E-mail: graduate.school@ua.edu
Admissions website: http://graduate.ua.edu/prospects/application/

Application deadlines
Fall admission:
U.S. students: January 15   *Int'l. students*: January 15
Spring admission:
U.S. students: November 1   *Int'l. students*: June 1

Application fee
U.S. students: $65   *Int'l. students*: $80
Admissions are considered after the deadlines if positions are available. Full consideration is only guaranteed if the deadlines are met.

Admissions information
For Fall of 2018:
   Number of applicants: 131
   Number admitted: 27
   Number enrolled: 15

Admission requirements
Bachelor's degree requirements: Bachelor's degree in Physics is required.
Minimum undergraduate GPA: 3.0

GRE requirements
The GRE is required.
The applicant must have a minimum of 300 on the GRE.

Subjective GRE requirements
The Subjective GRE is not required.

TOEFL requirements
The TOEFL exam is required for students from non-English-speaking countries.
   PBT score: 550
   iBT score: 79

Other admissions information
Undergraduate preparation assumed: Halliday and Resnick, Fundamentals of Physics; Serway, Moses, and Moyer, Modern Physics; Symon, Mechanics; Reitz, Milford, Foundation of Electromagnetic Theory; Eisberg, Resnick, Quantum Physics of Atoms; etc.

TUITION

Tuition year 2018–19:
Tuition for in-state residents
   Full-time students: $5,390 per semester
Tuition for out-of-state residents
   Full-time students: $14,615 per semester
Credit hours per semester to be considered full-time: 9
Deferred tuition plan: Yes
Health insurance: Available at the cost of $1,248 per year.
Academic term: Semester
Number of first-year students who received full tuition waivers: 15

Teaching Assistants, Research Assistants, and Fellowships
Number of first-year
   Teaching Assistants: 10
   Fellowship students: 5
Average stipend per academic year
   Teaching Assistant: $18,747
   Research Assistant: $18,747
   Fellowship student: $18,747
All first year students have guaranteed support for their first two semesters.

FINANCIAL AID

Application deadlines
Fall admission:
U.S. students: February 15   *Int'l. students*: February 15
Spring admission:
U.S. students: November 1   *Int'l. students*: June 1

Loans
Loans are available for U.S. students.
Loans are available for international students.
GAPSFAS application required: No

FAFSA application required: No

For further information

Address financial aid inquiries to: Office of Student Financial Aid, Box 870162, 106 Student Services Center, The University of Alabama, Tuscaloosa, AL 35487.
Phone: (855) 469-2262
E-mail: financialaid@ua.edu
Financial aid website: http://financialaid.ua.edu/

HOUSING

Availability of on-campus housing

Single students: No
Married students: No
Childcare Assistance: No

For further information

Address housing inquiries to: Julie Elmore, Assistant Director for Off-Campus Housing, 133 Parham East, Box 870399.
Phone: 205-348-0200
E-mail: offcampushousing@sa.ua.edu
Housing aid website: https://offcampushousing.ua.edu

Table A—Faculty, Enrollments, and Degrees Granted

Research Specialty	2017–18 Faculty	Enrollment Fall 2017		Number of Degrees Granted 2017–18 (2013–18)		
		Master's	Doctorate	Master's	Terminal Master's	Doctorate
Astronomy	5	–	10	–(8)	2(4)	2(5)
Astrophysics	2	–	4	–(4)	1(2)	–(2)
Condensed Matter Physics	10	–	25	–(13)	–(4)	3(14)
Engineering Physics/Science	–	–	4	–	–	–
Experimental particle physics	2	–	6	–(4)	–(2)	1(3)
Theoretical particle physics	10	–	8	–(8)	–(1)	2(7)
Other	–	–	2	–	–	–
Total	29	2	59	–(37)	3(13)	8(31)
Full-time Grad. Stud.	–	–	59	–	–	–
First-year Grad. Stud.	–	–	15	–	–	–

GRADUATE DEGREE REQUIREMENTS

Master's: Plan I: 24 graduate semester hours in an approved program with satisfactory performance required; "B" average; one semester in residence; master's examination required; thesis required; no language requirement. Plan II: 30 graduate semester hours in an approved program with satisfactory performance required; master's examination required; thesis not required; no language requirement.

Doctorate: A minimum of 48 graduate semester hours required in an approved program with satisfactory performance; one academic year in residence required; oral preliminary examination required; dissertation and dissertation examination required.

Thesis: Thesis may be written in absentia.

SPECIAL EQUIPMENT, FACILITIES, OR PROGRAMS

The Dept. of Physics and Astronomy at the University of Alabama are members of the SARA Telescope consortium, which operates a 0.9 meter telescope at Kitt Peak in Arizona, a 0.6 meter telescope at Cerro Tololo in Chile and a 1.0 meter telescope in La Palma, Canary Islands, Spain. The astronomy group at UA is a member of Galaxy Zoo, the Sloan Digital Sky Survey (SDSS) IV, the VERITAS and CTA gamma ray observatories, and the IceCube Neutrino Observatory at the South Pole. The experimental particle physics group at UA is a member of CMS experiment at CERN's Large Hadron Collider, the LZ direct Dark Matter detection experiment, the MoEDAL experiment at CERN, and the EXO-200 and nEXO neutrino experiments.

Condensed matter work is facilitated by two clean rooms. Several sputtering systems are available for sample synthesis. Characterization equipment includes alternating-gradient and superconducting vibrating-sample magnetometers, as well as scanning and transmission electron microscopes, scanning atomic force and tunneling microscopes, and Auger and x-ray photoelectron spectroscopy.

On site facilities further include well-equipped laboratories for research in condensed-matter physics, high-energy physics, and image processing.

Supporting facilities include a machine shop, electronics shop, computer workstations, and direct access to the campus mainframe computer and the Alabama supercomputer. Faculty and students participate in the Center for Materials for Information Technology and the Tri-Campus Material Science Ph.D. Program.

Table B—Separately Budgeted Research Expenditures by Source of Support

Source of Support	Departmental Research	Physics-related Research Outside Department
Federal government	$9,536,490	
State/local government		
Non-profit organizations		
Business and industry	$90,000	
Other		
Total	$9,626,490	

Table C—Separately Budgeted Research Expenditures by Research Specialty

Research Specialty	No. of Grants	Expenditures ($)
Astronomy	18	$1,946,210
Astroparticle physics	4	$183,090
Condensed Matter Physics	30	$4,664,210
Experimental particle physics	29	$2,570,980
Theoretical particle physics	9	$262,000
Total	90	$9,626,490

FACULTY

Professor

Busenitz, Jerome K., Ph.D., University of Illinois, 1985. *High Energy Physics, Particles and Fields*. Experimental elementary particle physics.

Harms, Benjamin C., Ph.D., Florida State University, 1969. *Particles and Fields*. Theoretical particle physics.

Keel, William C., Ph.D., University of California, Santa Cruz, 1982. *Astronomy*. Galactic nuclei, jets, and galaxy interactions.

LeClair, Patrick R., Ph.D., Eindhoven University of Technology, 2002. *Condensed Matter Physics, Materials Science, Metallurgy*. Experimental condensed matter physics.

Mankey, Gary J., Ph.D., Pennsylvania State University, 1992. *Condensed Matter Physics*. Experimental condensed matter physics.

Mewes, Tim, Ph.D., University of Kaisersleutern, 2002. *Condensed Matter Physics*. Experimental condensed matter physics.

Piepke, Andreas, Ph.D., Heidelberg University, 1990. *High Energy Physics, Particles and Fields*. Experimental elementary particle physics.

Sarker, S. K., Ph.D., Cornell University, 1980. *Condensed Matter Physics*. Theoretical condensed matter physics.

Schad, Rainer, Ph.D., University of Hannover, 1991. *Condensed Matter Physics*. Experimental condensed matter physics.

Stancu, Ion, Ph.D., Rice University, 1990. *High Energy Physics, Particles and Fields*. Experimental elementary particle physics.

Stern, Allen, Ph.D., Syracuse University, 1980. *Particles and Fields*. Theoretical particle physics.

White, Raymond E., Ph.D., University of Virginia, 1986. *Astronomy, Astrophysics*. Dynamics and hydrodynamics in galaxies and galaxy clusters.

Williams, Dawn R., Ph.D., University of California, Los Angeles, 2004. *Astrophysics, Particles and Fields*. Experimental particle astrophysics.

Associate Professor

Bailin, Jeremy, Ph.D., University of Arizona, 2004. *Astronomy, Astrophysics*. Galaxy formation and evolution.

Henderson, Conor, Ph.D., Massachusetts Institute of Technology, 2005. *High Energy Physics, Particles and Fields*. Experimental elementary particle physics.

Irwin, Jimmy, Ph.D., University of Virginia, 1997. *Astronomy, Astrophysics*. Accreting black holes and neutron stars.

Mewes, Claudia K.A., Ph.D., University of Kaiserslautern, 2004. *Condensed Matter Physics*. Theoretical condensed matter physics.

Okada, Nobuchika, Ph.D., Tokyo Metropolitan University, 1998. *Cosmology & String Theory, Particles and Fields*. Physics beyond the standard model.

Rumerio, Paolo G., Ph.D., Northwestern University, 2003. *Particles and Fields*. Experimental elementary particle physics.

Townsley, Dean M., Ph.D., University of California, Santa Barbara, 2004. *Astrophysics*. White dwarf supernovae.

Assistant Professor

Araujo, Paulo T., Ph.D., Universidade Federal de Minas Gerais, 2010. *Condensed Matter Physics, Nano Science and Technology*. Experimental condensed matter physics.

Hauser, Adam, Ph.D., Ohio State University, 2010. Experimental condensed matter physics. *Condensed Matter Physics*. Experimental condensed matter physics.

Kaminski, Matthias, Ph.D., Ludwig-Maximilians University, 2008. *High Energy Physics, Particles and Fields*. string theory, AdS/CFT correspondence, numerical gravity, quantum field theory.

Nair, Preethi, Ph.D., University of Toronto, 2009. *Astronomy*. Galaxy formation and evolution, using large astronomical surveys.

Ostrovskiy, Igor, Ph.D., University of Alabama, 2011. *High Energy Physics, Particles and Fields*. Experimental elementary particle physics.

Santander, Juan M., Ph.D., University of Wisconsin-Madison, 2013. *Astrophysics, Particles and Fields*. Experimental particle astrophysics.

Schwiete, Georg, Ph.D., University Bochum, 2004. *Condensed Matter Physics*. Theoretical condensed matter physics.

Tse, Wang-Kong, Ph.D., University of Maryland, 2008. *Condensed Matter Physics*. Theoretical condensed matter physics.

Professor Emeritus

Alexander, Chester, Ph.D., Duke University, 1968. *Condensed Matter Physics*. Experimental condensed matter and chemical physics.

Buta, Ronald J., Ph.D., University of Texas, Austin, 1984. *Astronomy*. Galaxy morphology catalogs.

Butler, William H., Ph.D., University of California, San Diego, 1969. *Condensed Matter Physics*. Theoretical condensed matter physics.

Byrd, Gene G., Ph.D., University of Texas, Austin, 1974. *Astrophysics*. Theoretical astrophysics.

Clavelli, Louis J., Ph.D., University of Chicago, 1967. *Particles and Fields*. Theoretical particle physics.

Coulter, Philip W., Ph.D., Stanford University, 1965. *Particles and Fields*. Theoretical particle physics.

Fujiwara, Hideo, Ph.D., University of Tokyo, 1969. *Condensed Matter Physics*. Experimental condensed matter physics.

Hardee, Philip E., Ph.D., University of Maryland, 1976. *Astrophysics*. Theoretical and observational astrophysics.

Harrell, J. W., Ph.D., University of North Carolina, Chapel Hill, 1969. *Condensed Matter Physics*. Experimental condensed matter physics.

Jones, Stanley T., Ph.D., University of Illinois, 1970. *Physics and other Science Education*. Physics education.

Sulentic, Jack W., Ph.D., SUNY, Albany, 1975. *Astronomy*. Observational astrophysics.

Tipping, Richard H., Ph.D., Pennsylvania State University, 1969. *Atomic, Molecular, & Optical Physics*. Theoretical physics; molecular spectroscopy.

Visscher, Pieter B., Ph.D., University of California, Berkeley, 1971. *Condensed Matter Physics*. Theoretical condensed matter physics; computer simulation.

Adjunct Professor

Biermann, Peter L., Ph.D., University of Gottingen, 1971. Theoretical astrophysics.

Crocker, Deborah A., Ph.D., University of Virginia, 1987. Observational astrophysics.

Gupta, Arunava, Ph.D., Stanford University, 1980. Experimental condensed-matter physics.

DEPARTMENTAL RESEARCH SPECIALTIES AND STAFF

Theoretical

Astrophysics. Galactic dynamics; galaxy formation; galactic structure; extragalactic astronomy; high-energy astrophysics; stellar evolution; supernovae. Bailin, Biermann, Townsley.

Condensed Matter Physics. Electronic structure of solids; magnetic properties; hierarchical and renormalization-group methods; magnetic lattice models. Butler, Claudia Mewes, Sarker, Schwiete, Tse, Visscher.

High Energy Physics. Harms, Kaminski, Okada, Stern.

Particles and Fields. Supersymmetry phenomenology; field theory; quantum black holes; particle astrophysics. Biermann, Harms, Kaminski, Okada, Stern.

Experimental

Astronomy. Black holes; galaxy evolution; galaxy morphology; spectroscopy of AGN; galaxy clusters; globular clusters; X-ray astronomy; X-ray binaries. Buta, Irwin, Keel, Nair, White.

Condensed Matter Physics. Magnetic materials and thin films; nanoparticles spintronics. Araujo, Gupta, Harrell, Hauser, LeClair, Mankey, Tim Mewes, Schad.

High Energy Physics. Detector research and development; neutrino physics; particle astrophysics. Busenitz, Henderson, Ostrovskiy, Piepke, Rumerio, Santander, Stancu, Williams.

THE UNIVERSITY OF ALABAMA AT BIRMINGHAM

DEPARTMENT OF PHYSICS

Birmingham, Alabama 35294-1170
http://www.uab.edu/cas/physics

General University Information

President: Ray L. Watts
Dean of Graduate School: Lori L. McMahon
University website: http://www.uab.edu
School Type: Public
Setting: Urban
Total Faculty: 2,605
Total Graduate Faculty: 1,690
Total number of Students: 20,902
Total number of Graduate Students: 6,622

Department Information

Department Chairman: Prof. Ilias Perakis, Chair
Department Contact: Amanda H. Watkins, Administrative
  Associate
  Total full-time faculty: 13
  Total number of full-time equivalent positions: 17
  Full-Time Graduate Students: 34
  Female Full-Time Graduate Students: 6
  First-Year Graduate Students: 7
  Total Post Doctorates: 5

Department Address

1720 2nd Avenue South
Campbell Hall 310
Birmingham, AL 35294-1170
Phone: (205) 934-4736
Fax: (205) 934-8042
E-mail: physics@uab.edu
Website: http://www.uab.edu/cas/physics

ADMISSIONS

Admission Contact Information

Address admission inquiries to: UAB Graduate School, LHL
  G03, 1720 2nd Avenue South, Birmingham, AL 35294-0013
Phone: (205) 934-8227
E-mail: gradschool@uab.edu
Admissions website: www.uab.edu/graduate/

Application deadlines

Fall admission:
U.S. students: July 1   *Int'l. students*: April 1

Application fee

U.S. students: $50   *Int'l. students*: $60

Admissions information

For Fall of 2018:
  Number of applicants: 46
  Number admitted: 12
  Number enrolled: 5

Admission requirements

Bachelor's degree requirements: A Bachelor's degree in Physics
  is required.

GRE requirements

The GRE is required.

The average GRE score for 2017–2018 admissions was 158
(quantitative) and 149 (verbal).

Subjective GRE requirements

The Subjective GRE is recommended.
No minimum GRE scores are set.

TOEFL requirements

The TOEFL exam is required for students from non-English-
  speaking countries.
PBT score: 550
iBT score: 80

Other admissions information

Undergraduate preparation assumed: Halliday and Resnick &
  Walker, Fundamentals of Physics; Thornton & Rex, Modern
  Physics; Morin, Introduction to Classical Mechanics; Grif-
  fiths, Introduction to Electrodynamics; Reif, Fundamentals of
  Statistical and Thermal Physics, Berkeley Course Vol. 5; Li-
  boff, Introductory Quantum Mechanics.

TUITION

Tuition year 2018–19:
Tuition for in-state residents
  Full-time students: $450 per credit
Tuition for out-of-state residents
  Full-time students: $1,030 per credit
In state tuition for first credit hour $626.00 and $396.00 for each
  additional credit hour. Out of state tuition for first credit hour
  is $1,167.00 and $935.00 for each additional credit hour.
Credit hours per semester to be considered full-time: 9
Deferred tuition plan: No
Health insurance: Yes, $1,966.00.
Academic term: Semester

Teaching Assistants, Research Assistants, and Fellowships

Number of first-year
  Teaching Assistants: 5
  Fellowship students: 2
Average stipend per academic year
  Teaching Assistant: $24,000
  Research Assistant: $24,000
  Fellowship student: $26,000
We support our top students with very competitive UAB
Blazer Fellowships.

FINANCIAL AID

Application deadlines

Fall admission:
U.S. students: March 1   *Int'l. students*: March 1

Loans

Loans are available for U.S. students.
Loans are available for international students.
GAPSFAS application required: No
FAFSA application required: Yes

For further information

Address financial aid inquiries to: Financial Aid, LHL 120, 1720 2nd Avenue South Birmingham, AL 35294-0013.
Phone: (205) 934-8223
E-mail: finaid@uab.edu
Financial aid website: www.uab.edu/students/paying-for-college

HOUSING

Availability of on-campus housing

Single students: Yes
Married students: No
Childcare Assistance: No

For further information

Address housing inquiries to: Student Housing and Residential Life, NSRH 103, 1720 2nd Avenue S, Birmingham, AL 35294-1230.
Phone: (205) 996-0400
E-mail: studenthousing@uab.edu
Housing aid website: www.uab.edu/students/housing

Table A—Faculty, Enrollments, and Degrees Granted

Research Specialty	2016–17 Faculty	Enrollment Fall 2016 Master's	Enrollment Fall 2016 Doctorate	Number of Degrees Granted 2016–17 (2012–17) Master's	Number of Degrees Granted 2016–17 (2012–17) Terminal Master's	Number of Degrees Granted 2016–17 (2012–17) Doctorate
Astrophysics	–	–	1	–(1)	–	–
Biophysics	–	–	–	–	–(1)	–(1)
Computational Physics	3	–	4	–(1)	–	1(2)
Condensed Matter Physics	6	1	18	4(13)	–(1)	1(9)
Optics	4	–	10	4(7)	1(2)	–(9)
Total	**13**	**1**	**32**	**8(22)**	**1(4)**	**3(21)**
Full-time Grad. Stud.	–	1	31	–	–	–
First-year Grad. Stud.	–	–	7	–	–	–

GRADUATE DEGREE REQUIREMENTS

Master's: Thirty semester hours of credit with thesis; minimum B (3.0 average); no residency requirements. Thesis is optional with approval of faculty. An additional "interdisciplinary track" for an M.S. degree with thesis option is also offered to non-physics majors and requires a minimum of 12 hours of graduate-level courses offered by other departments.

Doctorate: Minimum residence of three full-time academic years or equivalent periods of part-time enrollment with minimum GPA of B (3.0). Pass: oral placement examination on basic physics concepts; comprehensive examination covering the areas of classical mechanics, quantum mechanics, electromagnetic theory, oral examination on area of research specialization; oral defense of written dissertation proposal; and oral final defense of dissertation. In addition, there is an "applied physics track" for the Ph.D. degree that requires students to complete successfully a sequence of core graduate physics classes in classical mechanics, electromagnetism, quantum mechanics, statistical mechanics, and scientific communication seminars totaling 14 credit hours; 12 credit hours of elective courses in applied physics; 3 credit hours of an applied physics training course; and dissertation research hours.

Thesis: Thesis may be written in absentia.

SPECIAL EQUIPMENT, FACILITIES, OR PROGRAMS

The department has active research programs in experimental, computational and theoretical condensed-matter physics, materials science, nanophysics, optics, lasers, and laser spectroscopy. Opportunities exist for interaction with major government laboratories, including NASA Marshall Space Flight Center, Advanced Photon Source (APS) at Argonne National Laboratory, National Synchrotron Light Source (NSLS) at Brookhaven National Laboratory, and the following National Laboratories: Lawrence Livermore, Oak Ridge, and Sandia; the Naval Research Laboratory, the National Cancer Institute at the National Institutes of Health, National High Magnetic Field Laboratory (Tallahassee, FL), and Center for Integrated Nanotechnology-Los Alamos National Laboratory.

Table B—Separately Budgeted Research Expenditures by Source of Support

Source of Support	Departmental Research	Physics-related Research Outside Department
Federal government	$1,977,218.44	
State/local government	$545,451.56	
Non-profit organizations		
Business and industry		
Other		
Total	$2,522,670	

Table C—Separately Budgeted Research Expenditures by Research Specialty

Research Specialty	No. of Grants	Expenditures ($)
Condensed Matter Physics	12	$664,756
Optics	9	$1,252,929
Other	5	$604,985
Total	26	$2,522,670

FACULTY

Chair Professor

Perakis, Ilias, Ph.D., University of Illinois at Urbana - Champaign, 1992. Chair of the Department of Physics. *Computational Physics, Condensed Matter Physics, Optics.* Theory and Computation of non-equilibrium processes in condensed matter and complex quantum materials (superconductors, magnets, nano-structures, and semiconductors). Emphasis on femtosecond time-dependent correlations and quantum dynamics induced by strong femtosecond laser pulses for fundamental physics and next-generation device applications.

Professor

Lawson, Chris M., Ph.D., Oklahoma State University, 1981. Executive Director, Alabama Experimental Program to Stimulate Competitive Research (Alabama EPSCoR); Vice Chair, Coalition of EPSCoR States. Optics. Nonlinear optics; fiber optics; optical sensors. *Optics.* Nonlinear optics; fiber optics; optical sensors; optical coherence imaging and tomography.

Mirov, Sergey B., Ph.D., Lebedev Physical Institute, Moscow, 1983. P.N. University Professor of Physics; Director, Center for Optical Sensors and Spectroscopies (COSS). Optics. Experimental quantum electronics; physics of color centers; solid-state tunable lasers; laser spectroscopy. *Optics.* Experimental quantum electronics; solid-state lasers; physics of color centers; laser spectroscopy.

Vohra, Yogesh K., Ph.D., Bombay University, 1980. University Scholar/Associate Dean (College of Arts and Science); Director, UAB Center for Nanoscale Materials & Biointegrations: (www.uab.edu/cnmb) and Campus Director, NASA-Alabama Space Grant Consortium.*Applied Physics, Condensed Matter Physics*. High-pressure physics and materials under extreme environments; synthesis and characterization of single crystal-line diamond, nanostructured materials for biomedical applications.

Zvanut, Mary Ellen, Ph.D., Lehigh University, 1988. Associate Chair (Physics); Graduate Program Director. *Condensed Matter Physics*. Electrical studies and EPR studies of insulators and semiconductors; microelectronics and optoelectronics.

Associate Professor

Camata, Renato P., Ph.D., California Institute of Technology, 1998. Director of Undergraduate Physics Program. *Applied Physics, Condensed Matter Physics*. Synthesis and properties of metal and semiconductor nanoparticles; nanostructured materials; aerosol strategies in nanomaterials fabrication; pulsed laser deposition of thin films and nanostructured materials.

Catledge, Aaron S., Ph.D., University of Alabama at Birmingham, 1999. *Atomic, Molecular, & Optical Physics, Condensed Matter Physics*. Synthesis and properties of nanostructured super-hard materials; chemical vapor deposition (CVD) of diamond films and novel nanostructured coatings for biomedical implants; composite scaffolds for tissue engineering; mechanical properties.

Hilton, David J., Ph.D., Cornell University, 2002. *Applied Physics, Condensed Matter Physics, Optics*. Ultrafast spectroscopy and ultrashort pulse generations; ultrafast terahertz spectroscopy; correlated electron materials; superconductivity; high-magnetic field spectroscopy; magnetic semiconductors; complex functional nanomaterials; materials in extreme environments.

Kawai, Ryoichi, Ph.D., Waseda University, 1985. *Computational Physics, Condensed Matter Physics*. Condensed-matter theory; biophysics theory; materials physics theory; computational physics; complex systems.

Stanishevsky, Andrei V., Ph.D., Belarus Academy of Sciences, 1996. *Condensed Matter Physics, Nano Science and Technology*. Focused ion beam micro- and nanofabrication; PVD thin films deposition, characterization, and application; nanoparticle research.

Assistant Professor

Appavoo, Kannatassen, Ph.D., Vanderbilt University, 2012. *Applied Physics, Atomic, Molecular, & Optical Physics, Computational Physics, Electromagnetism, Engineering Physics/Science, Nano Science and Technology, Nonlinear Dynamics and Complex Systems, Optics, Solar Physics, Solid State Physics*. Functional nanophotonics; Metamaterials; Plasmonics; Phase-change materials; Strongly correlated systems; Light-harvesting and energy-to-fuel nanomaterials; Hybrid organic-inorganic perovskites; Electron-beam lithography; Ultrafast time-resolved spectroscopy; Advanced optical microscopy; Low-cost large-scale nanofabrication; Computational electro-magnetic simulations.

Chen, Cheng-Chien, Ph.D., Stanford University, 2011. *Computational Physics, Condensed Matter Physics, Solid State Physics, Theoretical Physics*. strongly correlated electron materials; unconventional superconductors; quantum magnets; theory of x-ray spectroscopies; quantum many-body algorithms; materials modeling; scientific supercomputing.

Simien, Clayton E., Ph.D., Rice University, 2008. *Atomic, Molecular, & Optical Physics*. Laser Cooling and Trapping, Ultracold Neutral Plasmas, Strongly Correlated Cold Atoms, Precision Spectroscopy, and Nanotechnology.

Emeritus

Agresti, David G., Ph.D., California Institute of Technology, 1967. Professor Emeritus. *Astrophysics, Condensed Matter Physics*. Extraterrestrial Mossbauer spectroscopy, planetary science, Martian regolith; meteorites; origin of life; laser raman instrument development.

Bauman, Robert P., Ph.D., University of Pittsburgh, 1954. Professor Emeritus. *Physics and other Science Education*. Physics Education.

Harrison, Joseph G., Ph.D., University of Wisconsin-Madison, 1981. *Computational Physics, Condensed Matter Physics*. Solid-state theory; atomic and molecular physics; MRI modeling; chemical kinetics; simulation of nanoparticle-facilitated hyperthermia.

Martin, James C., Ph.D., Georgia Institute of Technology, 1978. *Non-specialized*. Conformations of biological macromolecules; laser light scattering; optical pattern recognition; Raman spectroscopy.

Nordlund, Thomas M., Ph.D., University of Illinois, 1977. *Biophysics, Physics and other Science Education*. Physics education research; physics textbooks for non-traditional audiences; optical imaging of self-assembly.

Wills, Edward L., Ph.D., University of Virginia, 1968. Research Associate Professor Emeritus. *Nuclear Physics*. extraterrestrial Mossbauer spectroscopy.

Young, John H., Ph.D., Clark University, 1969. Professor Emeritus. *Electromagnetism, Non-specialized*. general relativity; electromagnetic theory.

Professor Emeritus

Shealy, David L., Ph.D., University of Georgia, 1973. *Computational Physics, Optics*. Geometrical optics; laser beam shaping optics; radiative transfer; caustic and optical aberration theory.

Wenger, Lowell E., Ph.D., Purdue University, 1975. Professor (Physics); Magnetic Materials and Superconductors. *Condensed Matter Physics*. Synthesis and characterization of magnetic materials and nanostructures; superconductivity.

Research Associate Professor

Fedorov, Vladimir V., Ph.D., General Physics Institute, Russian Academy of Sciences, 1999. *Non-specialized*. Physical and mathematical science; coherent and laser spectroscopic characterization of doped laser materials; solid-state lasers; laser spectroscopy for molecular-sensing applications.

Research Assistant Professor

Martyshkin, Dmitri V., Ph.D., University of Alabama at Birmingham, 2004. Development and spectroscopic characterization of doped laser materials; solid-state lasers; laser spectroscopy for molecular-sensing applications.

Instructor

Devore, Todd, Ph.D., University of Alabama at Birmingham, 1999. Coordinator of Undergraduate Laboratories. *Computational Physics, Physics and other Science Education*. Computational physics.

Mohr, Rob, Ph.D., University of Alabama, 2001. *Astronomy*. Computational applications to theoretical astrophysical problems.

DEPARTMENTAL RESEARCH SPECIALTIES AND STAFF

Theoretical

Astrophysics. Computer modeling of astrochemical processes and planetary data from Mars and the outer solar system; origin of the solar system; impact. Agresti.

Biophysics. Macromolecular structure; assembly and dynamics by computer modeling. Harrison, Kawai, Nordlund.

Computational Physics. The research programs in Computational and Theoretical Physics span projects from theoretical studies studying the effect of surface adsorption; ab initio molecular dynamics simulations; computational algorithms applicable to massively parallel computers; quantum Monte Carlo simulations; non-equilibrium statistical mechanics; stochastic processes; non-equilibrium processes in condensed matter systems and quantum materials (superconductors, magnets, nano-structures, and semiconductors) with emphasis on femtosecond correlations and quantum dynamics induced by strong femtosecond laser pulses; strongly correlated electron materials; unconventional superconductors; quantum magnets; theory of x-ray spectroscopies; quantum many-body algorithms; materials modeling; scientific supercomputing; non-equilibrium fluctuations; numerical simulations utilizing finite elements to test the effect of RF heating on brain tissue; developing a multilevel, integrative genomics approach for studying diabetes. In the above programs, statistical mechanics, thermodynamics, many-body theory, nonlinear dynamics, percolation theory, network theory, and electromagnetic theory are utilized. Appavoo, Chen, Harrison, Kawai, Perakis, Shealy.

Condensed Matter Physics. Low-dimensional systems; defects in insulators and semiconductors; positron states in condensed matter; simulation of chemical vapor deposition processes; computational electromagnetics; surface adsorption; ab initio molecular dynamics simulations; computational algorithms applicable to massively parallel computers; quantum Monte Carlo simulations; non-equilibrium statistical mechanics; stochastic processes; theoretical and computational studies of non-equilibrium condensed matter systems and quantum materials (superconductors, magnets, nano-structures, and semiconductors) with emphasis on femtosecond correlations and quantum dynamics induced by strong femtosecond laser pulses; strongly correlated electron materials; unconventional superconductors; quantum magnets; theory of x-ray spectroscopies; materials modeling. Agresti, Camata, Harrison, Kawai, Perakis, Shealy, Simien.

Optics. Laser physics; laser spectroscopy; fiber, laser, soft X-ray/UV optics; geometrical optics; nonlinear optics; laser beam shaping; optical design; caustic and optical aberration theory; nonlinear coupling of femtosecond and Terahertz laser pulses with quantum materials; theoretical and computational studies of non-equilibrium condensed matter systems and quantum materials (superconductors, magnets, nano-structures, and semiconductors) with emphasis on femtosecond correlations and quantum dynamics induced by strong femtosecond laser pulses; theory of x-ray spectroscopies. Chen, Hilton, Mirov, Perakis, Shealy.

Experimental

Astrophysics. Astrochemistry of cosmic ices and complex interstellar molecules; molecular evolution and precursors of life; hydrothermal systems; instruments for in situ planetary science and life search; participation in the Mars Rover exploration missions; mass extinctions and Pre-Cambrian paleontology; bringing to bear tools such as Mössbauer, uv/vis/ir, Raman, and mass spectroscopies, XRD, and chemical analysis. Agresti, Mohr.

Biophysics. DNA and protein structure and function via continuous and time-resolved fluorescence spectroscopy and molecular calculations; fiber-optic biosensors; TIRF; FRET; transient kinetics of molecular interactions; energy transfer and photophysics of sunscreens; spectroscopy and imaging of assembly and interactions between biomolecules and nanoparticles. Camata, Catledge, Fedorov, Mirov, Nordlund, Vohra.

Condensed Matter Physics. Nanophotonics; Plasmonics; Metamaterials; Light-harvesting nanomaterials; Energy-to-fuel photocatalysts; Ultrafast spectroscopy; EPR studies of bulk crystals and thin films; optical Mössbauer effect; design and construction of portable Mössbauer spectrometer for use in extraterrestrial studies; high-pressure physics; electrical studies of semiconducting and insulating materials; electrical and optical properties of bulk synthetic diamond and diamond thin films; radiational defects in crystals; optical properties of laser crystals; time-resolved laser spectroscopy; synthesis and characterization of metallic, semiconducting, and magnetic materials and nanostructures; superconductivity; aerosol strategies. Agresti, Appavoo, Camata, Catledge, Fedorov, Hilton, Lawson, Martyshkin, Mirov, Stanishevsky, Vohra, Wenger, Zvanut.

Materials Science, Metallurgy. Nanostructured materials; carbon nanotube synthesis and properties; nanoscale direct writing and patterning; nanocomposite biomaterials. Camata, Catledge, Stanishevsky, Vohra, Wenger.

Nano Science and Technology. Functional nanophotonics; 2D layered materials; Metamaterials; Plasmonics; Phase-change materials; Strongly correlated nanosystems; Light-harvesting nanomaterials; Water-splitting photocatalysts for energy-to-fuel conversion; Hybrid organic-inorganic perovskite; Nano-diamonds; Nanowires; Electron-beam lithography; Photolithography; Nanoimprinting. Appavoo, Camata, Catledge, Hilton, Stanishevsky, Vohra.

Optics. Nanophotonics; Broadband ultrafast dynamics; Time-resolved emission; Nanophotonics; Plasmonics; Metamaterials; In situ nanoparticle growth studies; In situ spectroscopy of photocatalysts; Hybrid organic-inorganic perovskites; Time-correlated single photon counting; Laser optics; laser resonators; solid-state laser materials; tunable lasers; laser spectroscopy; UV holographic projection processing of materials; physiological optics; nonlinear optics and nonlinear optical materials; diamond windows for optical spectroscopy; fiber optics; optical sensors; optical imaging; optical coherence; tomography. Appavoo, Camata, Catledge, Fedorov, Hilton, Lawson, Martyshkin, Mirov, Shealy, Stanishevsky, Vohra.

Solar Physics. Nanomaterials for light harvesting; Water-splitting photocatalysts for solar-to-fuel conversion; ultrafast time-resolved spectroscopy; Charge carrier dynamics; Time-resolved emission and absorption studies; In situ spectroscopy of nanostructured catalysts; Nanowires; Thin films; Plasmonics; Metamaterials. Appavoo.

View additional information about this department at www.gradschoolshopper.com. Check out the "Why Choose Us?" section, find out more about the department's culture and get links to social media networks.

UNIVERSITY OF ALASKA, FAIRBANKS

PHYSICS DEPARTMENT

Fairbanks, Alaska 99775-5920
http://www.uaf.edu/physics/graduate-programs/

General University Information
President: Jim Johnsen
Dean of Graduate School: Michael Castellini
University website: http://www.uaf.edu
School Type: Public
Setting: Urban
Total Faculty: 1,024
Total number of Students: 11,149
Total number of Graduate Students: 1,117

Department Information
Department Chairman: Prof. Renate Wackerbauer, Chair
Department Contact: Dr. Renate Wackerbauer, Graduate
  Program Coordinator
  Total full-time faculty: 11
  Total number of full-time equivalent positions: 7
  Full-Time Graduate Students: 24
  Female Full-Time Graduate Students: 3
  First-Year Graduate Students: 4
  Female First-Year Students: 1
  Total Post Doctorates: 1

Department Address
900 Yukon Drive, REIC 102
UAF Physics
Fairbanks, AK 99775-5920
Phone: (907) 474-6108
Fax: (907) 474-6130
E-mail: uaf-physics@alaska.edu
Website: http://www.uaf.edu/physics/graduate-programs/

ADMISSIONS

Admission Contact Information
Address admission inquiries to: Admissions, P.O. Box 757480,
  Fairbanks, AK 99775-7480
Phone: (800) 478-1823
E-mail: admissions@uaf.edu
Admissions website: http://www.uaf.edu/admissions

Application deadlines
Fall admission:
U.S. students: June 1   *Int'l. students*: March 1
Spring admission:
U.S. students: October 15   *Int'l. students*: September 1

Application fee
U.S. students: $60   *Int'l. students*: $60
Applicants interested in financial support (TA) are encouraged
  to apply as early as possible, since applications are reviewed
  and assistantships awarded starting in January for fall admission.

Admissions information
For Fall of 2018:
  Number of applicants: 30
  Number admitted: 6
  Number enrolled: 4

Admission requirements
Bachelor's degree requirements: A degree in Physics or in a
  closely related field is required.
Minimum undergraduate GPA: 3.0

GRE requirements
The GRE is required.

Subjective GRE requirements
The Subjective GRE is recommended.

TOEFL requirements
The TOEFL exam is required for students from non-English-
  speaking countries.
  PBT score: 550
  iBT score: 79
Must meet minimum TOEFL score to apply and be considered
  by department.

Other admissions information
Additional requirements: Three letters of recommendation, tran-
  scripts, resume, and statement of goals.
Undergraduate preparation assumed: Mathematical Physics,
  Computational Physics, Classical Mechanics, Electricity and
  Magnetism, Mathematical Physics, Computational Physics,
  Quantum Mechanics, Thermodynamics and Statistical Phys-
  ics, Differential equations, Linear Algebra.

TUITION

Tuition year 2017–18:
Tuition for in-state residents
  Full-time students: $3,996 per semester
  Part-time students: $444 per credit
Tuition for out-of-state residents
  Full-time students: $8,163 per semester
  Part-time students: $907 per credit
Tuition is included with TA/RA positions.
Credit hours per semester to be considered full-time: 9
Deferred tuition plan: Yes
Health insurance: Yes, included with TA/RA positions.
Other academic fees: Approximately $525/semester. These are
  mandatory fees incurred by UAF. www.uaf.edu/register/
  expenses/fee-chart/
Academic term: Semester
Number of first-year students who received full tuition waivers: 8

Teaching Assistants, Research Assistants, and Fellowships
Number of first-year
  Teaching Assistants: 7
Average stipend per academic year
  Teaching Assistant: $18,678
  Research Assistant: $18,678
  Fellowship student: $20,845
In addition, assistantships include a tuition waiver (not more
than 20 credits per academic year) and a basic student medical
insurance plan.

FINANCIAL AID

Application deadlines

Fall admission:
U.S. students: June 1   *Int'l. students*: March 1
Spring admission:
U.S. students: September 1   *Int'l. students*: October 15

Loans

Loans are available for U.S. students.
Loans are not available for international students.
GAPSFAS application required: No
FAFSA application required: No

For further information

Address financial aid inquiries to: UAF Financial Aid, 101 Eielson Building, P.O. Box 756360, Fairbanks, AK 99775-6360.
Phone: (907) 474-7256 Toll free: (888) 474-7256
E-mail: financialaid@uaf.edu
Financial aid website: http://www.uaf.edu/finaid/

HOUSING

Availability of on-campus housing

Single students: Yes
Married students: Yes
Childcare Assistance: No

For further information

Address housing inquiries to: UAF Department of Residence Life, 732 Yukon Drive, P.O. Box 756860, Fairbanks, AK 99775.
Phone: (907) 474-7247
E-mail: housing@uaf.edu
Housing aid website: http://www.uaf.edu/reslife/

Table A—Faculty, Enrollments, and Degrees Granted

Research Specialty	2017–2018 Faculty	Enrollment Fall 2017		Number of Degrees Granted 2017–2018 (2013–18)		
		Master's	Doctorate	Master's	Terminal Master's	Doctorate
Atmospheric Infrasound	–	–	–	–	–(2)	–(1)
Condensed Matter Physics	1	–	–	–	–	–
Geophysics	1	1	–	–	1(1)	–(1)
Nonlinear Dynamics and Complex Systems	2	1	3	–	–(3)	–(1)
Space Physics	6	2	14	–	–(3)	2(9)
Other	–	1	1	–	–	–
Total	10	5	18	–	1(9)	2(12)
Full-time Grad. Stud.	–	5	18	–	–	–
First-year Grad. Stud.	–	1	3	–	–	–

GRADUATE DEGREE REQUIREMENTS

Master's: The Master's degree in Physics is offered with a concentration in Physics, or Computational Physics, or Space Physics. (a) Thesis Option: The minimum number of credits that must be earned is 30 semester hours. A maximum of 12 credits may be devoted to thesis or to thesis and research. At least 21 credits in any master's program, including thesis and research, must be at the 600 level. A maximum of 9 semester hours of credit from another institution may be transferred to UAF and applied toward a master's degree upon approval of the student's advisory committee and the dean of the college or school in which the student is enrolled. A thesis is required and an oral defense of the thesis must be taken in conjunction with a comprehensive/final examination. The examining committees shall consist of the candidate's advisory committee. (b) Project Option: A non-thesis Master's degree requires a minimum of 33 credits. Three credits must be devoted to a short research project resulting in a written report. Coursework requirements, totaling a maximum of 30 credits, are the same as those listed for part (a) Thesis Option. A student may apply for admission to candidacy for a specific master's degree if he/she is in good standing and has satisfied the following requirements: the student must have (1) satisfactorily completed at least 9 credits of graduate study at UAF, (2) received approval for the provisional thesis title if a thesis is required, and (3) received approval of the finalized Graduate Study Plan. All work toward the fulfillment of a master's degree must be completed in 7 years.

Doctorate: We offer a Ph.D. degree in Physics and a Ph.D. degree in Space Physics. In both cases, the degree of Doctor of Philosophy is granted for proven ability and scholarly attainment. There are no fixed credit requirements for this degree. However, coursework will be set by individual student's background, coursework requirements for passing Ph.D. comprehensive examination, and research requirements. The student chooses a major line of study and, with the advice of his/her advisory committee, such lines of study in related fields as are necessary for achievement of a thorough and scholarly knowledge of his/her subject. The committee and the student will prepare the student's graduate study plan for the degree, which, including applicable and acceptable work transferred from other institutions, shall represent approximately 3 full years of study beyond the bachelor's degree. Admission to graduate study does not imply admission to candidacy for a degree. The student should seek admission to candidacy approximately 1 year before completing the requirements for the doctorate. A student may be accepted as a candidate by his/her advisory committee after (1) completing the full-time equivalent of 2 academic years of graduate study, (2) completing at least 1 semester in residence at UAF, (3) finalizing the graduate study plan, (4) obtaining approval by the advisory committee of the title and synopsis of the dissertation, and (5) passing a written comprehensive examination administered by the Department. The dissertation, which is expected to represent the equivalent of at least 1 full academic year's work at the University of Alaska Fairbanks, must be a substantial contribution to knowledge. After submitting the dissertation, the candidate must pass an oral examination supporting the dissertation. The examining committee will consist of the student's advisory committee supplemented by additional examiners, including one from outside the candidate's college or school representing the Office of the Graduate School. All work toward the fulfillment of a Ph.D. degree must be completed within 10 years.

Other Degrees: Interdisciplinary Degrees (M.S. or Ph.D.). Students can create their own Master's or Doctorate degree program by combining course work in more than one discipline. They have the responsibility to design the program, organize a committee of faculty members to serve as advisors and make sure that it conforms to rigorous academic standards. The proposed program must differ significantly from and may not substitute for an existing UAF graduate degree program. The student may select no more than one half of his/her program credits from one existing graduate degree program.

SPECIAL EQUIPMENT, FACILITIES, OR PROGRAMS

The University houses a number of research centers and institutes that provide support facilities and services for graduate student research. A majority of department faculty hold joint appointments with the Geophysical Institute. Many are also affiliated with the International Arctic Research Center and/or the Arctic Region Supercomputing Center. Examples of facilities are: 1152-CPU processor Cray XK6m and 2816-processor Penguin Computing Cluster; the Poker Flat Research Range with an active rocket launching facility; research and a major state-of-the-art satellite remote-sensing facility to receive, process, and analyze synthetic aperture radar (SAR) data from European Space Agency, Japanese, Canadian, and U.S. spacecraft, machine, and electronic shops; a network of field sites including stations in Antarctica, Spitzbergen, and sites throughout Alaska; specialized optical, radiation and infrasound instrumentation.

FACULTY

Professor

Conde, Mark, Ph.D., University of Adelaide, 1991. *Astronomy, Atmosphere, Space Physics, Cosmic Rays*. Auroral processes and space weather.

Delamere, Peter A., Ph.D., University of Alaska, Fairbanks, 1998. *Atmosphere, Space Physics, Cosmic Rays, Computational Physics*. Comparative magnetospheric physics; numerical simulation of space plasmas using hybrid and multi-fluid techniques.

Makarevich, Roman, Ph.D., University of Saskatchewan, Saskatoon, 2003. *Atmosphere, Space Physics, Cosmic Rays*. Radio remote sensing of the ionosphere and magnetosphere.

Newman, David E., Ph.D., University of Wisconsin-Madison, 1993. *Computational Physics, Nonlinear Dynamics and Complex Systems, Plasma and Fusion*. Complex systems; turbulence; nonlinear dynamics; fusion plasma physics.

Truffer, Martin, Ph.D., University of Alaska, Fairbanks, 1999. *Computational Physics, Geophysics*. Glacier dynamics; application of geophysical and borehole techniques to glaciology; numerical modeling of ice flow.

Wackerbauer, Renate A., Ph.D., Ludwig Maximilian University, Munich, 1995. Graduate Program Coordinator, Department Chair. *Computational Physics, Nonlinear Dynamics and Complex Systems*. Complex systems; nonlinear dynamics and chaos, modeling of biological systems and Arctic sea ice.

Associate Professor

Chowdhury, Ataur, Ph.D., Clark University, 1985. *Condensed Matter Physics*. Condensed matter physics.

Ng, Chung-Sang, Ph.D., Auburn University, Alabama, 1994. *Atmosphere, Space Physics, Cosmic Rays, Computational Physics, Plasma and Fusion*. Theoretical and computational plasma physics, with applications in space and fusion plasmas.

Szuberla, Curt, Ph.D., University of Alaska, Fairbanks, 1997. *Acoustics, Atmosphere, Space Physics, Cosmic Rays*. Atmospheric infrasound; digital signal processing.

Zhang, Hui, Ph.D., Boston University, 2008. *Atmosphere, Space Physics, Cosmic Rays*. Space plasma physics; magnetospheric physics; solar wind-magnetosphere interaction.

Assistant Professor

Connor, Hyunju, Ph.D., University of New Hampshire, 2012. *Atmosphere, Space Physics, Cosmic Rays, Computational Physics*. Magnetosphere-Ionosphere coupling processes; numerical simulations of space plasma.

Affiliate Professor

Bailey, Scott, Ph.D., University of Colorado, 1995. Aeronomy of the atmosphere.

Bristow, William, Ph.D., University of Alaska, Fairbanks, 1992. *Atmosphere, Space Physics, Cosmic Rays, Electrical Engineering*. Space physics and upper atmospheric physics.

Carreras, Benjamin A., Ph.D., Valencia University, Spain, 1968. *Nonlinear Dynamics and Complex Systems, Plasma and Fusion*. Fusion plasma physics; complex systems; turbulence and transport.

Collins, Richard, Ph.D., University of Illinois, 1994. *Climate/Atmospheric Science*. Laser studies (LIDAR) of the atmosphere.

Hampton, Donald, Ph.D., University of Alaska, Fairbanks, 1996. Optical Science Manager, Poker Flat Research Range. *Atmosphere, Space Physics, Cosmic Rays, Climate/Atmospheric Science, Optics, Systems Science/Engineering*. Space physics.

Lummerzheim, Dirk, Ph.D., University of Alaska, Fairbanks, 1987. *Atmosphere, Space Physics, Cosmic Rays*. Penetration of auroral electrons and protons into the atmosphere and the subsequent optical emissions.

Pettit, Erin, Ph.D., University of Washington, 2003. Assistant Professor of Geophysics. *Energy Sources & Environment, Geophysics*. Glacier dynamics with applications ranging from paleoclimatology to ice/ocean interactions.

Sanchez, Raul, Ph.D., Universidad Complutense de Madrid (Spain), 1997. *Nonlinear Dynamics and Complex Systems, Plasma and Fusion*. Computational physics; complex systems; turbulent transport; fusion plasma physics.

Simpson, William, Ph.D., Stanford University, 1995. Associate Professor of Physical Chemistry. *Chemical Physics, Climate/Atmospheric Science*. Spectroscopy to study environmental/atmospheric chemistry.

Weingartner, Tom, Ph.D., North Carolina State University, 1990. Professor, Physical Oceanography. *Marine Science/Oceanography*. Physical oceanography of Alaskan continental shelves and slopes; interdisciplinary marine research; wind- and buoyancy-forced shelf circulation systems.

DEPARTMENTAL RESEARCH SPECIALTIES AND STAFF

Theoretical

Computational Physics. Computational plasma physics with applications in space and fusion plasmas, hybrid and multi-fluid techniques for space plasmas, numerical modeling of ice flow, nonlinear dynamics and chaos, turbulence, modeling of complex systems. Delamere, Newman, Ng, Truffer, Wackerbauer.

Geophysics. Glacier dynamics, numerical modeling of ice flow. Truffer.

Nonlinear Dynamics and Complex Systems. Complex systems, nonlinear dynamics and chaos, turbulence, network dynamics, modeling and time series analysis. Newman, Wackerbauer.

Space Physics. Theoretical and computational space plasma physics, magnetospheric physics, solar wind-magnetosphere interaction, auroral processes, comparative magnetospheric physics. Delamere, Ng.

Experimental

Acoustics. Atmospheric infrasound, digital signal analysis, installation and operation of infrasonic arrays across the world. Szuberla.

Condensed Matter Physics. Semiconductors. Chowdhury.

Geophysics. Glacier dynamics, application of geophysical and borehole techniques to glaciology. Truffer.

Space physics. Space plasma physics, magnetospheric physics, solar wind - magnetosphere interaction, auroral processes and space weather; active launching of sounding rockets, radio remote sensing of the ionosphere and magnetosphere, satellite data analysis. Conde, Delamere, Makarevich, Zhang.

ARIZONA STATE UNIVERSITY

DEPARTMENT OF PHYSICS

Tempe, Arizona 85287-1504
https://physics.asu.edu/

General University Information
President: Michael M. Crow
Dean of Graduate School: Andrew Webber
University website: http://www.asu.edu
School Type: Public
Setting: Urban
Total Faculty: 3,122
Total Graduate Faculty: 1,839
Total number of Students: 103,567
Total number of Graduate Students: 20,016

Department Information
Department Chairman: Dr. Peter Bennett, Chair
Department Contact: Ixchell Paape, Department Manager
  Total full-time faculty: 53
  Total number of full-time equivalent positions: 53
  Full-Time Graduate Students: 113
  Female Full-Time Graduate Students: 21
  First-Year Graduate Students: 22
  Female First-Year Students: 2
  Total Post Doctorates: 10

Department Address
P.O. Box 871504
Bateman Physical Sciences F-Wing
Tempe, AZ 85287-1504
Phone: (480) 965-0355
Fax: (480) 965-7954
E-mail: physics.info@asu.edu
Website: https://physics.asu.edu/

ADMISSIONS

Admission Contact Information
Address admission inquiries to: 1151 S. Forest Avenue, #SSV112, Tempe, AZ 85287-1003
Phone: (480) 965-6113
E-mail: grad-ges@asu.edu
Admissions website: https://students.asu.edu/graduate

Application deadlines
Fall admission:
U.S. students: January 31   *Int'l. students*: January 31

Application fee
U.S. students: $70   *Int'l. students*: $90
Arizona State University maintains minimum standards for consideration for admission to graduate degree programs. Applicants should review these standards and also review standards, application materials and timelines for submitting your application for the degree program of your interest.

Admissions information
For Fall of 2018:
  Number of applicants: 105
  Number admitted: 60
  Number enrolled: 23

Admission requirements
Bachelor's degree requirements: Bachelor's degree in physics or a closely related program is required with a minimum undergraduate GPA of 3.0 specified and a minimum Junior-Senior GPA of 3.0.
Minimum undergraduate GPA: 3.0

GRE requirements
The GRE is required.
  Quantitative score: 150
  Verbal score: 150
  Analytical score: 3.0
  Mean GRE score range (25th–75th percentile): 1240-1380
Mean GRE scores have been calculated using the old grading scale.

Subjective GRE requirements
The Subjective GRE is required.
  Minimum accepted Advanced GRE score: 600
  Mean Advanced GRE score range (25th–75th percentile): 650-800
Minimum and Mean Physics GRE scores have been calculated using the old grading scale.

TOEFL requirements
The TOEFL exam is required for students from non-English-speaking countries.
  PBT score: 550
  iBT score: 84
At the department level, we look for scores about 15% above these minimal scores, since language skills are critical for teaching assistant positions.

Other admissions information
Undergraduate preparation assumed: Sturge, Statistical and Thermal Physics; Griffiths, Introduction to Electrodynamics; Arfken, Mathematical Methods for Physicists; Fowles and Cassiday, Analytic Mechanics; Griffiths, Introduction to Quantum Mechanics; Zettili, Quantum Mechanics, Concepts and Applications.

TUITION

Tuition year 2017–18:
Tuition for in-state residents
  Full-time students: $12,134 annual
  Part-time students: $1,038 per credit
Tuition for out-of-state residents
  Full-time students: $23,372 annual
  Part-time students: $1,482 per credit
Tuition is waived for students who obtain research or teaching assistantships, provided the student maintains satisfactory progress in the program.
Credit hours per semester to be considered full-time: 9
Deferred tuition plan: No
Health insurance: Yes, $1,875.00.
Other academic fees: Health and Wellness Fee; Technology Fee; Recreation Fee; FA Trust Fee; Tempe Arizona Student Associate Fee; Student Programs Fee.
Academic term: Semester
Number of first-year students who received full tuition waivers: 23

Teaching Assistants, Research Assistants, and Fellowships

Number of first-year
Teaching Assistants: 19
Research Assistants: 3
Fellowship students: 1
Average stipend per academic year
Teaching Assistant: $15,631
Research Assistant: $17,560
Research Assistant: TBD

FINANCIAL AID

Application deadlines
Fall admission:
U.S. students: June 30   *Int'l. students*: June 30

Loans
Loans are available for U.S. students.
Loans are available for international students.
GAPSFAS application required: No
FAFSA application required: No

For further information
Address financial aid inquiries to: Graduate Admissions, Interdisciplinary B-Wing, Room-285.
Phone: (480) 965-3521
E-mail: grad-financial@asu.edu
Financial aid website: http://graduate.asu.edu/financing

HOUSING

Availability of on-campus housing
Single students: Yes
Married students: No
Childcare Assistance: No

For further information
Address housing inquiries to: Residence Life, Student Services Bldg., 1151 S. Forest Ave., Tempe, AZ 85281.
Phone: (480) 965-3515
E-mail: housing@asu.edu
Housing aid website: https://housing.asu.edu

Table A—Faculty, Enrollments, and Degrees Granted

Research Specialty	2017–18 Faculty	Enrollment Fall 2016 Master's	Enrollment Fall 2016 Doctorate	Number of Degrees Granted 2016–17 Master's	Number of Degrees Granted 2016–17 Terminal Master's	Number of Degrees Granted 2016–17 Doctorate
Biophysics	18	–	13	–	–	2
Nano Science and Technology	22	10	36	3	7	3
Particles and Fields	14	–	23	2	–	3
Physics and other Science Education	6	4	–	–	1	–
Total	60	14	72	–	–	8
Full-time Grad. Stud.	–	7	72	–	–	–
First-year Grad. Stud.	–	5	10	–	–	–

GRADUATE DEGREE REQUIREMENTS

Master's: The department does not offer a traditional masters degree in physics.
Doctorate: 84 credit hours with a 3.0 average; qualifying exam; supervisory committee; written and oral comprehensive exams; thesis prospectus; oral dissertation required.

Other Degrees: Professional Sciences Master's in Nanoscience degree Master's in Natural Science degree.

SPECIAL EQUIPMENT, FACILITIES, OR PROGRAMS

Center for Solid State Electronics Research; Center for High-Resolution Electron Microscopy; Surface Science and Ion Beam Analysis facilities; The Biodesign Institute; Barry M. Goldwater Center for Science and Engineering; access to University of Arizona and other national and international facilities.

Table B—Separately Budgeted Research Expenditures by Source of Support

Source of Support	Departmental Research	Physics-related Research Outside Department
Federal government	$6,112,833.73	$997,662.2
State/local government	$9,229.71	
Non-profit organizations	$64,695	
Business and industry	$974,093.21	$517,731.46
Other	$28,502.98	$11,967.96
Total	$7,189,354.63	$1,527,361.62

Table C—Separately Budgeted Research Expenditures by Research Specialty

Research Specialty	No. of Grants	Expenditures ($)
Biophysics	69	$1,872,374
Nano Science and Technology	128	$2,835,841.57
Particles and Fields	30	$944,803.25
Physics and other Science Education	15	$46,274
Total	242	$5,699,292.82

FACULTY

Chair Professor
Bennett, Peter A., Ph.D., University of Wisconsin-Madison, 1980. Department Chair. *Condensed Matter Physics*. Experimental surface physics; epitaxial growth.

Professor
Alarcon, Ricardo O., Ph.D., Ohio University, 1985. Department Associate Chair. *Astrophysics, Nuclear Physics, Particles and Fields*. Experimental intermediate-energy nuclear physics.
Belitsky, Andrei V., Ph.D., Bogoliubov Laboratory of Theoretical Physics, Joint Institute for Nuclear Research, Dubna, Russia, 1996. *Particles and Fields*. Elementary particle physics, field theory, string theory.
Chamberlin, Ralph V., Ph.D., University of California, Los Angeles, 1984. Graduate Program Director. *Condensed Matter Physics*. Experimental condensed matter physics; dynamics of complex systems; nanothermodynamics.
Davies, Paul C. W., Ph.D., University College London, 1970. Director of Beyond Center for Fundamental Concepts in Science & Co-Director of Cosmology Initiative. *Astrophysics*. Astrophysics and cosmology.
Drucker, Jeff, Ph.D., University of California, Santa Barbara, 1986. *Condensed Matter Physics*. Synthesis and characterization of nanostructured electronic materials for novel opto electronic and photonic applications.
Krauss, Lawrence M., Ph.D., Massachusetts Institute of Technology, 1982. Foundation Professor, and Inaugural Director of the Origins Initiative & Co-Director of the Cosmology Initiative. *Cosmology & String Theory, Particles and Fields*. Elementary particle physics and cosmology.

Lebed, Richard F., Ph.D., University of California, Berkeley, 1994. *Particles and Fields*. Elementary particle theory. Hadronic physics, fundamental symmetries.

Lindsay, Stuart M., Ph.D., University of Manchester, 1976. Director of the Center for Single Molecule Biophysics. *Biophysics*. Biophysics and nanoscale physics; scanning probe microscopy and nanofabrication; molecular electronics.

Liu, Jingyue, Ph.D., Arizona State University, 1990. Director of the Professional Science Masters-Nanoscience Program. *Nano Science and Technology*. Nanomaterials for catalysis and application of high resolution electron microscopy to nanomaterials.

Lunardini, Cecilia, Ph.D., SISSA, Trieste, 2001. *Astrophysics, Particles and Fields*. Supernovae neutrinos, neutrino-matter interactions, particle astrophysics.

Matyushov, Dmitry, Ph.D., Kiev State University, Ukraine, 1987. Director of the Center of Biological Physics. *Biophysics*. Biophysics, electron transfer, theoretical chemistry.

Mauskopf, Philip, Ph.D., University of California, Berkeley, 1997. *Astrophysics, Particles and Fields*. Cosmology and astronomical measurements at millimeter/sub-millimeter wavelengths.

McCartney, Martha, Ph.D., Arizona State University, 1989. *Condensed Matter Physics*. Electron microscopy techniques, leading expert on electron holography.

Menendez, José, Ph.D., Stüttgart University, 1985. *Condensed Matter Physics*. Experimental condensed matter physics.

Nemanich, Robert J., Ph.D., University of Chicago, 1976. Department Chair. *Condensed Matter Physics*. Experimental surface science and nanoscience.

Ponce, Fernando A., Ph.D., Stanford University, 1997. *Materials Science, Metallurgy, Nano Science and Technology*. Microscopic properties of electronic materials for applications in microelectronics, photonics and optoelectronics.

Rez, Peter, Ph.D., University of Oxford, 1976. *Biophysics*. Electron diffraction and microscopy; medical physics; biophysics; solid-state theory.

Ritchie, Barry, Ph.D., University of South Carolina, 1979. Vice Provost. *Nuclear Physics*. Experimental medium-energy nuclear physics.

Ros, Robert, Ph.D., University of Basel, 2000. *Biophysics*. Nanobiophysics, structural biology, molecular recognition.

Schmidt, Kevin E., Ph.D., University of Illinois at Urbana-Champaign, 1979. *Condensed Matter Physics*. Theoretical solid-state physics; computational many-body theory.

Smith, David J., Ph.D., University of Melbourne, 1978. *Condensed Matter Physics*. Electron diffraction and high-resolution electron microscopy; electron holography; magnetic materials, and semiconductors.

Spence, John C. H., Ph.D., University of Melbourne, 1974. *Condensed Matter Physics*. Ultrahigh resolution electron microscopy; electron channeling; electron microscope contrast theory; excitations in solids by inelastic electron scattering; surface physics; STM; biophysics; X-ray imaging; nanolithography by stem.

Treacy, Mike, Ph.D., University of Cambridge, 1980. Director of Undergraduate Programs. *Condensed Matter Physics*. Diffraction physics, complex materials. Fluctuation microscopy of disordered materials; enumeration of hypothetical framework materials; diffraction phenomena.

Tsen, Kong-Thon, Ph.D., Purdue University, 1983. *Condensed Matter Physics*. Experimental condensed matter physics.

Vachaspati, Tanmay, Ph.D., Tufts University, 1985. Director of the Cosmology Initiative. *Particles and Fields*. Theoretical cosmology, particle physics, and gravitational physics.

Associate Professor

Culbertson, Robert J., Ph.D., Pennsylvania State University, 1979. Director of the Masters of Natural Science Program. *Condensed Matter Physics, Physics and other Science Education*. Studies of surface modification and characterization of materials, crystal surfaces, and interfaces using ion beams.

Easson, Damien A., Ph.D., Brown University, 2002. *Particles and Fields*. Particle cosmology; cosmology of the early universe; quantum aspects of gravity.

Ozkan, S. Banu, Ph.D., Bogazici University, Istanbuly, 2001. *Biophysics*. Biophysics, modeling, protein folding dynamics.

Parikh, Maulik, Ph.D., Princeton University, 1998. *Cosmology & String Theory*. Theoretical physics; black holes; cosmology; classical and quantum gravity; string theory.

Vaiana, Sara M., Ph.D., University of Palermo, 2004. *Biophysics*. Biophysics, protein self-assembly.

Assistant Professor

Baumgart, Matthew, Ph.D., Harvard University, 2009. *Astronomy, Astrophysics*. Baumgart is an Assistant Professor in the Department of Physics. He is a high energy theorist, interested in particle physics, cosmology, and gravity. His research employs effective field theory, a formalism that efficiently selects relevant degrees of freedom at an energy scale of interest. He applies it to topics in beyond the Standard Model particle physics and questions about cosmological spacetimes.

Beckstein, Oliver, Ph.D., University of Oxford, 2005. *Biophysics*. Biophysics.

Chen, Tingyong, Ph.D., Johns Hopkins University, 2006. *Condensed Matter Physics*. Experimental condensed matter physics; magnetism, superconductivity, nanostructures and nanomaterials.

Keeler, Cindy, Ph.D., University of California-Berkeley, 2008. *High Energy Physics, Theoretical Physics*.

Kirian, Richard, Ph.D., Arizona State University, 2011. *Biophysics*. X-ray diffraction methods and related free-electron laser science. Sample delivery methods (liquid jets and aerosol injectors).

Qing, Quan, Ph.D., Peking University, 2006. *Biophysics*.

Emeritus

Bauer, Ernst, Ph.D., Universitat Munchen, 1955. Distinguished Research Professor. *Condensed Matter Physics*. Surface and thin film physics, in particular surface electron growth.

Comfort, Joseph R., Ph.D., Yale University, 1968. *Nuclear Physics, Particles and Fields*. Experimental nuclear physics; low- and medium-energy nuclear reactions and spectroscopy; reaction mechanisms; nuclear structure models.

Herbots, Nicole, Ph.D., U. Catholique de Louvain, Belgium, 1984. *Condensed Matter Physics*. Synthesis of new thin-film heterostructures by combined ion and molecular deposition and characterization by a wide variety of modern analysis techniques.

Hestenes, David O., Ph.D., University of California, Los Angeles, 1963. *Physics and other Science Education*. Theoretical foundations of physics; relativistic electron theory; physics education research and development.

Jacob, Richard J., Ph.D., University of Utah, 1963. *Nuclear Physics, Particles and Fields*. Elementary particle theory; intermediate-energy hadronic interactions.

Kaufmann, William B., Ph.D., University of California, Berkeley, 1968. *Nuclear Physics, Particles and Fields*. Theoretical intermediate-energy; nuclear and elementary particle physics.

Marzke, Robert, Ph.D., Columbia University, 1966. *Condensed Matter Physics*. Experimental solid-state and chemical physics; NMR, studies of molten ceramics, electrolytes, catalysts and collagen. Biomechanics of hand function.

Page, John B., Ph.D., University of Utah, 1966. *Condensed Matter Physics*. Condensed matter theory; dynamical localization in nonlinear lattices, first-principles studies of fullerenes and fullerene polymers; resonance Raman scattering; phonons and electron-phonon interactions in solids.

Sankey, Otto F., Ph.D., Washington University, 1979. *Biophysics, Condensed Matter Physics*. Theoretical solid-state physics; molecular electronics; biophysics.

Thorpe, Michael F., Other, University of Oxford, 1968. *Biophysics, Condensed Matter Physics*. Theoretical molecular biophysics and soft condensed matter physics.

Venables, John A., Ph.D., University of Cambridge, 1961. *Condensed Matter Physics*. Electron microscopy and surface physics; atomic processes in adsorption and crystal growth; modeling and graduate education, using the Internet.

Research Professor

Jiang, Nan, Ph.D., The University of Birmingham, 1998. *Biophysics*.

Weierstall, Uwe, Ph.D., Eberhard Karls University Tübingen, 1994. *Condensed Matter Physics*. Multidisciplinary research based on electron and X-ray diffraction.

Research Associate Professor

Dugger, Michael, Ph.D., Arizona State University, 2001. *Nuclear Physics, Particles and Fields*. Medium energy nuclear and particle physics.

Research Assistant Professor

Zatsepin, Nadia, Ph.D., Monash University, 2011. *Biophysics*.

Lecturer

Adams, Gary, Ph.D., Arizona State University, 1992. First principles simulations of semiconductor surfaces and fullerenes, fullerene derivatives and carbon nanotubes.

Covatto, Carl, Ph.D., Arizona State University, 2002. Focused on calculating the evolution of grain size distributions in the outflows of cool starts.

Hakhoyan, Armen, Ph.D., Ukrainian National Academy of Sciences, 1986. *Physics and other Science Education*. Instructional resource development and teaching.

Makarova, Darya V., Ph.D., Herzen State Pedagogical University of Russia, 2006. *Physics and other Science Education*. Theory and methods of physics teaching.

Associate Research Scientist

Koeck, Franz, M.S., North Carolina State University, 2003. *Nano Science and Technology*. Efficient energy conversion, thermionic electron sources, diamond power electronics, diamond surfaces.

DEPARTMENTAL RESEARCH SPECIALTIES AND STAFF

Theoretical

Biological Physics and Biophysics. The biological physics group studies biological systems from the molecular to the cell level. With improved experimental data, biology is becoming much more quantitative. At ASU, we are researching the underlying principles involved in the machinery of living things and searching for unifying themes both within and between organisms in an interdisciplinary environment. Biological physics at ASU is a leader in this area and welcomes inquiries from prospective physics graduate students who would like to join one of our exciting research areas. Beckstein, Kirian, Lindsay, Matyushov, Qing, Rez, Ros, Sankey, Spence, Thorpe, Vaiana, Weierstall.

Cosmology, Particle Physics and Astrophysics. Cosmology, Particle Physics and Astrophysics research at ASU specializes in several areas. Major focus is upon particles whose constituents interact so strongly that their interactions cannot be handled using perturbative techniques, and is upon key experiments designed to test nature's fundamental symmetries. For example, the structure of hadrons (particles composed of quarks and gluons, which interact by means of the quantum field theory called quantum chromodynamics [QCD]), is one of our areas of theoretical and experimental specialty. Alarcon, Baumgart, Belitsky, Comfort, Davies, Dugger, Easson, Keeler, Krauss, Lebed, Lunardini, Mauskopf, Parikh, Ritchie, Vachaspati.

Education and Societal Impact. Physics interacts with society in many important ways. Within the university, the physics department teaches many undergraduate classes needed for future engineers and for many other professions. The general studies program involves most of our faculty and our graduate students who serve as teaching assistants. We offer professional degrees through the Master of Natural Science (M.N.S.) and Professional Science Master (P.S.M.) programs. Adams, Covatto, Culbertson, Hakhoyan, Makarova.

Nanoscience and Materials Physics. At the nanometer length scale, materials and structures behave differently, offering exciting new opportunities for scientific discoveries as well as technological advances. Our faculty are working to define the cutting edge in many aspects of nanoscale physics. ASU is well-known for its John M. Cowley Center for High Resolution Electron Microscopy, where researchers use and develop new techniques for probing structural, magnetic, electronic and optical properties at the nanoscale. Bauer, Chamberlin, Chen, Culbertson, Drucker, Herbots, Koeck, Liu, Marzke, McCartney, Menendez, Nemanich, Page, Ponce, Rez, Schmidt, Smith, Treacy, Tsen, Venables.

Experimental

Biological Physics and Biophysics. The biological physics group studies biological systems from the molecular to the cell level. With improved experimental data, biology is becoming much more quantitative. At ASU, we are researching the underlying principles involved in the machinery of living things and searching for unifying themes both within and between organisms in an interdisciplinary environment. Biological physics at ASU is a leader in this area and welcomes inquiries from prospective physics graduate students who would like to join one of our exciting research areas. Beckstein, Kirian, Lindsay, Matyushov, Qing, Rez, Ros, Sankey, Spence, Thorpe, Vaiana, Weierstall.

Cosmology, Particle Physics and Astrophysics. Cosmology, Particle Physics, and Astrophysics research at ASU specializes in several areas. Major focus is upon particles whose constituents interact so strongly that their interactions cannot be handled using perturbative techniques, and is upon key experiments designed to test nature's fundamental symmetries. For example, the structure of hadrons (particles composed of quarks and gluons, which interact by means of the quantum field theory called quantum chromodynamics [QCD]), is one of our areas of theoretical and experimental specialty. Alarcon, Belitsky, Comfort, Davies, Dugger, Easson, Krauss, Lebed, Lunardini, Mauskopf, Parikh, Ritchie, Vachaspati.

Education and Societal Impact. Physics interacts with society in many important ways. Within the university, the physics department teaches many undergraduate classes needed for future engineers and for many other professions. The general studies program involves most of our faculty and our graduate students who serve as teaching assistants. We offer professional degrees through the Master of Natural Science (M.N.S.) and Professional Science Master (P.S.M.) programs. Adams, Covatto, Hakhoyan, Makarova.

Nanoscience and Materials Physics. At the nanometer length scale, materials and structures behave differently, offering exciting new opportunities for scientific discoveries as well as technological advances. Our faculty are working to define the cutting edge in many aspects of nanoscale physics. ASU is well known for its John M. Cowley Center for High Resolution Electron Microscopy, where researchers use and develop new techniques for probing structural, magnetic, electronic and optical properties at the nanoscale. Bauer, Chamberlin, Chen, Culbertson, Drucker, Herbots, Koeck, Liu, Marzke, McCartney, Menendez, Nemanich, Page, Ponce, Rez, Schmidt, Smith, Treacy, Tsen, Venables, Weierstall.

View additional information about this department at www.gradschoolshopper.com. Check out the "Why Choose Us?" section, find out more about the department's culture and get links to social media networks.

NORTHERN ARIZONA UNIVERSITY

PHYSICS & ASTRONOMY

Flagstaff, Arizona 86011
http://www.physics.nau.edu

General University Information
President: Rita Cheng
Dean of Graduate School: Maribeth Watwood
University website: http://www.nau.edu/
School Type: Public
Setting: Urban
Total Faculty: 2,316
Total number of Students: 30,368
Total number of Graduate Students: 3,555

Department Information
Department Chairman: Prof. Nadine Barlow, Chair
Department Contact: Judene Mclane, Administrative Assistant
  Total full-time faculty: 23
  Total number of full-time equivalent positions: 23
  Full-Time Graduate Students: 32
  Female Full-Time Graduate Students: 10
  First-Year Graduate Students: 18
  Female First-Year Students: 3
  Total Post Doctorates: 7

Department Address
PO Box 6010
Flagstaff, AZ 86011
Phone: (928) 523-2661
Fax: (928) 523-1371
E-mail: astro.physics@nau.edu
Website: http://www.physics.nau.edu

ADMISSIONS

Admission Contact Information
Address admission inquiries to: NAU Graduate College, P.O. Box 4125, Flagstaff, AZ 86011-4125
Phone: (928) 523-4348
E-mail: graduate@nau.edu
Admissions website: http://nau.edu/gradcol/

Application deadlines
Fall admission:
U.S. students: January 15   *Int'l. students*: January 15

Application fee
U.S. students: $65

Admissions information
For Fall of 2018:
  Number of applicants: 62
  Number admitted: 13
  Number enrolled: 9

Admission requirements
Bachelor's degree requirements: Bachelors degree in Physics, Astronomy, Planetary Science, or a related field is required.
Minimum undergraduate GPA: 3.0

GRE requirements
The GRE is required.
No minimum GRE General scores were reported.

Subjective GRE requirements
The Subjective GRE is not required.

TOEFL requirements
The TOEFL exam is required for students from non-English-speaking countries.
  iBT score: 80
No PBT option

Other admissions information
Additional requirements: No minimum score is specified. The average GRE scores for admissions were not specified.

TUITION

Tuition year 2018–19:
Tuition for in-state residents
  Full-time students: $9,240 annual
  Part-time students: $458 per credit
Tuition for out-of-state residents
  Full-time students: $21,588 annual
  Part-time students: $1,199 per credit
Credit hours per semester to be considered full-time: 9
Health insurance: Yes, $230.00.
Academic term: Semester
Number of first-year students who received full tuition waivers: 9

Teaching Assistants, Research Assistants, and Fellowships
Number of first-year
  Teaching Assistants: 7
  Research Assistants: 3
  Fellowship students: 4
Average stipend per academic year
  Teaching Assistant: $14,250
  Fellowship student: $8,000
The GTA stipend in the MS program is $13,500 per academic year. The minimum GTA stipend in the PhD program is $15,000 per academic year. Outstanding PhD students are eligible for a Presidential Fellowship that includes an additional $8,000 per academic year. The GRA stipend in the PhD program ranges from $15,000 to $22,500 per academic year.

FINANCIAL AID

Application deadlines
Fall admission:
U.S. students: March 1   *Int'l. students*: March 1

Loans
Loans are available for U.S. students.
Loans are not available for international students.
GAPSFAS application required: No
FAFSA application required: Yes

For further information
Address financial aid inquiries to: Office of Student Financial Aid, Northern Arizona University, Box 4108, Flagstaff, AZ 86011.
Phone: (928) 523-4951
E-mail: Financial.Aid@nau.edu

Financial aid website: http://www.nau.edu/FinAid/Welcome

HOUSING

Availability of on-campus housing
Single students: Yes
Married students: Yes

For further information
Address housing inquiries to: Office of Residence Life, Northern
Arizona University, Box 6100, Flagstaff, AZ 86011.
Phone: (928) 523-3978
E-mail: Residence.Life@nau.edu
Housing aid website: http://www.nau.edu/Residence-Life/

Table A—Faculty, Enrollments, and Degrees Granted

Research Specialty	2018–19 Faculty	Enrollment Fall 2018 Master's	Enrollment Fall 2018 Doctorate	Number of Degrees Granted 2017–18 (2013–2018) Master's	Number of Degrees Granted 2017–18 (2013–2018) Terminal Master's	Number of Degrees Granted 2017–18 (2013–2018) Doctorate
Astronomy	4	–	13	–(8)	–	–
Astrophysics	1	–	–	–(5)	–	–
Condensed Matter Physics	2	4	–	–(10)	–	–
Nano Science and Technology	1	2	–	1(1)	–	–
Optics	2	2	–	2(4)	–	–
Physics and other Science Education	1	–	–	–(5)	–	–
Planetary Science	5	–	7	–(4)	–	–
Solid State Physics	5	4	–	–(3)	–	–
Total	17	12	20	3(39)	–	–
Full-time Grad. Stud.	–	14	–	–	–	–
First-year Grad. Stud.	–	9	–	–	–	–

GRADUATE DEGREE REQUIREMENTS

Master's: The M.S. in Applied Physics consists of thirty-six hours of graduate courses, including both thesis and non-thesis options. There is no foreign language requirement. This program can be interdisciplinary, integrating a broad range of subject areas to enhance student opportunities in the industrial or research world. Individual programs may be customized to meet specific student needs. The M.S. in Applied Physics is independent of the Ph.D. in Astronomy and Planetary Science.

Doctorate: The Ph.D. in Astronomy and Planetary Science is accepting students for the Fall 2018 semester. The program consists of ninety hours of graduate classes including thirty hours of formal core-courses and 60 hours of dissertation. There is no foreign language requirement. Each student must submit a written prospectus and make an oral presentation of the original research they propose to carry out. The student must write and submit a dissertation to a committee that approves the content. Each student must present an oral, public presentation of their research findings that meets with the approval the committee. The Ph.D. in Astronomy and Planetary Science is independent of the M.S. program in Applied Physics.

Thesis: The thesis of the M.S. program and the dissertation of the Ph.D. program may be written in absentia.

SPECIAL EQUIPMENT, FACILITIES, OR PROGRAMS

The Department has access to the large research-grade telescopes of the University of Arizona and Lowell Observatory. It has optics, nano-physics, photoelectron spectroscopy,and astrophysical ice laboratories. The Department has a cluster for work in computational physics and astronomy.

Table B—Separately Budgeted Research Expenditures by Source of Support

Source of Support	Departmental Research	Physics-related Research Outside Department
Federal government	$3,366,644	
State/local government		
Non-profit organizations		
Business and industry		
Other		
Total	$3,366,644	

Table C—Separately Budgeted Research Expenditures by Research Specialty

Research Specialty	No. of Grants	Expenditures ($)
Astrophysics	22	$3,054,774
Nano Science and Technology	3	$279,950
Physics and other Science Education	1	$31,920
Total	26	$3,366,644

FACULTY

Professor
Barlow, Nadine, Ph.D., University of Arizona, 1987. Planetary astronomy.
Delinger, William G., Ph.D., University of Iowa, 1972. Solid state, electronic instrumentation, solar energy, computers.
Dillingham, T. Randall, Ph.D., Kansas State University, 1983. Surface physics, x-ray photoelectron spectroscopy, surface chemistry of ices.
Tegler, Stephen C., Ph.D., Arizona State University, 1989. Optical and infrared astronomy, Kuiper belt objects, icy dwarf planets, laboratory astrophysics.

Associate Professor
Koerner, David, Ph.D., California Institute of Technology, 1994. Origin of planetary systems.
Montaño, Inés, Ph.D., Technical University of Berlin, 2004. Theoretical, solid state.
Trilling, David, Ph.D., University of Arizona, 1999. Planetary science, asteroids, near earth objects, kuiper belt objects.

Assistant Professor
Behunin, Ryan, Ph.D., University of Maryland, 2012. Solid state, optics.
Edwards, Christopher S., Ph.D., Arizona State University, 2012. Planetary geology, Mars, optics, flight instrumentation.
Gibbs, John G., Ph.D., University of Georgia, 2011. Complex and hybrid nanomaterial fabrication, soft-matter physics, condensed matter physics, plasmonics, metamaterials, active and non-equilibrium driven colloidal systems, colloidal science, catalytic nanomotors, magnetic colloidal systems, optical properties of nanomaterials.
Loeffler, Mark J., Ph.D., University of Virginia, 2002. Astrophysics, laboratory astrophysics, astrochemistry.
Mann, Christopher J., Ph.D., University of South Florida, 2006. Optics, interferometry, digital holography.

Robinson, Tyler D., Ph.D., University of Washington, 2012. Planetary science, exoplanets.

Salvatore, Mark R., Ph.D., Brown University, 2013. Planetary science, Mars.

Thomas, Cristina A., Ph.D., Massachusetts Institute of Technology, 2009. Asteroids, spectroscopy, planetary science, near earth objects, Kuiper belt objects.

Trujillo, Chadwick A., Ph.D., University of Hawaii, 2000. Kuiper belt, inner Oort cloud, the outer Solar System, planet formation, Titan, active asteroids.

Instructor

Chien, Lisa, Ph.D., University of Hawaii, 2009. extra-galactic astronomy.

Fobar, Brad, M.S., Northern Arizona University, 2009. Science education.

Hodges, Jimmy, M.S., Northern Arizona University, 2016. Science education.

Mitchell, Radford, Ph.D., Georgia Institute of Technology, 2013. Theoretical physics, fluid dynamics.

Senior Lecturer

Cole, David M., Ph.D., Texas A&M University, 1997. Magnetic resonance imaging, science education.

Lecturer

Dolle, Ethan, Ph.D., University of Arizona, 2009. Physics beyond the Standard Model, particle phenomenology, particle dark matter.

DEPARTMENTAL RESEARCH SPECIALTIES AND STAFF

Experimental

Astronomy. Planetary science, origins of solar systems, star formation and evolution, optical and infrared astronomy, Kuiper Belt objects, unmanned space missions. Loeffler, Robinson, Tegler, Thomas, Trilling, Trujillo.

Astrophysics. Laboratory astrophysics & astrochemistry. Loeffler, Tegler.

Condensed Matter Physics. Inorganic/Organic materials, semiconductor physics, microsensor development, polymer physics. Delinger, Dillingham, Gibbs.

Nano Science and Technology. Nano-science and technology. Gibbs.

Optics. Interferometry, digital holography. Mann.

Physics and other Science Education. Science education. Cole, Dolle.

Planetary Science. Planetary geology, Mars, optics, flight instrumentation, exoplanets, origin of planetary systems. Barlow, Edwards, Koerner, Robinson, Salvatore.

View additional information about this department at www.gradschoolshopper.com. Check out the "Why Choose Us?" section, find out more about the department's culture and get links to social media networks.

THE UNIVERSITY OF ARIZONA

COLLEGE OF OPTICAL SCIENCES

Tucson, Arizona 85721
http://www.optics.arizona.edu

General University Information
President: Dr. Robert C. Robbins
Dean of Graduate School: Andrew Comrie
University website: http://www.arizona.edu
School Type: Public
Setting: Urban
Total Faculty: 3,144
Total Graduate Faculty: 2,774
Total number of Students: 43,625
Total number of Graduate Students: 7,946

Department Information
Department Chairman: Dr. Thomas L. Koch, Dean
Department Contact: R. John Koshel, Associate Dean,
  Academic Programs
  Total full-time faculty: 63
  Total number of full-time equivalent positions: 38
  Full-Time Graduate Students: 308
  Female Full-Time Graduate Students: 77
  First-Year Graduate Students: 81
  Female First-Year Students: 21
  Total Post Doctorates: 15

Department Address
1630 E. University Boulevard
Tucson, AZ 85721
Phone: (520) 621-4112
Fax: (520) 626-1480
E-mail: admissions@optics.arizona.edu
Website: http://www.optics.arizona.edu

ADMISSIONS

Admission Contact Information
Address admission inquiries to: Dr. John Koshel, Associate Dean
  of Academic Programs, College of Optical Sciences, 1630 E.
  University Blvd., P.O. Box 210094, Tucson, AZ 85721-0094
Phone: (520) 621-4112
E-mail: admissions@optics.arizona.edu
Admissions website: http://www.optics.arizona.edu/academics/
  for-prospective-students/admissions/graduate

Application deadlines
Fall admission:
U.S. students: January 15   *Int'l. students*: January 15
Spring admission:
U.S. students: January 1   *Int'l. students*: October 10

Application fee
U.S. students: $85   *Int'l. students*: $95
Ph.D. applications are not accepted for spring semester admissions. M.S. applications are accepted for spring semester admission. Spring M.S. application deadline is December 10/
  2018 for domestic students and 9/1/2018 form international
  students.

Admissions information
For Fall of 2017:
  Number of applicants: 291
  Number admitted: 139
  Number enrolled: 92

Admission requirements
Bachelor's degree requirements: A Bachelor's degree in En-
  gineering, Physics, Mathematics, or Optics is required.
Minimum undergraduate GPA: 3.0

GRE requirements
The GRE is required.
  Quantitative score: 75
  Verbal score: 65
GRE subject is not required.

Subjective GRE requirements
The Subjective GRE is not required.

TOEFL requirements
The TOEFL exam is required for students from non-English-
  speaking countries.
  PBT score: 600
  iBT score: 79
Students may submit an IELTS score of 7.0 in lieu of a TOEFL

Other admissions information
Additional requirements: The minimum acceptable GRE score
  for admission is analytical: 65 percent; quantitative: 75 percent.
Undergraduate preparation assumed: Applicants should hold a
  Bachelor's degree in optics, engineering, physics, mathematics, or a related field. Before beginning graduate-level
  coursework, students should have taken four semesters of advanced mathematics, including calculus, vector calculus, and
  differential equations. A course in linear algebra is also recommended. Two semesters of introductory physics: Mechanics /
  Electricity and Magnetism is also recommended.

TUITION

Tuition year 2018–2019:
Tuition for in-state residents
  Full-time students: $5,858 per semester
  Part-time students: $837 per credit
Tuition for out-of-state residents
  Full-time students: $16,032 per semester
  Part-time students: $1,781 per credit
A limited number of graduate tuition scholarships and fellow-
  ships are available. Applicants from WRGP-participating
  states may qualify for in-state tuition. For more information,
  see http://www.optics.arizona.edu/academics/funding.
Credit hours per semester to be considered full-time: 9
Deferred tuition plan: Yes
Health insurance: Available at the cost of $2,088 per year.
Other academic fees: Additional mandatory fees are $1,328.26
  per academic year.
Academic term: Semester
Number of first-year students who received full tuition waivers: 31

Teaching Assistants, Research Assistants, and Fellowships

Number of first-year
Fellowship students: 23
Average stipend per academic year
Teaching Assistant: $17,379
Research Assistant: $17,379
Fellowship student: $24,344.5
Students with graduate research and teaching assistantships qualify for in-state tuition. They are required to enroll in a minimum of six units for full-time status (as opposed to the nine units required of other students). Assistantships include student health insurance coverage.

FINANCIAL AID

Application deadlines
Fall admission:
U.S. students: January 15   *Int'l. students*: January 15
Spring admission:
U.S. students: November 1   *Int'l. students*: November 1

Loans
Loans are available for U.S. students.
Loans are not available for international students.
GAPSFAS application required: No
FAFSA application required: Yes

For further information
Address financial aid inquiries to: Dr. John Koshel, Associate Dean of Academic Programs, College of Optical Sciences, P.O. Box 210094, Tucson, AZ 85721-0094.
Phone: (520) 621-4112
E-mail: jkoshel@optics.arizona.edu
Financial aid website: http://www.optics.arizona.edu/academics/funding

HOUSING

Availability of on-campus housing
Single students: Yes
Married students: Yes

For further information
Address housing inquiries to: Department of Residence Life., 501 N. Highland Avenue, Tucson, AZ 85721.
Phone: (520) 626-0336
E-mail: laaldea@life.arizona.edu
Housing aid website: http://www.life.arizona.edu/

Table A—Faculty, Enrollments, and Degrees Granted

Research Specialty	2017–2018 Faculty	Enrollment Fall 2018 Master's	Enrollment Fall 2018 Doctorate	Number of Degrees Granted 2017–2018 (2012–18) Master's	Number of Degrees Granted 2017–2018 (2012–18) Terminal Master's	Number of Degrees Granted 2017–2018 (2012–18) Doctorate
Optics	38	162	146	37(246)	37(213)	12(144)
Total	38	162	146	37(246)	37(213)	12(144)
Full-time Grad. Stud.	–	162	146	–	–	–
First-year Grad. Stud.	–	50	31	–	–	–

GRADUATE DEGREE REQUIREMENTS

Master's: Thesis option: a minimum of 32 units of graduate credit in optics or optics-related courses, including eight units of OPTI 910 (thesis) and at least two optics laboratory courses, and a final oral examination, based primarily on the thesis. Non-thesis option: a minimum of 35 units of graduate credit in optics or optics-related courses, including at least two units of optics laboratory courses; three units' credit for demonstrated competence in written communication, either for writing an acceptable master's report or successfully completing an appropriate course in technical writing; and a final oral examination, based primarily on the subject matter of the courses taken. A cumulative GPA of 3.0 is required for an M.S. degree to be awarded. The M.S. in Optical Sciences can be completed by distance with one visit to campus. The Master of Science in Photonics Communication has a core curriculum: http://www.optics.arizona.edu/academics/degree-programs/master-science-photonic-communications-engineering The M.S. in Optical Sciences and MBA Dual Degree offers the opportunity to earn two degrees concurrently: http://www.optics.arizona.edu/academics/degree-programs/master-science-optical-sciences-and-mba-dual-degree.

Doctorate: The equivalent of six semesters of full-time graduate coursework is required, including at least two optics laboratory courses, for a total of 54 units. The equivalent of two semesters of full-time study must be spent in residence, and 30 units of graduate credit must be earned at the University of Arizona. Students are also required to earn 18 dissertation units. To receive a Ph.D., students must maintain a cumulative GPA of 3.0. A foreign language is not required. Required examinations are the written and oral comprehensive examinations (usually completed during the fifth or sixth semester), the dissertation proposal examination, and the final oral examination.

Other Degrees: The Graduate Professional Certificate in Optical Sciences requires completion of 15 units of graduate-level course work in optics.

Thesis: Theses and dissertations for master's and doctoral degrees may be written in absentia.

SPECIAL EQUIPMENT, FACILITIES, OR PROGRAMS

The College of Optical Sciences is recognized internationally for its innovative and unusually comprehensive research programs. Research encompasses a broad set of technologies and techniques for exploiting the properties and applications of light, touching virtually every field of science and industry. The extensive research facilities at the college provide the resources for both theoretical and applied research programs in all areas related to optics and the optical sciences. We continually refine and upgrade our facilities to expand our research capabilities and programs.

Table B—Separately Budgeted Research Expenditures by Source of Support

Source of Support	Departmental Research	Physics-related Research Outside Department
Federal government	$14,416,028	
State/local government	$10,555,057	
Non-profit organizations	$93,062	
Business and industry	$5,485,517	
Other	$6,901,551	
Total	$37,451,215	

Table C—Separately Budgeted Research Expenditures by Research Specialty

Research Specialty	No. of Grants	Expenditures ($)
Optics	170	$25,265,867
Total	170	$25,265,867

FACULTY

Professor

Anderson, Brian P., Ph.D., Stanford University, 1999. *Applied Physics, Atomic, Molecular, & Optical Physics, Physics of Beams, Other*. Atomic gas Bose-Einstein condensates held in combined optical and magnetic potentials; vortices, solitons, and superfluid dynamics; atom interferometry, phase transitions, and BEC manipulation using tailored optical potentials.

Angel, J. Roger P., Ph.D., University of Oxford, 1967. *Astronomy, Atmosphere, Space Physics, Cosmic Rays, Atomic, Molecular, & Optical Physics, Optics, Other*. Adaptive optics; instrumentation; extrasolar planets; telescope design and optical fabrication; interferometry.

Armstrong, Neal, Ph.D., University of New Mexico, 1974. *Atomic, Molecular, & Optical Physics, Chemical Physics, Optics, Other*. New molecular materials through self-assembly and patterning; interface characterization through surface analysis and scanning probe microscopies; electrochemistry; chemical sensors; analytical chemistry.

Banerjee, Bhaskar, Other, University of London, 1983. *Medical, Health Physics*. Optical detection of gastrointestinal cancer using native fluorophores; receptor-targeted imaging of gastrointestinal cancer.

Barrett, Harrison H., Ph.D., Harvard University, 1969. *Medical, Health Physics, Nuclear Engineering, Optics, Other*. Inverse problems in medicine; applications of statistical decision theory; medical imaging; three-dimensional reconstruction; nuclear medicine.

Barton, Jennifer, Ph.D., University of Texas, Austin, 1998. *Medical, Health Physics, Other*. Optical imaging (optical coherence tomography); laser-tissue interaction; bioinstrumentation.

Binder, Rolf, Ph.D., Universität Dortmund, 1988. *Applied Physics, Optics, Physics of Beams, Other*. Theoretical investigations of the optical properties of semiconductor structures and modeling of semiconductor lasers.

Chipman, Russell, Ph.D., University of Arizona, 1987. *Optics, Other*. Optical polarization; ophthalmic optics.

Clarkson, Eric, Ph.D., Arizona State University, 1985. *Medical, Health Physics, Optics, Other*. Image science; mathematical optics; medical imaging; inverse problems; image quality assessment.

Dallas, William John, Ph.D., University of California, San Diego, 1973. *Electrical Engineering, Medical, Health Physics, Optics, Other*. Picture archiving and communications systems; electrical current imaging from biomagnetic field measurements; medical image processing; image display; cardiac imaging.

Denninghoff, Kurt R., Ph.D., Vanderbilt University School of Medicine, 1987. Also an M.D. *Medical, Health Physics, Other*. Emergency medicine; ophthalmic technologies.

Djordjevic, Ivan B., Ph.D., University of Nis, 1999. *Electrical Engineering, Other*. Optical networks; error control coding, constrained coding, and coded modulation; turbo equalization; OFDM applications; quantum error correction.

Fallahi, Mahmoud, Ph.D., Toulouse University/CNRS, 1988. *Atomic, Molecular, & Optical Physics, Electrical Engineering, Nano Science and Technology, Optics, Other*. High-power semiconductor lasers; DFB/DBR lasers; grating-assisted integrated optics; photonic integrated circuits; optical communication; wavelength multiplexers and demultiplexers; wavelength filters; sol-gel-semiconductor integration; WDM components; sensors, design, and microfabrication; nanofabrication and nanostructures; sol-gel PIC.

Furenlid, Lars, Ph.D., Georgia Institute of Technology, 1988. *Medical, Health Physics, Optics, Other*. Development and application of novel detectors; optical configurations; readout electronics; data-processing methods for biomedical imaging systems with special emphasis on biological questions related to cancer, cardiovascular, and neurodegenerative diseases.

Gmitro, Arthur, Ph.D., University of Arizona, 1982. *Medical, Health Physics, Optics, Other*. Magnetic resonance imaging; optics in medicine; optical computing.

Greivenkamp, John E., Ph.D., University of Arizona, 1980. *Optics, Other*. Ophthalmic and visual optics; ophthalmic instrumentation and measurements; interferometry and optical testing of aspheric surfaces; optical fabrication; optical system design; optical metrology systems; distance measurement systems; sampled imaging theory; optics of electronic imaging systems.

Hua, Hong, Ph.D., Beijing Institute of Technology, 1999. *Medical, Health Physics, Optics, Other*. Development of 2D and 3D display systems, imaging systems, tracking systems, and interaction methods; stereoscopic displays; human-computer interface techniques; virtual and augmented environments.

Jessen, Poul S., Ph.D., University of Aarhus, 1993. Chair of Quantum Information & Control. *Atomic, Molecular, & Optical Physics, Physics of Beams, Other*. Quantum state preparation; coherent control; quantum tunneling and transport phenomena in optical lattices; quantum computation; macroscopic superposition states and coherent evolution in dissipative quantum systems; few-body quantum state preparation in optical lattices; matter-wave equivalent of the laser/micromaser; atom-optics in nano-fabrication; laser cooling, trapping, and manipulation of atoms and ions.

Koch, Thomas, Ph.D., California Institute of Technology, 1982. Dean of the College of Optical Sciences Professor of Electrical and Computer Engineering. *Electrical Engineering*. Semiconductor optoelectronics; optical fiber communications; photonic integrated circuits; silicon photonics.

Koshel, Richard J., Ph.D., University of Rochester, 1996. *Optics, Other*. Optical system engineering; illumination engineering; non-imaging optics; radiometry; solar energy.

Kostuk, Raymond K., Ph.D., Stanford University, 1986. *Electrical Engineering, Optics, Other*. Holographic techniques, systems, and materials; ion-exchange waveguide devices-interfacing to polymer and PBG layers; fiber-optic systems including OCDMA, error-correction codes, and all-optical network issues; medical imaging sensors including OCT and holographic filtering of coherent image data.

Kupinski, Matthew, Ph.D., University of Chicago, 2000. *Applied Mathematics, Medical, Health Physics, Statistical & Thermal Physics, Other*. Task-based assessment of image quality for both tumor detection and parameter estimation tasks; statistical characteristics of images and the objects being imaged; imaging hardware optimization; human-observer models for image analysis.

Liang, Rongguang, Ph.D., University of Arizona, 2001. *Medical, Health Physics, Optics, Other*. Biomedical imaging; optical design.

Mansuripur, Masud, Ph.D., Stanford University, 1981. Chair of Optical Data Storage. *Electrical Engineering, Electromagnetism, Optics, Other*. Optical data storage; magneto-optics; optics of polarized light in systems of high numerical aperture; magnetic and magneto-optical properties of thin solid films; magnetization dynamics; integrated optics for optical heads (data storage systems); information theory; optical signal processing; biological data storage; erbium-doped fiber amplifiers and lasers.

Marcellin, Michael, Ph.D., Texas A&M, 1987. *Computational Physics*. Digital communication and data storage systems; image and video compression; image processing; digital signal processing.

Mazumdar, Sumit, Ph.D., Princeton University, 1980. *Engineering Physics/Science, Nonlinear Dynamics and Complex Systems, Optics, Polymer Physics/Science, Other*. Linear and nonlinear optical properties of organic conjugated molecules and polymers; effects of strong Coulomb correlations, excitons, and multiexcitons in organic systems; organic optoelectronic devices; strong Coulomb interactions and broken symmetries; charge and spin density waves and superconductivity in organic and inorganic materials with emphasis on organic charge-transfer solids and transition metal oxides.

Meystre, Pierre, Ph.D., Ecole Polytechnique Federale, 1974. Director of Biosphere 2. *Atomic, Molecular, & Optical Physics, Electrical Engineering, Energy Sources & Environment, Optics, Other*. Theoretical quantum optics; statistical properties of radiation; laser theory; nonlinear optics; atomic physics; ultracold atoms; Bose condensation and atom lasers; cavity quantum electrodynamics; atom optics.

Miller, Joseph M., Ph.D., Northeastern Ohio Universities College of Medicine, 1985. *Medical, Health Physics, Optics, Other*. The effect of astigmatism on visual development; non-invasive assessment of buried optical elements.

Milster, Thomas, Ph.D., University of Arizona, 1987. *Optics, Other*. Improving data density and signal readout quality in optical storage systems; design and implementation of novel storage modalities; signal detection and components.

Moloney, Jerome, Ph.D., University of Western Ontario, 1977. *Electrical Engineering, Nonlinear Dynamics and Complex Systems, Optics, Physics of Beams, Other*. Mathematical modeling and simulation of photonics systems; fundamental theory of semiconductor lasers; modeling high-power femtosecond atmospheric light strings; nonlinear theory of partial differential equations and chaos synchronization in extended complex spatiotemporal interacting systems; algorithm development for large-scale computational photonics systems simulations.

Neifeld, Mark A., Ph.D., California Institute of Technology, 1991. *Electrical Engineering, Optics, Other*. Nontraditional imaging; pattern recognition and neural networks; parallel coding and signal processing; volume optical storage; multiple-quantum-well photonics.

Nofziger, Michael, Ph.D., University of Arizona, 1995. Outreach Coordinator, College of Optical Sciences. *Optics, Physics and other Science Education, Other*.

Norwood, Robert, Ph.D., University of Pennsylvania, 1988. *Optics, Polymer Physics/Science, Other*. Electro-optic polymers and devices; photorefractive polymers; sol-gels; materials for linear and nonlinear photonic crystals; organic light-emitting diodes; solar cells; sensors.

Pau, Stanley, Ph.D., Stanford University, 1996. *Computer Science, Electrical Engineering, Nano Science and Technology, Optics, Other*. Micro-optics, MEMS/NEMS for imaging and sensing applications; optical lithography and novel techniques for nanofabrication; microfabricated neutral atom trap and ion trap for mass spectrometry and quantum computing; microfluidic and microfabricated chemical reactor.

Peyghambarian, Nasser, Ph.D., Indiana University, 1982. Chair, Photonics and Lasers; Director, ERC NSF CIAN. *Electrical Engineering, Nonlinear Dynamics and Complex Systems, Optics, Physics and other Science Education, Polymer Physics/Science, Other*. Optical telecommunication; fiber optics; fiber amplifiers and fiber lasers; integrated optics; femtosecond laser spectroscopy and dynamics of optical phenomena in semiconductors and organic materials; nonlinear photonics and high-speed optical switching; characterization of optical materials in terms of speed and nonlinearities; polymer op-

toelectronics; photorefractive polymers; organic light-emitting diodes and lasers.

Potter, Kelly Simmons, Ph.D., University of Arizona, 1994. *Electrical Engineering, Optics, Other*. Elements for integrated optical systems using both optically active and passive novel photowritable materials; examination of single- and multiphoton processes leading to both linear and nonlinear response in optical materials as a result of exposure to either ionizing or non-ionizing radiation; research into the impact of defect physics on material optical behavior, waveguide device design, and optical device performance.

Potter Jr., Barrett G., University of Florida, 1991. Professor of Materials Science and Engineering. *Materials Science, Metallurgy, Nano Science and Technology*. Synthesis and study of glass, ceramic, and molecular hybrid materials for photonic and electronic applications: optically driven molecular assembly strategies; nanostructured photovoltaic energy conversion materials; photoactivated phenomena in glass and hybrid thin films; solution and physical vapor phase deposition of thin films and nanocomposites (oxides, inorganic-organic hybrids); thermal stability of complex oxide optical materials; environmental sensing; optical behavior of rare-earth-doped matrices; semiconductor quantum-dot ensembles; optical spectroscopy.

Saavedra, Scott, Ph.D., Duke University, 1986. *Optics, Other*. Bioanalytical chemistry; Surface spectroscopy and spectroelectrochemistry; Waveguides and interfacial optics; Chemical and biological sensors; Biointerfaces and biomaterials; Photovoltaic materials.

Sasian, José M., Ph.D., University of Arizona, 1988. *Astronomy, Atomic, Molecular, & Optical Physics, Medical, Health Physics, Optics, Other*. Lens and mirror design; optical fabrication; optomechanics; illumination optics; optical instrumentation for astronomy and biomedical sciences; conformal optics; microlithography; novel optical systems.

Schwiegerling, James, Ph.D., University of Arizona, 1995. *Medical, Health Physics, Optics, Other*. Visual system modeling with ray tracing software; corneal topographic analysis for disease detection and visual performance assessment following surgery; optimization of refractive surgery techniques and development of ophthalmic instrumentation.

Seraphin, Supapan, Ph.D., Arizona State University, 1990. Green chemistry approach to synthesizing nanoparticles for waste water treatment and CO2.

Shadman, Farhang, Ph.D., University of California, Berkeley, 1972. Regents Professor of Chemical & Environmental Engineering; Director of the Semiconductor Research Corporation Engineering Research Center for Environmentally Benign Semiconductor Manufacturing. *Chemical Physics, Energy Sources & Environment, Other*. Applications of chemical reaction engineering in semiconductor and optoelectronics manufacturing; advanced materials processing and environmental contamination control.

Su, Tsu-Te J., Ph.D., California Institute of Technology, 2014. *Biophysics, Medical, Health Physics, Optics*. Imaging, microfabrication and optical instrument building for biological and medical applications. Specifically, biosensing and imaging, label-free single molecule detection, medical diagnostics, microfluidics, micropatterning of extracellular matrix molecules for cellular control, optical resonators, and sing magnetic and optical tweezers to study cellular dynamics.

Uhlmann, Donald R., Ph.D., Harvard University, 1963. *Materials Science, Metallurgy, Other*. Sol-gel synthesis of ceramics nanocomposites; optical materials; hybrid silicone materials and devices; ferroelectric and pyroelectric materials and devices; kinetic processes in materials.

Walker, Christopher K., Ph.D., University of Arizona, 1988. *Astronomy, Optics, Other*. Star formation; millimeter instrumentation.

Wright, Ewan M., Ph.D., Heriot-Watt University, 1983. *Applied Physics, Atomic, Molecular, & Optical Physics, Engineering Physics/Science, Low Temperature Physics, Nano Science and Technology, Nonlinear Dynamics and Complex Systems, Optics, Physics and other Science Education, Physics of Beams, Other*. Theory and simulation of light-string propagation in air; electromagnetic pulse emission from light-string-induced plasmas; supercontinuum generation and self-guiding in condensed media; Bose-Einstein condensation in atomic vapors; mean-field theory and beyond for small BECs; quantum theory of 1-D gases in the Tonks-Girardeau regime; theory of 1-D atom waveguides and interferometers; theory of light-induced waveguides for cold atoms; optically bound matter; theory of anyon matter in planar chiral nanostructures.

Ziolkowski, Richard, Ph.D., University of Illinois at Urbana-Champaign, 1980. *Applied Mathematics, Electromagnetism, Other*. Application of new mathematical and numerical methods to linear and nonlinear problems dealing with the interaction of acoustic and electromagnetic waves with complex media, metamaterials, and realistic structures.

Associate Professor

Ashok, Amit, Ph.D., University of Arizona, 2008. *Electrical Engineering, Optics, Other*. Optical imaging and sensing; physical optics; statistical inference and information theory.

Ellis, Jonathan D., Ph.D., Delft University of Technology, 2010. *Mechanics, Optics, Other*. freeform optics metrology; laser-based manufacturing; and defense systems. Interests in the intersections between traditional engineering and science disciplines relating to mechanical, optical, and electrical engineering, as well as vision science and biology.

Guha, Saikat, Ph.D., Massachusetts Institute of Technology, 2008. *Atomic, Molecular, & Optical Physics, Optics, Quantum Foundations, Other*. Quantum Information Theory; Optical Communications; Quantum Key Distribution; Optical and Quantum Computing; Optical Sensing and Imaging; Network Theory.

Guyon, Olivier, Ph.D., Pierre-and-Marie-Curie University, 2002. Assistant Professor of Astronomy. *Astronomy*. Innovative techniques for extrasolar planets; new wavefront sensing techniques for adaptive optics; Phase-Induced Amplitude Apodization coronagraph; high-contrast imaging techniques.

Hart, Michael, Ph.D., University of Arizona, 1991. *Astronomy, Optics, Other*. Adaptive optics r large astronomical telescopes and other optical systems, including tomographic wavefront sensing and deformable mirror development.

Jacquod, Philippe, Ph.D., University of Neuchâtel, 1997. *Nano Science and Technology, Quantum Foundations, Other*. Quantum Transport; Quantum Spintronics; Nano-optics; Thermoelectricity.

Jones, Ronald Jason, Ph.D., University of New Mexico, 2001. *Atomic, Molecular, & Optical Physics, Electrical Engineering, Optics, Other*. Ultrafast laser science; femtosecond frequency combs; extreme nonlinear light/matter interactions and generation; optical frequency metrology; high-resolution spectroscopy.

Kieu, Khanh, Ph.D., The University of Arizona, 2007. Quantum electronics, ultra-fast lasers, and nonlinear optics; optical fiber technologies such as fiber lasers, fiber optical sensors, nonlinear effects, and devices in waveguiding structures; developing new advanced components and instruments.

Kolesik, Miroslav, Ph.D., Slovak Academy of Sciences, 1992. *Nonlinear Dynamics and Complex Systems, Physics of Beams, Other*. Semiconductor laser simulation; femtosecond light-matter interactions; computational nonlinear optics.

Peng, Leilei, Ph.D., Purdue University, 2005. *Optics, Other*. High-speed Fourier transform fluorescence spectrometer for hyperspectral imaging.

Sandhu, Arvinder S., Ph.D., Tata Institute of Fundamental Research, 2005. *Atomic, Molecular, & Optical Physics, Engineering Physics/Science, High Energy Physics, Other*. High-harmonic generation in hollow waveguides/XUV sources; generation and applications of attosecond pulse trains; carrier envelope phase stabilization techniques for grating-based Ti: Sapphire ultrashort pulse amplifier systems; cold target recoil ion momentum spectroscopy (a.k.a. reaction microscope) for coincidence imaging of molecular or atomic fragments; time-resolved experiments to probe ultrafast dynamics in atoms, molecules, and plasmas using X-ray and electrons in both high-average-power and high-peak-power regime.

Takashima, Yuzuru, Ph.D., Stanford University, 2007. *Electrical Engineering, Optics, Other*. Optical systems for high-density bit-based holographic data storage systems.

Utzinger, Urs, Ph.D., Federal Institute of Technology, 1995. *Medical, Health Physics, Optics, Other*. Optical tissue spectroscopy; optical biosignatures and bioinstrumentation.

Visscher, Koen, Ph.D., University of Amsterdam, 1993. *Applied Physics, Optics, Other*. Regulation of gene expression by mechanical force; RNA structure; optical tweezers.

Witte, Russell, Ph.D., Arizona State University, 2002. *Medical, Health Physics, Optics, Other*. Electrical brain mapping during neurosurgery (epilepsy, brain cancer); novel paradigms to diagnose and treat neurological disorders (Alzheimer's); neural prostheses; functional electrical stimulation; neural engineering: muscular disease, sports injury, rehabilitation, fatigue, and aging.

Assistant Professor

Cronin, Alexander, Ph.D., University of Washington, 1999. *Atomic, Molecular, & Optical Physics, Optics, Other*. Atom interferometry.

Fan, Linran, Ph.D., Yale University, 2017. *Nano Science and Technology, Optics*. Development of on-chip photon control technology using nonlinear optical, mechanical, and electro-optic effects at nanometer scale with applications targeting quantum and classical information processing.

Hassan, Mohammed, Ph.D., Max-Planck Institute of Quantum Optics, 2013. *Optics, Other*. Attomicroscopy: Attosecond electron microscopy; Attosecond pump-attosecond probe spectroscopy; Imaging and controlling the electron dynamics in atoms, molecules, and solids.

Kang, Dongkyun, Ph.D., Korea Advanced Institute of Science and Technology, 2006. *Medical, Health Physics, Optics, Other*. Low-cost smartphone in vivo microscopy; High-speed in vivo endomicroscopy; Ultraminiature endomciroscopy; Optical imaging for low-resource settings.

Kim, Dae Wook, Ph.D., University of Arizona, 2009. *Electrical Engineering, Optics*. Large precision optics fabrication using Computer Controlled Optical Surfacing (CCOS) process; optical testing for large optical components using computer generated holograms, laser tracker, interferometer, etc.; optical system design and manufacturing; open-source data analysis and visualization S/W platform development for optical engineering.

McLeod, Euan, Ph.D., Princeton University, 2009. *Nano Science and Technology, Optics*. Nano-photonics, surface science, soft materials science, optical tweezers, holographic microscopy, computational imaging, 3D additive manufacturing, self-assembly, directed assembly, lab-on-chip imaging, biosensing & medical diagnostics.

Wilson, Dalziel, Ph.D., California Institute of Technology, 2011. *Atomic, Molecular, & Optical Physics, Quantum Foundations, Other*. Quantum optics; Optomechanics,.

Zhang, Zheshen, Ph.D., Georgia Institute of Technology, 2011. *Electrical Engineering, Optics, Other*. Experimental and theoretical aspects of quantum information science; new materials and light-matter interactions.

Emeritus

Burge, James H., Ph.D., University of Arizona, 1993. *Astronomy, Atmosphere, Space Physics, Cosmic Rays, Optics, Other*. Optical system engineering; optical design opto-mechanics; pointing and tracking; detectors; cryogenic systems; optical testing and precision metrology; aspheric surfaces; ultralightweight mirrors for space; diffractive optics; stellar interferometry; astronomical instrumentation.

Dereniak, Eustace L., Ph.D., University of Arizona, 1976. *Electrical Engineering, Optics, Physics of Beams, Other*. Infrared-radiation detection; imaging spectrometers; cryogenically cooled detector/electronics technology; CCD and CMOS devices; infrared detectors using charge-transfer concepts; image processing of infrared sensors.

Falco, Charles, Ph.D., University of California, Irvine, 1974. Chair of Condensed Matter Physics. *Energy Sources & Environment, Optics, Other*. Metallic superlattices; X-ray optics; magnetism; magneto-optics; far-IR detector materials; superconductivity; nucleation and epitaxy of thin films; multilayered materials and superlattices.

Professor Emeritus

Strickland, Robin, Ph.D., Sheffield University, 1979. Professor of Electrical and Computer Engineering. *Computer Science, Electrical Engineering, Other*. Digital image processing; computer vision; signal processing.

Wyant, James C., Ph.D., University of Rochester, 1968. Founding Dean of College of Optical Sciences. *Optics, Other*. Implementation of microcomputers and software to interferometric techniques for optical measurements, in particular for optical testing; testing of supersmooth optical surfaces; measurement of optically rough surfaces; testing of complex aspheric surfaces; development of commercial optical test equipment based on phase-shifting interferometry.

Research Professor

Biggar, Stuart F., Ph.D., University of Arizona, 1990. *Optics, Other*. Spacecraft and aircraft optical sensors; optical system design, evaluation, and absolute radiometric calibration; reflectance measurement.

Chavez-Pirson, Arturo, Ph.D., University of Arizona, 1989. *Optics, Other*. Fiber-based light sources for applications in optical sensing, laser ranging, metrology, optical telecommunications, industrial machining, biomedical imaging and related areas; Specialty glass and optical fibers; Single-frequency fiber lasers; High-power fiber lasers and amplifiers; Short-pulse fiber amplifiers; Mid-infrared optical fibers.

Hessenius, Chris, Ph.D., The University of Arizona, 2013. *Optics, Other*. Semiconductor materials; High-power semiconductor lasers; Extended cavity lasers; Nonlinear optical devices; Pulsed lasers; Intracavity sum and difference frequency generation.

Kaneda, Yushi, Ph.D., University of Tokyo, 1998. Task-relevant metrics for imaging system design and post-processing; Estimation/detection theory and practice, prior work in medical imaging; Stochastic systems analysis and information quantitation. *Nonlinear Dynamics and Complex Systems*. Solid-state lasers; optically pumped semiconductor lasers; fiber lasers; nonlinear frequency conversion.

Kilper, Daniel, Ph.D., The University of Michigan, 1996. *Optics, Other*. Photonics; Fiber Optics; Optical Communications; Simulations; Telecommunications; Optoelectronics, Network Design; Optical Fibet.

Kwong, Nai-Hang, Ph.D., California Institute of Technology, 1983. *Quantum Foundations*. Microscopic theory of nonlinear optics of semiconductor quantum well structures; quantum mechanics of interacting electrons and/or excitons in the semiconductor; electromagnetically induced transparency in quantum wells, Raman coherences, four-wave mixing in microcavities, and optically induced polarization shift in quantum well Bragg structures; conceptual issues such as the bosonic aspects of quantum well excitons.

LaComb, Lloyd, Ph.D., Stanford University, 1989. *Optics*. Holography; interferometry; spectroscopy; ellipsometry; reflectometry; image formation; image processing; image analysis and correction; fiber optics; lasers; film thickness measurement; surface measurements.

Rastegarfar, Houman, Ph.D., University of Toronto, 2014. *Optics, Other*. Optical networking for 5G mobile and wireless communications; Network and switch architecture; Network control and management; Cross-layer network design and analysis; Optical communications systems.

Stapelbroek, Maryn G., Ph.D., University of Connecticut, 1976. *Optics, Other*. Detectors and focal plane arrays for both infrared and visible applications;Semiconductor devices; solid-state physics and sensor systems.

Wissinger, John, Ph.D., Massachusetts Institute of Technology, 1994. *Computer Science*. Optical communications networks; network monitoring and control; distributed sensor networks; distributed inference and learning.

Research Associate Professor

Blanche, Pierre-Alexandre, Ph.D., University of Liege, 1999. *Nano Science and Technology, Optics*. Photorefractive materials and their applications; holography and recording materials; technical holographic applications; dispersive volume phase holographic gratings and holographic optical elements; photovoltaic materials; nano-structuring and nanoparticles for optics and photonics; nonlinear optics; space instrumentation.

Czapla-Myers, Jeffrey, Ph.D., University of Arizona, 2006. *Optics, Other*. Preflight and postlaunch radiometric calibration of airborne and satellite sensors; design and testing of field and laboratory radiometers.

Dubin, Matthew, Ph.D., University of Arizona, 2002. *Optics, Systems Science/Engineering, Other*. Optical systems and engineering; innovation; design, prototyping, and use of systems involving interferometry, alignment, imaging, opto-mechanical design, display design, and illumination combining conceptual and analytical skills with system design and practical implementation.

Hader, Jorg, Ph.D., Philipp University of Marburg, 1997. Semiconductor many-body physics; carrier recombination processes in semiconductors; nonequilibrium dynamics in semiconductor lasers; modeling of vertical external cavity surface emitting lasers; microscopic optoelectronics of wide bandgap nitride-based and mid- to far-infrared semiconductor lasers and laser diodes.

Jiang, Linan, Ph.D., Hong Kong University of Science and Technology, 1999. *Nano Science and Technology, Optics, Other*. microscale heat transfer and microfluidics; MEMs/nano technology, microsensors, microstructures, thin films and integrated microsystems; optofluidics for bio-sensing and detecting.

Kupinski, Meredith K., Ph.D., University of Arizona, 2008. *Optics, Physics and other Science Education, Other*. Task-relevant metrics for imaging system design and post-processing; Estimation/detection theory and practice, prior work in medical imaging; Stochastic systems analysis and information quantitation.

Polynkin, Pavel, Ph.D., Texas A&M University, 2000. High-intensity ultrafast laser science; plasma generation in intense laser fields; material processing with ultrafast lasers; free-space communications through turbid media; nonlinear wavelength conversion; optical fiber lasers and amplifiers; optical sensors.

Zhu, Xiushan, Ph.D., The University of Arizona, 2008. *Nano Science and Technology, Optics*. Optical fibers, fiber devices, fiber lasers, and solid-state lasers; novel materials for fiber laser and amplifiers, high power ZBLAN fiber lasers, single-frequency fiber lasers and amplifiers, advanced fiber devices and nonlinear optics.

Research Assistant Professor

Lacaplain, Caroline, Ph.D., University of Rouen, 2010. *Optics, Other*. generation of high energy ultrashort pulses in passively mode-locked fiber oscillators; behavior of large set of solitons in mode-locked fiber lasers; mid-infrared Kerr frequency combs based on crystalline microresonators.

Smith, Gregory A., Ph.D., The University of Arizona, 2006. *Engineering Physics/Science, Optics*. Polarization software design and polarization engineering; hands-on design for quantum physics; optical simulation and analysis.

Young Sik, Kim, Ph.D., Yonsei University, 2005. *Optics, Other*.

Adjunct Professor

Creath, Katherine, Ph.D., University of Arizona, 1985. *Optics, Other*. Interference microscopy; Interferometric metrology; Optical testing; Optical instrumentation; Image and signal processing; Nondestructive testing and speckle.

Jiang, Shibin, Ph.D., Universite de Rennes 1, 1996. *Optics*. Photonics; fiber lasers; fiber amplifiers and photonic devices using nonsilica glasses and fibers.

Koch, Stephan W., Ph.D., University of Frankfurt, 1979. *Atomic, Molecular, & Optical Physics, Nano Science and Technology, Theoretical Physics*. Condensed matter theory; optical and electronic properties of semiconductors; many-body interactions; semiconductor quantum optics; quantum confinement in solids; coherent and ultrafast phenomena; semiconductor laser theory; microcavity and photonic crystal effects.

Kost, Alan, Ph.D., University of Texas, Austin, 1983. Administrative Director, CIAN Engineering Research Center. *Electrical Engineering, Optics, Other*. Nano-photonics (photonic integrated circuits, fiber optics, and nonlinear optical materials); optical data storage.

Kyle, Myers, Ph.D., University of Arizona, 1985. *Optics, Other*. Image science.

Mahajan, Virendra, Ph.D., University of Arizona, 1974. *Optics, Other*. Aberration theory; Optical Imaging.

McClain, Stephen, Ph.D., Cornell University, 1992. *Optics, Other*. Polarization modeling, design and analysis; Optical system design and lens design.

Novak, Erik, Ph.D., University of Arizona, 1998. *Optics, Other*.

Pompea, Stephen, Ph.D., University of Arizona, 1989. *Optics, Other*. Science education program and instructional materials design; Science communication and engagement strategies, especially for groups underrepresented in STEM; Optical system design and analysis, stray light, and optical materials.

Schmit, Joanna, Ph.D., University of Arizona, 1996. *Optics, Other*.

Su, Peng, Ph.D., University of Arizona, 2008. Optical metrology for testing aspheric surfaces: swing arm profilometer, CGH test, interferometry, large flat test, and scanning pentaprism test; optical design; diffractive optics; adaptive optics; global warming; solar reflector; optical system engineering.

Turner, Mary, Ph.D., University of Arizona, 1993. *Optics, Other*.

Tyo, J. Scottt, Ph.D., University of Pennsylvania, 1997. *Optics, Other*. Enabling technologies for optical and microwave remote sensing: processing of high-dimensional spectropolarimetric data; Investigation of statistical properties of hyperspectral imagery; Optimization of polarimetric sensors for remote sensing applications.

Adjunct Associate Professor

Parks, Robert E., M.A., Williams College, 1966. Optical testing and test instrumentation; optical fabrication methods.

Posdoctoral Research Associate

Babicheva, Victoriia, Ph.D., Technical University of Denmark, 2013. *Nano Science and Technology, Optics, Other*. Nanophotonics; nano-optics; materials for optical and optoelectronic devices.

Ding, Yijun, Ph.D., University of Arizona, 2016. *Optics, Other*.

Gagatsos, Christos, Ph.D., Université Libre de Bruxelles, École Polytechnique, 2014. *Optics, Other*. Quantum Information Theory; Quantum Technologies; Quantum Sensing and Imaging; Open Quantum Systems.

Lukowski, Michal, Ph.D., University of Arizona, 2016. *Optics, Other*. VECSEL; tunable laser technology.

Rosenow, Phil, Ph.D., The Philipp University of Marburg, 2016. *Optics, Other*.

Seshadreesan, Kaushik, Ph.D., Louisiana State University, 2015. *Optics, Other*. Quantum Information Theory; Quantum Communications; Quantum Sensing and Imaging; Quantum Key Distribution.

DEPARTMENTAL RESEARCH SPECIALTIES AND STAFF

Theoretical

Image Science. http://www.optics.arizona.edu/research/faculty-specialties/image-science Ashok, Barrett, Barton, Chipman, Furenlid, Gmitro, Kang, Matthew Kupinski, Meredith Kupinski, Peng.

Optical Engineering. http://www.optics.arizona.edu/research/faculty-specialties/optical-engineering Czapla-Myers, Dubin, Ellis, Greivenkamp, Hua, Kim, Koshel, Liang, Milster, Sasian, Schwiegerling, Takashima.

Optical Physics. http://www.optics.arizona.edu/research/faculty-specialties/optical-physics Anderson, Binder, Jessen, Jones, Kolesik, Moloney, Polynkin, Wilson, Wright.

Photonics. http://www.optics.arizona.edu/research/faculty-specialties/photonics Blanche, Fallahi, Fan, Guha, Kilper, Thomas Koch, LaComb, Mansuripur, McLeod, Norwood, Pau, Peyghambarian, Tsu-Te Su, Zhu.

View additional information about this department at www.gradschoolshopper.com. Check out the "Why Choose Us?" section, find out more about the department's culture and get links to social media networks.

UNIVERSITY OF ARIZONA

DEPARTMENT OF PHYSICS

Tucson, Arizona 85721
http://www.physics.arizona.edu

General University Information
President: Robert C. Robbins
Dean of Graduate School: Andrew Carnie
University website: http://www.arizona.edu
School Type: Public
Setting: Urban
Total Faculty: 3,144
Total Graduate Faculty: 2,774
Total number of Students: 43,625
Total number of Graduate Students: 7,946

Department Information
Department Chairman: Prof. Sumit Mazumdar, Chair
Department Contact: Gardie Lueders, Graduate Coordinator
  Total full-time faculty: 32
  Full-Time Graduate Students: 116
  Female Full-Time Graduate Students: 20
  First-Year Graduate Students: 31
  Female First-Year Students: 10
  Total Post Doctorates: 10

Department Address
1118 E. 4th Street
Tucson, AZ 85721
Phone: (520) 621-2290
Fax: (520) 621-4721
E-mail: gradcoord@physics.arizona.edu
Website: http://www.physics.arizona.edu

ADMISSIONS

Admission Contact Information
Address admission inquiries to: University of Arizona, Department of Physics, Graduate Coordinator, 1118 E. 4th St., Tucson, AZ 85721
Phone: (520) 621-2290
E-mail: gradcoord@physics.arizona.edu
Admissions website: http://grad.arizona.edu/admissions

Application deadlines
Fall admission:
U.S. students: January 1   *Int'l. students*: December 1

Application fee
U.S. students: $85   *Int'l. students*: $95
http://w3.physics.arizona.edu/grad/apply. No Spring Admissions, except under special circumstances.

Admissions information
For Fall of 2018:
  Number of applicants: 164
  Number admitted: 85
  Number enrolled: 29

Admission requirements
Bachelor's degree requirements: A Bachelor's degree in Physics or a related field is required.
Minimum undergraduate GPA: 3.0

GRE requirements
The GRE is required.
No minimum score has been set.

Subjective GRE requirements
The Subjective GRE is required.
No minimum score has been set.

TOEFL requirements
The TOEFL exam is required for students from non-English-speaking countries.
  PBT score: 550
  iBT score: 79

Other admissions information
Undergraduate preparation assumed: Tipler, Modern Physics; (Phys. 242); Symon, Mechanics (Phys. 321); Wangsness, Griffiths, Electromagnetic Fields (Phys. 331/332); Hecht and Zajac, Optics (Phys. 320); Fermi, Thermodynamics; Callen, Thermodynamics (Phys. 325); Liboff, Griffiths, Quantum Physics (Phys. 371); Gasiorowicz, Quantum Physics (Phys. 472); Herzberg, Kodak, Beveridge, Atomic Spectra and Atomic Structure (Phys. 473/474); Kittel, Introduction to Solid State Physics (Phys. 460); Arfken, Mathematical Methods for Physics (Phys. 475); Melissinos, Experiments in Modern Physics; Young, Statistical Treatment of Experimental Data; Taylor, An Introduction to Error Analysis (all 3 optional); (Phys. 381, 481).

TUITION

Tuition year 2018–2019:
Tuition for in-state residents
  Full-time students: $5,858 per semester
Tuition for out-of-state residents
  Full-time students: $16,032.5 per semester
Graduate Assistants receive a Non-Resident Tuition Waiver and a Tuition Remission.
Credit hours per semester to be considered full-time: 9
Deferred tuition plan: Yes
Health insurance: Yes, $2,088 per year, included in assistantship.
Other academic fees: Miscellaneous fees total $664.13 per semester for full-time students.
Academic term: Semester

Teaching Assistants, Research Assistants, and Fellowships
Number of first-year
  Teaching Assistants: 26
  Research Assistants: 3
  Fellowship students: 4
Average stipend per academic year
  Teaching Assistant: $18,400
  Research Assistant: $18,400
Typically every student admitted into our PhD program is given an assistantship, normally in the form of a Teaching Assistantship.

FINANCIAL AID

Application deadlines
Fall admission:
U.S. students: January 1   *Int'l. students*: December 1

Loans

Loans are available for U.S. students.

Loans are available for international students.

GAPSFAS application required: No

FAFSA application required: Yes

For further information

Address financial aid inquiries to: Office of Student Financial Aid, 203 Administration Building, University of Arizona.

Phone: (520) 621-1858

Financial aid website: https://financialaid.arizona.edu

HOUSING

Availability of on-campus housing

Single students: Yes

Married students: Yes

For further information

Address housing inquiries to: Graduate Housing: La Aldea, 825 E. Fifth Street, Tucson, AZ 85719.

Phone: (520) 626-0336

E-mail: housing@life.arizona.edu

Housing aid website: http://www.life.arizona.edu

Table A—Faculty, Enrollments, and Degrees Granted

Research Specialty	2016–2017 Faculty	Enrollment Fall 2017		Number of Degrees Granted 2016–2017		
		Master's	Doctorate	Master's	Terminal Master's	Doctorate
Astrophysics	4	–	28	–	–	1
Atomic, Molecular, & Optical Physics	3	–	20	–	–	2
Biophysics	2	–	5	2	–	–
Chemical Physics	2	–	4	–	–	1
Computational Physics	–	–	1	–	–	–
Condensed Matter Physics	7	–	10	–	1	6
Cosmology & String Theory	–	–	1	–	–	–
High Energy Physics	9	–	11	1	1	1
Lattice Gauge Theory	–	–	1	–	–	–
Materials Science, Metallurgy	–	–	1	–	–	–
Medical, Health Physics	1	7	–	–	–	–
Nonlinear Dynamics and Complex Systems	–	–	2	–	–	–
Nuclear Physics	3	–	7	–	–	–
Optics	1	–	6	–	–	1
Physics of Beams	–	–	1	1	–	–
Theoretical Physics	–	–	7	2	–	–
Non-specialized	–	–	1	–	–	–
Total	32	7	109	6	2	12
Full-time Grad. Stud.	–	7	109	–	–	–
First-year Grad. Stud.	–	2	29	–	–	–

GRADUATE DEGREE REQUIREMENTS

Master's: To qualify for the M.S. degree, the student must complete at least 30 units of graduate work, at least 15 of which must be in physics. The student must pass the written comprehensive exam at the M.S. level and maintain a 3.0 average. No foreign language required. The student must also satisfy one of the following options: (1) Write a Master's Report (for which up to six units may be allowed) and pass an oral examination. (2) Take six additional graduate credits in physics and pass a final oral examination. Under this option, the stu-dent completes a total of at least 21 units in physics out of the total of 30 units required. (3) Pass the written and oral parts of the comprehensive examination for the Ph.D. Students are not normally admitted into the M.S. program; students with bachelors degrees who seek the Ph.D. as the terminal degree should apply directly for admission into the Ph.D. program. Such students may then earn the M.S. degree en route to the Ph.D. Masters in Medical Physics: This degree requires completion of at least 36 units of graduate work, including 6 units of internship, 12 units of physics, up to 6 units of business, and 9 units of other specialty courses.

Doctorate: The Ph.D. degree requires completion of 36 units of graduate work in physics, with 9 additional units in the minor, with a 3.0/4.0 grade average (exclusive of dissertation credits); passing the qualifying and comprehensive examinations; submitting a dissertation based on independent research; and defending this dissertation in a final examination. Note that independent study research can be used to earn a substantial portion of the required graduate units.

Other Degrees: Interdisciplinary work with other departments is possible, especially in the areas of materials and surface physics, chemical physics, astrophysics, space physics, optical science, medical physics, biophysics, applied math, and mathematical physics.

Thesis: Thesis may be written in absentia.

SPECIAL EQUIPMENT, FACILITIES, OR PROGRAMS

Our graduate program is dedicated to research at the cutting edge of discovery. We also have strong interdisciplinary initiatives, with campus-wide programs in theoretical astrophysics, lunar and planetary sciences, geosciences, optical sciences, biophysics, and applied mathematics. Additional connections to biology, chemistry, and medicine provide additional research opportunities. Moreover, in addition to a traditional Ph.D. program, we are also one of the few institutions nationwide to have a Master's program in Medical Physics. Graduate students have excellent resources at their disposal.

General facilities include a shop for students and staff. An extensive collection of physics journals and more than 5,000 physics books are located in the science library building. The University is connected to Internet2 for high-speed connectivity to the NSF supercomputer centers, other universities, and other supercomputer centers. The University also operates a large SGI supercomputer, numerous UNIX servers, Windows PC and Macintosh public access sites, and a computerized library information system (sabio.arizona.edu). The Physics Department has a large number of Linux PCs, Windows PCs, and laser printers (color and b/w) available for general department use.

Facilities and equipment for particular research areas in physics include a 3-MV tandem accelerator, spectrographs, spectrometers, superconducting magnets for solid state physics, electron microscopes, electron probes (including Auger, RHEED, and LEED), a materials-processing laboratory, thin-film molecular beam epitaxy (MBE) and sputter epitaxy equipment, thin-film X-ray diffraction facilities, an atomic force microscope, optical tweezers and single molecule detection for biophysics, cryogenic systems covering the entire temperature range of 300 K down to 0.02 K, a computerized Mössbauer spectroscopy system, ultrahigh-resolution infrared and visible lasers, atomic-beam machines, and an observatory for work in experimental relativity and solar seismology. The high-energy experimental group does work at Fermilab and CERN. There is an active program in theoretical physics covering atomic, nuclear, condensed matter, astrophysics, and high-energy theory. The Departments of Physics and Geosciences jointly operate a facility, sponsored by the National Science Foundation, that uses accelerators for radioisotope dating.

Table B—Separately Budgeted Research Expenditures by Source of Support

Source of Support	Departmental Research	Physics-related Research Outside Department
Federal government	$2,134,550	
State/local government		
Non-profit organizations	$901,688	
Business and industry		
Other	$74,821	
Total	**$3,111,059**	

Table C—Separately Budgeted Research Expenditures by Research Specialty

Research Specialty	No. of Grants	Expenditures ($)
Astrophysics	3	$186,208
Atomic, Molecular, & Optical Physics	11	$439,159
Biophysics	2	$67,911
Condensed Matter Physics	8	$507,213
High Energy Physics	12	$1,764,276
Nuclear Physics	1	$116,687
Physics and other Science Education	1	$20,645
Other	1	$8,960
Total	**39**	**$3,111,059**

FACULTY

Professor

Cheu, Elliott, Ph.D., Cornell University, 1991. Associate Dean, College of Science. *High Energy Physics*. Experimental high energy.

Cronin, Alexander D., Ph.D., University of Washington, 1999. *Atomic, Molecular, & Optical Physics*. Experimental atomic physics.

Dienes, Keith R., Ph.D., Cornell University, 1991. *High Energy Physics*. Theoretical high-energy physics.

Fleming, Sean, Ph.D., Northwestern University, 1995. Director of Graduate Studies. *Nuclear Physics*. Nuclear theory; high-energy theory.

Johns, Ken, Ph.D., Rice University, 1986. Associate Department Head. *High Energy Physics*. Experimental high energy.

Lebed, Andrei, Ph.D., Landau Institute for Theoretical Physics, 1986. *Condensed Matter Physics*. Theoretical condensed matter.

Mazumdar, Sumit, Ph.D., Princeton University, 1980. Department Head. *Condensed Matter Physics*. Condensed matter theory.

Melia, Fulvio, Ph.D., Massachusetts Institute of Technology, 1985. *Astrophysics*. Theoretical astrophysics.

Meystre, Pierre, Ph.D., Swiss Federal Institute of Technology, 1974. *Optics*. Theoretical quantum optics.

Rafelski, Johann, Ph.D., University of Frankfurt, 1973. *Nuclear Physics, Particles and Fields*. Relativistic nuclear theory; laser particle physics; nuclear cosmology.

Rutherfoord, John P., Ph.D., Cornell University, 1968. *High Energy Physics*. Experimental high-energy physics.

Sarcevic, Ina, Ph.D., University of Minnesota, 1986. *High Energy Physics, Nuclear Physics*. High-energy theory; nuclear theory.

Stafford, Charles A., Ph.D., Princeton University, 1992. Condensed matter theory.

Su, Shufang, Ph.D., Massachusetts Institute of Technology, 2000. *High Energy Physics*. Theoretical high-energy physics.

Toussaint, Douglas, Ph.D., Princeton University, 1978. *High Energy Physics*. High-energy theory.

van Kolck, Ubirajara, Ph.D., University of Texas, Austin, 1993. *Nuclear Physics*. Effective field theories in particle, nuclear, atomic, and astro physics.

Varnes, Erich W., Ph.D., University of California, Berkeley, 1997. *High Energy Physics*. Experimental high-energy physics.

Wolgemuth, Charles W., Ph.D., University of Arizona, 2000. *Biophysics*. Biological physics.

Zhang, Shufeng, Ph.D., New York University, 1991. *Condensed Matter Physics*. Condensed matter theory.

Associate Professor

LeRoy, Brian, Ph.D., Harvard University, 2003. *Condensed Matter Physics*. Experimental nanoscience.

Manne, Srinivas, Ph.D., University of California, Santa Barbara, 1994. *Condensed Matter Physics*. Experimental condensed matter.

Sandhu, Arvinder, Ph.D., Tata Institute of Fundamental Research, 2004. *Atomic, Molecular, & Optical Physics*. Experimental atomic, molecular, and optical physics.

Visscher, Koen, Ph.D., University of Amsterdam, 1993. *Biophysics*. Biophysics.

Assistant Professor

Gralla, Samuel E., Ph.D., University of Chicago, 2011. *Astrophysics*. Physics and astrophysics of strong gravitational and electromagnetic fields; Dynamics of compact objects; Self-force effects; Sources of gravitational radiation; Black hole thermodynamics; Modified gravity theories; Force-free magnetospheres.

Hassan, Mohammed, Ph.D., Ludwig-Maximillian University of Munich, Germany/Max Planck Institute of Quantum Optics, Munich, Germany, 2013. *Atomic, Molecular, & Optical Physics, Condensed Matter Physics*. Real time control, tracing and imaging of electron dynamics in matter.

Meinel, Stefan, Ph.D., Cambridge University, 2010. *High Energy Physics, Nuclear Physics*. High Energy Physics Nuclear Physics.

Rozo, Eduardo, Ph.D., University of Chicago, 2006. *Astrophysics, Cosmology & String Theory, Particles and Fields*. Understanding the physical origin behind our Universe's current phase of accelerated expansion.

Schaibley, John R., Ph.D., University of Michigan, 2013. *Atomic, Molecular, & Optical Physics, Condensed Matter Physics*. Quantum and non-linear optics and spin physics of low dimensional semi-conductor systems, and their applications to device physics and quantum information science.

Wang, Weigang, Ph.D., University of Delaware, 2008. *Condensed Matter Physics*. Experimental condensed matter.

Emeritus

Bickel, William S., Ph.D., Pennsylvania State University, 1965. *Biophysics, Optics*. Optical biophysics; atomic physics; physics of music.

Chambers, Robert H., Ph.D., Carnegie Mellon University, 1957. Science education; dislocation dynamics; internal friction.

Donahue, Douglas J., Ph.D., University of Wisconsin-Madison, 1952. Atomic and nuclear physics; accelerator mass spectrometry.

Emrick, Roy M., Ph.D., University of Illinois, 1960. Experimental solid-state physics.

Garcia, Jose D., Ph.D., University of Wisconsin-Madison, 1966. Collision theory; atomic physics; physics education.

Hill, Henry A., Ph.D., University of Minnesota, 1957. Astrophysics and experimental general relativity.

Hsieh, Ke Chiang, Ph.D., University of Chicago, 1969. Experimental cosmic-ray and space physics.

Huffman, Donald R., Ph.D., University of California, Riverside, 1966. Optical properties of solids; astrophysics.

Jenkins, Edgar W., Ph.D., Columbia University, 1962. Experimental elementary particle physics.

Just, Kurt W., Ph.D., Berlin University, 1954. Gauge theories of gravity and particles.

Kessler, John O., Ph.D., Columbia University, 1953. Applied physics; biophysics and fluids.

Kilkson, Rein, Ph.D., Yale University, 1956. Molecular biophysics.

Kohler, Sigurd, Uppsala, University of Sweden, 1959. Nuclear many-body theory; heavy-ion collisions.

Mahmoud, Hormoz M., Ph.D., Indiana University, 1953. Field theory.

McIntyre, Laurence C., University of Wisconsin-Madison, 1965. Ion-beam analysis.

Scadron, Michael D., Ph.D., University of California, Berkeley, 1964. Theoretical elementary particle physics.

Stark, Royal W., Ph.D., Case Western Reserve University, 1962. Experimental solid-state physics.

Stoner, John O., Ph.D., Princeton University, 1964. Experimental atomic spectroscopy; thin-film optics.

Tomizuka, Carl T., University of Illinois, 1954. Experimental solid-state physics.

Vuillemin, Joseph J., Ph.D., University of Chicago, 1965. Experimental solid-state physics.

Wing, William H., Ph.D., University of Michigan, 1968. Experimental atomic physics and quantum optics.

Research Professor

Beck, Warren, Ph.D., University of Minnesota, 1988. *Accelerator.* AMS Facility.

Hodgins, Gregory, Ph.D., Oxford University, 1999. *Accelerator.* Compound-specific isotope analysis, environmental isotope analysis and archaeology.

Research Associate Professor

Loch, Peter, Ph.D., University of Hamburg, 1992. *High Energy Physics.* High energy physics.

Research Assistant Professor

Biddulph, Dana, Ph.D., University of Arizona, 2004. *Accelerator.* Accelerator Mass Spectrometry.

Cheng, Li, Ph.D., University of Arizona, 2000. *Other.* Laboratory of Tree-Ring Research.

Adjunct Professor

Coon, Sidney, Ph.D., University of Maryland, 1972. Nuclear theory.

Affiliate Professor

Özel, Feryal, Ph.D., Harvard University, 2002. *Astrophysics.* Theoretical astrophysics.

Adamowicz, Ludwik, Ph.D., Institute of Physical Chemistry of the Polish Academy of Sciences, 1977. *Chemical Physics.* Theoretical chemistry; chemical physics.

Anderson, Brian, Ph.D., Stanford University, 1999. *Atomic, Molecular, & Optical Physics.* Experimental Bose-Einstein condensation.

Binder, Rudolf, Ph.D., University of Dortmund, 1988. *Atomic, Molecular, & Optical Physics.* AMO physics.

Brown, Michael, Ph.D., University of California, Santa Cruz, 1975. *Biophysics, Chemical Physics.* Physical chemistry and biochemistry; nuclear magnetic resonance spectroscopy.

Falco, Charles M., Ph.D., University of California, Irvine, 1974. *Condensed Matter Physics, Optics.* Condensed matter physics; optics.

Jessen, Poul, Ph.D., University of Aarhus, 1993. *Atomic, Molecular, & Optical Physics.* Atomic and optical physics.

Jull, Timothy, Ph.D., University of Bristol, 1976. *Geophysics.* Geosciences.

Kennedy, Thomas G., Ph.D., University of Virginia, 1984. Mathematical physics.

Maier, Robert S., Ph.D., Rutgers State University of New Jersey, 1983. *Applied Mathematics.* Applied mathematics; mathematical physics.

Pinto, Philip A., Ph.D., University of California, Santa Cruz, 1988. *Astronomy.* Astronomy.

Psaltis, Dimitrios, Ph.D., University of Illinois at Urbana-Champaign, 1998. *Astrophysics.* Theoretical astrophysics.

Wright, Ewan, Ph.D., Heriot-Watt University, 1983. *Optics.* Theory and stimulation of light string propagation in air.

Xin, Hao, Ph.D., Massachusetts Institute of Technology, 2000. *Condensed Matter Physics.* Microwave and millimeter wave technology.

Affiliate Associate Professor

Trouard, Theodore P., Ph.D., University of Virginia, 1992. *Biophysics.* Biomedical engineering.

Affiliate Assistant Professor

Watchman, Christopher J., Ph.D., University of Florida, 2005. *Medical, Health Physics.* Radiation Dosimetry (macro and microscopic), Lung Radiotherapy, IGRT, Molecular Radiotherapy, Bone Marrow Dosimetry.

Lecturer

Jackson, Shawn S., M.A., Washington University, St. Louis, 1988. *Astrophysics.* Astrophysics.

Milsom, John A., Ph.D., Northwestern University, 1996. Director of Undergraduate Studies. *Astrophysics.* Astrophysics.

DEPARTMENTAL RESEARCH SPECIALTIES AND STAFF

Theoretical

Astrophysics. Black holes, compact objects, AGN's particle astrophysics, cosmology. Özel, Gralla, Melia, Milsom, Psaltis, Rafelski, Rozo, Sarcevic.

Atomic, Molecular, & Optical Physics. Ultracold atoms, Bose condensation and atom lasers, cavity QED, ion-atom collision theory, atomic structure calculations. Binder, Hassan, Meystre, Wright.

Biophysics. Theory and experiment of cell motility. Wolgemuth.

Condensed Matter Physics. Strongly correlated electron systems, mesoscopic and nanoscopic materials, disordered systems, nonlinear dynamics, quantum chaos, quantum spin systems, superconductivity. Adamowicz, Lebed, Mazumdar, Schaibley, Stafford.

High Energy Physics. Theory and phenomenology of strong and electroweak interactions, lattice QCD, neutrino physics, Higgs physics, physics beyond the standard model, supersymmetry, grand unification, extra dimensions, and string theory. Dienes, Fleming, Sarcevic, Su, Toussaint.

Nuclear Physics. Nuclear many-body theory, heavy ion collisions, quark-gluon substructure of nuclear matter, effective field theories of nuclear forces, chiral perturbation theory, Soft-collinear effective theory, heavy-quark systems, laser-induced particle phenomena. Fleming, Kohler, Rafelski, van Kolck.

Experimental

Atomic, Molecular, & Optical Physics. Cold atom trapping, Bose-Einstein condensates, atom interferometry, quantum computation, attosecond spectroscopy. Anderson, Cronin, Jessen, Sandhu.

Biophysics. Theory and experiment of cell motility, chemotaxis, pattern formation by swimming cells, membrane proteins and membrane biophysics, solid-state NMR, nucleic acid structure, single-molecule biophysics, optical tweezers, molecular dynamics simulations. Brown, Kessler, Visscher, Wolgemuth.

Condensed Matter Physics. Self-assembly at solid/liquid interfaces, fullerenes, graphene, scanning tunneling microscopy, magnetic nanostructures, ultrafast optical spectroscopy. Huffman, LeRoy, Manne, Sandhu, Wang.

High Energy Physics. Accelerator-based experiments at Fermilab and CERN, including: direct CP violation in kaon decay, search for Higgs, top quark physics, jets, search for extra dimensions, electroweak physics. Cheu, Johns, Rutherfoord, Varnes.

Other. Radiocarbon dating, cosmic ray effects in terrestrial materials, climate change, geophysical studies. Beck, Jull.

View additional information about this department at www.gradschoolshopper.com. Check out the "Why Choose Us?" section, find out more about the department's culture and get links to social media networks.

CALIFORNIA STATE UNIVERSITY, LONG BEACH

DEPARTMENT OF PHYSICS & ASTRONOMY

Long Beach, California 90840-9505
http://www.physics.csulb.edu

General University Information
President: Jane C. Conoley
Dean of Graduate School: Jody Cormack
University website: http://www.csulb.edu/
School Type: Public
Setting: Urban
Total Faculty: 2,250
Total Graduate Faculty: 13
Total number of Students: 32,079
Total number of Graduate Students: 5,367

Department Information
Department Chairman: Prof. Andreas Bill, Chair
Department Contact: Korin Coombs, Administrative
   Coordinator
   Total full-time faculty: 13
   Total number of full-time equivalent positions: 13
   Full-Time Graduate Students: 63
   Female Full-Time Graduate Students: 14
   First-Year Graduate Students: 15
   Female First-Year Students: 4

Department Address
1250 Bellflower Boulevard
Long Beach, CA 90840-9505
Phone: (562) 985-7925
Fax: (562) 985-7924
E-mail: korin.coombs@csulb.edu
Website: http://www.physics.csulb.edu

ADMISSIONS

Admission Contact Information
Address admission inquiries to: Professor Prashanth Jaikumar,
   Department of Physics & Astronomy, 1250 Bellflower Blvd.,
   Long Beach, CA 90840-9505
Phone: (562) 985-5592
E-mail: Prashanth.Jaikumar@csulb.edu
Admissions website: http://www.csulb.edu/divisions/aa/projects/
   grad/

Application deadlines
Fall admission:
U.S. students: June 1   *Int'l. students*: April 1
Spring admission:
U.S. students: November 1   *Int'l. students*: October 1

Application fee
U.S. students: $55   *Int'l. students*: $55
Application Website: https://calstate.liaisoncas.com/applicant-
   ux/#/login Information about the program: http://web.
   csulb.edu/depts/physics/students/graduateStudents.shtml

Admissions information
For Fall of 2018:
   Number of applicants: 65
   Number admitted: 20
   Number enrolled: 15

Admission requirements
Bachelor's degree requirements: Bachelor degree in Physics is
   preferred. Closely related bachelor degrees are accepted under
   certain conditions. Contact the graduate advisor.
Minimum undergraduate GPA: 2.5

GRE requirements
The GRE is not required.
Applicants are encouraged to indicate their GRE score if they
   have one. It will be used for assessing our program, not for
   admissions.

Subjective GRE requirements
The Subjective GRE is not required.
Applicants are encouraged to indicate their GRE score if they
   have one. It will be used for assessing our program, not for
   admissions.

TOEFL requirements
The TOEFL exam is required for students from non-English-
   speaking countries.
   PBT score: 550
   iBT score: 80

Other admissions information
Additional requirements: Submit a half to one page statement
   of purpose (personal statement) that indicates what your
   dreams and goals are, and how/why you think the Master's
   degree in Physics will move you closer to them. Three letters
   of recommendation to be sent to the graduate advisor
   Prashanth Jaikumar.
Undergraduate preparation assumed: B.S./B.A. in Physics or
   closely related discipline. Contact Graduate Advisor
   Prashanth Jaikumar for advice if B.S. in is a different discipline.

TUITION

Tuition year 2018–19:
Tuition for in-state residents
   Full-time students: $4,116 per semester
   Part-time students: $2,447 per semester
Tuition for out-of-state residents
   Full-time students: $7,284 per semester
   Part-time students: $4,986 per semester
The information above is for 8 units (full-time) or up to 6 units
   (part-time). All graduate students (US citizens, permanent res-
   idents and international students) who are enrolled in 8 units
   are considered full-time graduate students. International stu-
   dents must be full-time students at all time.
Credit hours per semester to be considered full-time: 8
Deferred tuition plan: Yes
Health insurance: Available.
Other academic fees: Health insurance: Domestic students are
   insured after the "covered CA." International Students Services provides information for non-residents.
Academic term: Semester

Teaching Assistants, Research Assistants, and Fellowships

Number of first-year
- *Teaching Assistants*: 15

Average stipend per academic year
- *Teaching Assistant*: $10,088

TA for 1 laboratory section is $2,522 for one semester. The maximum teaching load is 4 laboratory sections per semester. Usually, only 1 or 2 sections are given to requesting students.

FINANCIAL AID

Application deadlines
Fall admission:
U.S. students: June 1   *Int'l. students*: April 1
Spring admission:
U.S. students: November 1   *Int'l. students*: October 1

Loans
Loans are available for U.S. students.
Loans are not available for international students.
GAPSFAS application required: No
FAFSA application required: Yes

For further information
Address financial aid inquiries to: CSULB Office of Financial Aid, In person: 101 Brotman Hall, CSU Long Beach, 1250 Bellflower Blvd, Long Beach 90840-0106.
Phone: (562) 985-8403
E-mail: rebecca.araujo@csulb.edu
Financial aid website: http://www.csulb.edu/depts/enrollment/financial_aid/

HOUSING

Availability of on-campus housing
Single students: No
Married students: No
Childcare Assistance: No

For further information
Address housing inquiries to: Housing and Residential Life, California State University, Long Beach, 1250 Bellflower Boulevard, MS 8701, Long Beach, CA 90840-8701.
Phone: (562) 985-4187
E-mail: housing@csulb.edu
Housing aid website: http://www.csulb.edu/divisions/students/housing/

Table A—Faculty, Enrollments, and Degrees Granted

Research Specialty	2018–19 Faculty	Enrollment Fall 2018		Number of Degrees Granted 2017–18		
		Master's	Doctorate	Master's	Terminal Master's	Doctorate
Astrophysics	3	–	–	–	–	–
Condensed Matter Physics	7	–	–	–	–	–
Nuclear Physics	1	–	–	–	–	–
Theoretical Physics	2	–	–	–	–	–
Total	–	63	–	20	–	–
Full-time Grad. Stud.	–	63	–	–	–	–
First-year Grad. Stud.	–	15	–	–	–	–

GRADUATE DEGREE REQUIREMENTS
Master's: 31 units (18 core, 6 research, 7 elective).

SPECIAL EQUIPMENT, FACILITIES, OR PROGRAMS

Many experimental facilities are housed in the department, including a Physical Properties Measurement System Evercool (PPMS), Teslatron (300mK, 12T), multi-target Sputtering systems, EBeam Evaporator, Magneto-Optical Kerr Effect (MOKE), X-ray diffraction system, Photo-current measurement systems, Vibrating Sample Magnetometer, Multimode Scanning Proble Microscope, Scanning Electron Microscope (SEM), Atomic Force Microscope (AFM), etc.

The Department also has a modern Computational Physics Laboratory and a shared 200 core computer. Several faculty members have their own clusters and all have 12-core computers.

Most equipment has been funded by various external grants, including NSF, DoD, DOE and the Army Research Laboratory.

FACULTY

Professor

Bill, Andreas, Ph.D., University of Stuttgart, 1995. Department chair. *Applied Physics, Computational Physics, Condensed Matter Physics, Low Temperature Physics, Nano Science and Technology, Solid State Physics, Theoretical Physics.* Quantum phases in hybrid structures, superconductivity, magnetism, low-dimensional systems, condensed matter theory, quantum mechanics, crystallization of solids. http://www.csulb.edu/~pjaikuma/Compuphys/comp.html

Gredig, Thomas, Ph.D., University of Minnesota, Twin Cities, 2002. *Applied Physics, Condensed Matter Physics, Materials Science, Metallurgy, Nano Science and Technology, Solar Physics, Solid State Physics.* Organic semiconductors, thin film crystallography, nanomagnetism.

Gu, Jiyeong, Ph.D., Seoul National University, 1998. Director of undergraduate studies. *Applied Physics, Condensed Matter Physics, Low Temperature Physics, Materials Science, Metallurgy, Nano Science and Technology, Solid State Physics.* Thin films; nanomagnetism; superconductivity.

Hintzen, Paul, Ph.D., University of Arizona, 1975. *Astronomy, Astrophysics.* Astronomy.

Hlousek, Zvonimir T., Ph.D., Brown University, 1987. *High Energy Physics, Particles and Fields, Physics and other Science Education, Theoretical Physics.* Quantum Field Theory, Quantum Gravity, Online Education.

Kwon, Chuhee, Ph.D., University of Maryland, College Park, 1995. *Applied Physics, Condensed Matter Physics, Low Temperature Physics, Materials Science, Metallurgy, Nano Science and Technology, Physics and other Science Education, Solid State Physics.* Condensed Matter Physics, Materials Science, Physics Education.

Papp, Zoltan, Ph.D., University of Debrecen, 1986. *Atomic, Molecular, & Optical Physics, Computational Physics, High Energy Physics, Nuclear Physics, Theoretical Physics.* Few body systems, computational physics, quantum mechanics.

Pickett, Galen T., Ph.D., University of Chicago, 1995. *Computational Physics, Condensed Matter Physics, Mechanics, Physics and other Science Education, Polymer Physics/Science, Surface Physics, Theoretical Physics.* Condensed matter theory, membranes.

Rajpoot, Subhash, Ph.D., Imperial College, London, 1979. *Cosmology & String Theory, High Energy Physics, Particles and Fields, Theoretical Physics.* Unification of all interactions. Study of supersymmetry, supergravity, superstring theory, and super membrane theory.

Associate Professor

Jaikumar, Prashanth, Ph.D., Stony Brook University, 2002. Director of graduate studies. *Astrophysics, Computational*

Physics, Nuclear Physics, Relativity & Gravitation, Theoretical Physics. Nuclear astrophysics; quantum chromodynamics (QCD); neutron stars; gravitational waves. http://www.csulb.edu/~pjaikuma/Compuphys/comp.html Computational Physics: http://www.csulb.edu/~pjaikuma/Compuphys/comp.html

Peterson, Michael, Ph.D., Pennsylvania State University, 2005. Society of Physics Students advisor. *Computational Physics, Condensed Matter Physics, Nano Science and Technology, Solid State Physics, Theoretical Physics*. Strongly correlated systems; quantum topological phases; condensed matter theory; quantum mechanics. http://www.csulb.edu/~pjaikuma/Compuphys/comp.html

Assistant Professor

Klaehn, Thomas, Ph.D., University of Rostock, 2005. *Astrophysics, Computational Physics, Relativity & Gravitation, Theoretical Physics*. Astrophysics; extremely dense matter; hadron and quark matter; neutron stars; gravitational waves.

Ojeda-Artistizabal, Claudia, Ph.D., Université Paris-sud XI, Orsay, 2010. *Applied Physics, Low Temperature Physics, Nano Science and Technology, Solid State Physics*. Low dimensional systems, Quantum coherent transport, Layered materials, Graphene.

Lecturer

Asbell, Jessica, M.S., California State University Long Beach, 2016. Director of "Night at the Observatory". *Astronomy, Astrophysics*.

Chuang, Kuan-Wen, Ph.D., University of California, Riverside, 1990.

Geier, Montserrat, Ph.D., Ruprecht Karls Universität Heidelberg, 1989.

Nishino, Hitoshi, Ph.D., University of Tokyo, 1981. *Cosmology & String Theory, High Energy Physics, Particles and Fields, Theoretical Physics*. Unification of all interactions. Study of supersymmetry, supergravity, superstring theory, and super membrane theory.

Sharma, Deepak, M.S., California State University Long Beach, 1999.

Woodhouse, Robert M., Ph.D., UCLA.

DEPARTMENTAL RESEARCH SPECIALTIES AND STAFF

Theoretical

Astrophysics. Gravitational waves, nuclear astrophysics. Jaikumar, Klaehn.

Computational Physics. This is an overarching specialty for most of our theoretical work. We provide training in computational physics for any path chosen by students but have research projects in condensed matter, nuclear, particle physics and astrophysics. Bill, Jaikumar, Klaehn, Papp, Peterson, Pickett.

Condensed Matter Physics. We study phenomena in superconductivity, magnetism, quantum Hall systems, topological phases, strongly correlated system, and low-dimensional systems. Bill, Peterson, Pickett.

High Energy Physics. Hlousek, Jaikumar, Klaehn, Nishino, Papp, Rajpoot.

Low Temperature Physics. Superconductivity. Bill, Peterson.

Nuclear Physics. We study the quantum mechanics of few-body systems, and nuclear astrophysics. Jaikumar, Klaehn, Papp.

Solid State Physics. Bill, Peterson.

Experimental

Applied Physics. Most of our research in experimental physics studies fundamental properties of matter but have applications in mind. Gredig, Gu, Kwon, Ojeda-Artistizabal.

Condensed Matter Physics. We have a strong emphasis in condensed matter experiments and materials science. Gredig, Gu, Kwon, Ojeda-Artistizabal.

Nano Science and Technology. We have state-of-the-art experiments, including sputtering machines to study nano particles, thin films and combinations thereof. Gredig, Gu, Kwon, Ojeda-Artistizabal.

Solar Physics. We study solar cells built of organic semiconductors. Gredig.

SAN DIEGO STATE UNIVERSITY

DEPARTMENT OF PHYSICS

San Diego, California 92182-1233
http://www.physics.sdsu.edu

General University Information
President: Adela de la Torre
Dean of Graduate School: Stephen C. Welter
University website: http://www.sdsu.edu
School Type: Public
Setting: Urban
Total Faculty: 1,795
Total Graduate Faculty: 894
Total number of Students: 32,576
Total number of Graduate Students: 4,981

Department Information
Department Chairman: Prof. Usha Sinha, Chair
Department Contact: Dennis Pornan, Department Buyer
  Total full-time faculty: 12
  Total number of full-time equivalent positions: 12
  Full-Time Graduate Students: 40
  Female Full-Time Graduate Students: 9
  First-Year Graduate Students: 20
  Female First-Year Students: 5
  Total Post Doctorates: 1

Department Address
5500 Campanile Drive
San Diego, CA 92182-1233
Phone: (619) 594-6165
Fax: (619) 594-1263
E-mail: dpornan@sdsu.edu
Website: http://www.physics.sdsu.edu

ADMISSIONS

Admission Contact Information
Address admission inquiries to: Admission Office
Phone: (800) 468-6927
E-mail: support@CSUMentor.edu
Admissions website: http://arweb.sdsu.edu/es/admissions/grad/index.html

Application deadlines
Fall admission:
U.S. students: February 28   *Int'l. students*: February 28
Spring admission:
U.S. students: November 1   *Int'l. students*: November 1

Application fee
U.S. students: $55   *Int'l. students*: $55
Early application will make it more likely you will receive a teaching assistantship or an out-of-state tuition waiver.

Admissions information
For Fall of 2017:
  Number of applicants: 84
  Number admitted: 43
  Number enrolled: 14

Admission requirements
Bachelor's degree requirements: Bachelor's degree in Physics, Engineering, or Mathematics is required.
Minimum undergraduate GPA: 2.85

GRE requirements
The GRE is required.
  Quantitative score: 150
  Verbal score: 150
  Analytical score: 3.0
We will also review applicants with lower GRE scores than those stated above.

Subjective GRE requirements
The Subjective GRE is not required.

TOEFL requirements
The TOEFL exam is required for students from non-English-speaking countries.
  PBT score: 550
  iBT score: 80

TUITION

Tuition year 2018–19:
Tuition for in-state residents
  Full-time students: $4,461 per semester
  Part-time students: $2,955 per semester
Tuition for out-of-state residents
  Full-time students: $396 per credit
  Part-time students: $396 per credit
Credit hours per semester to be considered full-time: 9
Deferred tuition plan: Yes
Health insurance: Not available.
Other academic fees: 0–6 units, $2,686; 6.1 or more units, $4,231.
Academic term: Semester
Number of first-year students who received full tuition waivers: 2

Teaching Assistants, Research Assistants, and Fellowships
Number of first-year
  Teaching Assistants: 10
  Research Assistants: 5
Average stipend per academic year
  Teaching Assistant: $16,932
  Research Assistant: $16,000

FINANCIAL AID

Loans
Loans are available for U.S. students.
Loans are not available for international students.
GAPSFAS application required: Yes
FAFSA application required: No

For further information
Address financial aid inquiries to: Office of Financial Aid and Scholarships, 5500 Campanile Drive, San Diego, CA 92182-7436.
Phone: (619) 594-6323
E-mail: fao@sdsu.edu
Financial aid website: http://go.sdsu.edu/student_affairs/financialaid/

HOUSING

Availability of on-campus housing
Single students: Yes
Married students: No
Childcare Assistance: No

For further information
Address housing inquiries to: Office of Housing Administration, 5500 Campanile Drive, San Diego, CA 92182-1802.
Phone: (619) 594-5742
E-mail: oha@sdsu.edu
Housing aid website: http://housing.sdsu.edu

Table A—Faculty, Enrollments, and Degrees Granted

Research Specialty	2016–17 Faculty	Enrollment Fall 2017 Master's	Enrollment Fall 2017 Doctorate	Number of Degrees Granted 2016–17 (2012–17) Master's	Number of Degrees Granted 2016–17 (2012–17) Terminal Master's	Number of Degrees Granted 2016–17 (2012–17) Doctorate
Astrophysics	1	2	1	–	1	1
Computational Physics	4	6	4	–	3	1
Condensed Matter Physics	2	2	–	–	–	–
Energy Sources & Environment	–	–	–	–	–	–
Medical, Health Physics	2	16	–	–	7	–
Nuclear Physics	3	4	4	–	1	1
Optics	3	6	2	–	2	–
Non-specialized	–	2	–	–	5	–
Other	–	–	–	–	–	–
Total	11	33	–	–	14	–
Full-time Grad. Stud.	–	33	–	–	–	–
First-year Grad. Stud.	–	18	–	–	–	–

GRADUATE DEGREE REQUIREMENTS

Master's: Master of Science (Physics): The student must complete a graduate program in which 18 of the 30 units must include graduate course work in quantum mechanics, statistical mechanics, classical mechanics, electricity and magnetism, and thesis. The remaining units must be approved by the graduate advisor. There is a minimum of 24 units in residence. The student must pass a final oral examination on his/her thesis and maintain a 3.0 GPA. There is no foreign language requirement. Master of Science (Medical Physics): The student must complete a graduate program in which 24 of the 30 units must include graduate course work in radiological physics, physics of medical imaging, radiation therapy physics, nuclear medicine physics, and radiation biology in addition to 6 units for research/thesis. Other requirements are as for the graduate M.S. degree in Physics. Master of Art (Physics): The student must complete a graduate program in which 21 of the 30 units include graduate course work in electricity and magnetism, quantum mechanics, statistical mechanics, and classical mechanics. The remaining units must be approved by the students' graduate committee. The student must pass a comprehensive examination and maintain a 3.0 GPA. There is a minimum of 24 units in residence.

Doctorate: Several of our faculty have students in the Computational Science Ph.D. program, see http://www.csrc.sdsu.edu/doctoral.html for more information. Also, contact computational physics faculty directly (Baljon, Johnson, Nollett and Weber). In addition, faculty in the optics and in the Medical Physics program also have students in the Computational Sciences Ph.D. program. Please contact Dr. Kuzne-tosva for Optics and Drs. Sinha and Tambasco for Medical Physics if you are interested in the Computational Sciences Ph.D. program in these areas.

Other Degrees: Student may get an M.S. or a Ph.D. in Computational Science while working with a Physics faculty member as their thesis mentor.

Thesis: Thesis may be written in absentia; however, residency is required.

SPECIAL EQUIPMENT, FACILITIES, OR PROGRAMS

Condensed matter physics laboratory, radiation therapy treatment planning systems, radiation biology lab, laser optics, holography facility; electro-optics measurements laboratory; image processing facility; materials laboratory, ultrafast laser; computational physics lab; Beowulf cluster, 3T Siemens Prisma MRI system (up since March 2018).

Table B—Separately Budgeted Research Expenditures by Source of Support

Source of Support	Departmental Research	Physics-related Research Outside Department
Federal government	$375,167	
State/local government	$31,654	
Non-profit organizations		
Business and industry	$246,201	
Other		
Total	$653,022	

Table C—Separately Budgeted Research Expenditures by Research Specialty

Research Specialty	No. of Grants	Expenditures ($)
Computational Physics	2	$198,992
Condensed Matter Physics	1	$8,675
Medical, Health Physics	1	$17,154
Optics	2	$246,201
Physics and other Science Education	1	$182,000
Total	7	$653,022

FACULTY

Professor

Davis, Jeffrey A., Ph.D., Cornell University, 1970. Director of Electro-optics Program. *Optics*. Optics; optical pattern recognition; computer generated holograms.

Goldberg, Fred M., Ph.D., University of Michigan, 1971. *Physics and other Science Education*. Physics education.

Johnson, Calvin W., Ph.D., University of Washington, 1989. *Astrophysics, Computational Physics, Nuclear Physics, Theoretical Physics*. Theoretical nuclear physics; astrophysics; computational nuclear physics and many-body physics; high-performance computing.

Sinha, Usha, Ph.D., Indian Institute of Science, Bangalore, 1985. Chair of Department and Director of Medical Physics Program. *Medical, Health Physics*. Medical physics; magnetic resonance imaging.

Sweedler, Alan R., Ph.D., University of California, San Diego, 1970. Assistant Vice President of International Programs and Director of SDSU's Center for Energy Studies. *Energy Sources & Environment*. Physical and environmental science; computer modeling of energy systems.

Torikachvili, Milton S., Ph.D., University of Campinas, 1978. *Condensed Matter Physics*. Experimental condensed matter physics.

Weber, Fridolin, Ph.D., University of Munich, Germany, 1985. Graduate Advisor and Associate Chair. *Astrophysics, Nuclear Physics, Relativity & Gravitation, Theoretical Physics.* Theoretical nuclear physics; astrophysics.

Associate Professor

Anderson, Matt, Ph.D., University of Oregon, 1998. Undergraduate Advisor. *Optics.* Ultrafast laser physics.

Baljon, Arlette R.C., Ph.D., University of Chicago, 1993. *Biophysics, Computational Physics, Fluids, Rheology, Polymer Physics/Science.* Computational soft condensed matter physics.

Tambasco, Mauro, Ph.D., University of Western Ontario, 2002. Associate Director, Medical Physics Associate Director, Medical Physics Residency. *Medical, Health Physics.* Medical physics.

Assistant Professor

Kuznetsova, Lyuba, Ph.D., Cornell, 2008. *Computational Physics, Nano Science and Technology, Optics, Solid State Physics.* Laser Physics, nanophotonics.

Nollett, Kenneth, Ph.D., University of Chicago, 2000. *Astrophysics, Computational Physics, Cosmology & String Theory, Nuclear Physics, Theoretical Physics.* Nuclear astrophysics; nuclear reactions; nucleosynthesis; Big Bang cosmology.

Perez, Rodrigo N., Ph.D., Universidad de Granada, 2015. *Computational Physics, Nuclear Physics, Theoretical Physics.* Nuclear density functional theory, density matrix expansion, heavy nuclei. Effective interactions, Gogny force. Nucleon-Nucleon interaction, chiral potentials. Nuclear structure calculations, few body problems. Uncertainty quantification, error propagation. High performance computing.

Sundqvist, Kyle, Ph.D., University of California at Berkeley, 2012. *Condensed Matter Physics, Low Temperature Physics, Optics.* Superconducting circuits and Josephson junctions Engineered microwave quantum-optical systems Design and characterization of nano-electronic devices Cryogenics at millikelvin temperatures Low-noise instrumentation, at both low and microwave frequencies Nonequilibrium semiconductor physics of carrier transport and recombination.

DEPARTMENTAL RESEARCH SPECIALTIES AND STAFF

Theoretical

Astrophysics. Nuclear astrophysics and nucleosynthesis; neutron stars, quark stars, and other compact objects. Option for Ph.D. through Computational Science. Nollett, Perez, Weber.

Computational Physics. We have specialties in astrophysics, medical imaging, nuclear and polymers. SDSU also offers a Ph.D. in Computational Science. Many students in this program are supported on research assistantships. Baljon, Johnson, Kuznetsova, Nollett, Perez, Sinha, Weber.

Nuclear Physics. Computational theoretical nuclear physics, including nuclear structure and reactions, nuclear astrophysics, and compact stellar objects. Option for Ph.D. through Computational Science. Johnson, Nollett, Perez, Weber.

Polymer Physics/Science. Modeling of polymers and their properties. Baljon.

Theoretical Physics. We specialize in computational approaches to a variety of theoretical problems; option for Ph.D. through Computational Science program. Baljon, Johnson, Nollett, Perez, Weber.

Experimental

Condensed Matter Physics. Specializing in materials and superconductivity. Sundqvist, Torikachvili.

Low Temperature Physics. Superconducting circuits and Josephson junctions Engineered microwave quantum-optical systems Design and characterization of nano-electronic devices. Sundqvist.

Medical, Health Physics. Medical image processing and imaging informatics, magnetic resonance imaging, radiation therapy physics, dose calculations. CAMPEP accredited. Option for clinical internships. Sinha, Tambasco.

Optics. Optics; optical pattern recognition; computer generated holograms, Ultrafast laser physics.nanophotonics. Anderson, Davis, Kuznetsova.

SAN JOSE STATE UNIVERSITY

DEPARTMENT OF PHYSICS AND ASTRONOMY

San Jose, California 95192-0106
http://www.sjsu.edu/physics

General University Information
President: Dr. Mary A. Papazian
Dean of Graduate School: Dr. Thalia Anagnos
University website: http://www.sjsu.edu
School Type: Public
Setting: Urban
Total Faculty: 1,740
Total number of Students: 28,007
Total number of Graduate Students: 5,766

Department Information
Department Chairman: Dr. Monika Kress, Chair
Department Contact: Bertha Aguayo, Administrative
 Analyst/Specialist
 Total full-time faculty: 14
 Total number of full-time equivalent positions: 22
 Full-Time Graduate Students: 35
 Female Full-Time Graduate Students: 2
 First-Year Graduate Students: 11
 Female First-Year Students: 2

Department Address
One Washington Square
San Jose, CA 95192-0106
Phone: (408) 924-5210
Fax: (408) 924-2917
E-mail: Bertha.Aguayo@sjsu.edu
Website: http://www.sjsu.edu/physics

ADMISSIONS

Admission Contact Information
Address admission inquiries to: Graduate Admissions Office
Phone: (408) 924-2480
E-mail: graduate@sjsu.edu
Admissions website: http://www.sjsu.edu/gape

Application deadlines
Fall admission:
U.S. students: April 1   *Int'l. students*: April 1

Application fee
U.S. students: $55

Admissions information
For Fall of 2016:
 Number of applicants: 25
 Number enrolled: 11

Admission requirements
Bachelor's degree requirements: A Bachelor's degree is required.
Minimum undergraduate GPA: 2.5

GRE requirements
 The GRE is not required.

Subjective GRE requirements
The Subjective GRE is not required.

TOEFL requirements
The TOEFL exam is required for students from non-English-speaking countries.
 PBT score: 550

Other admissions information
Additional requirements: The GRE Physics is not required for admission to the program, but it must be taken with a score of 550 no later than two semesters prior to graduation.
Undergraduate preparation assumed: Young and Freedman, University Physics; Marion, Classical Dynamics of Particles & Systems; Beiser, Concepts of Modern Physics; Griffiths, Introduction to Electrodynamics; Griffiths, Introduction to Quantum Mechanics.

TUITION

Tuition year 2017–2018:
Tuition for in-state residents
 Full-time students: $4,615 per semester
 Part-time students: $3,109 per semester
Tuition for out-of-state residents
 Full-time students: $9,367 per semester
Academic term: Semester

Teaching Assistants, Research Assistants, and Fellowships
 Number of first-year
 Teaching Assistants: 5

FINANCIAL AID

Loans
Loans are available for U.S. students.
Loans are not available for international students.
GAPSFAS application required: No
FAFSA application required: No

HOUSING

Availability of on-campus housing
 Single students: Yes
 Married students: Yes

For further information
Address housing inquiries to: Attn.: Housing Office.
Housing aid website: http://housing.sjsu.edu

Table A—Faculty, Enrollments, and Degrees Granted

Research Specialty	2015–2016 Faculty	Enrollment Fall 2015		Number of Degrees Granted 2014–2015 (2000–07)		
		Master's	Doctorate	Master's	Terminal Master's	Doctorate
Acoustics	1	–	–	–	–	–
Applied Physics	1	–	–	–	–	–
Astronomy	4	–	–	–	–	–
Astrophysics	4	–	–	–	–	–
Biophysics	1	–	–	–	–	–
Condensed Matter Physics	3	–	–	–	–	–
Optics	3	–	–	–	–	–
Plasma and Fusion	1	–	–	–	–	–
Non-specialized	–	23	–	–	11	–
Total	–	23	–	–	11(36)	–
Full-time Grad. Stud.	–	–	–	–	–	–
First-year Grad. Stud.	–	10	–	–	–	–

GRADUATE DEGREE REQUIREMENTS

Master's: A total of 30 semester units with a B average is required. Fifteen semester units in mathematical physics, advanced dynamics, electromagnetic theory, statistical physics, and quantum mechanics and at least six semester units of other graduate physics courses must be included. Twelve units of graduate level and/or upper division courses in mathematics, science, engineering, or other appropriate fields, selected with the approval of the graduate advisor, complete the course requirements. Twenty-four semester units must be completed in residence. All graduate students must attend weekly department seminars in at least one semester and must satisfy the English writing requirement prior to the semester of graduation. A comprehensive oral examination, literature review, or a thesis presentation is required.

Thesis: Optional.

SPECIAL EQUIPMENT, FACILITIES, OR PROGRAMS

The Department has academic options in optics and condensed matter and offers a concentration in computational physics. The Institute for Modern Optics coordinates optics research and collaboration with local industries. A 4,000-sq. ft. instruction and research facility contains equipment for laser spectroscopy, nolinear optics, Fourier optics, holography, and optical metrology. A world-class center for novel laser materials research and modeling of laser systems is located here. The solid state laboratory includes equipment for measuring magnetic susceptibility over a 4–1,000 K temperature range. Computing equipment consists of on-campus workstations and internet access to remote facilities and databases. A 10,000-sf Nuclear Science Facility is used by all science departments. Equipment includes neutron and gamma irradiators; x-ray fluorescence, magnetic resonance, and Mössbauer spectrometers; and a range of radiation analyzing equipment. Several faculty carry out research with colleagues at NASA Ames Research Center. Located in "Silicon Valley," we have research and instructional collaborations with many local instrumentation, materials, semiconductor, and optics companies.

Table B—Separately Budgeted Research Expenditures by Source of Support

Source of Support	Departmental Research	Physics-related Research Outside Department
Federal government	$500,000	
State/local government		
Non-profit organizations		
Business and industry	$840,000	$820,000
Other	$4,843,000	$720,000
Total	$6,183,000	$1,540,000

Table C—Separately Budgeted Research Expenditures by Research Specialty

Research Specialty	No. of Grants	Expenditures ($)
Astronomy	2	$100,000
Astronomy	2	$10,000
Atmosphere, Space Physics, Cosmic Rays	4	$200,000
Materials Science, Metallurgy	2	$490,000
Physics and other Science Education	1	$75,000
Solid State Physics	1	$188,000
Other	6	$4,570,000
Total	18	$5,633,000

FACULTY

Professor

Bahuguna, Ramendra D., Ph.D., Indian Institute of Technology, Delhi, 1979. Holographic interferometry; laser speckle metrology; display holography; Fourier optics; fingerprint verification.

Beyersdorf, Peter T., Ph.D., Stanford University, 2001. Gravitational wave detection; precision measurements and optical interferometry.

Garcia, Alejandro, Ph.D., University of Texas, Austin, 1984. Computational fluid mechanics; statistical mechanics.

Kaufman, Michael J., Ph.D., Johns Hopkins University, 1995. Astrophysics: interstellar medium, interactions of young stars with molecular clouds, dynamics and chemistry of molecular shocks, and infrared/submillimeter observations.

Kress, Monika, Ph.D., Rensselaer Polytechnic Institute, 1997. Astrophysics and planetary science; computer modeling of protoplanetary disks, comet impacts, and planetary environments; meteorites; astrobiology.

Wharton, Kenneth B., Ph.D., University of California, Los Angeles, 1998. Plasma physics, laser-plasma interactions; subpicosecond x-ray sources, foundations of quantum mechanics, relativistic quantum mechanics.

Associate Professor

Heindl, Ranko, Ph.D., University of South Florida, 2006. Magnetism, spintronics, and nonvolatile memories.

Khatami, Ehsan, Ph.D., University of Cincinnati, 2009. Strongly-correlated electronic systems, ultracold atoms in optical lattices, frustrated magnetism, numerical methods in condensed matter physics.

Paul, Cassandra, Ph.D., University of California, Davis, 2012. Physics education research; astronomy education research.

Romanowsky, Aaron, Ph.D., Harvard University, 1999. Astrophysics (galaxies, dark matter, and computation).

Assistant Professor

Harrer, Benedikt, Ph.D., University of Maine, 2013. Physics Education Research (PER).

Madura, Thomas, Ph.D., University of Delaware, 2010. Theoretical and computational astrophysics, 3-D printing, astronomy outreach and education with a focus on blind/visually-impaired students, massive stars, Eta Carinae, stellar winds and mass loss, radiative transfer theory, scientific data visualization.

Smallwood, Christopher, Ph.D., University of California, Berkeley, 2014. Experimental optics and condensed matter physics.

Switz, Neil, Ph.D., University of California, Berkeley, 2012. Optical microscopy and medical diagnostics.

Emeritus

Anderson, Merlin F., Ph.D., Oregon State University, 1966. Gas dynamics; computer applications.

Becker, Joseph F., Ph.D., New York University, 1976. Spectroscopy; biophysics; optics; optoelectronic devices.

Bloomer, Iris L., Ph.D., University of London, 1976. General relativity; optical properties of materials.

Boekema, Carolus, Ph.D., University of Groningen, Netherlands, 1977. Magnetism and superconductivity in solids; computational condensed matter physics; muon spin research: Mössbauer spectroscopy.

Finkelstein, Jerome, Ph.D., University of California, Berkeley, 1967. Theoretical physics; elementary particles.

Gruber, John B., Ph.D., University of California, Berkeley, 1961. Engineering physics; solid-state spectroscopy; rare-earth/transition-metal ion solid state lasers; chemical physics; quantum electronics.

Hamill, Patrick, Ph.D., University of Arizona, 1971. Atmospheric physics; aerosol physics; celestial mechanics.

Holmes, Brian W., Ph.D., Boston University, 1980. Musical acoustics; sports physics; physics education.

Lam, Lui, Ph.D., Columbia University, 1973. Histophysics; nonlinear physics; liquid crystals; pattern formation; complex systems.

Morris, Marvin L., Ph.D., University of Utah, 1966. High-energy cosmic rays; computer-aided instruction; physics education.

Parvin, Kiumars, Ph.D., University of California, Riverside, 1978. Experimental solid-state physics; magnetic materials.

Strandburg, Donald L., Ph.D., Iowa State University, 1961. Low-temperature physics; magnetism.

Tomley, Leslie J., Ph.D., University of Washington, 1968. *Astrophysics*. Astrophysics.

Tucker, Allen B., Ph.D., Stanford University, 1965. Nuclear physics; cosmic rays; accelerator mass spectrometry; health physics.

Williams, Gareth T., Ph.D., University of Wales, 1960. Optics; holography.

Adjunct Professor

Batalha, Natalie M., Ph.D., University of California, Santa Cruz, 1997. Stellar astrophysics: variable stars, magnetic activity, T Tauri stars; extra-solar planet detection.

Freund, Friedemann, Ph.D., University of Marburg, 1959. Defects in crystals; proton conductivity.

Lecturer

Hubickyj, Olenka, Ph.D., City University of New York, 1983. RR Lyrae stars' instability strip; primordial atmosphere of Earth; convection turbulence in the solar nebula; formation and evolution of gas giant planets.

Mosqueira, Ignacio, Ph.D., Cornell University, 1995. Planetary formation.

Sauke, Todd B., Ph.D., University of Illinois at Urbana-Champaign, 1989. Tunable diode laser technology; development of planetary exploration applications for the measurement of isotopic ratios in planetary surface and atmospheric samples.

DEPARTMENTAL RESEARCH SPECIALTIES AND STAFF

Experimental

Acoustics.
Applied Physics.
Astrophysics.
Biophysics.
Optics.
Plasma and Fusion.

View additional information about this department at www.gradschoolshopper.com. Check out the "Why Choose Us?" section, find out more about the department's culture and get links to social media networks.

STANFORD UNIVERSITY

DEPARTMENT OF APPLIED PHYSICS

Stanford, California 94305–4090
http://appliedphysics.stanford.edu

General University Information

President: Marc Tessier-Lavigne
Dean of Graduate School: Richard P. Saller
University website: http://www.stanford.edu
School Type: Private
Setting: Suburban
Total Faculty: 2,180
Total Graduate Faculty: 2,180
Total number of Students: 16,336
Total number of Graduate Students: 9,304

Department Information

Department Chairman: Prof. Martin M. Fejer, Chair
Department Contact: Patrice O'Dwyer, Department Academic Manager
Total full-time faculty: 24
Total number of full-time equivalent positions: 24
Full-Time Graduate Students: 142
Female Full-Time Graduate Students: 28
First-Year Graduate Students: 28
Female First-Year Students: 6
Total Post Doctorates: 26

Department Address

348 Via Pueblo Mall
Stanford, CA 94305–4090
Phone: (650) 723-4027
E-mail: podwyer@stanford.edu
Website: http://appliedphysics.stanford.edu

ADMISSIONS

Admission Contact Information

Address admission inquiries to: Graduate Admissions-Office of the University Registrar, 408 Panama Mall, Suite 217, Stanford, CA 94305-6032
Phone: (866) 432-7472
E-mail: gradadmissions@stanford.edu
Admissions website: http://gradadmissions.stanford.edu

Application deadlines

Fall admission:
U.S. students: December 12   *Int'l. students*: December 12

Application fee

U.S. students: $125   *Int'l. students*: $125
Application deadline of December 12/2018 is subject to change. Application fee to be paid by credit/debit card only (Visa or MasterCard). An application to only one department at a time is allowed.

Admissions information

For Fall of 2018:
Number of applicants: 263
Number admitted: 41
Number enrolled: 24

Admission requirements

Bachelor's degree requirements: Bachelor's degree in Physics, Mathematics, Chemistry, or Electrical Engineering is required.

GRE requirements

The GRE is required.
We do not set minimum accepted GRE scores.

Subjective GRE requirements

The Subjective GRE is required.
We do not set minimum accepted GRE Physics scores. GRE Physics is not required for the M.S. degree.

TOEFL requirements

The TOEFL exam is required for students from non-English-speaking countries.
PBT score: 600
iBT score: 100
For Stanford's policy on TOEFL scores, refer to: http://studentaffairs.stanford.edu/gradadmissions/applying/exams

Other admissions information

Additional requirements: We do not set a minimum undergraduate GPA.
Undergraduate preparation assumed: Intermediate undergraduate (junior and senior) courses in mechanics, electricity and magnetism, modern physics, statistical mechanics, and thermodynamics.

TUITION

Tuition year 2017–18:
Full-time students: $10,620 per quarter
$10,620/quarter is the standard rate for graduate students with the exception that a few outside fellowships provide the University's full tuition rate of $16,329/quarter.
Credit hours per semester to be considered full-time: 8
Deferred tuition plan: Yes
Health insurance: Yes, varies per year.
Other academic fees: Fees vary. Student health insurance is required. Partial subsidies from the University are available depending on the student's level of funding.
Academic term: Quarter

Teaching Assistants, Research Assistants, and Fellowships

Number of first-year
Research Assistants: 18
Fellowship students: 5
The number of first-year fellowships includes both full internal and outside fellowships the first-year students have been awarded to date. Research Assistantship stipends vary, depending on the year of study and which specific department requirements have been met. We do not have a Teaching Assistantship program, but there are Teaching Assistantship opportunities in other departments on a quarterly basis.

FINANCIAL AID

Application deadlines
Fall admission:
U.S. students: December 4　　　*Int'l. students*: December 4

Loans
Loans are available for U.S. students.
Loans are available for international students.
GAPSFAS application required: No
FAFSA application required: No

For further information
Address financial aid inquiries to: Patrice O'Dwyer, Academic Manager, Department of Applied Physics, Spilker Building - Room 118, Stanford University, Stanford, CA 94305-4090.
Phone: (650) 723-4027
E-mail: podwyer@stanford.edu
Financial aid website: http://financialaid.stanford.edu

HOUSING

Availability of on-campus housing
Single students: Yes
Married students: Yes
Childcare Assistance: Yes

For further information
Address housing inquiries to: Student Housing Office, 565 Cowell Lane, Stanford University, Stanford, CA 94305-8581.
Phone: (650) 725-1600
E-mail: studenthousing@stanford.edu
Housing aid website: http://studenthousing.stanford.edu

Table A—Faculty, Enrollments, and Degrees Granted

Research Specialty	2016–17 Faculty	Enrollment Fall 2016		Number of Degrees Granted 2016–17 (2012–17)		
		Master's	Doctorate	Master's	Terminal Master's	Doctorate
Applied Physics	60	9	133	9(33)	5(11)	26(106)
Total	60	9	133	9(33)	5(11)	26(106)
Full-time Grad. Stud.	–	8	133	–	–	–
First-year Grad. Stud.	–	4	24	–	–	–

GRADUATE DEGREE REQUIREMENTS

Master's: Subject matter: advanced mechanics, electrodynamics, and quantum mechanics. A "B" average is required. Total number of course units required is 45. There is no foreign language requirement, no comprehensive and/or qualification examination, and no thesis option. A terminal M.S. degree program is offered. A Master's can be earned en route to the PhD degree.

Doctorate: Subject matter: advanced mechanics, electrodynamics, quantum mechanics, statistical physics, and one advanced laboratory, with the remaining required courses to be distributed between major and minor fields. Total number of course units required is 135. A "B" average is required. Departmental qualification examination, fourth-year research progress report, dissertation, and oral defense of dissertation are required. There is no foreign language requirement.

Other Degrees: Coterminal Master's degree for Stanford undergraduates only.

Thesis: Required for the Doctorate degree.

SPECIAL EQUIPMENT, FACILITIES, OR PROGRAMS

The Applied Physics Department participates in the Honors Cooperative Program, which offers the opportunity to qualified engineers and scientists employed by companies in the general vicinity of the University to pursue graduate work on a part-time basis leading to the M.S. degree.

NOTE: Data for the separately budgeted research expenditures by source of support or by research specialty will not be provided. That information is not available at the reporting unit's level.

FACULTY

Professor

Block, Steven M., Ph.D., California Institute of Technology, 1983. Biophysics.

Bucksbaum, Philip H., Ph.D., University of California, Berkeley, 1980. Atomic, molecular, and optical physics; ultrafast science.

Byer, Robert L., Ph.D., Stanford University, 1969. Nonlinear optics.

Doniach, Sebastian, Ph.D., University of Liverpool, 1958. Theory of cooperative phenomena; biophysics.

Fejer, Martin M., Ph.D., Stanford University, 1986. Department Chair. Quantum electronics; guided-wave optics; optical materials.

Fisher, Daniel S., Ph.D., Harvard University, 1979. Theoretical condensed matter physics; biophysics; evolutionary dynamics.

Fisher, Ian R., Ph.D., University of Cambridge, 1996. Condensed matter physics; materials physics.

Heinz, Tony F., Ph.D., University of California, Berkeley, 1982. Condensed matter physics; laser and nonlinear spectroscopy; properties and applications of nanoscale materials.

Hwang, Harold Y., Ph.D., Princeton University, 1997. Materials physics; emergent phenomena in oxide heterostructures; devices.

Kapitulnik, Aharon, Ph.D., Tel Aviv University, 1984. Theoretical and experimental low-temperature and condensed matter physics; superconductivity.

Kasevich, Mark A., Ph.D., Stanford University, 1992. Atomic, molecular, and optical physics.

Lee, Young S., Ph.D., Massachusetts Institute of Technology, 2000. Condensed matter physics; materials physics; neutron scattering spectroscopy; synchrotron radiation.

Mabuchi, Hideo, Ph.D., California Institute of Technology, 1998. Quantum optics and electronics; quantum information and control.

Moler, Kathryn A., Ph.D., Stanford University, 1995. Condensed matter physics; materials physics; physics of small structures and of novel materials.

Petrosian, Vahé, Ph.D., Cornell University, 1967. Theoretical astrophysics and cosmology.

Quake, Stephen R., Ph.D., University of Oxford, 1994. Biophysics.

Shen, Zhi-Xun, Ph.D., Stanford University, 1989. Condensed matter physics; electronic structure; photoelectron spectroscopy; synchrotron radiation.

Suzuki, Yuri, Ph.D., Stanford University, 1995. Condensed matter physics; materials and device physics.

Associate Professor

Lev, Benjamin L., Ph.D., California Institute of Technology, 2005. Atomic, molecular, and optical physics; novel microscopy and imaging; condensed matter physics; materials research.

Reis, David A., Ph.D., University of Rochester, 1999. Condensed matter physics; ultrafast science.

Schnitzer, Mark J., Ph.D., Princeton University, 1999. Biophysics.

Assistant Professor

Ganguli, Surya, Ph.D., University of California, Berkeley, 2004. Theoretical neuroscience; biophysics.

Safavi-Naeini, Amir H., Ph.D., California Institute of Technology, 2013. Nanoscience and technology; quantum optics and electronics; atomic, molecular and optical physics; materials and device physics.

Emeritus

Beasley, Malcolm R., Ph.D., Cornell University, 1968. Low-temperature and condensed matter physics; superconductivity.

Bienenstock, Arthur I., Ph.D., Harvard University, 1962. Synchrotron radiation.

Fetter, Alexander L., Ph.D., Harvard University, 1963. Theoretical condensed matter physics.

Geballe, Theodore H., Ph.D., University of California, Berkeley, 1949. Low-temperature and condensed matter physics; superconductivity.

Harris, Stephen E., Ph.D., Stanford University, 1963. Quantum electronics and XUV lasers.

Harrison, Walter A., Ph.D., University of Illinois, 1956. Theoretical condensed matter physics: electronic structure.

Sturrock, Peter A., Ph.D., University of Cambridge, 1951. Theoretical solar physics and astrophysics.

Wiedemann, Helmut, Ph.D., University of Hamburg, 1971. Accelerator physics; electron storage rings.

Winick, Herman, Ph.D., Columbia University, 1957. Synchrotron radiation.

Yamamoto, Yoshihisa, Ph.D., University of Tokyo, 1978. Quantum optics and electronics; mesoscopic physics.

Research Professor

Digonnet, Michel, Ph.D., Stanford University, 1984. Fiber optics; sensors; slow and fast light.

Faculty by Courtesy

Brongersma, Mark L., Ph.D., FOM-Institute, 1998. Nanophotonics; materials physics.

Clemens, Bruce M., Ph.D., California Institute of Technology, 1983. Metal-metal multilayers; interfaces and interface reactions; magnetic thin films; x-ray diffraction.

Fan, Shanhui, Ph.D., Massachusetts Institute of Technology, 1993. Theoretical and computational studies of nano-photonic structures. Photonic crystals. Plasmonics; meta-materials; computational electromagnetics; solar cells; control of thermal radiation; non-reciprocal photonics; quantum transport of few photon states.

Goldhaber-Gordon, David, Ph.D., Harvard University, 1994. Condensed matter physics; nanoelectronics.

Greenleaf, William J., Ph.D., Stanford University, 2008. Biophysics.

Harris, James S., Ph.D., Stanford University, 1969. Optoelectronic device structures; quantum electronics.

Hesselink, Lambertus, Ph.D., California Institute of Technology, 1977. Nonlinear optics.

Huang, Zhirong, Ph.D., Stanford University, 1998. Accelerator physics; free-electron laser physics.

Miller, David A. B., Ph.D., Heriot-Watt University, 1979. Electro-optic wave devices; engineering physics.

Moerner, W. E., Ph.D., Cornell University, 1982. Quantum optics.

Osheroff, Douglas D., Ph.D., Cornell University, 1973. Low-temperature and condensed matter physics.

Spakowitz, Andrew J., Ph.D., California Institute of Technology, 2004. Biophysics.

Vuckovic, Jelena, Ph.D., California Institute of Technology, 2002. Nanophotonics; quantum photonics.

Zhang, Shoucheng, Ph.D., Stony Brook University, 1987. Theoretical condensed-matter physics.

DEPARTMENTAL RESEARCH SPECIALTIES AND STAFF

Theoretical
Astrophysics.
Biophysics.
Condensed Matter Physics.
Nanoscience and Technology.
Neuroscience/Neuro Physics.

Experimental
Atomic, Molecular, & Optical Physics.
Biophysics.
Condensed Matter Physics. Materials research.
Materials Science, Metallurgy.
Nanoscience and Technology.
Novel Microscopy and Imaging.
Optics.
Quantum Optics and Electronics.
Relativity & Gravitation.
Synchrotron Radiation.

View additional information about this department at www.gradschoolshopper.com. Check out the "Why Choose Us?" section, find out more about the department's culture and get links to social media networks.

STANFORD UNIVERSITY

DEPARTMENT OF PHYSICS

Stanford, California 94305
http://physics.stanford.edu

General University Information

President: Marc Tessier-Lavigne
Dean of Graduate School: Richard Saller
University website: http://www.stanford.edu
School Type: Private
Setting: Suburban
Total Faculty: 1,651
Total Graduate Faculty: 360
Total number of Students: 17,178
Total number of Graduate Students: 10,116

Department Information

Department Chairman: Prof. Shamit Kachru, Chair
Department Contact: Maria Frank, Student Services Officer
  Total full-time faculty: 50
  Total number of full-time equivalent positions: 48
  Full-Time Graduate Students: 187
  Female Full-Time Graduate Students: 32
  First-Year Graduate Students: 39
  Female First-Year Students: 7
  Total Post Doctorates: 60

Department Address

382 Via Pueblo Mall
Stanford, CA 94305
Phone: (650) 723-4344
E-mail: phys-admissions@lists.stanford.edu
Website: http://physics.stanford.edu

ADMISSIONS

Admission Contact Information

Address admission inquiries to: Before calling or emailing Graduate Admissions, please look for answers to your questions on the Applying to Graduate Admissions page http://studentaffairs.stanford.edu/gradadmissions/applying, and the Frequently Asked Questions page https://gradadmissions.stanford.edu/applying/frequently-asked-questions
Phone: (866) 432-7472
E-mail: gradadmissions@stanford.edu
Admissions website: http://gradadmissions.stanford.edu

Application deadlines

Fall admission:
U.S. students: December 18   *Int'l. students*: December 18

Application fee

U.S. students: $125   *Int'l. students*: $125
Application Fee Waiver Information: https://graddiversity.stanford.edu/graduate-fee-waiver/graduate-fee-waivers

Admissions information

For Fall of 2018:
  Number of applicants: 691
  Number admitted: 68
  Number enrolled: 33

Admission requirements

Bachelor's degree requirements: Bachelor's degree in Physics (or a related field) is required. International academic credential information can be found here: https://gradadmissions.stanford.edu/applying/international-applicants.

GRE requirements

The GRE is required.
No minimum scores specified. We strongly advise you to take the general and physics GRE tests no later than September, so that your scores will be received by the application deadline or shortly thereafter.

Subjective GRE requirements

The Subjective GRE is required.
No minimum scores specified. We strongly advise you to take the general and physics GRE tests no later than September, so that your scores will be received by the application deadline or shortly thereafter.

TOEFL requirements

The TOEFL exam is required for students from non-English-speaking countries.
  PBT score: 600
  iBT score: 100
Scores must be submitted from a test taken within the last eighteen months. Exemptions are granted to applicants who have earned (or will earn, before enrolling at Stanford) a U.S. bachelor's, master's, or doctoral degree from a college or university accredited by a regional accrediting association in the United States, or the international equivalent degree from a university of recognized standing in a country in which all instruction is provided in English. U.S. citizenship does not automatically exempt an applicant from taking the TOEFL if the applicant's first language is not English. More detailed information regarding the TOEFL can be found here: https://gradadmissions.stanford.edu/applying/starting-your-application/required-exams

Other admissions information

Additional requirements: No minimum scores specified.
  The average GRE scores for admitted students to the 2018–19 academic year were: Verbal-164, Quantitative–167; Analytical–4.54; Physics Subject–879.

TUITION

Tuition year 2018–19:
  Full-time students: $46,800 annual
Further Info: https://registrar.stanford.edu/students/tuition-and-fees
Credit hours per semester to be considered full-time: 10
Deferred tuition plan: No
Health insurance: Available at the cost of $5,208 per year.
Other academic fees: Varies (student health insurance is required). Health insurance subsidy available for qualifying students. See https://vaden.stanford.edu/insurance/cardinal-care-overview-and-benefits/cost-and-coverage-dates for more information.
Academic term: Quarter
Number of first-year students who received full tuition waivers: 30

FINANCIAL AID

Loans

Loans are available for U.S. students.
Loans are not available for international students.
GAPSFAS application required: No
FAFSA application required: Yes

For further information

Address financial aid inquiries to: Financial Aid Office, Stanford
University, Montag Hall, 355 Galvez Street, Stanford, CA
94305-6106.
Phone: (888) 326-3773
E-mail: financialaid@stanford.edu
Financial aid website: http://financialaid.stanford.edu/grad/

HOUSING

Availability of on-campus housing

Single students: Yes
Married students: Yes

For further information

Address housing inquiries to: R&DE Student Housing, 565 Cow-
ell Lane, Stanford, CA 94305.
Phone: (650) 725-1600
E-mail: studenthousing@stanford.edu
Housing aid website: https://rde.stanford.edu/studenthousing

Table A—Faculty, Enrollments, and Degrees Granted

Research Specialty	2017–18 Faculty	Enrollment Fall 2017		Number of Degrees Granted 2017–18 (2016–2017)		
		Mas-ter's	Doc-torate	Mas-ter's	Terminal Master's	Doc-torate
Astrophysics	16	–	24	–	–	2(5)
Atomic, Molecular, & Optical Physics	6	–	22	–	–	2(2)
Biophysics	–	–	10	–	–	–(3)
Condensed Matter Physics	11	–	37	–	–	6(4)
Particles and Fields	13	–	63	–	–	8(9)
Physics and Science Education Research	1	–	–	–	–	–
Non-specialized	–	–	26	4(5)	2(1)	–
Other	1	–	5	–	–	4
Total	48	–	187	4(5)	2(1)	22(23)
Full-time Grad. Stud.	–	–	187	–	–	–
First-year Grad. Stud.	–	–	39	–	–	–

GRADUATE DEGREE REQUIREMENTS

Master's: The Physics Department does not offer a separate program for the master of science degree, but this degree may
be awarded for a portion of the doctoral degree; one-year residency is required. http://exploredegrees.stanford.edu/school
ofhumanitiesandsciences/physics/#masterstext.

Doctorate: See website http://exploredegrees.stanford.edu/
schoolofhumanitiesandsciences/physics/#doctoraltext.

Thesis: Thesis may be written in absentia.

SPECIAL EQUIPMENT, FACILITIES, OR PROGRAMS

Access to SLAC National Accelerator Laboratory; Teaching
Center-Science and Engineering Quad; Hansen Experimental
Physics Laboratory; Edward L. Ginzton Laboratory; Kavli In-
stitute for Particle Astrophysics and Cosmology; Center for
Space Science and Astrophysics; Laboratory for Advanced Mate-
rials.

FACULTY

Professor

Abel, Thomas, Ph.D., L. Maxemillian Univ. Munich, 2000. Director of Kavli Institute of Particle Astrophysics and Cosmology. *Astrophysics, Theoretical Physics*. Theoretical astrophysics and cosmology.

Allen, Steven, Ph.D., University of Cambridge, 1994. *Astrophysics*. Experimental and observational astrophysics and cosmology.

Blandford, Roger, Ph.D., Magdalene College, 1974. Professor
at SLAC National Accelerator Laboratory. *Astrophysics, Theoretical Physics*. Theoretical astrophysics and cosmology.

Bucksbaum, Philip, Ph.D., University of California, Berkeley,
1980. Director, Ultrafast Science Center, SLAC National Accelerator Laboratory. *Atomic, Molecular, & Optical Physics*.
Optics; atomic, molecular, and optical physics.

Burchat, Patricia, Ph.D., Stanford University, 1986. *Astrophysics*. Experimental and observational astrophysics and cosmology; experimental particle physics.

Cabrera, Blas, Ph.D., Stanford University, 1975. *Astrophysics*.
Experimental and observational astrophysics and cosmology;
experimental particle physics.

Chu, Steven, Ph.D., University of California, Berkeley, 1976.
Professor Physics and Molecular and Cellular Physiology.
Atomic, Molecular, & Optical Physics, Biophysics. Atomic,
molecular, and optical physics.

Church, Sarah E., Ph.D., University of Cambridge, 1991. Professor by Courtesy, SLAC. *Astrophysics*. Experimental and observational astrophysics and cosmology.

Dimopoulos, Savas, Ph.D., University of Chicago, 1978. *Astrophysics, Theoretical Physics*. Theoretical particle physics.

Doniach, Sebastian, Ph.D., University of Liverpool, 1958. Professor of Applied Physics. *Biophysics, Condensed Matter
Physics, Theoretical Physics*. Biophysics; theoretical condensed matter physics.

Drell, Persis, Ph.D., University of California, Berkeley, 1983.
Provost; Professor of Physics and Material Science & Engineering. *Astrophysics, Particles and Fields*. Experimental
and observational astrophysics and cosmology; experimental
particle physics.

Goldhaber-Gordon, David, Ph.D., Massachusetts Institute of
Technology, 1999. *Condensed Matter Physics*. Experimental
condensed matter physics.

Gratta, Giorgio, Ph.D., Laurea, University of Rome, 1986. *Particles and Fields*. Experimental particle physics.

Hayden, Patrick, Ph.D., Oxford University, 2001. *Quantum
Foundations, Theoretical Physics*. Theoretical physics; quantum information.

Irwin, Kent, Ph.D., Stanford University, 1995. *Astrophysics,
Particles and Fields*. Experimental and observational astrophysics and cosmology; experimental particle physics.

Kachru, Shamit, Ph.D., Princeton University, 1994. Department
Chair. *Theoretical Physics*. Theoretical physics.

Kahn, Steven M., Ph.D., University of California, Berkeley,
1980. *Astrophysics*. Experimental and observational astrophysics and cosmology.

Kallosh, Renata, Ph.D., Lebedev Physical Institute, Moscow,
1968. *Theoretical Physics*. Theoretical particle physics.

Kapitulnik, Aharon, Ph.D., Tel Aviv University, 1984. *Condensed Matter Physics*. Experimental condensed matter physics.

Kasevich, Mark, Ph.D., Stanford University, 1992. *Atomic, Molecular, & Optical Physics*. Atomic, molecular, and optical physics.

Kivelson, Steven A., Ph.D., Harvard University, 1979. *Condensed Matter Physics, Theoretical Physics*. Theoretical condensed matter physics.

Laughlin, Robert, Ph.D., Massachusetts Institute of Technology, 1979. *Condensed Matter Physics, Theoretical Physics*. Theoretical condensed matter physics.

Linde, Andrei, Ph.D., Lebedev Physical Institute, Moscow, 1974. *Particles and Fields, Theoretical Physics*. Theoretical particle physics and cosmology.

Macintosh, Bruce, Ph.D., UCLA, 1994. *Astrophysics*. Experimental and observational astrophysics.

Michelson, Peter, Ph.D., Stanford University, 1979. Associate Chair. *Astrophysics*. Experimental and observational astrophysics and cosmology.

Moler, Kathryn A., Ph.D., Stanford University, 1995. Vice Provost and Dean of Research. *Condensed Matter Physics*. Experimental condensed matter physics.

Petrosian, Vahe, Ph.D., Cornell University, 1967. *Astrophysics, Theoretical Physics*. Theoretical astrophysics and cosmology.

Romani, Roger, Ph.D., California Institute of Technology, 1987. *Astrophysics, Theoretical Physics*. Theoretical astrophysics and cosmology.

Shen, Zhi-Xun, Ph.D., Stanford University, 1989. Professor of Physics, Applied Physics, and Photon Science - SLAC National Accelerator Laboratory. *Condensed Matter Physics*. Experimental condensed matter physics.

Shenker, Stephen H., Ph.D., Cornell University, 1980. *Theoretical Physics*. Theoretical physics.

Silverstein, Eva, Ph.D., Princeton University, 1996. *Theoretical Physics*. Theoretical physics.

Susskind, Leonard, Ph.D., Cornell University, 1965. *Theoretical Physics*. Theoretical physics.

Wieman, Carl, Ph.D., Stanford University, 1977. Professor, School of Education. *Atomic, Molecular, & Optical Physics, Physics and other Science Education*. Physics education and atomic and molecular physics.

Zhang, Shoucheng, Ph.D., Stony Brook University, 1987. *Condensed Matter Physics, Theoretical Physics*. Theoretical condensed matter physics.

Associate Professor

Graham, Peter, Ph.D., Stanford University, 2007. *Particles and Fields, Theoretical Physics*. Theoretical particle physics.

Hartnoll, Sean, Ph.D., University of Cambridge, 2005. *Particles and Fields, Theoretical Physics*. Theoretical particle physics.

Kuo, Chao-Lin, Ph.D., University of California, Berkeley, 2003. *Astrophysics*. Experimental and observational astrophysics and cosmology.

Lev, Benjamin, Ph.D., California Institute of Technology, 2005. Asociate Professor of Applied Physics and Physics. *Atomic, Molecular, & Optical Physics*. Atomic, molecular, and optical physics.

Manoharan, Hari, Ph.D., Princeton University, 1997. *Condensed Matter Physics*. Experimental condensed matter physics.

Qi, Xiaoliang, Ph.D., Tsinghua University, 2007. *Condensed Matter Physics, Theoretical Physics*. Theoretical condensed matter physics.

Raghu, Srinivas, Ph.D., Princeton University, 2006. *Condensed Matter Physics, Theoretical Physics*. Theoretical condensed matter physics.

Senatore, Leonardo, Ph.D., Massachusetts Institute of Technology, 2006. *Particles and Fields, Theoretical Physics*. Theoretical particle physics and cosmology.

Stanford, Douglas, Ph.D., Stanford University, 2014. *Theoretical Physics*. Theoretical particle physics.

Wechsler, Risa, Ph.D., University of California, Santa Cruz, 2001. *Astrophysics, Theoretical Physics*. Theoretical astrophysics and cosmology.

Assistant Professor

Feldman, Benjamin E., Ph.D., Harvard University, 2013. *Condensed Matter Physics*. Experimental condensed matter physics.

Hogan, Jason M., Ph.D., Stanford University, 2010. *Atomic, Molecular, & Optical Physics*. Atomic, molecular, and optical physics, precision measurement, and experimental gravitational physics.

Schleier-Smith, Monika, Ph.D., Massachusetts Institute of Technology, 2011. *Atomic, Molecular, & Optical Physics*. Atomic, molecular, and optical physics.

Tompkins, Lauren A., Ph.D., University of Calif. at Berkeley, 2011. *Particles and Fields*. Experimental particle physics.

Professor Emeritus

Fetter, Alexander L., Ph.D., Harvard University, 1963. Theoretical Condensed Matter Physics. *Condensed Matter Physics, Theoretical Physics*.

Lipa, John A., Ph.D., University of Western Australia, 1969. Professor (Research) Emeritus. *Condensed Matter Physics, Low Temperature Physics*. Experimental Condensed Matter Physics.

Little, William A., Ph.D., Rhodes, 1955. *Condensed Matter Physics, Low Temperature Physics*. Experimental Condensed Matter Physics.

Osheroff, Douglas D., Ph.D., Cornell University, 1973. *Condensed Matter Physics, Low Temperature Physics*. Experimental Condensed Matter Physics.

Ritson, David M., Ph.D., University of Oxford, 1948. *High Energy Physics, Particles and Fields*. Experimental Particle Physics.

Schwettman, H. Alan, Ph.D., Rice University, 1962. *Atomic, Molecular, & Optical Physics, Low Temperature Physics*. Atomic, Molecular and Optical Physics.

Smith, Todd I., Ph.D., Rice University, 1965. Professor (Research) Emeritus. *Atomic, Molecular, & Optical Physics*. Free electron laser physics.

Sturrock, Peter, Ph.D., University of Cambridge, 1951. Professor (Emeritus) by Courtesy. *Astrophysics, Solar Physics, Theoretical Physics*. Theoretical Astrophysics and Cosmology.

Turneaure, John, Ph.D., Stanford University, 1967. Professor (Research) Emeritus. *Relativity & Gravitation*. Experimental General Relativity and Superconductivity.

Wagoner, Robert V., Ph.D., Stanford University, 1965. *Astrophysics, Relativity & Gravitation, Theoretical Physics*. Theoretical Astrophysics and Cosmology.

Walecka, John D., Ph.D., Massachusetts Institute of Technology, 1958. *Nuclear Physics, Particles and Fields, Theoretical Physics*. Theoretical Nuclear and Particle Physics.

Wojcicki, Stanley G., Ph.D., University of California, Berkeley, 1961. *High Energy Physics, Particles and Fields*. Experimental Particle Physics.

Yearian, Mason, Ph.D., Stanford University, 1959. *High Energy Physics, Particles and Fields*. Experimental Particle Physics.

Research Professor

Hollberg, Leo, Ph.D., University of Colorado Boulder, 1984. *Atomic, Molecular, & Optical Physics*. Atomic, Molecular, and Optical Physics.

Scherrer, Philip H., Ph.D., University of California, Berkeley, 1973. *Astrophysics, Solar Physics*. Observational astrophysics; solar physics.

Courtesy Professor

Akerib, Daniel S., Ph.D., Princeton University, 1991. Professor, SLAC National Accelerator Laboratory. *Astrophysics.* CDMS.

Levin, Craig, Ph.D., Yale University, 1993. Prof. of Radiology and by courtesy, Physics, Electrical Engineering and Bioengineering. *Biophysics.* Molecular Imaging Instrumentation.

Quake, Stephen, Ph.D., University of Oxford, 1999. Professor of Bioengineering and by courtesy, Physics. *Biophysics.* Biophysics.

Shutt, Thomas A., Ph.D., UC Berkeley, 1993. Professor, SLAC National Accelerator Laboratory. *High Energy Physics.* High energy phyiscs.

Zare, Richard N., Ph.D., Harvard University, 1964. Professor of Chemistry and by courtesy, Physics. *Other.* Laser Chemistry.

Courtesy Assistant Professor

Das, Rhiju, Ph.D., Stanford University, 2005. Assistant Professor of Biochemistry and, by courtesy, Physics. *Biophysics.* Biophysics.

DEPARTMENTAL RESEARCH SPECIALTIES AND STAFF

Theoretical

Quantum Information. Hayden.

Theoretical Astrophysics and Cosmology. Calculating and modeling the physics of the cosmos. First objects in the universe, relativistic astrophysics, neutron stars, black holes, inflation, cosmic evolution and structure. Current research in theoretical astrophysics and cosmology at Stanford explores a wide range of critical questions. Major topics include numerical simulations of the formation of structure from small scales (first stars) to large scales (dark matter structure), galaxy formation, black holes (evolution, jets, accretion disks and orbiting objects), neutron stars (pulsars, magnetars), particle acceleration (relativistic shocks, origin of cosmic rays), gravitational lensing, and the very early universe (inflation). For more info: https://physics.stanford.edu/research/theoretical-astrophysics-and-cosmology Abel, Blandford, Petrosian, Romani, Wechsler.

Theoretical Condensed Matter. Predicting the behavior of material systems based on their structure and composition. Exotic phases of matter, emergent phenomena, origin of physical law, topological phenomena. Theoretical condensed matter physics at Stanford is focused on understanding the macroscopic and collective properties of condensed matter systems. What is the relation between the macroscopic properties and the microscopic physics at the single electron or single molecule scale? In particular what are the consequences of strong correlation effects in electronic materials and devices where the low energy properties are qualitatively different from those of a noninteracting electron gas? How do new phases of matter fit into field theories that describe the collective behavior of electrons in solids and how can these be detected in experiments? Central areas of research include quantum entanglement, the quantum spin Hall effect, topological insulators, quantum spintronics, cuprate and pnictide superconductors, superfluidity, and holographic duality. For more info: https://physics.stanford.edu/research/theoretical-condensed-matter-physics Doniach, Kivelson, Laughlin, Qi, Raghu, Zhang.

Theoretical Particle Physics. Understanding the fundamental nature of forces, particles, and space-time geometry. The origin of mass, grand unification of the forces, general relativity, quantum field theory and string theory and their applications, early universe cosmology including inflation and eternal inflation, holography, quantum gravity. Research in the Stanford Institute for Theoretical Physics (SITP) includes a strong focus on fundamental questions about the new physics underlying the Standard Models of particle physics and cosmology, and on the nature and applications of our basic frameworks (quantum field theory and string theory) for attacking these questions. For more info: https://physics.stanford.edu/research/theoretical-particle-physics Dimopoulos, Graham, Hartnoll, Kachru, Kallosh, Linde, Senatore, Shenker, Silverstein, Stanford, Susskind.

Experimental

Atomic, Molecular, & Optical Physics. Examining and manipulating matter at the scale of the atom and molecule. Attosecond to femtosecond processes, quantum properties of atoms and photons, testing fundamental physics. Research in atomic, molecular, laser and X-ray physics at Stanford takes place in the Physics and Applied Physics Departments and in the Photon Science Department at SLAC National Accelerator Laboratory. A rich set of topics are explored in the Varian Physics Laboratory, the Ginzton Lab and through the PULSE Institute for Ultrafast Energy Science. SLAC houses both the Stanford Synchrotron Radiation Lightsource and the Linac Coherent Light Source. For further info: https://physics.stanford.edu/research/atomic-molecular-and-optical-physics Bucksbaum, Chu, Hogan, Hollberg, Kasevich, Lev, Schleier-Smith.

Experimental and Observational Astrophysics and Cosmology. Viewing the formation and evolution of stars, galaxies, and the cosmos. Galaxy clusters, cosmic microwave background radiation, ultra high-energy sources, large scale structure in the universe and cosmic evolution. Current research in observational astrophysics and cosmology at Stanford covers a wide range of approaches to tackling the most important frontiers. Major topics include direct detection of dark matter, probes of dark energy (via gravitational lensing, surveys of galaxy clusters and supernovae), sources of gamma rays (pulsars, blazars, supernova remnants, dark matter annihilation or decay), the structure of clusters of galaxies and their use as probes of cosmology, the development of next generation detectors of photons (radio through gamma-ray), the origins of solar variability on a wide range of time scales, and experiments in gravitation (detection of gravitational waves, probes of gravity at short distance scales). For further info: https://physics.stanford.edu/research/experimental-observational-astrophysics-and-cosmology Allen, Burchat, Cabrera, Church, Drell, Irwin, Kahn, Kuo, Macintosh, Michelson, Scherrer.

Experimental Condensed Matter Physics. Measuring the behavior of electrons in material systems. Semiconductor nanostructures, superconductivity and low-temperature physics, atomic and molecular measurement and control, novel quantum materials. News: Stanford researchers create exotic electrons that may lead to new materials, devices Research in experimental condensed matter physics at Stanford takes place in the Physics and Applied Physics Departments and has strong connections with the Photon Science Department at the SLAC National Accelerator Laboratory. A broad set of topics are explored in the Varian Physics Laboratory, Geballe Laboratory for Advanced Materials and through the Stanford Institute for Materials and Energy Science. For more info: https://physics.stanford.edu/research/experimental-condensed-matter-physics Feldman, Goldhaber-Gordon, Kapitulnik, Lev, Manoharan, Moler, Shen.

Experimental Particle Physics. Understanding the fundamental forces and particles of the universe. Electroweak symmetry breaking, heavy flavor physics, searches for physics beyond the Standard Model, matter/antimatter asymmetry, dark matter, single-photon detection, neutrino properties, dark energy, instrumentation and detector development. At Stanford, studies of the fundamental interactions and the elementary particles are enhanced by close collaboration between the Physics Department and the SLAC National Accelerator Center. The Cryogenic Dark Matter Search (CDMS) and the LUX-ZEPLIN Experiment (LZ) focus on the development and operation of new detector technologies to increase the sensitivity of searches for weakly interacting massive particles. The goal of the Enriched Xenon Experiment (EXO) is to detect "neutrinoless double-beta decay" using large amounts of xenon enriched in the isotope 136. The MINOS Experiment is a long-baseline neutrino experiment designed to observe the phenomenon of neutrino oscillations, an effect that is related to neutrino mass. The BABAR data set provides opportunities for studying matter/antimatter asymmetries (CP violation) and heavy flavor physics. SLAC plays a major role on the ATLAS experiment at the Large Hadron Collider, focusing on the pixel detector, the high-level trigger system, detector simulations and the exploration of TeV-scale physics. For more info: https://physics.stanford.edu/research/experimental-particle-physics Gratta, Hogan, Tompkins.

Physics and Science Education Research. Wieman.

View additional information about this department at www.gradschoolshopper.com. Check out the "Why Choose Us?" section, find out more about the department's culture and get links to social media networks.

UNIVERSITY OF CALIFORNIA, BERKELEY

DEPARTMENT OF PHYSICS

Berkeley, California 94720-7300
http://www.physics.berkeley.edu

General University Information
Chancellor: Carolyn Christ
Dean of Graduate School: Fiona Doyle
University website: http://www.grad.berkeley.edu/
School Type: Public
Setting: Urban
Total Faculty: 2,082
Total number of Students: 36,142
Total number of Graduate Students: 10,257

Department Information
Department Chairman: Prof. Wick Haxton, Chair
Department Contact: Brian Underwood, Deputy Director of
   Administration
   Total full-time faculty: 65
   Total number of full-time equivalent positions: 51
   Full-Time Graduate Students: 278
   Female Full-Time Graduate Students: 0
   First-Year Graduate Students: 45
   Female First-Year Students: 6
   Total Post Doctorates: 44

Department Address
366 Le Conte Hall
MC 7300
Berkeley, CA 94720-7300
Phone: (510) 642-3317
Fax: (510) 643-8497
E-mail: physicsap@berkeley.edu
Website: http://www.physics.berkeley.edu

ADMISSIONS

Admission Contact Information
Address admission inquiries to: Donna K. Sakima, Graduate Stu-
   dent Affairs, Physics Student Services, 370 LeConte Hall
   #7300, University of California, Berkeley, CA 94720-7300
Phone: (510) 642-0596
E-mail: sakima@berkeley.edu
Admissions website: http://www.grad.berkeley.edu/admissions/
   index.shtml

Application deadlines
Fall admission:
U.S. students: December 17   *Int'l. students*: December 17

Application fee
U.S. students: $105   *Int'l. students*: $125

Admissions information
For Fall of 2018:
   Number of applicants: 898
   Number admitted: 127
   Number enrolled: 45

Admission requirements
Bachelor's degree requirements: Bachelor's degree in Physics
   and/or related field is required.
Minimum undergraduate GPA: 3.0

GRE requirements
The GRE is required.
The average percentiles of the General GRE scores for admission
   are: verbal–45% or better; quantitative–90% or better; and
   analytical writing–45% or better.

Subjective GRE requirements
The Subjective GRE is required.
   Minimum accepted Advanced GRE score: 730
   Mean Advanced GRE score range (25th–75th percentile): 910
   - 990
Mean GRE Physics percentile range: 86th - 94th.

TOEFL requirements
The TOEFL exam is required for students from non-English-
   speaking countries.
   PBT score: 570
   iBT score: 68
Students who do not speak English as a native language and do
   not hold a Bachelor's degree from a U.S. institution must
   demonstrate oral English proficiency to be appointed as a
   Graduate Student Instructor. Oral English proficiency can be
   demonstrated by a passing iBT speaking section score (26
   or better).

Other admissions information
Additional requirements: Supervised undergraduate research is
   strongly encouraged.
Undergraduate preparation assumed: Three semesters-General
   Physics, Giancoli; 1 semester-Mechanics, Taylor; 2
   semesters-Electromagnetism and Optics, Griffiths; 1 semes-
   ter-Thermal/Statistical, Kittel & Kroemer, Reif; 2 semesters-
   Atomic Physics and Quantum Mechanics, Griffiths, Bransden
   & Joachain; 2 semesters-Advanced Undergraduate Laboratory, no required textbook. Plus mathematics courses in vector
   calculus, linear algebra, ordinary and partial differential equations, complex variable. (Berkeley undergraduates have in addition 1 semester of physics electives; for example, solid state
   physics, plasma physics, nuclear and particle physics, relativity.).

TUITION

Tuition year 2017–18:
Tuition for in-state residents
   Full-time students: $18,631.5 annual
Tuition for out-of-state residents
   Full-time students: $33,733.5 annual
Fees subject to change.
Credit hours per semester to be considered full-time: 12
Deferred tuition plan: No
Health insurance: Available at the cost of $4,462 per year.
Other academic fees: Cost of the Student Health Insurance Pro-
   gram ($4,462) is included in tuition information.
Academic term: Semester
Number of first-year students who received full tuition waivers: 45

Teaching Assistants, Research Assistants, and Fellowships

Number of first-year
Teaching Assistants: 36
Research Assistants: 2
Fellowship students: 7
Average stipend per academic year
Teaching Assistant: $20,652
Research Assistant: $34,030
Fellowship student: $34,000
TAs are appointed for 10 months, whereas RAs are appointed throughout the calendar year.

FINANCIAL AID

Loans

Loans are available for U.S. students.
Loans are not available for international students.
GAPSFAS application required: No
FAFSA application required: Yes

For further information

Address financial aid inquiries to: Financial Aid and Scholarships Office, UC Berkeley, 201 Sproul Hall #1960, Berkeley, CA 94720-1960.
Phone: (510) 664-9181
Financial aid website: http://financialaid.berkeley.edu/

HOUSING

Availability of on-campus housing

Single students: Yes
Married students: Yes
Childcare Assistance: Yes

For further information

Address housing inquiries to: Cal Rentals, 2610 Channing Way, #2272, University of California, Berkeley CA 94720-2272.
Phone: (510) 642-3644
E-mail: calrentals@berkeley.edu
Housing aid website: https://housing.berkeley.edu/graduate

Table A—Faculty, Enrollments, and Degrees Granted

Research Specialty	2017–2018 Faculty	Enrollment Fall 2017 Master's	Enrollment Fall 2017 Doctorate	Number of Degrees Granted 2017–18 (2013–18) Master's	Number of Degrees Granted 2017–18 (2013–18) Terminal Master's	Number of Degrees Granted 2017–18 (2013–18) Doctorate
Astrophysics	12	–	40	–	–	3(23)
Atomic, Molecular, & Optical Physics	7	–	27	–	–	4(18)
Biophysics	9	–	15	–	–	1(11)
Condensed Matter Physics	17	–	80	–	–	7(58)
High Energy Physics	15	–	60	–	–	8(33)
Nuclear Physics	–	–	1	–	–	–(1)
Plasma and Nonlinear Dynamics	4	–	10	–	–	1(9)
Non-specialized	–	–	46	–	–	–
Total	**64**	**–**	**279**	**34**	**–**	**24(153)**
Full-time Grad. Stud.	–	–	279	–	–	–
First-year Grad. Stud.	–	–	45	–	–	–

GRADUATE DEGREE REQUIREMENTS

Master's: Thirty-five semester units in approved program with satisfactory performance; comprehensive exam required; thesis not required; two semester residence requirement; no language requirement.

Doctorate: Thirty-eight graduate units in approved program with satisfactory performance, preliminary examination, candidacy qualifying examination, and dissertation required; four semester residency requirement; no language requirement.

Other Degrees: Interdepartmental research: Some graduate students are engaged in research problems involving interdepartmental collaboration of which the following are examples: (1) nuclear physics, in programs with the Chemistry Department or the Lawrence Berkeley National Laboratory; (2) astrophysics, with the Department of Astronomy, the Berkeley Center for Cosmological Physics, or the Space Sciences Laboratory; (3) solid-state physics, with the Departments of Electrical Engineering and Computer Sciences, and Materials Science and Engineering; (4) plasma physics, with the Departments of Electrical Engineering and Computer Sciences and Nuclear Engineering or the Lawrence Berkeley National Laboratory; and (5) Biophysics and medical physics. Interdisciplinary groups: there are a number of graduate Interdisciplinary Groups with Ph.D. programs separate from the Ph.D. in Physics, particle physics, with the Berkeley Center for Theoretical Physics.

SPECIAL EQUIPMENT, FACILITIES, OR PROGRAMS

In addition to our own research programs and facilities, our dynamic collaborations bring access to local research facilities such as Lick Observatory (University of California, Mount Hamilton, San Jose CA); Space Sciences Laboratory (University of California, Berkeley, CA); Lawrence Berkeley National Laboratory/ LBNL (DOE, Berkeley, CA); Advanced Light Source (LBNL); National Center for Electron Microscopy (LBNL); The Molecular Foundry, a nanoscience user research facility (LBNL); and Lawrence Livermore National Laboratory (Livermore, CA).

The following local, national, and international laboratories also make facilities available for graduate student research: Brookhaven National Laboratory (New York); Fermi National Accelerator Laboratory (Illinois); NASA Ames Center (California); Kitt Peak National Observatory (Arizona); SLAC National Accelerator Laboratory (California); University of California, Berkeley Micro/Nanofabrication Facility (California); the University of California, Berkeley Radio Astronomy Laboratory (California); Argonne National Laboratory (Illinois); W. M. Keck Observatory (Hawaii); CERN (Headquarters Switzerland); Gran Sasso Underground Laboratory (Italy); Assergi (Italy); Kamioka Observatory (Japan); Institute for the Physics and Mathematics of the Universe/IPMU (Japan); Paul Scherrer Institute (Switzerland); and TRIUMF (Canada).

Table B—Separately Budgeted Research Expenditures by Source of Support

Source of Support	Departmental Research	Physics-related Research Outside Department
Federal government	$21,486,790	$10,000,000
State/local government	$1,179,957	$5,000,000
Non-profit organizations	$4,712,258	
Business and industry	$383,653	
Other	$1,305,391	
Total	**$29,068,049**	**$15,000,000**

Table C—Separately Budgeted Research Expenditures by Research Specialty

Research Specialty	No. of Grants	Expenditures ($)
Astrophysics	30	$2,603,111
Atomic, Molecular, & Optical Physics	56	$4,043,444
Condensed Matter Physics	107	$10,271,531
Nuclear Physics	14	$2,103,523
Particles and Fields	37	$1,955,455
Plasma and Fusion	11	$1,150,063
Other	34	$2,505,239
Total	289	$24,632,366

FACULTY

Chair Professor

Haxton, Wick, Ph.D., University of California, Santa Cruz, 1971. *Astrophysics, Nuclear Physics, Particles and Fields.* Theoretical Particle Physics, Astrophysics, & Nuclear Physics.

Professor

Aganagic, Mina, Ph.D., California Institute of Technology, 1999. Theoretical Particle Physics.

Altman, Ehud, Ph.D., Technion-Israel Institute of Technology, 2002. *Condensed Matter Physics.* Strongly correlated many-body physics; Theoretical Condensed Matter Physics & Atomic, Molecular & Optical Physics.

Bale, Stuart, Ph.D., University of Minnesota, 1994. Director, Space Science Laboratory, UC Berkeley. *Astrophysics.* Experimental Astrophysics.

Betzig, Eric, Ph.D., Cornell University, 1988. 2014 Nobel Laureate in Chemistry. *Biophysics, Nano Science and Technology, Optics.* Biological Imaging; Nanofluorescence Microscopy.

Birgeneau, Robert J., Ph.D., Yale University, 1966. Chancellor Emeritus. *Condensed Matter Physics, Materials Science, Metallurgy.* Experimental Condensed Matter Physics & Materials Science.

Bousso, Raphael, Ph.D., University of Cambridge, 1998. *Particles and Fields.* Theoretical Particle Physics.

Bustamante, Carlos J., Ph.D., University of California, Berkeley, 1981. *Biophysics.* Experimental Biophysics.

Crommie, Michael, Ph.D., University of California, Berkeley, 1991. *Condensed Matter Physics, Materials Science, Metallurgy.* Experimental Condensed Matter Physics & Materials Science.

Fajans, Joel, Ph.D., Massachusetts Institute of Technology, 1985. *Nonlinear Dynamics and Complex Systems, Plasma and Fusion.* Experimental Plasma & Nonlinear Dynamics.

Hall, Lawrence J., Ph.D., Harvard University, 1981. *Particles and Fields.* Theory of Elementary Particles.

Hellman, Frances D., Ph.D., Stanford University, 1985. Dean, Division of Math and Physical Science, College of Letters and Science. *Condensed Matter Physics, Materials Science, Metallurgy.* Experimental Condensed Matter Physics & Materials Science.

Hoava, Petr, Ph.D., Czech Academy of Sciences, 1981. *Particles and Fields.* Theoretical Particle Physics.

Holzapfel, William L., Ph.D., University of California, Berkeley, 1996. *Astrophysics.* Experimental Astrophysics.

Jacak, Barbara, Ph.D., Michigan State, 1984. Director of the Nuclear Science Division and Senior Scientist, Lawrence Berkeley National Lab. *Particles and Fields.* Experimental Particle Physics. Experimental study of quark gluon plasma; this plasma is formed in relativistic heavy ion collisions where nuclei are heated to trillions of degrees and quarks are no longer confined in hadrons.

Jacobsen, Robert G., Ph.D., Stanford University, 1991. Dean, Undergraduate Studies, College of Letters & Science. *Particles and Fields.* Experimental Elementary Particle Physics.

Knobloch, Edgar, Ph.D., Harvard University, 1978. *Nonlinear Dynamics and Complex Systems, Plasma and Fusion.* Theoretical Astrophysics; Fluid Dynamics; Plasma & Nonlinear Dynamics.

Kolomensky, Yury, Ph.D., University of Massachusetts, 1997. *Nuclear Physics, Particles and Fields.* Experimental Particle Physics & Nulcear Physics. BaBar, B hadron decays, with particular emphasis on understanding the origin of CD noninvariance.

Lanzara, Alessandra, Ph.D., University of Rome, 1999. *Condensed Matter Physics, Materials Science, Metallurgy.* Experimental Condensed Matter Physics & Materials Science.

Lee, Adrian, Ph.D., Stanford University, 1993. Associate Director of the Radio Astronomy Laboratory, UC Berkeley. *Astrophysics.* Experimental Astrophysics; Cryogenic far-infrared and mm-wave detector development.

Lee, Dung-Hai, Ph.D., Massachusetts Institute of Technology, 1982. *Condensed Matter Physics, Materials Science, Metallurgy.* Theory of Condensed Matter & Materials Science; quantum phase transitions; strongly correlating electronic systems.

Leone, Stephen R., Ph.D., University of California, Berkeley, 1974. Director, Chemical Dynamics Beamline, Lawrence Berkeley National Lab. *Atomic, Molecular, & Optical Physics.* Experimental Atomic, Molecular, and Optical Physics; Gas phase laser spectroscopy.

Louie, Steven G., Ph.D., University of California, Berkeley, 1976. *Condensed Matter Physics, Materials Science, Metallurgy.* Theory of Condensed Matter Physics & Materials Science.

Luk, Kam-Biu, Ph.D., Rutgers University, 1983. *Particles and Fields.* Experimental Elementary Particle Physics.

Ma, Chung-Pei, Ph.D., Massachusetts Institute of Technology, 1993. Professor of Astronomy. *Astrophysics.* Theoretical Astrophysics.

McKinsey, Daniel, Ph.D., Harvard University, 2002. *Astrophysics, Particles and Fields.* Experimental Particle Physics and Astrophysics. The search for WIMPs using noble liquids (liquid xenon, argon, neon, and helium) as detector materials.

Moore, Joel E., Ph.D., Massachusetts Institute of Technology, 2000. *Condensed Matter Physics, Materials Science, Metallurgy.* Theory of Condensed Matter Physics & Materials Science and statistical physics-theory/biophysics theory.

Murayama, Hitoshi, Ph.D., University of Tokyo, 1991. Founding Director, The Kavli Institute for Physics and Mathematics of the Universe (KAVLI IPMU)Japan. *Particles and Fields.* Theory of Elementary Particles.

Neaton, Jeffrey B., Ph.D., Cornell University, 2000. Director: Molecular Foundry & Senior Scientist/ Materials Sciences Division, Lawrence Berkeley National Lab. *Condensed Matter Physics, Materials Science, Metallurgy.* Theory of Condensed Matter & Materials Science.

Nomura, Yasunori, Ph.D., University of Tokyo, 2000. Director, Berkeley Center for Theoretical Physics (BCTP). *Particles and Fields.* Theoretical Particle Physics.

Orenstein, Joseph W., Ph.D., Massachusetts Institute of Technology, 1980. *Condensed Matter Physics.* Experimental Condensed Matter Physics & Materials Science.

Perlmutter, Saul, Ph.D., Harvard University, 1986. 2011 Nobel Laureate; Director, Berkeley Center for Cosmological Physics (BCCP). *Astrophysics.* Experimental Astrophysics.

Qiu, Zi Qiang, Ph.D., Johns Hopkins University, 1990. *Condensed Matter Physics.* Experimental Condensed Matter Physics & Materials Science.

Quataert, Eliot, Ph.D., Harvard University, 1999. Director, Theoretical Astrophysics Center (TAC), UC Berkeley. *Astronomy, Astrophysics*. Astronomy and Theoretical Astrophysics.

Ramesh, Ramamoorthy, Ph.D., University of California, Berkeley, 1987. Associate Laboratory Director of Energy Technologies at Lawrence Berkeley National Lab. *Condensed Matter Physics, Materials Science, Metallurgy*. Experimental Condensed Matter Physics & Materials Science.

Rokhsar, Daniel S., Ph.D., Cornell University, 1987. *Biophysics*. Statistical and many-body physics; Biophysics.

Sadoulet, Bernard, Ph.D., d'Etude es Sciences, Orsay, 1971. *Astrophysics*. Experimental Astrophysics.

Seljak, Uroš, Ph.D., Massachusetts Institute of Technology, 1995. Director, Berkeley Center for Cosmological Physics (BCCP). *Astrophysics*. Cosmology and Theoretical Astrophysics.

Shapiro, Marjorie, Ph.D., University of California, Berkeley, 1984. *Particles and Fields*. Experimental Elementary Particle Physics.

Siddiqi, Irfan, Ph.D., Yale University, 2002. Director, Quantum Nanoelectronics Lab, UC Berkeley. *Condensed Matter Physics, Materials Science, Metallurgy*. Experimental Condensed Matter Physics & Materials Science.

Stamper-Kurn, Dan, Ph.D., Massachusetts Institute of Technology, 1999. *Atomic, Molecular, & Optical Physics, Condensed Matter Physics, Materials Science, Metallurgy*. Experimental Atomic, Molecular, and Optical Physics; Bose-Einstein Condensation (BEC) of Atoms; Condensed Matter Physics & Materials Science.

Vishwanath, Ashvin, Ph.D., Princeton University, 2001. *Condensed Matter Physics, Materials Science, Metallurgy*. Theoretical Condensed Matter Physics & Materials Science.

Wang, Feng, Ph.D., Columbia University, 2004. *Condensed Matter Physics, Materials Science, Metallurgy*. Experimental Condensed Matter Physics & Materials Science.

White, Martin, Ph.D., Yale University, 1992. *Astrophysics*. Theoretical Astrophysics.

Witherell, Michael, Ph.D., University of Wisconsin, Madison, 1973. Director, Lawrence Berkeley National Lab. *Particles and Fields*. Currently working on the LUX experiment in South Dakota; member of the LUX-ZEPLIN collaboration. Interested in the search for dark matter and for neutrinoless double beta decay; Experimental Particle Physics.

Wurtele, Jonathan S., Ph.D., University of California, Berkeley, 1979. *Nonlinear Dynamics and Complex Systems, Plasma and Fusion*. Theoretical Plasma Physics & Nonlinear Dynamics.

Zettl, Alex, Ph.D., University of California, Los Angeles, 1983. *Condensed Matter Physics, Materials Science, Metallurgy*. Experimental Condensed Matter Physics & Materials Science.

Associate Professor

DeWeese, Michael, Ph.D., Princeton University, 1995. *Biophysics*. Experimental Biophysics.

Ganor, Ori, Ph.D., Tel Aviv University, 1996. *Particles and Fields*. Theoretical Particle Physics.

Ginsberg, Naomi, Ph.D., Harvard University, 2007. Associate Professor in the Department of Chemistry. *Atomic, Molecular, & Optical Physics, Chemical Physics, Condensed Matter Physics*. Physical & Biophysical Chemistry; Light harvesting; Spectroscopy & Imaging; Experimental Atomic, Molecular, & Optical Physics; Condensed Matter Physics & Materials Science.

Häffner, Hartmut, Ph.D., University of Mainz, 2000. *Atomic, Molecular, & Optical Physics*. Experimental Atomic Molecular and Optical Physics.

Ji, Na, Ph.D., UC Berkeley, 2005. *Biophysics, Optics*. Experimental Biophysics.

Kasen, Daniel, Ph.D., University of California, Berkeley, 2004. Assistant Professor, Astronomy. *Astrophysics, Nuclear Physics*. Theoretical Astrophysics & Nuclear Physics.

Müller, Holger, Ph.D., Humboldt University, Berlin, 2004. *Atomic, Molecular, & Optical Physics*. Experimental Atomic, Molecular, and Optical Physics.

Yildiz, Ahmet, Ph.D., University of Illinois, 2004. *Biophysics*. Experimental Biophysics.

Assistant Professor

Analytis, James, Ph.D., University of Oxford, 2006. *Condensed Matter Physics, Materials Science, Metallurgy*. Experimental Condensed Matter Physics & Materials Science.

Garcia, Hernan, Ph.D., California Institute of Technology, 2011. Assistant Professor in Department of Molecular and Cell Biology. *Biophysics*. Optics, Physics, Molecular and Developmental Biology. Seeking a quantitative and predictive analyses of microscopic genetic expression data through the use of equilibrium thermodynamic methods of analysis.

Hallatschek, Oskar, Ph.D., Free University of Berlin, 2004. *Biophysics*. Theoretical Biophysics.

Orebi-Gann, Gabriel, Ph.D., University of Oxford, 2008. *Particles and Fields*. Experimental Particle Physics & Nuclear Physics.

Pyle, Matt C., Ph.D., Stanford University, 2012. *Astrophysics, Nuclear Physics*. Experimental Astrophysics & Nuclear Physics; Dark matter; Detector technology.

Rajendran, Surjeet, Ph.D., Stanford University, 2009. *Particles and Fields, Theoretical Physics*. Theoretical Particle Physics. Inventing new experimental avenues to help answer questions on the nature of Dark Matter, the origins of the electroweak scale and the cosmological constant as well as the quantum nature of gravity.

Yao, Norman, Ph.D., Harvard University, 2014. *Atomic, Molecular, & Optical Physics, Condensed Matter Physics, Materials Science, Metallurgy, Optics*. Theoretical Atomic, Molecular, and Optical Physics; Quantum Optics; Condensed Matter Physics and Materials Science.

Zaletel, Michael, Ph.D., University of California, Berkeley, 2014. *Particles and Fields*. Theory of Particle Physics.

Emeritus

Arons, Jonathan, Ph.D., Harvard University, 1970. Professor of the Graduate School. *Astrophysics*. Theoretical High-energy Astrophysics; X-ray sources.

Bardakci, Korkut, Ph.D., University of Rochester, 1962. *Particles and Fields*. Theory of Elementary Particles Physics.

Budker, Dmitry, Ph.D., University of California, Berkeley, 1993. Professor of the Graduate School. *Atomic, Molecular, & Optical Physics*. Experimental Atomic, Molecular, and Optical Physics.

Chew, Geoffrey F., Ph.D., University of Chicago, 1948. Theory of Elementary Particles.

Chinowsky, William, Ph.D., Columbia University, 1955. *Astrophysics*. Astrophysics.

Clarke, John, Ph.D., University of Cambridge, 1968. Professor of the Graduate School. Experimental superconductivity and low-temperature physics; Condensed Matter Physics, and Materials Science.

Cohen, Marvin L., Ph.D., University of Chicago, 1964. Professor of the Graduate School. *Condensed Matter Physics, Materials Science, Metallurgy*. Theory of Condensed Matter Physics & Materials Science.

Davis, Marc, Ph.D., Princeton University, 1973. *Astrophysics*. Theoretical astrophysics; extragalactic astronomy; cosmology.

Dynes, Robert C., Ph.D., McMaster University, 1968. *Condensed Matter Physics*. Experimental condensed matter physics.

Ely, Robert P., Ph.D., Massachusetts Institute of Technology, 1959.

Falcone, Roger W., Ph.D., Stanford University, 1979. Director, Advanced Light Source, Lawrence Berkeley National Lab; Professor of the Graduate School. *Atomic, Molecular, & Optical Physics, Nonlinear Dynamics and Complex Systems, Plasma and Fusion*. Quantum electronics; Experimental Atomic, Molecular, and Optical Physics; Plasma and Nonlinear Dynamics.

Frazer, William R., Ph.D., University of California, Berkeley, 1959. *Particles and Fields*. Elementary Particle Theory; Cosmology.

Gaillard, Mary K., Ph.D., University of Paris, 1968. Professor of the Graduate School. *Particles and Fields*. Theory of Elementary Particles.

Genzel, Reinhard L., Ph.D., University of Bonn, 1978. Professor of the Graduate School. *Astrophysics*. Experimental Astrophysics; Infrared and Microwave Astronomy.

Halpern, Martin B., Ph.D., Harvard University, 1964. *Particles and Fields*. Theory of Elementary Particles.

Kaufman, Allan N., Ph.D., University of Chicago, 1953. *Nonlinear Dynamics and Complex Systems, Plasma and Fusion*. Plasma Theory and Nonlinear Dynamics.

Kittel, Charles, Ph.D., University of Wisconsin-Madison, 1941.

Littlejohn, Robert G., Ph.D., University of California, Berkeley, 1980. *Nonlinear Dynamics and Complex Systems, Plasma and Fusion*. Theoretical Plasma Physics and Nonlinear Dynamics.

Marrus, Richard, Ph.D., University of California, Berkeley, 1959. *Atomic, Molecular, & Optical Physics*. Experimental Atomic, Molecular, and Optical Physics; Beam Foil Spectroscopy.

McKee, Christopher F., Ph.D., University of California, Berkeley, 1970. Professor of the Graduate School. *Astrophysics*. Theoretical Astrophysics; Interstellar Medium; High-energy Astrophysics.

Mozer, Forrest S., Ph.D., California Institute of Technology, 1956. *Astrophysics*. Astrophysics.

Muller, R. A., Ph.D., University of California, Berkeley, 1969. *Astrophysics*. Experimental Astrophysics.

Packard, Richard E., Ph.D., University of Michigan, 1969. *Condensed Matter Physics*. Experimental condensed matter physics; experimental low-temperature physics.

Price, P. Buford, Ph.D., University of Virginia, 1958. *Astrophysics*. Astrophysics experiment; cosmic radiation and relativistic nuclear physics; high-energy neutrino astrophysics; microbes in polar ice.

Reif, Frederick, Ph.D., Harvard University, 1953.

Richards, Paul L., Ph.D., University of California, Berkeley, 1960. *Astrophysics*. Experimental condensed matter physics; infrared spectroscopy; infrared astrophysics.

Sachs, Rainer K., Ph.D., Syracuse University, 1958. *Biophysics*. Biophysics.

Schwartz, Charles L., Ph.D., Massachusetts Institute of Technology, 1954. *Atomic, Molecular, & Optical Physics*. Atomic, Molecular, and Optical Physics.

Shank, Charles V., Ph.D., University of California, Berkeley, 1969. *Condensed Matter Physics*. Experimental Condensed Matter Physics.

Shen, Yuen-Ron, Ph.D., Harvard University, 1963. Professor of the Graduate School. *Condensed Matter Physics, Nonlinear Dynamics and Complex Systems*. Experimental Condensed Matter Physics; Quantum and Nonlinear Optics.

Siegrist, James L., Ph.D., Stanford University, 1979. Director, Physics Division, Lawrence Berkeley National Laboratory. *Particles and Fields*. Experimental Elementary Particle Physics.

Smoot, George F., Ph.D., Massachusetts Institute of Technology, 1970. 2006 Nobel Laureate; Professor of the Graduate School. *Astrophysics*. Experimental Astrophysics.

Steiner, Herbert M., Ph.D., University of California, Berkeley, 1956. *Particles and Fields*. Experimental elementary particle physics.

Stevenson, M. Lynn, Ph.D., University of California, Berkeley, 1953. *Particles and Fields*. Experimental Elementary Particle Physics.

Strovink, Mark W., Ph.D., Princeton University, 1970. *Astrophysics*. Astrophysics.

Suzuki, Mahiko, Ph.D., University of Tokyo, 1965. *Particles and Fields*. Theory of Elementary Particles.

Trilling, George H., Ph.D., California Institute of Technology, 1955. *Particles and Fields*. Experimental Elementary Particle Physics.

Tripp, Robert D., Ph.D., University of California, Berkeley, 1955. *Particles and Fields*. Experimental Elementary Particle Physics.

Wichmann, Eyvind H., Ph.D., Columbia University, 1956. *Particles and Fields*. Theory of Elementary Particles; Mathematical Physics.

Yu, Peter, Ph.D., Brown University, 1972. *Condensed Matter Physics*. Experimental Condensed Matter Physics; Semiconductor Physics.

DEPARTMENTAL RESEARCH SPECIALTIES AND STAFF

Theoretical

Atomic, Molecular, & Optical Physics. Quantum optics; laser cooling and atom trapping; atom interferometers; the search for the electric dipole moment of the electron; including the search for dark matter; studies of the consequences of Bose-Einstein condensation; generation an application of ultra-short pulses of x-rays; antimatter research. Altman, Yao.

Biophysics. Detect and manipulate single molecules to elucidate molecular motors, protein folding, polymer (biopolymer) physics, single molecule rheology, dynamics of complex processes such as transcription, replication, and translation, etc. Hallatschek.

Condensed Matter and Materials Physics. Uncover new states of matter and understand their physical properties. Theoretical and computational studies of the behaviors of novel materials and nanostructures, including electronic, vibrational, optical, thermal, transport, magnetic, and superconducting properties; emergent phenomena, quantum phase transitions, and strongly correlated electron systems; many-body effects in bulk, reduced-dimensional, and nanostructured systems; surface, interface, phase transition, and alloy properties. Altman, Cohen, Dung-Hai Lee, Louie, Moore, Neaton, Vishwanath, Yao.

Nonlinear Dynamics, Plasma and Beam Physics, and Complex Systems. Dynamics of neutral and nonneutral plasmas with applications to antihydrogen trapping, laser-plasma interaction and particle acceleration; Chaos and approach to chaos; bifurcation theory; pattern formation; fluid dynamics; semiclassical mechanics; climate change. Knobloch, Littlejohn, Wurtele.

Nuclear Physics. Low-energy neutrino physics, including solar and supernova neutrinos; nuclear astrophysics, including the origin of elements and the nuclear physics of dark matter direct and indirect detection; studies of ultra-relativistic heavy ion collisions, to probe the properties of strongly interacting matter at extreme energy densities. Haxton, Kasen.

Particles and Fields. Gauge theory of weak and electromagnetic interactions and perturbative QCD; theories of physics beyond the standard model, including grand unification, supersymmetry, supergravity, and extra dimensions; quantum field theory; string theory; theories of gravity. Aganagic, Bousso, Gaillard, Ganor, Hall, Haxton, Hoava, Kasen, Murayama, Nomura, Rajendran.

Theoretical Astrophysics. Interstellar medium; star formation; binary stars; stellar convection; pulsars; X-ray sources; active galactic nuclei and quasars; galaxy formation; cosmology. Arons, Haxton, Kasen, Ma, McKee, Quataert, Seljak, White.

Experimental

Atmosphere, Space Physics, Cosmic Rays. Magnetospheric physics: space plasmas and fields; auroras; isotopic and elemental composition of cosmic rays; search for new particles and antimatter in cosmic rays; spectrum and anisotropy of the universal microwave radiation; infrared astronomical spectroscopy and spatial interferometry; millimeter and submillimeter spectra; the galactic center; star formation; new astronomical detectors; automated supernova search; X-ray spectroscopy and laboratory astrophysics; high-energy gamma-ray astrophysics; experimental cosmology including particle astrophysics. Bale.

Atomic, Molecular, & Optical Physics. Precision measurements; ultra-cold quantum gases; quantum information; attosecond physics; X-ray lasers; tests of fundamental symmetries; variation of fundamental constants; quantum phase transitions; ion trapping; hybrid quantum systems; antihydrogen trapping and spectroscopy; optomechanical systems; magnetometry; low-field NMR; frequency combs; precision spectroscopy of atomic systems near and in bulk materials; NV-centers; novel approaches to microscopy; energy transfer in complex molecules; nonlinear interaction of light with matter; hot and dense plasmas. Budker, Falcone, Ginsberg, Häffner, Leone, Müller, Stamper-Kurn.

Biophysics. Molecular biophysics and structural biology. Application of atomic force spectroscopy and optical tweezers to biological problems. Betzig, Bustamante, DeWeese, Garcia, Ginsberg, Ji, Rokhsar, Yildiz.

Condensed Matter Physics. Synthesis and experimental investigation of novel condensed phase materials, including high-Tc superconductors, low-dimensional materials, strongly correlated materials, thin-film oxides, and topological insulators. Understand the fundamental electrical, magnetic, optical, superconducting, and superfluidic behavior using state-of-the-art experimental techniques, including electrical and magnetic transport, scanning tunneling microscopy, in-situ transmission electron microscopy, ultrafast laser spectroscopy, angle-resolved photoemission, and neutron scattering. Applications of superconducting devices for quantum measurements and quantum information; quantum bits; superconducting parametric amplifiers. Analytis, Birgeneau, Clarke, Crommie, Dynes, Ginsberg, Hellman, Lanzara, Orenstein, Packard, Qiu, Ramesh, Shank, Shen, Siddiqi, Stamper-Kurn, Wang, Zettl.

Energy Sources & Environment. The Center for Building Science, in the Applied Science Division at Lawrence Berkeley National Laboratory.

Experimental Astrophysics. Dark matter searches; astroparticle physics; observations of the cosmic microwave background; cosmology; studies of galaxy clusters; studies of star forming galaxies; study of dark energy using supernovae, galaxy counts, and Baryon acoustic oscillations; Studies of astrophysical neutrinos, solar physics, and high-energy neutrino astrophysics. Bale, Davis, Genzel, Holzapfel, Adrian Lee, McKinsey, Muller, Perlmutter, Price, Pyle, Richards, Sadoulet, Smoot.

High Energy Physics. Neutrino physics, including studies of neutrinos produced in solar, atmospheric and reactor interactions; nuclear astrophysics; studies of symmetry breaking in nuclear systems; searches for neutrinoless double beta decay; weak interactions in nuclei; heavy ion collisions. Jacobsen, Kolomensky, Luk, McKinsey, Orebi-Gann, Shapiro, Siegrist.

Nonlinear Dynamics, Plasma and Beam Physics, and Complex Systems. Nonneutral plasmas and antihydrogen synthesis; laser-driven particle acceleration in plasmas; high-brightness electron and ion beams. Fajans.

Particles and Fields. Experiments utilizing particle accelerators such as electron-positron and hadron colliders, as well as fixed target machines to test and extend the standard model and to search for physics beyond the standard model; studies of neutrino physics using neutrinos produced in accelerators and reactors; searches for dark matter and other experimental studies in the field of particle astrophysics; development and fabrication of detectors appropriately matched to these goals. Jacobsen, Kolomensky, Luk, McKinsey, Orebi-Gann, Pyle, Shapiro, Siegrist, Witherell.

Plasma and Fusion. Plasma production and heating; magnetic confinement of high-temperature plasma; development and application of plasma diagnostic methods; atomic physics problems related to controlled fusion; accelerator research for heavy-ion driven pellet fusion; single species plasma. Fajans, Falcone.

View additional information about this department at www.gradschoolshopper.com. Check out the "Why Choose Us?" section, find out more about the department's culture and get links to social media networks.

UNIVERSITY OF CALIFORNIA, DAVIS

DEPARTMENT OF PHYSICS

Davis, California 95616
http://www.physics.ucdavis.edu/

General University Information

Chancellor: Gary S. May
Dean of Graduate School: Prasant Mohapatra
University website: http://www.ucdavis.edu/index.html
School Type: Public
Setting: Suburban
Total Faculty: 1,878
Total Graduate Faculty: 1,878
Total number of Students: 33,300
Total number of Graduate Students: 5,203

Department Information

Department Chairman: Prof. Robert Svoboda, Chair
Department Contact: Angela Sharma, Graduate Program
  Coordinator
  Total full-time faculty: 56
  Total number of full-time equivalent positions: 50
  Full-Time Graduate Students: 160
  Female Full-Time Graduate Students: 37
  First-Year Graduate Students: 30
  Female First-Year Students: 7
  Total Post Doctorates: 28

Department Address

One Shields Avenue
Physics Department
Davis, CA 95616
Phone: (530) 752-1501
Fax: (530) 752-4717
E-mail: grad-info@physics.ucdavis.edu
Website: http://www.physics.ucdavis.edu/

ADMISSIONS

Admission Contact Information

Address admission inquiries to: Graduate Program, Department
  of Physics, One Shields Avenue, Davis, CA 95616
Phone: (530) 752-1501
E-mail: grad-info@physics.ucdavis.edu
Admissions website: http://www.physics.ucdavis.edu/resources_
  for_graduates/index.html

Application deadlines

Fall admission:
U.S. students: January 5   *Int'l. students*: January 5

Application fee

U.S. students: $105   *Int'l. students*: $125
All applications completed by January 5 are evaluated fully. If
  room remains in the program, further applications are accepted until May 31.

Admissions information

For Fall of 2018:
  Number of applicants: 416
  Number admitted: 100
  Number enrolled: 30

Admission requirements

Bachelor's degree requirements: Bachelor's degree from an accredited college or university with a grade-point average of
  3.0 or better (on a scale where A = 4.0) in upper division
  coursework and in any graduate courses taken.
Minimum undergraduate GPA: 3.0

GRE requirements

The GRE is required.
  Mean GRE score range (25th–75th percentile): 319-331

Subjective GRE requirements

The Subjective GRE is recommended.
  Mean Advanced GRE score range (25th–75th percentile): 745-
  930

TOEFL requirements

The TOEFL exam is required for students from non-English-
  speaking countries.
  PBT score: 550
  iBT score: 80

Other admissions information

Additional requirements: No minimum score specified.
Undergraduate preparation assumed: Typical texts: Tipler,
  Physics for Scientists and Engineers; Serway, Moses, and
  Moyer, Modern Physics; Boas, Mathematical Methods in the
  Physical Sciences; Marion and Thornton, Classical Dynamics;
  Griffiths, Introduction to Electrodynamics; Reif, Fundamen-
  tals of Statistical and Thermal Physics; Griffiths, Quantum
  Mechanics.

TUITION

Tuition year 2018–19:
Tuition for in-state residents
  Full-time students: $17,581.3 annual
  Part-time students: $11,971.3 annual
Tuition for out-of-state residents
  Full-time students: $32,683.3 annual
  Part-time students: $19,522.3 annual
Health insurance included with in-state tuition.
Credit hours per semester to be considered full-time: 12
Deferred tuition plan: No
Health insurance: Available
Other academic fees: None
Academic term: Quarter
Number of first-year students who received full tuition waivers: 26
Number of first-year students who received partial tuition waivers: 3

Teaching Assistants, Research Assistants, and Fellowships

Number of first-year
  Teaching Assistants: 27
  Fellowship students: 3
Average stipend per academic year
  Teaching Assistant: $24,540
  Research Assistant: $25,032
  Fellowship student: $24,540

Most first-year fellowships are much smaller, since they supplement rather than replace Teaching Assistantships positions. In later years, fellowships are intended as full support. All numbers are for 12 months of support.

FINANCIAL AID

Application deadlines
Fall admission:
U.S. students: January 5   *Int'l. students*: January 5

Loans
Loans are available for U.S. students.
Loans are not available for international students.
GAPSFAS application required: No
FAFSA application required: Yes

For further information
Address financial aid inquiries to: Graduate Financial Aid Office, One Shields Avenue, Davis, CA 95616.
Phone: (530) 752-9246
E-mail: gradfinaid@ucdavis.edu
Financial aid website: http://financialaid.ucdavis.edu/graduate/index.html

HOUSING

Availability of on-campus housing
Single students: Yes
Married students: Yes

For further information
Address housing inquiries to: Student Housing Office, One Shields Avenue, Davis, CA 95616.
Phone: (530) 752-2033
E-mail: studenthousing@ucdavis.edu
Housing aid website: http://www.housing.ucdavis.edu/

Table A—Faculty, Enrollments, and Degrees Granted

Research Specialty	2017–18 Faculty	Enrollment Fall 2017 Master's	Enrollment Fall 2017 Doctorate	Number of Degrees Granted 2017–18 (2017–18) Master's	Number of Degrees Granted 2017–18 (2017–18) Terminal Master's	Number of Degrees Granted 2017–18 (2017–18) Doctorate
Astrophysics	10	1	26	–	1	3(19)
Biophysics	1	–	5	–	–	–(6)
Computational Physics	2	–	13	–	–	2(7)
Condensed Matter Physics	14	2	35	–	–(1)	7(36)
Nuclear Physics	3	–	12	–	–	–(5)
Particles and Fields	12	1	27	–	1(1)	6(19)
Physics and other Science Education	1	–	2	–	–	–(3)
Relativity & Gravitation	3	–	12	–	–	–(3)
Non-specialized	–	1	19	14(62)	2(10)	–
Total	46	5	151	14(62)	4(12)	18(98)
Full-time Grad. Stud.	–	5	151	–	–	–
First-year Grad. Stud.	–	–	27	–	–	–

GRADUATE DEGREE REQUIREMENTS

Master's: Two master's programs are offered. Plan I requires 32 quarter hours of graduate and upper division coursework and a master's thesis. Plan II requires 36 quarter hours of graduate and upper division coursework, of which at least 18 hours must be at the graduate level, and passing the preliminary examination at the master's level. The preliminary

examination covers senior undergraduate and first-year graduate level physics. Both plans require coursework in classical physics, quantum mechanics, and mathematical methods.

Doctorate: The Ph.D. degree requires a thorough understanding of the foundations of physics and mathematical methods as evidenced by performance on the preliminary examination and oral examination and submission of a dissertation, which must include an original contribution to fundamental physics. Ph.D. students must also complete the graduate core courses in classical physics, statistical physics, quantum mechanics, and mathematical methods. The required curriculum can be tailored to fit the individual student's preparation and needs. Each graduate student selects a course of study in consultation with a graduate advisor. A student with weaknesses in preparation may be advised to audit or take for credit specific advanced undergraduate courses. A student entering with advanced preparation may skip the core courses by passing the written examination upon entrance to the program. Students are to take a cluster of advanced graduate courses determined by their field of specialization. For more information, please visit http://www.physics.ucdavis.edu.

Thesis: Thesis may be written in absentia.

SPECIAL EQUIPMENT, FACILITIES, OR PROGRAMS

At UC Davis our students have access to a wide range of physics research facilities at national and international laboratories and observatories. A list of facilities by discipline is available at http://physics.ucdavis.edu/research/research-facilities.

Table B—Separately Budgeted Research Expenditures by Source of Support

Source of Support	Departmental Research	Physics-related Research Outside Department
Federal government	$6,918,450	
State/local government	$166,479	
Non-profit organizations		
Business and industry	$2,065,096	$12,788
Other	$200,188	
Total	$9,350,213	$12,788

Table C—Separately Budgeted Research Expenditures by Research Specialty

Research Specialty	No. of Grants	Expenditures ($)
Cosmology	61	$2,691,329
Complexity Sciences	15	$1,584,781
Condensed Matter Physics	47	$1,983,254
Geophysics	1	$31,835
Nuclear Physics	1	$373,602
Particles and Fields	34	$2,698,200
Total	159	$9,363,001

FACULTY

Distinguished University Professor
Albrecht, Andreas, Ph.D., University of Pennsylvania, 1983. *Cosmology & String Theory*. Cosmology; high-energy theory.
Fong, Ching-Yao, Ph.D., University of California, Berkeley, 1968. *Condensed Matter Physics*. Theoretical solid-state physics.
Pickett, Warren E., Ph.D., Stony Brook University, 1975. *Condensed Matter Physics*. Theoretical condensed matter physics; metals and superconductors.

Rundle, John B., Ph.D., University of California, Los Angeles, 1976. *Computational Physics, Geophysics*. Dynamics of complex nonlinear systems.

Tyson, J. Anthony, Ph.D., University of Wisconsin-Madison, 1967. *Astrophysics, Cosmology & String Theory*. Observational cosmology; development of new astronomical surveys, detectors, astronomical instrumentation, and analysis algorithms.

Professor

Calderón de la Barca Sánchez, Manuel, Ph.D., Yale University, 2001. *Nuclear Physics*. Relativistic heavy-ion physics.

Carlip, Steven, Ph.D., University of Texas, Austin, 1987. *Relativity & Gravitation*. Theoretical high-energy physics; quantum gravity.

Cebra, Daniel A., Ph.D., Michigan State University, 1990. *Nuclear Physics*. Relativistic heavy-ion physics.

Cheng, Hsin-Chia, Ph.D., University of California, Berkeley, 1996. *High Energy Physics*. Theoretical particle physics.

Chertok, Maxwell B., Ph.D., Boston University, 1997. *High Energy Physics*. Experimental high-energy physics; hadron collider physics.

Chiang, Shirley, Ph.D., University of California, Berkeley, 1983. *Condensed Matter Physics, Surface Physics*. Experimental condensed matter physics and surface physics.

Conway, John, Ph.D., University of Chicago, 1987. Vice Chair. *High Energy Physics*. Experimental high-energy physics.

Cox, Daniel L., Ph.D., Cornell University, 1985. *Biophysics, Condensed Matter Physics*. Theoretical biological physics.

Crutchfield, James, Ph.D., University of California, Santa Cruz, 1983. *Computational Physics*. Nonlinear dynamics; condensed matter physics; physics of computation; evolutionary dynamics; pattern discovery; dynamics of learning; distributed robotics.

Curro, Nicholas, Ph.D., University of Illinois at Urbana-Champaign, 1998. *Condensed Matter Physics*. Experimental condensed matter physics with a focus on nuclear magnetic resonance of condensed matter electron systems, especially phenomena associated with magnetism, unconventional superconductivity, and heavy fermion physics.

Erbacher, Robin, Ph.D., Stanford University, 1998. *High Energy Physics*. Experimental high-energy particle physics: top quark physics; searches for new particles and phenomena; particle detector development.

Fassnacht, Christopher D., Ph.D., California Institute of Technology, 1999. *Astronomy*. Observational cosmology; galaxy structure; cosmological parameter measurement through gravitational lensing.

Ferenc, Daniel, Ph.D., University of Zagreb, Croatia, 1992. *Astrophysics, Nuclear Physics*. Relativistic universe; high-energy astrophysics; gamma-ray astronomy; next-generation underground laboratory for proton decay and neutrino physics.

Hubeny, Veronika E., Ph.D., University of California, Santa Barbara, 2001. *Cosmology & String Theory, High Energy Physics, Particles and Fields, Relativity & Gravitation*. String theory; quantum gravity.

Kaloper, Nemanja, Ph.D., University of Minnesota, Minneapolis, 1992. *Cosmology & String Theory, High Energy Physics*. Cosmology; high-energy theory.

Knox, Lloyd D., Ph.D., University of Chicago, 1995. *Cosmology & String Theory*. Cosmology.

Liu, Kai, Ph.D., Johns Hopkins University, 1998. *Condensed Matter Physics*. Experimental condensed matter.

Lubin, Lori M., Ph.D., Princeton University, 1995. Vice Chair. *Astronomy*. Observational cosmology.

Luty, Markus, Ph.D., University of Chicago, 1992. *High Energy Physics*. Theoretical particle physics; theoretical gravity.

Prebys, Eric, Ph.D., University of Rochester, 1990. Director of Crocker Nuclear Laboratory. *Accelerator, High Energy Physics, Particles and Fields*.

Rangamani, Mukund, Ph.D., Princeton University, 2002. *Cosmology & String Theory, High Energy Physics, Particles and Fields, Relativity & Gravitation*. String theory; quantum gravity.

Savrasov, Sergey Y., Ph.D., Lebedev Physical Institute, Moscow, 1994. *Condensed Matter Physics*. Theoretical condensed matter physics; electronic structure of solids; computational approaches to strongly correlated systems.

Scalettar, Richard T., Ph.D., University of California, Santa Barbara, 1986. *Condensed Matter Physics*. Theoretical condensed matter physics; statistical mechanics; many-body theory; highly correlated systems.

Singh, Rajiv R. P., Ph.D., Stony Brook University, 1986. *Biophysics, Condensed Matter Physics*. Theoretical condensed matter physics; spin glasses; critical phenomena; low-dimensional systems, biological physics.

Svoboda, Robert, Ph.D., University of Hawaii, 1985. Department Chair. *High Energy Physics*. Neutrino physics.

Terning, John, Ph.D., University of Toronto, 1990. *High Energy Physics*. Theoretical particle physics; electroweak symmetry breaking; supersymmetry; cosmology; extra dimensions; AdS/CFT correspondence.

Tripathi, S. Mani, Ph.D., University of Pittsburgh, 1986. *High Energy Physics*. Experimental high-energy physics; productions of direct photons in hadronic interactions.

Zhu, Xiangdong, Ph.D., University of California, Berkeley, 1989. *Biophysics, Condensed Matter Physics*. Experimental condensed matter physics; nonlinear optics; laser studies of surfaces.

Zieve, Rena, Ph.D., University of California, Berkeley, 1992. Vice Chair, Graduate Affairs. *Condensed Matter Physics, Low Temperature Physics*. Experimental condensed matter physics; low-temperature physics; unconventional superconductors.

Zimanyi, Gergely, Ph.D., Eotvos Lorand University, 1985. *Condensed Matter Physics*. Theoretical condensed matter physics; localization; electron gas; low-dimensional system; superconductivity.

Associate Professor

Bradac, Marusa, Ph.D., University of Bonn, 2004. *Astronomy*. Cosmology gravitational lensing; first galaxies; dark matter.

Mulhearn, Michael J., Ph.D., Massachusetts Institute of Technology, 2004. *High Energy Physics*. Experimental high-energy physics.

Wittman, David M., Ph.D., University of Arizona, 1997. *Astronomy*. Observational cosmology; deep lens survey; weak lensing.

Yu, Dong, Ph.D., University of Chicago, 2005. *Condensed Matter Physics*. Synthesis and characterization of colloidal nanocrystals, including measurements of their optical, electrical, and low temperature transport properties. Vapor phase synthesis and characterization of phase-change nanowires, the fabrication and transport studies of nanodevices, and scanning photocurrent imaging of nanowire-polymer photovoltaic devices.

Assistant Professor

da Silva Neto, Eduardo, Ph.D., Princeton University, 2013. *Condensed Matter Physics, Solid State Physics*. Scanning tunneling microscopy, resonant x-ray scattering, and other synchrotron-based experiments of quantum materials.

Jones, Tucker, Ph.D., California Institute of Technology, 2012. *Astronomy, Astrophysics*. Understanding how galaxies form and evolve.

Pantic, Emilija, Ph.D., Technical University Munich/MPI, 2008. *Astrophysics, Particles and Fields*. Experimental astroparticle physics.

Taufour, Valentin, Ph.D., Universite Joseph Fourier, 2011. *Condensed Matter Physics, Materials Science, Metallurgy*. Design, synthesis and study of novel electronic and magnetic materials.

Trnka, Jaroslav, Ph.D., Princeton University, 2013. *Cosmology & String Theory, Particles and Fields*. Quantum field theory, supersymmetry, and string theory.

Valenti, Stefano, Ph.D., University of Ferrara, 2008. *Astrophysics*. Stellar evolution and supernovae; surveys and time domain phenomena; cosmology; AGN reverberation mapping; spectroscopic and photometric data analysis.

Vishik, Inna, Ph.D., Stanford University, 2013. *Condensed Matter Physics, Solid State Physics*. High-resolution angle-resolved photoemission spectroscopy and ultrafast optical studies of quantum materials.

Wetzel, Andrew, Ph.D., UC Berkeley, 2010. *Astronomy, Astrophysics*. Cosmological hydrodynamic simulations, near-field cosmology, galaxy formation and evolution, dwarf galaxies, The Local Group, galactic archaeology, galaxy groups and clusters.

Emeritus

Breedon, Richard, Ph.D., Rockefeller University, 1988. *High Energy Physics*. High-energy experimental physics.

Professor Emeritus

Becker, Robert, Ph.D., University of Maryland, 1975. *Astronomy*. Creating new astronomical surveys; radioastronomy.

Brady, F. Paul, Ph.D., Princeton University, 1960. *Nuclear Physics*. Experimental nuclear physics; neutron physics and relativistic nuclear collisions.

Cahill, Thomas A., Ph.D., University of California, Los Angeles, 1965. Experimental nuclear and atomic physics; analytical applications of accelerator beams; atmospheric physics.

Chau, Ling-Lie, Ph.D., University of California, Berkeley, 1966. Theoretical particle physics.

Coleman, Lawrence B., Ph.D., University of Pennsylvania, 1975. *Condensed Matter Physics*. Experimental condensed matter physics; far infrared spectroscopy; phase transitions in solids; structure-property relationships.

Corruccini, Linton R., Ph.D., Cornell University, 1972. *Condensed Matter Physics, Low Temperature Physics*. Experimental low-temperature and condensed matter physics; liquid helium.

Draper, James E., Ph.D., Cornell University, 1952. Experimental nuclear physics; particle-gamma and ion-beam atomic spectroscopy.

Erickson, Glen W., Ph.D., University of Minnesota, 1960. Theoretical physics; quantum field theory.

Fadley, Charles S., Ph.D., University of California, Berkeley, 1970. *Condensed Matter Physics*. Advanced light source; surfaces and interfaces via angle-resolved photo-electron spectroscopy.

Garrod, Claude, Ph.D., New York University, 1963. *Statistical & Thermal Physics*. Theoretical physics; quantum-mechanical many-particle systems; statistical mechanics.

Gunion, John F., Ph.D., University of California, San Diego, 1970. *High Energy Physics*. Theoretical particle physics.

Kiskis, Joseph E., Ph.D., Stanford University, 1974. *High Energy Physics*. Theoretical particle physics; lattice gauge theory.

Klein, Barry M., Ph.D., New York University, 1969. *Condensed Matter Physics*. Theoretical condensed matter.

Ko, Winston T., Ph.D., University of Pennsylvania, 1971. Dean, Division of Mathematical and Physical Sciences. *High Energy Physics*. Experimental particle physics.

Lander, Richard L., Ph.D., University of California, Berkeley, 1958. *High Energy Physics*. Experimental particle physics.

McColm, Douglas W., Ph.D., Yale University, 1961. Experimental atomic physics; molecular beam studies.

Pellett, David E., Ph.D., University of Michigan, 1966. Experimental particle physics.

Webb, David J., Ph.D., University of Maryland, 1983. *Physics and other Science Education*. Physics education.

Yager, Philip M., Ph.D., University of California, San Diego, 1973. Experimental particle physics.

Adjunct Professor

de Roeck, Albert, Ph.D., University of Antwerp, Belgium. Experimental particle physics.

Radousky, Harry B., Ph.D., University of Illinois, 1982. *Condensed Matter Physics*. Experimental condensed matter physics.

Vogt, Ramona, Ph.D., Stony Brook University, 1989. *Nuclear Physics*. Theoretical nuclear physics.

Lecturer with Rank of Professor

Boeshaar, Patricia, Ph.D., Ohio State University, 1976. *Astrophysics*. Physics and astronomy education.

Lecturer

Weideman, Thomas, Ph.D., University of California, Davis, 1990.

Professional Specialist

Klavins, Peter, M.S., Iowa State University, 1987. Experimental materials physics.

Project Physicist

Cox, Peter Timothy, Ph.D., University of Michigan, 1980. High-energy experimental physics.

Smith, John R., Ph.D., University of California, Davis, 1982. *High Energy Physics*. High-energy experimental physics.

Researcher

Gregg, Michael D., Ph.D., Yale University, 1985. *Astronomy, Astrophysics, Cosmology & String Theory*. Cosmology.

Richter, Matthew J., Ph.D., University of California, Berkeley, 1995. *Astronomy, Astrophysics*. Infrared astronomical spectroscopy; infrared studies of interstellar molecules; development of high-resolution infrared spectrographs.

Stanford, Spencer Adam, Ph.D., University of Wisconsin-Madison, 1990. *Astronomy, Astrophysics*. Cosmology.

DEPARTMENTAL RESEARCH SPECIALTIES AND STAFF

Theoretical

Computational Physics. Computational simulations of complex physical and biological systems; data mining of massive and multidimensional data sets; understanding emergent patterns and coherent structures in nonlinear systems; prediction and forecasting; scaling; network and cluster formation and dynamics. Crutchfield, Rundle.

Condensed Matter Physics. Studies of macroscopic phases of matter, including metals, insulators, superconductors, superfluids, magnets, spin-glasses, supersolids, etc.; thermal and quantum-phase transitions and critical phenomena; microscopic theory and phenomenology of high-temperature superconductivity and of superconductivity coexisting with magnetism; microscopic studies of strongly correlated electron systems; Hubbard, t-J, and Heisenberg models; mesoscopic physics and nanostructures; electronic structure calculations. Quantum Monte Carlo and other advanced numerical methods are used to study alloy phase stability, semiconductor nanostructures, spintronic materials, and surface physics properties from first principles. Daniel Cox, Fong, Pickett, Savrasov, Scalettar, Singh, Zimanyi.

Cosmology & String Theory. Physics of the early universe and the formation of cosmic structure; cosmic inflation; dark energy models and probes; cosmic microwave background; precision cosmology. Albrecht, Gregg, Kaloper, Knox, Trnka.

Nuclear Physics. Relativistic heavy-ion collisions; quark-gluon plasma. Vogt.

Particles and Fields. Gauge theories of the electromagnetic, weak, and strong interactions; perturbative and nonperturbative analysis; lattice gauge theory; unification, supersymmetry; extra dimension; symmetry breaking; phenomenology; heavy quark systems; soluble models; quantum gravity. Cheng, Gunion, Kiskis, Luty, Terning, Trnka.

Relativity & Gravitation. Conceptual issues in quantum gravity; low-dimensional models for quantum gravity; black hole thermodynamics; physical and mathematical foundations of general relativity. Carlip, Hubeny, Rangamani.

Experimental

Astrophysics. Physics of the early universe; evolution of active galactic nuclei (AGN); quasar absorption line systems; clusters of galaxies; gravitational lenses; large-scale surveys; supernovas. Becker, Boeshaar, Bradac, Fassnacht, Ferenc, Gregg, Jones, Lubin, Stanford, Tyson, Valenti, Wetzel, Wittman.

Condensed Matter Physics. Surfaces and interfaces; magnetism; low-temperature physics; lattice dynamics; quantum fluctuations; transport properties; high-temperature superconductivity; granular materials; light scattering on biological materials and nanostructured materials. Systems under study include atoms, molecules, and nanostructures on surfaces; nanoparticles and nanowires; epitaxial multilayer thin films; patterned nanostructures; organic and biological nanostructures; 4 He vortices; dipolar magnets and frustrated antiferromagnets; exotic superconductors; complex magnetic and ferroelectric materials; and disordered media. Sample synthesis and processing are by magnetron sputtering; thermal and e-beam evaporation; electrodeposition; high-temperature sintering and single-crystal growth; and photo- and e-beam lithography. Characterizations are by photoelectron spectroscopy, diffraction, and holography using laboratory sources and high-brightness synchrotron radiation at the nearby Lawrence Berkeley National Laboratory; X-ray diffraction; scanning electron microscopy; ultra-high-vacuum scanning tunneling and atomic force microscopy; low-energy electron microscopy and diffraction; surface magneto-optical Kerr effect; Raman spectroscopy; far infrared spectroscopy; SQUID and local Hall probe magnetometry; metallographic and thermal analyses; semi-adiabatic calorimetry from dilution refrigerator range to high temperatures; transport measurements; and vibrating wire studies. Chiang, Coleman, Corruccini, Curro, da Silva Neto, Fadley, Klavins, Liu, Taufour, Vishik, Yu, Zhu, Zieve.

Nuclear Physics. Study of relativistic heavy-ion collisions; creation of quark-antiquark pairs; discovery and study of quark matter (or quark-gluon plasma, as it is often called). Brady, Calderón de la Barca Sánchez, Cebra, Draper, Ferenc.

Particles and Fields. Experiments using particle accelerators and colliders around the world to probe the structure of matter at the deepest possible level; design and construction of neutrino and WIMP dark-matter detectors to search for dark matter and make precision measurements of neutrino properties; properties of and the forces between quarks and leptons and searches for new particles; extensive computer utilization for data analysis and design modeling; development of new detectors such as micron-size silicon pixel devices; design and fabricate read-out electronics using new techniques such as ASIC (application specific integrated circuit) and flip chip bump bonding. Breedon, Chertok, Conway, de Roeck, Erbacher, Ko, Lander, Mulhearn, Pantic, Pellett, Smith, Svoboda, Tripathi.

Physics and other Science Education. The process of how students come to an understanding of physics/science concepts; instructional models; use of visual models in understanding atomic phenomena. Webb.

View additional information about this department at www.gradschoolshopper.com. Check out the "Why Choose Us?" section, find out more about the department's culture and get links to social media networks.

UNIVERSITY OF CALIFORNIA, IRVINE

DEPARTMENT OF PHYSICS AND ASTRONOMY

Irvine, California 92697-4575
http://www.physics.uci.edu/

General University Information
Chancellor: Howard Gillman
Dean of Graduate School: Frances Leslie
University website: http://www.uci.edu/
School Type: Public
Setting: Urban
Total Faculty: 2,298
Total number of Students: 32,443
Total number of Graduate Students: 5,908

Department Information
Department Chairman: Prof. James Bullock, Chair
Department Contact: My Banh, Graduate Affairs Officer
   Total full-time faculty: 49
   Full-Time Graduate Students: 141
   Female Full-Time Graduate Students: 30
   First-Year Graduate Students: 21
   Female First-Year Students: 2
   Total Post Doctorates: 35

Department Address
4129 Frederick Reines Hall
Irvine, CA 92697-4575
Phone: (949) 824-6911
Fax: (949) 824-2174
E-mail: physics@uci.edu
Website: http://www.physics.uci.edu/

ADMISSIONS

Admission Contact Information
Address admission inquiries to: University of California, Irvine, Graduate Admissions Committee, Department of Physics and Astronomy, 4129 Frederick Reines Hall, Irvine, CA 92697-4575
Phone: (949) 824-3496
E-mail: physgrad@uci.edu
Admissions website: http://www.physics.uci.edu/graduate

Application deadlines
Fall admission:
U.S. students: January 1   *Int'l. students*: January 1

Application fee
U.S. students: $105   *Int'l. students*: $125

Admissions information
For Fall of 2018:
   Number of applicants: 374
   Number admitted: 74
   Number enrolled: 21

Admission requirements
Bachelor's degree requirements: A Bachelor's degree is required.
Minimum undergraduate GPA: 3.0

GRE requirements
The GRE is required.

In the admissions process, we look at the complete file of students, with particular emphasis on undergraduate grades, especially in subject-related courses, research experience, letters of recommendation, and physics GRE score.

Subjective GRE requirements
The Subjective GRE is required.
In the admissions process, we look at the complete file of students, with particular emphasis on undergraduate grades, especially in subject-related courses, research experience, letters of recommendation, and physics GRE score.

TOEFL requirements
The TOEFL exam is required for students from non-English-speaking countries.
   PBT score: 550
   iBT score: 80

Other admissions information
Additional requirements: No minimum scores on the General GRE and Physics GRE are specified.
Undergraduate preparation assumed: The following texts (or their equivalents): Halliday & Resnick, General Physics; Marion, Mechanics; Griffiths, E and M; Liboff, Quantum Mechanics; Reif, Thermal and Statistical Physics; Arfken, Mathematics for Physics; and advanced undergraduate laboratory.

TUITION

Tuition year 2017–2018:
Tuition for in-state residents
   Full-time students: $17,331.5 annual
   Part-time students: $11,580.5 annual
Tuition for out-of-state residents
   Full-time students: $32,433.5 annual
   Part-time students: $19,131.5 annual
Credit hours per semester to be considered full-time: 12
Deferred tuition plan: No
Health insurance: Yes, $3932.00.

Teaching Assistants, Research Assistants, and Fellowships
   Number of first-year
      Teaching Assistants: 19
      Research Assistants: 2
      Fellowship students: 8
   Average stipend per academic year
      Teaching Assistant: $20,653.02
      Research Assistant: $20,187

FINANCIAL AID

Application deadlines
Fall admission:
U.S. students: March 2

Loans
Loans are available for U.S. students.
Loans are not available for international students.
GAPSFAS application required: No
FAFSA application required: Yes

For further information

Address financial aid inquiries to: Financial Aid and Scholarships Office, 102 Aldrich Hall, Irvine, CA 92697-2825.
Phone: (949) 824-8262
E-mail: finaid@uci.edu
Financial aid website: http://www.ofas.uci.edu/content/default. aspx

HOUSING

Availability of on-campus housing

Single students: Yes
Married students: Yes
Childcare Assistance: Yes

For further information

Address housing inquiries to: Student Housing Services, G458 Student Center, Irvine, CA 92697-5225.
Phone: (949) 824-6811
E-mail: housing@uci.edu
Housing aid website: http://www.housing.uci.edu

Table A—Faculty, Enrollments, and Degrees Granted

Research Specialty	2017–2018 Faculty	Enrollment Fall 2018 Master's	Enrollment Fall 2018 Doctorate	Number of Degrees Granted 2017–2018 (2013–2018) Master's	Number of Degrees Granted 2017–2018 (2013–2018) Terminal Master's	Number of Degrees Granted 2017–2018 (2013–2018) Doctorate
Astrophysics	13	–	30	–(10)	–(2)	5(20)
Atmosphere, Space Physics, Cosmic Rays	–	–	–	–	–	–
Biophysics	–	–	4	1(3)	–(3)	–(7)
Chemical Physics	–	–	29	4(31)	–(4)	7(34)
Condensed Matter Physics	16	–	25	–(6)	3(5)	1(18)
Medical, Health Physics	–	–	1	–	–	–(1)
Particles and Fields	14	–	32	2(7)	3(8)	4(15)
Plasma and Fusion	6	–	20	1(4)	–(1)	1(8)
Total	49	–	141	8(61)	6(23)	18(103)
Full-time Grad. Stud.	–	–	141	–	–	–
First-year Grad. Stud.	–	–	21	–	–	–

GRADUATE DEGREE REQUIREMENTS

Master's: The requirements for the M.S. degree are: (1) at least three quarters of residence; (2) Mastery of graduate course material, which must be demonstrated by passing, with a grade of "B" or better, a minimum of seven quarter courses including 211, 212A, 213A, 213B or 240C, 214A, 215A-B, two courses numbered between 200-259, and two other courses approved by the graduate advisor; and (3) either option A, a research project and written thesis, or option B, a comprehensive written examination. Students pursuing option A typically complete three quarters of research, enrolling in Physics 295 or 296. Students following option B should take Physics 215B. There is no foreign language requirement. For option A, the thesis need be of no specified length or format, but must report significant results in readable, meaningful form while at the same time revealing the student's general grasp of the field and awareness of related work. For option B, the comprehensive examination for the M.S. degree is identical to that for the Ph.D. degree. The level of performance required for the M.S. degree by examination is identical to the required level of performance for the Ph.D. degree.

Doctorate: The principal requirements for the Ph.D. degree are a minimum of six quarters of residence, passage of a written and an oral examination, and successful completion and defense of a dissertation reporting results of original research. In addition, the Ph.D. candidate must complete certain graduate course requirements. Experience in teaching is an integral part of the graduate program, and all Ph.D. students are required to participate in the teaching program for at least one quarter during their graduate careers. Foreign students must pass a campus-approved spoken English proficiency examination (required in order to be a teaching assistant) by the time they advance to candidacy. There is no foreign language requirement for the Ph.D. degree.

Thesis: The thesis need be of no specified length or format, but must report significant results in readable, meaningful form while at the same time revealing the student's general grasp of the field and awareness of related work.

Table B—Separately Budgeted Research Expenditures by Source of Support

Source of Support	Departmental Research	Physics-related Research Outside Department
Federal government		$7,249,285.35
State/local government		$876,899.98
Non-profit organizations		
Business and industry		$4,378,713.47
Other		$497,880.63
Total		$13,002,779.43

Table C—Separately Budgeted Research Expenditures by Research Specialty

Research Specialty	No. of Grants	Expenditures ($)
Astrophysics	119	$2,361,882.87
Biophysics	42	$1,802,502.98
Condensed Matter Physics	71	$3,810,602.36
Particles and Fields	67	$3,627,153.05
Plasma and Fusion	33	$1,703,284.08
Total	332	$13,305,425.34

FACULTY

Distinguished University Professor

Fisk, Zachary, Ph.D., University of California, San Diego, 1969. Emeritus. *Condensed Matter Physics*. Experimental condensed matter physics.

Professor

Barth, Aaron, Ph.D., University of California, Berkeley, 1998. *Astrophysics*. Observational astrophysics. Supermassive black holes, quasars and active galactic nuclei.

Barty, Christopher P. J., Ph.D., Stanford University, 1990. *Plasma and Fusion*.

Barwick, Steven, Ph.D., University of California, Berkeley, 1986. *Astronomy*. Experimental particle physics, astrophysics.

Bullock, James, Ph.D., University of California, Santa Cruz, 1999. Department Chair of Physics & Astronomy. *Astrophysics*. Theoretical cosmology; astrophysics; astronomy. Galaxy formation theory and simulations, dark matter, near-field cosmology.

Buote, David, Ph.D., Massachusetts Institute of Technology, 1995. *Astrophysics*. Observational astrophysics; cosmology. X-ray astronomy, dark matter, massive galaxies, and galaxy clusters.

Chen, Mu-Chun, Ph.D., University of Colorado Boulder, 2002. *Particles and Fields*. Theoretical particle physics.

Chernyshev, Alexander L., Ph.D., Novosibirsk, 1995. *Condensed Matter Physics*. Theoretical condensed matter physics.

Collins, Philip G., Ph.D., University of California, Berkeley, 1998. *Biophysics, Condensed Matter Physics*. Experimental condensed matter physics.

Cooray, Asantha, Ph.D., University of Chicago, 2001. *Astronomy*. Theoretical cosmology; astrophysics; planetary science. infrared surveys and galaxy evolution.

Dennin, Michael, Ph.D., University of California, Santa Barbara, 1995. *Biophysics, Condensed Matter Physics*. Experimental condensed matter physics; biological physics.

Dollar, Franklin, Ph.D., University of Michigan - Ann Arbor, 2012. *Plasma and Fusion*. High intensity laser plasma interactions.

Feng, Jonathan L., Ph.D., Stanford University, 1995. *Particles and Fields*. Elementary particle theory; cosmology.

Hamber, Herbert, Ph.D., University of California, Santa Barbara, 1980. *Particles and Fields*. Elementary particle theory; general relativity.

Heidbrink, William, Ph.D., Princeton University, 1984. *Plasma and Fusion*. Experimental plasma physics.

Ho, Wilson, Ph.D., University of Pennsylvania, 1979. *Condensed Matter Physics*. Experimental condensed matter physics; chemistry.

Kaplinghat, Manoj, Ph.D., Ohio State University, 1999. *Astrophysics*. Theoretical cosmology; astrophysics. Dark matter, dark energy, gravitational lensing, and near-field cosmology.

Kirkby, David P., Ph.D., California Institute of Technology, 1995. *Astrophysics*. Astrophysics & Cosmology. Experimental particle physics. Observational cosmology, large surveys, dark matter and dark energy.

Krivorotov, Ilya, Ph.D., University of Minnesota, 2002. *Condensed Matter Physics*. Experimental condensed matter physics.

Lankford, Andrew, Ph.D., Yale University, 1978. *Particles and Fields*. Experimental particle physics.

Lin, Zhihong, Ph.D., Princeton University, 1996. *Plasma and Fusion*. Theoretical plasma physics.

McWilliams, Roger D., Ph.D., Princeton University, 1980. Associate Dean of the School of Physical Sciences and Professor of Physics & Astronomy. *Plasma and Fusion*. Experimental plasma physics.

Molzon, William, Ph.D., University of Chicago, 1979. *Particles and Fields*. Experimental particle physics.

Pan, Xiaoqing, Ph.D., Saarland University, 1991. *Condensed Matter Physics*. Experimental Condensed Matter Physics.

Rajaraman, Arvind, Ph.D., Stanford University, 1998. *Particles and Fields*. Elementary particle theory.

Ratz, Michael, Ph.D., TU Munchen, 2002. *Particles and Fields*. Theoretical Particle Physics.

Ritz, Thorsten, Ph.D., University of Ulm, 2001. *Biophysics, Condensed Matter Physics*. Theoretical biological physics; theoretical condensed matter physics.

Shirman, Yuri, Ph.D., University of California, Santa Cruz, 1997. *Particles and Fields*. Theoretical particle physics.

Siryaporn, Albert, Ph.D., University of Pennsylvania, 2008. *Biophysics*. Biological Physics.

Siwy, Zuzana, Ph.D., Silesian Univ. of Tech., 1997. *Biophysics, Condensed Matter Physics*. Experimental biological physics; experimental condensed matter physics.

Taborek, Peter, Ph.D., California Institute of Technology, 1980. *Condensed Matter Physics*. Experimental condensed matter physics.

Taffard, Anyes, Ph.D., University of Liverpool, 2002. *Particles and Fields*. Experimental particle physics.

Tait, Timothy, Ph.D., Michigan State University, 1999. *Particles and Fields*. Theoretical particle physics.

Trimble, Virginia L., Ph.D., California Institute of Technology, 1968. *Astrophysics*. Theoretical astronomy. History of science and scientometrics, binary star astrophysics.

Tucker, Laura, Ph.D., UC San Diego, 2010. *Plasma and Fusion*. Science. Education.

White, Steven, Ph.D., Cornell University, 1988. *Condensed Matter Physics*. Theoretical condensed matter physics.

Whiteson, Daniel, Ph.D., University of California, Berkeley, 2003. *Particles and Fields*. Experimental particle physics.

Wu, Ruqian, Ph.D., Peking University, 1989. *Condensed Matter Physics*. Theoretical condensed matter physics.

Yu, Clare, Ph.D., Princeton University, 1984. *Biophysics, Condensed Matter Physics*. Theoretical condensed matter physics; biological physics.

Associate Professor

Abazajian, Kevork, Ph.D., University of California, San Diego, 2001. *Astrophysics*. Theoretical cosmology. Dark matter, precision cosmology, neutrino physics, galaxy formation theory.

Allard, Jun, Ph.D., University of British Columbia, 2011. Mathematics. *Biophysics*. Theoretical biological physics.

Casper, David W., Ph.D., University of Michigan, 1990. *Particles and Fields*. Experimental particle physics.

Cooper, Michael, Ph.D., University of California, Berkeley, 2007. *Astrophysics*. Observational astrophysics and cosmology. Galaxy evolution, large multiwavelength surveys, data reduction and analysis pipelines.

Murgia, Simona, Ph.D., Michigan State University, 2002. *Astrophysics, Particles and Fields*. Experimental particle physics; astrophysics. High-energy astrophysics, observational cosmology, dark matter, dark energy.

Smecker-Hane, Tammy, Ph.D., Johns Hopkins University, 1993. *Astrophysics*. Observational astrophysics; astronomy. Galaxy evolution, stellar populations, astronomy education, UCI Observatory.

Xia, Jing, Ph.D., Stanford University, 2008. *Condensed Matter Physics, Medical, Health Physics*. Experimental condensed matter physics.

Assistant Professor

Ashok Parameswaran, Sid, Ph.D., Princeton, 2011. *Condensed Matter Physics*. Theory Condensed Matter Physics.

Bian, Jianming, Ph.D., Insitute of High Energy Physics, Chinese Academy of Sciences, 2009. *Particles and Fields*. Experimental Particle Physics.

Robertson, Paul M., Ph.D., University of Texas, Austin, 2013. *Astrophysics*. His current research focuses on the development of the Habitable Zone Planet Finder and NEID instruments, and continuing a detailed study of stellar activity for old, low-mass stars. These research avenues together advance his overall goal of finding potentially habitable exoplanets around nearby stars.

Shields, Aomawa, Ph.D., University of Washington, 2014. *Astrophysics*. Climate and habitability of planetary systems.

Emeritus

Benford, Gregory, Ph.D., UC San Diego, 1967. *Plasma and Fusion*.

Dzyaloshinskii, Igor, Ph.D., Institute for Physical Problems, 1957. *Condensed Matter Physics*. Theoretical condensed matter physics.

Hopster, Herbert, Ph.D., Technische Hochschule Aachen, 1977. *Condensed Matter Physics*. Experimental condensed matter physics.

Lawrence, Jon, Ph.D., University of Rochester. *Condensed Matter Physics*. Experimental condensed matter physics.

Rutledge, James, Ph.D., University of Illinois, 1978. Emeritus. *Condensed Matter Physics*. Experimental condensed matter physics.

Rynn, Nathan, Ph.D., Stanford University, 1956.

Schultz, Jonas, Ph.D., Columbia University, 1962. *Particles and Fields*. Experimental particle physics.

Silverman, Dennis, Ph.D., Stanford University, 1968. *Particles and Fields*. Theoretical particle physics.

Research Professor

Chanan, Gary A., Ph.D., University of California, Berkeley, 1978. *Astrophysics*. Observational astrophysics. Optics and wavefront sensing for segmented-mirror telescopes.

Chen, Liu, Ph.D., University of California, Berkeley, 1972. Emeritus. *Plasma and Fusion*. Theoretical plasma physics.

Mandelkern, Mark A., Ph.D., UC Berkeley, 1967. *Medical, Health Physics, Particles and Fields*. Experimental particle physics.

Maradudin, Alexei A., Ph.D., University of Bristol, 1957. Emeritus. *Condensed Matter Physics*. Theoretical condensed matter physics.

Newman, Riley, Ph.D., University of California, Berkeley, 1966. Emeritus. Experimental particle physics; gravitational physics.

Parker, William H., Ph.D., University of Pennsylvania, 1967. Emeritus. *Condensed Matter Physics*. Experimental condensed matter physics.

Sobel, Henry, Ph.D., Case Institute of Technology, 1968. *Particles and Fields*. Experimental particle physics.

Yodh, Gaurang, Ph.D., University of Chicago, 1955. Emeritus. Experimental particle astrophysics.

Adjunct Faculty

Tajima, Toshiki, Ph.D., University of Califorina, Irvine, 1975. Plasma physics.

Vagins, Mark, Ph.D., Yale University, 1994. Experimental particle physics.

Lecturer

Guerra, Arnold, Ph.D., UC Irvine, 1999.

Kirkby, Anne, Ph.D., Theoretical Physics California Institute of Technology.

Minassian, Eric, Ph.D., UC Davis, 2003.

Tajima, Fumiko, Ph.D., University of Tokyo, 1983.

Joint Appointment

Burke, Kieron, Ph.D., University of California, Santa Barbara, 1989. *Condensed Matter Physics*. Theoretical condensed matter physics.

Gratton, Enrico, Ph.D., University of Rome, 1969. *Biophysics, Medical, Health Physics*. Biomedical physics.

Gross, Steven, Ph.D., University of Texas, Austin, 1995. *Biophysics, Medical, Health Physics*. Experimental biological physics.

Gulsen, Gultekin, Ph.D., Bogazici University, 1999. *Medical, Health Physics*. Experimental biological physics.

Mukamel, Shaul, Ph.D., Tel Aviv University, 1976. Chemistry.

Su, Lydia, Ph.D., University of California, Irvine, 1993. *Medical, Health Physics*. Radiological sciences; medical physics.

DEPARTMENTAL RESEARCH SPECIALTIES AND STAFF

Theoretical

Astrophysics. Galaxy formation and evolution; large-scale structure; cosmology; high-energy astrophysics; dark matter; the early universe. Abazajian, Barth, Bullock, Buote, Chanan, Cooper, Cooray, Kaplinghat, David Kirkby, Murgia, Robertson, Shields, Smecker-Hane, Trimble.

Biophysics. Biological Physics and Medical Physics cover a broad range of disciplines that apply quantitative physical methods to the study of fundamental biological problems as well as the more practical concerns of human physiology, disease, and medical diagnosis and treatment. Allard, Dennin, Gratton, Ritz, Siryaporn, Siwy, Yu.

Condensed Matter Physics. Surfaces, superlattices, and ultrathin films; electromagnetic interactions with solids; lattice dynamics; semiconductors. Ashok Parameswaran, Burke, Chernyshev, Dzyaloshinskii, Maradudin, Ritz, White, Wu, Yu.

Cosmology & String Theory.

High Energy Physics. Researchers in the group are engaged in theoretical research in a broad range of areas in particle physics, astroparticle physics, and cosmology. These include electroweak symmetry breaking, supersymmetry, extra dimensions, grand unified theories, neutrinos, flavor physics and CP violation, astroparticle physics, dark matter and dark energy, cosmology, string theory, and quantum gravity. Mu-Chun Chen, Feng, Hamber, Rajaraman, Ratz, Shirman, Silverman, Tait.

History & Philosophy of Physics/Science.

Medical, Health Physics. Gross, Gulsen, Su, Xia.

Plasma and Fusion. Wave and particle dynamics in plasmas; nonlinear theories and large-scale numerical simulations. Barty, Benford, Liu Chen, Dollar, Heidbrink, Lin, McWilliams, Toshiki Tajima.

Experimental

Astrophysics. Optical, infrared, and X-ray astronomy; high-energy astrophysics; galaxy evolution; quasars and active galactic nuclei; cosmic background radiation; black holes and dark matter, large telescope optics.

Biophysics. Photosynthesis, magnetonavigation, nanopores, cancer, systems biology.

Condensed Matter Physics. Electronic, mechanical, and optical properties of solids and liquids, especially at interfaces or at the nanoscale; surface physics; materials science; superconductivity, magnetism, and topological phases of matter; spintronics; nanotechnology. Collins, Dennin, Fisk, Ho, Hopster, Krivorotov, Lawrence, Pan, Parker, Rutledge, Siwy, Taborek, Xia.

High Energy Physics. Antarctic Muon and Neutrino Detector Array, Super-Kamiokande neutrino and proton decay experiment, T2K and LBNE long-baseline experiments, NUANCE neutrino physics simulation software, Minerva experiment. Barwick, Bian, Casper, David Kirkby, Lankford, Mandelkern, Molzon, Murgia, Newman, Schultz, Sobel, Taffard, Whiteson, Yodh.

Medical, Health Physics. Biological Physics and Medical Physics cover a broad range of disciplines that apply quantitative physical methods to the study of fundamental biological problems as well as the more practical concerns of human physiology, disease, and medical diagnosis and treatment. Gross, Gulsen, Mandelkern, Xia.

Plasma and Fusion. Relativistic electron beams; fast ion dynamics; plasma waves and turbulence; collective accelerators. Benford, Liu Chen, Dollar, Heidbrink, Lin, McWilliams, Toshiki Tajima.

UNIVERSITY OF CALIFORNIA MERCED

DEPARTMENT OF PHYSICS

Merced, California 95343
http://physics.ucmerced.edu/

General University Information

Chancellor: Dorothy Leland
Dean of Graduate School: Marjorie S. Zatz
University website: http://www.ucmerced.edu/
School Type: Public
Setting: Rural
Total Faculty: 390
Total Graduate Faculty: 232
Total number of Students: 8,535
Total number of Graduate Students: 670

Department Information

Department Chairman: Prof. Ajay Gopinathan, Chair
Department Contact: David Strubbe, admissions chair
  Total full-time faculty: 17
  Total number of full-time equivalent positions: 17
  Full-Time Graduate Students: 55
  Female Full-Time Graduate Students: 13
  First-Year Graduate Students: 14
  Female First-Year Students: 4
  Total Post Doctorates: 8

Department Address

5200 N. Lake Road
Merced, CA 95343
Phone: (209) 228-4481
E-mail: dstrubbe@ucmerced.edu
Website: http://physics.ucmerced.edu/

ADMISSIONS

Admission Contact Information

Address admission inquiries to: Graduate Division, University of California, Merced, 5200 N. Lake Road, SSB 310, Merced, CA 95343
Phone: (209) 228-4723
E-mail: gradadmissions@ucmerced.edu
Admissions website: https://graduatedivision.ucmerced.edu/admissions

Application deadlines

Fall admission:
U.S. students: January 15   *Int'l. students*: January 15

Application fee

U.S. students: $105   *Int'l. students*: $125
Applications received by 15 Dec 2018 will receive priority review. A limited number of graduate application fee waivers are available based on financial need. Contact Prof Strubbe to request. See also http://physics.ucmerced.edu/academics/graduate-studies.

Admissions information

For Fall of 2018:
  Number of applicants: 69
  Number admitted: 33
  Number enrolled: 14

Admission requirements

Bachelor's degree requirements: Bachelor's degree in a science or engineering discipline, preferably with a physics emphasis.
Minimum undergraduate GPA: 3.0

GRE requirements

The GRE is required.
No minimum cut-off.

Subjective GRE requirements

The Subjective GRE is required.
No minimum cut-off.

TOEFL requirements

The TOEFL exam is required for students from non-English-speaking countries.
  PBT score: 550
  iBT score: 80
Either TOEFL or IELTS is required for students from non-English-speaking countries. See full information at https://graduatedivision.ucmerced.edu/admissions/how-apply/international-applicants

Other admissions information

Undergraduate preparation assumed: Quantum Mechanics at the level of "Introduction to Quantum Mechanics," by D. J. Griffiths; Electrodynamics at the level of "Introduction to Electrodynamics," by D. J. Griffiths; Classical Mechanics at the level of "Classical Mechanics" by J. R. Taylor.

TUITION

Tuition year 2018–2019:
Tuition for in-state residents
  Full-time students: $5,751 per semester
Tuition for out-of-state residents
  Full-time students: $13,302 per semester
All tuition for PhD students is covered by appointment as teaching assistant or Graduate Student Researcher, or by fellowships.
Credit hours per semester to be considered full-time: 12
Deferred tuition plan: Yes
Health insurance: Yes, $2,517.29.
Other academic fees: $882.50 total fees for student services, transportation, recreation, etc.
Academic term: Semester
Number of first-year students who received full tuition waivers: 14

Teaching Assistants, Research Assistants, and Fellowships

Number of first-year
  Teaching Assistants: 14
Average stipend per academic year
  Teaching Assistant: $27,000
  Research Assistant: $27,000
  Fellowship student: $27,000
Five years of funding (including tuition and fees) is guaranteed for graduate students in good standing. This funding may take the form of TA positions, research positions, or fellowships. All students are required to TA for one semester, typically done in the first semester.

FINANCIAL AID

Loans

Loans are available for U.S. students.
Loans are not available for international students.
GAPSFAS application required: No
FAFSA application required: Yes

For further information

Address financial aid inquiries to: University of California, Merced, ATTN: Graduate Division, 5200 N. Lake Road, SSB 310, Merced, CA 95343.
Phone: 209-228-4622
E-mail: gradfunding@ucmerced.edu
Financial aid website: http://graduatedivision.ucmerced.edu/financial-support

HOUSING

Availability of on-campus housing

Single students: No
Married students: No
Childcare Assistance: Yes

For further information

Address housing inquiries to: UC Merced Housing & Residential Life, 5200 N. Lake Road, Merced, CA 95343.
Phone: 209.228.4663
E-mail: housing@ucmerced.edu
Housing aid website: http://housing.ucmerced.edu/

Table A—Faculty, Enrollments, and Degrees Granted

Research Specialty	2018–2019 Faculty	Enrollment Fall 2018 Master's	Enrollment Fall 2018 Doctorate	Number of Degrees Granted 2017–2018 (2007–18) Master's	Number of Degrees Granted 2017–2018 (2007–18) Terminal Master's	Number of Degrees Granted 2017–2018 (2007–18) Doctorate
Atomic, Molecular, & Optical Physics	5	–	14	1(4)	–	2(7)
Condensed Matter, Nanoscience and Energy	4	–	13	–	–	3(10)
Soft Matter and Biophysics	7	–	14	–(1)	–	3(7)
Total	16	–	41	–(5)	–	8(24)
Full-time Grad. Stud.	–	1	55	–	–	–
First-year Grad. Stud.	–	1	14	–	–	–

GRADUATE DEGREE REQUIREMENTS

Master's: Students are normally admitted to the graduate program in Physics to work toward the Ph.D. degree. Requirements for the M.S. degree: Complete at least two semesters of full-time academic residence (12 units minimum) at UC Merced; Pass the preliminary examinations on undergraduate-level classical mechanics, quantum mechanics, and electromagnetism; Complete at least 24 semester hours of upper-division and graduate course work with a cumulative grade-point average of at least 3.0. At least 16 semester hours must be from regular, letter-graded lecture or discussion courses, while the remaining 8 hours may be research or similar courses; Pass a comprehensive oral examination administered by the faculty committee of at least 3 members. This examination will test the student's understanding of the main concepts in the field at the graduate level.

Doctorate: The recipient of a Ph.D. degree is understood to possess thorough knowledge of a broad field of learning and to have given evidence of distinguished accomplishment in that field; the degree is a warrant of critical ability and powers of imaginative synthesis. The degree also signifies that the recipient has presented a doctoral dissertation containing an original contribution to knowledge in his or her chosen field of study. To complete a Ph.D. degree in physics at UC Merced students are required to: Complete at least four semesters of full-time academic residence (12 units minimum) at UC Merced; Complete the required courses with a letter grade of at least "B" in each course ("S" in seminar courses graded S/U); Serve as a teaching assistant for at least one semester; Pass the preliminary examinations on undergraduate-level classical mechanics, quantum mechanics, and electromagnetism; Pass the oral Ph.D. qualifying examination; Present and successfully defend a doctoral dissertation containing an original contribution to knowledge in the field.

SPECIAL EQUIPMENT, FACILITIES, OR PROGRAMS

As the 10th campus of the University of California, UC Merced draws on the outstanding resources of the UC system, a world-renowned center for research and education. Physics graduate students have access to major facilities, such as state-of-the-art lasers, electron microscopes, a nanofabrication facility, a high-performance computing cluster, and an NMR on campus. Other large facilities, such as synchrotron light sources, located at Stanford, Lawrence Livermore, and Lawrence Berkeley National Laboratories, are within two hours' drive and are routinely used by students and faculty members. We collaborate extensively with other nearby institutions such as UC Berkeley, Davis, Santa Cruz, and San Francisco. Students have access to the extensive library holdings and journal subscriptions of the UC system. Students work with the system-wide University of California Advanced Solar Technologies Institute (headquartered here), the NSF-CREST Center for Cellular and Biomolecular Machines, the Health Sciences Research Institute, and the NASA-funded Merced nAnomaterials Center for Energy and Sensing, all located at UC Merced.

Table B—Separately Budgeted Research Expenditures by Source of Support

Source of Support	Departmental Research	Physics-related Research Outside Department
Federal government	$1,146,900	
State/local government	$582,200	
Non-profit organizations		
Business and industry		
Other	$326,000	
Total	$2,055,100	

FACULTY

Professor

Gopinathan, Ajay, Ph.D., University of Chicago, 2003. Co-Director of CCBM, chair of physics unit. *Biophysics, Computational Physics, Condensed Matter Physics, Energy Sources & Environment, Nonlinear Dynamics and Complex Systems, Polymer Physics/Science, Statistical & Thermal Physics, Theoretical Physics*. Theoretical biophysics: molecular motors, disordered proteins, bacterial physics, swarming, and soft condensed matter physics.

Hirst, Linda S., Ph.D., Manchester University, 2001. *Applied Physics, Biophysics, Condensed Matter Physics, Nano Science and Technology, Polymer Physics/Science*. Experimental soft condensed matter physics, biophysics, liquid crystals, nano-materials and polymers.

Mitchell, Kevin, Ph.D., University of California, Berkeley, 2000. *Atomic, Molecular, & Optical Physics, Biophysics, Computational Physics, Fluids, Rheology, Nonlinear Dynamics and Complex Systems, Theoretical Physics.* Nonlinear dynamics and chaos, with applications to AMO (atomic, molecular, and optical) physics and fluid dynamics.

Winston, Roland, Ph.D., University of Chicago, 1963. Director of UC Solar. *Energy Sources & Environment, High Energy Physics, Optics, Particles and Fields, Other.* Solar power and renewable energy; elementary particle physics; non-imaging optics.

Associate Professor

Ghosh, Sayantani, Ph.D., University of Chicago, 2003. Chair of graduate group. *Applied Physics, Atomic, Molecular, & Optical Physics, Condensed Matter Physics, Energy Sources & Environment, Low Temperature Physics, Nano Science and Technology, Optics.* Experimental condensed matter physics; magnetism, strongly correlated systems, spintronics, quantum information.

Scheibner, Michael, Ph.D., University of Würzburg, 2006. *Applied Physics, Atomic, Molecular, & Optical Physics, Condensed Matter Physics, Low Temperature Physics, Nano Science and Technology, Optics, Quantum Foundations.* Experimental quantum science & technology for applications in sensing, metrology, phononics, photonics, materials engineering, information processing, resource sustainability & extreme environments.

Sharping, Jay E., Ph.D., Northwestern University, 2003. *Atomic, Molecular, & Optical Physics, Biophysics, Engineering Physics/Science, Optics.* Ultrafast laser technology and applications in physics, chemistry, and biology.

Tian, Lin, Ph.D., Massachusetts Institute of Technology, 2002. *Atomic, Molecular, & Optical Physics, Condensed Matter Physics.* Theoretical questions in solid-state quantum computing, quantum simulation, hybrid quantum systems, optomechanics, decoherence, and noise models.

Xu, Jing, Ph.D., University of California, Santa Barbara, 2006. *Biophysics, Condensed Matter Physics, Nonlinear Dynamics and Complex Systems.* Experimental biophysics, soft condensed matter physics, and nonlinear dynamics and complex systems, with interest in biomaterials including molecular motors and microtubules. Research methods include optical trapping, fluorescence microscopy, and Monte Carlo simulations.

Assistant Professor

Beller, Daniel, Ph.D., University of Pennsylvania, 2014. *Biophysics, Computational Physics, Condensed Matter Physics, Fluids, Rheology, Nonlinear Dynamics and Complex Systems, Statistical & Thermal Physics, Theoretical Physics.* Theoretical soft condensed matter, liquid crystals, active matter, and biophysics.

Chien, Chih-Chun, Ph.D., University of Chicago, 2009. *Atomic, Molecular, & Optical Physics, Condensed Matter Physics, Nano Science and Technology.* Theoretical atomic and molecular physics, theoretical condensed matter physics, geometrical and topological effects in physics, thermal transport, hybrid quantum systems.

Dasbiswas, Kinjal, Ph.D., University of Florida, 2012. *Biophysics, Computational Physics, Condensed Matter Physics, Fluids, Rheology, Low Temperature Physics, Mechanics, Statistical & Thermal Physics, Theoretical Physics.* Theoretical biological physics and soft condensed matter: mechanobiology, cell and tissue physics, pattern formation, out-of-equilibrium soft and biological materials.

Kleckner, Dustin P., Ph.D., University of California, Santa Barbara, 2010. *Condensed Matter Physics, Electromagnetism, Fluids, Rheology, Nonlinear Dynamics and Complex Systems,* *Optics, Statistical & Thermal Physics.* Experiments on geometry and topology in soft matter and fluids.

Liu, Bin, Ph.D., New York University, 2006. *Biophysics, Computational Physics, Fluids, Rheology, Nonlinear Dynamics and Complex Systems, Polymer Physics/Science.* Experimental soft condensed matter physics, biophysics, biological transport, non-Newtonian fluids, and mechanical metamaterials.

Strubbe, David, Ph.D., University of California, Berkeley, 2012. Admissions committee chair. *Chemical Physics, Computational Physics, Condensed Matter Physics, Materials Science, Metallurgy, Nano Science and Technology, Solid State Physics.* Theoretical condensed matter and materials science, electronic and optical properties, amorphous materials, photovoltaics, nanoscience, high-performance computing.

Professor Emeritus

Chiao, Raymond, Ph.D., Massachusetts Institute of Technology, 1965. *Atomic, Molecular, & Optical Physics, Condensed Matter Physics, Nano Science and Technology, Optics, Quantum Foundations, Relativity & Gravitation.* Nonlinear and quantum optics, experiment, and theory; detection and generation of gravitational radiation via quantum mechanical systems, such as a pair of charged mini-magnets levitated above superconductors (in collaboration with Prof. Sharping).

Teaching Associate Professor

Menke, Carrie, Ph.D., University of California, Irvine, 2005. *Physics and other Science Education.* physics education.

DEPARTMENTAL RESEARCH SPECIALTIES AND STAFF

Theoretical

Atomic, Molecular, & Optical Physics. The ability to manipulate matter at the atomic scale and its interactions with light have led to transformative advances in atomic, molecular and optical physics (AMO). Research areas include theoretical nonlinear dynamics for atomic and molecular systems, and quantum optics and quantum information in nanoscale systems including superconducting quantum computing, semiconductor optics, and nanomechanics. Chien, Mitchell, Tian.

Biophysics. Biophysics is by definition an interdisciplinary science where ideas and techniques from physics (including soft condensed matter physics) are utilized to understand biological systems and phenomena. The biophysics group at UC Merced collaborates extensively between theory and experiment, and with chemistry, biology, applied math, and bioengineering groups. Research areas include macromolecular transport, biopolymers (structure, dynamics and function), bacterial physics (growth, division, motility), and molecular motors and intracellular transport. Beller, Dasbiswas, Gopinathan.

Condensed Matter Physics. Condensed matter physics investigates the physical, electronic and magnetic properties of the various forms of solid and liquid matter, ranging from naturally occurring crystals to engineered micro- and nanostructures as well as more exotic condensed phases and phenomena such as superconductivity and the quantum Hall effect. Research areas include nanoscience, strongly correlated systems, quantum information processing and magneto-optical phenomena, optical properties of nanostructures, and theoretical and computational tools for condensed-matter physics. Chien, Strubbe, Tian.

Nano Science and Technology. The ability to fabricate, control, and study matter on the nanometer scale has opened up new possibilities in science and technology. Research areas include optical properties of nanostructures, quantum optics and quantum information in nanoscale systems, superconducting quantum computing, semiconductor optics, and nanomechanics. Chien, Strubbe, Tian.

Nonlinear Dynamics and Complex Systems. Most processes encountered in nature are inherently nonlinear. Nonlinear dynamics and statistical physics find applications across a wide range of disciplines from mathematics and physics to chemistry, biology, and engineering. Research areas include chaotic dynamics, thermal transport, collective phenomena in swarming and foraging, anomalous transport in complex environments, and fundamental studies of topological dynamics. Beller, Chien, Gopinathan, Mitchell.

Soft Matter. Soft condensed matter is the study of materials that are neither crystalline solids, nor simple liquids — they are somewhere in between. Everyday examples of soft matter include soaps, paints, gels, plastics, liquid crystals and most of your own body and the food you eat. Research areas include liquid crystals, active matter, and polymer physics and elasticity. Beller, Dasbiswas, Gopinathan.

Experimental

Affiliated faculty in other departments. The physics group also includes affiliate faculty from other UC Merced graduate groups. Physics students may also carry out their physics graduate research with these groups. Venkattraman Ayyaswamy: plasma physics (mechanical engineering); Mehmet Z. Baykara: tribology and surface science (mechanical engineering); Mike Colvin: biomolecular simulation (chemistry and chemical biology); Arvind Gopinath: soft matter and biophysics (bioengineering and small-scale technologies); Sarah Kurtz: solar energy (bioengineering and small-scale technologies); Jennifer Lu: functional material synthesis (bioengineering and small-scale technologies); Victor Muñoz: biophysics of proteins (bioengineering and small-scale technologies); Alex Noy: biomaterials (Lawrence Livermore National Laboratory); Anand Subramaniam: biomaterials (bioengineering and small-scale technologies); Tao Ye: bio/nano interfaces (chemistry and chemical biology).

Atomic, Molecular, & Optical Physics. The ability to manipulate matter at the atomic scale and its interactions with light have led to transformative advances in atomic, molecular and optical physics (AMO). Research areas include photonic and electronic coupling for applications in quantum information, non-imaging optics, laboratory research at the boundary between relativity and quantum mechanics, ultrafast laser systems and their applications, and use of optical traps to manipulate nature's nano-machines: molecular motors. Ghosh, Scheibner, Sharping, Winston, Xu.

Biophysics. Biophysics is by definition an interdisciplinary science where ideas and techniques from physics (including soft condensed matter physics) are utilized to understand biological systems and phenomena. The biophysics group at UC Merced collaborates extensively between theory and experiment, and with chemistry, biology, applied math, and bioengineering groups. Research areas include structure and function of cell membranes, biopolymers (structure, dynamics and function), biophotonics, bacterial physics (growth, division, motility), and molecular motors and intracellular transport. Hirst, Liu, Sharping, Xu.

Condensed Matter Physics. Condensed matter physics investigates the physical, electronic and magnetic properties of the various forms of solid and liquid matter, ranging from naturally occurring crystals to engineered micro- and nanostructures as well as more exotic condensed phases and phenomena such as superconductivity and the quantum Hall effect. Research areas include nanoscience, strongly correlated systems, quantum information processing and magneto-optical phenomena, optical properties of nanostructures, and emergence of complex phenomena when transitioning from single molecule to small ensemble studies. Chiao, Ghosh, Scheibner, Xu.

Nano Science and Technology. The ability to fabricate, control, and study matter on the nanometer scale has opened up new possibilities in science and technology. Research areas include directed assembly of nanostructures for information and energy transfer, optical properties of nanostructures, and combination of physics and biochemistry methodologies to tune the nano-machinery of molecular motors. Ghosh, Hirst, Scheibner, Xu.

Soft Matter. Soft condensed matter is the study of materials that are neither crystalline solids, nor simple liquids — they are somewhere in between. Everyday examples of soft matter include soaps, paints, gels, plastics, liquid crystals and most of your own body and the food you eat. Research areas include liquid crystals, active matter, polymer physics and elasticity, fluid dynamics and granular systems, membranes, and experiments on geometry and topology in soft matter and fluids. Hirst, Kleckner, Liu.

Solar and Energy Sciences. As the first new research university in the 21st century, UC Merced was established with the mission to address new challenges facing humanity, including development of inexpensive renewable energy. Research areas include design of novel optics for light energy collection and development of novel materials for energy conversion. The University of California Advanced Solar Technologies Institute (UC Solar) is a multi-campus research institute across the UC system. Headquartered at UC Merced, UC Solar conducts cross-disciplinary research that leads to new and improved solar energy generation technologies and educates the energy industry and the next generation of energy scholars. Ghosh, Hirst, Strubbe, Winston.

View additional information about this department at www.gradschoolshopper.com. Check out the "Why Choose Us?" section, find out more about the department's culture and get links to social media networks.

UNIVERSITY OF CALIFORNIA, RIVERSIDE

DEPARTMENT OF PHYSICS AND ASTRONOMY

Riverside, California 92521
http://www.physics.ucr.edu

General University Information
Chancellor: Kim A. Wilcox
Dean of Graduate School: Shaun Bowler
University website: http://www.ucr.edu
School Type: Public
Setting: Suburban
Total Faculty: 1,145
Total Graduate Faculty: 713
Total number of Students: 23,278
Total number of Graduate Students: 3,209

Department Information
Department Chairman: Prof. Kenneth Barish, Chair
Department Contact: Derek Beving, Student Affairs Officer
  Total full-time faculty: 44
  Total number of full-time equivalent positions: 44
  Full-Time Graduate Students: 131
  Female Full-Time Graduate Students: 0
  First-Year Graduate Students: 34
  Female First-Year Students: 4
  Total Post Doctorates: 21

Department Address
900 University Avenue, PHYS 3047
Riverside, CA 92521
Phone: (951) 827-5332
E-mail: gophysics@ucr.edu
Website: http://www.physics.ucr.edu

ADMISSIONS

Admission Contact Information
Address admission inquiries to: Graduate Advisor, Department
  of Physics and Astronomy, University of California, River-
  side, CA 92521
Phone: (951) 827-5332
E-mail: gophysics@ucr.edu
Admissions website: http://www.physics.ucr.edu/graduate

Application deadlines
Fall admission:
U.S. *students*: January 5   Int'l. *students*: January 5
Spring admission:
U.S. *students*: September 1   Int'l. *students*: June 1

Application fee
U.S. *students*: $105   Int'l. *students*: $125

Admissions information
For Fall of 2017:
  Number of applicants: 325
  Number admitted: 87
  Number enrolled: 32

Admission requirements
Bachelor's degree requirements: Bachelor's degree in Physics
  or equivalent is required.
Minimum undergraduate GPA: 3.25

GRE requirements
The GRE is required.
  Quantitative score: 155
  Mean GRE score range (25th–75th percentile): 312-324
GRE combined minimum 300. Average GRE score: 318

Subjective GRE requirements
The Subjective GRE is required.
  Mean Advanced GRE score range (25th–75th percentile): 695-
  880
Average PGRE is 793.

TOEFL requirements
The TOEFL exam is required for students from non-English-
  speaking countries.
  PBT score: 550
  iBT score: 80

Other admissions information
Undergraduate preparation assumed: Kittel, Thermal Physics;
  Fowles, Analytical Mechanics; Lorrain and Corson, Elec-
  tromagnetic Fields and Waves; Liboff, Introductory Quantum
  Mechanics.

TUITION

Tuition year 2017–18:
Tuition for in-state residents
  Full-time students: $11,502 annual
Tuition for out-of-state residents
  Full-time students: $26,604 annual
Based on proposed graduate student tuition/fees. Amounts sub-
  ject to change. The University of California covers 6 years
  of non-resident tuition costs for international students (non-
  resident tuition is the difference between in-state and out-
  of-state annual tuition). UC Riverside also covers 1 year of
  non-resident tuition for national students (national students
  become residents after this period).
Credit hours per semester to be considered full-time: 12
Deferred tuition plan: Yes
Health insurance: Available
Other academic fees: Health insurance included in student fees.
Academic term: Quarter
Number of first-year students who received full tuition waivers: 13

Teaching Assistants, Research Assistants, and Fellowships
Number of first-year
  Teaching Assistants: 5
  Fellowship students: 13
Average stipend per academic year
  Teaching Assistant: $20,051
  Research Assistant: $20,101
  Fellowship student: $12,578
The Teaching Assistant and Fellowships cover all fees. RA
  positions, when available, are open only for students who
  have advanced to candidacy

FINANCIAL AID

Application deadlines
Fall admission:

U.S. students: January 5   *Int'l. students*: January 5

Loans
Loans are available for U.S. students.

Loans are not available for international students.

GAPSFAS application required: No

FAFSA application required: No

For further information
Address financial aid inquiries to: Graduate Advisor, Department of Physics and Astronomy, University of California, Riverside, Riverside, CA 92521-0413, USA.

Phone: (951) 827-5332

E-mail: gophysics@ucr.edu

Financial aid website: http://www.physics.ucr.edu./graduate/apply.html

HOUSING

Availability of on-campus housing
Single students: Yes

Married students: Yes

For further information
Address housing inquiries to: Graduate Advisor, Department of Physics and Astronomy, University of California, Riverside, Riverside, CA 92521-0413, USA.

Phone: 951-827-6350

E-mail: housinginfo@ucr.edu

Housing aid website: http://www.housing.ucr.edu

Table A—Faculty, Enrollments, and Degrees Granted

Research Specialty	2015–16 Faculty	Enrollment Fall 2015 Master's	Enrollment Fall 2015 Doctorate	Number of Degrees Granted 2016–17 (2010–17) Master's	Number of Degrees Granted 2016–17 (2010–17) Terminal Master's	Number of Degrees Granted 2016–17 (2010–17) Doctorate
Astrophysics	11	–	28	6(26)	–(7)	4(16)
Biophysics	2	–	9	–(5)	–	1(5)
Condensed Matter Physics	14	–	47	3(65)	–(4)	12(69)
High Energy Physics	10	–	26	–(23)	–(6)	5(27)
Nuclear Physics	2	–	3	–(5)	–(1)	2(6)
Other	4	–	8	1(6)	–(2)	–(3)
Total	43	–	121	10(129)	–(20)	24(126)
Full-time Grad. Stud.	–	–	131	–	–	–
First-year Grad. Stud.	–	–	32	–	–	–

GRADUATE DEGREE REQUIREMENTS

Master's: (1) Satisfactory completion of a minimum of 36 quarter units of approved physics courses taken for a letter grade after admission to graduate study; of these, at least 24 quarter units must be in the 200 series. (2) Either: (a) satisfactory completion of a thesis in a field of physics to be chosen in consultation with a faculty supervisor or (b) satisfactory performance on the comprehensive examination. See the general catalog for more details: http://www.catalog.ucr.edu.

Doctorate: (1) Coursework: Each course must be passed with a grade of "B-" or better. Each student must maintain an average of "B" or better for all courses. (2) Written comprehensive examination to be taken at the end of the student's first year. In the event of a failure, a make-up examination is offered in the winter quarter of the second year. The examination cov-

ers mechanics, statistical and thermal physics, quantum mechanics, and electromagnetism. The comprehensive examination for students pursuing the astronomy specialization consists of an examination that covers mechanics, statistical and thermal physics, electromagnetism, and fundamental astrophysics. (3) Oral qualifying examination in the general area of the student's proposed research. This examination is conducted by a doctoral committee charged with general supervision of the student's research. (4) Dissertation containing a review of existing knowledge relevant to the area of the candidate's research and the results of the candidate's original research. This research must be of sufficiently high quality to constitute a contribution to knowledge in the subject area. (5) Final oral examination may be required. See the general catalog for more details: http://www.catalog.ucr.edu.

Table B—Separately Budgeted Research Expenditures by Source of Support

Source of Support	Departmental Research	Physics-related Research Outside Department
Federal government	$7,727,197	
State/local government	$2,412,546	
Non-profit organizations	$446,631	
Business and industry	$101,067	
Other	$150,259	
Total	$10,837,700	

Table C—Separately Budgeted Research Expenditures by Research Specialty

Research Specialty	No. of Grants	Expenditures ($)
Astronomy	14	$2,124,280
Biophysics	1	
Condensed Matter Physics	25	$6,993,795
High Energy Physics	5	$1,220,514
Nuclear Physics	1	$499,110
Total	46	$10,837,699

FACULTY

Distinguished University Professor

Barish, Barry C., Ph.D., University of California, Berkeley, 1962. Nobel Laureate in Physics (2017). *Accelerator, High Energy Physics, Particles and Fields, Relativity & Gravitation*. Physics and detection of gravitational waves. Physics of future colliders.

Hanson, Gail G., Ph.D., Massachusetts Institute of Technology, 1973. *High Energy Physics, Particles and Fields*. Experimental high-energy physics.

Professor

Barish, Kenneth N., Ph.D., Yale University, 1996. *Nuclear Physics*. Experimental relativistic heavy ion and spin physics.

Canalizo, Gabriela, Ph.D., University of Hawaii, 2000. *Astronomy, Astrophysics*. Astrophysics, Observational Extragalactic Astrophysics, Active Galactic Nuclei, Quasar host galaxies and their environments, Ultraluminous Infrared Galaxies (ULIGs).

Clare, Robert B., Ph.D., Massachusetts Institute of Technology, 1982. *High Energy Physics, Particles and Fields*. Experimental high-energy physics.

Ellison, John A., Ph.D., Imperial College of London, 1987. *High Energy Physics, Particles and Fields*.

Gary, John W., Ph.D., University of California, Berkeley, 1985. *High Energy Physics, Particles and Fields*. Experimental high-energy physics.

Hamann, Frederick, Ph.D., State University of New York at Stony Brook, 1987. *Astronomy, Astrophysics*. Astrophysics. Quasars and active galaxies. Super-massive black holes in galactic nuclei.

Long, Owen, Ph.D., University of Pennsylvania, 1997. *High Energy Physics, Particles and Fields*. Experimental High Energy Physics: CP violation and physics beyond the standard model.

Mills, Allen P., Ph.D., Brandeis University, 1967. *Atomic, Molecular, & Optical Physics, Condensed Matter Physics, Solid State Physics*. Experimental Solid State and Atomic Physics.

Mobasher, Braham, Ph.D., University of Durham, UK, 1988. Director, Fellowships and Internships in Extremely Large Data Sets (FIELDS) NASA MIRO Center. *Astronomy, Astrophysics*. Observational astrophysics.

Mohideen, Umar, Ph.D., Columbia University, 1992. *Biophysics, Condensed Matter Physics, Optics, Quantum Foundations*. Experimental Condensed Matter Physics. Fundamental precision measurements; biophysics; laser spectroscopy and nonlinear optics.

Pryadko, Leonid P., Ph.D., Stanford University, 1996. *Condensed Matter Physics, Solid State Physics, Statistical & Thermal Physics, Surface Physics, Theoretical Physics*. Theoretical condensed matter physics.

Seto, Richard, Ph.D., Columbia University, 1983. *Nuclear Physics*. Experimental heavy ion physics.

Shi, Jing, Ph.D., University of Illinois, 1994. University of California Presidential Chair, Director Spins and Heat in Nanoscale Electronic Systems (SHINES) Energy Frontier Research Center. *Condensed Matter Physics, Nano Science and Technology*. Experimental condensed matter physics.

Shtengel, Kirill, Ph.D., University of California, Los Angeles, 1999. *Condensed Matter Physics, Solid State Physics, Statistical & Thermal Physics, Theoretical Physics*. Theoretical condensed matter physics.

Tom, Harry W. K., Ph.D., University of California, Berkeley, 1984. *Atomic, Molecular, & Optical Physics, Condensed Matter Physics, Optics*. Surface nonlinear optics studies of metal, semiconductor and water/solid interface systems,Ultrafast physical and chemical processes on surfaces, Terahertz spectroscopy of liquid water, confined water, and biomolecules in liquid water.

Wilson, Gillian, Ph.D., University of Durham, 1996. *Astronomy, Astrophysics*. Observational astrophysics.Galaxy Clusters and Mapping Dark Matter, Observational Cosmology, Dark Matter and Dark Energy, $1 < z < 3$ Clusters of Galaxies, "SpARCS" & "GCLASS" cluster surveys, Galaxy Evolution, Structure Formation, Infrared Galaxy Studies.

Wimpenny, Stephen J., Ph.D., Sheffield University (England), 1980. *High Energy Physics, Particles and Fields*. Experimental high-energy physics.

Wudka, Jose, Ph.D., Massachusetts Institute of Technology, 1986. *High Energy Physics, Particles and Fields, Theoretical Physics*. Theoretical high-energy and astroparticle physics.

Yarmoff, Jory A., Ph.D., University of California, Los Angeles, 1985. *Condensed Matter Physics, Nano Science and Technology, Surface Physics*. Experimental Surface Science, Nanometer-Scale Physics, Environmental Physics.

Zandi, Roya, Ph.D., University of California, Los Angeles, 2001. *Biophysics, Condensed Matter Physics*. Theoretical Condensed Matter Physics & Biophysics.

Associate Professor

Aji, Vivek, Ph.D., University of Illinois at Urbana-Champaign, 2002. *Condensed Matter Physics, Solid State Physics, Statistical & Thermal Physics, Theoretical Physics*. Theoretical condensed matter physics.

Anderson, Michael, Ph.D., UC Davis, 2006. *Physics and other Science Education*. Physics Education Research.

Beyermann, Ward, Ph.D., University of California, Los Angeles, 1988. *Condensed Matter Physics, Solid State Physics, Statistical & Thermal Physics*. Experimental condensed matter physics.

Gabor, Nathaniel, Ph.D., Cornell University, 2010. *Condensed Matter Physics, Statistical & Thermal Physics*. Experimental condensed matter physics.

Reddy, Naveen, Ph.D., California Institute of Technology, 2006. *Astronomy, Astrophysics*. Galaxy formation and evolution, multi-wavelength star formation indicators, stellar populations and dust properties of high redshift galaxies, and the connection between galaxies and the inter-galactic medium.

Siana, Brian, Ph.D., University of California, San Diego, 2005. *Astronomy, Astrophysics*. Galaxy formation in the early universe and its effects on the intergalactic medium.

Tsai, Shan-Wen, Ph.D., Brown University, 2000. *Condensed Matter Physics, Optics, Solid State Physics, Statistical & Thermal Physics*. Theoretical Condensed Matter Physics, Theoretical Atomic, Molecular and Optical Physics.

Assistant Professor

Barsukov, Igor, Ph.D., University Duisburg-Essen. Duisburg, 2012. *Condensed Matter Physics, Statistical & Thermal Physics*. Experimental Condensed Matter Physics, Spintronics.

Barton, John, Ph.D., Rutgers University, 2012. *Biophysics, Statistical & Thermal Physics*. Theoretical and Computational Biophysics, Statistical Physics.

Becker, George, Ph.D., California Institute of Technology, 2006. *Astronomy, Astrophysics*. Extragalactic Astronomy, Intergalactic Medium, Cosmic Reionization, First Stars and Galaxies, Chemical Enrichment, Dark Matter, Optical and Infrared Spectroscopy.

Bird, Simeon, Ph.D., University of Cambridge, 2011. *Astrophysics, Cosmology & String Theory*. Cosmology, Galaxy formation, theory of the intergalactic medium. Dark matter and massive neutrinos.

Cui, Yanou, Ph.D., University of Michigan, 2008. *High Energy Physics, Particles and Fields, Theoretical Physics*. Theoretical High Energy Physics-Particle Physics, Cosmology/Astrophysics.

Cui, Yontao, Ph.D., Cornell University, 2012. *Condensed Matter Physics, Statistical & Thermal Physics*. Experimental Condensed Matter Physics, Nanoscale Physics.

D'Aloisio, Anson, Ph.D., Yale University, 2011. *Astrophysics, Cosmology & String Theory*. Theoretical astrophysics and cosmology: cosmological structure formation, reionization, quasar absorption spectra, gravitational lensing, and primordial non-Gaussianity.

Hemmerling, Boerge, Ph.D., Gottfried Wilhelm Leibniz Universität Hannover, 2011. *Atomic, Molecular, & Optical Physics, Optics*. Experimental Atomic, Molecular and Optical Physics, Experimental Quantum Optics.

Kuhlman, Thomas, Ph.D., University of California, San Diego, 2007. *Biophysics*. Experimental biological physics; regulation of gene expression in prokaryotes; role of chromosomal organization in transcriptional regulation.

Lui, Chun-Hung, Ph.D., Columbia University, 2011. *Condensed Matter Physics, Nano Science and Technology, Optics, Statistical & Thermal Physics*. Experimental Condensed Matter Physics, Ultrafast Nano-Optics.

Mulligan, Michael, Ph.D., Stanford University. *Condensed Matter Physics, Solid State Physics, Statistical & Thermal Physics, Theoretical Physics*. Condensed Matter Theory. Strongly correlated systems, quantum field theory.

Sales, Laura, Ph.D., Facultad de Matematica, Astronomia y Fisica, Universidad Nacional de Cordoba, 2007. *Astrophysics.* Galaxy Formation and Evolution, Dynamical modeling of galaxies, Dwarf galaxies, Milky Way and Local Group cosmology, Nature of feedback, Physics of the ISM, Hydrodynamics, Numerical simulations.

Tanedo, Philip (Flip), Ph.D., Cornell University, 2013. *High Energy Physics, Particles and Fields, Theoretical Physics.* Theoretical Particle Physics.

Wei, Peng, Ph.D., Uniersity of California, Riverside, 2011. *Condensed Matter Physics, Solid State Physics, Statistical & Thermal Physics.* Experimental Condensed Matter Physics, Mesoscopic Quantum Physics.

Yu, Hai-Bo, Ph.D., University of Maryland, 2007. *Astrophysics, High Energy Physics, Particles and Fields, Theoretical Physics.* Theoretical Particle Physics and Astrophysics; Cosmology.

Professor Emeritus

Desai, Bipin R., Ph.D., University of California, Berkeley, 1961. *High Energy Physics, Particles and Fields, Theoretical Physics.* Theoretical high-energy physics.

Ma, Ernest, Ph.D., University of California, Irvine, 1970. Professor of Graduate Division. *High Energy Physics, Particles and Fields, Theoretical Physics.* Theoretical particle physics.

MacLaughlin, Douglas E., Ph.D., University of California, Berkeley, 1966. Research Professor. *Condensed Matter Physics, Solid State Physics, Statistical & Thermal Physics.* Experimental condensed-matter physics: high-temperature superconductivity; heavy-fermion compounds; magnetic resonance techniques.

Varma, Chandra M., Ph.D., University of Minnesota, 1968. *Condensed Matter Physics, Solid State Physics, Statistical & Thermal Physics, Theoretical Physics.* Theoretical condensed matter physics.

Zych, Allen D., Ph.D., Case Western Reserve University, 1968. Experimental space physics; gamma-ray astronomy; atmospheric and solar gamma-rays and neutrons.

DEPARTMENTAL RESEARCH SPECIALTIES AND STAFF

Theoretical

Astrophysics and cosmology.

Biophysics. Virus structure and structure formation kinetics; elastic and Casimir-type interaction between particles embedded in bilayer lipid membranes. There is one postdoctoral physicist. Barton, Mohideen, Zandi.

Condensed Matter Physics. Research in quantum and statistical mechanics of many-body systems, including studies of quantum critical phenomena, novel phases, and phase transitions in strongly correlated matter; superconductivity; singular Fermi liquids; low-dimensional systems including graphene, quantum computation, Casimir interactions, and cold atom physics. There are seven postdoctoral physicists. Aji, Barsukov, Beyermann, Yontao Cui, Gabor, Lui, MacLaughlin, Mohideen, Mulligan, Pryadko, Shi, Shtengel, Tsai, Varma, Wei, Yarmoff.

Particles and Fields. Gauge theories; extensions of the standard model; effective theories of electroweak interactions and their potential impact on present and future colliders; neutrinos and related physics beyond the standard model; higher gauge symmetries, as well as models of extra spacetime dimensions. Dark matter and dark energy, astro particle physics and cosmology. Clare, Yanou Cui, Desai, Gary, Hanson, Long, Ma, Tanedo, Wimpenny, Wudka, Yu.

Physics and other Science Education. Anderson.

Experimental

Astronomy. Astronomy/astrophysics/cosmology. The main research area in the astronomy group at UCR is observational extragalactic astronomy. Using data from space and ground-based facilities (i.e., the Hubble and Spitzer Space Telescopes, Keck and Gemini telescopes, etc.), we study the following topics: formation and evolution of galaxies at different look-back times, high-redshift universe, large-scale structure and clustering of galaxies, gravitational lensing, active galactic nuclei, and multi-waveband galaxy surveys. The UCR astronomy group is an active member of a number of large collaborations aimed at studying the evolution of galaxies. There are 20 graduate students and five postdoctoral physicists. Becker, Canalizo, Hamann, Mobasher, Reddy, Sales, Siana, Wilson.

Atomic, Molecular, & Optical Physics. Positronium atom physics; Bose-Einstein condensation of a dense collection of positronium atoms; measuring the energy structure of the positronium atom; making a Bose-Einstein condensed positronium annihilation gamma-ray laser. Mills.

Atomic, Molecular, & Optical Physics. Laser spectroscopy and nonlinear optics: femtosecond and picosecond laser pulses are used to time-resolve chemical processes at surfaces, the rotational dynamics of liquids, electron-phonon coupling in solids, and the orientation of molecules at environmentally significant interfaces. Novel laser sources in the far infrared are being developed. Picosecond time-resolved nanoscale microscopy is used to study the electronic properties of quantum dot structures and the mobility of ferroelectric and ferromagnetic domain walls. There is one postdoctoral physicist. Hemmerling, Mills, Tom.

Biophysics. Virus structure and structure formation kinetics; elastic and Casimir-type interactions between particles embedded in bilayer lipid membranes. There is one postdoctoral physicist. Mohideen.

Condensed Matter Physics. Strongly correlated electron systems such as heavy-fermion materials, biological materials, high-temperature superconductors, non-Fermi liquids, Bose-Einstein condensates, quantum magnets, magnetic superconductors, spin glasses, fullerenes, and impurity systems. Experimental techniques include nuclear magnetic resonance (NMR) and muon spin rotation (muSR), terahertz spectroscopy, and both elastic and inelastic neutron scattering. NMR experiments are carried out at UCR, and the group travels to "meson factory" facilities such as TRIUMF in Vancouver, Canada, to perform muSR experiments using accelerator-produced beams of muons. Transport and thermodynamic properties are also investigated as functions of temperature and magnetic fields. In some cases, experiments are conducted down to mK temperatures or in pulsed magnetic fields up to 60T. Some of this research is performed offsite at user facilities such as Paul Scherrer Institute, LANSCE, and NHMFL. Research is also being conducted on devising an analog neural network computer based on the interactions of DNA molecules. There are three postdoctoral physicists. Barsukov, Beyermann, Yontao Cui, Gabor, Lui, MacLaughlin, Mills, Mohideen, Shi, Tom, Wei, Yarmoff.

Environmental Physics. Environmental physics: surface physics of the air/water/solid interface and complex materials such as zeolites with application to atmospheric and soil sciences, chemical and bioremediation, and chemical and biological sensors. Tom, Yarmoff.

Fundamental Precision Measurements. Precision measurements and theory of the Casimir force and other effects of the zero point fields for different shapes of the interacting bodies made using microcantilever-based techniques such as in atomic force microscopy. There is one postdoctoral physicists. Mohideen, Zandi.

Joint Programs. A joint Ph.D. in Physics and an M.S. in Soil Physics, a joint Ph.D. in Soil Physics and an M.S. in Physics, and a Ph.D. in Physics with emphasis on environmental physics are offered in conjunction with the Department of Soil and Environmental Sciences. Interdisciplinary training is offered in the area of chemical physics through collaboration with faculty members in the Department of Chemistry. Tom.

Nano Science and Technology. Properties of graphene and carbon nanotubes, including quantum transport, strain engineering, spin transport, thermoelectric, and nanomechanical properties; synthesis of oxide heterostructures, semiconductors, topological insulators, ultrathin magnetic films, large area graphene, and carbon nanotubes; optical probes of interface dynamics, magnetism, and spin coherence; spintronics in semiconductor, metal, and carbon-based materials; fundamental properties and fabrication of metal nanoclusters; thermoelectric and thermo-spintronic phenomena; nanoscale superconductivity; physics of information storage devices. Techniques include nanofabrication by electron beam lithography and focused ion beam milling, electron transport in He3 and dilution refrigerators, pulsed laser and nonlinear optical spectroscopy, scanning probe microscopy, molecular beam epitaxy (MBE), laser-MBE, muon spin relaxation, and SQUID magnetometry. There are four postdoctoral physicists. Yontao Cui, Lui, Shi, Tom, Yarmoff.

Nucleon Structure. Proton spin research: what are the gluon and antiquark contributions to the proton spin? Spin is a property of particles as fundamental as charge and mass. The spin of the proton was first determined in 1927, yet, we still do not understand the spin structure of the proton. We are investigating the longitudinal and transverse spin structure of the proton

at Brookhaven National Laboratory. There is one postdoctoral physicist and two graduate students. Kenneth N. Barish.

Particles and Fields. High-energy physics: research efforts are ongoing in the study of proton-proton collisions at CERN. The CMS experiment at the CERN Large Hadron Collider is the highest-energy collider in the world. Our detector efforts focus on the end-cap muon chambers, the silicon strip tracker, and the hadron calorimeter, as well as upgrades for future high-luminosity running. Physics interests include tracking software, top quark physics, the study of the properties of the Higgs boson, and search of new physics beyond the Standard Model, such as supersymmetry. There are four postdoctoral physicists. Clare, Ellison, Gary, Hanson, Long, Wimpenny.

Relativistic Heavy-ion Physics. The experimental group studies relativistic nucleus-nucleus collisions at high energies to explore the behavior of extended nuclear matter under extreme conditions of density and temperature, i.e., the Quark Gluon Plasma (QGP). These studies use the PHENIX and sPHENIX detectors at the Brookhaven Relativistic Heavy Ion Collider (RHIC), where energies of 100 GeV per nucleon are available. The initial goal for creating the QGP has been accomplished: a strongly interacting plasma behaving like a liquid has been found. The main goal now is to characterize this new state of matter. There are two postdoctoral physicists, six graduate students, and two undergraduate students. Kenneth N. Barish, Seto.

Surface Physics. The geometric, electronic, chemical, and magnetic properties of solid surfaces are investigated with a wide variety of modern surface spectroscopies. We have particular expertise in studying ion-surface and laser-surface interactions. In addition, the surface properties of novel materials are investigated. There are two postdoctoral physicists. Tom, Yarmoff.

View additional information about this department at www.gradschoolshopper.com. Check out the "Why Choose Us?" section, find out more about the department's culture and get links to social media networks.

UNIVERSITY OF CALIFORNIA, SAN DIEGO

DEPARTMENT OF PHYSICS

La Jolla, California 92093–0319
http://physics.ucsd.edu/

General University Information
Chancellor: Pradeep K. Khosla
Dean of Graduate School: Kit Pogliano
University website: http://www.ucsd.edu/
School Type: Public
Setting: Suburban
Total Faculty: 1,460
Total Graduate Faculty: 1,460
Total number of Students: 36,624
Total number of Graduate Students: 6,113

Department Information
Department Chairman: Prof. Benjamin Grinstein, Chair
Department Contact: Sharmila Poddar, Graduate Coordinator
 Total full-time faculty: 60
 Total number of full-time equivalent positions: 60
 Full-Time Graduate Students: 180
 Female Full-Time Graduate Students: 28
 First-Year Graduate Students: 48
 Female First-Year Students: 6
 Total Post Doctorates: 55

Department Address
9500 Gilman Drive
La Jolla, CA 92093–0319
Phone: (858) 822-1074
E-mail: apply@physics.ucsd.edu
Website: http://physics.ucsd.edu/

ADMISSIONS

Admission Contact Information
Address admission inquiries to: Graduate Admissions Office, Department of Physics (0319), 9500 Gilman Dr., La Jolla, CA 92093–0319
Phone: (858) 534-3293
E-mail: apply@physics.ucsd.edu
Admissions website: https://apply.grad.ucsd.edu/home

Application deadlines
Fall admission:
U.S. students: December 15   *Int'l. students*: December 15

Application fee
U.S. students: $105   *Int'l. students*: $125

Admissions information
For Fall of 2018:
 Number of applicants: 569
 Number admitted: 151
 Number enrolled: 48

Admission requirements
Bachelor's degree requirements: Entering graduate students are required to have a sound knowledge of undergraduate mechanics, electricity, and magnetism; to have had senior courses or their equivalent in atomic and quantum physics, nuclear physics, and thermodynamics; and to have taken upper division laboratory work.
Minimum undergraduate GPA: 3.0

GRE requirements
The GRE is required.
 The GRE examinations must be taken no later than November in order for the scores to be considered by the Admissions Committee. Incomplete files and applications received after December 15th will be considered only if space is available.

Subjective GRE requirements
The Subjective GRE is required.
It is recommended that applicant score in the 50th percentile or higher on the GRE Physics exam.

TOEFL requirements
The TOEFL exam is required for students from non-English-speaking countries.
 PBT score: 550
 iBT score: 85
The minimum TOEFL score required is 213 for computer-based (CBT) and 85 for internet based (iBT). The minimum TOEFL score for the speaking section is 23. The minimum International English Language Testing System (IELTS) score required is Band Score 7. The minimum IELTS Spoken score is 8. The Test for Spoken English (TSE) is highly recommended. International Students whose native language is not English will be required to demonstrate English language proficiency before they may serve as teaching assistants.

Other admissions information
Additional requirements: The average GRE scores for admitted students for 2017–2018 were verbal–161; quantitative–167; subjective–895.
Undergraduate preparation assumed: Griffiths, Introduction to Electrodynamics; Dubin, Numerical and Analytical Methods for Scientists and Engineers; Thornton and Marion, Classical Dynamics; Barnaal, Analog Electronics for Scientific Application; Horowitz and Hill, The Art of Electronics; Griffiths, Introduction to Quantum Mechanics; Gasiorowicz, Quantum Physics; Sakurai, Advanced Quantum Mechanics; Carter, Classical and Statistical Thermodynamics; Kittel and Zetti, Introduction to Solid State Physics; Luth and Ibach, Solid-State Physics: An Introduction to Principles of Materials Science.

TUITION

Tuition year 2018–19:
Tuition for in-state residents
 Full-time students: $17,005.86 annual
Tuition for out-of-state residents
 Full-time students: $32,107.86 annual
Based on a proposed graduate student fees/tuition. Amounts subject to change.
Credit hours per semester to be considered full-time: 12
Deferred tuition plan: No
Health insurance: Yes, $3,609.00.
Other academic fees: Health insurance is included in student fees.
Academic term: Quarter

Teaching Assistants, Research Assistants, and Fellowships
Number of first-year
 Teaching Assistants: 22
 Research Assistants: 2
 Fellowship students: 4

Average stipend per academic year
Teaching Assistant: $20,653
Research Assistant: $21,123
Fellowship student: $12,500
Only select students receive a fellowship stipend.

FINANCIAL AID

Loans
Loans are available for U.S. students.
Loans are not available for international students.
GAPSFAS application required: No
FAFSA application required: Yes

For further information
Address financial aid inquiries to: Student Financial Services, 0013 Graduate Division, 9500 Gilman Dr., La Jolla, CA 92093–0013.
Phone: (858) 534-4480
E-mail: finaid@ucsd.edu
Financial aid website: http://grad.ucsd.edu/financial/index.html

HOUSING

Availability of on-campus housing
Single students: Yes
Married students: Yes
Childcare Assistance: Yes

For further information
Address housing inquiries to: ARCH (Associated Residential Community Housing), 9500 Gilman Drive, Department 0907, La Jolla, CA 92093–0907.
Phone: (858) 534-2724
E-mail: archinfo@ucsd.edu
Housing aid website: http://hdh.ucsd.edu/arch/pages/

Table A—Faculty, Enrollments, and Degrees Granted

Research Specialty	2017–18 Faculty	Enrollment Fall 2017 Master's	Enrollment Fall 2017 Doctorate	Number of Degrees Granted 2016–17 (2011–17) Master's	Number of Degrees Granted 2016–17 (2011–17) Terminal Master's	Number of Degrees Granted 2016–17 (2011–17) Doctorate
Acoustics	1	–	–	–	–	–
Applied Mathematics	1	–	4	–	–	1(3)
Astrophysics/ Astronomy	17	–	30	–	–	7(29)
Atomic, Molecular, & Optical Physics	5	–	2	–	–	–
Biophysics	9	–	36	–	–	2(24)
Computational Science	5	–	5	–	–	3(8)
Condensed Matter Physics	17	–	36	–	–	5(36)
Elementary Particles	–	–	2	–	–	–
High Energy Physics	16	–	11	–	–	–(18)
Materials Science, Metallurgy	8	–	3	–	–	–
Nonlinear Dynamics	1	–	7	–	–	1(5)
Physics Education	3	–	–	–	–	–
Plasma and Fusion	3	–	6	–	–	1(8)
Non-specialized	–	–	13	–	–(18)	–
Total	–	–	146	–	–(18)	20(130)
Full-time Grad. Stud.	–	–	146	–	–	–
First-year Grad. Stud.	–	–	27	–	–	–

GRADUATE DEGREE REQUIREMENTS

Master's: A "B" average in 36 units of graduate work and a comprehensive written examination are required. A thesis is not required. There is no language requirement. Three quarters of residency are required. UCSD does not offer a terminal master's degree in Physics.

Doctorate: A "B" average must be maintained in all coursework. A comprehensive departmental examination at the beginning of the second year, completion of five advanced courses, completion of teaching requirement, followed by an oral qualifying examination for advancement to candidacy are required. A dissertation and successful oral defense of dissertation are required. There is no language requirement. Six quarters residency are required.

Other Degrees: A Ph.D. in Physics (Biophysics) is also available. This option has the same requirements as the regular Ph.D., except that the departmental examination can be taken at beginning of the third year and five courses related to the life sciences are required. A Ph.D. with a specialization in computational science (CSME) is designed to allow students to obtain training in their chosen field of science, mathematics, or engineering, with additional training in computational science integrated into their graduate studies. Prospective students must apply and be admitted into the Ph.D. program in physics, and then be admitted into the CSME program.

Thesis: Thesis may not be written in absentia.

SPECIAL EQUIPMENT, FACILITIES, OR PROGRAMS

Departmental facilities include excellent electronics and machine shops, a liquid He facility, and extensive computing facilities. Additional computing support is available from the campus-based San Diego Supercomputing Center (SDSC).

Table B—Separately Budgeted Research Expenditures by Source of Support

Source of Support	Departmental Research	Physics-related Research Outside Department
Federal government	$18,080,678.16	
State/local government	$389,777	
Non-profit organizations	$27,807,655.48	
Business and industry	$371,596	
Other		
Total	$46,649,706.64	

Table C—Separately Budgeted Research Expenditures by Research Specialty

Research Specialty	No. of Grants	Expenditures ($)
Astrophysics/Astronomy	47	$30,765,317.08
Biophysics	23	$3,345,900
Condensed Matter Physics	40	$7,207,501.56
Elementary Particles/High Energy	15	$4,682,311
Plasma and Fusion	3	$648,677
Other	–	
Total	128	$46,649,706.64

FACULTY

Distinguished University Professor

Abarbanel, Henry D. I., Ph.D., Princeton University, 1966. *Biophysics*. Nonlinear dynamics of fluids; optical systems and neural assemblies; geophysical fluid dynamics and physical oceanography.

Boggs, Steven, Ph.D., UC Berkeley, 1998. Dean of the Division of Physical Sciences. *Astronomy.* Experimental Astrophysics. Research is focused on high-energy astrophysics, in particular the development of novel gamma-ray and X-ray instruments with an emphasis on high-resolution spectroscopy. Primary interest is the detailed measurement of radioactive nuclei produced in the inner regions of a supernova explosion.

Chivukula, R. Sekhar, Ph.D., Harvard University, 1987. *Particles and Fields.* Theoretical Particle Physics. Theory and phenomenology of physics beyond the standard model.

Diamond, Patrick H., Ph.D., Massachusetts Institute of Technology, 1979. Theoretical plasma physics and astrophysics; nonlinear dynamics.

Fuller, George M., Ph.D., California Institute of Technology, 1981. *Astrophysics.* Astrophysics/Astronomy. My research centers on nuclear and particle astrophysics and a few issues in gravitation. Recent work by my group and me includes calculation of neutrino flavor transformation in supernovae and the early universe, neutrino mass in cosmology, sterile neutrino dark matter, and general relativistic instability of super-massive stars.

Grinstein, Benjamin, Ph.D., Harvard University, 1984. Elementary particle theory. Interested in mathematical models of the interactions of elementary particles: creating models, developing methods to analyze them and confronting them with experiment. Interested as well in formal aspects of Quantum Field Theory.

Hwa, Terence T.-L., Ph.D., Massachusetts Institute of Technology, 1990. *Biophysics, High Energy Physics.* Statistical mechanics; biological physics; systems biology; molecular evolution; genomics; condensed matter physics; dynamics of complex systems; polymer physics.

Kleinfeld, David, Ph.D., University of California, San Diego, 1984. *Biophysics, Neuroscience/Neuro Physics.* Experimental and computational neuroscience and neurovascular studies at the cellular through systems level; Advancements in electrical instrumentation, molecular probes, and optical microscopy for imaging and manipulation.

Kuti, Julius, Ph.D., Hungary, 1967. Elementary particles and fields.

Manohar, Aneesh V., Ph.D., Harvard University, 1983. *High Energy Physics.* Elementary particle physics. Theoretical high-energy physics and cosmology.

Maple, M. Brian, Ph.D., University of California, San Diego, 1969. Superconductivity; magnetism, strongly correlated electron phenomena; high-pressure physics; surface science.

Norman, Michael L., Ph.D., University of California, Davis, 1980. *Astrophysics.* Computational astrophysics and cosmology.

Schuller, Ivan K., Ph.D., Northwestern University, 1976. *Condensed Matter Physics.* Experimental condensed matter physics; materials science (thin films, heterostructures, magnetism, nanostructures, and superconductivity).

Simmons, Elizabeth H., Ph.D., Harvard University, 1990. Executive Vice Chancellor, Academic Affairs. *High Energy Physics.* Theoretical particle physics. Focus is on theories of the origins of mass. Presently studying how physics beyond the Standard Model might manifest in experiments at the CERN Large Hadron Collider.

Surko, Clifford M., Ph.D., University of California, Berkeley, 1968. *Atomic, Molecular, & Optical Physics.* Experimental studies of nonlinear non-equilibrium phenomena, plasma physics using positrons and positron–matter interactions.

Professor

Arovas, Daniel P., Ph.D., University of California, Santa Barbara, 1986. *Condensed Matter Physics.* Condensed matter theory; statistical mechanics.

Averitt, Richard D., Ph.D., Rice University, 1998. *Condensed Matter Physics.* Experimental condensed matter. Correlated electron materials; transition metal oxides; metamaterials; plasmonics; ultrafast optical and terahertz spectroscopy.

Branson, James G., Ph.D., Princeton University, 1977. *High Energy Physics.* Experimental elementary particle physics. My group has recently found a new "Higgs-like" boson at the Large Hadron Collider in the decay mode into two photons. We have played a leading role in the search for the Higgs in this mode, where the strongest signal has been observed. Now we are working on measuring the properties of this new particle to determine whether it is simply a Standard Model Higgs or something much more interesting.

Burgasser, Adam, Ph.D., California Institute of Technology, 2001. *Astrophysics.* Astrophysics/Astronomy. Observational astrophysics; low mass stars, brown dwarfs and extrasolar planets; near-infrared instrumentation.

Butov, Leonid V., Ph.D., Institute of Solid State Physics, 1991. *Condensed Matter Physics, Optics.* Experimental condensed matter physics. Studies of basic properties of electron-hole systems in semiconductors and development of new methods for optoelectronic signal processing.

Coil, Alison, Ph.D., University of California, Berkeley, 2004. *Astrophysics.* Astrophysics/Astronomy. Observer, studying distant, high-redshift galaxies and accreting supermassive black holes, as well as outflowing galactic winds.

Di Ventra, Massimiliano, Ph.D., Ecole Polytechnique Federale de Lausanne, 1997. *Condensed Matter Physics.* Condensed matter physics. Interests are in the theory of non-equilibrium phenomena in nanoscale and biological systems, with particular focus on applicative contexts. Employs both analytical and numerical approaches to understand and predict the behavior of many-body systems out of equilibrium.

Dubin, Daniel H. E., Ph.D., Princeton University, 1984. *Computational Physics.* Theoretical plasma physics. I am a plasma theorist working mainly on nonneutral plasmas, such as pure electron plasmas or pure ion plasmas. In addition to plasma physics this work involves statistical physics, nonlinear dynamics and advanced computer simulation methods.

Dudko, Olga K., Ph.D., Institute for Low Temperature Physics and Engineering, Kharkov, Ukraine, 2001. *Biophysics.* Theoretical biophysics.

Fogler, Michael M., Ph.D., University of Minnesota, 1997. *Condensed Matter Physics.* Condensed matter theory. Theoretical study of low dimensional and nanoscale electron systems, in particular, graphene, semiconductor nanowires and quantum wells. Investigation of correlations, disorder, and quantum effects in transport and optical properties of such materials.

Groisman, Alexander, Ph.D., Weizmann Institute of Science, 2001. *Biophysics.* Experimental biophysics, fluid mechanics, microfluidics, mechanobiology.

Hirsch, Jorge E., Ph.D., University of Chicago, 1980. *Condensed Matter Physics.* Theoretical condensed matter physics.

Holst, Michael, Ph.D., University of Illinois at Urbana-Champaign, 1993. Director: Mathematical and Computational Physics Research Group. Co-Director: Center for Computational Mathematics. *Biophysics.* Biophysics, mathematical physics, general relativity.

Intriligator, Kenneth A., Ph.D., Harvard University, 1992. *High Energy Physics.* Elementary particle physics. High-energy theory topics: quantum field theory, supersymmetry, string theory, and dualities.

Jenkins, Elizabeth, Ph.D., Harvard University, 1989. *Nuclear Physics.* Elementary particle physics.

Keating, Brian, Ph.D., Brown University, 2000. *Astrophysics.* Astrophysics/Astronomy. Cosmic Microwave Background, Experimental cosmology, low noise electronics, and detector physics.

McGreevy, John, Ph.D., Stanford University, 2002. *High Energy Physics*. High-energy theory.

Murphy, Thomas M., Ph.D., California Institute of Technology, 2000. Vice Chair of Education, Physics. *Astrophysics*. Astrophysics/Astronomy. Tests fundamental gravitation by measuring the Earth-Moon separation to millimeter precision using an apparatus he and his group constructed for the Apache Point Observatory in New Mexico.

Sharma, Vivek A., Ph.D., Syracuse University, 1990. *High Energy Physics*. Prof. Sharma's group is engaged in Higgs boson physics with the CMS detector at the Large Hadron collider at CERN.

Shpyrko, Oleg, Ph.D., Harvard University, 2004. *Condensed Matter Physics*. Condensed matter physics. We use X-ray, light and neutron scattering, as well as scanning probes to understand and manipulate the behavior of materials at the nanoscale, including problems that range from soft to hard condensed matter.

Smith, Douglas E., Ph.D., Stanford University, 1999. *Biophysics*. Biophysics. We conduct research in experimental biophysics, primarily using optical tweezers to manipulate single DNA molecules. Topics include viral DNA packaging, molecular motors, and protein-DNA interactions.

Tytler, David, Ph.D., University of London, 1982. *Astrophysics*. Cosmology and galaxy formation; quasars; ultraviolet, optical and infrared observations; telescopes and astronomical instrumentation; other planetary systems.

Vergassola, Massimo, Ph.D., University Nice Sophia-Antipolis, 1994. *Biophysics*. Biological physics, statistical physics. Current topics include bacterial motility and physiology, biological sensory systems and turbulent transport.

Wu, Congjun, Ph.D., Stanford University, 2005. *Condensed Matter Physics*. Condensed matter physics. Wu's research interest covers the theoretical study of new states of matter in condensed matter systems, including unconventional magnetism and superconductivity, orbital physics, spin-orbit coupling and spintronics, excitons, quantum phase transitions and criticality, strongly correlated bosonic and fermionic systems with cold atoms, and numerical algorithms for two dimensional quantum systems.

Wuerthwein, Frank, Ph.D., Cornell University, 1995. Elementary particle physics. Interested in search for new physics at the LHC. CMS SUSY convener for 2013/14.

Yagil, Avraham, Ph.D., Weizmann Institute of Science, 1989. *High Energy Physics*. Experimental high-energy physics at the large hadron collider.

Associate Professor

Jun, Suckjoon, Ph.D., Simon Fraser University, 2004. *Biophysics*. Experimental biophysics.

Keres, Dusan, Ph.D., University of Massachusetts, Amherst, 2007. *Astrophysics*. Astrophysics/Astronomy. Galaxy formation and evolution; cosmological simulations.

Ni, Kaixuan, Ph.D., Columbia University, 2006. *Particles and Fields*. Experimental Particle Physis. Research interest: dark matter direct detection, neutrino-less double beta decay. Our group is developing sensitive detectors, especially based on liquid xenon, to search for dark matter at deep underground laboratories.

Wright, Shelley, Ph.D., University of California, Los Angeles, 2008. *Astrophysics*. Experimental astrophysics. We design and build optical and near-infrared astronomical instrumentation and specialize in their use with adaptive optics.

Assistant Professor

Arnold, Kam, Ph.D., UC Berkeley, 2010. *Astrophysics*. Experimental Astrophysics.

Barreiro, Julio T., Ph.D., University of Illinois at Urbana-Champaign, 2008. *Atomic, Molecular, & Optical Physics, Condensed Matter Physics*. Experimental atomic, molecular, and optical physics; ultracold atoms in optical lattices; trapped ions; quantum computation; quantum simulations.

Flauger, Raphael, Ph.D., The University of Texas, 2009. *High Energy Physics*. Early universe cosmology, cosmic microwave background, quantum field theory.

Frano, Alex, Ph.D., Max Planck Institute/Technical University of Berlin, 2014. *Condensed Matter Physics*. Experimental Condensed Matter Physics. We design thin films, superlattices, and heterostructures based on "quantum materials"- and characterize the macroscopic properties that emerge due to having highly correlated electronic wave functions: magnetism, charge/orbital order, high-temperature superconductivity, etc. We use synchrotron-based x-ray techniques as well as advanced probes here at UCSD.

Green, Daniel R., Ph.D., Stanford University, 2009. *Astrophysics, High Energy Physics*. Theoretical Astropysics and High Energy Physics.

Grover, Tarun, Ph.D., Massachusetts Institute of Technology, 2010. *Condensed Matter Physics*. Condensed Matter Theory, Quantum information, Statistical mechanics.

Konopacky, Quinn M., Ph.D., University of California, Los Angeles, 2009. *Astrophysics*. Planet formation and evolution; high contrast imaging; star formation; stellar and substellar evolution; orbital dynamics; high angular resolution imaging and spectroscopy; adaptive optics; astrometry; speckle interferometry; optical and infrared astronomy.

Koslover, Elena F., Ph.D., Stanford, 2013. *Biophysics, Theoretical Physics*. We study collective physical phenomena in living cells, pulling together techniques from statistical and continuum mechanics to shed light on cell biology, and using the intracellular world as inspiration for new insights into the behavior of active soft matter.

Lin, Tongyan, Ph.D., Harvard University, 2012. *Astrophysics, High Energy Physics*. High Energy Physics, Particle Astrophysics. Theoretical studies of particle dark matter models, phenomena, and searches.

Palacci, Jeremie, Ph.D., Universite de Lyon, 2010. *Condensed Matter Physics*. Soft Condensed Matter, Active Colloids, Self-Organization, Non-equilibrium, Experimental Physics.

Popmintchev, Tenio, Ph.D., University of Colorado, Boulder, 2010. *Atomic, Molecular, & Optical Physics*. Quantum and extreme nonlinear optics design of laser-like X-rays with arbitrary spectral, temporal, and spatial shape, and spin and orbital angular momentum. Dynamic imaging of bio- and nanosystems at the space-time resolution extreme.

Sandstrom, Karin M., Ph.D., University of California, Berkeley, 2009. *Astrophysics*. Multiwavelength observational studies of the interstellar medium and star formation in nearby galaxies. The properties and evolution of interstellar dust.

You, Yi-Zhuang, Ph.D., Tsinghua University, 2013. *Condensed Matter Physics*. Condensed Matter theory. Quantum many-body physics, topological phases of matter, quantum information, machine learning and physics.

Emeritus

McIlwain, Carl E., Ph.D., University of Iowa, 1960. Research Professor. Space physics; experimental and theoretical studies of planetary magnetospheres; observational and instrumental astrophysics.

Ohkawa, Tihiro, Ph.D., University of Tokyo, 1955. *Plasma and Fusion*. Experimental plasma physics and controlled fusion.

Pathria, Raj K., Ph.D., University of Delhi, 1957. *Statistical & Thermal Physics*. Statistical physics; quantum physics; low-temperature physics.

Peterson, Laurence E., Ph.D., University of Minnesota, 1960. Research Professor. *Astrophysics*. X- and gamma-ray astronomy; cosmic rays; space physics; balloon and satellite instrumentation.

Sinha, Sunil K., Ph.D., University of Cambridge, 1964. *Condensed Matter Physics*. Neutron and X-ray scattering studies of condensed matter.

Professor Emeritus

Berkowitz, Ami E., Ph.D., University of Pennsylvania, 1953. Magnetic materials investigations; correlation of microstructures with magnetic behavior; surface effects; relaxation phenomena.

Burbidge, E. Margaret, Ph.D., London Observatory, 1943. Extragalactic studies; spectrophotometric and imaging; observational work on normal galaxies; galaxies with active nuclei, especially radio galaxies; quasars using Lick Observatory 3-M telescope and Keck Observatory 10-M telescope.

Chen, Joseph C.Y., Ph.D., University of Notre Dame, 1961. Theory of atomic and molecular structure and processes; history and philosophy of science.

Driscoll, C. Fred, Ph.D., University of California, San Diego, 1976. Experimental plasma physics; waves and transport in pure electron and pure ion plasmas; 2D fluid dynamics and turbulence.

Dynes, Robert C., Ph.D., McMaster University, 1968. Experimental condensed matter physics; solid-state physics.

Feher, George, Ph.D., University of California, Berkeley, 1954. *Biophysics*. Biophysics; photosynthesis; magnetic resonance; mechanisms of crystallization of macromolecules.

Fredkin, Donald R., Ph.D., Princeton University, 1961. Solid-state theory; applied magnetics; biophysics.

Goodkind, John M., Ph.D., Duke University, 1960. *Condensed Matter Physics*. Low-temperature experimental research; 2D electrons; solid He; geophysical and fundamental gravity; quantum computing.

Griest, Kim, Ph.D., University of California, Santa Cruz, 1987. *Astrophysics*. Theoretical and observational astrophysic; theoretical elementary particle physics; dark matter.

Jones, Barbara, Ph.D., University of London, 1976. *Astrophysics*. Infrared astrophysics; galactic and extragalactic astronomy; astronomical instrumentation; research in physics education.

Liebermann, Leonard N., Ph.D., University of Chicago, 1940. Magnetism; propagation of underwater sound; molecular and chemical physics; extremely low-frequency electromagnetic waves.

Lovberg, Ralph H., Ph.D., University of Minnesota, 1955. Experimental plasma physics; geophysics.

Nguyen-Huu, Xuong, Ph.D., University of California, Berkeley, 1962. *Biophysics*. Biophysics; protein crystallography; electron microscopy, detectors for X-rays and electrons.

O'Neil, Thomas M., Ph.D., University of California, San Diego, 1965. Theoretical plasma physics.

Okamura, Melvin Y., Ph.D., Northwestern University, 1970. *Biophysics*.

Onuchic, José, Ph.D., California Institute of Technology, 1987. *Biophysics*. Theoretical biophysics and chemical physics; theoretical studies in electron-transfer reactions in chemical and biological systems and in the protein-folding problem; bioinformatics.

Sham, Lu Jeu, Ph.D., University of Cambridge, 1963. *Condensed Matter Physics*. Theoretical condensed matter physics.

Suhl, Harry, Ph.D., University of Oxford, 1948. Theoretical solid-state physics, particularly superconductivity, magnetism, and surface kinetics; nonlinear dynamics.

Swanson, Robert A., Ph.D., University of Chicago, 1958. Experiments involving properties and interactions of elementary particles; interference and decay of neutral K-mesons; deep inelastic muon scattering; nucleon structure and fragmentation; rare kaon decays and CP violation.

Ticho, Harold, Ph.D., University of Chicago, 1949. Experimental elementary particle physics.

Wong, David Y., Ph.D., University of Maryland, 1958. *High Energy Physics*. Theoretical high-energy physics.

Teaching Assistant Professor

Paddock, Mark, Ph.D., UC San Diego, 1991. *Physics and other Science Education*. Physics for Life Sciences. Developing and incorporating both biologically-linked curricula and pedagogical best practices. Recent efforts included developmental work on an online textbook/homework system (kudu.com) and implementing in-class workbooks and associated clicker questions in a large lecture class setting.

Shotwell, Brian S., Ph.D., UC San Diego, 2015. *High Energy Physics, Physics and other Science Education*. Physics Education Research.

Tsai, Philbert S., Ph.D., UC San Diego, 2004. *Biophysics, Physics and other Science Education*. Research interests include microscopy and bio-photonics as well as modern pedagogical techniques in interdisciplinary sciences. Lab Coordinator for the UC San Diego Hacker Lab for interdisciplinary graduate specialization in Quantitative Biology.

Adjunct Faculty

Basov, Dmitri N., Ph.D., Lebedev Institute, USSR, 1991. Chair, Department of Physics. *Condensed Matter Physics*. Experimental condensed matter. Novel electronic and magnetic materials; meta-materials; advanced methods for optical spectroscopy and nano-imaging.

Schoetz-Collins, Eva-Mara, Ph.D., University of Dresden, 2007. *Biophysics*. Experimental biophysics.

Adjunct Professor

Sharpee, Tatyana O., Ph.D., Michigan State University, 2001. *Biophysics*. Our group works on theoretical principles of how the brain processes information. We are interested in how sensory processing in the brain is shaped by the animal's need to create parsimonious representations of events in the outside world. Our approaches are often derived from methods in statistical physics, mathematics, and information theory.

Waltz, Ronald, Ph.D., University of Chicago, 1970. Theoretical plasma physics; numerical simulation of turbulence in plasma.

DEPARTMENTAL RESEARCH SPECIALTIES AND STAFF

Theoretical

Acoustics. Abarbanel.

Astrophysics. Diamond, Fuller, Green, Keres, Lin, Norman.

Biophysics. Abarbanel, Dudko, Hwa, Koslover, Vergassola.

Condensed Matter Physics. Arovas, Di Ventra, Fogler, Grover, Hirsch, Hwa, McGreevy, Wu, You.

High Energy Physics. Chivukula, Flauger, Green, Grinstein, Intriligator, Jenkins, Kuti, Lin, Manohar, McGreevy, Simmons.

Nonlinear Dynamics and Complex Systems. Abarbanel, Diamond, Groisman, Hwa, Surko.

Plasma and Fusion. Diamond, Dubin.

Statistical & Thermal Physics. Arovas, Diamond, Dubin, Hwa.

Experimental

Astronomy. Arnold, Boggs, Burgasser, Coil, Keating, Konopacky, Murphy, Sandstrom, Tytler, Wright.

Biophysics. Groisman, Jun, Kleinfeld, Schoetz-Collins, Sharpee, Smith.

Condensed Matter Physics. Averitt, Barreiro, Basov, Butov, Frano, Maple, Palacci, Popmintchev, Schuller, Shpyrko, Sinha, Smith.

High Energy Physics. Boggs, Branson, Ni, Sharma, Wuerthwein, Yagil.

Plasma and Fusion. Surko.

Polymer Physics/Science. Hwa.

View additional information about this department at www.gradschoolshopper.com. Check out the "Why Choose Us?" section, find out more about the department's culture and get links to social media networks.

UNIVERSITY OF CALIFORNIA, SANTA BARBARA

DEPARTMENT OF PHYSICS

Santa Barbara, California 93106-9530
http://www.physics.ucsb.edu

General University Information
Chancellor: Henry T. Yang
Dean of Graduate School: Carol Genetti
University website: http://www.ucsb.edu
School Type: Public
Setting: Suburban
Total Faculty: 1,102
Total Graduate Faculty: 1,102
Total number of Students: 23,497
Total number of Graduate Students: 2,772

Department Information
Department Chairman: Prof. Claudio Campagnari, Chair
Department Contact: Jennifer Farrar, Staff Graduate Advisor
   Total full-time faculty: 49
   Total number of full-time equivalent positions: 45
   Full-Time Graduate Students: 138
   Female Full-Time Graduate Students: 20
   First-Year Graduate Students: 27
   Female First-Year Students: 3
   Total Post Doctorates: 31

Department Address
UNIVERSITY OF CALIFORNIA, SANTA BARBARA
PHYSICS DEPARTMENT, 3019 BROIDA HALL
Santa Barbara, CA 93106-9530
Phone: (805) 893-4646
Fax: (805) 893-4646
E-mail: gradapp@physics.ucsb.edu
Website: http://www.physics.ucsb.edu

ADMISSIONS

Admission Contact Information
Address admission inquiries to: University of California, Santa
   Barbara, Physics Department, Broida Hall, Attn: Staff Gradu-
   ate Advisor, Santa Barbara, CA 93106-9530
Phone: (805) 893-4646
E-mail: physics-gradapp@ucsb.edu
Admissions website: http://www.graddiv.ucsb.edu/admissions

Application deadlines
Fall admission:
U.S. students: December 15   *Int'l. students*: December 15

Application fee
U.S. students: $105   *Int'l. students*: $125

Admissions information
For Fall of 2018:
   Number of applicants: 787
   Number admitted: 146
   Number enrolled: 43

Admission requirements
Bachelor's degree requirements: For admission to the graduate
   programs (only Ph.D. offered), a bachelor's degree in physics
   or a related field is required.
Minimum undergraduate GPA: 3.0

GRE requirements
The GRE is required.
   Quantitative score: 152
   Verbal score: 142
   Analytical score: 3.0
   Mean GRE score range (25th–75th percentile): 326-335

Subjective GRE requirements
The Subjective GRE is required.
   Minimum accepted Advanced GRE score: 650
   Mean Advanced GRE score range (25th–75th percentile): 860-
   970
For students interested in astrophysics, the Physics Subject GRE
   is optional.

TOEFL requirements
The TOEFL exam is required for students from non-English-
   speaking countries.
   PBT score: 550
   iBT score: 80
The minimum IELTS score for consideration is an Overall Band
   Score of 7 or higher. TOEFL or IELTS scores can be no more
   than two years old at the time of application.

TUITION

Tuition year 2018–19:
Tuition for in-state residents
   Full-time students: $4,523.10 per quarter
Tuition for out-of-state residents
   Full-time students: $5,034 per quarter
The total cost of a non-resident includes both fees and non-
   resident tuition which is $9,557.10 per quarter.
Credit hours per semester to be considered full-time: 12
Deferred tuition plan: No
Health insurance: Available at the cost of $3,324 per year.
Other academic fees: Student Technology Fee is $2.50 per unit
   capped at 15 Letters & Science course units, a maximum of
   $37.50 per quarter. For more information, please visit: http://
   www.collaborate.ucsb.edu/tech-fee.
Academic term: Quarter
Number of first-year students who received full tuition waivers: 43

Teaching Assistants, Research Assistants, and Fellowships
   Number of first-year
      Teaching Assistants: 36
      Fellowship students: 43
   Average stipend per academic year
      Teaching Assistant: $20,653
      Research Assistant: $25,620
      Fellowship student: $30,000

FINANCIAL AID

Application deadlines
Fall admission:
U.S. students: March 2

Loans

Loans are available for U.S. students.

Loans are not available for international students.

GAPSFAS application required: No

FAFSA application required: Yes

For further information

Address financial aid inquiries to: University of California, Santa Barbara, Office of Financial Aid and Scholarships, 2103 SAASB, Santa Barbara, CA 93106-3180.

Phone: (805) 893-2432

E-mail: faweb@sa.ucsb.edu

Financial aid website: http://www.finaid.ucsb.edu

HOUSING

Availability of on-campus housing

Single students: Yes

Married students: Yes

Childcare Assistance: Yes

For further information

Address housing inquiries to: Community Housing Office, For information on childcare assistance, please visit, http://www.graddiv.ucsb.edu/financial/parenting-employment/child-care-reimbursement-programs.

Phone: (805) 893-4021

E-mail: aptcontracts@housing.ucsb.edu

Housing aid website: http://www.housing.ucsb.edu/index.asp

Table A—Faculty, Enrollments, and Degrees Granted

Research Specialty	2017–18 Faculty	Enrollment Fall 2017 Master's	Enrollment Fall 2017 Doctorate	Number of Degrees Granted 2017–18 (2013–18) Master's	Number of Degrees Granted 2017–18 (2013–18) Terminal Master's	Number of Degrees Granted 2017–18 (2013–18) Doctorate
Astrophysics	10	–	27	–	–(6)	4(30)
Atomic, Molecular, & Optical Physics	3	–	2	–	–	2(2)
Biophysics	9	–	11	3(5)	–	3(12)
Condensed Matter Physics	17	–	64	3(64)	2(5)	17(61)
High Energy Physics	12	–	29	6(24)	–(1)	6(33)
Relativity & Gravitation	5	–	4	–(5)	–	2(6)
Other	1	–	1	–	–(1)	–
Total	49	–	138	12(98)	2(13)	34(145)
Full-time Grad. Stud.	–	–	138	–	–	–
First-year Grad. Stud.	–	–	27	–	–	–

GRADUATE DEGREE REQUIREMENTS

Master's: The Department of Physics does not offer a terminal M.A. program. Admission is to the Ph.D. program only. Master's degrees may be awarded only in the case of students who leave the Ph.D. program or for continuing students advanced to candidacy for the Ph.D. program who request the M.A. degree. The requirements for the M.A. are: (1) completion of 36 quarter-units of work, with a minimum of 32 units of graduate-level courses and the rest approved by the student's academic advisory committee and (2) successful completion of an M.A. examination administered by the student's graduate advisory committee (successful completion of the advancement to candidacy examination fulfills this requirement).

Doctorate: Requirements include, but are not limited to, directed-preparatory coursework, an oral Advancement to Candidacy examination, and the completion and successful defense of a doctoral dissertation. At least six regular aca-

demic quarters in residence, three of which must be completed consecutively prior to advancement to candidacy, are required. The minimum acceptable GPA is 3.0.

Other Degrees: In addition to the standard Physics Ph.D., a student may also choose to receive the Physics Ph.D. with an Astrophysics emphasis. This emphasis is similar except for the course requirements.

Thesis: Thesis may be written in absentia.

SPECIAL EQUIPMENT, FACILITIES, OR PROGRAMS

The UCSB Physics Department has outstanding resources for both experimental and theoretical research. The physics building, Broida Hall, has unusually well-equipped laboratories engaged in a broad range of research in biophysics, condensed matter physics (including spintronics, nanotechnology, and quantum information science), and for the development and construction of innovative detector technologies in astrophysics and particle physics. A new, state-of-the-art laboratory is also now being renovated for ultracold atomic physics experiments. A unique high-power, tunable, far-infrared free-electron laser is the center of a broad research program in terahertz phenomena. The California Nanosystems Institute, the Materials Research Laboratory, and Microsoft's Station Q are other key on-campus facilities with strong interactions with our graduate program and faculty. Off-campus research is performed at CERN (Geneva) and at special low-background laboratories designed for dark matter searches. Astrophysicists use the Keck telescopes in Hawaii, as well as a variety of other ground-based and space-based observing facilities. The Department has a strong association with the Las Cumbres Observatory Global Telescope Network, a worldwide network of telescopes that is now being constructed and is headquartered near the campus. The resources for theoretical physics are outstanding. The Kavli Institute for Theoretical Physics (KITP), supported by the National Science Foundation, is located in a nearby building on campus. The Institute conducts research programs across a broad range of areas of astrophysics, biophysics, condensed matter physics, fundamental particle physics, nuclear physics, string theory, and gravity/relativity, inviting eminent physicists from around the world to participate in these programs for months at a time. As a center for theoretical study, the Institute also has a strong influence on the Department's graduate program.

Table B—Separately Budgeted Research Expenditures by Source of Support

Source of Support	Departmental Research	Physics-related Research Outside Department
Federal government	$19,354,903	$3,617,574
State/local government		
Non-profit organizations		
Business and industry	$986,157	
Other		
Total	$20,341,060	$3,617,574

Table C—Separately Budgeted Research Expenditures by Research Specialty

Research Specialty	No. of Grants	Expenditures ($)
Astrophysics	43	$6,450,360
Biophysics	3	$853,440
Condensed Matter Physics	27	$4,667,880
Particles and Fields	18	$5,796,000
Relativity & Gravitation	3	$1,293,600
Total	94	$19,061,280

FACULTY

Professor

Antonucci, Robert, Ph.D., University of California, Santa Cruz. *Astronomy, Astrophysics*. Observational astrophysics-experimental.

Balents, Leon, Ph.D., Harvard University. *Condensed Matter Physics*. Condensed matter physics-theoretical.

Berenstein, David, Ph.D., University of Texas. Graduate Advisor. *High Energy Physics, Particles and Fields*. High energy physics-theoretical.

Bildsten, Lars, Ph.D., Cornell University. *Astrophysics*. Astrophysics-theoretical.

Blaes, Omer M., Ph.D., International School for Advanced Studies, Trieste, Italy. *Astrophysics*. Astrophysics-theoretical.

Bleszynski Jayich, Ania, Ph.D., Harvard University. *Condensed Matter Physics*. Condensed matter-experimental.

Bouwmeester, Dik, Ph.D., University of Leiden, Netherlands. *Condensed Matter Physics*. Condensed matter-experimental.

Brown, Frank L., Ph.D., Massachusetts Institute of Technology. Professors in the Department of Chemistry and Biochemistry Professor and the Biomolecular Science and Engineering graduate program; Co-Director UCSB Center for Scientific Computing. *Biophysics, Chemical Physics, Statistical & Thermal Physics, Theoretical Physics*. Biophysics-theoretical, chemical physics-theoretical.

Campagnari, Claudio F., Ph.D., Yale University. Vice Chair. *High Energy Physics, Particles and Fields*. High energy physics-experimental.

Carlson, Jean M., Ph.D., Cornell University. *Condensed Matter Physics, Nonlinear Dynamics and Complex Systems*. Condensed matter physics: theoretical, complex systems; materials; geophysics; biophysics; neuroscience ecology networks.

Dogic, Zvonimir, Ph.D., Brandeis U. *Biophysics, Condensed Matter Physics*. Soft matter physics, active matter, strongly-out-of-equilibrium systems, self-assembly.

Eardley, Douglas, Ph.D., University of California, Berkeley. *Astrophysics, Relativity & Gravitation*. Relativistic astrophysics.

Fisher, Matthew P. A., Ph.D., University of Illinois. *Condensed Matter Physics*. Condensed matter-theoretical.

Giddings, Steve, Ph.D., Princeton University. *High Energy Physics, Particles and Fields*. High-energy physics-theoretical.

Gross, David J., Ph.D., University of California, Berkeley. 2004 Physics Nobel Laureate. *High Energy Physics, Particles and Fields*. Particle physics-theoretical.

Gwinn, Elisabeth G., Ph.D., Harvard University. *Condensed Matter Physics*. Condensed matter physics-experimental.

Horowitz, Gary, Ph.D., University of Chicago. *Relativity & Gravitation*. Gravitational physics.

Incandela, Joseph, Ph.D., University of Chicago. *High Energy Physics, Particles and Fields*. High energy physics-experimental.

Lubin, Philip M., Ph.D., University of California, Berkeley. *Astrophysics*. Astrophysics and cosmology-experimental.

Ludwig, Andreas W. W., Ph.D., University of California, Santa Barbara. *Condensed Matter Physics*. Condensed matter physics-theoretical.

Marchetti, Cristina, Ph.D., University of Florida. *Biophysics, Condensed Matter Physics*. Soft Matter Theory and Biological Physics.

Marolf, Donald, Ph.D., University of Texas. Chair. *Relativity & Gravitation*. Gravitational physics.

Martin, Crystal, Ph.D., University of Arizona. *Astronomy, Astrophysics*. Observational astrophysics.

Martinis, John, Ph.D., University of California, Berkeley. *Condensed Matter Physics*. Condensed matter physics-experimental; quantum computing.

Mazin, Ben, Ph.D., California Institute of Technology. *Astrophysics, Condensed Matter Physics, Cosmology & String Theory*. Astrophysics.

Morrison, David, Ph.D., Harvard University. *High Energy Physics, Particles and Fields*. Mathematical physics.

Nayak, Chetan, Ph.D., Princeton University. *Condensed Matter Physics*. Theoretical condensed matter physics.

Nelson, Harry N., Ph.D., Stanford University. *High Energy Physics, Particles and Fields*. Elementary particle physics-experimental.

Oh, Siang-Peng, Ph.D., Princeton University. *Astrophysics*. Astrophysics-theoretical.

Pincus, Philip A., Ph.D., University of California, Berkeley. Joint appointment with the Department of Materials; Biomolecular Science and Engineering. *Biophysics, Condensed Matter Physics*. Theoretical soft condensed matter: biomolecules, self assembly, hydrogen bond networks, highly charged surfaces.

Richman, Jeffrey, Ph.D., California Institute of Technology. *High Energy Physics, Particles and Fields*. High energy physics-experimental.

Shea, Joan-Emma, Ph.D., Massachusetts Institute of Technology. Professor, Department of Chemistry & Biochemistry. *Chemical Physics*. Theoretical biophysical chemistry.

Sherwin, Mark, Ph.D., University of California, Berkeley. *Condensed Matter Physics*. Condensed matter-experimental.

Shraiman, Boris, Ph.D., Harvard University. *Biophysics, Condensed Matter Physics*. Biophysics-theoretical.

Srednicki, Mark, Ph.D., Stanford University. *High Energy Physics, Particles and Fields*. High energy physics-theoretical.

Stuart, David, Ph.D., University of California, Davis. *High Energy Physics, Particles and Fields*. Particle physics; high-energy physics-experimental.

Wiltzius, Pierre, Ph.D., E.T.H. Zurich. Dean of Mathematical, Life and Physical Sciences. *Condensed Matter Physics*. Soft condensed matter and complex fluids.

Xu, Cenke, Ph.D., University of California, Berkeley. *Condensed Matter Physics*. Condensed matter-theoretical.

Zee, Anthony, Ph.D., Harvard University. *High Energy Physics, Particles and Fields*. Particle physics-theoretical.

Associate Professor

Craig, Nathaniel, Ph.D., Stanford University, 2010. *High Energy Physics, Particles and Fields, Theoretical Physics*. Theoretical particle physics, physics beyond the Standard Model, quantum field theory.

Fygenson, Deborah K., Ph.D., Princeton University. Joint appointment with the Department of Biomolecular Science & Engineering. *Biophysics*. Biophysics-experimental.

Hennawi, Joseph, Ph.D., Princeton University. *Astrophysics*. observational and theoretical cosmology, the intergalactic medium, supermassive black holes and active galaxies cosmic reionization events, galaxy formation, data mining, machine learning and statistical methods.

Lipman, Everett, Ph.D., University of California, Berkeley. *Biophysics*. Experimental biological physics; single-molecule spectroscopy.

Van Dam, Wim, Ph.D., University of Amsterdam. *Computer Science, Quantum Foundations*. Computer science.

Assistant Professor

Brandt, Timothy, Ph.D., Princeton University. *Astrophysics*. Astrophysics and Cosmology.

Dong, Xi, Ph.D., Stanford University. *High Energy Physics, Particles and Fields, Quantum Foundations*. Elementary particle physics-theoretical, string theory, quantum information.

Jayich, Andrew, Ph.D., Yale University. *Condensed Matter Physics*. Fundamental symmetries and quantum chemical reactions.

Patterson, David, Ph.D., Harvard University. *Atomic, Molecular, & Optical Physics, Condensed Matter Physics*. Molecular physics-experimental, quantum information-experimental high precision measurement.

Streichan, Sebastian, Ph.D., Universitaet des Saarlandes. *Biophysics*. Biophysics-experimental.

Weld, David, Ph.D., Stanford University. *Atomic, Molecular, & Optical Physics, Condensed Matter Physics*. Atomic, molecular, and optical physics; condensed matter physics-experimental.

Young, Andrea, Ph.D., Columbia University, 2012. *Condensed Matter Physics*. Experimental condensed matter physics, low dimensional systems, scanned probe microscopy.

Emeritus

Ahlers, Guenter, Ph.D., University of California, Berkeley. *Fluids, Rheology, Statistical & Thermal Physics*. Statistical mechanics-experimental.

Allen, S. James, Ph.D., Massachusetts Institute of Technology. *Condensed Matter Physics*. Condensed matter physics-experimental.

Gwinn, Carl, Ph.D., Princeton University. *Astronomy, Astrophysics*. Astrophysics-experimental.

Hansma, Paul K., Ph.D., University of California, Berkeley. *Biophysics, Medical, Health Physics*. Scanning probe microscopy-experimental.

Hartle, James B., Ph.D., California Institute of Technology. *Relativity & Gravitation*. General relativity and quantum cosmology.

Heeger, Alan J., Ph.D., University of California, Berkeley. 2000 Chemistry Nobel Laureate. Joint appointment with the Department of Materials. *Condensed Matter Physics, Polymer Physics/Science*. Condensed matter physics-experimental.

Hone, Daniel W., Ph.D., University of Illinois. *Condensed Matter Physics*. Condensed matter theory.

Langer, James S., Ph.D., University of Birmingham. *Condensed Matter Physics, Nonlinear Dynamics and Complex Systems*. Nonlinear dynamics and materials.

Roig, Francesc, Ph.D., University of Massachusetts. *Physics and other Science Education*. Physics instruction.

Sawyer, Raymond F., Ph.D., Harvard University. *Nuclear Physics*. Nuclear physics.

Scalapino, Douglas J., Ph.D., Stanford University. *Condensed Matter Physics*. Condensed matter physics-theoretical.

Sugar, Robert L., Ph.D., Princeton University. *Particles and Fields*. Lattice gauge theory.

Professor Emeritus

Cannell, David S., Ph.D., Massachusetts Institute of Technology. *Condensed Matter Physics*. Experimental study of fluctuations in non-equilibrium fluids.

Adjunct Professor

Awschalom, David D., Ph.D., Cornell University. *Condensed Matter Physics, Nano Science and Technology*. Condensed matter physics-experimental.

Cleland, Andrew N., Ph.D., University of California, Berkeley. *Condensed Matter Physics, Nano Science and Technology*. Condensed matter physics-experimental.

Howell, Dale Andrew, Ph.D., University of Texas, Austin. *Astronomy, Astrophysics*. Astrophysics.

Affiliate Professor

Safinya, Cyrus R., Ph.D., Massachusetts Institute of Technology. *Biophysics, Materials Science, Metallurgy*. Materials; biophysics.

Witherell, Michael, Ph.D., University of Wisconsin-Madison. *High Energy Physics, Particles and Fields*. High energy physics-experimental.

Affiliate Associate Professor

Murray-Clay, Ruth, Ph.D., University of California, Berkeley. *Astronomy, Astrophysics*. Astrophysics.

Lecturer

Bibilashvili, Tengiz, Ph.D., Tbilisi State University. Joint appointment in the College of Creative Studies. *Theoretical Physics*. Physics instruction.

Freedman, Roger, Ph.D., Stanford University. Lecturer with Security of Employment. *Physics and other Science Education*. Physics instruction.

Geller, Robert, Ph.D., University of California, Santa Barbara. Continuing Lecturer. *Astronomy, Physics and other Science Education*. Physics instruction.

Guruswamy, Sathya, Ph.D., University of Rochester. *Particles and Fields, Physics and other Science Education*. Physics instruction.

DEPARTMENTAL RESEARCH SPECIALTIES AND STAFF

Theoretical

Astrophysics. Cosmology; galaxy formation; accretion disks and magnetic turbulence; structure of evolved stars and stellar systems; superdense nuclear matter. Bildsten, Blaes, Brandt, Eardley, Hennawi, Oh.

Biophysics. Biomolecular physics of polymers, charged surfaces, polyelectrolytes, and lamellar phases. Brown, Carlson, Dogic, Pincus, Safinya, Shea, Shraiman.

Condensed Matter Physics. Superconductivity; magnetism; phase transitions; systems of reduced dimensionality; disordered materials; surface physics; polymers and colloids; complex systems; materials; geophysics; biophysics; neuroscience; ecology networks. Balents, Brown, Carlson, Dogic, Fisher, Ludwig, Nayak, Patterson, Shea, Shraiman, Van Dam, Xu, Young.

High Energy Physics. String theory; particle phenomenology; gauge/gravity duality and applications; algebraic geometry; quantum chaos. Berenstein, Craig, Dong, Giddings, Gross, Morrison, Srednicki, Zee.

Relativity & Gravitation. Black holes; quantum gravity; quantum fields in curved space; gravitational aspects of string theory; applications to gauge/gravity duality. Dong, Eardley, Giddings, Horowitz, Marolf.

Experimental

Astrophysics. Evolution of galaxies; galactic structure and mass distribution; multiwavelength studies of active galaxies and active galactic nuclei; studies of pulsars and the interstellar medium; ground-based and balloon-borne observations of the cosmic microwave background; detector development. Antonucci, Carl Gwinn, Lubin, Martin, Mazin.

Atomic, Molecular, & Optical Physics. Quantum analysis and control of atoms, ions, molecules, and photons; precision measurement and spectroscopy; degenerate quantum gases; quantum simulation of many-body and non-equilibrium states of matter; quantum information. Jayich, Patterson, Weld.

Biophysics. Mechanics and dynamics of biological assemblies; scanning probe microscopy for biophysical applications. Fygenson, Lipman, Streichan.

Condensed Matter Physics. Basic properties of novel materials; studies of complex fluids and nonlinear phenomena; development and study of nanometer-scale electronic, spintronic, superconducting, and optical systems. The advanced technology required to pursue this research is provided by several unique, shared research facilities, including molecular beam epitaxy chambers for atomically-precise sample fabrication, a world-class clean room and nanofabrication laboratory for turning wafers into devices, research and student machine shops, and a free-electron laser facility for exploring terahertz science and technology. In addition, our students have access to the wide range of shared experimental facilities within the Materials Research Laboratory and the new California Nanosystems Institute. Bleszynski Jayich, Bouwmeester, Cannell, Cleland, Dogic, Elisabeth Gwinn, Heeger, Martinis, Patterson, Sherwin, Weld, Young.

Particles and Fields. Experiments are conducted at the CERN Large Hadron Collider (CMS), Fermilab (CDF), Stanford Linear Accelerator Center (BaBar), particle astrophysics, and non-accelerator searches for dark matter (CDMS). Design and construction of particle detectors, especially silicon tracking systems and high-sensitivity, low-background experiments are performed. Campagnari, Incandela, Nelson, Richman, Stuart, Witherell.

Polymer Physics/Science. Fundamental physics of one-dimensional systems; electronic and magnetic properties of conducting polymers and organic compounds. Pincus.

Statistical & Thermal Physics. Studies of critical phenomena in classical fluids and liquid helium; the behavior of enzymes that undergo structural changes. Brown, Pincus, Shea.

View additional information about this department at www.gradschoolshopper.com. Check out the "Why Choose Us?" section, find out more about the department's culture and get links to social media networks.

UNIVERSITY OF CALIFORNIA, SANTA CRUZ

DEPARTMENT OF PHYSICS

Santa Cruz, California 95064
http://physics.ucsc.edu

General University Information
President: Janet Napolitano
Dean of Graduate School: Tyrus Miller
University website: http://www.ucsc.edu
School Type: Public
Setting: Suburban
Total Faculty: 860
Total Graduate Faculty: 860
Total number of Students: 17,577
Total number of Graduate Students: 1,880

Department Information
Department Chairman: Prof. Robert Johnson, Chair
Department Contact: Ben Miller, Graduate Program
  Coordinator
  Total full-time faculty: 24
  Total number of full-time equivalent positions: 24
  Full-Time Graduate Students: 68
  Female Full-Time Graduate Students: 9
  First-Year Graduate Students: 9
  Total Post Doctorates: 11

Department Address
1156 High Street
Santa Cruz, CA 95064
Phone: (831) 459-4121
Fax: (831) 459-5265
E-mail: benmiller@ucsc.edu
Website: http://physics.ucsc.edu

ADMISSIONS

Admission Contact Information
Address admission inquiries to: University of California, Santa
  Cruz, Graduate Application Processing, 1156 High Street,
  Santa Cruz, CA 95064
Phone: (831) 459-5905
E-mail: gradadm@ucsc.edu
Admissions website: http://graddiv.ucsc.edu

Application deadlines
Fall admission:
U.S. students: January 15   *Int'l. students*: January 15

Application fee
U.S. students: $105   *Int'l. students*: $125

Admissions information
For Fall of 2018:
  Number of applicants: 211
  Number admitted: 48
  Number enrolled: 11

Admission requirements
Bachelor's degree requirements: A bachelor's degree in Physics
  is required.
Minimum undergraduate GPA: 3.0

GRE requirements
The GRE is not required.

We no longer require that you submit a GRE score. If you would
like to submit your scores officially or unofficially then we
will use this information while evaluating your application.
There is no minimum GRE score required for admission. You
will not be penalized for failing to submit a GRE score.

Subjective GRE requirements
The Subjective GRE is recommended.
  The GRE Physics exam is recommended but not required. We
  will evaluate your application, without penalty, even if you
  don't submit a GRE Physics score.

TOEFL requirements
The TOEFL exam is required for students from non-English-
  speaking countries.
  PBT score: 550
  iBT score: 83

Other admissions information
Additional requirements: None.

TUITION

Tuition year 2017–18:
Tuition for in-state residents
  Full-time students: $6,088.36 per quarter
  Part-time students: $4,171.36 per quarter $11,122.36
  $6,668.36
Credit hours per semester to be considered full-time: 10
Deferred tuition plan: No
Health insurance: Available at the cost of $4,428 per year.
Academic term: Quarter
Number of first-year students who received full tuition waivers: 9

Teaching Assistants, Research Assistants, and Fellowships
  Number of first-year
    Teaching Assistants: 11
  Average stipend per academic year
    Teaching Assistant: $20,051
    Research Assistant: $24,156
    Fellowship student: $24,000

FINANCIAL AID

Loans
Loans are available for U.S. students.
Loans are not available for international students.
GAPSFAS application required: No
FAFSA application required: No

For further information
Address financial aid inquiries to: Financial Aid and Scholarship
  Office, University of California, Santa Cruz, 1156 High Street,
  205 Hahn Student Services Building, Santa Cruz, CA 95064.
Phone: (831) 459-2963
Financial aid website: http://www2.ucsc.edu/fin-aid

HOUSING

Availability of on-campus housing
Single students: Yes
Married students: Yes

For further information
Address housing inquiries to: Graduate Housing Office, University of California, Santa Cruz, 1156 High Street, Santa Cruz, CA 95064.
Phone: (831) 459-5712
E-mail: gradhsg@ucsc.edu
Housing aid website: http://housing.ucsc.edu

Table A—Faculty, Enrollments, and Degrees Granted

Research Specialty	2018–19 Faculty	Enrollment Fall 2017		Number of Degrees Granted 2017–18 (2013–18)		
		Master's	Doctorate	Master's	Terminal Master's	Doctorate
Physics and other Science Education	24	1	70	–	–	–
Total	24	–	70	–	–	–
Full-time Grad. Stud.	–	1	70	–	–	–
First-year Grad. Stud.	–	1	11	–	–	–

GRADUATE DEGREE REQUIREMENTS

Master's: Coursework plus a master's thesis or qualifying examinations are required.

Doctorate: Oral qualifying examination and a dissertation are required.

Other Degrees: Combined BS/MS Program.

SPECIAL EQUIPMENT, FACILITIES, OR PROGRAMS

Research laboratories are accessible in particle physics, astrophysics, cosmology, condensed matter physics, biophysics, and applied physics. For example the Santa Cruz Institute for Particle Physics gives access to numerous facilities and staff support. The Institute presently occupies 14,521 square feet of space. A large portion of this is used for Experimental High Energy and Astroparticle Physics laboratories, a clean room and a machine shop. The University of California High-Performance AstroComputing Center based at UCSC also provides access to state-of-the-art supercomputers. Condensed matter experimentalists benefit from faculty laboratory facilities on campus. Established on-campus facilities for condensed matter and materials include a low temperature laboratory and a solar energy laboratory as well as the construction of two new labs. One is for molecular beam epitaxy (MBE) and the other for scanning tunneling microscopy (STM).

Physics students and faculty use a number of UCSC research facilities: Santa Cruz Institute for Particle Physics (SCIPP), Institute of Marine Sciences, and the Institute of Tectonics. There is strong interaction with other disciplines, especially astronomy and astrophysics, biology, chemistry, Earth sciences, electrical engineering, and mathematics. Proximity to the Stanford Linear Accelerator Center and the Stanford Synchrotron Radiation Laboratory provides additional local research opportunities. UCSC faculty and graduate students are actively working at the Large Hadron Collider at CERN (ATLAS experiment), on GLAST, and conducting research at Los Alamos National Laboratory, Oak Ridge National Laboratory, NASA Ames, NREL, Lucent, Xerox, IBM, Bell Labs, and other national and international laboratories.

The Center for Adaptive Optics (CfAO) is also headquartered at UCSC. Education is central to the CfAOs mission, with a particular focus on graduate students. In addition to research facilities, the center provides access to an interdisciplinary nationwide network of scientists in astronomy and vision science.

FACULTY

Distinguished University Professor

Dine, Michael, Ph.D., Yale University, 1978. Past Chair, Department of Physics. *Cosmology & String Theory, High Energy Physics, Particles and Fields, Theoretical Physics*. Particle theory.

Haber, Howard, Ph.D., University of Michigan, 1978. Chair, Graduate Recruitment Committee (Physics). *Particles and Fields, Theoretical Physics*. Theory and phenomenology of fundamental particles and their interactions.

Shastry, B. Sriram, Ph.D., Tata Institute of Fundamental Research. *Condensed Matter Physics, Theoretical Physics*. Condensed matter theory.

Professor

Aguirre, Anthony, Ph.D., Harvard University. *Astrophysics, Quantum Foundations, Relativity & Gravitation, Theoretical Physics*. Particle theory. Theoretical cosmology.

Belanger, David P., Ph.D., University of California, Santa Barbara, 1981. *Condensed Matter Physics*. Experimental condensed matter physics; phase transitions.

Carter, Sue, Ph.D., University of Chicago. *Condensed Matter Physics*. Applied Physics,Condensed Matter Physics. Materials, photovoltaics, optoelectronics.

Deutsch, Joshua, Ph.D., University of Cambridge, 1983. *Applied Mathematics, Biophysics, Chemical Physics, Computational Physics, Condensed Matter Physics, Materials Science, Metallurgy, Nonlinear Dynamics and Complex Systems, Polymer Physics/Science, Quantum Foundations, Statistical & Thermal Physics, Theoretical Physics*. Condensed matter theory.

Johnson, Robert P., Ph.D., Stanford University, 1986. Department Chair. *Astrophysics, Heliophysics and Space Weather, High Energy Physics, Medical, Health Physics*. Experimental high-energy physics; astrophysics.

Lederman, David, Ph.D., University of California, Santa Barbara, 1991. Director, Materials Science Initiative. *Applied Physics, Biophysics, Condensed Matter Physics, Low Temperature Physics, Materials Science, Metallurgy, Solid State Physics, Statistical & Thermal Physics, Surface Physics*. Nanotechnology, electronics in reduced dimensions, novel magnetoelectronic materials.

Narayan, Onuttom, Ph.D., Princeton University. *Condensed Matter Physics, Theoretical Physics*. Condensed matter theory.

Nielsen, Jason A., Ph.D., University of Wisconsin-Madison. *High Energy Physics, Particles and Fields*. Experimental high-energy physics.

Profumo, Stefano, Ph.D., International School for Advanced Studies (Trieste). Chair, Graduate Committee (Physics). *Astronomy, Astrophysics, Atmosphere, Space Physics, Cosmic Rays, Computational Physics, Cosmology & String Theory, High Energy Physics, Nuclear Physics, Particles and Fields, Relativity & Gravitation, Theoretical Physics*. Theory of particle physics and particle astrophysics.

Ramirez, Arthur, Ph.D., Yale University, 1984. Former dean of the Jack Baskin School of Engineering. *Condensed Matter Physics*. Condensed matter physics and materials science.

Ritz, Steven, Ph.D., University of Wisconsin-Madison. Director, SCIPP. *Accelerator, Astrophysics, Atmosphere, Space Physics, Cosmic Rays, Cosmology & String Theory, High Energy*

Physics, Particles and Fields. Particle physics and astrophysics.

Schlesinger, Zack, Ph.D., Cornell University. *Computational Physics, Condensed Matter Physics, Solid State Physics*. Condensed matter experimental.

Schumm, Bruce, Ph.D., University of Chicago. *High Energy Physics, Particles and Fields*. Particle experimental.

Smith, David M., Ph.D., University of California, Berkeley. *Astronomy, Astrophysics, Atmosphere, Space Physics, Cosmic Rays, Climate/Atmospheric Science, Geophysics, Heliophysics and Space Weather, Nuclear Physics, Solar Physics*. Particle experiment; high-energy astrophysics.

Associate Professor

Jeltema, Tesla, Ph.D., Massachusetts Institute of Technology. *Astronomy, Astrophysics, Cosmology & String Theory, High Energy Physics*. Large-scale structure; galaxy evolution; indirect detection of dark matter.

Sher, Alexander, Ph.D., University of Pittsburgh. *Biophysics*. Development of experimental techniques for recording and stimulation of activity at hundreds of neurons and use of these techniques to study neural function, structure, and development.

Assistant Professor

Altmannshofer, Wolfgang, Ph.D., University of Technology Munich, 2010. Particle Physics High Energy Physics Theoretical Particle Physics Standard Model Supersymmetry Elementary Particle Physics Flavor Physics. *High Energy Physics, Particles and Fields, Theoretical Physics*.

Gori, Stefania, Ph.D., Technical University Munich, 2010. *High Energy Physics, Particles and Fields, Theoretical Physics*. Particle Physics Beyond the Standard Model, Higgs Physics, Collider Physics, Dark Matter, Flavor Models & CP Violation, Neutrino Physics.

Hance, Michael, Ph.D., University of Pennsylvania, 2011. *High Energy Physics, Particles and Fields*. High-energy experimental physics.

Syzranov, Sergey, Ph.D., Ruhr-Universitat Bochum, 2011. *Atomic, Molecular, & Optical Physics, Condensed Matter Physics, Low Temperature Physics, Nano Science and Technology, Solid State Physics, Statistical & Thermal Physics, Surface Physics, Theoretical Physics*. Transport in disordered materials, localisation-delocalisation transitions Physics of topological and Dirac materials (Weyl semimetals, graphene, topological insulators, etc.) Strongly correlated systems (high-temperature superconductors, transport near quantum criticality, superconductor-insulator transitions, etc.) Quantum information and decoherence (open-system dynamics, quantum-chaotic systems, quantum information scrambling, etc.) Physics of trapped ultracold gases.

Velasco, Jairo, Ph.D., University of California, Riverside, 2012. *Condensed Matter Physics, Low Temperature Physics, Materials Science, Metallurgy, Solid State Physics, Surface Physics*. Electronic Transport of Graphene, Topological Insulators, Superconductivity, Physics, Graphene, Correlated Electron Systems, Integer quantum hall effect, Bilayer graphene, Quantum Many-Body Physics, and Quantum Hall effects.

Emeritus

Primack, Joel, Ph.D., Stanford University. Director, University of California Systemwide High Performance Astro-Computing Center. Cosmology; galaxy; formation and evolution; particle astrophysics; nature of dark matter; gamma-ray astronomy.

Young, A. Peter, Ph.D., University of Oxford. Condensed matter theory.

Research Professor

Bridges, Frank, Ph.D., University of California, San Diego, 1968. *Condensed Matter Physics*. Local structure in the vicinity of specific atoms using X-ray Absorption Fine Structure spectroscopy (XAFS). The study of atomic defects.

Seiden, Abraham, Ph.D., University of California, Santa Cruz. Particle experimental physics.

Adjunct Professor

Fischer, Peter, Ph.D., Technical University of Munich, 1993. Deputy Division Director Senior Staff Scientist Materials Science Division Lawerence Berkeley National Lab. magnetism on the nano- and mesoscale magnetic x-ray microscopy and spectroscopy (ultra-)fast spin dynamics soft x-ray tomography of condensed matter x-ray optics.

Adjunct Associate Professor

Williams, David, Ph.D., Harvard, 1987. *Astronomy, Astrophysics, Atmosphere, Space Physics, Cosmic Rays*. high-energy gamma-rays from astrophysical objects.

DEPARTMENTAL RESEARCH SPECIALTIES AND STAFF

Theoretical

Materials Program. The Condensed Matter Program at UCSC performs research in both statistical physics and highly correlated materials. A newly formed campus Materials Program includes condensed matter faculty and students from physics as well as from Chemistry, Earth Sciences and Electrical Engineering. The materials graduate group will allow a more coordinated research effort, both fundamental and applied, in novel materials such as graphene, complex oxides, and materials suitable for solar cells. It will allow graduate students to gain a broad interdisciplinary training that will lead to positions in industry and academia. The Materials Program is expected to significantly increase research funding and the number of graduate students in the participating departments. Condensed matter experimentalists benefit from faculty laboratory facilities on campus. Established on-campus facilities for condensed matter and materials include low temperature laboratories and solar energy laboratories. Two new laboratories being constructed for molecular beam epitaxy (MBE) and scanning tunneling microscopy (STM). Deutsch, Narayan, Shastry, Syzranov.

Santa Cruz Institute for Particle Physics (SCIPP). Research in high-energy particle physics and astrophysics is done in the organized research unit, the Santa Cruz Institute for Particle Physics (SCIPP), with which two dozen faculty are affiliated. Both they and students play major roles in the ATLAS experiment at the CERN Large Hadron Collider and in planning future accelerators. They are intensely engaged with the Fermi Gamma-ray space Telescope, the Dark Energy Survey (DES), development of the Large Synoptic Survey Telescope (LSST) and the Bayon Oscillation Spectroscopic Survey (BOSS). They collaborate in major cosmic ray experiments (VERITAS and HAWC) and use satellites to study X-rays from space as well as questions about the atmosphere. SCIPP is a world leader in the development of custom readout electronics and silicon micro-strip sensors for state-of-the-art particle detection systems. SCIPP researchers apply these technologies in other scientific fields such as neurophysiology and biomedicine; the principal instrument on the Fermi satellite is another such application. SCIPP theorists work on the phenomenology of the Higgs particle and possible new physics which might be observed at the LHC, on building models to address limitations of the Standard Model, on dark matter and dark energy, on inflationary cosmology, and on simulations of the growth of structure in the universe. Particularly notable (and unusual) is the close connection between theorists and experimentalists on topics like the properties of the Higgs. . . . Aguirre, Dine, Haber, Primack, Profumo.

Experimental

Materials Group. The Condensed Matter Program at UCSC performs research in both statistical physics and highly correlated materials. A newly formed campus Materials Program includes condensed matter faculty and students from physics as well as from Chemistry, Earth Sciences and Electrical Engineering. The materials graduate group will allow a more coordinated research effort, both fundamental and applied, in novel materials such as graphene, complex oxides, and materials suitable for solar cells. It will allow graduate students to gain a broad interdisciplinary training that will lead to positions in industry and academia. The Materials Program is expected to significantly increase research funding and the number of graduate students in the participating departments. Condensed matter experimentalists benefit from faculty laboratory facilities on campus. Established on-campus facilities for condensed matter and materials include low temperature laboratories and solar energy laboratories. Two new laboratories being constructed for molecular beam epitaxy (MBE) and scanning tunneling microscopy (STM). Belanger, Bridges, Lederman, Schlesinger, Smith, Velasco.

NeuroProject. The NeuroProject involves Proton Computed Tomography for cancer therapy. This effort, supported by the NIH and other agencies, is a collaborative endeavor with biologists on the UCSC campus as well as at Stanford University and elsewhere. This program has extensive graduate student involvement. Sher.

Santa Cruz Institute for Particle Physics (SCIPP). Research in high-energy particle physics and astrophysics is done in the organized research unit, the Santa Cruz Institute for Particle Physics (SCIPP), with which two dozen faculty are affiliated. Both they and students play major roles in the ATLAS experiment at the CERN Large Hadron Collider and in planning future accelerators. They are intensely engaged with the Fermi Gamma-ray space Telescope, the Dark Energy Survey (DES), development of the Large Synoptic Survey Telescope (LSST) and the Bayon Oscillation Spectroscopic Survey (BOSS). They collaborate in major cosmic ray experiments (VERITAS and HAWC) and use satellites to study X-rays from space as well as questions about the atmosphere. SCIPP is a world leader in the development of custom readout electronics and silicon micro-strip sensors for state-of-the-art particle detection systems. SCIPP researchers apply these technologies in other scientific fields such as neurophysiology and biomedicine; the principal instrument on the Fermi satellite is another such application. SCIPP theorists work on the phenomenology of the Higgs particle and possible new physics which might be observed at the LHC, on building models to address limitations of the Standard Model, on dark matter and dark energy, on inflationary cosmology, and on simulations of the growth of structure in the universe. Particularly notable (and unusual) is the close connection between theorists and experimentalists on topics like the properties of the Higgs boson, supersymmetry, the nature of dark matter, and the development of cosmic structure. Hance, Jeltema, Johnson, Nielsen, Ritz, Schumm, Seiden.

View additional information about this department at www.gradschoolshopper.com. Check out the "Why Choose Us?" section, find out more about the department's culture and get links to social media networks.

UNIVERSITY OF SOUTHERN CALIFORNIA

DEPARTMENT OF PHYSICS AND ASTRONOMY

Los Angeles, California 90089-0484
http://dornsife.usc.edu/physics/

General University Information
President: C. L. Max Nikias
Dean of Graduate School: Sally (Sarah) Pratt, Vice Provost
University website: http://www.usc.edu/
School Type: Private
Setting: Urban
Total Faculty: 4,190
Total Graduate Faculty: 4,190
Total number of Students: 44,000
Total number of Graduate Students: 25,000

Department Information
Department Chairman: Prof. Stephan Haas, Chair
Department Contact: Betty Byers, Graduate Coordinator
  Total full-time faculty: 40
  Total number of full-time equivalent positions: 30
  Full-Time Graduate Students: 77
  Female Full-Time Graduate Students: 11
  First-Year Graduate Students: 11
  Female First-Year Students: 3
  Total Post Doctorates: 6

Department Address
825 Bloom Walk
ACB 439
Los Angeles, CA 90089-0484
Phone: (213) 740-8685
E-mail: physics@dornsife.usc.edu
Website: http://dornsife.usc.edu/physics/

ADMISSIONS

Admission Contact Information
Address admission inquiries to: Department of Physics and Astronomy,
  University of Southern California, Los Angeles, CA 90089-0484
Phone: (213) 740-8685
E-mail: physicsgradadmis@dornsife.usc.edu
Admissions website: http://www.usc.edu/admission/graduate/

Application deadlines
Fall admission:
U.S. students: December 1   *Int'l. students*: December 1

Application fee
U.S. students: $90   *Int'l. students*: $90

Admissions information
For Fall of 2018:
  Number of applicants: 157
  Number admitted: 29
  Number enrolled: 15

Admission requirements
Bachelor's degree requirements: Bachelor's degree in the Physi-
  cal Sciences is required.
Minimum undergraduate GPA: 3.2

GRE requirements
The GRE is required.
  Quantitative score: 160
  Verbal score: 150

  Analytical score: 3.0
  Mean GRE score range (25th–75th percentile): 315

Subjective GRE requirements
The Subjective GRE is required.
  Minimum accepted Advanced GRE score: 780
  Mean Advanced GRE score range (25th–75th percentile): 900

TOEFL requirements
The TOEFL exam is required for students from non-English-
  speaking countries.
  PBT score: 600
  iBT score: 100

Other admissions information
Additional requirements: The minimum acceptable score suggested for
  admission is verbal—550; quantitative—750; total—1,300.
  The GRE Advanced is required, the minimum acceptable score suggested for admission is 780.
  A minimum TOEFL score of 100 or higher with no less than 20
  on each of the four individual sections of the Internet-based TOEFL
  (iBT) or (600 on paper-based/250 or higher on the computer-based
  TOEFL) is required for Teaching Assistants.
Undergraduate preparation assumed: Reitz and Milford, Foundations of Electromagnetic Theory; Eisberg, Quantum Physics for Atoms, Molecules, Solids, Nuclei, and Particles;
  Saxon, Elementary Quantum Mechanics; Reif, Foundation of
  Statistical and Thermal Physics; Boyce and DiPrima, Elementary Differential Equations and Boundary Value Problems.

TUITION

Tuition year 2018–19:
  Full-time students: $21,600 per semester
  Part-time students: $1,800 per credit
Credit hours per semester to be considered full-time: 6
Deferred tuition plan: Yes
Health insurance: Available at the cost of $1,816 per year.
Other academic fees: New Student Orientation Fee $55.00 (first semes-
  ter); Student Programming Fee $40.00 per semester; Student Ser-
  vices Fee $14.00 per semester; Norman Topping Student Aid Fund
  $8.00 per semester.
Academic term: Semester

Teaching Assistants, Research Assistants, and Fellowships
Number of first-year
  Fellowship students: 10
Average stipend per academic year
  Teaching Assistant: $30,000
  Research Assistant: $30,000
  Fellowship student: $30,000
Fellowship offers can be combinations of RA, TA, and top
off awards. These guarantee a minimum of $30,000 for the
academic first year. Academic year covers the fall and spring
semesters which is 9 months.

FINANCIAL AID

Application deadlines
Fall admission:
U.S. students: December 1   *Int'l. students*: December 1

Loans
Loans are available for U.S. students.
Loans are not available for international students.
GAPSFAS application required: No
FAFSA application required: No

For further information
Address financial aid inquiries to: Department of Physics and Astronomy, University of Southern California, Los Angeles, CA 90089-0484.
Phone: (213) 740-8685
E-mail: physicsgradadmis@dornsife.usc.edu
Financial aid website: http://dornsife.usc.edu/physics/financial-support/

HOUSING

Availability of on-campus housing
Single students: Yes
Married students: Yes
Childcare Assistance: No

For further information
Address housing inquiries to: Housing Services Office, University of Southern California, Los Angeles, CA 90089-1332.
Phone: (800) 872-4632
E-mail: housing@usc.edu
Housing aid website: http://housing.usc.edu/

Table A—Faculty, Enrollments, and Degrees Granted

Research Specialty	2017–18 Faculty	Enrollment Fall 2017 Master's	Enrollment Fall 2017 Doctorate	Number of Degrees Granted 2017–18 (2013–18) Master's	Number of Degrees Granted 2017–18 (2013–18) Terminal Master's	Number of Degrees Granted 2017–18 (2013–18) Doctorate
Astronomy	3	–	1	–	–	–
Astrophysics	2	–	2	–	–	–(2)
Atmosphere, Space Physics, Cosmic Rays	1	–	–	–	–	–
Atomic, Molecular, & Optical Physics	8	–	–	–	–(1)	–(1)
Biophysics	3	–	8	–	–	3(8)
Chemical Physics	3	–	1	–	–	–(1)
Computational Physics	1	–	13	–	–	–(3)
Condensed Matter Physics	13	–	11	–	–(1)	1(9)
Cosmology & String Theory	6	–	2	–	–	–
Electrical Engineering	2	–	5	–	–	1(1)
High Energy Physics	6	–	7	–	–	1(8)
Low Temperature Physics	3	–	–	–	–	–
Materials Science, Metallurgy	1	–	–	–	–	–(1)
Nano Science and Technology	2	–	2	–	–	1(4)
Plasma and Fusion	2	–	–	–	–	–(1)
Quantum Foundations	–	–	13	–	–	–(2)
Statistical & Thermal Physics	1	–	–	–	–	–
Non-specialized	–	–	15	1(3)	–(12)	–
Other	–	–	–	–	–	–
Total	57	–	80	1(3)	–(14)	7(41)
Full-time Grad. Stud.	–	–	80	–	–	–
First-year Grad. Stud.	–	–	15	–	–	–

GRADUATE DEGREE REQUIREMENTS

Master's: The M.S. Physics degree requires satisfactory completion of seven courses of which no more than one course may be directed research. The M.A. Physics degree requires satisfactory completion of eight courses (exclusive of directed research) plus a comprehensive exam. For all master's degrees, a GPA of 3.0 and one-year residency is required; there is no language requirement.

Doctorate: A minimum of 11 courses exclusive of dissertation and directed research courses, taken at this university and elsewhere with a minimum GPA of 3.0; comprehensive exam, qualifying exam, dissertation, and dissertation exam required; one-year residency required; there is no language requirement.

Thesis: Thesis may not be written in absentia.

SPECIAL EQUIPMENT, FACILITIES, OR PROGRAMS

Molecular beam laboratory, low temperature laboratories, laser optics laboratories, biological physics laboratories, electron microscopy, nanofabrication laboratories, nanomaterials synthesis.

Large-scale parallel computing facilities, quantum computing (D-Wave).

Table B—Separately Budgeted Research Expenditures by Source of Support

Source of Support	Departmental Research	Physics-related Research Outside Department
Federal government	$5,300,000	
State/local government		
Non-profit organizations		
Business and industry		
Other		
Total	$5,300,000	

Table C—Separately Budgeted Research Expenditures by Research Specialty

Research Specialty	No. of Grants	Expenditures ($)
Astrophysics	10	$1,280,000
Atomic, Molecular, & Optical Physics	1	$70,000
Biophysics	6	$600,000
Computational Physics	15	$2,500,000
Condensed Matter Physics	6	$495,000
Nano Science and Technology	2	$300,000
Particles and Fields	7	$355,000
Total	47	$5,600,000

FACULTY

Professor
Bars, Itzhak, Ph.D., Yale University, 1971. *Cosmology & String Theory, High Energy Physics, Particles and Fields, Quantum Foundations, Theoretical Physics*. High Energy Physics, Field Theory and String Theory, Cosmology, the cosmological role of the Higgs boson, Two-Time Physics, Completion of space time beyond gravitational singularities such as big bang and black holes.

Bergmann, Gerd, Ph.D., University of Göttingen, 1963. *Condensed Matter Physics*. Experimental condensed matter physics.

Bickers, Nelson E., Ph.D., Cornell University, 1986. *Condensed Matter Physics*. Theoretical condensed matter physics.

Bozler, Hans, Ph.D., Stony Brook University, 1972. Department Chair. *Condensed Matter Physics, Low Temperature Physics.* Experimental low-temperature and condensed matter physics.

Feinberg, Jack, Ph.D., University of California, Berkeley, 1977. *Optics.* Experimental laser physics; nonlinear optics.

Gould, Christopher, Ph.D., Cornell University, 1978. *Condensed Matter Physics, Low Temperature Physics.* Experimental low-temperature and condensed matter physics.

Haas, Stephan, Ph.D., Florida State University, 1995. Chair of the Department of Physics and Astronomy. *Computational Physics, Condensed Matter Physics.* Stephan Haas is engaged in theoretical research on the physics of strongly correlated electrons in solids. His recent interests include microscopic modeling and phenomenology of strongly correlated many-body systems, in particular the analysis of dynamical spectra and phase diagrams. He is using a range of numerical approaches to study low-dimensional antiferromagnets, spin ladders, spin-Peierls systems, and superconductors. Furthermore, his research extends to disordered quantum systems, including random-exchange antiferromagnets, dirty superconductors, and systems with impurity-induced spin and charge textures.

Johnson, Clifford V., Ph.D., University of Southampton, 1992. *Cosmology & String Theory, High Energy Physics, Theoretical Physics.* Theoretical quantum gravity; string theory.

Kalia, Rajiv, Ph.D., Northwestern University, 1976. *Computational Physics, Condensed Matter Physics.* Computational condensed matter physics.

Kresin, Vitaly, Ph.D., University of California, Berkeley, 1992. *Atomic, Molecular, & Optical Physics, Chemical Physics, Condensed Matter Physics, Nano Science and Technology, Solid State Physics.* Nanoscience; atomic and molecular clusters; electronic and structural properties, superconductivity, and superfluidity of nanoparticles.

Lu, Jia Grace, Ph.D., Harvard University, 1997. *Condensed Matter Physics, Nano Science and Technology.* Experimental condensed matter physics; nanoscale materials and electronics.

Nemeschansky, Dennis, Ph.D., Princeton University, 1984. *High Energy Physics, Theoretical Physics.* Theoretical high-energy physics.

Pierpaoli, Elena, Ph.D., SISSA - ISAS, Trieste, Italy, 1998. *Astrophysics, Cosmology & String Theory.* Cosmology and theoretical astrophysics.

Pilch, Krzysztof, Ph.D., University of Wroclaw, 1979. *High Energy Physics, Theoretical Physics.* Theoretical elementary particle physics.

Rhodes, Edward J., Ph.D., University of California, Los Angeles, 1977. *Astronomy.*

Saleur, Hubert, Ph.D., Universite Paris 6, 1987. *High Energy Physics, Theoretical Physics.* Theoretical elementary particle physics.

Shakeshaft, Robin, Ph.D., University of Nebraska-Lincoln, 1972. *Atomic, Molecular, & Optical Physics.* Interaction of two-electron systems with intense light.

Wagner, William G., Ph.D., California Institute of Technology, 1962. *Quantum Foundations, Theoretical Physics.* Theoretical quantum electronics; elementary particle physics.

Warner, Nicholas P., Ph.D., University of Cambridge, 1982. *High Energy Physics, Theoretical Physics.* Theoretical elementary particle physics.

Zanardi, Paolo, Ph.D., Università di Roma, 1995. *Theoretical Physics.* Quantum Information and computation, many-body physics, mathematical physics.

Associate Professor

Di Felice, Rosa, Ph.D., University of Rome Tor Vergata, 1996. National Research Council of Italy, Institute of Nanoscience, Modena, Italy (Senior Researcher, equivalent to Associate Professor). *Biophysics, Chemical Physics, Nano Science and Technology.* Electronic structure of biomaterials; charge transfer through DNA and proteins; molecular dynamics simulations of protein-DNA complexes.

El-Naggar, Moh, Ph.D., California Institute of Technology, 2006. *Biophysics.* Biological nanostructure.

Haselwandter, Christoph A., Ph.D., Imperial College, 2007. *Biophysics, Computational Physics, Condensed Matter Physics, Statistical & Thermal Physics, Theoretical Physics.* The research of the Haselwandter group focuses on the theoretical physics of biological systems.

Assistant Professor

Boedicker, James, Ph.D., University of Chicago, 2010. *Applied Physics, Biophysics.* Biophysics.

Levenson-Falk, Eli, Ph.D., University of California, Berkeley, 2013. *Quantum Foundations.* The use of superconductors in quantum information science (QIS); quantum information applications, including quantum computing and quantum simulation, and studying the basic mechanisms of quantum mechanics.

Professor Emeritus

Chang, Tu-nan, Ph.D., University of California, Riverside, 1972. *Atomic, Molecular, & Optical Physics.* Theoretical atomic physics.

Dappen, Werner, Ph.D., ETH, Zurich, 1978. *Astronomy, Astrophysics, Atomic, Molecular, & Optical Physics, Solar Physics.* Theoretical atomic physics; astronomy.

Hellwarth, Robert W., Ph.D., University of Oxford, 1955. Theoretical and experimental laser physics; solid-state and statistical physics.

Thompson, Richard S., Ph.D., Harvard University, 1965. *Condensed Matter Physics, Low Temperature Physics.* Theoretical superconductivity and low-temperature physics.

Wu, Robert, Ph.D., University of Illinois, 1973. *Chemical Physics.* Chemical physics.

Research Professor

Didkovsky, Leonid, Ph.D., Main Astronomical Observatory of Ukraine, 1990. *Astrophysics, Atmosphere, Space Physics, Cosmic Rays.*

Peters, Geraldine, Ph.D., University of California, Los Angeles, 1974. *Astrophysics.* Stellar astrophysics.

Research Assistant Professor

Campos Venuti, Lorenzo, Ph.D., University of Stuttgart, 2003. Research Professor. *Condensed Matter Physics, Quantum Foundations, Statistical & Thermal Physics, Theoretical Physics, Other.* Quantum computation and simulation and the reverse problem of classical "simulation" of quantum systems. Adiabatic approaches. Equilibration and thermalization. Closed and open dynamics.

Teaching Associate Professor

Peroomian, Vahe, Ph.D., UCLA, 1994. *Geophysics.*

Adjunct Professor

Yu, Nan, Ph.D., University of Arizona, 1988. *Atomic, Molecular, & Optical Physics.* Atomic frequency standards and clocks; Quantum sensors; Microwave photonics; Lasers and Optical metrology; Atomic molecular and optical physics; Molecular spectroscope and spectrometer development.

Adjunct Associate Professor

Bretschger, Orianna, Ph.D., University of Southern California, 2008. *Biophysics.* Research efforts are focused on understanding the metabolism and electron transfer mechanisms within mixed microbial communities with the goal of applying this knowledge to biotechnology development.

Adjunct Assistant Professor

Albash, Tameem, Ph.D., University of Southern California, 2010. *Computational Physics, Condensed Matter Physics, Quantum Foundations.* quantum adiabatic algorithm, quantum annealing, quantum information theory.

Hen, Itay, Ph.D., Tel-Aviv University, 2008. *Computational Physics, Condensed Matter Physics, Quantum Foundations.* Quantum computing and algorithms, Adiabatic quantum computing, Quantum phase transitions, numerical and computational physics, Foundations of Quantum Mechanics.

Senior Lecturer

Burke, Douglas, Ph.D., UC Irvine, 1989.

Joint Appointment

Brun, Todd, Ph.D., California Institute of Technology, 1994. Professor of Electrical Engineering, with joint appointments in Physics and Astronomy, and in Computer Science. *Atomic, Molecular, & Optical Physics, Quantum Foundations, Theoretical Physics, Other.* Quantum information and computation, decoherence and quantum error correction and general quantum theory.

Cherezov, Vadim, Ph.D., Moscow Institute of Physics and Technololgy, 1997. Professor of Chemistry, Bridge Institute.

Cronin, Stephen B., Ph.D., Massachusetts Institute of Technnology, 2002. *Optics, Quantum Foundations.* Photonics and Quantum Electronics.

Dapkus, Daniel, Ph.D., University of Illinois, 1970. I am a Distinguished Professor of Electrical Engineering, Materials Science and Physics. *Condensed Matter Physics, Electrical Engineering, Energy Sources & Environment, Materials Science, Metallurgy, Nano Science and Technology, Optics, Solid State Physics.* My research involves the study of light matter interactions and their exploitation to create novel lasers and efficient light sources and detectors.

Farley, Robert A., Ph.D., University of Rochester, 1975. *Biophysics, Medical, Health Physics.* the structure and mechanism of ion channels, active transport proteins, and neurotransmitter transporters; molecular dynamics simulations of ion channels and alternate access; transport proteins; electrophysiology; molecular characterization of inherited disorders of ion transport; biophysical determinants of cell membrane structure and dynamics.

Gundersen, Martin A., Ph.D., University of Southern California, 1972. Lloyd F. Hunt Professor of Electrical Power Engineering and Professor of Electrical Engineering, Physics and Astronomy, and Chemical Engineering and Materials Science at the University of Southern California. *Applied Physics, Biophysics, Electromagnetism, Energy Sources & Environment, Other.* Researches pulsed power, applications in medicine and energy. ≈350 papers, 25 graduated PhD students. Dr. Gundersen's interests include engineering new pulsed power technology, new therapeutic methods for treatment of cancer based on intense electric field generation, diagnostic methodologies for the study of processes in biological cells and systems, including apoptosis (the generation of programmed cell death). In a very different area, nanosecond pulsed power is being researched for engine technologies for emissions reduction and improved efficiencies in gasoline, hybrid fuels, natural gas, and diesel, through generation of non-equilibrium, transient plasmas based on nanosecond pulsed power switching. A further area is agriculture, including the enhancement of juice extraction quality in wine grapes.

Kunc, Joseph, Ph.D., Warsaw Technical University, 1974. Plasma physics.

Levi, Anthony F. J., Ph.D., University of Cambridge, 1983. Photonic devices.

Lidar, Daniel, Ph.D., Hebrew University of Jerusalem, 1997. *Chemical Physics, Quantum Foundations.* Physical theoretical chemistry.

Madhukar, Anupam, Ph.D., California Institute of Technology, 1971. Experimental and theoretical quantum-well physics.

Nakano, Aiichiro, Ph.D., University of Tokyo, 1989. *Computational Physics, Computer Science, Materials Science, Metallurgy.* Computational physics.

Pinaud, Fabien, Ph.D., University of California, Los Angeles, 2007. Assistant Professor of Biological Sciences and Chemistry. *Biophysics, Chemical Physics, Nano Science and Technology, Neuroscience/Neuro Physics, Optics, Other.* We use light-based microscopy techniques to detect, study and understand the properties of biomolecules at the cellular, subcellular and molecular levels, with spatial resolution of a few nanometers. Our lab focuses on using a variety of single molecule fluorescence microscopy techniques to study how nanoscale cellular compartments modulate the diffusion and the activity of proteins involved in normal and pathological cellular signaling and responses. We are particularly interested in understanding how plasma and nuclear membrane scaffolds, microdomains and cavities influence the diffusion an.

Povinelli, Michelle, Ph.D., Massachusetts Institute of Technology, 2004. *Applied Physics, Biophysics, Electrical Engineering, Electromagnetism, Medical, Health Physics, Nano Science and Technology, Optics.* Nanophotonics, including: optical trapping and self assembly, optofluidics for lab-on-chip, nanostructured photovoltaics, integrated photonics.

Prezhdo, Oleg, Ph.D., University of Texas, Austin, 1997. Professor of Chemistry.

Rohs, Remo, Ph.D., Freie Universitat Berlin, 2003. Computational structural biology; statistical machine learning; high-throughput prediction of DNA shape; genome-wide analysis of sequence and structure; Monte Carlo simulation; electrostatics.

Shera, Christopher A., Ph.D., California Institute of Technology, 1992. *Biophysics, Medical, Health Physics, Neuroscience/Neuro Physics.* Studies how the ear amplifies, analyzes, and creates sound.

Takahashi, Susumu, Ph.D., University of Florida, 2005. Assistant Professor of Chemistry. *Biophysics, Chemical Physics, Condensed Matter Physics, Nano Science and Technology, Quantum Foundations, Solid State Physics.* We are an interdisciplinary experimental research group overlapping in the areas of Condensed Matter Physics, Chemical Physics and Biophysics. Our current research interests include, - Spin dynamics of a single nitrogen-vacancy (NV) center in diamond, - Development of single-molecule magnetic resonance techniques - Nanomagnetism in quantum molecular magnets, - Conformational dynamics in biological systems.

Tanguay, Armand, Ph.D., Yale University, 1977. *Applied Physics, Biophysics, Electrical Engineering, Engineering Physics/Science, Medical, Health Physics, Neuroscience/Neuro Physics, Optics, Solid State Physics.* Biomedical optics, intraocular retinal prostheses, hybrid electronic/photonic systems integration for artificial vision applications.

Vashishta, Priya, Ph.D., Indian Institute of Technology, Kampur, 1967. *Computational Physics, Materials Science, Metallurgy.* Computational physics.

Vilesov, Andrey, Ph.D., St. Petersburg State University, 1985. Professor of Chemistry. *Atomic, Molecular, & Optical Physics, Chemical Physics, Condensed Matter Physics, Low Temperature Physics.* Spectroscopy of molecules and molecular clusters isolated in superfluid He droplets. Quantum vorticity in superfluid nano-droplets. X-ray coherent diffractive imaging in nano-droplets.

DEPARTMENTAL RESEARCH SPECIALTIES AND STAFF

Theoretical

Astrophysics. Theoretical solar physics uses the Sun as a plasma physics laboratory. On the one hand, this work involves state-of-the-art solar modeling and an analysis of helioseismic data. On the other hand, helioseismology is the first accurate experiment that puts strong constraints on the thermodynamic quantities of the plasma of stellar interiors. Cosmology is interested in a variety of scientific issues including dark matter and dark energy models, the early Universe, cosmological parameter determination, data analysis and interpretation. The group offers the opportunity of collaborative research with scientists at the Jet Propulsion Laboratory on current and future space missions. Pierpaoli.

Atomic, Molecular, & Optical Physics. Interactions of strong electromagnetic radiation (lasers) with matter; multiphoton processes; energy development related basic atomic transitions; many-body approach to atomic transitions; multiply excited atomic resonances; atomic optics; collective properties in atomic traps and confined Bose-Einstein condensates; atomic lithography; atoms and ions in dense stellar plasmas; interactions of high-power laser beams with matter leading to nonlinear optical phenomena; propagation of light in dense inhomogeneous plasmas; free-electron lasers; high-power unstable laser oscillators. Chang, Didkovsky, Feinberg, Gundersen, Hellwarth, Kresin, Kunc, Shakeshaft, Takahashi, Tanguay, Wu.

Biophysics. The area is characterized by the use of quantitative methods, modeling, and physics based experimental methods to make discoveries related to biological systems. This subdiscipline anticipates the movement of both basic biological science and medical applications to areas where physics has an ever greater impact. Bretschger, El-Naggar, Farley, Haas, Haselwandter, Kalia, Madhukar.

Computational Physics. Large-scale simulations of quantum spin liquids, atomic spectra, time-dependent atomic processes in intense fields, multi-scale hybrid simulations of materials, algorithm design, high performance programming environments for massively parallel machines, interactive three-dimensional scientific visualization. Brun, Campos Venuti, Haas, Kalia, Nakano, Vashishta.

Condensed Matter Physics. Superconductivity, superfluidity in 3He; nonlinear transport phenomena in reduced dimensionality; electronic structures, strongly correlated metals; nonlinear phenomena in metals; high-Tc superconductors; quantum magnetism. Bergmann, Bickers, Bozler, Brun, Campos Venuti, Dapkus, El-Naggar, Gould, Haas, Kalia, Kresin, Levenson-Falk, Levi, Lidar, Lu, Madhukar, Nakano, Povinelli, Saleur, Vashishta, Wagner, Zanardi.

High Energy Physics. Quantum field theory and unification of fundamental interactions; cosmology; superstring theory; M-theory; gauge theories; supersymmetry and supergravity; conformal field theory; statistical mechanics; mathematical physics; integrable models. Bars, Johnson, Nemeschansky, Pilch, Saleur, Warner.

Quantum Foundations. Use of quantum mechanical resources for computation, communication, and other information-processing tasks. Effect of noise and decoherence; quantum error correction and suppression, dynamical decoupling, and decoherence-free subspaces and subsystems; weak and continuous measurements and quantum trajectories; quantum random walks; quantification of entanglement; quantum information theory; algebraic description of quantum states and observables; quantum information and many-body physics; entanglement and quantum phase transitions; quantum algorithms for classical statistical physics; quantum process tomography; geometric phases; adiabatic, holonomic, and topological quantum computation; quantum computing implementations, using quantum dots, linear optics, and magnetic resonance force microscopy; quantum information. Brun, Campos Venuti, Haas, Levenson-Falk, Lidar, Zanardi.

Experimental

Astrophysics. Study of the overall structure, composition, origins and evolution of the Universe; analysis of cosmic microwave background data and the study of dark matter and galaxy clusters. Study of the structure and dynamics of the solar atmosphere and interior using observations and theory of solar local and global oscillations; use of helioseismology to probe properties of dense plasmas. Didkovsky, Peters, Pierpaoli, Rhodes, Wu.

Atmosphere, Space Physics, Cosmic Rays. Laser spectroscopy, highly excited atomic states, study of planetary atmospheres from space flight experiments; photoabsorption and emission in planetary atmospheres; vacuum ultraviolet radiation interacting with gaseous plasmas. Didkovsky, Wu.

Biophysics. Research at the interface between biological and inorganic systems. Cell-surface interactions. Microbe-inorganic interactions. Bioenergy production in microbial fuel cells. Electronic and enzymatic activity of extracellular nanostructures. Intersection of information and biological sciences. Biochemical sensors and intelligent bio-mimetic coatings for neural prostheses. Optical imaging and spectroscopic studies of intracellular biochemical processes. Boedicker, El-Naggar.

Condensed Matter Physics. Electronic transport and quantum-interference in two-dimensional metals, superconducting films, magnetic surface impurities, anomalous Hall effect and spin-orbit scattering, quantum wires; quasi-one-dimensional conductors; localization; magnetoresistance. Superfluidity in 3He; transport properties of anisotropic conductors and thin alkali metal films; phase transitions in metals of low dimensionality; two-dimensional magnetism of 3He films; development of primary thermometry at ultralow temperatures. Electronic and thermal properties of size-quantized metal nanoclusters; photodissociation, transport, and particle growth in ultra-cold liquid helium clusters. Bergmann, Bozler, Feinberg, Hellwarth, Kresin, Levenson-Falk, Levi, Lu, Povinelli, Wu.

Optics. Laser spectroscopy; nonlinear optical mixing; optical fibers and devices; phase-conjugation, photorefractive effect; Raman-induced Kerr effect spectroscopy; spectroscopy of glassy solids; laser plasma studies; photochemistry of simple molecular systems; interaction in wave guides. Feinberg, Hellwarth.

COLORADO SCHOOL OF MINES

DEPARTMENT OF PHYSICS

Golden, Colorado 80401
http://physics.mines.edu

General University Information
President: Paul C. Johnson
Dean of Graduate School: Wendy Zhou
University website: http://www.mines.edu
School Type: Public
Setting: Suburban
Total Faculty: 307
Total number of Students: 6,117
Total number of Graduate Students: 1,323

Department Information
Department Chairman: Prof. Uwe Greife, Head
Department Contact: LeeAnna Grauel, Program Assistant
  Total full-time faculty: 23
  Total number of full-time equivalent positions: 23
  Full-Time Graduate Students: 58
  Female Full-Time Graduate Students: 10
  First-Year Graduate Students: 13
  Female First-Year Students: 4
  Total Post Doctorates: 3

Department Address
1523 Illinois Street
Suite 382
Golden, CO 80401
Phone: (303) 384-2578
Fax: (303) 273-3919
E-mail: lgrauel@mines.edu
Website: http://physics.mines.edu

ADMISSIONS

Admission Contact Information
Address admission inquiries to: Professor Kyle Leach, Department of Physics, Colorado School of Mines, 1523 Illinois Street, Golden, CO 80401
E-mail: kleach@mines.edu
Admissions website: https://www.mines.edu/graduate-admissions/

Application deadlines
Fall admission:
U.S. students: July 1   *Int'l. students*: March 1

Application fee
U.S. students: $75   *Int'l. students*: $80
Submit Mines online application by January 5th for priority funding consideration. Application Fee is discounted for U.S. citizens and U.S. permanent residents if applications are received prior to: March 1:$60 Fall. Current Mines undergraduate students: $25.

Admissions information
For Fall of 2018:
  Number of applicants: 73
  Number admitted: 33
  Number enrolled: 21

Admission requirements
Bachelor's degree requirements: Bachelor's degree in physics is required.
Minimum undergraduate GPA: 3.0

GRE requirements
The GRE is required.

Subjective GRE requirements
The Subjective GRE is recommended.

TOEFL requirements
The TOEFL exam is required for students from non-English-speaking countries.
PBT score: 550
iBT score: 79
Minimum accepted IELTS Score of 6.5.

Other admissions information
Additional requirements: The Advanced GRE Test is recommended and is required for financial aid.
Undergraduate preparation assumed: One semester of classical mechanics at the level of Marion, two semesters of electromagnetism at the level of Griffiths, one year of modern physics, and one semester each of thermodynamics, optics, mathematical physics, and electronics.

TUITION

Tuition year 2018–19:
Tuition for in-state residents
  Full-time students: $8,325 per semester
  Part-time students: $3,237.5 per semester
Tuition for out-of-state residents
  Full-time students: $18,135 per semester
  Part-time students: $7,052.5 per semester
Part-time tuition is for 1 to 4 credit hours.
Credit hours per semester to be considered full-time: 9
Deferred tuition plan: Yes
Health insurance: Yes, $2,400.00.
Other academic fees: $1,157.00 per academic semester Mandatory Student Fees: Academic Construction Building, Associated Students, Athletic, Health Services, Intermodal Transportation, Recreation Center, Student Services, Technology
Academic term: Semester

Teaching Assistants, Research Assistants, and Fellowships
Number of first-year
  Teaching Assistants: 7
  Research Assistants: 4
  Fellowship students: 2
Average stipend per academic year
  Teaching Assistant: $25,000
  Research Assistant: $26,000
  Fellowship student: $25,000
All listed stipends are for initial appointments. More senior graduate students receive larger stipends. Most appointments also pay full tuition, fees, and health insurance.

FINANCIAL AID

Application deadlines
Fall admission:
U.S. students: June 30

Loans
Loans are available for U.S. students.
Loans are not available for international students.
GAPSFAS application required: No
FAFSA application required: No

For further information
Address financial aid inquiries to: Prof. Kyle Leach, Department of Physics, Colorado School of Mines, 1232 West Campus Road #T1-1, Golden, CO 80401.
E-mail: kleach@mines.edu
Financial aid website: https://www.mines.edu/graduate-admissions/pay-for-graduate-school/

HOUSING

Availability of on-campus housing
Single students: Yes
Married students: Yes

For further information
Address housing inquiries to: Amy Baccei, Assistant Director for Housing Operations, 1795 Elm Street, Golden, CO 80401.
Phone: (800) 446-9488 x-5433
E-mail: Housing@mines.edu
Housing aid website: https://minesresidencelife.com/housing/

Table A—Faculty, Enrollments, and Degrees Granted

Research Specialty	2017–18 Faculty	Enrollment Fall 2017		Number of Degrees Granted 2017–18 (2014–18)		
		Master's	Doctorate	Master's	Terminal Master's	Doctorate
Applied Optics	5	3	2	–	2(3)	–(5)
Condensed Matter						
Physics	8	1	2	–(1)	1(16)	6(17)
Sub-Atomic Physics	4	3	3	–	2(13)	2(8)
Other	6	–	–	–	–(1)	2(5)
Total	23	7	7	–(1)	5(33)	10(35)
Full-time Grad. Stud.	–	13	45	–	–	–
First-year Grad. Stud.	–	7	7	–	–	–

GRADUATE DEGREE REQUIREMENTS

Master's: Twenty semester hours coursework, 16 hours of research credit. Coursework includes 9 hours in a specialty area (see Doctorate for areas). Thesis is required.

Doctorate: Thirty-two semester hours coursework, 40 hours of research credit. Coursework includes 12 hours in a specialty area, which includes courses in Optical Science and Engineering, Condensed Matter Physics, Photovoltaics, Nanotechnology, Materials Physics, Quantum Computing, Nuclear Physics, and Astroparticle Physics in addition to topic areas in the other degree programs at Mines. Ph.D. candidacy is established by grades or oral examination. Thesis is required.

Other Degrees: Faculty in the Department participate in a variety of interdisciplinary fields of research primarily through the Materials Science, as well as the Nuclear Science and Engineering programs. The M.S. and Ph.D. degrees granted are in Materials Science and Nuclear Engineering.

Thesis: Off-campus Work: Due to strong collaboration with national laboratories, students can often be placed off-site to research and write their thesis. Recent examples include: National Renewable Energy Laboratory, Los Alamos National Laboratory and Lawrence Livermore National Laboratory.

SPECIAL EQUIPMENT, FACILITIES, OR PROGRAMS

The Department aims at covering selected areas in both fundamental and applied physics and operates appropriate facilities and equipment.

The experimental condensed matter group has traditionally been taking advantage of the nearby National Renewable Energy Laboratory (NREL) and has access to their facilities through joint appointments. At this time we operate materials processing and lithography facilities which provide extensive capabilities for making and characterizing nanocrystalline, amorphous and organic semiconductors, patterned nanostructures, and self-assembled nanostructures. Capabilities also include growth systems (e.g., PECVD, low pressure CVD, MOCVD, sputtering, and electrochemical deposition), transmission electron microscopy, reactive ion etching, ion implantation, wet etching and cleaning stations, oxide and nitride growth and deposition, dopant diffusion, annealing furnaces, and a clean room with optical lithography.

Materials characterization capabilities include surface profilometers, visible and IR spectrometers, visible and FTIR spectroscopic ellipsometers, a complete X-ray analysis laboratory, an imaging X-ray photoelectron spectroscopy system, scanning Auger electron spectroscopy system, temperature-dependent Seebeck and Hall effect systems, and characterization of photovoltaic devices and integrated circuits. Also included are an electron microprobe, an atomic force microscope, transmission electron microscopy and field-emission scanning electron microscopy, atom probe tomography, near-field microscopy, confocal and conventional Raman spectroscopy, and various chemical techniques for determining elemental compositions. Laboratories are also equipped with electron paramagnetic resonance (EPR) and nuclear magnetic resonance (NMR) as well as instruments for temperature-dependent electroluminescence and photoluminescence (PL), PL excitation spectroscopy, and microwave modulated PL.

The applied optics group maintains a state-of-the-art ultrafast (femtosecond) spectroscopy laboratory, including a 1 terawatt, 1 kHz, Ti:sapphire laser system, a 6 terawatt, 20 Hz, Ti:sapphire laser system used for development of novel X-ray sources, an extended cavity Ti:sapphire oscillator and a diode-pumped Nd:glass laser used for multiphoton imaging, and a fiber oscillator used for ultrafast spectroscopy and nonlinear imaging. Biophotonics laboratories are equipped with multifunctional total internal reflection fluorescence (TIRF) microscopy and complete facilities for E. coli based molecular biology, and GE AKTA FPLC for protein purification.

The subatomic physics group specializes in experiments in low energy nuclear physics, as well as astroparticle physics, and in both cases, works in small to large collaborations with scientists from national laboratories (TRIUMF in Vancouver, Canada, FRIB in East Lansing, Michigan, USA and Pierre Auger Observatory in Malargüe, Argentina) and other universities. Local laboratories are equipped for the development of instrumentation to be used in large, off-site experiments and specialize in detector development, as well as laser-based atmospheric monitoring instrumentation. The group recently built the payload for a NASA Super Pressure Balloon flight launched from New Zealand to monitor cosmic radiation in the Earth's atmosphere.

Computational physics is conducted on a massively parallel 10,496-core 656-node supercomputer with 17.4 TB of memory, capable of a peak speed of 154 Tflop. The group has grown to cover the field of quantum information systems.

Table B—Separately Budgeted Research Expenditures by Source of Support

Source of Support	Departmental Research	Physics-related Research Outside Department
Federal government	$4,523,770	
State/local government	$10,250	
Non-profit organizations		
Business and industry	$186,294	
Other	$556,945	
Total	**$5,277,259**	

Table C—Separately Budgeted Research Expenditures by Research Specialty

Research Specialty	No. of Grants	Expenditures ($)
Condensed Matter Physics	20	$2,390,712
Subatomic Physics	9	$1,394,129
Applied Optics	3	$324,451
Other	5	$1,167,967
Total	**37**	**$5,277,259**

FACULTY

Professor

Carr, Lincoln, Ph.D., University of Washington, 2001. *Atomic, Molecular, & Optical Physics, Computational Physics, Condensed Matter Physics, Nonlinear Dynamics and Complex Systems, Quantum Foundations, Theoretical Physics.* Theoretical condensed matter physics.

Collins, Reuben T., Ph.D., California Institute of Technology, 1984. REMRSEC Associate Director. *Applied Physics, Energy Sources & Environment, Materials Science, Metallurgy, Nano Science and Technology, Solid State Physics, Surface Physics.* Electronic materials and devices.

Durfee, Charles G., Ph.D., University of Maryland, 1994. *Applied Physics, Optics.* Generation, characterization of ultrashort laser pulses; interactions with atoms and plasmas.

Greife, Uwe, Ph.D., University of Bochum, 1994. Department Head. *Applied Physics, Astrophysics, Nuclear Engineering, Nuclear Physics.* Experimental nuclear physics and astrophysics.

Lusk, Mark T., Ph.D., California Institute of Technology, 1992. *Condensed Matter Physics.* Quantum Field Theory and Quantum Optics.

Sarazin, Frederic, Ph.D., University of Caen, 1999. *Astrophysics, Atmosphere, Space Physics, Cosmic Rays, Nuclear Engineering, Nuclear Physics.* Experimental nuclear physics; astroparticle physics.

Squier, Jeff, Ph.D., University of Rochester, 1992. Department Head. MOABC Co-Director. *Applied Physics, Optics.* Ultrafast optics; nonlinear optics; biological imaging; microscopy; micromachining.

Wiencke, Lawrence, Ph.D., Columbia University, 1992. *Astrophysics, Atmosphere, Space Physics, Cosmic Rays, Engineering Physics/Science.* Astroparticles, multi-messengers, and atmospheric science instrumentation.

Associate Professor

Kapit, Eliot, Ph.D., Cornell University, 2012. *Computer Science, Condensed Matter Physics, Quantum Foundations, Theoretical Physics.* Quantum information, quantum many-body physics and dynamics, open quantum systems, superconducting quantum device design, quantum simulation and error correction.

Ohno, Timothy R., Ph.D., University of Maryland, 1989. *Applied Physics, Condensed Matter Physics, Energy Sources & Environment, Materials Science, Metallurgy, Solid State Physics, Surface Physics.* Experimental solid state physics; surface physics; photovoltaics.

Toberer, Eric S., Ph.D., University of California, Santa Barbara, 2006. Staff Scientist, NREL. *Condensed Matter Physics, Crystallography, Energy Sources & Environment, Solid State Physics.* Thermoelectric and photovoltaic materials.

Assistant Professor

Eley, Serena, Ph.D., University of Illinois Urbana-Champaign, 2012. *Applied Physics, Condensed Matter Physics, Low Temperature Physics, Materials Science, Metallurgy.* Applied Superconductivity, Vortex Physics, Disorder in Quantum Materials, Materials Issues affecting Superconducting Quantum Circuits, and Skyrmions.

Gong, Zhexuan, Ph.D., University of Michigan, 2013. NIST Associate, Boulder CO. *Atomic, Molecular, & Optical Physics, Condensed Matter Physics, Theoretical Physics.* Quantum computing, quantum simulation, and quantum many-body physics.

Leach, Kyle G., Ph.D., University of Guelph, 2012. *Nuclear Physics.* Precision tests of the Standard Model, High-Precision Gamma-Ray Spectroscopy; Light-Ion Nuclear Transfer Reactions.

Sarkar, Susanta K., Ph.D., University of Oregon, 2006. *Biophysics, Nano Science and Technology, Optics.* Single-molecule microscopy.

Singh, Meenakshi, Ph.D., University of Pennsylvania, 2012.

Zimmerman, Jeramy D., Ph.D., University of California, Santa Barbara, 2008. Materials Science Program. *Applied Physics, Condensed Matter Physics, Materials Science, Metallurgy.* Electronic materials, III-V growth, atom probe tomography, organic electronics, small molecule electronics devices, organic light emitting diodes, and photovoltaics.

Professor Emeritus

Cecil, F. Edward, Ph.D., Princeton, 1973. *Applied Physics.* Fusion reactor diagnostics.

Furtak, Thomas E., Ph.D., Iowa State University, 1975. *Applied Physics, Condensed Matter Physics, Energy Sources & Environment, Materials Science, Metallurgy, Nano Science and Technology, Optics, Surface Physics.* Soft-matter physics; Raman spectroscopy; optical properties of materials and interfaces.

Kowalski, Frank V., Ph.D., Stanford University, 1978. *Applied Physics, Atomic, Molecular, & Optical Physics, Optics, Physics and other Science Education.* Experimental laser physics; technology-assisted learning.

Taylor, P. Craig, Ph.D., Brown University, 1969. Founding Director, Renewable Energy Materials Research Science and Engineering Center and Co-Editor in Chief, Journal of Renewable and Sustainable Energy. *Applied Physics, Condensed Matter Physics, Engineering Physics/Science, Materials Science, Metallurgy, Nano Science and Technology, Solid State Physics.* Optical, electronic, and structural properties of Amorphous and Nano-Crystalline Materials.

Williamson, Don L., Ph.D., University of Washington, 1971. *Applied Physics, Condensed Matter Physics, Energy Sources & Environment, Materials Science, Metallurgy, Solid State*

Physics. Experimental solid state physics; Mössbauer effect; x-ray scattering.

Wood, David M., Ph.D., Cornell University, 1981. *Computational Physics, Condensed Matter Physics, Materials Science, Metallurgy, Solid State Physics, Theoretical Physics.* Solid state theory.

Research Professor

Coffey, Mark W., Ph.D., Iowa State University, 1991. *Computational Physics, Condensed Matter Physics, Solid State Physics, Theoretical Physics.* Quantum computing algorithms; superconducting and magnetic systems.

Scales, John A., Ph.D., University of Colorado, 1984. *Applied Physics, Atomic, Molecular, & Optical Physics, Condensed Matter Physics, Electromagnetism, Theoretical Physics.* Mesoscopic materials; electromagnetics; wave phenomena.

Shayer, Zeev, Ph.D., Tel-Aviv University. Fission nuclear battery based on gas cooled reactor technology for space and terrestrial applications.

Research Associate Professor

Adams Spencer, Wendy K., Ph.D., University of Colorado Boulder, 2008. Co-Director TEAM-UP (Teacher Education Alliance Mines - UNC Partnership). *Physics and other Science Education.* Physics Education Research; Assessment, problem solving, teacher preparation, curriculum development.

Research Assistant Professor

Flammer, P. David, Ph.D., Colorado School of Mines, 2014. *Electromagnetism, Relativity & Gravitation, Theoretical Physics.* Fundamental Electromagnetic Theory and Computational Electromagnetism.

Kumar, Nitin, Ph.D., Pennsylvania State University, 2012.

Steirer, K. Xerxes, Ph.D., Colorado School of Mines, 2010. Facilities Director for Renewable Energy Materials Research Science and Engineering Center (REMRSEC), and X-ray Facilities Manager for Alliance for the Development of Additive Processing Technologies. Renewable Energy Materials and Devices and Surface Science.

Teaching Professor

Callan, Kristine E., Ph.D., Duke University, 2013. Co-Director of Teacher Preparation. *Applied Physics, Optics, Physics and other Science Education.*

Flournoy, Alex T., Ph.D., University of Colorado, 2003. *Cosmology & String Theory, Particles and Fields, Relativity & Gravitation, Theoretical Physics.* Theoretical particle physics; string theory and cosmology.

Kohl, Patrick, Ph.D., University of Colorado, 2007. *Physics and other Science Education.* Physics education research.

Kuo, Hsia-Po Vincent, Ph.D., University of Minnesota, 2004. *Physics and other Science Education.* Physics education research and development and Qualitative and quantitative educational research methodologies.

Ruskell, Todd G., Ph.D., University of Arizona, 1996. Assistant Department Head. *Applied Physics, Atomic, Molecular, &*

Optical Physics, Optics, Physics and other Science Education, Surface Physics. Computer-assisted instruction.

Stone, Charles A., Ph.D., University of California, Los Angeles, 1990. *Applied Physics, Other.* The Physics of Sound, STEM Education Research, Science Education Outreach' Ethics in Science & Engineering, Applied Plasma Physics & Fusion Engineering, Applications & Principles of Renewable Energy Technologies, and Enhancing the Appreciation & Understanding of Engineering Physics.

DEPARTMENTAL RESEARCH SPECIALTIES AND STAFF

Theoretical

Condensed Matter Physics. Theoretical many body quantum and classical mechanics in application to ultracold quantum gases: quantum phase transitions; atomic and molecular superfluidity and superconductivity; atom lasers; nonlinear waves; fractals, solitons, and vortices; quantum information science; mathematical physics and inverse problems; novel semiconductor materials and structures; semiconductor alloys; phonon properties; surfaces and interfaces; nanostructures; plasmonic phenomena. Carr, Coffey, Collins, Eley, Furtak, Gong, Kapit, Lusk, Scales, Singh, Taylor.

Experimental

Applied Optics. Laser physics and ultrafast optical phenomena, plasmonic electronic systems, nonlinear microscopy and micromachining, ultra-high-intensity lasers, ultrafast X-ray diffraction, frequency shifted feedback lasers, precision measurement, radio-frequency wave propagation in random media, ultrasonics, mesoscopic phenomena, quantum chaos, biophotonics, single-molecule microscopy. Durfee, Sarkar, Scales, Squier.

Condensed Matter Physics. Semiconductor science, electronic devices, optical properties of materials and interfaces, transport phenomena, soft condensed matter and liquid crystals, self-assembled monolayers, bioinorganic composites, quantum nanostructures, surface physics and catalysis, transport phenomena, nonlinear optical properties of surfaces, amorphous materials. Collins, Flammer, Furtak, Ohno, Scales, Taylor, Toberer, Williamson, Zimmerman.

Renewable Energy. Solar photovoltaics, third-generation photoconversion, nanostructures, thermoelectrics, artificial photosynthesis, organic photovoltaics, photoelectrochemistry, optical and electronic properties of crystalline and amorphous semiconductors, thin-film photovoltaic materials, photoexcitation and relaxation in nanostructures. Collins, Furtak, Ohno, Toberer, Williamson, Zimmerman.

Sub-Atomic Physics. Nuclear astrophysics, low-energy nuclear physics, astrophysics with radioactive beams, ultra-high-energy cosmic ray physics, astroparticle physics, low-energy nuclear reactions, fusion diagnostics, nuclear engineering. Greife, Leach, Sarazin, Wiencke.

COLORADO STATE UNIVERSITY

DEPARTMENT OF PHYSICS

Fort Collins, Colorado 80523
http://www.physics.colostate.edu

General University Information
President: Tony Frank
Dean of Graduate School: Jodie Redditi Hanzlik, Vice Provost for Graduate Affairs and Dean of the Graduate School
University website: http://www.colostate.edu
School Type: Public
Setting: Urban
Total Faculty: 1,846
Total Graduate Faculty: No separate graduate faculty
Total number of Students: 33,198
Total number of Graduate Students: 3,962

Department Information
Department Chairman: Prof. Jacob Roberts, Chair
Department Contact: Kristin McLaughlin, Administrative Assistant II
   Total full-time faculty: 22
   Total number of full-time equivalent positions: 22
   Full-Time Graduate Students: 61
   Female Full-Time Graduate Students: 6
   First-Year Graduate Students: 11
   Female First-Year Students: 2
   Total Post Doctorates: 7

Department Address
Campus Delivery 1875
Fort Collins, CO 80523
Phone: (970) 491-6206
Fax: (970) 491-7947
E-mail: physics_grad_admissions@mail.colostate.edu
Website: http://www.physics.colostate.edu

ADMISSIONS

Admission Contact Information
Address admission inquiries to: Graduate Admissions Committee, Department of Physics, 1875 Campus Delivery, Colorado State University, Fort Collins, CO 80523
Phone: (970) 491-6207
E-mail: physics_grad_admissions@Mail.colostate.edu
Admissions website: http://www.physics.colostate.edu/graduate-program/how-do-i-apply/

Application deadlines
Fall admission:
U.S. students: February 1   *Int'l. students*: February 1

Application fee
U.S. students: $60   *Int'l. students*: $70
Initial application (no fee until after admissions notification). Late applications can be considered until all positions are filled.

Admissions information
For Fall of 2018:
   Number of applicants: 133
   Number admitted: 44
   Number enrolled: 15

Admission requirements
Bachelor's degree requirements: Bachelor's degree in Physics or a related field is required.
Minimum undergraduate GPA: 3.0

GRE requirements
The GRE is required.
   Mean GRE score range (25th–75th percentile): 314-324

Subjective GRE requirements
The Subjective GRE is required.
   Mean Advanced GRE score range (25th–75th percentile): 660-830

TOEFL requirements
The TOEFL exam is required for students from non-English-speaking countries.
   PBT score: 600
   iBT score: 100

Other admissions information
Undergraduate preparation assumed: Mechanics: Marion, Classical Dynamics; Electromagnetism: Reitz and Milford, Foundations of Electromagnetic Theory; Thermal Physics: Kittel and Kroemer, Thermal Physics; Quantum Mechanics: Griffith, Introduction to Quantum Mechanics.

TUITION

Tuition year 2018–2019:
Tuition for in-state residents
   Full-time students: $780.85 per credit
   Part-time students: $780.75 per credit
Tuition for out-of-state residents
   Full-time students: $1,604.55 per credit
   Part-time students: $1,604.55 per credit
These figures include the student fees.
Credit hours per semester to be considered full-time: 9
Deferred tuition plan: No
Health insurance: Available.
Academic term: Semester
Number of first-year students who received full tuition waivers: 11

Teaching Assistants, Research Assistants, and Fellowships
   Number of first-year
      Teaching Assistants: 11
   Average stipend per academic year
      Teaching Assistant: $18,225
      Research Assistant: $18,225
The stipends listed are for 9 months. Most students are able to secure 12 month salaries, which equal $24,300.00 annually.

FINANCIAL AID

Application deadlines
Fall admission:
U.S. students: February 15   *Int'l. students*: February 15

Loans

Loans are available for U.S. students.

Loans are not available for international students.

GAPSFAS application required: Yes

FAFSA application required: Yes

For further information

Address financial aid inquiries to: Colorado State University, Student Financial Services, Campus Delivery 1065, Fort Collins, CO 80523.

Phone: (970) 491-6321

E-mail: FinancialAid@colostate.edu

Financial aid website: http://sfs.colostate.edu

HOUSING

Availability of on-campus housing

Single students: Yes

Married students: Yes

Childcare Assistance: No

For further information

Address housing inquiries to: CSU - Housing, Palmer Center, 1005 W. Laurel St., Fort Collins, CO 80523-8032.

Phone: (970) 491-6511

E-mail: housing@colostate.edu

Housing aid website: http://www.housing.colostate.edu/

Table A—Faculty, Enrollments, and Degrees Granted

Research Specialty	2017–2018 Faculty	Enrollment Fall 2017		Number of Degrees Granted 2017–2018 (2013–2018)		
		Master's	Doctorate	Master's	Terminal Master's	Doctorate
Atomic, Molecular, & Optical Physics	5	–	17	1(18)	–(2)	2(14)
Condensed Matter Physics	11	–	31	7(26)	2(4)	2(14)
High Energy and Particle Astrophysics	5	–	13	1(14)	–(5)	2(11)
Total	21	–	61	9(68)	2(11)	6(39)
Full-time Grad. Stud.	–	–	61	–	–	–
First-year Grad. Stud.	–	–	11	–	–	–

GRADUATE DEGREE REQUIREMENTS

Master's: Two options. Thesis Option: A student must complete a minimum of 30 semester credits. These must include 18 credits in physics classroom courses at the 500 level or higher and two credits of PH692 (Seminar). The student must also perform research and prepare a thesis. The final examination for the Plan A M.S. Degree is the thesis defense. Non-Thesis Option: A student must complete a minimum of 32 semester credits. These must include 21 credits in physics classroom courses at the 500 level or higher, three additional credits in the physics classroom courses at the 500 level or higher or in PH693 (Current Topics in Physics Research), and two credits of PH692 (Seminar). The final examination for the Plan B M.S. degree is the seminar/examination.

Doctorate: Seventy-two credits in course work and research in an approved program, 24 credits in core physics courses with another 6 in 500-level physics courses or above; a minimum of 32 credits must be earned at Colorado State University; one-year residency required; no language requirement. Oral examination to determine mastery of specialized field of proposed dissertation required. Dissertation and dissertation defense required.

Thesis: Thesis may be written in absentia.

SPECIAL EQUIPMENT, FACILITIES, OR PROGRAMS

Research programs in our department have received the designation of Programs of Research and Scholarly Excellence (PRSE) from Colorado State University because they have achieved great distinction and set a standard for excellence in research, teaching and service. PRSE programs are High Energy Physics and Particle Astrophysics, Center for Advanced Magnetics, and Center for Extreme Ultraviolet Science and Technology.

Faculty members in particle physics, particle astrophysics and nuclear physics are actively involved in large external collaborations such as DUNE, T2K, NOvA, DRIFT, Auger, EXO-200 and nEXO, for the search for fundamental neutrino properties and dark matter. Faculty in AMO physics are collaborators in the CERN-ATRAP antihydrogen experiment. Condensed matter and AMO faculty have developed joint research program with Argonne National Laboratory, the National Institute of Standards and Technology, Los Alamos National Laboratory, Lawrence Livermore National Laboratory, National Center for Atmospheric Research, the National Renewable Energy Laboratory, and many other American and international universities and research institutions.

The department is well equipped to conduct state-of-the-art research in atomic, molecular and optical physics, condensed matter physics, particle and particle astrophysics, nuclear physics and theoretical physics. In addition, major research facilities for condensed matter and materials research include conventional and superconducting magnets, microwave spectrometer for ferromagnetic-resonance studies, ESR spectrometers, vibrating-sample magnetometer, facilities for semiconductor fabrication and analysis, microelectronic fabrication, thin film deposition systems, and high-speed workstations. Other facilities available on campus include state-of-the-art transmission and scanning electron microscopes, X-ray diffraction instrumentation, a SQUID magnetometer, and nuclear magnetic resonance.

Table B—Separately Budgeted Research Expenditures by Source of Support

Source of Support	Departmental Research	Physics-related Research Outside Department
Federal government	$3,253,542	
State/local government	$11,374	
Non-profit organizations	$14,998	
Business and industry		
Other		
Total	**$3,279,914**	

Table C—Separately Budgeted Research Expenditures by Research Specialty

Research Specialty	No. of Grants	Expenditures ($)
Atomic, Molecular, & Optical Physics	–	$629,830
Condensed Matter Physics	–	$1,373,494
High Energy Physics	–	$1,261,592
Total	–	**$3,264,916**

FACULTY

Professor

Bradley, R. Mark, Ph.D., Stanford University, 1985. Department of Physics Associate Chair. *Condensed Matter Physics, Nonlinear Dynamics and Complex Systems, Statistical & Thermal*

Physics, Theoretical Physics. Condensed-matter theory; pattern formation in non-equilibrium systems.

Fairbank, William M., Ph.D., Stanford University, 1974. *Atomic, Molecular, & Optical Physics, Chemical Physics, High Energy Physics, Nuclear Physics, Optics, Particles and Fields.* Neutrino physics, neutrinoless double beta decay, single atom detection, nucleon decay, laser spectroscopy.

Harton, John L., Ph.D., Massachusetts Institute of Technology, 1988. *Astrophysics, Atmosphere, Space Physics, Cosmic Rays, High Energy Physics, Particles and Fields.* Experimental particle physics, high energy cosmic rays, dark matter searches.

Krueger, David A., Ph.D., University of Washington, 1967. Graduate Admissions Committee. *Atomic, Molecular, & Optical Physics, Climate/Atmospheric Science, Fluids, Rheology, Statistical & Thermal Physics.* Lidar studies of the atmosphere.

Roberts, Jacob L., Ph.D., University of Colorado Boulder, 2001. Department of Physics Chair. Society of Physics Students Faculty Sponsor. *Atomic, Molecular, & Optical Physics, Optics, Plasma and Fusion.* Laser cooling; ultra-cold plasmas.

Rocca, Jorge J., Ph.D., Colorado State University, 1983. *Applied Physics, Atomic, Molecular, & Optical Physics, Nano Science and Technology, Optics, Plasma and Fusion.* Lasers, plasmas, and quantum electronics. Extreme UV and X-ray laser development and applications.

Sites, James R., Ph.D., Cornell University, 1969. Associate Dean for Research, College of Natural Sciences. *Condensed Matter Physics, Energy Sources & Environment, Materials Science, Metallurgy, Solid State Physics.* Semiconductor physics; photovoltaics, solar cells.

Toki, Walter H., Ph.D., Massachusetts Institute of Technology, 1976. Undergraduate Advisor. *High Energy Physics, Particles and Fields.* Experimental particle physics.

Wilson, Robert J., Ph.D., Purdue University, 1983. Graduate Advising Committee. *High Energy Physics, Particles and Fields.* Experimental particle physics.

Wu, Mingzhong, Ph.D., Huazhong University of Science and Technology, 1999. Graduate Admissions Committee. *Applied Physics, Condensed Matter Physics, Materials Science, Metallurgy, Nano Science and Technology.* Magnetics.

Associate Professor

Buchanan, Kristen, Ph.D., University of Alberta, 2004. Women in Physics Chair. *Condensed Matter Physics, Materials Science, Metallurgy, Nano Science and Technology.* Magnetics.

Buchanan, Norm, Ph.D., University of Alberta, 2003. Graduate Admissions Committee. *Astrophysics, High Energy Physics, Particles and Fields.* Experimental particle physics.

Eykholt, Richard E., Ph.D., University of California, Irvine, 1984. *Applied Mathematics, Climate/Atmospheric Science, Condensed Matter Physics, Fluids, Rheology, Nonlinear Dynamics and Complex Systems, Theoretical Physics.* Nonlinear dynamics; chaos; mathematical physics.

Field, Stuart B., Ph.D., University of Chicago, 1986. Graduate Advising Committee Chair. *Condensed Matter Physics, Low Temperature Physics, Nonlinear Dynamics and Complex Systems.* Vortices in superconductors; non-linear dynamics.

Gelfand, Martin P., Ph.D., Cornell University, 1990. Department of Physics Associate Chair. Undergraduate Key Advisor. *Computational Physics, Condensed Matter Physics, Statistical & Thermal Physics, Theoretical Physics.* Condensed matter theory.

Assistant Professor

Chen, Hua, Ph.D., University of Tennessee, Knoxville, 2012. *Computational Physics, Condensed Matter Physics, Solid State Physics, Theoretical Physics.*

de la Venta, Jose, Ph.D., Universidad Complutense, 2009. *Condensed Matter Physics, Materials Science, Metallurgy, Nano Science and Technology.* Nanoscience.

Mooney, Michael, Ph.D., Princeton University, 2014. *Accelerator, Astrophysics, Computational Physics, High Energy Physics, Particles and Fields.*

Ross, Kathryn, Ph.D., McMaster University, 2012. CIFAR Global Scholar. Vice-Chair of the SNS-HFIR User Group Executive Committee. *Chemical Physics, Condensed Matter Physics, Materials Science, Metallurgy, Nano Science and Technology.* Quantum magnetism, Frustrated magnetism, Correlated electron systems; Research specialties include inelastic neutron Scattering, crystal growth, magnetic thermodynamic characterizations.

Yost, Dylan C., Ph.D., University of Colorado, 2011. *Atomic, Molecular, & Optical Physics, Optics.* Precision Laser Spectroscopy of atomic hydrogen and anti-hydrogen, frequency comb metrology, high power cw ultraviolet laser development.

Professor Emeritus

Culver, Roger B., Ph.D., Ohio State University, 1971. *Astronomy, Astrophysics.* Astronomy; experimental astrophysics.

Hochheimer, Hans D., Ph.D., Universitaet Regensberg, 1974. *Condensed Matter Physics, Materials Science, Metallurgy.* High pressure physics with diamond anvil cell and large volume cells, Brillouin scattering spectroscopy of conducting polymers and incommensurate systems at high pressure.

Kern, Sanford, Ph.D., Purdue University, 1963. *Condensed Matter Physics, Crystallography, Solid State Physics.* Neutron scattering study of rare earth and actinide materials.

Lee, Siu Au, Ph.D., Stanford University, 1976. Graduate Admissions Committee Chair. *Atomic, Molecular, & Optical Physics, Optics.* Laser manipulation of atoms; precision tests of fundamental theories, quantum information.

Leisure, Robert G., Ph.D., Washington University, 1967. *Condensed Matter Physics, Solid State Physics.* Ultrasonics.

Lundeen, Stephen R., Ph.D., Harvard University, 1975. *Atomic, Molecular, & Optical Physics.* Atomic, molecular, and optical physics.

Patton, Carl E., Ph.D., California Institute of Technology, 1967. *Condensed Matter Physics.* Magnetism and magnetic materials.

Robinson, Raymond S., Ph.D., Colorado State University, 1979. *Applied Physics, Plasma and Fusion.* Low-density plasmas; space electric propulsion; ion-beam applications, including surface microtexturing.

She, Chiao-Yao, Ph.D., Stanford University, 1964. *Atomic, Molecular, & Optical Physics, Climate/Atmospheric Science, Optics.* Lidar study of the atmosphere.

DEPARTMENTAL RESEARCH SPECIALTIES AND STAFF

Theoretical

Theoretical Condensed Matter Physics. Pattern formation in systems driven far from equilibrium; nanoscale pattern formation induced by ion bombardment of solid surfaces; ion beam assisted deposition of thin films; non-linear dynamical systems; chaos and fractals; mathematical physics; novel materials and phases; statistical and computational physics. Bradley, Chen, Eykholt, Gelfand.

Experimental

Atomic, Molecular, & Optical Physics. The research in the experimental atomic, molecular and optical physics group range from fundamental studies to applications. Research topics include exploration of novel non-evaporative cooling techniques for ultra-cold atom gases; experimental investigations of ultra-cold plasmas; studies of radiation trapping and transport in ultracold gases; laser cooling/slowing of atomic hydrogen; precision UV laser development; UV and VUV laser development for cooling anti-hydrogen (CERN-ATRAP collaboration), development of Si-based quantum computer; laser cooled single atom on demand source for ion deposition; new techniques for quantum information; Na fluorescence Lidar for both day and night measurements of temperature, zonal wind and meridional wind in the upper atmosphere; studies of atmospheric wave and global changes; fast beam high-precision laser-RF spectroscopy of Rydberg atoms; ultra-sensitive single-atom detection for tagging Ba+ ion in the neutrinoless double-beta decay (EXO collaboration); EUV research includes x-ray laser development and applications to nanolithography and ultra-high resolution imaging; high power optical laser development; studies of ultra-intense laser matter interactions. The Center for EUV Science and Technology has been designated a Colorado State University Program of Research and Scholarly Excellence. Fairbank, Krueger, Lee, Lundeen, Roberts, Rocca, Yost.

Condensed Matter Physics. The experimental condensed matter physics group has strong programs in magnetism, photovoltaics, and superconductivity. The Center for Advanced Magnetics is a Program of Research and Scholarly Excellence at Colorado State University. Current research topics include thin-film semiconductors, semiconductor surfaces, solar cells; magnetic thin films, multi-ferroics, nanomagnetism; quantum magnetism, frustrated magnetism, correlated electron system, study of emergence in quantum phases of matter, spin liquids; neutron scattering, crystal growth; vortex physics in magnetic nanodots, spintronics, magnetic recording physics and materials, ferrite materials, magnetodynamics and magnetic relaxation, magnon Brillouin light scattering, chaos and solitons in magnetic films, surface plasmon resonance and exchange bias; low temperature physics, superconducting vortex dynamics, scanning Hall probe microscopy. Kristen Buchanan, de la Venta, Field, Gelfand, Sites, Wu.

High Energy Physics and Particle Astrophysics. Members of the CSU High Energy Physics and Particle Astrophysics research group work on several forefront experiments to explore the fundamental properties of neutrinos: the Deep Underground Neutrino Experiment (DUNE), T2K, NOvA, Fermilab Short-Baseline Neutrino (SBN) program, EXO-200 and nEXO. DUNE, T2K, SBN and NOvA study neutrino flavor oscillations, neutrino interactions and evidence for sterile neutrinos, while EXO searches for neutrinoless double beta decay. Particle astrophysics experiments include dark matter searches (DRIFT) and study of ultra-high energy cosmic rays (Auger). The T2K, DRIFT, EXO and Auger collaborations are analyzing data. Major components for the T2K Near Detector in Japan and the Pierre Auger Observatory in Argentina were constructed at CSU and the group hosts remote operation centers for the NOvA and EXO experiments. R&D on technologies for neutrino detection in liquid argon for DUNE and for a new 1200 square-meter cosmic ray tagger for the world's largest liquid argon detector are underway at CSU. Towards next generation experiments, single atom Ba tagging research and nucleon decay studies for EXO are being conducted at CSU. The HEPPA program has been designated a Colorado State University Program of Research and Scholarly Excellence. Norm Buchanan, Fairbank, Harton, Mooney, Toki, Wilson.

View additional information about this department at www.gradschoolshopper.com. Check out the "Why Choose Us?" section, find out more about the department's culture and get links to social media networks.

UNIVERSITY OF COLORADO, BOULDER

DEPARTMENT OF PHYSICS

Boulder, Colorado 80309
http://www.colorado.edu/physics/

General University Information
President: Bruce Benson
Dean of Graduate School: Ann Schmiesing
University website: http://www.colorado.edu/
School Type: Public
Setting: Urban
Total Faculty: 1,658
Total number of Students: 33,246
Total number of Graduate Students: 5,581

Department Information
Department Chairman: Prof. John Cumalat, Chair
Department Contact: Jeanne Nijhowne, Graduate Program
  Assistant
  Total full-time faculty: 73
  Total number of full-time equivalent positions: 54
  Full-Time Graduate Students: 266
  Female Full-Time Graduate Students: 42
  First-Year Graduate Students: 52
  Female First-Year Students: 8
  Total Post Doctorates: 99

Department Address
2000 Colorado Avenue
Boulder, CO 80309
Phone: (303) 735-0519
Fax: (303) 492-3352
E-mail: jeanne.nijhowne@colorado.edu
Website: http://www.colorado.edu/physics/

ADMISSIONS

Admission Contact Information
Address admission inquiries to: Jeanne Nijhowne, Graduate Pro-
  gram Assistant, 390 UCB, University of Colorado, Depart-
  ment of Physics, Boulder, CO 80309
Phone: (303) 735-0519
E-mail: jeanne.nijhowne@colorado.edu
Admissions website: http://www.colorado.edu/physics/
  admissions/graduate-application-info-and-deadlines

Application deadlines
Fall admission:
U.S. students: December 15   *Int'l. students*: December 15

Application fee
U.S. students: $60   *Int'l. students*: $80

Admissions information
For Fall of 2018:
  Number of applicants: 802
  Number admitted: 201
  Number enrolled: 55

Admission requirements
Bachelor's degree requirements: A 4 year Bachelors degree is
  required.
Minimum undergraduate GPA: 3.0

GRE requirements
The GRE is required.
  Mean GRE score range (25th–75th percentile): 320-335
There are no minimum score requirements.

Subjective GRE requirements
The Subjective GRE is required.
  Mean Advanced GRE score range (25th–75th percentile): 830-
  960
There are no minimum score requirements. Applicants to the
  Geophysics program are not required to submit physics GRE
  scores.

TOEFL requirements
The TOEFL exam is required for students from non-English-
  speaking countries.
  iBT score: 85

Other admissions information
Additional requirements: The average GRE scores for admitted
  (matriculating) students for 2018 from the USA were 163
  (161), 165 (165), and 848 (825) for verbal, quantitative, and
  physics, respectively. The corresponding values for international students were 158 (159), 168 (169), and 937 (945) for
  verbal, quantitative, and physics, respectively. The lowest
  scores of students admitted for 2018 were 140, 146, and 520
  for verbal, quantitative, and physics, respectively.
Undergraduate preparation assumed: An undergraduate program
  for students entering graduate study in physics should typically
  include the following: ; Physics: 3 Semesters Introductory Physics; 1 Semester Advanced Classical Mechanics; 1 Semester
  Quantum Mechanics; 1 Semester Statistical Mechanics; 2 Semesters Advanced Electricity and Magnetism; 2 Semesters Advanced Laboratory Course/Project Work; 1 Semester Advanced
  Course in modern Physics such as Condensed Matter, Geophysics,; Atomic, Nuclear, or Particle Physics; Math: 3 Semesters Calculus; 1 Semester Linear Algebra; 1 Semester Differential Equations; Computing: ; General knowledge.

TUITION

Tuition year 2018–19:
Tuition for in-state residents
  Full-time students: $5,742 per semester
Tuition for out-of-state residents
  Full-time students: $15,192 per semester
Tuition is for 9 credits per semester. Tuition is covered by the
  department for all students in the Ph.D. program.
Credit hours per semester to be considered full-time: 6
Deferred tuition plan: Yes
Health insurance: Available at the cost of $4000 per year.
Other academic fees: $1,762 graduate student fees for AY
  2018–19 assuming 9 credit hours per semester.
Academic term: Semester
Number of first-year students who received full tuition waivers: 52

Teaching Assistants, Research Assistants, and Fellowships
Number of first-year
  Teaching Assistants: 35
  Research Assistants: 17

Average stipend per academic year
Teaching Assistant: $21,451.45
Research Assistant: $23,148
Fellowship student: $23,148
Stipends are for 9 months. During the 3 months of summer, the total RA stipend ranges from $7716 to $15432. RA salaries increase by 3% after admission to candidacy.

FINANCIAL AID

Application deadlines
Fall admission:
U.S. students: December 15　　*Int'l. students*: December 15

Loans
Loans are available for U.S. students.
Loans are not available for international students.
GAPSFAS application required: No
FAFSA application required: No

For further information
Address financial aid inquiries to: University of Colorado Boulder Office of Financial Aid, 556 UCB, Boulder, Colorado 80309-0556.
Phone: (303) 492-5091
E-mail: finaid@colorado.edu
Financial aid website: http://www.colorado.edu/finaid/grad.html

HOUSING

Availability of on-campus housing
Single students: Yes
Married students: Yes
Childcare Assistance: No

For further information
Address housing inquiries to: University of Colorado Housing and Dining Services, 159 UCB, Boulder, CO 80309-0159.
Phone: (303) 492-6384
E-mail: familyhousing@colorado.edu
Housing aid website: http://housing.colorado.edu/residences/graduate-family

Table A—Faculty, Enrollments, and Degrees Granted

Research Specialty	Faculty	Enrollment Fall 2018		Number of Degrees Granted 2017–18 (2013–18)		
		Master's	Doctorate	Master's	Terminal Master's	Doctorate
Total	–	–	265	31(134)	2(5)	27(158)
Full-time Grad. Stud.	–	–	265	–	–	–
First-year Grad. Stud.	–	–	52	–	–	–

GRADUATE DEGREE REQUIREMENTS

Master's: We do not generally admit students intending to just pursue a Masters degree. Graduate students are admitted directly into the Ph.D. program and generally obtain a Masters degree en route to the Ph.D.

Doctorate: Students must complete five of the six required Comps I courses with a "B-" or better. Five additional graduate courses are needed to complete the 30 hours of required coursework of which at least 27 must be physics courses. Students must maintain a 3.0 GPA. All students are required to take the Comps II examination. When students are ready, they take a Comps III examination and are admitted into candidacy. They then write a doctoral thesis that they must defend. Students have six years to complete their doctorate, although this limit may be extended.

Other Degrees: There are programs in geophysics, applied physics, chemical physics, materials science, and interdisciplinary quantitative biology that have different requirements.

SPECIAL EQUIPMENT, FACILITIES, OR PROGRAMS

Two large centers are led by CU physicists: the Soft Material Research Center (SMRC) and the Center on Read-Time Functional Imaging (STROBE). There are many interdisciplinary programs with physics participation: Geophysics, Materials Science and Engineering (MSE), Chemical Physics, and Integrated Quantitative Biology (IQBio). Professional Research Experience Program (PREP)is a special partnership with the National Institute of Standards and Technology (NIST)that places undergraduates, graduate students and post-doctoral researchers in NIST labs to gain research experience alongside NIST scientists and applicable majors include most engineering departments, biochemistry, chemistry and physics.There are many institutes with a physics presence: JILA, Renewable and Sustainable Energy Institute (RASEI), the Cooperative Institute for Research in Environmental Sciences (CIRES), and the Institute for Modeling Plasma Atmospheres and Cosmic Dust (IMPACT); the last one hosts a unique 3 MV dust accelerator. Other facilities in the physics building include multiple shops, an optical metrology lab, and a micro and nanofabrication lab. Experimental and theoretical research opportunities are also available in Boulder at JILA, the National Institute for Standards & Technology (NIST), the Laboratory for Atmospheric and Space Physics (LASP), the High Altitude Observatory (HAO), the National Center for Atmospheric Research (NCAR), the National Solar Observatory (NSO), and the U.S. Geological Survey (USGS), as well as the National Renewable Energy Laboratory (NREL) in nearby Golden. Groups additionally work at facilities around the world including CERN, JPARC, Fermilab, Brookhaven, Spallation Neutron Source, and Advanced Photon Source.

Table B—Separately Budgeted Research Expenditures by Source of Support

Source of Support	Departmental Research	Physics-related Research Outside Department
Federal government	$25,782,085	$31,722,611
State/local government	$4,938	$229,756
Non-profit organizations	$1,680,194	$2,199,805
Business and industry	$627,765	$837,299
Other	$151,546	
Total	**$28,246,528**	**$34,989,471**

Table C—Separately Budgeted Research Expenditures by Research Specialty

Research Specialty	No. of Grants	Expenditures ($)
Atomic, Molecular, & Optical Physics	–	$29,639,286
Biophysics	–	$597,231
Condensed Matter Physics	–	$5,409,293
Geophysics	–	$654,780
Nuclear Physics	–	$701,971
Professional Research Experience Program	–	$13,169,804
Particles and Fields	–	$1,908,556
Physics and other Science Education	–	$2,876,933
Plasma and Fusion	–	$8,278,145
Total	–	**$63,235,999**

FACULTY

Professor

Anderson, Dana Z., Ph.D., University of Arizona, 1981. *Nano Science and Technology, Optics.* Experimental nonlinear optics, atom optics and optical precision measurements.

Baker, Daniel N., Ph.D., University of Iowa, 1974. Joint appointment with Astrophysical & Planetary Sciences and Laboratory for Atmospheric and Space Physics. *Heliophysics and Space Weather, Solar Physics.*

Beale, Paul D., Ph.D., Cornell University, 1982. *Condensed Matter Physics, Theoretical Physics.* Theoretical Physics, thermodynamics and statistical mechanics of condensed matter systems.

Becker, Andreas, Ph.D., Beilefeld University, 1997. JILA fellow. *Atomic, Molecular, & Optical Physics, Theoretical Physics.* Analysis and simulation of ultrafast phenomena in atoms, molecules and clusters, in particular attosecond electron dynamics, coherent control and molecular imaging.

Betterton, Meredith D., Ph.D., Harvard University, 2000. *Biophysics, Chemical Physics.* Theoretical and experimental biophysics; systems biology; bioinformatics; pattern formation.

Cao, Gang, Ph.D., Temple University, 1993. *Condensed Matter Physics, Crystallography, Materials Science, Metallurgy.* Research program combines a methodical search for novel quantum materials in single-crystal form, and a systematic effort to elucidate the underlying physics of these materials.

Cary, John, Ph.D., University of California, Berkeley, 1979. *Computational Physics, Electromagnetism, Physics of Beams, Plasma and Fusion.* Theoretical and computational physics of plasmas, nonlinear dynamics, and electromagnetics.

Clark, Noel A., Ph.D., Massachusetts Institute of Technology, 1970. Director of Soft Materials Research Center. *Chemical Physics, Condensed Matter Physics, Crystallography.* understanding and using the properties of Research on condensed phases, ranging from experiments on the fundamental physics of phase transitions, such as melting, to the development of liquid crystal electro-optic light valves.

Cumalat, John P., Ph.D., University of California, Santa Barbara, 1977. Department chair. *High Energy Physics, Particles and Fields.* Experimental particle physics (CMS experiment).

de Alwis, Senarath P., Ph.D., University of Cambridge, 1969. *High Energy Physics, Particles and Fields, Theoretical Physics.* Theoretical particle physics with interests in string theory, supersymmetry breaking, and cosmology.

DeGrand, Thomas A., Ph.D., Massachusetts Institute of Technology, 1976. *High Energy Physics, Particles and Fields, Theoretical Physics.* Study of the properties of strongly-interacting systems, most of which appear in the context of elementary particle physics, with a combination of analytic and numerical techniques.

Dessau, Daniel, Ph.D., Stanford University, 1992. *Condensed Matter Physics, Materials Science, Metallurgy.* Experimental condensed matter interests center around using femtosecond optics and electron spectroscopic tools for the study of the electronic structure, magnetic structure, and phase transitions of novel materials systems such as high temperature superconductors (HTSCs or cuprates) and colossal magnetoresistive oxides (CMRs or manganites).

Finkelstein, Noah, Ph.D., Princeton University, 1998. Director of the Physics Education Research group Director of the Center for STEM Learning. *Physics and other Science Education.* Physics Education Research that focuses on studying the conditions that support students' interest and ability in physics – developing models of context. These research projects range from the specifics of student learning particular concepts, to the departmental and institutional scales of sustainable educational transformation.

Glenn, Jason, Ph.D., University of Arizona, 1997. Joint appointment with Astrophysical & Planetary Science. *Astrophysics.*

Goldman, Martin, Ph.D., Harvard University, 1965. *Plasma and Fusion, Solar Physics.* Plasma physics research centered around linear and nonlinear wave phenomena excited in plasmas (ionized gases) by electron and radiation beams.

Gurarie, Victor, Ph.D., Princeton University, 1996. Director of Center for Theory of Quantum Matter (CTQM). *Condensed Matter Physics, Theoretical Physics.* Theoretical condensed matter physics.

Hamilton, Andrew J. S., Ph.D., University of Virginia, 1983. Joint appointment with Astrophysical & Planetary Science. *Astrophysics, Relativity & Gravitation.*

Hasenfratz, Anna, Ph.D., Lorand Eotvos University, 1982. *High Energy Physics, Particles and Fields, Theoretical Physics.* Theoretical particle physics (lattice gauge theory).

Holland, Murray, Ph.D., University of Oxford, 1994. JILA fellow. *Atomic, Molecular, & Optical Physics, Theoretical Physics.* Theoretical research on properties of quantum gases with a focus on transport in optical lattices and on strongly interacting superfluids. Also, research on superradiant cavity QED with group-II elements to develop a mHz linewidth "laser".

Horanyi, Mihaly, Ph.D., Lorand Eotvos University, Budapest, 1982. Laboratory for Atmospheric and Space Physics (LASP). *Atmosphere, Space Physics, Cosmic Rays, Plasma and Fusion.* Theoretical and experimental investigations of space and laboratory complex (dusty) plasmas.

Kapteyn, Henry, Ph.D., University of California, Berkeley, 1989. JILA fellow. *Atomic, Molecular, & Optical Physics, Chemical Physics, Optics.* Ultrafast laser technology, ultrafast dynamics in Molecular and materials systems, and development of tabletop coherent x-ray sources.

Kinney, Edward R., Ph.D., Massachusetts Institute of Technology, 1988. *Nuclear Physics.* Experimental nuclear physics research focused on the elucidation of how the basic constituents of the nucleon, quarks, are bound in a gluonic field.

Munsat, Tobin, Ph.D., Princeton University, 2001. Associate Chair for Graduate Studies. *Atmosphere, Space Physics, Cosmic Rays, Plasma and Fusion.* Experimental plasma physics research follows several lines of study, including fluctuation measurements in plasmas, the relationship of turbulent quantities to cross-field plasma transport, and the microphysics of dust impacts which drive the dusty plasma equilibria.

Murnane, Margaret, Ph.D., University of California, Berkeley, 1989. JILA fellow. *Atomic, Molecular, & Optical Physics, Chemical Physics, Optics.* Ultrafast laser and x-ray science, ultrafast femtosecond-to-attosecond dynamics in molecular and materials systems, development of tabletop coherent x-ray sources and their application in science and technology.

Nagle, Jamie, Ph.D., Yale University, 1996. *Nuclear Physics.* Research is in the field of experimental high-energy heavy ion physics. Studying the quark-gluon plasma with the PHENIX experiment at RHIC and working on the upgraded detector sPHENIX.

Parker, Scott, Ph.D., University of California, Berkeley, 1990. *Plasma and Fusion.* Research in the area of the kinetic theory and simulation of plasmas, currently in the area of direct numerical simulation of tokamak plasma turbulence on large massively parallel computers.

Piestun, Rafael, Ph.D., Israel Institute of Technology, 1998. Joint appointment with Electrical, Computer & Energy Engineering. *Electrical Engineering, Optics.*

Pollock, Steven, Ph.D., Stanford University, 1987. *Physics and other Science Education.* Physics Education Research, including issues of teacher preparation, large-scale classes, and upper-division classes.

Price, John C., Ph.D., Stanford University, 1986. *Condensed Matter Physics, Low Temperature Physics, Nano Science and Technology*. Experimental condensed matter physics including low temperature physics, molecular electronics, and molecular crystals.

Radzihovsky, Leo, Ph.D., Harvard University, 1993. *Condensed Matter Physics, Theoretical Physics*. Theoretical physics research that spans a broad spectrum of condensed matter, ranging from liquid crystals, colloids, membranes, rubber and other "soft" matter to degenerate atomic gases, superconductors, and quantum Hall systems. The unifying theme is the collective universal behavior that emerges at long scales and low energies, driven by a combination of strong interactions, fluctuations, and/or local heterogeneity.

Rankin, Patricia, Ph.D., University of London, 1982. *High Energy Physics, Particles and Fields, Other*. Experimental particle physics; investigating leadership and the under representation of women in physics.

Raschke, Markus B., Ph.D., Technical University of Munich, 1999. *Atomic, Molecular, & Optical Physics, Chemical Physics, Condensed Matter Physics, Nano Science and Technology, Optics*. Experimental nonlinear and ultrafast nano-optics. Spatio-temporal optical control, optical antennas, surface plasmon and phonon polaritons, extreme nonlinear optics, strong light matter interaction. Scanning probe near-field optical microscopy and spectroscopy, optical forces, and opto-thermal phenomena. Dynamics and phase behavior of complex oxides, semiconductor nanostructures, and polymer nano-composites.

Ritzwoller, Michael H., Ph.D., University of California, San Diego, 1987. Director of Center for Imaging the Earth's Interior (CIEI). *Geophysics*. Observational seismology concentrated on developing methods to focus seismic models derived from surface wave dispersion information to tectonic scales, particularly in the US and China. Recent emphasis has focused on developing methods for exploiting ambient noise and earthquakes in surface wave tomography and combining this information to produce 3-D models of the crust and uppermost mantle.

Rogers, Charles T., Ph.D., Cornell University, 1987. *Condensed Matter Physics*. Experimental condensed matter physics of thin films and very small systems. Presently, studying the nanoelectromechanical behavior of nanowires and fabricated electromechanical structures, buried interfaces in photovoltaic systems, and surface molecular dipole systems. Nanoscale objects are made with a combination of photolithography, electron-beam lithography, epitaxial thin-film growth.

Smalyukh, Ivan, Ph.D., Kent State University, 2003. *Chemical Physics, Condensed Matter Physics, Materials Science, Metallurgy, Nano Science and Technology*. Experimental soft condensed matter physics styding the organizing principles of mesoscale self-assembly phenomena that lead to creation of artificial materials and structures with emergent physical behavior and properties arising from the patterning of molecular order combined with the organization of nano- and micro-sized particles into precisely controlled configurations.

Zhong, Shijie, Ph.D., University of Michigan, 1994. *Geophysics*. Geophysics research aimed at understanding the physical processes that control the evolution of terrestrial planets (Earth, Moon, Mars, . . .).

Zimmerman, Eric, Ph.D., University of Chicago, 1998. *High Energy Physics*. Experimental particle physics studying the properties of neutrinos with the T2K experiment at JPARC, the NA61/Shine experiment at CERN, and the DUNE experiment at Fermilab/Homestake.

Associate Professor

DeWolfe, Oliver, Ph.D., Massachusetts Institute of Technology, 2000. *High Energy Physics, Particles and Fields, Theoretical Physics*. Theoretical particle physics focusing on string theory and supergravity and their applications to other phenomena via holography, particle physics, cosmology and quantum field theory.

Gopinath, Juliet, Ph.D., Massachusetts Institute of Technology, 2005. Joint appointment with Electrical, Computer & Energy Engineering. *Electrical Engineering, Optics*.

Halverson, Nils, Ph.D., University of California, Berkeley, 2002. Joint appointment with Astrophysical & Planetary Sciences. *Astrophysics*. Observational cosmology.

Hermele, Michael, Ph.D., University of California, Santa Barbara, 2005. *Condensed Matter Physics, Theoretical Physics*. Theoretical condensed matter physics focused on strongly correlated quantum systems. These are systems, occurring both in solid state materials and ultracold atomic gases, where quantum mechanics and interactions among the constituent particles combine to give rise to striking collective behavior. Study is done using modern techniques of quantum field theory and other tools to study the collective behavior of correlated systems.

Kempf, Sascha, Ph.D., Friedrich Schiller University, Jena, 1999. LASP. *Atmosphere, Space Physics, Cosmic Rays, Plasma and Fusion*. Dusty plasmas, specializing in dust detectors and analysis with CCLDAS.

Lewandowski, Heather, Ph.D., University of Colorado, Boulder, 2002. Associate Chair of Engineering Physics. JILA fellow. *Atomic, Molecular, & Optical Physics, Physics and other Science Education*. Experimental study of collisions and reactions of simple cold molecules to understand the quantum mechanical processes involved in making and breaking a chemical bond. We aim to control the reacting molecules external and internal degrees of freedom in the quantum regime. To accomplish this control, we slow down a supersonically cooled molecular beam using time-varying inhomogeneous electric fields (Stark deceleration). The cold (~ 100 mK) molecules are then loaded into an electrostatic trap for study.

Marino, Alysia, Ph.D., University of California, Berkeley, 2004. *High Energy Physics, Particles and Fields*. Experimental particle physics studying the properties of neutrinos with the T2K experiment at JPARC, the NA61/Shine experiment at CERN, and the DUNE experiment at Fermilab/Homestake.

Regal, Cindy, Ph.D., University of Colorado, Boulder, 2006. JILA fellow. *Atomic, Molecular, & Optical Physics*. Engineering and exploring isolated quantum systems for quantum information and quantum optics with a focus on manipulating single and few neutral atoms and the quest to control single phonons in mesoscopic mechanical oscillators. This experimental work relies on low-loss optical interfaces and laser cooling and trapping techniques.

Reznik, Dmitry, Ph.D., University of Illinois at Urbana-Champaign, 1993. *Condensed Matter Physics, Materials Science, Metallurgy*. Experimental condensed matter and materials physics focusing on using neutron, x-ray, and Raman scattering to investigate the physics of correlated electrons and electron-phonon coupling in perovskite oxides (including high Tc supercondcutors, manganites, etc.) and other exotic materials.

Romatschke, Paul, Ph.D., Technical University of Vienna, 2003. *Nuclear Physics, Theoretical Physics*. Theoretical study of cold dense matter, relativistic viscous hydrodynamics, non-Abelian plasma instabilities, nonlinear gravity, and other topics.

Schibli, Thomas, Ph.D., University of Karlsruhe, 2001. JILA adjunct fellow. *Atomic, Molecular, & Optical Physics, Con-*

densed *Matter Physics, Materials Science, Metallurgy, Nano Science and Technology, Optics.* Experimental research to advance science and technology in the fields of optics and photonics through advanced functional materials, novel laser systems, and measurement techniques.

Shaheen, Sean E., Ph.D., University of Arizona, 1999. Joint appointment with Electrical, Computer & Energy Engineering. *Biophysics, Electrical Engineering, Energy Sources & Environment, Materials Science, Metallurgy.*

Stenson, Kevin, Ph.D., University of Wisconsin, Madison, 1998. *High Energy Physics, Particles and Fields.* Experimental particle physics with the CMS experiment at the CERN LHC searching for physics beyond the standard model (for example supersymmetry) and working on upgrades to the detector.

Uzdensky, Dmitri A., Ph.D., Princeton University, 1998. Director of Center for Integrated Plasma Studies (CIPS). *Astrophysics, Atmosphere, Space Physics, Cosmic Rays, Plasma and Fusion, Solar Physics.* Theoretical plasma physics, including both basic plasma physics and its applications to understand various natural phenomena, usually those involving magnetized plasmas far beyond Earth. Main interests lie in the realm of plasma astrophysics, including high-energy astrophysics, but I am also strongly interested in various topics in space physics and solar physics, as well as certain areas of magnetic fusion.

Assistant Professor

Calkins, Michael A., Ph.D., University of California, Los Angeles, 2010. *Geophysics.* Geophysical and astrophysical fluid dynamics studying the generation of planetary magnetic fields via the inductive action of turbulent motions, and the physics of fluid motion in planetary atmospheres.

Hough, Loren E., Ph.D., University of Colorado, Boulder, 2007. *Biophysics.* Currently studying intrinsically disordered proteins using solution NMR. Proteins containing disordered domains perform many important cellular functions. The aggregations of this family of proteins is implicated in neuodegenerative diseases such as Alzheimer's and Parkinson's diseases. In-cell nuclear magnetic resonance techniques are used to study the disordered proteins that form the selective barrier of the nuclear pore complex. This is being extended to study similar proteins, especially those involved in transcriptional regulation.

Lee, Minhyea, Ph.D., University of Chicago, 2004. *Condensed Matter Physics.* Experimental condensed matter and materials physics research focusing on understanding collective behavior in condensed matter systems via electrical and thermal transport properties, under the control parameters of high pressure and magnetic field. The systems of interest include anomalous Hall effect materials, itinerant magnetic systems, novel superconductivity in the vicinity of other ground states, and high thermoelectric materials. We also use nanofabrication and microwave measurements to develop novel probes for correlated electron systems based on shot noise.

Litos, Michael, Ph.D., Boston University, 2010. *Physics of Beams, Plasma and Fusion.* Experimental plasma physics, beam-driven and laser-driven plasma wakefield acceleration and interactions.

Nandkishore, Rahul, Ph.D., Massachusetts Institute of Technology, 2012. *Condensed Matter Physics, Theoretical Physics.* Theoretical condensed matter physics focusing on the search for new emergent phenomena in quantum many body systems with strong interactions and/or strong randomness in systems both in and out of equilibrium. Particular topics of interest include: non-equilibrium quantum statistical mechanics, many body localization and thermalization, field theory of correlated systems, Dirac fermions, unconventional superconductors, and the interplay of disorder and interactions.

Neil, Ethan T., Ph.D., Yale University, 2011. *High Energy Physics, Particles and Fields, Theoretical Physics.* Theoretical particle physics: Lattice gauge theory, physics beyond the standard model, collider and dark matter phenomenology, strongly-coupled quantum field theory.

Perepelitsa, Dennis, Ph.D., Columbia University, 2014. *Nuclear Physics.* Experimental nuclear physics. Study of phenomena of heavy ion collisions using the ATLAS detector at CERN.

Smith, Graeme, Ph.D., California Institute of Techonology, 2006. JILA associate fellow. *Atomic, Molecular, & Optical Physics, Quantum Foundations, Theoretical Physics.* Theory of quantum information and quantum computing. Identification of the fundamental limits that physics places on communication, information processing, and sensing and understand the implications of these limits both in terms of practical technologies and fundamental physics. This involves finding new ways to think about information and computation, and new ideas for analyzing them. Past work includes error correction, quantum channel capacities, additivity questions, characterization of quantum annealers, and mathematical properties of entropy.

Ulmer, Keith, Ph.D., University of Colorado, Boulder, 2007. *High Energy Physics, Particles and Fields.* Experimental particle physics with the CMS experiment at the CERN LHC searching for physics beyond the standard model (for example supersymmetry) and working on upgrades to the detector.

Wilcox, Bethany, Ph.D., University of Colorado, 2015. *Physics and other Science Education.*

Yin, Xiaobo, Ph.D., Stanford University, 2008. Joint appointment with Mechanical Engineering. *Materials Science, Metallurgy, Nano Science and Technology.* Nanoscale materials and engineering.

Research Professor

Bohn, John, Ph.D., University of Chicago, 1995. JILA fellow. *Atomic, Molecular, & Optical Physics, Theoretical Physics.* Theory of cold collisions and few-body physics.

Research Associate Professor

Jaron-Becker, Agnieszka, Ph.D., Warsaw University Institute of Theoretical Physics, 2000. JILA associate fellow. *Atomic, Molecular, & Optical Physics, Theoretical Physics.* Theoretical atomic physics.

Research Assistant Professor

D'Incao, Jose P., Ph.D., University of Sao Paulo, Institute of Physics Sao Carlos - Brazil, 2002. *Atomic, Molecular, & Optical Physics, Theoretical Physics.* Theoretical atomic physics.

Adjunct Professor

Nesbitt, David, Ph.D., University of Colorado, Boulder, 1981. JILA fellow. *Biophysics, Chemical Physics.* Chemical physics, including high resolution laser spectroscopy, chemical reaction dynamics, quantum nanostructures and single-molecule biophysics.

Perkins, Thomas T., Ph.D., Stanford University, 1997. JILA fellow. *Biophysics, Chemical Physics, Optics.* Single molecule measurements of biological systems using applying high precision measurements based on optical traps and atomic force microscopes.

Professor Adjoint

Cornell, Eric, Ph.D., Massachusetts Institute of Technology, 1990. JILA fellow. *Atomic, Molecular, & Optical Physics.* Experimental precision measurements and Bose-Einstein condensation and related topics in ultracold atoms. Current projects include an experiment to put an improved limit on the electron electric dipole moment and developing technology for extracting electricity from waste heat.

Diddams, Scott, Ph.D., University of New Mexico, 1996. NIST physicist. *Atomic, Molecular, & Optical Physics, Optics*. Experimental laser physics; femtosecond lasers and ultrafast phenomena; nonlinear optics; precision spectroscopy; optical frequency combs; metrology.

Hall, John, Ph.D., Carnegie Institute of Technology, 1961. JILA fellow. *Atomic, Molecular, & Optical Physics, Optics*. Development of laser stabilization and measurement techniques that lead toward the creation of phase-stable optical frequency sources and their application to precision tests of fundamental principles.

Lehnert, Konrad, Ph.D., University of California, Santa Barbara, 1999. JILA fellow. *Atomic, Molecular, & Optical Physics, Nano Science and Technology*. Studying quantum coherence in macroscopic mechanical oscillators, developing quantum-coherent networks of microwave signals for control and measurement, and implementing quantum-limited measurements in astrophysics and condensed matter experiments.

Levine, Judah, Ph.D., New York University, 1966. JILA fellow NIST fellow. *Geophysics, Relativity & Gravitation*. Developing statistical methods for estimating the performance of frequency standards and for distributing time and frequency information.

Rey, Ana Maria, Ph.D., University of Maryland, 2004. JILA fellow. *Atomic, Molecular, & Optical Physics, Theoretical Physics*. Theory of optical lattices, quantum degenerate Fermi gases, and ultracold Boson-Fermion mixtures.

Wineland, David, Ph.D., Harvard University, 1970. NIST physicist. *Atomic, Molecular, & Optical Physics*. Laser-cooled trapped ions in the areas of high-resolution spectroscopy, basic plasma physics, and quantum information.

Ye, Jun, Ph.D., University of Colorado, Boulder, 1997. JILA fellow. *Atomic, Molecular, & Optical Physics, Optics*. Atomic and optical physics and precision measurement.

Associate Professor Adjoint

Thompson, James K., Ph.D., Massachusetts Institute of Technology, 2003. JILA fellow. *Atomic, Molecular, & Optical Physics, Low Temperature Physics*. Ultracold atoms, quantum optics, and precision measurements.

Assistant Professor Adjoint

Kaufman, Adam, Ph.D., University of Colorado, Boulder, 2015. *Atomic, Molecular, & Optical Physics*.

Professor Attendant Rank

Glaser, Matthew A., Ph.D., University of Colorado, Boulder, 1991. *Biophysics, Computational Physics, Condensed Matter Physics*. Computer simulation techniques for problems in condensed-matter physics and statistical physics.

Maclennan, Joseph, Ph.D., University of Colorado, Boulder, 1988. *Condensed Matter Physics*. Ferroelectric liquid crystals; freely suspended liquid crystal films; instrumentation.

Wagner, Stephen, Ph.D., Johns Hopkins University, 1983. *High Energy Physics, Particles and Fields*. Experimental particle physics (CMS experiment).

Associate Professor Attendant Rank

Perkins, Katherine, Ph.D., Harvard University, 2000. Director of PhET Interactive Simulations Project and CU's Science Education Initiative. *Physics and other Science Education*. Physics education research with a focus on the use of interactive simulations for teaching and learning physics, students' beliefs about physics (and chemistry), and sustainable course reform.

Instructor

Bolton, Daniel R., Ph.D., University of Washington, 2011. *Nuclear Physics, Theoretical Physics*. Nuclear theory and lattice QCD.

Dubson, Michael, Ph.D., Cornell University, 1984. Associate Chair of Arts and Sciences Undergraduate Physics. *Physics and other Science Education*. Physics education research.

Hodby, Eleanor, Ph.D., University of Oxford, 2002. *Physics and other Science Education*. AMO, PER.

West, Colin, Ph.D., C.N. Yang Institute for Theoretical Physics, Stony Brook University, 2016. *Physics and other Science Education*. quantum information theory; physics education research.

Wilkerson, Donald, M.A., University of Colorado, 1990. *Other*. writing courses for science and engineering students.

Lecturer

Cundiff, Steven, Ph.D., University of Michigan, 1992. Professor of physics at University of Michigan. *Optics*. Telecommunications; fiber optics; ultrafast optical studies of semiconductors.

Knill, Emanuel, Ph.D., University of Colorado, Boulder, 1991. NIST physicist. *Applied Mathematics, Theoretical Physics*. Quantum information science.

Leibrandt, David, Ph.D., Massachusetts Institute of Technology, 2009. NIST physicist. *Atomic, Molecular, & Optical Physics*.

Papp, Scott, Ph.D., University of Colorado, Boulder, 2007. NIST physicist. *Applied Physics, Atomic, Molecular, & Optical Physics*.

Simmonds, Raymond W., Ph.D., University of California, Berkeley, 2002. NIST physicist. *Atomic, Molecular, & Optical Physics, Optics*.

Ullom, Joel, Ph.D., Harvard University, 1997. NIST physicist. *Applied Physics, Electrical Engineering, Low Temperature Physics, Materials Science, Metallurgy*. Experimental condensed-matter physics: superconductivity, low-temperature physics, and radiation detectors and their applications.

Senior Research Scientist

Wieman, Carl E., Ph.D., Stanford University, 1977. Senior advisor to PhET. *Atomic, Molecular, & Optical Physics, Physics and other Science Education*. Bose-Einstein condensation; AMO physics; physics education research.

DEPARTMENTAL RESEARCH SPECIALTIES AND STAFF

Theoretical

Astrophysics. Astrophysics is concentrated in the Department of Astrophysical and Planetary Sciences, but many of our Ph.D. students work with faculty at APS, JILA, CASA, and LASP. Hamilton.

Atmosphere, Space Physics, Cosmic Rays. Solar, space, and atmospheric plasma studies and lunar surface environment. Horanyi.

Atomic, Molecular, & Optical Physics. Our AMO physics is concentrated in JILA, one of the leading research institutes in the world in this area. Research at JILA includes high-precision spectroscopy and precision measurement, ultracold cold atoms and molecules, ultrafast and ultra-high-power lasers, and micron- and nanometer-scale optics. Becker, Bohn, D'Incao, Holland, Jaron-Becker, Knill, Rey, Smith.

Biophysics. Molecular motors and motors that can change their track; DNA-protein interactions; self-assembly of cytoskeletal materials; liquid crystalline aggregates. Betterton, Glaser.

Chemical Physics. Theory of ultracold chemical reactions; chemical reaction dynamics. Bohn.

Condensed Matter Physics. Theoretical condensed-matter research on soft materials, strongly interacting quantum systems, fractional quantum Hall effect, exotic quantum states, and statistical mechanics of spin systems. Beale, Glaser, Gurarie, Hermele, Maclennan, Nandkishore, Radzihovsky, Romatschke.

Geophysics. Physics of earth dynamics, including both gravitational and magnetic fields and tectonics and volcanism. Ritzwoller, Zhong.

High Energy Physics. Non-perturbative QCD lattice gauge theories; grand unified theories; supersymmetry; string theory. de Alwis, DeGrand, DeWolfe, Hasenfratz, Neil.

History & Philosophy of Physics/Science. History and philosophy of 20th-century physics, especially high-energy physics.

Nuclear Physics. Theory of highly relativistic ion collisions, relativistic fluids, and the quark-gluon plasma. Bolton, Romatschke.

Optics. Ultrafast and ultra-high-power lasers and interactions. Becker, Jaron-Becker.

Particles and Fields. Non-perturbative QCD lattice gauge theories; grand unified theories; supersymmetry; string theory. de Alwis, DeGrand, DeWolfe, Hasenfratz, Neil.

Physics and other Science Education. Uses of technology in physics education; assessments (conceptual, epistemological, and belief oriented); curricular and classroom materials at the middle- and upper-division levels; theoretical models of students learning physics; social and contextual foundations of student learning; examination of successful educational reforms and replication studies of such reforms; student problem-solving in physics. Finkelstein, Hodby, West, Wilcox, Wilkerson.

Plasma and Fusion. Theory of space and laboratory plasmas; plasma turbulence; magnetic reconnection. The Center for Integrated Plasma Studies is used. Cary, Goldman, Horanyi, Parker, Uzdensky.

Experimental

Applied Physics. Research in materials science; nanomechanical systems; nano-optics; ultrafast, and ultra-high-power lasers. Anderson, Kapteyn, Lehnert, Levine, Murnane, Papp, Price, Rogers, Schibli, Ullom, Yin.

Astrophysics. Astrophysics is concentrated in the Department of Astrophysical and Planetary Science, but many of our Ph.D. students work with faculty at APS, JILA, CASA, and LASP. Glenn, Halverson.

Atmosphere, Space Physics, Cosmic Rays. Solar, space, and atmospheric plasma studies; lunar surface environment. Baker, Goldman, Horanyi, Kempf, Munsat.

Atomic, Molecular, & Optical Physics. Our AMO physics is concentrated in JILA, one of the leading research institutes in the world in this area. Research at JILA includes high-precision spectroscopy and precision measurement, ultracold cold atoms and molecules, ultrafast and ultra-high-power lasers, and micron- and nanometer-scale optics. Anderson, Cornell, Cundiff, Diddams, Gopinath, Hall, Kapteyn, Kaufman, Lehnert, Leibrandt, Levine, Lewandowski, Murnane, Papp, Piestun, Raschke, Regal, Schibli, Simmonds, Thompson, Ullom, Wineland, Ye.

Biophysics. Atomic force spectroscopy of biological molecules; nanoassembly. Betterton, Hough, Thomas Perkins.

Chemical Physics. Laser spectroscopy of molecules; ultracold molecules; state-resolved chemical reactions; nanometer/femtosecond measurements of electrons in molecules. Betterton, Kapteyn, Lewandowski, Murnane, Nesbitt, Thomas Perkins, Raschke, Smalyukh.

Condensed Matter Physics. Soft condensed-matter and liquid crystal physics; femtosecond optical, electron, and neutron spectroscopy on materials; nanoscale electronic structure studies of surfaces; electrical and mechanical properties of nanofabricated materials; low-temperature properties of exotic materials. Cao, Clark, Dessau, Lee, Lehnert, Maclennan, Price, Raschke, Reznik, Rogers, Schibli, Shaheen, Smalyukh, Yin.

Geophysics. Physics of earth dynamics, including both gravitational and magnetic fields and tectonics and volcanism. Calkins.

High Energy Physics. The high-energy physics experimentalists are members of the CMS experiment at CERN, the T2K neutrino experiment at JPARC, the DUNE project at Fermilab/Homestake, and the NA61/Shine experiment at CERN. Cumalat, Marino, Rankin, Stenson, Ulmer, Wagner, Zimmerman.

Low Temperature Physics. Low-temperature properties of exotic materials. Cornell, Lewandowski, Price, Regal, Thompson, Ye.

Materials Science, Metallurgy. Electronic and mechanical properties of nanostructures. Cao, Dessau, Price, Raschke, Reznik, Rogers, Smalyukh, Yin.

Nuclear Physics. Relativistic heavy ion collisions and medium-energy nuclear structure studies. Kinney, Nagle, Perepelitsa.

Optics. Ultrafast and ultra-high-power lasers; femtosecond/nanoscale optics; nonlinear optics; integrated nano-optics. Anderson, Cundiff, Diddams, Gopinath, Hall, Kapteyn, Murnane, Piestun, Raschke, Schibli, Ye.

Particles and Fields. The particle physics experimentalists are members of the CMS experiment at CERN, the T2K neutrino experiment at JPARC, the DUNE project at Fermilab/Homestake, and the NA61/Shine experiment at CERN. Cumalat, Marino, Stenson, Ulmer, Wagner, Zimmerman.

Physics and other Science Education. Uses of technology in physics education; assessments (conceptual, epistemological, and belief oriented); curricular and classroom materials at the middle- and upper-division levels; theoretical models of students learning physics; social and contextual foundations of student learning; examination of successful educational reforms and replication studies of such reforms; student problem-solving in physics. Dubson, Lewandowski, Katherine Perkins, Pollock, Wieman.

Physics of Beams. Theoretical and experimental development of advanced beams, primarily through plasma wakefield acceleration. Cary, Litos.

Plasma and Fusion. Laboratory and space plasmas; measurement and assessment of turbulence and cross-field transport in magnetically confined plasmas; solar plasma observations; dusty plasmas; lunar surface environment. The Center for Integrated Plasma Studies, Colorado Center for Lunar Dust and Atmospheric Studies, is used. Baker, Goldman, Horanyi, Kempf, Litos, Munsat.

View additional information about this department at www.gradschoolshopper.com. Check out the "Why Choose Us?" section, find out more about the department's culture and get links to social media networks.

UNIVERSITY OF COLORADO, COLORADO SPRINGS

PHYSICS & ENERGY SCIENCE

Colorado Springs, Colorado 80918
http://www.uccs.edu/~physics/

General University Information
Chancellor: Venkateshwar K. Reddy
Dean of Graduate School: Kelli Klebe
University website: http://www.uccs.edu
School Type: Public
Setting: Urban
Total Faculty: 828
Total number of Students: 12,435
Total number of Graduate Students: 1,832

Department Information
Department Chairman: Prof. Robert Camley, Chair
Department Contact: Kristina Woods, Program Assistant
  Total full-time faculty: 13
  Full-Time Graduate Students: 31
  Female Full-Time Graduate Students: 8
  First-Year Graduate Students: 5
  Female First-Year Students: 2
  Total Post Doctorates: 4

Department Address
1420 Austin Bluffs Pkwy
Colorado Springs, CO 80918
Phone: 719-255-3164
Fax: 719-262-3013
E-mail: kwoods@uccs.edu
Website: http://www.uccs.edu/~physics/

ADMISSIONS

Admission Contact Information
Address admission inquiries to: Professor Anatoliy Pinchuk, Department of Physics, University of Colorado, Colorado Springs, 1420 Austin Bluffs Parkway, Colorado Springs, CO 80918, USA
Phone: 719-255-3556
E-mail: apinchuk@uccs.edu
Admissions website: http://www.uccs.edu/graduateschool/prospective-students/admissions.html

Application deadlines
Fall admission:
U.S. students: July 1   *Int'l. students*: July 1
Spring admission:
U.S. students: December 1   *Int'l. students*: December 1

Application fee
U.S. students: $60   *Int'l. students*: $100
Rolling admissions. Students may start in Fall, Spring or Summer semesters. However, to be eligible for certain teaching assistant positions, students should apply by April 1. Also, students must apply for financial aid by March 1. Many university scholarships require that you are accepted and complete scholarship applications before the March 1st university scholarship deadline.

Admissions information
For Fall of 2017:
  Number of applicants: 7
  Number admitted: 7
  Number enrolled: 5

Admission requirements
Bachelor's degree requirements: A Bachelors degree in Physics or in a closely related field, from an accredited college or university.
Minimum undergraduate GPA: 3.0 0 0 0.0 GRE Required in some cases

Subjective GRE requirements
The Subjective GRE is not required.
The GRE is not generally required. Students with international transcripts, however, are required to submit Physics Subject Exam GRE scores. A minimum acceptable score is 520.

TOEFL requirements
The TOEFL exam is required for students from non-English-speaking countries.
  PBT score: 560
  iBT score: 83
International students are encouraged to speak with Physics faculty to demonstrate their English skills.

Other admissions information
Additional requirements: Students who have not completed all the undergraduate core Physics classes with a grade of B- or better may be accepted provisionally and asked to take these undergraduate classes.
Undergraduate preparation assumed: Modern Physics,; Statistical Mechanics,; Electricity and Magnetism (2 semesters),; Quantum Mechanics,; Classical Mechanics,; Mathematical Methods,; Some math classes beyond the Calculus series (Linear Algebra, Differential Equations, etc).

TUITION

Tuition year 2018–19:
Tuition for in-state residents
  Full-time students: $3,671 per semester
  Part-time students: $2,026 per semester
Tuition for out-of-state residents
  Full-time students: $7,307 per semester
  Part-time students: $3,844 per semester
Full-time tuition cost provided is for 6 credit hours per semester. Part-time tuition provided is for 3 credit hours per semester.
Credit hours per semester to be considered full-time: 5
Deferred tuition plan: No
Health insurance: Not available.
Other academic fees: Fees vary with class selection, academic level, and academic load. Please see the UCCS Bursar's website for current cost estimates: https://www.uccs.edu/bursar/
Academic term: Semester
Number of first-year students who received full tuition waivers: 3
Number of first-year students who received partial tuition waivers: 3

Teaching Assistants, Research Assistants, and Fellowships

Number of first-year
Teaching Assistants: 5
Research Assistants: 2
Fellowship students: 2

Average stipend per academic year
Teaching Assistant: $8,000
Research Assistant: $8,000
Fellowship student: $5,000

UCCS also has a variety of internal graduate fellowships that are based on merit. If you receive one of these fellowships, the support typically ranges from from $5,000 to $25,000

FINANCIAL AID

Application deadlines
Fall admission:
U.S. students: March 1   *Int'l. students*: March 1
Spring admission:
U.S. students: March 1   *Int'l. students*: March 1

Loans
Loans are available for U.S. students.
Loans are not available for international students.
GAPSFAS application required: No
FAFSA application required: Yes

For further information
Address financial aid inquiries to: Office of Financial Aid/Student Employment, University of Colorado at Colorado Springs, 1420 Austin Bluffs Parkway, Colorado Springs, CO 80918-3733.
Phone: (719) 255-3460
E-mail: finaidse@uccs.edu
Financial aid website: https://www.uccs.edu/finaid/

HOUSING

Availability of on-campus housing
Single students: Yes
Married students: No
Childcare Assistance: No

For further information
Address housing inquiries to: UCCS Office of Residence Life and Housing, University of Colorado at Colorado Springs, 1420 Austin Bluffs Parkway, Colorado Springs, CO 80918, USA.
Phone: (719) 255-4326
E-mail: housing@uccs.edu
Housing aid website: https://www.uccs.edu/residence/

Table A—Faculty, Enrollments, and Degrees Granted

Research Specialty	2017–18 Faculty	Enrollment Fall 2017		Number of Degrees Granted 2017–18 (2013–18)		
		Master's	Doctorate	Master's	Terminal Master's	Doctorate
Condensed Matter, Magnetism, Liquid crystals, thin films, plasmonics, radon, microwave, nanotechnology, biophysics	13	–	31	3(11)	–	2(8)
Total	13	–	31	3(11)	–	2(8)
Full-time Grad. Stud.	–	–	31	–	–	–
First-year Grad. Stud.	–	–	6	–	–	–

GRADUATE DEGREE REQUIREMENTS

Master's: MASTERS NON-THESIS OPTION. - 30 hours of course work. - Regular degree students must maintain at least a 3.0 grade point average each semester or summer term on all work taken, whether or not it is to be applied toward the advanced degree intended. - The Master's Comprehensive Exam is an exit oral exam that must be passed by all students. Students in the non-thesis option are required to write a short (15 page, double-spaced) typed paper summarizing either some original research or summarizing a research topic in current physics. The paper should be at a graduate physics level. The exam consists of a 30-40 minute presentation of the paper with questions on the topic from the faculty.

Doctorate: The student must complete a minimum of 66 hours of coursework and dissertation. This includes: 1) A minimum of 36 hours of course work with GPA above 3.0. - 21 hours of Core courses. - 15 hours of Specialization, Elective or Interdisciplinary courses. 2) A minimum of 30 hours of dissertation work, pass the comprehensive exam/proposal, and complete and successfully defend the dissertation.

Thesis: MASTERS THESIS OPTION. - 24 hours of course work, plus 6 credit hours of thesis. - Regular degree students must maintain at least a 3.0 grade point average each semester or summer term on all work taken, whether or not it is to be applied toward the advanced degree intended. - Submission of an original thesis to the Thesis Committee. - The Master's Comprehensive Exam is an exit oral exam that must be passed by all students. The exam consists of a 30-40 minute defense of the thesis, followed by questions from the faculty.

SPECIAL EQUIPMENT, FACILITIES, OR PROGRAMS

Physics and BioFrontiers labs include:
- liquid crystal lab
- ultrafast optics lab
- Brillouin light scattering
- microwave lab (50 MHz - 110 GHz)
- clean room (photolithography & etching)
- scanning electron microscope with EDX and electron beam lithography
- total internal reflection microscope (TIRF)
- confocal microscope
- atomic force microscope (AFM, STM, MFM)
- scanning near-field optical microscope
- cell-culturing facilities
- flow cytometer
- IBM computer cluster
- SQUID, MOKE and FMR magnetometry
- molecular beam epitaxy
- sputtering & electron beam thin film deposition
- x-ray diffraction system
- Raman scattering
- NSOM

Table B—Separately Budgeted Research Expenditures by Source of Support

Source of Support	Departmental Research	Physics-related Research Outside Department
Federal government		$844,949
State/local government		$13,732
Non-profit organizations		
Business and industry	$529,743	$111,030
Other	$21,466	
Total	**$551,209**	**$969,711**

FACULTY

Distinguished University Professor

Camley, Robert E., Ph.D., University of California Irvine, 1979. Director of the UCCS Biofrontiers Center. Department Chair (2018–19). *Applied Physics, Biophysics, Computational Physics, Condensed Matter Physics, Electromagnetism, Nonlinear Dynamics and Complex Systems, Theoretical Physics.* Theoretical solid state physics, Magnetic and electromagnetic properties of multilayers, Surface excitations, Magnetic dynamics - spin waves.

Celinski, Zbigniew J., Ph.D., Simon Fraser University, 1992. Director of Center for Magnetism and Magnetic Nanostructures. *Condensed Matter Physics, Electromagnetism, Engineering Physics/Science, Nano Science and Technology, Solid State Physics.* Experimental solid state physics, Growth and characterization of ultra-thin metallic films and multilayers, Magnetic materials, Brillouin light scattering, Ferromagnetic resonance, Exchange coupling in magnetic thin films, Microwave signal processing devices.

Professor

Christensen, Tom, Ph.D., Cornell University, 1985. Provost and Executive Vice Chancellor for Academic Affairs (not currently in the department). *Condensed Matter Physics, Materials Science, Metallurgy, Physics and other Science Education, Solid State Physics, Surface Physics.* Experimental surface and thin film physics, X-ray diffraction, Physics education.

Glushchenko, Anatoliy, Ph.D., Institute of Physics, Ukrainian Academy of Sciences, 1997. Director for the Center for Advanced Technologies & Optical Materials. *Condensed Matter Physics, Fluids, Rheology, Nano Science and Technology, Optics, Other.* Soft matter physics, Liquid crystals, Applied optics, Materials science.

Pinchuk, Anatoliy, Ph.D., National Academy of Science of Ukraine, 1999. Graduate Co-Adviser (in-coming students and recruitment). *Biophysics, Condensed Matter Physics, Nano Science and Technology, Optics.* Nanooptics, Plasmonics, Photonics, Colloidal chemistry, Negative index of refraction, Metamaterials.

Associate Professor

Grabowski, Marek, Ph.D., University of Kentucky, 1981. *Nonlinear Dynamics and Complex Systems, Polymer Physics/Science, Theoretical Physics.* Theoretical solid state physics, Chaos, Nonlinear physics, Solitons, One and two dimensional systems, Polymers, Complex systems.

Livesey, Karen L., Ph.D., University of Western Australia, 2009. Graduate Co-Adviser (enrolled students). *Applied Physics, Condensed Matter Physics, Statistical & Thermal Physics, Theoretical Physics.* Nano-magnetism, Liquid crystals, Multiferroic materials, Nonlinear magnetization dynamics, Domain walls.

Assistant Professor

Spendier, Kathrin, Ph.D., University of New Mexico, 2012. *Biophysics, Optics, Statistical & Thermal Physics.* Role of cell surface curvature in disease models, Metallic nanoparticles for biomedical application, Cell membrane protein dynamics, Reaction-diffusion calculations.

DEPARTMENTAL RESEARCH SPECIALTIES AND STAFF

Theoretical

Condensed Matter Physics. The three theorists in our department specialize in the study of magnetic and low-dimensional electronic systems, plus nonlinear physics. There is additional theoretical work in biophysics, nanoparticles, microwave devices, and electromagnetism. There are strong collaborations with the experimentalists in the department and world-wide. Projects are both very applied (bio-engineering and device applications) plus purely theoretical in nature. Camley, Grabowski, Livesey.

Experimental

Biophysics. Biophysics research in the department is centered on the application of nano-materials to image, diagnose and treat disease. The interaction of nanoparticles with cells and mucus is studied using a variety of techniques and using equipment shared by Physics and the UCCS Biofrontiers Center. Pinchuk, Spendier.

Condensed Matter Physics. Experimental condensed matter physics expertise in our department includes the areas of liquid crystals, soft matter, plasmonics, nanotechnology, magnetism, microwave, infrared and interface physics. The department has state-of-the-art equipment totaling several millions of dollars to make, characterize, image, test, and apply nano-materials for many exciting applications. Celinski, Christensen, Glushchenko, Pinchuk.

View additional information about this department at www.gradschoolshopper.com. Check out the "Why Choose Us?" section, find out more about the department's culture and get links to social media networks.

UNIVERSITY OF DENVER

DEPARTMENT OF PHYSICS AND ASTRONOMY

Denver, Colorado 80208-2238
http://www.physics.du.edu

General University Information
Chancellor: Rebecca Chopp
Dean of Graduate School: Andrei Kutateladze, Dean of Natural
  Sciences and Mathematics (NSM)
University website: http://www.du.edu
School Type: Private
Setting: Suburban
Total Faculty: 678
Total Graduate Faculty: N/A
Total number of Students: 11,614
Total number of Graduate Students: 5,860

Department Information
Department Chairman: Dr. Davor Balzar, Chair
Department Contact: Faun Lee, Assistant to Chair
  Total full-time faculty: 12
  Total number of full-time equivalent positions: 12
  Full-Time Graduate Students: 20
  Female Full-Time Graduate Students: 6
  First-Year Graduate Students: 6
  Female First-Year Students: 1
  Total Post Doctorates: 1

Department Address
2112 E. Wesley Ave
Denver, CO 80208-2238
Phone: (303) 871-2238
Fax: (303) 871-4405
E-mail: Faun.lee@du.edu
Website: http://www.physics.du.edu

ADMISSIONS

Admission Contact Information
Address admission inquiries to: Davor Balzar, Chair, Department
  of Physics and Astronomy, University of Denver, 2112 E
  Wesley Ave, Denver, CO 80208
Phone: (303) 871-2238
E-mail: Davor.Balzar@du.edu
Admissions website: https://www.du.edu/admission-aid/
  graduate/admission-policies-procedures.html

Application deadlines
Fall admission:
U.S. students: February 1   *Int'l. students*: January 4

Application fee
U.S. students: $65   *Int'l. students*: $65

Admissions information
For Fall of 2018:
  Number of applicants: 61
  Number admitted: 10
  Number enrolled: 6

Admission requirements
Bachelor's degree requirements: A Bachelor's degree in Physics
  (or a Physics and Mathematics background equivalent to that
  required for a Bachelor of Science degree in Physics) is required.

Minimum undergraduate GPA: 3.0

GRE requirements
The GRE is required.
No minimum scores are set.

Subjective GRE requirements
The Subjective GRE is not required.
The GRE Physics is optional.

TOEFL requirements
The TOEFL exam is required for students from non-English-
  speaking countries.
  PBT score: 550
  iBT score: 80
Graduate Teaching Assistants (GTAs) must demonstrate fluency
  in spoken English by scoring a 26 on the TOEFL (iBT) speaking section or 8.0 on the IELTS speaking section.

TUITION

Tuition year 2018–19:
  Full-time students: $1,372 per credit
  Part-time students: $1,372 per credit
Full-time equivalent teaching and research assistants receive full
  tuition waivers for normal academic loads; the health fee is
  paid by the university for full-time graduate assistants.
Credit hours per semester to be considered full-time: 8
Deferred tuition plan: Yes
Health insurance: Yes, $2,976.00.
Other academic fees: Health insurance provided at no cost for
  students with GTA or GRA support. Student fees: $10.65/
  credit hour.
Academic term: Quarter

Teaching Assistants, Research Assistants, and Fellowships
Number of first-year
  Teaching Assistants: 6
Average stipend per academic year
  Teaching Assistant: $20,000
  Research Assistant: $20,000
  Fellowship student: $26,667

FINANCIAL AID

Application deadlines
Fall admission:
U.S. students: February 1   *Int'l. students*: January 4

Loans
Loans are available for U.S. students.
Loans are not available for international students.
GAPSFAS application required: No
FAFSA application required: No

For further information
Address financial aid inquiries to: Davor Balzar, Chair, De-
  partment of Physics and Astronomy, University of Denver,
  2112 E Wesley Ave, Denver, CO 80208.
Phone: (303) 871-2238
E-mail: gradservices@du.edu

Financial aid website: www.du.edu/financialaid

HOUSING

Availability of on-campus housing
Single students: Yes
Married students: Yes
Childcare Assistance: No

For further information
Address housing inquiries to: Housing and Residential Education, University of Denver, 2055 E. Evans Ave., Suite 200, Denver, CO 80208.
Phone: (303) 871-2246
E-mail: housing@du.edu
Housing aid website: http://www.du.edu/housing/

Table A—Faculty, Enrollments, and Degrees Granted

Research Specialty	2018–19 Faculty	Enrollment Fall 2018 Master's	Enrollment Fall 2018 Doctorate	Number of Degrees Granted 2017–18 (2013–18) Master's	Number of Degrees Granted 2017–18 (2013–18) Terminal Master's	Number of Degrees Granted 2017–18 (2013–18) Doctorate
Astrophysics	4	–	4	–	–(2)	1(7)
Atmosphere, Space Physics, Cosmic Rays	1	–	–	–	–	–
Biophysics	2	–	5	–	–(1)	1(4)
Condensed Matter Physics	6	–	10	–(1)	–(1)	1(11)
Physics and other Science Education	1	–	–	–	–	–
Total	14	–	19	–(1)	–(4)	3(21)
Full-time Grad. Stud.	–	–	19	–	–	–
First-year Grad. Stud.	–	–	7	–	–	–

GRADUATE DEGREE REQUIREMENTS

Master's: MS (with Research Thesis): 45 quarter hours in an approved course of study, up to 10 hours of which may be in Thesis research; Comprehensive Examination; Thesis Defense. MA (without Thesis): 45 quarter hours in an approved course of study.

Doctorate: Minimum of three years of full-time study beyond the Baccalaureate degree, with at least 90 quarter hours of approved graduate credit; Comprehensive Examination; Oral Dissertation Research Proposal; Dissertation Defense.

Thesis: Thesis may be written in absentia.

SPECIAL EQUIPMENT, FACILITIES, OR PROGRAMS

The Department has major research programs in: massive binary stars, circumstellar material, core-collapse supernovae, spectropolarimetry, polarized radiative transfer modeling; stellar Evolution, circumstellar-interstellar interactions; optical and infrared astronomy using the department's observatory at the summit of Mt. Evans (4,313 m) and other facilities and data sources; condensed matter and materials physics focusing on using nanofabrication techniques to control and measure thermal, magnetic, and electronic properties of thin films and nanostructures; studies of high resolution microcalorimeter X-ray and gamma-ray detectors; investigating spin transport in non-magnetic and magnetic metals and heterostructures, understanding the impact of spin-orbit coupling on magnetic dynamics; computational methods to study surface physics, especially focused on adsorption processes; using light-matter interactions to control and measure electron and phonon transport in nanostructures; nanoscale re-search on ferroelectrics, nano- and biomaterials research using X-ray and neutron diffraction and AFM techniques. (Some graduate research assistantships may be available in cooperation with several nearby Federal Laboratories, in particular the National Institute of Standards and Technology, NIST, and the National Renewable Energy Laboratory, NREL).

Table B—Separately Budgeted Research Expenditures by Source of Support

Source of Support	Departmental Research	Physics-related Research Outside Department
Federal government	$949,525	
State/local government		
Non-profit organizations	$38,637	
Business and industry		
Other		
Total	$988,162	

Table C—Separately Budgeted Research Expenditures by Research Specialty

Research Specialty	No. of Grants	Expenditures ($)
Astronomy	5	$129,537
Biophysics	3	$294,528
Condensed Matter Physics	7	$564,099
Total	15	$988,164

FACULTY

Professor

Stencel, Robert E., Ph.D., University of Michigan, 1977. Womble Chair in Astrophysics. *Astronomy, Astrophysics*. Stellar evolution and infrared instrumentation.

Zink, Barry, Ph.D., University of California, San Diego, 2002. *Applied Physics, Condensed Matter Physics, Materials Science, Metallurgy, Nano Science and Technology*. Uses micro- and nanofabrication techniques to control and measure the thermal, magnetic and electronic properties of systems to study the fundamental physics of new materials and apply this knowledge for new technologies.

Associate Professor

Balzar, Davor, Ph.D., University of Zagreb, Croatia, 1993. Department Chair. *Applied Physics, Condensed Matter Physics, Materials Science, Metallurgy, Nano Science and Technology*. Studying materials' properties by x-ray and neutron diffraction and computational techniques.

Calbi, M. Mercedes, Ph.D., University of Buenos Aires, Argentina, 2000. Chair, Graduate Committee. *Condensed Matter Physics, Nano Science and Technology*. Surface physics, especially focused on adsorption processes.

Ghosh, Kingshuk, Ph.D., University of Massachusetts, Amherst, 2003. *Biophysics*. Theoretical and computational models to understand physical biology: protein folding, gene networks and evolution.

Hoffman, Jennifer, Ph.D., University of Wisconsin-Madison, 2002. Chair, Undergraduate Committee. *Astrophysics*. Massive binary stars, circumstellar material, core-collapse supernovae, spectropolarimetry, polarized radiative transfer modeling.

Loerke, Dinah, Ph.D., University of Göttingen, Germany, 2004. *Biophysics*. Quantitative biophysical approaches to experimental cell biology.

Siemens, Mark, Ph.D., University of Colorado, 2009. *Condensed Matter Physics, Nano Science and Technology, Optics*. Using light-matter interactions to control and measure electron and phonon transport in nanostructures.

Ueta, Toshiya, Ph.D., University of Illinois at Urbana-Champaign, 2002. *Astronomy, Astrophysics*. Observational Astronomy (multi-wavelength from optical, near/mid/far-IR, sub-mm to radio), Stellar Evolution, Stellar Mass Loss, Circumstellar Shells, Circumstellar-Interstellar Interactions, Astronomical Dust, and Radiative Transfer Modeling.

Assistant Professor

Fan, Xin, Ph.D., University of Delaware, 2010. *Condensed Matter Physics, Nano Science and Technology*. Spintronics and magnetic properties of nano-scale materials.

Emeritus

Blatherwick, Ronald D., Ph.D., University of Denver, 1976. *Atmosphere, Space Physics, Cosmic Rays*. Atmospheric physics.

Goldman, Aaron, Technion-Israel Institute of Technology, 1965. John Evans Professor. *Atmosphere, Space Physics, Cosmic Rays, Atomic, Molecular, & Optical Physics*. Atmospheric physics; atomic and molecular spectroscopy.

Neumann, Herschel, Ph.D., University of Nebraska-Lincoln, 1965. *Physics and other Science Education, Other*. Physics education.

Olson, John R., Ph.D., Iowa State University, 1963. *Acoustics, Atmosphere, Space Physics, Cosmic Rays, Other*. Atmospheric physics; electronics.

van der Merwe, Alwyn J., Ph.D., University of Bern, Switzerland, 1971. *History & Philosophy of Physics/Science, Other*. Intermolecular forces; history and foundations of physics.

Williams, Walter John, M.S., University of Denver, 1963. *Atmosphere, Space Physics, Cosmic Rays*. Upper atmospheric physics.

Research Professor

Amme, Robert C., Ph.D., Iowa State University, 1958. *Atomic, Molecular, & Optical Physics, Condensed Matter Physics, Materials Science, Metallurgy, Mechanics*. Granular particle physics and the compaction of granular materials.

Ormes, Jonathan F., Ph.D., University of Minnesota, 1967. *Astrophysics, High Energy Physics, Other*. Cosmic rays.

Teaching Professor

Iona, Steven, Ph.D., University of Denver, 1994. *Physics and other Science Education*. Teacher preparation and student conceptual development specifically of physics topics.

Teaching Assistant Professor

Cisernos, Sophia, Ph.D., New Mexico State University, 2011. *Astrophysics*. Study of general relativity symmetry techniques in the case of galaxy dynamics, especially focused on the flat-rotation curve problem in spiral galaxies.

Adjunct Faculty

Alde, Douglas M., M.D./Ph.D., University of Illinois-Urbana.

Adjunct Professor

Mickle, Ronald, M.S., Swinburne University, 2008. *Astronomy*. Astronomy.

Sievers, Albert J., Ph.D., University of California at Berkeley, 1962. *Condensed Matter Physics*. Condensed Matter Physics.

DEPARTMENTAL RESEARCH SPECIALTIES AND STAFF

Theoretical

Astrophysics. Radiative transfer simulations of circumstellar material. Cisernos, Hoffman, Ueta.

Biophysics. Computational studies of protein-protein interactions. Ghosh.

Condensed Matter Physics. Gas adsorption on nanostructures. Calbi.

Experimental

Astronomy. Binary stars; stellar evolution; supernovae and supernova progenitors; spectropolarimetry; telescope design and instrumentation. Hoffman, Mickle, Stencel, Ueta.

Astrophysics. Stellar mass loss and mass transfer; stellar wind-ISM interaction; circumstellar material; dust composition and formation. Hoffman, Ormes, Stencel, Ueta.

Atmosphere, Space Physics, Cosmic Rays. Cosmic rays. Ormes.

Biophysics. Molecular dynamics of actin. Loerke.

Condensed Matter Physics. Materials physics and science; applied physics; low-temperature physics; thin films and nanostructures; measurements of thermal, magnetic, electronic, and mechanical properties; organic semiconductors; spintronics; strains and defects; X-ray and neutron diffraction; materials structure; compaction of granular materials; ultrafast laser optics. Balzar, Calbi, Fan, Siemens, Sievers, Zink.

View additional information about this department at www.gradschoolshopper.com. Check out the "Why Choose Us?" section, find out more about the department's culture and get links to social media networks.

SOUTHERN CONNECTICUT STATE UNIVERSITY

DEPARTMENT OF PHYSICS

New Haven, Connecticut 06515
http://www.southernct.edu/academics/schools/arts/departments/physics/

General University Information
President: Dr. Joe Bertolino
Dean of Graduate School: Dr. Christine Broadbridge
University website: http://www.southernct.edu
School Type: Public
Setting: Urban
Total Faculty: 683
Total Graduate Faculty: 320
Total number of Students: 10,320
Total number of Graduate Students: 2,357

Department Information
Department Chairman: Dr. Matthew J. Enjalran, Chair
Department Contact: Evan Finch, Graduate Program
  Coordinator
  Total full-time faculty: 9
  Total number of full-time equivalent positions: 9
  Full-Time Graduate Students: 6
  Female Full-Time Graduate Students: 1
  First-Year Graduate Students: 3
  Total Post Doctorates: 1

Department Address
501 Crescent Street
New Haven, CT 06515
Phone: (203) 392-6465
Fax: (203) 392-6466
E-mail: physics@southernct.edu
Website: http://www.southernct.edu/academics/schools/arts/
  departments/physics/

ADMISSIONS

Admission Contact Information
Address admission inquiries to: Dr. Evan Finch, Graduate Program Coordinator, Department of Physics, 501 Crescent Street, New Haven, CT 06515
Phone: (203) 392-6465
E-mail: FinchL3@southernct.edu
Admissions website: https://www.southernct.edu/academics/graduate/graduate-admissions/

Application deadlines
Fall admission:
U.S. students: July 1   *Int'l. students*: April 1
Spring admission:
U.S. students: November 1   *Int'l. students*: October 1

Application fee
U.S. students: $50   *Int'l. students*: $50

Admissions information
For Fall of 2017:
  Number of applicants: 6
  Number admitted: 2
  Number enrolled: 2

Admission requirements
Bachelor's degree requirements: A Bachelor's degree in Science, Engineering, or a related field is required.
Minimum undergraduate GPA: 3.0

GRE requirements
The GRE is not required.

Subjective GRE requirements
The Subjective GRE is not required.

TOEFL requirements
The TOEFL exam is required for students from non-English-speaking countries.
  PBT score: 550
  iBT score: 79

Other admissions information
Additional requirements: Undergraduate transcripts, two letters of recommendation, and a one-page personal statement are required to complete the admission package.
Undergraduate preparation assumed: An undergraduate preparation that includes at least six physics courses is assumed (the same as for a minor in physics at the undergraduate level at SCSU).

TUITION
Tuition year 2018–19:
Tuition for in-state residents
  Full-time students: $6,072 per semester
  Part-time students: $764 per credit
Tuition for out-of-state residents
  Full-time students: $12,244 per semester
  Part-time students: $764 per credit
The figures above include university fees for full-time students. For part-time students, per-credit costs decreases slightly as number of credits increases.
Credit hours per semester to be considered full-time: 9
Deferred tuition plan: No
Health insurance: Available at the cost of $2,953 per year.
Academic term: Semester
Number of first-year students who received partial tuition waivers: 1

Teaching Assistants, Research Assistants, and Fellowships
Number of first-year
  Research Assistants: 1
  Fellowship students: 1
Average stipend per academic year
  Research Assistant: $18,312
  Fellowship student: $9,600
Full-time fellowships come with some remission of fees.

FINANCIAL AID

Application deadlines
Fall admission:
U.S. students: March 15   *Int'l. students*: March 15
Spring admission:
U.S. students: November 1   *Int'l. students*: November 1

Loans

Loans are available for U.S. students.

Loans are available for international students.

GAPSFAS application required: No

FAFSA application required: Yes

For further information

Address financial aid inquiries to: Financial Aid, Southern Connecticut State University, Wintergreen Building, 501 Crescent St., New Haven, CT 06515.

Phone: (203) 392-5222

E-mail: financialaid@southernct.edu

Financial aid website: https://www.southernct.edu/financialaid/

HOUSING

Availability of on-campus housing

Single students: Yes

Married students: No

For further information

Address housing inquiries to: Office of Residence Life, Southern Connecticut State University, 501 Crescent St., Schwartz Hall RM 100, New Haven, CT 06515.

Phone: (203) 392-5870

E-mail: reslife@southernct.edu

Housing aid website: http://www.southernct.edu/student-life/campus-life/residencelife/index.html/

Table A—Faculty, Enrollments, and Degrees Granted

Research Specialty	2016–17 Faculty	Enrollment Fall 2017 Master's	Enrollment Fall 2017 Doctorate	Number of Degrees Granted 2017–18 (2013–18) Master's	Number of Degrees Granted 2017–18 (2013–18) Terminal Master's	Number of Degrees Granted 2017–18 (2013–18) Doctorate
Applied Physics	9	12	–	–	7(20)	–
Total	9	12	–	–	7(20)	–
Full-time Grad. Stud.	–	6	–	–	–	–
First-year Grad. Stud.	–	2	–	–	–	–

GRADUATE DEGREE REQUIREMENTS

Master's: The Master of Science degree in applied physics requires completion of a total of 36 credits with a "B" or better average. All students in the program must complete an interdisciplinary core consisting of the six courses with a "B" or better average. After the core, the student selects one of two tracks, nanotechology/materials science or optics/optical instrumentation. The student then completes two electives and a research capstone experience. An internship (not for class credit) with a local technology company is also required for graduation.

Thesis: A Master's thesis based on research acceptable to the department is one way to satisfy the research capstone requirement. For the thesis option, students must complete a thesis proposal and initial research, and then develop and write a thesis. A student must apply to the department for the thesis defense and provide a final draft of the completed thesis at least two weeks prior to the defense date.

SPECIAL EQUIPMENT, FACILITIES, OR PROGRAMS

The department has significant nanotechnology facilities, including sample preparation stations, scanning electron microscopy, transmission electron microscopy, atomic force microscopy and optical microscopy. Photonics and optical instrument development facilities exist for fiber optics, spectroscopy and high-resolution astronomy projects. The department also has high-speed computing facilities.

Table B—Separately Budgeted Research Expenditures by Source of Support

Source of Support	Departmental Research	Physics-related Research Outside Department
Federal government	$604,213	
State/local government	$11,213	
Non-profit organizations		
Business and industry	$77,500	
Other		
Total	**$692,926**	

Table C—Separately Budgeted Research Expenditures by Research Specialty

Research Specialty	No. of Grants	Expenditures ($)
Astronomy	4	$185,713
Biophysics	2	$6,213
High Energy Physics	1	$5,500
Nano Science and Technology	2	$345,500
Physics and other Science Education	1	$150,000
Total	**10**	**$692,926**

FACULTY

Professor

Bidarian, Akbar, Ph.D., University of Kentucky, 1990. *Applied Physics, Electrical Engineering, Engineering Physics/Science, Low Temperature Physics, Materials Science, Metallurgy, Polymer Physics/Science, Solid State Physics*. Properties of polymers; superconductors with high-critical temperatures; robotics; automation and electronic control systems.

Broadbridge, Christine C., Ph.D., Brown University, 1993. SCSU Executive Director of Research and Innovation. Education Director, Center for Research on Interface Structures and Phenomena, Yale University/SCSU; Director, Connecticut State University Center for Nanotechnology. *Applied Physics, Condensed Matter Physics, Materials Science, Metallurgy, Nano Science and Technology, Physics and other Science Education, Solid State Physics, Surface Physics, Systems Science/Engineering*. Advanced materials and nanostructures for microelectronics and optoelectronics; scanning probe and electron microscopy; X-ray diffraction and spectroscopy; best practices in professional development for STEM educators.

Cummings, Karen, Ph.D., State University of New York at Albany, 1996. Assessment Coordinator. *Physics and other Science Education*. Learning and teaching physics, including the effective use of technology, the development of problem-solving ability in introductory students, and the development of curricular materials for use in modern learning environments.

Dolan, James F., Ph.D., University of Connecticut, 1983. *Applied Physics, Optics*. Spectroscopy of solid-state lasers and effects of ultraviolet light on optical fibers; polarization effects in interferometric measurements. Fluorescence of biological specimens.

Enjalran, Matthew, Ph.D., University of California, Davis, 2000. Department Chairperson. *Applied Physics, Computational Physics, Condensed Matter Physics, Solid State Physics, Statistical & Thermal Physics, Theoretical Physics*. Condensed-matter many-body physics; frustrated magnetism and correlated electrons; statistical mechanics and phase transitions; numerical techniques for many-body systems.

Horch, Elliott P., Ph.D., Stanford University, 1994. Adjunct Astronomer, Lowell Observatory. *Applied Physics, Astronomy,*

Astrophysics, Optics. High-resolution imaging techniques for astronomy; design and construction of instrumentation for large telescopes; binary stars as probes of stellar and galactic evolution; exoplanets.

Associate Professor

Schwendemann, Todd C., Ph.D., University of Virginia, 2006. Associate Director, Connecticut State University Center for Nanotechnology; Visiting Assistant Professor, Yale University Department of Mechanical Engineering. *Applied Physics, Chemical Physics, Condensed Matter Physics, Engineering Physics/Science, Materials Science, Metallurgy, Nano Science and Technology, Solid State Physics, Surface Physics, Systems Science/Engineering.* Nanoscale friction/adhesion (nanotriboloy) through the manipulation of nanoparticles; thin-film and nanoparticle deposition by matrix-assisted processing (pulsed laser deposition); high-resolution scanning probe microscopy.

Assistant Professor

Finch, Leon E., Ph.D., Yale University, 1999. Graduate Program Coordinator. Member of STAR experimental collaboration at Brookhaven National Lab. *Applied Physics, High Energy Physics, Nuclear Physics.* Experimental nuclear and high-energy particle physics, particle astrophysics.

Wu, Binlin, Ph.D., City University of New York, 2013. *Applied Physics, Biophysics, Medical, Health Physics, Optics.* Biophysics and medical physics, optics, imaging and spectroscopy with special interests in biomedical applications.

DEPARTMENTAL RESEARCH SPECIALTIES AND STAFF

Theoretical

Condensed Matter Physics. Magnetism; correlated many-body systems; phase transitions; statistical mechanics; numerical methods. Enjalran.

Experimental

Astronomy. High-resolution imaging techniques for astronomy; binary stars as probes of stellar and galactic evolution; exoplanets. Horch.

Condensed Matter Physics. Properties of polymers; high Tc superconductors; thin-film and nanoparticle deposition by matrix assisted processing (pulsed laser deposition); spectroscopy of materials. Bidarian, Broadbridge, Cummings, Schwendemann.

Medical, Health Physics. Biomedical physics and biophysics, optical imaging methods of biological materials. Wu.

Nano Science and Technology. Advanced materials and nanostructures for microelectronics and optoelectronics; scanning probe and electron microscopy; X-ray diffraction and spectroscopy; nanoscale friction/adhesion (nanotriboloy) through the manipulation of nanoparticles; high-resolution scanning probe microscopy. Broadbridge, Schwendemann, Wu.

Nuclear Physics. High-energy nuclear physics, relativistic heavy ions. Finch.

Optics. Spectroscopy of solid-state lasers and effects of ultraviolet light on optical fibers; polarization effects in interferometric measurements. Fluorescence of biological specimens. Design and construction of optical instrumentation for large telescopes. Dolan, Horch, Wu.

Particles and Fields. High-energy astro-particle physics. Finch.

Physics and other Science Education. Learning and teaching physics, including the effective use of technology, the development of problem-solving ability in introductory students, the development of curricular materials for use in the modern learning environment, and professional development for STEM educators. Broadbridge, Cummings.

View additional information about this department at www.gradschoolshopper.com. Check out the "Why Choose Us?" section, find out more about the department's culture and get links to social media networks.

UNIVERSITY OF CONNECTICUT

DEPARTMENT OF PHYSICS

Storrs, Connecticut 06269-3046
http://www.physics.uconn.edu

General University Information
President: Susan Herbst
Dean of Graduate School: Kent Holsinger
University website: http://www.uconn.edu
School Type: Public
Setting: Rural
Total Faculty: 1,518
Total Graduate Faculty: 1,307
Total number of Students: 32,027
Total number of Graduate Students: 8,397

Department Information
Department Chairman: Prof. Barrett Wells, Head
Department Contact: Micki Bellamy, Academic Advisor
　Total full-time faculty: 33
　Total number of full-time equivalent positions: 33
　Full-Time Graduate Students: 85
　Female Full-Time Graduate Students: 12
　First-Year Graduate Students: 18
　Female First-Year Students: 3
　Total Post Doctorates: 13

Department Address
2152 Hillside Road
Storrs, CT 06269-3046
Phone: (860) 486-0449
Fax: (860) 486-3346
E-mail: micki.bellamy@uconn.edu
Website: http://www.physics.uconn.edu

ADMISSIONS

Admission Contact Information
Address admission inquiries to: The Whetten Graduate Center, Second Floor, University of Connecticut, 438 Whitney Road Extension, Unit-1152, Storrs, CT 06269-1152
Phone: (860) 486-0449
E-mail: micki.bellamy@uconn.edu
Admissions website: http://www.grad.uconn.edu

Application deadlines
Fall admission:
U.S. students: January 15　　　*Int'l. students*: January 15

Application fee
U.S. students: $75　　　*Int'l. students*: $75

Admissions information
For Fall of 2018:
　Number of applicants: 90
　Number admitted: 40
　Number enrolled: 18

Admission requirements
Bachelor's degree requirements: A bachelor's degree in Physics or a closely allied field with a sufficient concentration in physics is required.
Minimum undergraduate GPA: 3.0

GRE requirements
The GRE is required.
No minimum acceptable score is specified, but GRE scores are considered as part of application.

Subjective GRE requirements
The Subjective GRE is required.
No minimum acceptable score is specified, but GRE scores are considered as part of application.

TOEFL requirements
The TOEFL exam is required for students from non-English-speaking countries.
　iBT score: 92
minimum TOEFL speak score 22

Other admissions information
Additional requirements: Non-degree students may register under the Extended Education Program. Transfer to the Graduate Program may be possible for those with adequate academic performance.

TUITION

Tuition year 2018–19:
Tuition for in-state residents
　Full-time students: $8,830 per semester
　Part-time students: $853 per credit
Tuition for out-of-state residents
　Full-time students: $19,636 per semester
　Part-time students: $2,561 per credit
Tuition is waived for graduate assistants, veterans, and other certain groups of individuals (see graduate catalog for details).
Credit hours per semester to be considered full-time: 6
Deferred tuition plan: No
Health insurance: Available at the cost of $200 per year.
Other academic fees: General university fee, $278; Student Health Service fee, $193; Infrastructure fee, $117; Activity fee, $16; Matriculation fee, $42; Transit fee for on-campus residents to support campus shuttle, $80; Technology Fee, $75. (full-time per semester)
Academic term: Semester

Teaching Assistants, Research Assistants, and Fellowships
Average stipend per academic year
　Teaching Assistant: $22,910
　Research Assistant: $22,910
　Fellowship student: $22,910

FINANCIAL AID

Application deadlines
Fall admission:
U.S. students: January 15　　　*Int'l. students*: January 15

Loans
Loans are available for U.S. students.
Loans are not available for international students.
GAPSFAS application required: No
FAFSA application required: Yes

For further information

Address financial aid inquiries to: Caroline Cichocki, Physics Department, 2152 Hillside Road, U-3046, Storrs, CT 06269-3046.

Phone: (860) 486-4924

E-mail: caroline.cichocki@uconn.edu

Financial aid website: http://grad.uconn.edu/financial-resources/

HOUSING

Availability of on-campus housing

Single students: No

Married students: No

Childcare Assistance: No

For further information

Address housing inquiries to: The Whetten Graduate Center, Second Floor, University of Connecticut, 438 Whitney Road Extension, Unit-1152, Storrs, CT 06269-1152.

Phone: 860-486-3617

E-mail: gradschool@uconn.edu

Housing aid website: http://www.reslife.uconn.edu

Table A—Faculty, Enrollments, and Degrees Granted

Research Specialty	2017–18 Faculty	Enrollment Fall 2017		Number of Degrees Granted 2017–18 (2015–18)		
		Master's	Doctorate	Master's	Terminal Master's	Doctorate
Astrophysics	3	2	5	1(1)	1(2)	–(1)
Atomic, Molecular, & Optical Physics	8	–	21	–(2)	–(5)	3(9)
Condensed Matter Physics	8	1	19	1(2)	2(2)	5(15)
Geophysics	1	–	3	–	–	1(3)
Nuclear Physics	7	–	19	–	–(3)	2(6)
Particles and Fields	4	1	6	–(1)	–(1)	1(3)
Polymer Physics/Science	1	–	7	–	–	–
Total	33	4	81	2(6)	3(13)	12(36)
Full-time Grad. Stud.	–	2	81	–	–	–
First-year Grad. Stud.	–	2	15	–	–	–

GRADUATE DEGREE REQUIREMENTS

Master's: For the Thesis MS degree, 21 credits of graduate courses and 9 additional credits of Master's Thesis Research, and a thesis, are required. For the Non-Thesis MS degree, 30 credits of graduate courses are required. Either of these degrees may (but need not) be part of a Ph.D. program. The courses submitted must be approved in advance by the student's Advisory Committee. An average of B or better must be maintained. For the Thesis MS degree a final oral examination is required. There is no foreign language or residency requirement.

Doctorate: The student must complete a plan of study of extent and quality satisfactory to the student's Advisory Committee and the Dean of the Graduate School. Ordinarily, the program will include at least 15 credits beyond the master's degree, and 15 credits of Doctoral Dissertation Research. An average of B or better must be maintained. QMIII and EMII are required for the PhD degree. At least one year must be in residence. The General Examination must be taken by the end of the fifth semester. There is no foreign language or residency requirement.

Thesis: Thesis may be written in absentia.

SPECIAL EQUIPMENT, FACILITIES, OR PROGRAMS

The Physics Department occupies an 80,000-square-foot physics building and 25,000 square feet in the basement of an adjacent Biological Sciences/Physics building that provides research facilities for theoretical and experimental atomic, molecular, and optical physics; condensed matter physics; nuclear physics; theoretical particle physics; astrophysics; and general relativity. In addition, the Institute of Materials Science, adjacent to the Physics Department, provides research facilities for theoretical and experimental condensed matter physics.

The Physics Department's own computer research network includes three high-performance parallel clusters. The Department's computer laboratory provides students and faculty with access to Linux, Windows, and Mac workstations and a variety of software for numerical analysis, scientific visualization, symbolic processing, and program development.

Faculty from the Physics Department have developed joint research programs with Brookhaven National Laboratory in NY, the Thomas Jefferson National Accelerator Facility in VA, Argonne National Laboratory in IL, the NASA/Caltech Jet Propulsion Laboratory in CA, the Lawrence Livermore National Laboratory in CA, Oak Ridge National Laboratory in TN, the National Institute of Standards and Technology in MD and CO, the LCLS at SLAC in Stanford, CA, and many other American and foreign universities and research institutions.

Prospective students should visit http://www.phys.uconn.edu/research.

Table B—Separately Budgeted Research Expenditures by Source of Support

Source of Support	Departmental Research	Physics-related Research Outside Department
Federal government	$3,506,104	
State/local government		
Non-profit organizations		
Business and industry		
Other		
Total	$3,506,104	

Table C—Separately Budgeted Research Expenditures by Research Specialty

Research Specialty	No. of Grants	Expenditures ($)
Atomic, Molecular, & Optical Physics	13	$1,948,595
Condensed Matter Physics	4	$ 233,133
Geophysics	2	$ 184,797
Nuclear Physics	11	$ 879,360
Particles and Fields	2	$ 260,219
Polymer Physics/Science	–	
Total	32	$3,506,104

FACULTY

Professor

Balatsky, Alexander V., Ph.D., Landau Institute, Moscow, 1987. *Condensed Matter Physics, Polymer Physics/Science*. Condensed Matter Physics, Nanoscience, Biophysics and DNA, Materials Informatics. Quantum materials, Dirac materials, multiferroics, nonequilibrium states of matter.

Berrah, Nora, Ph.D., University of Virginia, 1987. Department Head. *Atomic, Molecular, & Optical Physics*. Atomic and molecular dynamics and spectroscopy; nonlinear physics; quantum control of atoms, molecules, and clusters; ultrafast time scales and strong laser fields. The research involves the use of intense femtosecond free electron lasers (FEL) in the vuv and X-ray regimes to probe physical and chemical processes that happen on ultrafast time scales.

Blum, Thomas, Ph.D., University of Arizona, 1995. Associate Department Head for Undergraduate Education. *High Energy Physics, Particles and Fields*. Theoretical high-energy physics; lattice gauge theory; quantum chromodynamics (QCD); electroweak physics.

Côté, Robin, Ph.D., Massachusetts Institute of Technology, 1995. Associate Department Head for Administration. *Atomic, Molecular, & Optical Physics*. Theoretical atomic and molecular physics; ultracold collisions; Bose-Einstein condensation.

Cormier, Vernon F., Ph.D., Columbia University, 1976. *Geology/Geochemistry, Geophysics*. Wave propagation in deep earth structures.

Dunne, Gerald V., Ph.D., Imperial College, London, 1988. *Particles and Fields*. Theoretical particle physics; quantum field theory; gauge theory; mathematical physics.

Dutta, Niloy K., Ph.D., Cornell University, 1978. Associate Department Head for Graduate Research and Education. *Condensed Matter Physics, Engineering Physics/Science, Optics*. Experimental condensed matter and optical physics; semiconductor laser technology; quantum wires; fiber-optic transmission systems.

Fernando, Gayanath W., Ph.D., Cornell University, 1985. *Condensed Matter Physics*. Theoretical condensed matter physics; properties of transition metals.

Gibson, George N., Ph.D., University of Illinois at Chicago, 1990. *Atomic, Molecular, & Optical Physics*. High-intensity, short-pulse laser physics; laser spectroscopy.

Gould, Phillip L., Ph.D., Massachusetts Institute of Technology, 1986. *Atomic, Molecular, & Optical Physics*. Experimental quantum optics; laser cooling and trapping of atoms.

Hamilton, Douglas S., Ph.D., University of Wisconsin-Madison, 1976. *Condensed Matter Physics, Optics*. Experimental condensed matter physics; nonlinear optics; light scattering; solid-state laser design; dynamics of ions in solids.

Javanainen, Juha, Ph.D., University of Helsinki, 1981. *Atomic, Molecular, & Optical Physics*. Theoretical quantum optics; interaction of light with atoms.

Joo, Kyungseon, Ph.D., Massachusetts Institute of Technology, 1997. *Nuclear Physics*. High-energy nuclear physics.

Kharchenko, Vasili A., Ph.D., Ioffe Institute, St. Petersburg, 1977. *Astrophysics, Atomic, Molecular, & Optical Physics, Planetary Science*. Theoretical physics and X-ray astrophysics; hot atoms in planetary atmospheres; kinetics and theory of atomic collisions.

Kovner, Alex, Ph.D., Tel Aviv University, 1985. *Particles and Fields*. Theoretical particle physics; strongly coupled gauge theories.

Mannheim, Philip D., Ph.D., Weizmann Institute of Science, 1970. *Astrophysics, Particles and Fields, Relativity & Gravitation*. Theoretical physics; elementary particle theory; general relativity; astrophysics.

Wells, Barrett O., Ph.D., Stanford University, 1992. *Condensed Matter Physics*. Experimental condensed matter physics; neutron scattering; superconductivity; photoemission.

Wuosmaa, Alan, Ph.D., University of Pennsylvania, 1988. *Nuclear Physics*. Experimental nuclear and hadronic physics; transfer reactions, structure of exotic nuclei, particle detectors and spectrometers.

Yelin, Susanne F., Ph.D., Ludwig-Maximilians University (Munich), 1998. *Atomic, Molecular, & Optical Physics, Condensed Matter Physics, Optics*. Theoretical quantum optics and condensed matter physics; spin physics in semiconduc-tors; quantum coherence and quantum information; nonlinear optics in atoms and semiconductors.

Associate Professor

Dormidontova, Elena, Ph.D., Moscow State University, 1994. *Biophysics, Condensed Matter Physics, Polymer Physics/Science, Theoretical Physics*. Theoretical soft condensed matter physics, biophysics; theoretical and computational soft matter physics; (bio)macromolecules, networks, associating systems, micelles, biomedical applications, polymer-modified nanoparticles, surfaces, phase separation.

Jain, Menka, Ph.D., University of Puerto Rico, 2004. *Condensed Matter Physics*. Experimental condensed matter physics.

Jones, Richard T., Ph.D., Virginia Polytechnic Institute and State University (Virginia Tech), 1988. *Nuclear Physics*. Experimental nuclear physics.

Schweitzer, Peter, Ph.D., University of Bochum, 2001. *Nuclear Physics, Particles and Fields*. Theoretical nuclear physics.

Sinkovic, Boris, Ph.D., University of Hawaii, 1986. *Condensed Matter Physics*. Experimental condensed matter physics; magnetic properties of films, surfaces, and nanostructures.

Trallero-Herrero, Carlos, Ph.D., Stony Brook University, 2007. Atomic, Molecular, and Optical Physics. Strong-field processes in atoms, molecules, solids and nanostructures. Ultrafast and attosecond optics and dynamics.

Assistant Professor

Battersby, Cara, Ph.D., University of Colorado, Boulder, 2013. *Astrophysics*. Star formation in galactic center. Massive stars and star cluster.

Hancock, Jason, Ph.D., University of California, Santa Cruz, 2005. *Condensed Matter Physics*. Topological insulators; superconductivity; correlated materials.

Jin, Luchang, Ph.D., Columbia University, 2016. Particle Physics. Lattice Quantum Chromodynamics(QCD).

McCarron, Daniel, Ph.D., University of Durham, 2012. Atomic, Molecular and Optical Physics. Ultracold atoms and molecules, quantum degenerate gases, new platforms for quantum computation and simulation using polar molecules, ultracold chemistry and precise tests of fundamental physics.

Puckett, Andrew, Ph.D., Massachusetts Institute of Technology, 2009. *High Energy Physics, Nuclear Physics, Particles and Fields*. Experimental nuclear/particle/hadronic physics; precision studies of the internal quark structure and QCD dynamics of strongly interacting matter in medium-energy fixed-target electron scattering experiments at Jefferson Laboratory.

Sochnikov, Ilya, Ph.D., Bar-Ilan University, 2011. *Condensed Matter Physics, Low Temperature Physics, Nano Science and Technology, Solid State Physics*. Nanoscale magnetic imaging, low dimensional systems & nanotechnology, topological insulators, superconductivity, correlated systems, quantum magnetism.

Trump, Jonathan, Ph.D., University of Arizona, 2010. *Astronomy*. Black holes and galaxy evolution. Spatially resolved spectroscopy and industrial-scale time-domain observations.

Whitaker, Katherine, Ph.D., Yale, 2012. *Astronomy*. Observational galaxy formation and evolution. Star formation and galaxy morphology.

Emeritus

Bartram, Ralph H., Ph.D., New York University, 1960. *Condensed Matter Physics*. Theoretical condensed matter physics; optical and magnetic properties of point imperfections in solids.

Best, Philip E., Ph.D., University of Western Australia, 1962. *Condensed Matter Physics*. Experimental surface physics; electron scattering.

Budnick, Joseph I., Ph.D., Rutgers University, 1955. *Condensed Matter Physics*. Experimental condensed matter physics; nuclear magnetic resonance; critical phenomena.

Gilliam, O. R., Ph.D., Duke University, 1950. *Condensed Matter Physics*. Experimental condensed matter physics; electron spin resonance.

Hahn, Yukap, Ph.D., Yale University, 1962. *Atomic, Molecular, & Optical Physics*. Theoretical atomic, molecular, and optical physics.

Hayden, Howard, Ph.D., University of Denver, 1967. *Condensed Matter Physics*. Experimental condensed matter physics.

Hines, William A., Ph.D., University of California, Berkeley, 1967. *Condensed Matter Physics*. Experimental condensed matter physics; nuclear magnetic resonance and magnetization studies of metals and alloys.

Islam, M. M., Ph.D., Imperial College, London, 1961. *High Energy Physics*. Theoretical physics; high-energy scattering; nucleon structure.

Kappers, Lawrence A., Ph.D., University of Missouri, Columbia, 1970. *Condensed Matter Physics*. Experimental condensed matter physics; color centers; optical properties; radiation damage.

Kessel, Quentin, Ph.D., University of Connecticut, 1966. *Astrophysics, Atomic, Molecular, & Optical Physics*. Experimental atomic and molecular physics; ionization; X-rays; Auger electrons; laboratory astrophysics.

Markowitz, David, Ph.D., University of Illinois, 1963. *Condensed Matter Physics*. Theoretical condensed matter physics.

Pease, Douglas M., Ph.D., University of Connecticut, 1972. *Condensed Matter Physics*. Experimental condensed matter physics; X-ray studies of alloys.

Peterson, Cynthia W., Ph.D., Cornell University, 1964. Manages the planetarium and observatory. *Astronomy, Biophysics, Condensed Matter Physics*. Experimental condensed matter physics; vacuum UV reflection spectroscopy; UV photoemission spectroscopy; biophysics.

Russek, Arnold, Ph.D., New York University, 1953. *Atomic, Molecular, & Optical Physics*. Theoretical atomic, molecular, and optical physics.

Smith, Winthrop W., Ph.D., Massachusetts Institute of Technology, 1963. *Atomic, Molecular, & Optical Physics*. Experimental atomic physics; ion-atom collisions; beam-foil spectroscopy; laser spectroscopy; laboratory astrophysics.

Stwalley, William C., Ph.D., Harvard University, 1969. *Atomic, Molecular, & Optical Physics*. Experimental atomic and molecular interactions; laser spectroscopy and dynamics of atoms and molecules; ultracold atoms and molecules.

Professor Emeritus

Mallett, Ronald L., Ph.D., Pennsylvania State University, 1973. *Astrophysics, Relativity & Gravitation*. Theoretical physics; relativity and gravitation; relativistic quantum theory.

Adjunct Professor

Bates, Stephen C., Ph.D., Massachusetts Institute of Technology, 1977. *Condensed Matter Physics*. Experimental condensed matter physics.

Deveney, Edward F., Ph.D., University of Connecticut, 1993. *Atomic, Molecular, & Optical Physics*. Experimental atomic and molecular physics.

Kussow, Adil-Gerai, Ph.D., A.F. Ioffe Institute of Physics and Technology (St. Petersburg), 1977. *Condensed Matter Physics, Solid State Physics*. Solid-state theory: electron excitations; magnetic properties of thin films; theory of defects and fracture; first-principle electronic structure calculations.

Affiliate Professor

Birge, Robert R., Ph.D., Wesleyan College, 1972. Molecular biophysics; biomolecular electronics; biomolecular spectroscopy.

Edson, James, Ph.D., Pennsylvania State University, 1989. *Climate/Atmospheric Science, Marine Science/Oceanography*. Boundary layer meteorology with a focus on surface layer turbulence and air-sea interaction.

Huber, Greg, Ph.D., Boston University, 1993. *Biophysics, Nonlinear Dynamics and Complex Systems*. Biological physics and mechanics; biocomplexity; soft matter physics; nonequilibrium and nonlinear dynamics.

Liu, Lambo, Ph.D., Stanford University, 1993. *Geophysics*. Applied and computational geophysics; continental tectonophysics.

Michels, H. Harvey, Ph.D., University of Delaware, 1960. *Atomic, Molecular, & Optical Physics, Chemical Physics*. Theoretical atomic and molecular physics.

Montgomery, John A., Ph.D., Columbia University, 1978. *Atomic, Molecular, & Optical Physics, Computational Physics*. Computational molecular physics.

O'Donnell, James, Ph.D., University of Delaware, 1986. *Fluids, Rheology, Marine Science/Oceanography*. Physics of the coastal ocean; environmental fluid dynamics; mathematical models of environmental processes.

Papadimitrakopoulos, Fotios, Ph.D., University of Massachusetts, 1993. *Biophysics, Condensed Matter Physics*. Self-assembly of organic, inorganic, biological, and hybrid nanostructures; devices and sensors; organic semiconductors; II-VI and Si nanocrystals; carbon nanotubes.

Roychoudhuri, Chandrasekhar, Ph.D., University of Rochester, 1973. *Optics*. Experimental optical physics; semiconductor laser technology.

Schweitzer, Jeffrey S., Ph.D., Purdue University, 1972. *Astrophysics, Nuclear Physics, Solar Physics*. Experimental nuclear physics; nuclear astrophysics; solar physics.

DEPARTMENTAL RESEARCH SPECIALTIES AND STAFF

Theoretical

Astrophysics. Dark matter, dark energy, and the cosmological constant problem; interplay of cosmology and particle physics; neutrino oscillations; applications of standard and alternate gravity theories to astrophysics and cosmology; astrophysical plasmas and neutral gas; physics of the heliosphere; new astrophysical sources of X-ray emission; applications of quantum collision theory to the physics of planetary atmospheres and interstellar gas. Battersby, Kharchenko, Mallett, Mannheim, Trump, Whitaker.

Atomic, Molecular, & Optical Physics. Atomic and molecular structure; interaction of light with atoms; Bose-Einstein condensation; ultracold collisions; quantum coherence and quantum information. Côté, Javanainen, Kharchenko, Yelin.

Condensed Matter Physics. Electronic properties of point imperfections in ionic solids; thermal and electronic properties of transition metals; thermal conduction by lattice waves and electrons; spin physics in semiconductors; light-matter interactions. Balatsky, Dormidontova, Fernando, Yelin.

High Energy Physics. Theoretical particle physics; lattice gauge theory, quantum chromodynamics, and quantum electrodynamics; neutrino oscillations. Blum, Dunne, Jin, Kovner, Mannheim, Peter Schweitzer.

Nuclear Physics. Scattering and rearrangement reactions of projectiles on nuclei; saturation physics; theory and phenomenology of strong interactions. Joo, Kovner, Peter Schweitzer.

Polymer Physics/Science. Self-assembling polymers; polymer/nanoparticle mixtures. Balatsky, Dormidontova.

Experimental

Atomic, Molecular, & Optical Physics. Cold ion-neutral collisions; quasimolecular processes in heavy ion collisions; laser spectroscopy and atomic and molecular interactions; laser cooling and trapping of atoms; high-intensity, short-pulse laser physics; precision laser spectroscopy; ultracold molecules and plasmas. Berrah, Gibson, Gould, McCarron, Stwalley, Trallero-Herrero.

Condensed Matter Physics. Electronic structure of alloys; magnetically ordered systems; high-temperature superconductivity; surface modification; point defects in nonmetallic crystals via ESR; NMR and magnetization studies of metals and alloys; point defects in ionic crystals via optical methods; laser spectroscopy of solids; angular-dependent electron spectroscopy from surfaces; semiconductor laser technology and fiber-optic transmission systems; neutron scattering; photoemission; X-ray absorption spectroscopy; very high-peak-power ps diodes for material processing; broadly tunable diodes and novel mux/demux devices for DWDM. Dutta, Hamilton, Hancock, Jain, Peterson, Sinkovic, Wells.

Geophysics. Deep earth and planetary structure; elastic wave propagation; earthquake source properties. Cormier.

Nuclear Physics. Nuclear astrophysics; nuclear structure; the structure of the nucleon; low-energy QCD; meson spectroscopy. Jones, Joo, Puckett, Wuosmaa.

View additional information about this department at www.gradschoolshopper.com. Check out the "Why Choose Us?" section, find out more about the department's culture and get links to social media networks.

WESLEYAN UNIVERSITY

PHYSICS DEPARTMENT

Middletown, Connecticut 06459-0155
https://www.wesleyan.edu/physics/

General University Information
President: Michael S. Roth
Dean of Graduate School: Martha S. Gilmore
University website: https://www.wesleyan.edu
School Type: Private
Setting: Suburban
Total Faculty: 400
Total Graduate Faculty: 400
Total number of Students: 2,971
Total number of Graduate Students: 240

Department Information
Department Chairman: Prof. Greg A. Voth, Chair
Department Contact: Dana Gordon Gannuscio, Administrative
Assistant
    Total full-time faculty: 12
    Total number of full-time equivalent positions: 12
    Full-Time Graduate Students: 16
    Female Full-Time Graduate Students: 7
    First-Year Graduate Students: 3
    Female First-Year Students: 1
    Total Post Doctorates: 7

Department Address
265 Church Street, 2nd floor
Exley Science Center
Middletown, CT 06459-0155
Phone: (860) 685-2030
Fax: (860) 685-2031
E-mail: gradappphys@wesleyan.edu
Website: https://www.wesleyan.edu/physics/

ADMISSIONS

Admission Contact Information
Address admission inquiries to: Wesleyan University, Physics
Department, 265 Church St., Middletown, CT 06459
Phone: 860-685-2030
E-mail: gradappphys@wesleyan.edu
Admissions website: https://www.wesleyan.edu/physics/
graduate/

Application deadlines
Fall admission:
U.S. students: January 31   *Int'l. students*: January 31
Spring admission:
U.S. students: September 30   *Int'l. students*: September 30

Application fee
There is no application fee required.
Online form found at http://www.wesleyan.edu/grad/apply.html

Admissions information
For Fall of 2018:
    Number of applicants: 60
    Number admitted: 3
    Number enrolled: 3

Admission requirements
Bachelor's degree requirements: Bachelor's degree in physics
is required.

GRE requirements
The GRE is recommended but not required.

Subjective GRE requirements
The Subjective GRE is recommended.

TOEFL requirements
The TOEFL exam is required for students from non-English-
speaking countries.
    PBT score: 550
    iBT score: 80
TOEFL waived for international students with a degree from a
U.S. University

Other admissions information
Additional requirements: Three letters of recommendation, statement of purpose, transcripts.

TUITION

Tuition year 2017–18:
All graduate students who are enrolled full-time receive a tuition
waiver and most receive a graduate assitantship stipend.
Deferred tuition plan: No
Health insurance: Available at the cost of $650 per year.
Other academic fees: Activity fee $20
Academic term: Semester
Number of first-year students who received full tuition waivers: 3

Teaching Assistants, Research Assistants, and Fellowships
    Average stipend per academic year
        Teaching Assistant: $33,000
    Students receiving teaching assistantship stipends from Wes-
leyan must TA one course each semester.

FINANCIAL AID

Loans
Loans are available for U.S. students.
Loans are not available for international students.
GAPSFAS application required: No
FAFSA application required: No

For further information
Address financial aid inquiries to: Wesleyan University, Office
of Financial Aid, 237 High Street, Middletown, CT 06459.
Phone: (860) 685-2800
E-mail: finaid@wesleyan.edu
Financial aid website: http://www.wesleyan.edu/finaid/
graduatestudent.html

HOUSING

Availability of on-campus housing
    Single students: Yes
    Married students: Yes
    Childcare Assistance: No

For further information

Address housing inquiries to: Wesleyan University, Office of Residential Life, 237 High Street, North College - Lower Level, Middletown, CT 06459.
Phone: 8606853500
E-mail: reslife@wesleyan.edu
Housing aid website: http://www.wesleyan.edu/reslife/grad_housing/index.html

Table A—Faculty, Enrollments, and Degrees Granted

Research Specialty	2017–18 Faculty	Enrollment Fall 2018 Master's	Enrollment Fall 2018 Doctorate	Number of Degrees Granted 2016–17 (2012–18) Master's	Number of Degrees Granted 2016–17 (2012–18) Terminal Master's	Number of Degrees Granted 2016–17 (2012–18) Doctorate
Atomic, Molecular, &						
Optical Physics	4	–	3	–	–	–(3)
Biophysics	1	–	1	–	–	3(3)
Condensed Matter						
Physics	4	4	5	–(2)	–	–(4)
Theoretical Physics	3	–	4	2(2)	–(1)	1(4)
Total	11	4	13	–(4)	–(1)	–(14)
Full-time Grad. Stud.	–	4	13	–	–	–
First-year Grad. Stud.	–	4	3	–	–	–

GRADUATE DEGREE REQUIREMENTS

Master's: A minimum of eight credits with grades of B- or better is required for the MA degree. These may include three credits in research leading to the thesis, which is also required. Course selection is flexible and is done in consultation with the faculty adviser and with the members of the student's committee. Only students receiving an undergraduate degree from Wesleyan may directly enroll in the Master's program. Students applying to the graduate program from other undergraduate institutions are expected to pursue Doctorates.

Doctorate: While there are no specific course requirements for the Ph.D. degree, each student is required to take one course during every semester of residence. Students must have demonstrated proficiency in the main subject areas of physics before completion of the program. These areas embody quantum theory, including atomic, nuclear, and elementary particle physics, electromagnetism and optics, classical dynamics and relativity theory, thermal, statistical, and solid state physics. Three formal examinations serve to define the student's progress toward the degree. The first, taken during September of the second year, is a short written exam on material at an advanced undergraduate level. During the spring of the second year each student presents to his or her graduate advisory committee a description and defense of a specific research topic. Finally, the dissertation, based on original and significant research, must be defended in an oral examination. The spirit of the program is to give the student an early opportunity to become a recognized and significant member of the department. Emphasis is placed on having students "do physics" right from the start, rather than spend one or two years solely on course work before getting into research. To this end, graduate students are expected to join in the research activities of the department upon arrival.

Other Degrees: Wesleyan offers a BA/MA program as a formal curricular option for Wesleyan undergraduate students who are interested in an intensive research experience. The two semesters of MA work immediately follow the completion of the BA degree requirements.

Thesis: Thesis may be written in absentia.

SPECIAL EQUIPMENT, FACILITIES, OR PROGRAMS

Our research facilities include the following:

High-Performance Computing Facility with an aggregate performance in excess of 100 teraflops. The facility current consists of 1800 compute cores and 20 GPUs, along with more than 100 TB of data storage. All Wesleyan graduate students are offered access to these facilities. Hardware is updated annually to ensure resources are current with the latest technologies.

Molecular Physics Lab with pulsed laser system, nanosecond gated CCD camera, high resolution spectrometer, molecular beam apparatus, time-of-flight mass spectrometer.

Fluid Dynamics and Soft Matter lab with two turbulence facilities, a vertical water tunnel and a flow between oscillating grids, several other experiments, high speed cameras with real-time image processing hardware, pulsed YAG laser for illumination.

A newly established Microwave Laboratory with a two-port Keysight E5080A vector network analyzer, supporting metamaterial and mesoscopic physics (transport in disordered media and chaotic cavities) research at frequencies up to 7 GHz. The lab is equipped with a custom-made high performance computing system to run simulations for electromagnetic propagation and has licensed COMSOL and CST Microwave Studio solvers.

Single-Molecule Biophysics Laboratory with a home-built total internal reflection fluorescence (TIRF) microscopy system equipped with an electron-multiplying CCD camera and capable of two-channel simultaneous imaging utilizing multiple laser illumination options at wavelengths spanning the visible spectrum.

Molecular Collisions laboratory with multiple single-frequency diode lasers, double monochromator with high-sensitivity CCD camera, heat-pipe ovens and ancillary optical analysis equipment.

High Energy Molecular Spectroscopy Lab with particle accelerator-laser apparatus including a pulsed two dye laser system and a 10 keV accelerator.

Carrier Dynamics and Ultrafast Spectroscopy lab with Ti:Sapphire femtosecond laser oscillator and amplifier, frequency lock-in detection system, home-built terahertz spectrometer with sub-picosecond time resolution and wide bandwidth terahertz generation source.

Central advance imaging facility with a scanning electron microscope, transmission electron microscope, confocal microsope.

Table B—Separately Budgeted Research Expenditures by Source of Support

Source of Support	Departmental Research	Physics-related Research Outside Department
Federal government	$2,894,000	
State/local government		
Non-profit organizations		
Business and industry		
Other		
Total	$2,894,000	

FACULTY

Professor

Blümel, Reinhold, Ph.D., Technical Univ. of Munich, 1983. *Atomic, Molecular, & Optical Physics, Nuclear Physics*. Theoretical atomic, molecular, optical, and nuclear physics. Ion trapping, quantum chaos, exact solutions of "unsolvable" problems.

Ellis, Fred M., Ph.D., University of Massachusetts, Amherst, 1983. *Low Temperature Physics.* Low-temperature physics of quantum fluids.

Hüwel, Lutz, Ph.D., Georg-August Univ., Göttingen, 1980. *Atomic, Molecular, & Optical Physics.* Photo-ionization and dissociation of small molecules, electronic lifetimes, and laser-induced plasma in gases and liquids.

Kottos, Tsampikos, Ph.D., University of Crete, Greece, 1997. *Applied Physics, Electromagnetism, Nonlinear Dynamics and Complex Systems, Optics, Theoretical Physics.* Linear and nonlinear optics and photonics, applied electromagnetism, non-hermitian wave transport, mesoscopic physics, wave chaos.

Morgan, Thomas J., Ph.D., University of California, Berkeley, 1971. *Atomic, Molecular, & Optical Physics.* High energy molecule states, heavy Rydberg states.

Starr, Francis, Ph.D., Boston University, 1999. Director, College of Integrative Sciences. *Biophysics, Computational Physics, Materials Science, Metallurgy, Nano Science and Technology, Polymer Physics/Science, Statistical & Thermal Physics.*

Computational and theoretical approaches to problems in soft matter physics and biophysics.

Stewart, Brian, Ph.D., Massachusetts Institute of Technology, 1987. *Atomic, Molecular, & Optical Physics.* Collisions of small molecules.

Voth, Greg, Ph.D., Cornell University, 2000. Department Chair. *Condensed Matter Physics, Fluids, Rheology, Nonlinear Dynamics and Complex Systems.* Fluid dynamics and soft condensed matter.

Assistant Professor

Etson, Candice, Ph.D., Harvard University, 2010. *Biophysics, Physics and other Science Education.* Single molecule biophysics.

Paily, George M., Ph.D., MSC Indian Institute of Technology.

Sher, Meng-Ju (Renee), Ph.D., Harvard University, 2013. *Condensed Matter Physics, Optics.* Optoelectronic properties of renewable energy materials.

Tu, Min-Feng, Ph.D., California Institute of Technology.

DEPARTMENTAL RESEARCH SPECIALTIES AND STAFF

Experimental

View additional information about this department at www.gradschoolshopper.com. Check out the "Why Choose Us?" section, find out more about the department's culture and get links to social media networks.

UNIVERSITY OF DELAWARE

DEPARTMENT OF PHYSICS AND ASTRONOMY

Newark, Delaware 19716
http://web.physics.udel.edu

General University Information
President: Dennis Assanis
Dean of Graduate School: Doug Doren (Interim Vice Provost)
University website: http://www.udel.edu
School Type: Public
Setting: Suburban
Total Faculty: 1,277
Total number of Students: 27,774
Total number of Graduate Students: 4,024

Department Information
Department Chairman: Prof. Edmund Nowak, Chair
Department Contact: Elle Bornemann, Academic Support
  Coordinator
  Total full-time faculty: 37
  Total number of full-time equivalent positions: 35
  Full-Time Graduate Students: 80
  Female Full-Time Graduate Students: 7
  First-Year Graduate Students: 12
  Female First-Year Students: 1
  Total Post Doctorates: 13

Department Address
104 The Green/ 217 Sharp Lab
Newark, DE 19716
Phone: (302) 831-1995
Fax: (302) 831-1637
E-mail: physics@physics.udel.edu
Website: http://web.physics.udel.edu

ADMISSIONS

Admission Contact Information
Address admission inquiries to: Chair of Graduate Admissions
  Committee
Phone: (302) 831-1995
E-mail: physics@physics.udel.edu
Admissions website: http://web.physics.udel.edu/graduate/apply

Application deadlines
Fall admission:
U.S. students: April 15   *Int'l. students*: April 15

Application fee
U.S. students: $75   *Int'l. students*: $75

Admissions information
For Fall of 2018:
  Number of applicants: 129
  Number admitted: 34
  Number enrolled: 12

Admission requirements
Bachelor's degree requirements: Admission to either the M.S.
  or Ph.D. program requires a Bachelor's degree in Physics or
  a closely related field.
Minimum undergraduate GPA: 3.2

GRE requirements
The GRE is required.
  Quantitative score: 160
  Mean GRE score range (25th–75th percentile): 313-326
GRE scores are on new scale

Subjective GRE requirements
The Subjective GRE is required.
  Minimum accepted Advanced GRE score: 650
  Mean Advanced GRE score range (25th–75th percentile): 670-
  850

TOEFL requirements
The TOEFL exam is required for students from non-English-
  speaking countries.
  PBT score: 600
  iBT score: 100
IELTS score of 7.0 is acceptable in place of TOEFL.

Other admissions information
Additional requirements: Advanced GRE score expected for financial aid consideration.
Undergraduate preparation assumed: Electricity and Magnetism, Classical Mechanics, Quantum Mechanics, Thermodynamics.

TUITION

Tuition year 2018–19:
Tuition for in-state residents
  Full-time students: $15,930 per semester
  Part-time students: $1,770 per credit
Tuition for out-of-state residents
  Full-time students: $15,930 per semester
  Part-time students: $1,770 per credit
Teaching and Research Assistant tuition is waived.
Credit hours per semester to be considered full-time: 6
Deferred tuition plan: Yes
Health insurance: Available at the cost of $200 per year.
Other academic fees: $454 (Health Service) per year.
Academic term: Semester
Number of first-year students who received full tuition waivers: 13

Teaching Assistants, Research Assistants, and Fellowships
  Number of first-year
    Teaching Assistants: 13
  Average stipend per academic year
    Teaching Assistant: $27,500
    Research Assistant: $27,500

FINANCIAL AID

Application deadlines
Fall admission:
U.S. students: February 15   *Int'l. students*: February 15

Loans
Loans are not available for U.S. students.
Loans are not available for international students.
GAPSFAS application required: No

FAFSA application required: No

For further information

Address financial aid inquiries to: Chair Graduate Admissions Committee.

E-mail: physics@physics.udel.edu

HOUSING

Availability of on-campus housing

Single students: Yes

Married students: Yes

For further information

Address housing inquiries to: Office of Housing and Residence Life, www.udrentals.com.

Phone: 302-831-4663

E-mail: reslife-housing@udel.edu

Housing aid website: http://www1.udel.edu/reslife/resources/students/grad.html

Table A—Faculty, Enrollments, and Degrees Granted

Research Specialty	2018–2019 Faculty	Enrollment Fall 2018 Master's	Enrollment Fall 2018 Doctorate	Number of Degrees Granted 2017–2018 (2013–18) Master's	Number of Degrees Granted 2017–2018 (2013–18) Terminal Master's	Number of Degrees Granted 2017–2018 (2013–18) Doctorate
Astrophysics	6	–	8	–	–	–(1)
Atmosphere, Space Physics, Cosmic Rays	5	–	7	–	–	–(3)
Atomic, Molecular, & Optical Physics	8	–	14	1(3)	–	3(5)
Biophysics	1	–	4	–	–	–
Condensed Matter Physics	9	–	23	3(2)	–	6(14)
Particles and Fields	7	–	9	–(1)	–	2(8)
Non-specialized	–	–	15	–	–	–
Total	26	–	80	4(6)	–	11(31)
Full-time Grad. Stud.	–	–	80	–	–	–
First-year Grad. Stud.	–	–	12	–	–	–

GRADUATE DEGREE REQUIREMENTS

Master's: Twenty-four credit hours of classroom courses plus six credits of M.S. thesis. Thirty credit hours for M.S. without thesis.

Doctorate: Thirty credit hours of classroom courses, passing the Ph.D. written and oral candidacy exam, Ph.D. thesis. Students entering the program with a Master's degree may follow the Ph.D. fast track which has a reduced course requirement of 12 credit hours.

Thesis: Thesis may be written in absentia.

SPECIAL EQUIPMENT, FACILITIES, OR PROGRAMS

The Department of Physics and Astronomy is housed in Sharp Laboratory, which has its own library, machine and electronics shops, as well as research and teaching laboratories, classrooms, and office space. The condensed matter and material science programs have in house scanning and transmission microscopes, a variety of magnetometers, X-ray diffractometers, differential scanning calorimeters, thin-film deposition systems and cryogenic facilities, and make use of accelerator based facilities for X-ray and neutron scattering. The atomic and molecular physics laboratories include femtosecond and high-power pulsed lasers for non-linear optical studies and high resolution multiphoton spectroscopy. The astro-particle physics programs include high-

altitude balloon flights and high-energy cosmic ray and neutrino experiments in Antarctica (ICECUBE and Anita). Space physics programs maintain a world-wide network of neutron monitors and are involved with MMS, the Magnetosphere Multiscale mission, and multispacecraft missions such as Cluster-2, to study the magnetosphere and the solar wind. Opportunities are available for participation in several NASA missions: ACE, The Spitzer infrared telescope, the Chandra X-ray satellite and the Hubble Space Telescope. UD is the lead institution for the Whole Earth Telescope (WET). Further programs on campus are the Institute for Energy Conversion and the Center for Composite Materials.

Table B—Separately Budgeted Research Expenditures by Source of Support

Source of Support	Departmental Research	Physics-related Research Outside Department
Federal government	$4,444,846.03	
State/local government	$3,166.93	
Non-profit organizations	$118,486.65	
Business and industry	$104,359.6	
Other	$559,443.49	
Total	$5,230,302.7	

Table C—Separately Budgeted Research Expenditures by Research Specialty

Research Specialty	No. of Grants	Expenditures ($)
Astronomy	7	$172,849.17
Astrophysics	7	$69,204.97
Atmosphere, Space Physics, Cosmic Rays	20	$2,582,826.69
Atomic, Molecular, & Optical Physics		$886,806.94
Condensed Matter Physics		$829,023.24
High Energy Physics	1	$91,437.81
Particles and Fields	5	$598,153.88
Total	40	$5,230,302.7

FACULTY

Professor

Barr, Stephen, Ph.D., Princeton University, 1978. Director of Bartol Research Institute. *Particles and Fields*. Elementary particle theory.

Chui, Siu-Tat, Ph.D., Princeton University, 1972. *Condensed Matter Physics*. Theoretical condensed matter physics; low-dimensional and amorphous materials; nanomagnetism.

Evenson, Paul A., Ph.D., University of Chicago, 1972. *Atmosphere, Space Physics, Cosmic Rays*. Space physics; solar and cosmic-ray studies.

Gaisser, Thomas K., Ph.D., Brown University, 1967. *Particles and Fields*. Particle astrophysics; neutrino astronomy.

Gizis, John, Ph.D., California Institute of Technology, 1998. *Astrophysics*. Astronomy; subdwarfs; brown dwarfs.

Hadjipanayis, George C., Ph.D., University of Manitoba, 1979. *Condensed Matter Physics*. Experimental condensed matter and materials physics; magnetism; nanocrystalline materials.

Holder, Jamie, Ph.D., University of Durham, UK, 1997. *Particles and Fields*. Gamma ray astronomy.

MacDonald, James, Ph.D., University of Cambridge, 1979. *Astrophysics*. Astronomy and astrophysics; white dwarfs; cataclysmic variables.

Matthaeus, William H., Ph.D., College of William and Mary, 1979. *Astrophysics, Atmosphere, Space Physics, Cosmic Rays*. Space physics; plasma physics; turbulence theory; computational physics.

Mullan, Dermott J., Ph.D., University of Maryland, 1969. *Astrophysics*. Astrophysics; solar and stellar physics.

Nikolic, Branislav, Ph.D., Stony Brook University, 2000. Graduate Program Director. *Condensed Matter Physics*. Theoretical and computational condensed matter physics; nonequilibrium many-body theory; quantum transport; spintronics; nanoelectronics; thermoelectrics.

Nowak, Edmund R., Ph.D., University of Minnesota, 1994. *Condensed Matter Physics*. Experimental condensed matter and materials physics; magnetism; spintronics; superconductivity; granular materials.

Owocki, Stanley P., Ph.D., University of Colorado, 1982. *Astrophysics*. Computational astrophysics; stellar winds; stellar magnetospheres.

Safronova, Marianna, Ph.D., University of Notre Dame, 2001. *Atomic, Molecular, & Optical Physics*. Quantum computing with neutral atoms; Rydberg atoms.

Seckel, David, Ph.D., University of Washington, 1983. *Particles and Fields*. Particle astrophysics; cosmology.

Shafi, Qaisar, Ph.D., Imperial College, London, 1971. *Particles and Fields*. Elementary particle theory; cosmology.

Shah, Ismat, Ph.D., University of Illinois, 1986. *Condensed Matter Physics*. Experimental condensed matter and materials physics; thin films; surface; interface; nanostructures.

Shay, Michael, Ph.D., University of Maryland, College Park, 1998. *Atmosphere, Space Physics, Cosmic Rays*. Plasma physics; space physics; astrophysics.

Shipman, Harry L., Ph.D., California Institute of Technology, 1971. *Astronomy*. Astronomy and astrophysics; white dwarfs.

Stanev, Todor, Ph.D., Sofia, Bulgaria, 1977. *Particles and Fields*. Cosmic-ray physics; particle astrophysics.

Szalewicz, Krzysztof, Ph.D., University of Warsaw, 1977. *Atomic, Molecular, & Optical Physics*. Theoretical and computational molecular physics.

Unruh, Karl M., Ph.D., Johns Hopkins University, 1983. *Condensed Matter Physics*. Experimental condensed matter and materials physics; thin films; nanomagnetism.

Walker, Barry, Ph.D., Stony Brook University, 1996. *Atomic, Molecular, & Optical Physics*. Light-matter interactions; optical physics.

Watson, George, Ph.D., University of Delaware, 1984. *Condensed Matter Physics*. Experimental condensed matter and materials physics; laser spectroscopy of condensed matter; photonic band structure.

Xiao, John Q., Ph.D., Johns Hopkins University, 1993. *Condensed Matter Physics*. Experimental condensed matter and materials physics; spintronics; nanomagnetism.

Associate Professor

Clem, John, Ph.D., Vanderbilt, 1990. *Atmosphere, Space Physics, Cosmic Rays*. Particle astrophysics; space physics; cosmic-ray physics.

DeCamp, Matthew F., Ph.D., University of Michigan, 2002. Undergraduate program director. *Atomic, Molecular, & Optical Physics*. Experimental atomic and molecular physics.

Dodson-Robinson, Sarah, Ph.D., University of California at Santa Cruz, 2008. *Astronomy, Astrophysics, Planetary Sci-*

ence, Theoretical Physics. Planetary science; theoretical astrophysics; observational astronomy.

Ji, Yi, Ph.D., Johns Hopkins University, 2003. *Condensed Matter Physics*. Experimental condensed matter and materials physics; spintronics.

Morgan, John D., Ph.D., University of California, Berkeley, 1978. *Atomic, Molecular, & Optical Physics*. Theoretical atomic and molecular physics.

Provencal, Judith L., Ph.D., University Texas Austin, 1994. Director of the Delaware Asteroseismic Research Center (DARC). *Astronomy*. Observational astronomy and asteroseismic research.

Assistant Professor

Gundlach, Lars, Ph.D., Free University of Berlin, 2005. *Atomic, Molecular, & Optical Physics*. Experimental atomic and molecular physics.

Jungfleisch, Matthias B., Ph.D., TU Kaiserslautern, 2013. *Condensed Matter Physics*. magnetic interactions and spin-orbital phenomena in nanodevices.

Lyman, Edward, Ph.D., Virginia Polytechnic Institute and State University (Virginia Tech), 2004. *Biophysics*. Computational biophysics; soft condensed matter.

Maruca, Bennett, Ph.D., Harvard, 2012. *Atmosphere, Space Physics, Cosmic Rays*. Solar wind.

Petit, Veronique, Ph.D., Université Laval, 2011. *Astrophysics*. Magnetic fields in massive stars; optical, ultraviolet, and X-ray spectroscopy.

Schroeder, Frank G., Ph.D., Karisruhe Institute of Technology. *Particles and Fields*. High-energy cosmic particles (nuclei, photons, neutrinos); detectors for cosmic-ray air showers; techniques for tie and amplitude calibration.

DEPARTMENTAL RESEARCH SPECIALTIES AND STAFF

Theoretical

Astrophysics. Dodson-Robinson, Gizis, MacDonald, Matthaeus, Mullan, Owocki, Petit, Shay, Shipman.

Atmosphere, Space Physics, Cosmic Rays. Clem, Evenson, Gaisser, Maruca, Matthaeus, Seckel, Shay, Stanev.

Atomic, Molecular, & Optical Physics. DeCamp, Gundlach, Lyman, Morgan, Safronova, Szalewicz, Walker.

Biophysics. Gundlach, Lyman.

Condensed Matter Physics. Chui, Hadjipanayis, Ji, Jungfleisch, Nikolic, Nowak, Shah, Unruh, Xiao.

Particles and Fields. Barr, Gaisser, Holder, Seckel, Shafi, Stanev.

Experimental

Astrophysics. Gizis, Holder, Petit, Provencal, Shipman.

Atmosphere, Space Physics, Cosmic Rays. Evenson, Gaisser, Holder, Maruca.

Atomic, Molecular, & Optical Physics. DeCamp, Gundlach, Walker.

Condensed Matter Physics. Hadjipanayis, Ji, Nowak, Shah, Unruh, Watson, Xiao.

Optics. DeCamp, Walker, Watson.

Particles and Fields. Schroeder.

View additional information about this department at www.gradschoolshopper.com. Check out the "Why Choose Us?" section, find out more about the department's culture and get links to social media networks.

GEORGE WASHINGTON UNIVERSITY

DEPARTMENT OF PHYSICS

Washington, D.C. 20052
http://physics.columbian.gwu.edu/

General University Information
President: Thomas LeBlanc
Dean of Graduate School: Jeffrey Brand
University website: http://www.gwu.edu/
School Type: Private
Setting: Urban
Total Faculty: 4,673
Total Graduate Faculty: N/A
Total number of Students: 21,000
Total number of Graduate Students: 10,000

Department Information
Department Chairman: Prof. William J Briscoe, Chair
Department Contact: William J Briscoe, Chair
  Total full-time faculty: 22
  Total number of full-time equivalent positions: 19
  Full-Time Graduate Students: 50
  Female Full-Time Graduate Students: 10
  First-Year Graduate Students: 5
  Female First-Year Students: 1
  Total Post Doctorates: 9

Department Address
Corcoran Hall
725 21st Street, NW
Washington, D.C. 20052
Phone: (202) 994-6275
Fax: (202) 994-3001
E-mail: phys@gwu.edu
Website: http://physics.columbian.gwu.edu/

ADMISSIONS

Admission Contact Information
Address admission inquiries to: Prof. Chryssa Kouveliotou, Director of Graduate Programs, Department of Physics, 725 21st Street, NW, Washington D.C. 20052
Phone: (202) 994-5898
E-mail: gradappl@gwu.edu
Admissions website: https://graduate.admissions.gwu.edu/admissions

Application deadlines
Fall admission:
U.S. students: January 15   *Int'l. students*: January 15
Spring admission:
U.S. students: September 1   *Int'l. students*: September 1

Application fee
U.S. students: $75   *Int'l. students*: $75
April 01/2017 for MS applicants

Admissions information
For Fall of 2017:
  Number of applicants: 70
  Number admitted: 35
  Number enrolled: 17

Admission requirements
Bachelor's degree requirements: Bachelor's degree in Physics or equivalent is required.
Minimum undergraduate GPA: 3.0

GRE requirements
The GRE is required.
We require GRE general with a good Q score and reasonable A and V scores. There are no set values required.

Subjective GRE requirements
The Subjective GRE is recommended.
GRE subject is optional but reporting a good score can enhance your chances.

TOEFL requirements
The TOEFL exam is required for students from non-English-speaking countries.
  PBT score: 600
  iBT score: 100

Other admissions information
Undergraduate preparation assumed: Subjects at the level of Taylor, Classical Mechanics; Griffiths, Intro to Electrodynamics; Kittel and Kroemer, Thermal Physics; Griffiths, Intro to Quantum Mechanics.

TUITION

Tuition year 2018–19:
  Full-time students: $1,710 per credit
  Part-time students: $1,710 per credit
Credit hours per semester to be considered full-time: 9
Deferred tuition plan: Yes
Health insurance: Available at the cost of $1,100 per year.
Other academic fees: One time matriculation fee of $300.
Academic term: Semester
Number of first-year students who received full tuition waivers: 4
Number of first-year students who received partial tuition waivers: 1

Teaching Assistants, Research Assistants, and Fellowships
  Number of first-year
    Teaching Assistants: 5
    Fellowship students: 1
  Average stipend per academic year
    Teaching Assistant: $24,000
    Research Assistant: $24,000
    Fellowship student: $25,000

FINANCIAL AID

Application deadlines
Fall admission:
U.S. students: February 15   *Int'l. students*: February 15
Spring admission:
U.S. students: July 1   *Int'l. students*: July 1

Loans
Loans are available for U.S. students.
Loans are not available for international students.
GAPSFAS application required: No
FAFSA application required: Yes

For further information

Address financial aid inquiries to: Cloyd Heck Marvin Center, Ground Floor, 800 21st Street, NW, Washington D.C. 20052, Fax: 202-994-9009.
Phone: (202) 994-9000
E-mail: ccentral@gwu.edu
Financial aid website: http://colonialcentral.gwu.edu/

HOUSING

Availability of on-campus housing

Single students: Yes
Married students: No

For further information

Address housing inquiries to: GW Housing, Division of Student Affairs, John Quincy Adams House, 2129 Eye Street, NW, Washington D.C. 20052, Fax: 202-994-1422.
Phone: (202) 994-2552
E-mail: gwhouse@gwu.edu
Housing aid website: http://living.gwu.edu/

Table A—Faculty, Enrollments, and Degrees Granted

Research Specialty	2015–16 Faculty	Enrollment Fall 2016 Master's	Enrollment Fall 2016 Doctorate	Number of Degrees Granted 2015–17 (2008–15) Master's	Number of Degrees Granted 2015–17 (2008–15) Terminal Master's	Number of Degrees Granted 2015–17 (2008–15) Doctorate
Astrophysics	7	–	6	–	–	1(2)
Biophysics	5	–	7	–	–(1)	1(6)
Medical, Health Physics	–	–	1	–	–	1(2)
Nuclear Physics	12	–	9	–(1)	–(2)	2(9)
Physics and other Science Education	4	–	1	–	–	1(2)
Non-specialized	–	–	9	–(1)	–(2)	–
Total	25	–	34	–(2)	–(4)	6(9)
Full-time Grad. Stud.	–	–	34	–	–	–
First-year Grad. Stud.	–	–	6	–	–	–

GRADUATE DEGREE REQUIREMENTS

Master's: M.A. degree with thesis or no thesis options: 30 semester hours of course work in physics plus thesis, or 36 semester hours of course work in physics and mathematics, including a tool requirement in computer programming. A 3.0 GPA is required.

Doctorate: A minimum of 72 semester hours of approved courses for students with only a baccalaureate. For students with a master's degree, a minimum of 48 semester hours is required. Tool requirement: completion of numerical methods course. A 3.0 GPA is required.

Thesis: Thesis may be written in absentia.

SPECIAL EQUIPMENT, FACILITIES, OR PROGRAMS

High-end central computing facility (Colonial One); several departmental computing facilities, including five high-end clusters, two CMP/biophysics research laboratories; machine shop; Virginia campus facilities contains laboratories for design, construction, and testing of particle and radiation detectors for use at major accelerator laboratories worldwide.

A new Science and Engineering Hall (SEH) opened in January 2015. Physics Building (Corcoran Hall) is being completely renovated, reopens in January 2018.

Table B—Separately Budgeted Research Expenditures by Source of Support

Source of Support	Departmental Research	Physics-related Research Outside Department
Federal government	$2,200,000	
State/local government		
Non-profit organizations		
Business and industry	$400,000	
Other	$200,000	
Total	$2,800,000	

Table C—Separately Budgeted Research Expenditures by Research Specialty

Research Specialty	No. of Grants	Expenditures ($)
Astrophysics	18	$500,000
Biophysics	2	$300,000
Nuclear Physics	7	$2,000,000
Physics and other Science Education	4	$150,000
Total	31	$2,950,000

FACULTY

Chair Professor

Briscoe, William, Ph.D., Catholic University of America, 1978. *Nuclear Physics*. Experimental nuclear physics and particle physics.

Professor

Eskandarian, Ali, Ph.D., George Washington University, 1967. *Astrophysics, Computational Physics, Nuclear Physics*. Theoretical nuclear physics; astrophysics.

Feldman, Gerald, Ph.D., University of Washington, 1987. *Nuclear Physics, Physics and other Science Education*. Experimental nuclear physics; physics education research.

Kouveliotou, Chryssa, Ph.D., Technical University of Munich, 1981. Director of the GWU Astronomy, Physics, and Statistics Institute of Sciences (APSIS). *Astrophysics*. High Energy Astrophysics: Gamma Ray Bursts, Magnetars, Compact Objects, Time Domain Astronomy, Multi-wavelength follow ups.

Lee, Frank X., Ph.D., Ohio University, 1993. *Computational Physics, Nuclear Physics*. Theoretical nuclear and particle physics.

Reeves, Mark E., Ph.D., University of Illinois, 1989. *Biophysics, Condensed Matter Physics, Physics and other Science Education*. Experimental condensed matter physics; biophysics; medical physics.

Zeng, Chen, Ph.D., Cornell University, 1994. *Biophysics, Computational Physics, Statistical & Thermal Physics*. Theoretical condensed matter physics; biophysics.

Associate Professor

Afanasev, Andrei V., Ph.D., Kharkov National University, 1990. *Condensed Matter Physics, Nuclear Physics*. Theoretical nuclear physics.

Alexandru, Andrei, Ph.D., Louisiana State University, 2001. *Nuclear Physics*. Theoretical nuclear physics.

Cobb Kung, Bethany, Ph.D., Yale University, 2008. Also teaches in the University Honors Program. *Astrophysics*. Astrophysics (gamma-ray bursts, time-domain, astronomy).

Dhuga, Kalvir S., Ph.D., University of Birmingham, 1980. *Astrophysics, Nuclear Physics*. Astrophysics, experimental nuclear physics.

Downie, Evangeline J., Ph.D., University of Gaslow, 2007. *Nuclear Physics*. Experimental nuclear physics.

Griesshammer, Harald, Ph.D., University of Erlangen-Nürnberg, 1996. *Nuclear Physics*. Theoretical nuclear and particle physics.

Haberzettl, Helmut, Ph.D., University of Bonn, 1979. *Nuclear Physics*. Theoretical nuclear and particle physics.

Kargaltsev, Oleg, Ph.D., Pennsylvania State University, 2004. *Astrophysics*. Observational high-energy astrophysics: neutron stars, pulsars, pulsar winds, high-mass XRBs, black holes, GeV/TeV sources, machine-learning in astronomy, astrostatistics.

Peng, Weiqun, Ph.D., University of Illinois, 2001. *Biophysics, Computational Physics*. Theoretical biophysics.

Qui, Xiangyun, Ph.D., Michigan State University, 2004. Experimental condensed-matter physics; biophysics.

Assistant Professor

Doering, Michael, Ph.D., University of Valencia, 2007. Theoretical nuclear physics; phenomenology.

Guiriec, Sylvain, Ph.D., Laboratoire de Physique Theorique et Astroparticules, 2008. *Astrophysics*. High-energy astrophysics: Fermi Gamma-ray Space Telescope – Gamma-Ray Bursts.

Lan, Ganhui, Ph.D., Johns Hopkins University, 2008. Computational biophysics.

van der Horst, Alexander J., Ph.D., University of Amsterdam, 2007. *Astrophysics*. Observational and theoretical astrophysics of high-energy transients in X-ray, gamma-ray and radio wavelengths. Big data pipelines.

Emeritus

Lehman, Donald R., Ph.D., George Washington University, 1970. Theoretical nuclear physics.

Research Professor

Strakovsky, Igor, Ph.D., Petersburg Nuclear Physics Institute, 1984. Experimental nuclear physics; phenomenology.

Research Associate Professor

Workman, Ron, Ph.D., University of British Columbia, 1987. Theoretical nuclear physics; phenomenology.

DEPARTMENTAL RESEARCH SPECIALTIES AND STAFF

Theoretical

Astrophysics. The Astrophysics Group has tripled in size over the past 3 years. Its faculty, postdocs, and students perform cutting-edge high-energy astrophysics research. We apply our expertise in astrophysics, nuclear and particle physics, to the exotic processes occurring near extremely dense and compact objects, such as white dwarfs, neutron stars and black holes. Some of these processes, such as extremely strong magnetic and gravity fields, stellar collapse, stellar mergers, and matter falling into black holes, are impossible to duplicate on Earth. They are responsible for powerful distant sources of light, neutrinos, and gravity waves. We study neutron stars, magnetars, black holes, X-ray and gamma-ray binaries, and gamma-ray bursts to understand the physics of these systems. Six astrophysics faculty are strongly committed to providing solid graduate education adopted to the needs of modern-day astronomy and astrophysics. We work hard to ensure that students get involved in research as early as possible and have enough time to publish their original research and make themselves noticeable. For further information, click on Astro physics Group Webpage. Cobb Kung, Dhuga, Eskandarian, Guiriec, Kargaltsev, Kouveliotou, van der Horst.

Biophysics. The Theoretical Biophysics Group currently consists of our four faculty members, and associated postdoctoral associates, graduate students, and undergraduate students. Current research interests of the faculty members are as follows: Ganhui Lan - Theoretical analysis of biochemical networks for cells to maintain their precise temporal and spatial regulation; computational modeling of intracellular assembling processes. Weiqun Peng - Computation study of functional genomics, epigenomics, and gene regulation; bioinformatics; mathematical modeling of evolutionary dynamics. Guanyu Wang - Physical Oncology, disease modeling, and bionetwork analysis. Chen Zeng - Computational modeling and design of protein structures and numerical studies of bionetworks' robustness and evolvability. To learn more, click on the Biophysics Group's Web site. Lan, Peng, Zeng.

Nuclear Physics. The theoretical nuclear physics research group aims to understand the structure and interactions of photons, hadrons, and nuclei at low and intermediate energy scales. It employs a variety of theoretical tools, such as lattice QCD and QCD sum rules, coupled-channels analysis, relativistic reaction theories, and effective field theories. For more information, click on the Theoretical Nulcear Physics Web site. Afanasev, Alexandru, Doering, Eskandarian, Griesshammer, Haberzettl, Lee, Lehman, Strakovsky, Workman.

Experimental

Astrophysics. The GWU Physics Faculty has a long tradition in Astrophysics going back to George Gamow, the developer of the hot Big Bang Theory of the Universe. The group has recently expanded with the hire of 3 new faculty members specializing in multiwavelength observational high-energy Astrophysics. Our current interests center on understanding the underlying physical processes of explosive transients (such as Gamma-Ray Bursts) and the emission processes near extremely compact and dense objects, such as magnetized neutron stars and black holes. We study these processes through the analysis of X-ray and gamma-ray data that have been collected by a number of space-borne telescopes. Astrophysics faculty and students use world's best space observatories (Hubble Space Telescope, Chandra X-ray Observatory, Fermi Gamma-ray Observatory) as well as state-of-the-art optical and radio observations on the ground (with with JVLA, LOFAR, GTC). The GW group closely collaborates with colleagues at NASA/Goddard Space Flight Center and Naval Research Laboratory. For further information, click on Astro physics Group Webpage. Cobb Kung, Dhuga, Kargaltsev, Kouveliotou, van der Horst.

Biophysics. The experimental biophysics group currently consists of faculty members, Mark Reeves and Xiangyun Qiu, and their graduate and undergraduate students. The group features expertise in scanning probe-based near-field microscopy; detection of biomolecules by localized surface plasmon sensing; analysis of biomolecular structure, interaction, and functional relationships; X-ray and neutron scattering; and osmotic stress methods for modifying cellular components. These techniques are being applied to the study of electronic materials, biomaterials, and to problems in cellular biological physics. Our expertise allows our students to study structural linkages in proteins and crystalline systems, and to study biological and electronic functionality through sub-wavelength length-scale probes of the electromagnetic response of materials. Collaborations with federal laboratories (NRL, ORNL, NIH, and NIST) and with faculty in chemistry, biology, and in the medical school allow us to address a wide array of research questions. New approaches to investigating protein functionality are being developed, based on the electronic and optical response of self-assembled nanoparticle systems. To learn more, click on the Biophysics Group's Web site. Qui, Reeves.

Nuclear Physics. The focus of the experimental nuclear physics group remains the understanding of the strong interaction in the nuclear medium. Our intention is to measure the elementary amplitudes for meson photoproduction and baryon excitation on the nucleon and see how they are modified in the nuclear medium, particularly in the light nuclei, where the nuclear density changes dramatically with very little change in nuclear size. To learn more, click on the GW Experimental Nuclear Physics Research Group's Web site. Briscoe, Dhuga, Downie, Feldman, Strakovsky, Workman.

Physics and other Science Education. Peer instruction: Developing and testing large collection of ConcepTests, organizing coherent sequences (ConcepModules), linking conceptual questions with numerical problems. Thinking skills curriculum: Taxonomy of physics problems (based on Marzano); develop cognitive skills necessary for problem-solving; problem-solving protocol (GW–ACCESS). Collaborative SCALEUP classroom: Students work in cooperatively groups; full integration of lecture; recitation and laboratory; entirely focused on students (instructor as coach). Briscoe, Feldman, Reeves, Workman.

View additional information about this department at www.gradschoolshopper.com. Check out the "Why Choose Us?" section, find out more about the department's culture and get links to social media networks.

GEORGETOWN UNIVERSITY, WASHINGTON D.C.

DEPARTMENT OF PHYSICS

Washington, D.C. 20057
http://physics.georgetown.edu/

General University Information
President: John J. DeGioia
Dean of Graduate School: Norberto Grzywacz
University website: http://www.georgetown.edu/
School Type: Private
Setting: Urban
Total Faculty: 2,546
Total number of Students: 15,398
Total number of Graduate Students: 8,199

Department Information
Department Chairman: Prof. Jeff Urbach, Chair
Department Contact: Paola Barbara, Director of Graduate
  Studies
  Total full-time faculty: 17
  Full-Time Graduate Students: 28
  Female Full-Time Graduate Students: 6
  First-Year Graduate Students: 10
  Female First-Year Students: 4
  Total Post Doctorates: 12

Department Address
37th & O Streets NW
Reiss Science Building, Room 506
Washington, D.C. 20057
Phone: (202) 687-6025
E-mail: graduatehelp@physics.georgetown.edu
Website: http://physics.georgetown.edu/

ADMISSIONS

Admission Contact Information
Address admission inquiries to: GSAS, Office of Graduate Ad-
  missions, Box 571004, Washington D.C. 20057-1004
Phone: (202) 687-5568
E-mail: gradmail@georgetown.edu
Admissions website: http://grad.georgetown.edu/admissions/

Application deadlines
Fall admission:
U.S. students: January 1   *Int'l. students*: January 1

Application fee
U.S. students: $90   *Int'l. students*: $90

Admissions information
For Fall of 2018:
  Number of applicants: 49
  Number admitted: 17
  Number enrolled: 3

Admission requirements
Bachelor's degree requirements: Bachelor's degree in Physics
  or related field is required, plus a personal statement, three
  letters of recommendation, and a resume/CV.
Minimum undergraduate GPA: 3.0

GRE requirements
The GRE is required.
  Mean GRE score range (25th–75th percentile): 75th

Subjective GRE requirements
The Subjective GRE is required.

TOEFL requirements
The TOEFL exam is required for students from non-English-
  speaking countries.
  PBT score: 600
  iBT score: 100

Other admissions information
Additional requirements: GRE physics subject test is required.
Undergraduate preparation assumed: Intermediate-level courses
  in classical mechanics, quantum mechanics, electricity and
  magnetism, and statistical and thermal physics, as well as a
  working knowledge of an advanced computer language.

TUITION

Tuition year 2018–2019:
  Full-time students: $2,065 per credit
Credit hours per semester to be considered full-time: 9
Deferred tuition plan: No
Health insurance: Yes, Provided to full-time students.
Other academic fees: Mandatory Yates recreation fee: $420 per
  year.
Academic term: Semester
Number of first-year students who received full tuition waivers: 10

Teaching Assistants, Research Assistants, and Fellowships
Number of first-year
  Teaching Assistants: 18
  Research Assistants: 8
Average stipend per academic year
  Teaching Assistant: $29,000
  Research Assistant: $29,000
  Fellowship student: $29,000
The program offers a summer stipend: $5,500

FINANCIAL AID

Application deadlines
Fall admission:
U.S. students: January 1   *Int'l. students*: January 1

Loans
Loans are available for U.S. students.
Loans are available for international students.
GAPSFAS application required: Yes
FAFSA application required: Yes

For further information
Address financial aid inquiries to: Graduate School of Arts &
  Sciences, Car Barn, Suite 400, 3520 Prospect Street, N.W.,
  Washington D.C. 20057-1005.
Phone: (202) 687-7753
E-mail: gradfinaid@georgetown.edu
Financial aid website: https://grad.georgetown.edu/financial-
  support

137

HOUSING

Availability of on-campus housing
Single students: No
Married students: No

For further information
Address housing inquiries to: Office of Neighborhood Life, 1300 36th Street, N.W., Washington, DC 20007.
Phone: (202) 687-5138
E-mail: neighborhoodlife@georgetown.edu
Housing aid website: https://studentliving.georgetown.edu

Table A—Faculty, Enrollments, and Degrees Granted

Research Specialty	2017–18 Faculty	Enrollment Spring 2017		Number of Degrees Granted 2017–2018 (2011–18)		
		Master's	Doctorate	Master's	Terminal Master's	Doctorate
Biophysics	4	–	4	–	–	–(1)
Condensed Matter Physics	12	–	8	–	–	3(21)
Engineering Physics/Science	1	–	2	–	–	–
Nano Science and Technology	5	–	2	–	–(1)	–(3)
Optics	4	–	1	–	–	–(2)
Statistical & Thermal Physics	4	–	1	–	–	–(1)
Non-specialized	–	–	10	4(17)	–(4)	–
Total	16	–	28	4(17)	–(5)	3(28)
Full-time Grad. Stud.	–	–	28	–	–	–
First-year Grad. Stud.	–	–	10	–	–	–

GRADUATE DEGREE REQUIREMENTS

Master's: The thesis option requires 31 credits of satisfactory graduate coursework plus a thesis; the non-thesis option requires 37 credits of satisfactory graduate coursework.

Doctorate: The Ph.D. requires 34 credits of satisfactory graduate coursework and a dissertation. Graduate examinations include comprehensive and qualifying examinations and a dissertation defense.

Other Degrees: The Ph.D. program offers a traditional physics track and an Industrial Leadership in Physics (ILP) track. The latter is intended for students interested in scientific careers in industry. The curriculum of the ILP track includes business electives and a year-long internship in industry. Both tracks emphasize communication skills and teamwork.

Thesis: Thesis may be written in absentia.

SPECIAL EQUIPMENT, FACILITIES, OR PROGRAMS

Georgetown GNμLab

GNμLab is a micro-fabrication and materials research facility that is wholly managed by the Department of Physics. GNμLab comprises a 2,000-square-foot facility including 1,200 square feet of clean room space and the following capabilities: optical and electron beam lithography, deposition, evaporation, and sputtering systems; etching: RIE/DRIE equipment and wet TMAH etching; high-temperature furnaces; measurement: stress, film thickness, and FESEM; and wire bonding. The Carbon Nanotube Synthesis facility (CVD) is located in GNμLab.

Soft Matter Institute

Georgetown's Institute for Soft Matter Synthesis and Metrology, or I(SM)2, serves to catalyze the development of fundamental principles and practical measurement tools that can be applied to soft matter synthesis and precision measurement and characterization (metrology). The institute maintains a shared laboratory outfitted with two scanning probe microscopes, two Anton Paar rheometers, two light scattering systems, and microcalorimeter and surface plasmon resonance capabilities. The institute also supports the regional conference series, The Mid-Atlantic Soft Matter (MASM) Workshops. MASM was established in 2007 by Georgetown scientists to encourage inter-institution collaboration and provides an effective venue for promoting interaction among soft matter researchers from academic, industrial, and national laboratories in the Mid-Atlantic region.

Soft Matter Lab

The Soft Matter Lab is a user facility with state-of-the-art instruments for materials measurements in the following categories: microscopy (AFM, bright field, fluorescence), rheometry, light scattering, microcalorimetry (ITC and DSC), spectroscopy (UV-visible-near IR), mechanical testing, and surface plasmon resonance. Multi-modal measurements are enabled by integrating optical microscopy with other techniques, in order to establish correlation between materials properties and their morphology. The facility also has equipment for materials processing, including spin-coating, blade-coating, plasma cleaning, and 3D printing.

Georgetown Laser Laboratory

The optical characterization comprises several systems for the measurement of nanoparticle formation, non-linear optical effects, and spectrally resolved imaging. High-powered laser systems include a nanosecond pulsed laser (Quanta-Ray GCR03) pumping an optical parametric oscillator (GWU), a multi-line Ar laser system (Spectra Physics Beamlok), and a number of diode lasers. Nanoparticle formation is studied using photon and fluorescence correlation spectroscopy based on a hardware autocorrelator (ALV5000) and a photon-counting avalanche photodiode. Spectrally resolved fluorescence imaging capabilities are provided by a FALCON chemical imaging microscope (ChemImage). A solar simulator (Abet Technologies) combined with a monochromator provides wavelength tunable incoherent light for measurement of the spectral response of photoconductive and photovoltaic materials. This equipment is augmented by advanced detection and signal processing instrumentation.

Dynamics Imaging Laboratory

The Dynamics Imaging Laboratory contains high-speed and high-resolution digital imaging systems; software for image acquisition, processing, and analysis; a high-speed confocal microscope; and a high-powered optical tweezer.

Computing Resources

The computational groups have parallel computation resources with about 500 CPUs on campus and access to large national supercomputing facilities.

The Industrial Leadership in Physics (ILP) Track

It is intended for students interested in scientific careers in industry. The curriculum of the ILP track includes business electives and a year-long internship in industry.

Superconductivity and Nanoelectronics Laboratory

The Superconductivity and Nanoelectronics Laboratory has a room-temperature testing station (with four micromanipulators); a Gas-Cell Kelvin Probe System (UHVKPM020-Cube0275 from KP Technology, with manual translator for sample stage (25.4 cm) and heated sample stage (550C)); a low-noise, low-temperature transport measurement setup with an optical cryostat (OPTIAC-V14A, Optistat Actively Cooled Optical Cryostat by Oxford Instruments, temperature range: 2.8K-325K, Cooling power of 0.5

W at 4.2 K); optical sources in the 100GHz- 1THz range, including a Quasi-Optical Source QS2-DT by Microtech Instruments Inc., with operating spectral windows: 100-180 GHz (1-100 mW), 200-350 GHz (1-20 mW) and 600-1000 GHz (20-100 μW). Lab members have access to a clean room (GNuLab), scanning microscopy tools (NTEGRA Prima scanning probe microscope), Raman spectroscopy tools (Horiba LabRam, HR Evolution, with 325 nm, 405 nm, 532 nm, and 785 nm laser lines) and furnaces with controlled gas flow for chemical vapor deposition of carbon nanotubes, graphene and transition metal dichalcogenides.

Table B—Separately Budgeted Research Expenditures by Source of Support

Source of Support	Departmental Research	Physics-related Research Outside Department
Federal government	$9,472,031	
State/local government		
Non-profit organizations		
Business and industry	$63,742	
Other		
Total	$9,535,773	

Table C—Separately Budgeted Research Expenditures by Research Specialty

Research Specialty	No. of Grants	Expenditures ($)
Atomic, Molecular, & Optical Physics	1	$46,450
/Condensed Matter	1	$120,000
Condensed Matter Physics	9	$1,892,851
/Polymer Physics/Science, Fluids/Rheology	2	$7,412,730
Polymer Physics/Science	1	$63,742
Total	14	$9,535,773

FACULTY

Professor

Barbara, Paola, Ph.D., Technical University of Denmark, 1995. Director of Graduate Studies. *Condensed Matter Physics.* Physical properties of nanoscale materials and devices.

Currie, John F., Ph.D., Cornell University, 1977. *Condensed Matter Physics.* Device microfabrication; biomedical devices.

Freericks, James K., Ph.D., University of California, Berkeley, 1991. *Atomic, Molecular, & Optical Physics, Computational Physics, Condensed Matter Physics, Nano Science and Technology.* Non-equilibrium physics; theoretical condensed matter; ultra-cold atomic physics.

Liu, Amy Y., Ph.D., University of California, Berkeley, 1991. *Condensed Matter Physics.* Theoretical condensed matter physics.

Liu, Kai, Ph.D., Johns Hopkins University, 1998. *Condensed Matter Physics.* Synthesis and experimental investigation of nanostructured materials, particularly in nanomagnetism and spintronics, which have potentially important technological applications in magnetic recording, low dissipation information storage and nanoelectronics.

Olmsted, Peter, Ph.D., University of Illinois at Urbana-Champaign, 1991. *Biophysics, Chemical Physics, Computational Physics, Condensed Matter Physics, Fluids, Rheology, Materials Science, Metallurgy, Nonlinear Dynamics and Complex Systems, Polymer Physics/Science, Statistical & Thermal Physics, Theoretical Physics.* Biophysics; soft condensed matter physics; materials physics.

Urbach, Jeffrey S., Ph.D., Stanford University, 1993. Department Chair. *Condensed Matter Physics.* Biophysics of cellular dynamics and mechanics, Physics of Soft Matter.

Associate Professor

Blair, Daniel L., Ph.D., Clark University, 2003. *Biophysics, Condensed Matter Physics.* Complex fluids; experimental soft matter physics.

Del Gado, Emanuela, Ph.D., University of Naples, 2001. *Applied Physics, Computational Physics, Condensed Matter Physics, Engineering Physics/Science, Fluids, Rheology, Materials Science, Metallurgy, Statistical & Thermal Physics, Theoretical Physics.* Statistical mechanics; computational physics; soft condensed matter physics; material physics; complex systems.

Dzakpasu, Rhonda, Ph.D., University of Michigan, 2003. *Biophysics, Computational Physics.* Neuroscience.

Egolf, David A., Ph.D., Duke University, 1994. *Computational Physics, Condensed Matter Physics, Particles and Fields.* Theoretical soft condensed matter physics; QCD.

Paranjape, Makarand, Ph.D., University of Alberta, 1993. *Engineering Physics/Science, Medical, Health Physics, Systems Science/Engineering.* Microelectromechanical systems; biomedical microdevices.

Van Keuren, Edward, Ph.D., Carnegie Mellon University, 1990. *Condensed Matter Physics, Optics.* Nanoparticles; optical characterization of materials.

Emeritus

Chiao-Yap, Lydia, Ph.D., University of California, Berkeley, 1961. *Condensed Matter Physics.* Phenomenological study of the collective and individual particle aspects of nuclear structure and the electronic structure of silicides.

Mathews, Wesley N., Ph.D., University of Illinois at Urbana-Champaign, 1966. *Condensed Matter Physics.* Statistical mechanics.

Serene, Joseph W., Ph.D., Cornell University, 1974. *Computational Physics, Condensed Matter Physics.* Theoretical condensed matter physics.

Research Professor

Esrick, Mark A., Ph.D., Georgetown University, 1981. *Biophysics.* Quantum mechanics.

Research Assistant Professor

Cothran, Christopher D., Ph.D., University of Virginia, 2000. Director of Instructional Laboratories. *Nuclear Physics, Particles and Fields, Plasma and Fusion, Solar Physics.*

Teaching Assistant Professor

Johnson, Patrick, Ph.D., Washington University in St. Louis, 2012. *Physics and other Science Education.*

Adjunct Professor

Lavine, James, Ph.D., University of California, Irvine, 1971. *Condensed Matter Physics.* Semiconductor physics.

DEPARTMENTAL RESEARCH SPECIALTIES AND STAFF

Theoretical

Atomic, Molecular, & Optical Physics. Ultra-cold gases, ion trap quantum simulators. Freericks.

Biophysics. Dzakpasu, Olmsted, Urbach.

Computational Physics. Computational fluid dynamics, molecular dynamics; non-equilibrium molecular dynamics; nonlinear dynamics and differential equations; Monte Carlo techniques. Del Gado, Egolf, Freericks, Amy Liu, Olmsted, Serene.

Hard condensed-matter physics. Interaction of light with matter; magnetism; strongly correlated materials; structural, electronic, and transport properties; superconductivity. Freericks, Amy Liu, Mathews, Serene.

Nano Science and Technology. Theoretical calculations of transport in multi-layered devices. Freericks.

Particles and Fields. Effective theories. Egolf.

Soft condensed-matter physics. Biomaterials; biomimetic materials; colloidal aggregation; gels; glasses; liquid crystals; nanocomposites; non-Newtonian fluids; polymers; rheology; self-assembling systems. Del Gado, Egolf, Olmsted.

Statistical & Thermal Physics. Critical phenomena; disordered systems; glass transition; non-equilibrium dynamical systems, both classical and quantum; phase transitions; statistical mechanics and non-equilibrium physics of soft matter. Del Gado, Egolf, Freericks, Olmsted.

Experimental

Biophysics. Biomaterials; cellular biophysics; pattern formation in neural systems. Blair, Dzakpasu, Urbach.

Hard Condensed Matter Physics. Sensors; superconductivity; superconducting devices; transport in nanostructures. Barbara, Currie, Kai Liu, Paranjape.

Nano Science and Technology. Applications to environmental monitoring, bioengineering, medical imaging; nanotube devices; organic photovoltaic; semiconductor technology; sensors and actuators. Barbara, Currie, Paranjape, Van Keuren.

Optics. Biomedical optics; imaging of soft materials; nanoparticle synthesis and characterization. Blair, Urbach, Van Keuren.

Soft condensed-matter physics. Biomaterials; colloidal and polymer physics; fluids; granular materials; non-linear dynamic soft glasses. Blair, Urbach, Van Keuren.

View additional information about this department at www.gradschoolshopper.com. Check out the "Why Choose Us?" section, find out more about the department's culture and get links to social media networks.

FLORIDA ATLANTIC UNIVERSITY

DEPARTMENT OF PHYSICS

Boca Raton, Florida 33431
http://www.physics.fau.edu/

General University Information
President: Dr. John Kelly
Dean of Graduate School: Khaled Sobhan, Ph.D.
University website: http://www.fau.edu
School Type: Public
Setting: Suburban
Total Faculty: 1,571
Total Graduate Faculty: N/A
Total number of Students: 30,598
Total number of Graduate Students: 4,847

Department Information
Department Chairman: Dr. Luc T. Wille, Chair
Department Contact: Shianne Noel, Senior Secretary
  Total full-time faculty: 15
  Full-Time Graduate Students: 42
  Female Full-Time Graduate Students: 15
  First-Year Graduate Students: 12
  Female First-Year Students: 3
  Total Post Doctorates: 2

Department Address
777 Glades Road
Boca Raton, FL 33431
Phone: (561) 297-3380
Fax: (561) 297-2662
E-mail: shiannenoel@fau.edu
Website: http://www.physics.fau.edu/

ADMISSIONS

Admission Contact Information
Address admission inquiries to: Jonathan Engle, Admissions
  Chair, Science Bldg (SE-43), Rm. 430
Phone: (561) 297-3380
E-mail: jengle7@fau.edu
Admissions website: http://www.physics.fau.edu/

Application deadlines
Fall admission:
U.S. students: July 1   *Int'l. students*: April 1
Spring admission:
U.S. students: November 15   *Int'l. students*: October 1

Application fee
U.S. students: $30   *Int'l. students*: $30

Admissions information
For Fall of 2018:
  Number of applicants: 20
  Number admitted: 14
  Number enrolled: 11

Admission requirements
Bachelor's degree requirements: Bachelor's degree in physics
  is required. PSMMP Admissions Requirements: A BS or BA
  in Physics. Candidates with a BS in Biology, Chemistry,
  Computer Science, or Engineering with a minor in Physics

are considered. At least a 3.0 (of a 4.0 maximum) grade point
average (GPA) in Science and Mathematics, courses. Have
taken the general portion of the GRE.
Minimum undergraduate GPA: 3.0

GRE requirements
The GRE is required.
There is no minimum GRE score required.

Subjective GRE requirements
The Subjective GRE is recommended.
There is no minimum GRE score required.

TOEFL requirements
The TOEFL exam is required for students from non-English-
  speaking countries.
  PBT score: 550
  iBT score: 79

Other admissions information
Undergraduate preparation assumed: Reitz and Milford, Foun-
  dations of Electromagnetic Theory; Symon, Mechanics;
  Saxon, Quantum Mechanics;* Boyce and Deprima, Elemen-
  tary Differential Equations and Boundary Value Problems;
  Reif, Statistical and Thermal Physics;* Boas, Mathematical
  Methods in the Physical Sciences.*; *May be taken during
  first year of graduate study.

TUITION
Tuition year 2018–2019:
Tuition for in-state residents
  Full-time students: $369.82 per credit
  Part-time students: $369.82 per credit
Tuition for out-of-state residents
  Full-time students: $1,024.81 per credit
  Part-time students: $1,024.81 per credit
Credit hours per semester to be considered full-time: 9
Deferred tuition plan: No
Health insurance: Available at the cost of $1,350 per year.
Academic term: Semester

Teaching Assistants, Research Assistants, and Fellowships
Number of first-year
  Teaching Assistants: 6
  Fellowship students: 3
Average stipend per academic year
  Teaching Assistant: $20,050
All first-year Ph.D. students are offered a TA stipend per ac-
ademic year.

FINANCIAL AID

Application deadlines
Fall admission:
U.S. students: March 1
Spring admission:
U.S. students: March 1

Loans

Loans are not available for U.S. students.

Loans are not available for international students.

GAPSFAS application required: No

FAFSA application required: Yes

For further information

Address financial aid inquiries to: Office of Student Financial
   Aid, Bldg. SU-80, Rm. 233.

Phone: (561) 297-3530

Financial aid website: http://www.fau.edu/finaid/getting-started/
   graduate-student.php

HOUSING

Availability of on-campus housing

Single students: Yes

Married students: No

For further information

Address housing inquiries to: Director of Student Housing, Bldg
   SH-46, RM 215.

Phone: (561) 297-2880

E-mail: housing@fau.edu

Housing aid website: http://www.fau.edu/housing/index.php

Table A—Faculty, Enrollments, and Degrees Granted

Research Specialty	2017–2018 Faculty	Enrollment Fall 2017		Number of Degrees Granted 2017–2018		
		Master's	Doctorate	Master's	Terminal Master's	Doctorate
Biophysics	2	–	4	–	–	–
Condensed Matter Physics	5	–	3	–	–	–
Medical, Health Physics	4	27	–	1	–	1
Relativity & Gravitation	4	–	6	–	–	1
Other	–	–	15	–	1	1
Total	15	27	28	1	1	3
Full-time Grad. Stud.	–	18	31	–	–	–
First-year Grad. Stud.	–	–	4	–	–	–

GRADUATE DEGREE REQUIREMENTS

Master's: Thirty credits in approved program with a 3.0 sustained GPA, including 7 credits of thesis research. Students must be in residence for two semesters. Final thesis.

Doctorate: Fifty credits in approved program with a 3.0 sustained GPA beyond the M.S., including 30 credits of dissertation research; comprehensive written examination covering mechanics, electromagnetism, quantum mechanics, and statistical mechanics. Dissertation and oral examination required.

Other Degrees: The MST in physics requires 30 credits with a 3.0 GPA, which may include 6 thesis credits. In addition, a 6-credit internship requirement must be satisfied for students without teaching experience. The Ed.D. degree in Curriculum and Instruction is offered for junior college teachers with physics as a first or second teaching field. Professional Science Master in Medical Physics: 41 credits and Thesis in PSMMP program. PSMMP is one of the 35 CAMPEP-accredited programs in the USA. PSMMP provides professional training in partnership with area hospitals, and focuses on Radiation Therapy.

Thesis: Thesis may be written in absentia.

SPECIAL EQUIPMENT, FACILITIES, OR PROGRAMS

The Department is rapidly growing and is poised to meet the new challenges for the field of physics in today's environment at a research university. Our research focus is in three main areas: (1) classical and quantum gravity, (2) the behavior of complex systems, particularly as it relates to neuroscience, and (3) medical and materials physics. While we have well-established M. S. and Ph.D. programs in physics, we also offer a CAMPEP accredited professional M.S. in Medical Physics. All are centered around our core research thrusts.

We host one of the largest general relativity groups which focuses on loop quantum gravity, numerical relativity, and discrete geometry (Regge calculus). The FAU spacetime (FAUST) physics group provides numerical and mathematical support for gravitational wave physics and general relativistic astrophysics. We have a large and growing quantum gravity effort, as well as a new thrust in quantum computing and quantum cryptography.

We have a close relationship and share faculty with the Center for Complex Systems and Brain Science. We are in the process of building a core biophysics effort to integrate with this center as well as FAU's broader neuroscience thrust. In addition, we are augmenting and integrating our core expertise in condensed matter physics with the growing fields of the Physics of Living Systems and Medical Physics.

Our research includes collaborations with National Labs and partnerships with hospitals under the Center of Biomedical and Materials Physics (CBAMP). Our growing efforts in all fields are tightly integrated with that of the other departments within the Charles E. Schmidt College of Science, as well as the strategic plan of the university at large.

Table B—Separately Budgeted Research Expenditures by Source of Support

Source of Support	Departmental Research	Physics-related Research Outside Department
Federal government	$814,882	
State/local government		
Non-profit organizations		
Business and industry		
Other	$150,000	
Total	$964,882	

FACULTY

Professor

Leventouri, Theodora, Ph.D., University of Athens Greece. *Condensed Matter Physics, Materials Science, Metallurgy, Medical, Health Physics, Nano Science and Technology*. Experimental condensed matter physics, biophysics, Medical Physics. X-ray diffraction of biocompatible materials.

Miller, Warner A., Ph.D., University of Texas, Austin. Classical and quantum gravity; general relativistic astrophysics, numerical relativity, foundations of quantum mechanics.

Qiu, Shen-Li, Ph.D., City University of New York. Experimental condensed matter; photoemission; electronic structure and magnetic behavior of metals and alloys.

Sarajedini, Vicki, Ph.D., University of Arizona. *Astronomy*. Surveys for active galaxies, AGN variability, X-ray and Infrared observations of AGN, AGN host galaxy morphology and environment.

Tichy, Wolfgang, Ph.D., Cornell University. Numerical relativity; binary black hole systems; gravitational wave physics.

Wille, Luc T., Ph.D., Ghent University. Theoretical condensed matter; non-linear systems; physics of living.

Associate Professor

Beetle, Christopher, Ph.D., Pennsylvania State University, University Park. Classical and quantum gravity; numerical relativity.

Engle, Jonathan, Ph.D., Pennsylvania State University. Loop quantum gravity.

Fuchs, Armin, Ph.D., University of Stuttgart. Nonlinear dynamical systems; complex systems and brain sciences.

Lau, Andy W. C., Ph.D., University of California, Santa Barbara. Theoretical soft condensed matter physics; biophysics and statistical mechanics.

Assistant Professor

Han, Muxin, Ph.D., Humboldt-Universität zu Berlin. *Relativity & Gravitation, Other*. Loop Quantum Gravity, Non-perturbative Gauge Theory, String Theory.

Kalantzis, Georgios, Ph.D., University of Texas-MD Anderson. *Accelerator, Biophysics, Computational Physics, Medical, Health Physics, Neuroscience/Neuro Physics, Nonlinear Dynamics and Complex Systems, Other*. Parallelization Methods in Medical Physics, Radiation Therapy, Treatment Planning.

Emeritus

Bruenn, Stephen W., Ph.D., Columbia University. Theoretical astrophysics; supernovae models; radiation transport.

Dean, Nathan W., Ph.D., University of Cambridge. Theoretical elementary particle physics; mathematical finance.

Faulkner, John S., Ph.D., Ohio State University. Theoretical physics; theory of alloys.

Jordan, Robin G., Ph.D., University of Sheffield. Experimental condensed matter; UV photoemission; alloys.

McGuire, James B., Ph.D., University of California, Los Angeles. Mathematical physics; three-body problem; statistical physics; quantum field theory.

Medina, Fernando D., Ph.D., Princeton University. Experimental condensed matter physics; spectroscopic studies of solids.

Instructor

Chen, De Huai, Ph.D., City University of New York.

Gross, Robert, Ph.D., Florida Atlantic University.

Hotiu, Angelica, Ph.D., Florida Atlantic University, 2010. n/a.

Associate Scientist

Sorge, Korey D., Ph.D., University of Tennessee, Knoxville. Condensed matter physics.

Associate Scholar / Scientist

Kreymerman, Grigoriy, Ph.D., Academy of Sciences, Soviet Union. *Optics*. Applied optics, liquid crystal display and diffractive optics, optical and acoustic imaging, fiber optic sensors.

Astronomer

Sarajedini, Ata, Ph.D., Yale. Dean of the Charles E. Schmidt College of Science. *Astronomy*.

DEPARTMENTAL RESEARCH SPECIALTIES AND STAFF

Theoretical

Astrophysics.

Condensed Matter Physics. Soft Condensed Matter Physics, Neuroscience; Electronic Structures.

Statistical & Thermal Physics. Nonlinear Phenomena, Complex System, Computational Medical Physics.

Experimental

Biophysics. Biomaterials Physics; X-ray and Neutron Powder Diffraction; Magnetic Nanomaterials; Medical Physics.

Condensed Matter Physics. Electrical, Magnetic, Structural, and Optical Properties of Solids.

View additional information about this department at www.gradschoolshopper.com. Check out the "Why Choose Us?" section, find out more about the department's culture and get links to social media networks.

FLORIDA INTERNATIONAL UNIVERSITY

DEPARTMENT OF PHYSICS

Miami, Florida 33199
http://physics.fiu.edu

General University Information
President: Mark Rosenberg
Dean of Graduate School: Andres Gil
University website: http://gradschool.fiu.edu
School Type: Public
Setting: Urban
Total Faculty: 1,208
Total Graduate Faculty: 893
Total number of Students: 56,886
Total number of Graduate Students: 8,700

Department Information
Department Chairman: Prof. Werner Boeglin, Chair
Department Contact: Jorge L. Rodriguez, Graduate Program
  Director
  Total full-time faculty: 25
  Total number of full-time equivalent positions: 25
  Full-Time Graduate Students: 43
  Female Full-Time Graduate Students: 8
  First-Year Graduate Students: 8
  Female First-Year Students: 1
  Total Post Doctorates: 4

ADMISSIONS

Admission Contact Information
Address admission inquiries to: Graduate Director, Physics Dept
Phone: (305) 348-2605
E-mail: jrodrig@fiu.edu
Admissions website: http://physics.fiu.edu/graduate-program/
  prospective-students/

Application deadlines
Fall admission:
U.S. students: February 15   *Int'l. students*: February 15

Application fee
U.S. students: $30   *Int'l. students*: $30
Please have your applications in by Jan 1 if you are interested in an
  assistantship. Our first round of offers are decided in early January

Admissions information
For Fall of 2017:
  Number of applicants: 81
  Number admitted: 9
  Number enrolled: 7

Admission requirements
Bachelor's degree requirements: Bachelor's degree in Physics
  or closely-related field is required.
Minimum undergraduate GPA: 3.0

GRE requirements
The GRE is required.

Subjective GRE requirements
The Subjective GRE is not required.

TOEFL requirements
The TOEFL exam is required for students from non-English-
  speaking countries.
  PBT score: 550
  iBT score: 80

Other admissions information
Undergraduate preparation assumed: Halliday and Resnick,
  Physics; Griffiths, Electromagnetic Theory; Thornton and
  Marion, Classical Mechanics; Griffiths, Quantum Mechanics;
  Sears and Salinger, Thermodynamics.

TUITION
Tuition year 2017–2018:
Tuition for in-state residents
  Full-time students: $10,935.36 annual
  Part-time students: $455.64 per credit
Tuition for out-of-state residents
  Full-time students: $24,040.56 annual
  Part-time students: $1,001.69 per credit
Tuition is waived for all students admitted on an assistantship.
Credit hours per semester to be considered full-time: 9
Deferred tuition plan: Yes
Health insurance: Yes, $542.25.
Other academic fees: Additional fees of $2,325.81/year not cov-
  ered by assistantships.
Academic term: Semester
Number of first-year students who received full tuition waivers: 8

Teaching Assistants, Research Assistants, and Fellowships
Number of first-year
  Teaching Assistants: 8
Average stipend per academic year
  Teaching Assistant: $23,460
  Research Assistant: $23,460

FINANCIAL AID

Application deadlines
Fall admission:
U.S. students: March 1

Loans
Loans are available for U.S. students.
Loans are not available for international students.
GAPSFAS application required: No
FAFSA application required: No

For further information
Address financial aid inquiries to: Financial Aid Office, University Park.
Phone: (305) 348-7000
Financial aid website: http://finaid.fiu.edu/index.php?id=4

HOUSING

Availability of on-campus housing
  Single students: Yes
  Married students: Yes

For further information
Address housing inquiries to: Housing and Residential Life,
  11200 SW 8th St., UT 121, Miami, FL 33199.
Phone: (305) 348-4190
E-mail: housing@fiu.edu
Housing aid website: http://www.housing.fiu.edu

Table A—Faculty, Enrollments, and Degrees Granted

Research Specialty	2017–18 Faculty	Enrollment Fall 2018		Number of Degrees Granted 2017–2018 (2001–18)		
		Master's	Doctorate	Master's	Terminal Master's	Doctorate
Astronomy	3	–	2	–	–(1)	1(4)
Atomic, Molecular, & Optical Physics	2	–	3	–	–(1)	–(2)
Computational	2	–	3	–	–(1)	–(7)
Condensed Matter Physics	5	–	10	–	–(5)	1(8)
Experiment	5	–	10	–	–(3)	1(15)
Experiment	1	–	–	–	–(1)	–(2)
High Energy Physics	2	–	–	–	–(2)	–(2)
Neuroscience/Neuro Physics	2	–	2	–	–	1
Nuclear	2	–	2	–	–(2)	1(6)
Physics and other Science Education	2	–	4	–	–(1)	2(5)
Plasma and Fusion	1	–	2	–	–	–(1)
Total	**24**	**1**	**43**	**–**	**–(12)**	**6(50)**
Full-time Grad. Stud.	–	–	43	–	–	–
First-year Grad. Stud.	–	–	8	–	–	–

GRADUATE DEGREE REQUIREMENTS

Master's: The program requires 45 credit hours including 15 hours of thesis work. Required courses include Mathematical Methods I, Computational Physics I, Advanced Quantum Mechanics I and II, Advanced Electromagnetic Theory I and II, Statistical Physics, and Advanced Classical Mechanics, as well as one three-credit elective in the area of research specialization. A Thesis is required to graduate.

Doctorate: The program requires 80 credit hours including at least 15 hours of dissertation credit. Course requirements are the same as for the master's degree with the addition of two three-credit electives. All doctoral candidates must pass the Ph.D.-qualifying examination no later than three years after entering the program. The examination will be given twice per year and requires a detailed knowledge of all areas of undergraduate and first-year graduate physics. Upon completion of course work, the student shall propose a dissertation topic and defend the proposal before his/her dissertation committee.

Thesis: Thesis may be written in absentia.

SPECIAL EQUIPMENT, FACILITIES, OR PROGRAMS

The department has in-house research laboratories in each area of specialization. Close affiliations with several off-site facilities include Jefferson Lab for nuclear physics, the Kitt Peak 1-m telescope for optical astronomy, and the Very Large Array radio telescope, in addition to numerous facilities at other universities.

Table B—Separately Budgeted Research Expenditures by Source of Support

Source of Support	Departmental Research	Physics-related Research Outside Department
Federal government	$6,692,257	
State/local government		
Non-profit organizations	$1,126,310	
Business and industry	$100,425	
Other		
Total	**$7,918,992**	

Table C—Separately Budgeted Research Expenditures by Research Specialty

Research Specialty	No. of Grants	Expenditures ($)
Atomic, Molecular, & Optical Physics	2	$450,156
Experiment	1	$96,391
Condensed Matter Physics	3	$718,750
Neuroscience/Neuro Physics	6	$1,832,721
Experiment	1	$1,309,905
Theory	2	$903,664
Education	4	$446,225
Physics and other Science Education	3	$786,702
Plasma and Fusion	1	$266,167
Total	**23**	**$6,810,681**

FACULTY

Professor

Boeglin, Werner, Ph.D., University of Basel, 1986. *Nuclear Physics, Plasma and Fusion.* Experimental medium-energy nuclear physics; electron scattering; plasma and fusion physics.

Bone, R. A., Ph.D., University of the West Indies, 1971. *Biophysics.* Biophysics; human visual system.

Darici, Yesim, Ph.D., University of Missouri, Columbia, 1985. *Condensed Matter Physics.* Solid-state physics; surface physics.

Gerstman, Bernard, Ph.D., Princeton University, 1981. Department Chair. *Biophysics.* Theoretical and computational investigations of the structure, dynamics, and function of proteins from the level of individual amino acids up to the level of multi-protein aggregates that are implicated in a variety of catastrophic diseases. In addition to interacting closely with experimentalists, we perform Molecular Dynamics and Monte Carlo simulations, and employ the theoretical tools of statistical physics, thermodynamics, non-linear dynamics, and transfer entropy.

Kramer, Laird, Ph.D., Duke University, 1992. *Physics and other Science Education.* Physics education research.

Laird, Angela, Ph.D., University of Wisconsin, Madison, 2002. *Neuroscience/Neuro Physics.* Computational cognitive neuroimaging; functional MRI of human brain networks; neuroinformatics; connectivity; data-driven statistical modeling.

Li, Wenzhi, Ph.D., Chinese Academy of Sciences, 1997. *Condensed Matter Physics.* Experimental condensed matter physics; nanoscience.

Markowitz, Pete, Ph.D., William and Mary, Virginia, 1992. *High Energy Physics, Nuclear Physics.* Experimental electromagnetic production of strange particles; hyper-nuclear spectroscopy; medium-energy tests of QCD. Angular distributions of gauge bosons; searches for dark matter; properties of gauge bosons.

Narayanan, Rajamani, Ph.D., University of California, 1990. *Particles and Fields.* Lattice QCD.

Raue, Brian, Ph.D., Indiana University, 1993. *Nuclear Physics.* Experimental electromagnetic production of strange particles; precision electron-proton elastic scattering.

Reinhold, Jörg, Ph.D., Technische Universität München, 1995. *Nuclear Physics.* Experimental medium-energy nuclear physics; electron scattering; hyper-nuclear spectroscopy.

Sargsian, Misak, Ph.D., Yerevan Physics Institute, 1993. *Nuclear Physics.* Theoretical nuclear physics.

Simpson, Caroline, Ph.D., University of Florida, 1995. *Astronomy.* Structure and evolution of dwarf galaxies; cold interstellar medium; star formation feedback; radio wavelength spectroscopy.

Van Hamme, Walter, Ph.D., Ghent, 1981. *Astronomy.* Stellar structure evolution; close binary stars.

Webb, James, Ph.D., University of Florida, 1987. *Astronomy.* Observational and theoretical work in Blazar variability. Using SARA optical telescopes and utilizing Radio through Gamma-ray multi-wavelength data, we investigate the physics and structure of the relativistic jets accelerated from the core of the Blazar.

Zhu, Yifu, Ph.D., U. Virginia, 1987. *Atomic, Molecular, & Optical Physics.* Quantum Optics: Cavity quantum electrodynamics, quantum coherence and interference, and their applications in quantum state manipulation and non-linear spectroscopic measurements.

Associate Professor

Chapagain, Prem, Ph.D., Florida International University, 2005. *Biophysics.* Theoretical and computational biophysics.

Guo, Lei, Ph.D., Vanderbilt University, 2004. *Nuclear Physics.* Experimental electromagnetic production of strange particles; exotic mesons; hadron spectroscopy.

He, Jin, Ph.D., Arizona State University, 2005. *Biophysics, Condensed Matter Physics.* Nanobiotechnology; single molecule cellular biophysics; bioimaging and bioanalytical instruments; biosensors/nano electronics.

Potvin, Geoff, Ph.D., University of Toronto, 2006. *Physics and other Science Education.* Diversity issues in physics and engineering, graduate education and the professional development of physicists, identity development in the physical sciences, novel methodologies in education research.

Rodríguez, Jorge, Ph.D., University of Florida, 1995. Graduate Program Director. *High Energy Physics, Nuclear Physics.* Elementary particle physics; searches for super symmetry (SUSY); development of high performance computing tools for large-scale data analysis.

Wang, Xuewen, Ph.D., Iowa State University, 1987. *Condensed Matter Physics.* Theoretical solid-state physics.

Assistant Professor

Li, Hebin, Ph.D., Wuhan University, 2001. *Atomic, Molecular, & Optical Physics.* Ultra-fast spectroscopy and quantum optics; multi-dimensional coherent spectroscopy; probe and manipulation of quantum dynamics in atomic/molecular vapors and semiconductor nanostructures.

Emeritus

Maxwell, O. V., Ph.D., Stony Brook University, 1978. *Nuclear Physics.* Theoretical electromagnetic production of strange quarks.

Research Scientist

Laird, Robert, Ph.D., Florida State University. *Neuroscience/ Neuro Physics.* Neuroimaging.

DEPARTMENTAL RESEARCH SPECIALTIES AND STAFF

Theoretical

Theoretical Biophysics. The Theoretical and Computational Biophysics research group investigates the structure, dynamics, and function of proteins from the level of individual amino acids up to the level of multi-protein aggregates that are implicated in a variety of catastrophic diseases. In addition to interacting closely with experimentalists, we also perform Molecular Dynamics and Monte Carlo simulations. We employ the theoretical mathematical physics tools of statistical physics, thermodynamics, non-linear dynamics, and transfer entropy. On the level of individual amino acids, we are investigating which sequences of amino acids are the best choices for inser-

tion into a protein in order to engineer a protein to take on a specific shape, and the effects of amino acid mutations on protein structure and dynamics. On an intermediate scale, we are examining the dynamics of a new class of "transformer" proteins that allows these proteins to transform the shape to perform different functions. Transformer proteins are crucial in the normal epigenetic operations of biological cells, and also are a crucial component in the potency of the Ebola virus. On a larger scale, we are investigating how amyloid-like proteins convert their structure and form aggregates that are implicated in various diseases, such as Alzheimer's and Parkinson's disease. Chapagain, Gerstman.

Theoretical nuclear and particle physics. Electromagnetic production of strange particles; Lattice QCD; high-energy nuclear physics; short range correlations; QCD and nuclei; confinement. Narayanan, Sargsian.

Experimental

Astronomy. Stellar evolution and structure; quasars; extra galactic radio astronomy. Simpson, Van Hamme, Webb.

Atomic, Molecular, & Optical Physics. Ultra-fast Spectroscopy: Multi-dimensional coherent spectroscopy, probe and manipulation of quantum dynamics in atomic/molecular vapors and semiconductor nanomaterials. Quantum Optics: Cavity quantum electrodynamics, quantum coherence and interference, and their applications in quantum state manipulation and non-linear spectroscopic measurements. Hebin Li, Zhu.

Biophysics. Physics of the visual system; macular pigment; temporal processing, protein folding, interactions of laser light with the human visual system. Bone.

Condensed Matter Physics. Physics of surfaces and thin films; nanomaterials and nanostructures and devices; nanobiotechnology; molecular and nano electronics. Darici, He, Wenzhi Li, Wang.

Medium energy nuclear physics. The group primarily conducts experiments at the Thomas Jefferson National Accelerator Facility in Newport News, VA, with affiliations in all four experimental halls. The group has been a leader in studying the electromagnetic production of strange quarks, both in production off of proton targets (elementary production) and in nuclei (hyper-nuclear spectroscopy). Baryon and meson spectroscopy experiments are conducted through both the CLAS/CLAS12 and GlueX collaborations. Experiments probing the short-range structure of A=2,3 nuclei are carried out with the Hall A/C collaborations. We have led efforts to produce the world's most precise measurement of two photon exchange in elastic electron-proton scattering. Boeglin, Guo, Markowitz, Raue, Reinhold, Rodríguez.

Nanobiotechnology. One goal of our research is to understand biophysical and chemical phenomena at nanoscale and fundamental properties and functions of nanostructured materials. The other goal is to transfer the research discoveries into new applications that are relevant to promoting health and combating disease. To reach the goals, we build and develop sophisticated scanning probe microscopy-based instruments. We also utilize various top-down and bottom-up micro/nano fabrication techniques to fabricate novel devices. The current research projects are in these fields: single molecule cellular biophysics, nanobiotechnology, nano and molecular electronics and bioimaging and analytical instruments. He.

Neuroimaging. Functional and structural organization of the human brain; magnetic resonance imaging; neurobiological mechanisms underlying behavior. Angela Laird, Robert Laird.

Physics and other Science Education. PER - active learning classrooms and reformed pedagogical practices, affective considerations in physics learning, student networks and physics learning, institutional change and instructional transformation. Kramer, Potvin.

Plasma and Fusion. Study of nuclear fusion rates as a function of space and time in a spherical tokamak and their response to plasma instabilities. Experiments are carried out at the NSTX-U (National Spherical Tokamak Experiment Upgrade) at the Princeton Plasma Physics Laboratory. Boeglin.

View additional information about this department at www.gradschoolshopper.com. Check out the "Why Choose Us?" section, find out more about the department's culture and get links to social media networks.

FLORIDA STATE UNIVERSITY

DEPARTMENT OF PHYSICS

Tallahassee, Florida 32306-4350
http://www.physics.fsu.edu/

General University Information
President: John Thrasher
Dean of Graduate School: Dr. Nancy Marcus
University website: http://fsu.edu
School Type: Public
Setting: Urban
Total number of Students: 32,528
Total number of Graduate Students: 8,981

Department Information
Department Chairman: Dr. Horst Wahl, Chair
Department Contact: Felicia Youngblood, Graduate
  Coordinator
  Total full-time faculty: 57
  Total number of full-time equivalent positions: 49
  Full-Time Graduate Students: 150
  Female Full-Time Graduate Students: 0
  First-Year Graduate Students: 27
  Female First-Year Students: 6
  Total Post Doctorates: 5

Department Address
77 Chieftan Way
Tallahassee, FL 32306-4350
Phone: (850) 644-4473
Fax: (850) 644-8630
E-mail: fky11@fsu.edu
Website: http://www.physics.fsu.edu/

ADMISSIONS

Admission Contact Information
Address admission inquiries to: FSU Office of Admissions, Florida State University, Tallahassee, FL USA 32306-2400
Phone: (850) 644-6200
E-mail: graduateadmissions@admin.fsu.edu
Admissions website: http://Admissions.fsu.edu

Application deadlines
Fall admission:
U.S. students: January 15   *Int'l. students*: January 15

Application fee
U.S. students: $30   *Int'l. students*: $30

Admissions information
For Fall of 2018:
  Number of applicants: 264
  Number admitted: 57
  Number enrolled: 27

Admission requirements
Bachelor's degree requirements: Bachelor's degree in physics or related science is required.
Minimum undergraduate GPA: 3.0

GRE requirements
The GRE is required.

Subjective GRE requirements
The Subjective GRE is not required.

TOEFL requirements
The TOEFL exam is required for students from non-English-speaking countries.
PBT score: 550
iBT score: 80

Other admissions information
Undergraduate preparation assumed: Optics, Author: Hecht, Publisher: AW, Edition: 4TH, ; Modern Physics, Author: Tipler, Publisher: FREEM, ; Thermal and Statistical Mechanics, Author: Schroeder, Publisher: Addison Wesley.

TUITION

Tuition year 2018–19:
Tuition for in-state residents
  Full-time students: $479.32 per credit
Tuition for out-of-state residents
  Full-time students: $1,110.72 per credit
Local Fees (Per Credit Hour) Athletics Fee $7.90 Activity and Services Fee $12.86 Health Fee $13.97 Subtotal: $34.73 Other Fees (Per Credit Hour) Transportation Fee $8.90 Facilities Use Fee $2.00 Technology Fee $5.25 Student Financial Aid Fee: $20.17 Capital Improve Trust Fee: $4.76 Subtotal: $43.4 Student Financial Aid Fee (out of state only): $30.06 Plus Per Semester Facilities Use Fee: $20.00
Credit hours per semester to be considered full-time: 9
Deferred tuition plan: Yes
Health insurance: Yes, $443-$589 after subsidy.
Other academic fees: Transportation Access Fee—$6.50/per cr. hr.
Academic term: Semester
Number of first-year students who received full tuition waivers: 27

Teaching Assistants, Research Assistants, and Fellowships
Number of first-year
  Teaching Assistants: 26
  Research Assistants: 1
Average stipend per academic year
  Teaching Assistant: $20,900
  Research Assistant: $23,900
  Fellowship student: $23,900

FINANCIAL AID

Application deadlines
Fall admission:
U.S. students: April 15   *Int'l. students*: April 15

Loans
Loans are available for U.S. students.
Loans are available for international students.
GAPSFAS application required: Yes
FAFSA application required: Yes

For further information
Address financial aid inquiries to: Office of Financial Aid, Suite 4400A University Center, Tallahassee, FL 32306-2430.
Phone: (850) 644-0539
E-mail: ofacs@admin.fsu.edu

Financial aid website: http://financialaid.fsu.edu/

HOUSING

Availability of on-campus housing
Single students: Yes
Married students: No
Childcare Assistance: Yes

For further information
Address housing inquiries to: University Housing, 942 Learning Way, P.O. Box 3064174, Tallahassee, FL, 32306-4174.
Phone: (850) 644-2860
E-mail: housinginfo@fsu.edu
Housing aid website: http://www.housing.fsu.edu/

Table A—Faculty, Enrollments, and Degrees Granted

Research Specialty	2017–2018 Faculty	Enrollment Fall 2017		Number of Degrees Granted 2017–2018 (2013–18)		
		Master's	Doctorate	Master's	Terminal Master's	Doctorate
Astrophysics	6	–	–	–	–	2(9)
Atomic, Molecular, & Optical Physics	1	–	–	–	–	–(2)
Biophysics	2	–	–	–	–	1(2)
Condensed Matter Physics	16	–	–	–	–	5(59)
High Energy Physics	12	–	–	–	–	4(25)
Nuclear Physics	15	–	–	–	–	3(27)
Total	52	–	141	33(128)	–	15(124)
Full-time Grad. Stud.	–	–	141	–	–	–
First-year Grad. Stud.	–	–	24	–	–	–

GRADUATE DEGREE REQUIREMENTS

Master's: To qualify for the M.S. degree, students must either (a) complete 21 hours of graduate work of which at least 18 hours must be in courses numbered 5,000 and above, or (b) take a program of courses that is acceptable to their Supervisor Committee that includes four courses from a select list of advanced courses and pass with a cumulative grade point average of no less than B in all six core graduate courses, or c) pass a written Qualifying Examination in the areas of mechanics, statistical mechanics, electrodynamics, and quantum mechanics. The classroom phase of the graduate program is designed to introduce students to the basic conceptual tools used in physics and to acquaint them with a variety of research areas. The well-prepared incoming student will have had advanced undergraduate courses in Mechanics, Electricity and Magnetism, Modern Physics, Quantum Mechanics, Thermodynamics, and Optics, comparable to the following undergraduate courses at Florida State: PHY 3221 (Mechanics), PHY 4323–4324 (Electricity and Magnetism), PHY 3101 (Intermediate Modern Physics), PHY 4604 (Quantum Theory of Matter AB), PHY 4513 (Thermal and Statistical Physics), PHY 3424 (Optics). Students deficient in one or more of these areas should include in their graduate program whatever undergraduate courses are necessary to remedy these deficiencies. The core graduate courses that contain the material with which every research physicist should be familiar are: PHY 5246 (Theoretical Mechanics); PHY 5524 (Statistical Mechanics); PHY 5346 and PHY 5347 (Electrodynamics A and B); PHY 5645, PHY 5646, (Quantum Mechanics A,B) and a third Quantum Mechanics course. Courses required for the M.S. Both thesis and non-thesis programs are offered leading to the Master of Science degree. Non-thesis degree: To qualify for a non-thesis degree, the student must complete at least thirty-three (33) hours in courses numbered 4000 or above, eighteen (18) of which must be in courses numbered 5000 or above. At least twenty-one (21) of the thirty-three (33) hours must be taken on a letter grade basis. At least three (3) of the courses must be from the seven core graduate courses listed above, including at least one Quantum Mechanics course. Thesis degree: To qualify for a thesis degree, the student must submit an acceptable thesis and complete at least thirty (30) hours in courses numbered 4000 or above, eighteen (18) of which must be in courses numbered 5000 or above. At least eighteen (18) of the thirty (30) hours must be on a letter grade basis. No more than three (3) semester hours of PHY 5918 credit and three (3) semester hours of PHY 5940 credit may be counted toward the Master of Science degree. A minimum of six (6) hours of credit must be earned for the thesis. Examinations: To qualify for the M.S. degree, students must pass an Oral Qualifying Examination on their graduate work. In the course Master's degree program, the Qualifying Examination focuses on the subjects of mechanics, statistical mechanics, electrodynamics and quantum mechanics. In the thesis program, the oral examination will consist primarily of defense of thesis. Residency: A minimum of two semesters or the equivalent must be completed in residence (must be enrolled for a minimum of 12 semester hours per semester). No language requirement. Minimum GPA of 3.0/4.0.

Doctorate: To qualify for a Ph.D., students must (a) make a formal presentation of some explicit research accomplishment satisfactory to their tentative Ph.D. Supervisory Committee; (b) take a program of courses that is acceptable to their Supervisory Committee that includes three courses from a select list of advanced courses; (c) pass with a cumulative grade average of no less than B in all six core graduate courses; (d) teach two elementary laboratory sections for two semesters; (e) pass a written Qualifying Examination in the advanced under graduate areas of mechanics, statistical mechanics, electrodynamics, and quantum mechanics; (f) pass a PHY 8964 Oral Qualifying Examination in the broad area of their particular specialization within the field of physics; (g) carry out research leading to an acceptable dissertation; and (h) pass orally the PHY 8985 Dissertation Defense of their dissertation. Residency: after having finished 30 semester hours of graduate work or being awarded the Master's degree, the student must be continuously enrolled on the Florida State University campus for a minimum of 24 graduate semester hours credit in any period of 12 consecutive months.

Thesis: Thesis may be written in absentia.

SPECIAL EQUIPMENT, FACILITIES, OR PROGRAMS

The Department of Physics has world class programs in experimental and theoretical research in the areas of astrophysics and cosmology, atomic physics, biophysics, condensed matter physics, high-energy physics, nuclear physics and statistical mechanics. The department has consistently been rated as one of the best in the Southeast United States and boasts internationally prominent faculty. Among the faculty are 18 Fellows of The American Physical Society and 5 Fellows of The American Association for the Advancement of Science.

In accord with emerging national trends and priorities in interdisciplinary science, synergistic connections and collaborations are evolving, notably between nuclear, high energy and astrophysics/cosmology; condensed matter and materials science; and theoretical and computational physics. As such, the department provides a rich variety of research opportunities to our undergraduate, graduate and postdoctoral communities.

The department occupies three adjacent buildings: the Keen Building, an eight-story Physics Research Building, The Leroy Collins Research Laboratory Building, and an undergraduate physics classroom and laboratory building. Extensive experimental facilities include a 9.5-MV Super FN Tandem Van de Graaff accelerator with superconducting post accelerator, a precision Penning trap mass spectrometer, a detector development laboratory for high-energy particle detectors, high-resolution Fourier-transform IR spectrometers, an ion implantation facility, instrumentation for research at liquid helium temperature and thin-film preparation, UHV (including surface analysis, molecular beam epitaxy, and atomic cluster facilities), facilities for high- and low-temperature superconductivity, small-angle and standard x-ray diffractometry, crystal growth facilities and ion implantation facility, scanning electron and tunneling microscopy, image analysis, quasi-elastic light scattering, polarized electron energy loss spectroscopy, a He atom beam-crystal surface scattering apparatus, and a unique aerosol physics-electron irradiation system.

Computational facilities at FSU include an IBM Multiprocessor Supercomputer, a state of the art visualization lab, and a 120 CPU Beowulf cluster in the department. Extensive networking facilities provide access to computers on- and off-campus.

The strong overlap of the department with the National High Magnetic Field Laboratory at FSU adds to the many research tools available, as do research partnerships with many other national and international facilities including the Thomas Jefferson National Accelerator Facility, Fermi National Accelerator Laboratory, Los Alamos National Laboratory, Oak Ridge National Laboratory and the European Laboratory for Particle Physics (CERN). The strength of the department's research and educational programs is reflected in the current level of $15.4 M active contracts and grants received, and the graduation of 18 PhD and 20 BS degrees per year.

The National High Magnetic Field Laboratory is the only user facility of its kind in the Western Hemisphere.

The in-house research program is built around leading scientists and engineers who concentrate on the study of strongly correlated electron systems, molecular conductors, magnetic materials, magnetic resonance, cryogenics, and new approaches to measuring materials properties in high magnetic fields.

The laboratory also has one of the world's foremost magnet and science technology groups, which designs and builds this new generation of magnets. In 1999, the lab brought online a new 45-Tesla hybrid magnet, the most powerful magnet of its kind in the world. In 2004, the laboratory commissioned the world's first ultra-wide bore 900 MHz NMR magnet for chemical and biomedical research.

The National High Magnetic Field laboratory has many exciting research opportunities for graduate students who wish to pursue research at the edge of parameter space in any area of science utilizing these world-class resources and instrumentation.

Trained as "problem solvers", physics graduates of our department have access to a broad range of career options leading to positions in the U.S. and abroad as post-doctoral fellows, university professors, researchers at national laboratories, or as scientific staff at technical institutes, medical centers, or industry.

Undergraduate students can choose from among four majors: Physics, Physics and Astrophysics, Physical Science, and Physical Science/FSU-Teach. Undergraduate research is strongly encouraged as work towards a senior thesis or honors thesis. The FSU chapter of the Society of Physics Students is very active, providing an opportunity for physics majors to build a community outside the classroom.

Table B—Separately Budgeted Research Expenditures by Source of Support

Source of Support	Departmental Research	Physics-related Research Outside Department
Federal government	$2,813,941.11	
State/local government		
Non-profit organizations		
Business and industry		
Other		
Total	$2,813,941.11	

Table C—Separately Budgeted Research Expenditures by Research Specialty

Research Specialty	No. of Grants	Expenditures ($)
Astrophysics	4	$437,602.98
Atomic, Molecular, & Optical Physics	1	$180,138
(Including the NHMFL)	24	$708,247.45
High Energy Physics	9	$763,342.22
Nuclear Physics	6	$602,610.46
Particles and Fields	1	$122,000
Total	45	$2,813,941.11

FACULTY

Professor

Adams, Todd, Ph.D., University of Notre Dame, 1997. *High Energy Physics, Particles and Fields.* Experimental high-energy physics; particle physics; supersymmetry.

Berg, Bernd, Ph.D., Free University., Berlin, 1977. *Computational Physics, High Energy Physics.* Theoretical physics; lattice gauge theory; computational physics.

Blessing, Susan, Ph.D., Indiana University, 1989. Women In Math Science and Engineering (WIMSE) director; Undergraduate Chair. *High Energy Physics.* Experimental high-energy physics; elementary particle physics.

Boebinger, Gregory, Ph.D., Massachusetts Institute of Technology, 1986. Director, National High Magnetic Field Laboratory. *Condensed Matter Physics, Electromagnetism.* Magnetism; experimental condensed matter physics; correlated electron systems.

Bonesteel, Nicholas, Ph.D., Cornell University, 1991. *Condensed Matter Physics, Electromagnetism.* Theoretical physics; condensed matter physics; many-body theory; magnetism, Quantum Hall Effect.

Cao, Jianming, Ph.D., University of Rochester, 1996. *Condensed Matter Physics.* Experimental condensed matter physics, ultrafast dynamics probed by Lasers.

Capstick, Simon, Ph.D., University of Toronto, 1986. Graduate Chair. *Computational Physics, Nuclear Physics, Particles and Fields.* Theoretical nuclear and particle physics; computational physics.

Cottle, Paul, Ph.D., Yale University, 1986. *Nuclear Physics.* Experimental heavy-ion nuclear physics.

Dobrosavljevic, Vladimir, Ph.D., Brown University, 1988. *Condensed Matter Physics.* Theoretical condensed matter physics; disordered systems and glasses; metal-insulator transitions.

Duke, Dennis, Ph.D., Iowa State University, 1974. *Computational Physics, History & Philosophy of Physics/Science.* Theoretical physics; elementary particles; computational physics.

Eugenio, Paul, Ph.D., University of Massachusetts, 1998. *Nuclear Physics, Particles and Fields.* Experimental hadronic nuclear physics; quark-gluon structure of matter and hadron spectroscopy; search for gluonic excitations.

Greene, Laura H., Ph.D., Cornell University, 1984. Chief Scientist, NHMFL. *Condensed Matter Physics, Materials Science, Metallurgy, Nano Science and Technology.* experimental condensed matter physics investigating strongly correlated electron systems, superconductivity.

Hill, Stephen, Ph.D., University of Oxford, 1994. *Condensed Matter Physics.* Experimental condensed matter.

Hoeflich, Peter, Ph.D., University of Heidelberg, 1986. *Astrophysics, Computational Physics.* Theoretical astrophysics; dark energy, dark matter and dark ages.

Manousakis, Efstratios, Ph.D., University of Illinois, 1985. *Condensed Matter Physics.* Theoretical physics; condensed matter; many-body theory; superconductivity.

Piekarewicz, Jorge, Ph.D., University of Pennsylvania, 1985. *Astrophysics, Nuclear Physics.* Theoretical nuclear physics; collective nuclear modes; equation of state of dense matter; neutron stars.

Prosper, Harrison B., Ph.D., University of Manchester, 1980. *High Energy Physics, Particles and Fields.* Experimental high-energy physics; particle physics.

Reina, Laura, Ph.D., University of Trieste, 1992. *High Energy Physics, Particles and Fields.* Theoretical high-energy physics; elementary particles.

Riley, Mark, Ph.D., University of Liverpool, 1985. Dean of the Graduate School. *Nuclear Physics.* Experimental physics; nuclear structure.

Roberts, Winston, Ph.D., University of Guelph, 1988. *Nuclear Physics, Particles and Fields.* Theoretical hadron physics.

Tabor, Samuel, Ph.D., Stanford University, 1972. Director, John D. Fox Superconducting Accelerator Laboratory. *Nuclear Physics.* Experimental physics; nuclei far from stability; high-spin states in nuclei.

Van Winkle, David, Ph.D., University of Colorado, 1984. *Condensed Matter Physics.* Experimental condensed matter physics; liquid crystal gels.

Wahl, Horst, Ph.D., Vienna, 1969. Department Chair. *High Energy Physics, Particles and Fields.* Experimental physics; elementary particles.

Wiedenhoever, Ingo, Ph.D., University of Cologne, 1995. Department Associate Chair. *Nuclear Physics.* Experimental nuclear physics; radioactive beams.

Xiong, Peng, Ph.D., Brown University, 1994. *Biophysics, Condensed Matter Physics, Nano Science and Technology.* Experimental condensed matter physics; nano-biophysics systems.

Yang, Kun, Ph.D., Indiana University, 1994. *Computational Physics, Condensed Matter Physics.* Theoretical physics; condensed matter, computational physics.

Associate Professor

Askew, Andrew, Ph.D., Rice University, 2004. *High Energy Physics.* Experimental high-energy physics.

Chiorescu, Irinel, Ph.D., University Joseph-Fourier, France, 2000. *Condensed Matter Physics, Low Temperature Physics, Nano Science and Technology.* Nanoscale experimental condensed matter, Quantum Magnetism, Superconducting Devices.

Crede, Volker, Ph.D., University of Bonn, 2000. *Nuclear Physics, Particles and Fields.* Experimental nuclear physics; hadronic physics.

Lind, David, Ph.D., Rice University, 1986. *Condensed Matter Physics.* Experimental condensed matter physics; magnetic superlattices.

Ng, Hon-Kie, Ph.D., McMaster University, 1984. *Condensed Matter Physics, Electromagnetism.* Experimental physics; far-infrared spectroscopy; superconductivity, highly correlated electron systems; spectroscopy in high magnetic fields.

Okui, Takemichi, Ph.D., University of California, Berkeley, 2003. *High Energy Physics, Particles and Fields.* Theoretical high-energy physics.

Volya, Alexander, Ph.D., Michigan State University, 2000. *Nuclear Physics.* Theoretical nuclear physics; nuclear structure models.

Assistant Professor

Almaraz-Calderon, Sergio, Ph.D., University of Notre Dame, 2012.

Beekman, Christianne, Ph.D., Leiden University, 2010. *Condensed Matter Physics, Materials Science, Metallurgy, Nano Science and Technology.*

Collins, David, Ph.D., University of California, San Diego, 2009. *Astrophysics.* I work on molecular cloud dynamics, focusing on the role of magnetic fields in the statistics and collapse of the cloud and the formation of prestellar cores. I work with adaptive mesh resolution (AMR) techniques, notably the code Enzo.

Dobbs, Sean, Ph.D., Northwestern University, 2012. searching for novel states beyond the "standard quark model" of quark-antiquark mesons and 3-quark baryons; photoproduction; hybrid mesons; nucleon structure with heavy quark probes; systems for managing and studying large data sets.

Gao, Hanwei, Ph.D., Northwestern University, 2009. *Condensed Matter Physics, Materials Science, Metallurgy, Nano Science and Technology.*

Hsiao, Eric Y., Ph.D., University of Victoria, 2009. *Astronomy, Astrophysics.* SuperNova observation and data analysis.

Huffenberger, Kevin, Ph.D., Princeton University, 2006. *Astrophysics.* Cosmology, CMB data analysis.

Kolberg, Ted, Ph.D., University of Notre Dame, 2011. *High Energy Physics, Particles and Fields.*

Murphy, Jeremiah, Ph.D., University of Arizona, 2008. *Astrophysics.* Astrophysics, core collapse SuperNovae, studies of progenitor systems and supernova remnants.

Vafek, Oskar, Ph.D., Johns Hopkins University, 2003. *Condensed Matter Physics.* Theoretical condensed matter physics; quantum phase transitions; superconductivity.

Yohay, Rachel, Ph.D., University of Virginia, 2012. *High Energy Physics.*

Professor Emeritus

Owens, Joseph, Ph.D., Tufts University, 1973. *High Energy Physics, Particles and Fields.* Theoretical physics; elementary particles.

Schlottmann, Pedro, Ph.D., Technical University, Munich, 1973. *Condensed Matter Physics, Electromagnetism.* Theoretical physics; high-Tc superconductors; heavy fermions; magnetism.

von Molnár, Stephen, Ph.D., University of California, Riverside, 1965. *Condensed Matter Physics, Electromagnetism, Nano Science and Technology.* Experimental physics; correlation effects in electronic systems; magnetic semiconductors; magnetic nano-structures.

Research Professor

Frawley, Anthony, Ph.D., Australian National University, 1977. *Nuclear Physics, Particles and Fields.* Experimental physics; Relativistic heavy ion physics; QCD matter; Quark gluon plasma.

Myers, Edmund, Ph.D., University of Oxford, 1982. *Atomic, Molecular, & Optical Physics.* Experimental atomic physics; precision measurement.

Scholar / Scientist

Balicas, Luis, Ph.D., University of Paris Xl-Orsay, 1995. *Condensed Matter Physics, Nano Science and Technology.* High temperature superconductivity and/or multiferroiticity; magnetic states of matter.

Engle, Lloyd, Ph.D., Princeton University, 1987. *Condensed Matter Physics, Electromagnetism.*

Kuhns, Philip, Ph.D., College of William and Mary, 1983. *Condensed Matter Physics, Electromagnetism.*

Popovic, Dragana, Ph.D., Brown University, 1989. *Condensed Matter Physics.* Experimental condensed matter physics; electronic properties of two-dimensional (2D) systems in semiconductor heterostructures; effects of disorder and strong electronic correlations; mesoscopic effects; 2D metal-insulator transition; glassy freezing and out-of-equilibrium dynamics; noise; charge dynamics and magnetotransport in cuprates.

Reyes, Arneil, Ph.D., University of California, Riverside, 1990. *Condensed Matter Physics.* Experimental Condensed Matter high-field nuclear magnetic resonance technique, rf, cryogenic, and high pressure instrumentation; exotic magnetism in strongly correlated electronic systems as in heavy fermion compounds, semiconductors, high temperature superconductors, nanomagnets, multiferroics, and low-dimensional electron systems.

Tozer, Stanley W., Ph.D., Johns Hopkins University, 1986. *Condensed Matter Physics.*

Associate Scholar / Scientist

Choi, Eun-Sang, Ph.D., Seoul National University, 1998. *Condensed Matter Physics.*

McGill, Stephen, Ph.D., University of Pennsylvania, 2004. *Condensed Matter Physics, Optics.*

Smirnov, Dmitry, Ph.D., A. F. Ioffe Physico-Technical Institute of Russian Academy of Sciences, 1996. *Condensed Matter Physics.*

DEPARTMENTAL RESEARCH SPECIALTIES AND STAFF

Theoretical

Astrophysics. Advanced stages of stellar evolution; core-collapse and thermonuclear supernovae; compact stellar remnants; thermonuclear astrophysical combustion; radiative transfer. Duke, Hoeflich, Piekarewicz.

Condensed Matter Physics. Many-body theory of magnetism; magnetic properties of solids; high-temperature superconductivity; heavy fermions; adsorption; phase transitions. Bonesteel, Dobrosavljevic, Manousakis, Schlottmann, Vafek, Yang.

High Energy Physics. Strong and electroweak interaction phenomenology in high-energy particle physics. Lattice gauge theory and numerical simulations of various physical systems. Berg, Okui, Owens, Reina.

Nuclear Physics. Nuclear structure studies emphasizing transitions; collective nuclear modes; structure and electromagnetic interactions of baryons and nuclei; structure and phases of neutron stars. Capstick, Piekarewicz, Roberts, Volya.

Experimental

Astrophysics. Collins, Hsiao, Huffenberger, Murphy.

Atomic, Molecular, & Optical Physics. Precision atomic measurements using Penning trap. Myers.

Condensed Matter Physics. Biomolecular ordering; nano/biophysics; liquid crystals; gels; spintronics; hard magnetic materials; surface physics; sub-picosecond spectroscopy; low- and high-temperature. superconductivity; highly correlated electron systems; organic crystals; quantum qubits. Balicas, Beekman, Boebinger, Cao, Chiorescu, Choi, Engle, Gao, Greene, Hill, Kuhns, Lind, McGill, Ng, Popovic, Reyes, Smirnov, Tozer, Van Winkle, von Molnár, Xiong.

High Energy Physics. Collider physics; strong and electroweak interactions in high-energy particle physics. Adams, Askew, Blessing, Kolberg, Prosper, Wahl, Yohay.

Nuclear Physics. Hadron spectroscopy; heavy-ion reactions and radioactive beams. Photoproduction of baryons and mesons; search for exotic and hybrid mesons; search for new strangeonia states; search for missing baryons, particle detector development and computational physics. Heavy-ion fusion and fragmentation studies. Properties of nuclear systems at high angular momentum and far from stability; laser-induced polarization; octupole structure in nuclei. Light-ion nuclear spectroscopy, alpha, beta, and gamma spectroscopy; relativistic heavy-ion reactions. Almaraz-Calderon, Cottle, Crede, Dobbs, Eugenio, Frawley, Riley, Tabor, Wiedenhoever.

View additional information about this department at www.gradschoolshopper.com. Check out the "Why Choose Us?" section, find out more about the department's culture and get links to social media networks.

UNIVERSITY OF CENTRAL FLORIDA

CREOL, THE COLLEGE OF OPTICS & PHOTONICS

Orlando, Florida 32816-2700
http://www.creol.ucf.edu

General University Information
President: Dale Whitaker
Dean of Graduate School: Elizabeth Klonoff
University website: http://www.ucf.edu
School Type: Public
Setting: Suburban
Total Faculty: 1,700
Total number of Students: 66,000
Total number of Graduate Students: 8,000

Department Information
Department Chairman: Dr. Bahaa Saleh, Dean
Department Contact: David Hagan, Associate Dean/Program
  Director
  Total full-time faculty: 36
  Total number of full-time equivalent positions: 14
  Full-Time Graduate Students: 120
  Female Full-Time Graduate Students: 22
  First-Year Graduate Students: 22
  Female First-Year Students: 5
  Total Post Doctorates: 15

Department Address
4304 Scorpius St
Orlando, FL 32816-2700
Phone: 407-823-6817
Fax: 407-823-6810
E-mail: gradprog@creol.ucf.edu
Website: http://www.creol.ucf.edu

ADMISSIONS

Admission Contact Information
Address admission inquiries to: Graduate Program Office
Phone: 407-823-4726
E-mail: gradprog@creol.ucf.edu
Admissions website: http://www.creol.ucf.edu

Application deadlines
Fall admission:
U.S. students: July 1   *Int'l. students*: January 15
Spring admission:
U.S. students: December 1   *Int'l. students*: July 1

Application fee
U.S. students: $30   *Int'l. students*: $30
January 15 is the priority deadline. *Applicants who plan to enroll full time in a degree program and who wish to be considered for university fellowships or assistantships should apply
by the priority deadline.

Admissions information
For Fall of 2018:
  Number of applicants: 164
  Number admitted: 45
  Number enrolled: 30

Admission requirements
Bachelor's degree requirements: Electrical Engineering, Physics,
  Optics & Photonics, and any related discipline.
Minimum undergraduate GPA: 3.0

GRE requirements
The GRE is required.
  Quantitative score: 160
  Verbal score: 150
  Mean GRE score range (25th–75th percentile): 80th
GRE is a requirement for the PhD program. There is no such
  requirement for the MS degree. These scores are typical if
  seeking a college fellowship, but not the minimum required.

Subjective GRE requirements
The Subjective GRE is not required.

TOEFL requirements
The TOEFL exam is required for students from non-English-
  speaking countries.
  iBT score: 80

Other admissions information
Undergraduate preparation assumed: Incoming students are expected to have a science or engineering bachelors degree that
  includes a strong background in calculus-based physics and
  electromagnetics.

TUITION

Tuition year 2017–2018:
Tuition for in-state residents
  Full-time students: $369.65 per credit
  Part-time students: $369.65 per credit
Tuition for out-of-state residents
  Full-time students: $1,194.05 per credit
  Part-time students: $1,194.05 per credit
Tuition is inclusive of fees.
Credit hours per semester to be considered full-time: 9
Deferred tuition plan:
Health insurance: Available at the cost of $2,141 per year.
Academic term: Semester
Number of first-year students who received full tuition waivers: 25

Teaching Assistants, Research Assistants, and Fellowships
Number of first-year
  Teaching Assistants: 3
  Research Assistants: 5
  Fellowship students: 30
Average stipend per academic year
  Teaching Assistant: $25,000
  Research Assistant: $25,000
  Fellowship student: $25,000
Students on first year fellowships usually continue on research
assistantships. These fellowships are for doctoral students.

FINANCIAL AID

Application deadlines
Fall admission:
U.S. students: December 1

Loans
Loans are available for U.S. students.
Loans are available for international students.
GAPSFAS application required: Yes
FAFSA application required: Yes

For further information
Address financial aid inquiries to: Office of Student Financial Assistance.
Phone: 407-823-2827
E-mail: finaid@ucf.edu
Financial aid website: http://www.finaid.ucf.edu

HOUSING

Availability of on-campus housing
Single students: Yes
Married students: Yes
Childcare Assistance: Yes

For further information
Address housing inquiries to: UCF Housing & Residence Life.
Phone: 407-823-4663
Housing aid website: http://www.housing.ucf.edu

Table A—Faculty, Enrollments, and Degrees Granted

Research Specialty	36 Faculty	Enrollment 136		Number of Degrees Granted 34 (181)		
		Master's	Doctorate	Master's	Terminal Master's	Doctorate
Optics and Photonics	36	35	116	7	12	15
Total	36	35	116	7(46)	12(55)	15(80)
Full-time Grad. Stud.	–	12	115	–	–	–
First-year Grad. Stud.	–	2	23	–	–	–

GRADUATE DEGREE REQUIREMENTS

Master's: Students admitted to the Master's program will be required to complete 30 credit hours. A comprehensive exam is mandatory if the thesis option is not selected. Students can expect to complete the degree in 4 semesters on average.

Doctorate: PhD students are required to complete 72 credit hours of coursework and research. There are 6 core courses, and a qualifying exam is taken at the end of the first year. Two laboratory courses are required, and an additional 7 elective courses. A candidacy exam is taken near the end of coursework. The remainder of the PhD is satisfied by taking research and dissertation hours. Up to 30 hours many be transferred from an earned Master's degree.

Thesis: The MS degree has thesis and non-thesis options.

SPECIAL EQUIPMENT, FACILITIES, OR PROGRAMS

The CREOL building houses 90 research laboratories equipped with state-of-the-art equipment including 3 clean rooms, nanophotonics fabrication facility, lasers covering THz - X-ray spectral range and CW to attosecond pulsewidths, scanning electron microscope, and numerous optical characterization facilities.

FACULTY

Distinguished University Professor
Chang, Zenghu, Ph.D., Chinese Academy of Sciences, 1988.
Christodoulides, Demetrios, Ph.D., John Hopkins University, 1986.

Delfyett, Peter, Ph.D., University Center of the City University of New York, 1988.
Deppe, Dennis, Ph.D., University of Illinois, 1988.
Dogariu, Aristide, Ph.D., Hokkaido University.
Hagan, David, Ph.D., Heriot-Watt University, 1985. Associate Dean.
Patel, Kumar, Ph.D., Stanford University, 1961.
Richardson, Kathleen, Ph.D., Alfred University, 1992.
Richardson, Martin, Ph.D., London University, 1967.
Saleh, Bahaa E. A., Ph.D., Johns Hopkins University, 1971. Dean.
Soileau, M.J., Ph.D., University of Southern California.
Van Stryland, Eric, Ph.D., University of Arizona, 1976.
Wu, Shin-Tson, Ph.D., University of Southern California.

Professor
Abouraddy, Ayman, Ph.D., Boston University, 2003.
Driggers, Ronald, Ph.D., University of Memphis, 1990.
Fathpour, Sasan, Ph.D., University of Michigan, 2005.
Kar, Aravinda, Ph.D., University of Illinois at Urbana-Champaign.
Li, Guifang, Ph.D., University of Wisconsin-Madison.
LiKamWa, Patrick, Ph.D., University of Sheffield.
Moharam, M.G. Jim, Ph.D., University of British Columbia, 1978.
Schoenfeld, Winston, Ph.D., University of California-Santa Barbara, 2000.
Schulzgen, Axel, Ph.D., Humboldt University, 1992.
Vodopyanov, Konstantin, Ph.D., Oscillations Lab of Lebedev Physical Institute.

Associate Professor
Chanda, Debashis, Ph.D., University of Toronto, 2008.
Gaume, Romain, Ph.D., Paris VI University, 2002.
Khajavikhan, Mercedeh, Ph.D., University of Minnesota, 2009.
Kik, Pieter, Ph.D., FOM Institute for Atomic & Molecular Physics.
Kuebler, Stephen, Ph.D., University of Oxford.

Assistant Professor
Amezcua Correa, Rodrigo, Ph.D., University of Southampton.
Argenti, Luca, Ph.D., Scuola Normale Superiore of Pisa, 2008.
Dong, Yajie, Ph.D., Harvard University, 2010.
Gelfand, Ryan, Ph.D., Northwestern University, 2013.
Han, Kyu, Ph.D., Seoul National University, 2010.
Pang, Shuo Sean, Ph.D., Caltech, 2013.
Renshaw, Christopher Kyle, Ph.D., University of Michigan.
Yu, Xiaoming, Ph.D., Kansas State University, 2016.

Emeritus
Bass, Michael, Ph.D., University of Michigan.
Boreman, Glenn, Ph.D., University of Arizona, 1984.
Phillips, Ronald, Ph.D., Arizona State University, 1970.
Silfvast, William, Ph.D., University of Utah, 1965.
Zeldovich, Boris, Ph.D., Ledebev Physics Institute.

Research Professor
Glebov, Leonid, Ph.D., State Optical Institute, 1976.

Joint Appointment
Baudelet, Matthieu, Ph.D., Laboratoire de Spectrométrie Ionique et Moléculaire.
Gesquiere, Andre, Ph.D., Catholic University Leuven, 2001.
Hernandez, Florencio Eloy, Ph.D., Universidad Central de Venezuela and L'Université Franche-Comté, 1996.
Lyakh, Arkadiy, Ph.D., University of Florida.
Shah, Mubarak, Ph.D., Wayne State University, 1986.
Sigman, Michael, Ph.D., Florida State University, 1986.

Thomas, Jayan, Ph.D., Cochin University of Science & Technology, 1990.

DEPARTMENTAL RESEARCH SPECIALTIES AND STAFF

Theoretical

Nonlinear & Quantum Optics. Nonlinear optics deals with the behavior of intense light in media exhibiting nonlinear response to the applied optical field. It enables wavelength conversion and multiphoton absorption, and plays essential roles in optical telecommunication, nonlinear microscopy and spectroscopy, and attosecond science. Quantum optics is concerned with light-matter interaction phenomena requiring quantum-mechanical description. It includes processing of quantum information at the photon level, and supports applications ranging from ultrasensitive measurement and secure communication to computing. Abouraddy, Argenti, Christodoulides, Khajavikhan, Kik, Saleh.

Experimental

Fiber Optics. Fiber optics allows us to transport and distribute optically encoded information over long distances with low losses as well as to collect and manipulate optical signals. Advances in optical fiber have revolutionized the fields of communication and information processing and continued research in materials science and optical engineering will aid in the development of next generation devices. In addition to telecommunication, modern fibers can be found as an integral component in many applications such as lighting and display hardware, lasers, and sensors. Core Technologies: Fiber Fabrication Technology; Multimaterial Fibers; Nanostructured Fibers; Mid Infrared Fibers; Fiber Lasers Applications: Fiber Optic Communication; Fiber Optic Networks; Fiber Optic Sensing. Abouraddy, Amezcua Correa, Christodoulides, Delfyett, Fathpour, Gaume, Li, LiKamWa, Kathleen Richardson, Martin Richardson, Schulzgen.

Imaging, Sensing, and Display. Optical sensing, imaging, and display involve the acquisition, manipulation, and presentation of optical information by use of optical irradiance, phase, coherence, polarization, luminescence, in one or more dimensions. The research in this area synergizes device development and signal processing. Optical sensing and imaging have unique advantages in biomedical imaging and industrial metrology, due to the non-invasive and high-specific nature of the visible light; display technologies, including solid-state lighting and liquid crystal display, play an major role in today's advancement in consumer electronics and entertainment industry. Abouraddy, Baudelet, Dogariu, Driggers, Gelfand, Han, Kar, Khajavikhan, Kik, Li, Pang, Renshaw, Kathleen Richardson, Martin Richardson, Van Stryland, Vodopyanov, Wu, Yu.

Nonlinear & Quantum Optics. Nonlinear optics deals with the behavior of intense light in media exhibiting nonlinear response to the applied optical field. It enables wavelength conversion and multiphoton absorption, and plays essential roles in optical telecommunication, nonlinear microscopy and spectroscopy, and attosecond science. Quantum optics is concerned with light-matter interaction phenomena requiring quantum-mechanical description. It includes processing of quantum information at the photon level, and supports applications ranging from ultrasensitive measurement and secure communication to computing. Abouraddy, Amezcua Correa, Argenti, Baudelet, Christodoulides, Delfyett, Fathpour, Glebov, Hagan, Khajavikhan, Kik, Kuebler, Li, LiKamWa, Kathleen Richardson, Martin Richardson, Saleh, Schoenfeld, Schulzgen, Thomas, Van Stryland, Vodopyanov, Yu.

Optoelectronics & Integrated Photonics. Optoelectronics enables the bi-directional conversion of energy between photons and electrons to generate, absorb and manipulate light within the context of electronic systems. Example devices include LEDs, semiconductor lasers, modulators, photodetectors, and solar cells. Integrated photonics combines such passive and active devices to make optics seamlessly integrated with electronics to revolutionize communication, information processing, sensing and imaging systems. Abouraddy, Chanda, Christodoulides, Delfyett, Deppe, Dong, Driggers, Fathpour, Glebov, Hagan, Han, Kar, Khajavikhan, Kik, Kuebler, LiKamWa, Moharam, Renshaw, Kathleen Richardson, Martin Richardson, Schoenfeld, Schulzgen, Thomas, Van Stryland, Vodopyanov, Wu, Yu.

View additional information about this department at www.gradschoolshopper.com. Check out the "Why Choose Us?" section, find out more about the department's culture and get links to social media networks.

UNIVERSITY OF CENTRAL FLORIDA

DEPARTMENT OF PHYSICS

Orlando, Florida 32816-2385
http://physics.cos.ucf.edu/

General University Information
President: Dr. Dale Whittaker
Dean of Graduate School: Dr. Elizabeth A. Klonoff
University website: http://www.ucf.edu
School Type: Public
Setting: Urban
Total Faculty: 2,481
Total Graduate Faculty: 1,889
Total number of Students: 66,183
Total number of Graduate Students: 8,726

Department Information
Department Chairman: Prof. Eduardo Mucciolo, Chair
Department Contact: Esperanza Soto Arcino, Graduate
   Program Assistant
   Total full-time faculty: 50
   Total number of full-time equivalent positions: 50
   Full-Time Graduate Students: 97
   Female Full-Time Graduate Students: 35
   First-Year Graduate Students: 18
   Female First-Year Students: 8
   Total Post Doctorates: 11

Department Address
4111 Libra Drive
Physical Sciences, Building 121, Room 430
Orlando, FL 32816-2385
Phone: (407) 823-2325
Fax: (407) 823-5112
E-mail: physics@ucf.edu
Website: http://physics.cos.ucf.edu/

ADMISSIONS

Admission Contact Information
Address admission inquiries to: Professor Abdelkader Kara,
   Graduate Program Director, Department of Physics, Univer-
   sity of Central Florida, Orlando, FL 32816-2385
Phone: (407) 823-1527
E-mail: Abdelkader.Kara@ucf.edu
Admissions website: http://www.graduate.ucf.edu

Application deadlines
Fall admission:
U.S. students: July 1   *Int'l. students*: January 15
Spring admission:
U.S. students: December 1   *Int'l. students*: July 1

Application fee
U.S. students: $30   *Int'l. students*: $30

Admissions information
For Fall of 2018:
   Number of applicants: 99
   Number admitted: 41
   Number enrolled: 18

Admission requirements
Bachelor's degree requirements: Bachelors degree in Physics is
   required.
Minimum undergraduate GPA: 3.0

GRE requirements
The GRE is required.
   Mean GRE score range (25th–75th percentile): 130-170
There is no minimum requirement.

Subjective GRE requirements
The Subjective GRE is recommended.
   Mean Advanced GRE score range (25th–75th percentile): 700-
   900
   A General GRE score of at least 1,000 on the combined verbal-
   quantitative sections of the Aptitude Test is recommended for
   admission to the Ph.D./M.S. program. Under the new GRE
   scoring system, a combined score of at least 310 is recommended.

TOEFL requirements
The TOEFL exam is required for students from non-English-
   speaking countries.
   PBT score: 550
   iBT score: 80
TOEFL score of 220 (computer test or equivalent score on the
   paper test)

Other admissions information
Additional requirements: The Versant English test is administered once the student arrives at the university. Students must
   score a minimum of 69 to be eligible as Graduate Teaching
   Associates.

TUITION

Tuition year 2018–19:
Tuition for in-state residents
   Full-time students: $369.65 per credit
Tuition for out-of-state residents
   Full-time students: $1,194.05 per credit
Students with graduate assistantships receive a stipend, tuition
   remission, and free health insurance. The department offers
   10-40 graduate teaching assistantships per academic year,
   pending funding (Tuition rates include fees and may change
   after August 1).
Credit hours per semester to be considered full-time: 9
Deferred tuition plan: No
Health insurance: Available
Other academic fees: International Students will have to pay a
   $50 fee per semester for services provided by UCF Global.
   In addition, all students must pay an annual ID/Access fee
   of $10. Additional fees may apply.
Academic term: Semester

Teaching Assistants, Research Assistants, and Fellowships
Number of first-year
   Teaching Assistants: 10
   Research Assistants: 4
   Fellowship students: 3

Average stipend per academic year
Teaching Assistant: $22,307
Fellowship stipends vary and range from $500.00 - $25000. Assistantship stipends range from $20,600 - $22,307 for GTA, and $21,000 - $30,900 for GRA.

FINANCIAL AID

Application deadlines
Fall admission:
U.S. students: May 30
Spring admission:
U.S. students: May 30

Loans
Loans are available for U.S. students.
Loans are not available for international students.
GAPSFAS application required: No
FAFSA application required: Yes

For further information
Address financial aid inquiries to: Office of Student Financial Assistance, 4000 Central Florida Blvd., Millican Hall, Room 107, Orlando, FL 32816-0113.
Phone: (407) 823-2827
E-mail: finaid@ucf.edu
Financial aid website: http://finaid.ucf.edu/

HOUSING

Availability of on-campus housing
Single students: Yes
Married students: No

For further information
Address housing inquiries to: Department of Housing and Residence Life, P.O. Box 163222, University of Central Florida, Orlando, FL 32816-3222.
Phone: (407) 823-4663
E-mail: housing@ucf.edu
Housing aid website: http://www.housing.ucf.edu/

Table A—Faculty, Enrollments, and Degrees Granted

Research Specialty	2018–19 Faculty	Enrollment Fall 2017 Master's	Enrollment Fall 2017 Doctorate	Number of Degrees Granted 2017–18 (2013–18) Master's	Number of Degrees Granted 2017–18 (2013–18) Terminal Master's	Number of Degrees Granted 2017–18 (2013–18) Doctorate
Atomic, Molecular, & Optical Physics	5	–	–	–	–	–
Biophysics	3	–	–	–	–	–
Computational Physics	4	–	–	–	–	–
Condensed Matter Physics	21	–	–	–	–	–
Geophysics	1	–	–	–	–	–
Physics and other Science Education	4	–	–	–	–	–
Planetary Science	12	1	13	–	–	–
Total	50	6	85	14(51)	–	13(74)
Full-time Grad. Stud.	–	6	85	–	–	–
First-year Grad. Stud.	–	3	17	–	–	–

GRADUATE DEGREE REQUIREMENTS

Master's: A total of 30 semester credit hours is required. The student has the option of choosing courses specialized in General Physics, Condensed Matter Physics, and Optical Physics, with either a thesis or a non-thesis option. All students must take a set of core courses. The thesis option requires additional semester hours of electives plus 6 semester hours of thesis. The non-thesis option requires electives, 3 semester hours of directed research plus a comprehensive exit exam. The Physics M.S. program includes the Bridge Program and a Planetary Science track. For more information, please visit our website, https://sciences.ucf.edu/physics/graduate/physics-program/curriculum/.

Doctorate: Students have the option of choosing from three specializations: General Physics, Condensed Matter Physics, and Optical Physics. A total of 72 semester credit hours, of which 15 are required dissertation hours, are needed for the doctoral degree. The remaining 57 hours are divided into 18 hours of core courses, and a combination of specialization specific electives and research. Upon completion of the core, the student must take the written part of the Ph.D. candidacy examination. The Physics Ph.D. program also offers a Planetary Science track with specific core course requirements geared towards this track. For more information, please visit our website, https://sciences.ucf.edu/physics/graduate/physics-program/curriculum/.

Thesis: Thesis may be written in absentia.

SPECIAL EQUIPMENT, FACILITIES, OR PROGRAMS

APS Bridge Site established in Fall 2015.

The Department has attosecond laser physics and NMR facilities. The Physical Science building, where the department is located, has it is own Helium Liquefier for research at very low temperatures. The new facility boasts a clean-room for microdevice prototyping and a separate location for UHV deposition techniques and spectrometry. For more detailed information regarding the available research facilities see the Physics research page.

The Department operates a Surface Physics Laboratory, which includes a heavy ion backscattering spectrometer, 400-KEV ion implanter, imaging X-ray photoemission spectrometer, imaging secondary ion mass spectrometer, ultrahigh vacuum atomic force microscope and scanning tunneling microscope, digital low-energy electron diffraction, digital reflection high-energy electron diffraction, angle resolved ultraviolet photoemission spectrometer, and equipment for ultra-thin epitaxial film growth.

Other Department laboratories provide equipment for Mössbauer spectroscopy, magnetic susceptibility measurements, SQUID magnetometry, X-ray diffraction, Fourier spectroscopy, Raman and FTIR spectroscopy, inductively coupled plasma etching, e-beam thermal thin film evaporation, sub-micron optical lithography, high-sensitivity on-chip magnetometry, ultralow temperature high magnetic field/high frequency EPR and FMR spectroscopy, and high temperature incubation of bacterial cultures.

Equipment for performing biophysical research include an autoclave, a probe sonicator, a PCR thermocycler, a BioSafety hood, multiple centrifuges, and a soft-wall clean room.

The Department has two ultrahigh vacuum systems with an e-beam evaporator, a quartz microbalance, a hybrid atom/ion plasma source, an argon sputter gun, a mass spectrometer, XPS and Auger spectrometers, UPS, TPD, and a variable temperature STM.

Computation facilities include several Linux clusters with several hundred nodes each. UCF has a state-of-the-art high-performance computer facility consisting of more than 1000 nodes is available.

Department faculty participate in several campus research centers which provide access to additional specialized equipment. Research in advance materials and microelectronics is supported by the Materials Characterization Facility (MCF), located in the campus Research Park. Department faculty and students using

MCF have access to Rutherford backscattering spectroscopy, imaging secondary ion mass spectroscopy, transmission and scanning electron microscopes, a focused ion beam system, a scanning Auger microprobe, X-ray photoelectron spectroscopy, and X-ray diffraction.

The Department is responsible for operating the Robinson Observatory, an on-campus research and education facility that houses a 0.51-m f/8.2 Ritchey-Chretien astronomical telescope. The primary instrumentation on the telescope is a camera with a research-grade 3072-by-2048 pixel CCD that allows for multi-wavelength imaging.

https://physics.cos.ucf.edu/research/research-facilities/

Table B—Separately Budgeted Research Expenditures by Source of Support

Source of Support	Departmental Research	Physics-related Research Outside Department
Federal government		$35,867,294
State/local government		$484,000
Non-profit organizations		$274,250
Business and industry		$572,391
Other	$374,457	$2,654,257
Total	$374,457	$39,852,192

Table C—Separately Budgeted Research Expenditures by Research Specialty

Research Specialty	No. of Grants	Expenditures ($)
Atomic, Molecular, & Optical Physics	10	$17,047,914
Biophysics	3	$142,750
Condensed Matter Physics	18	$10,744,638
Physics and other Science Education	10	$1,650,525
Planetary Science	31	$10,640,792
Total	72	$40,226,619

FACULTY

Distinguished University Professor

Chang, Zhenghu, Ph.D., Chinese Academy of Sciences, 1998. *Atomic, Molecular, & Optical Physics, Optics.* Atomic, Molecular, and Optical Physics, Optics and precision mechanics.

Rahman, Talat S., Ph.D., University of Rochester, 1977. *Computational Physics, Condensed Matter Physics, Physics and other Science Education, Surface Physics.* Chemical Physics, Computational Physics, Condensed Matter Physics, Nanoscience and Technology, Surface Physics.

Professor

Bhattacharya, Aniket, Ph.D., University of Maryland, 1992. *Biophysics, Condensed Matter Physics, Polymer Physics/Science, Theoretical Physics.* Polymer Physics/Science, Theoretical soft condensed matter; nonlinear dynamics.

Britt, Daniel T., Ph.D., Brown University, 1991. Director of the Center for Lunar and Asteroid Surface Science (CLASS). https://sciences.ucf.edu/class/*Geophysics, Planetary Science.* Geophysics; Planetary Science.

Campins, Humberto, Ph.D., University of Arizona, 1982. *Planetary Science.* Planetary science; comets and asteroids.

Chernyak, Leonid, Ph.D., Weizmann Institute of Science, 1996. *Applied Physics, Condensed Matter Physics, Materials Science, Metallurgy, Nano Science and Technology.* Condensed Matter Physics, Materials Science, Nanostructure device physics.

Chow, Lee, Ph.D., Clark University, 1981. *Condensed Matter Physics, Nano Science and Technology.* Nanoscience and Technology, Experimental condensed matter; carbon nanotubes and diamond-like carbon films.

Colwell, Joshua, Ph.D., University of Colorado Boulder, 1989. *Planetary Science.* Planetary science; planetary rings; planet formation; microgravity.

del Barco, Enrique, Ph.D., Barcelona, 2001. *Condensed Matter Physics, Low Temperature Physics, Nano Science and Technology.* Nanoscience and Technology; Experimental condensed matter; single-molecule magnets.

Harrington, Joseph, Ph.D., Massachusetts Institute of Technology, 1994. *Atmosphere, Space Physics, Cosmic Rays, Planetary Science.* Planetary science; spectroscopy; exoplanets.

Johnson, Michael D., Ph.D., University of Virginia, 1986. Dr. Michael Johnson is the Dean of the College of Sciences. *Condensed Matter Physics, Nano Science and Technology, Theoretical Physics.* Theoretical condensed matter; nanostructures.

Kara, Abdelkader, Ph.D., Lille, Saclay, 1985. Dr. Abdelkader Kara is the Graduate Program Director in the Department of Physics. *Chemical Physics, Computational Physics, Condensed Matter Physics, Surface Physics.* Chemical Physics, Computational Physics, Condensed Matter Physics, Nanoscience and Technology, Surface Physics.

Khondaker, Saiful I., Ph.D., University of Cambridge, 1999. *Condensed Matter Physics, Nano Science and Technology.* Experimental condensed matter; nanoelectronics.

Klemm, Richard, Ph.D., Harvard University, 1974. *Condensed Matter Physics, Nano Science and Technology, Theoretical Physics.* Theoretical condensed matter; superconductivity; nanomagnetism.

Kokoouline, Viatcheslav, Ph.D., St. Petersburg, 1999. *Atomic, Molecular, & Optical Physics, Theoretical Physics.* Theoretical atomic and molecular physics.

Leuenberger, Michael N., Ph.D., Basel, 2002. *Condensed Matter Physics, Quantum Foundations, Theoretical Physics.* Theoretical condensed matter; quantum computing.

Luo, Weili, Ph.D., University of California, Los Angeles, 1989. *Condensed Matter Physics, Fluids, Rheology.* Fluids, Experimental condensed matter; complex systems.

Mucciolo, Eduardo, Ph.D., Massachusetts Institute of Technology, 1994. Dr. Eduardo Mucciolo is the Chair of the Department of Physics. *Computer Science, Condensed Matter Physics, Quantum Foundations, Theoretical Physics.* Theoretical condensed matter; electronic transport; quantum information.

Peale, Robert E., Ph.D., Cornell University, 1989. *Applied Physics, Condensed Matter Physics, Optics.* Experimental condensed matter; far-infrared semiconductor lasers.

Saha, Haripada, Ph.D., Calcutta, 1978. *Atomic, Molecular, & Optical Physics, Optics, Theoretical Physics.* Theoretical atomic, molecular, and optical physics.

Schulte, Alfons F., University of Munich, 1985. *Biophysics.* Biophysics; dynamics of proteins and disordered systems.

Tatulain, Suren, Ph.D., St. Petersburg, 1979. *Biophysics.* Experimental bio-physics; catalysis.

Associate Professor

Chanda, Debashis, Ph.D., University of Toronto, 2008. Nanoscience Technology Center, The College of Optics and Photonics. *Nano Science and Technology, Optics.* Light confinement at nanoscale; novel device applications; energy harvesting; large-scale and low-cost fabrication of optical nanostructure; metamaterials, plasmonic nanostructures.

Chen, Bo, Ph.D., Northwestern University, 2007. *Biophysics.* Biological Physics, Nuclear Magnetic Resonance.

Donoghue, Joseph F., Ph.D., University of Southern California, 1981. *Geology/Geochemistry.* Sedimentary processes, environmental geology, causes and effects of sea-level and climate change, geology and geomorphology of coastal and aquatic environments, Quaternary geology and geochronology, contaminants in sediments.

Efthimiou, Costas, Ph.D., Cornell University, 1996. *Physics and other Science Education, Theoretical Physics*. Mathematical physics; physics education research.

Fernández, Yanga R., Ph.D., University of Maryland, 1999. *Planetary Science*. Planetary science, comets, and asteroids.

Ishigami, Masahiro, Ph.D., University of California, Berkeley, 2004. *Condensed Matter Physics*. He is an expert on scanning tunneling microscopy and spectroscopy, transport measurements on nanoscale materials, and nanoscale friction measurements at speeds reaching 1 m/sec.

Schelling, Patrick K., Ph.D., University of Minnesota, 1999. *Computational Physics, Condensed Matter Physics, Materials Science, Metallurgy, Theoretical Physics*. Theoretical condensed matter and materials physics.

Stolbov, Sergei, Ph.D., Rostov State University, 1982. *Chemical Physics, Computational Physics, Condensed Matter Physics, Surface Physics*. Computational condensed physics, surface physics, chemical physics, material design.

Assistant Professor

Argenti, Luca, Ph.D., Scuola Normale Superiore di Pisa, 2008. *Atomic, Molecular, & Optical Physics, Chemical Physics*. Theoretical description of the electronic continuum of atoms and molecules, with particular reference to the reconstruction and control of the photoionisation dynamics triggered in matter by attosecond light pulses.

Bennett, Christopher, Ph.D., University of Hawai'i at Manoa, 2009. *Planetary Science*. Physical & Analytical Chemistry Astrochemistry, Astrobiology, and Planetary Science.

Chen, Zhongzhou, Ph.D., University of Illinois Urbana Champaign, 2012. *Physics and other Science Education*. Understanding and modeling the cognitive mechanism behind learning. Developing online instructional methods that makes education more flexible, more cost-effective, and more scalable. Developing accurate, secure and informative means to assess both teaching and learning. Researching effective methods to categorize and curate online educational resources.

Chini, Jacquelyn, Ph.D., Kansas State University, 2010. *Physics and other Science Education*. Physics education research. Implementing and assessing course transformation; physics teacher preparation.

Chini, Michael, Ph.D., University of Central Florida, 2012. *Atomic, Molecular, & Optical Physics, Condensed Matter Physics, Optics*. Ultrafast and strong-field induced dynamics in solids.

Dove, Adrienne, Ph.D., University of Colorado, Dept. of Astrophysical and Planetary Sciences, 2012. *Planetary Science*. Dust/regolith on planetary surfaces, disturbances to planetary surfaces, plasma interactions with spacecraft and planetary surfaces.

Feng, Xiaofeng, Ph.D., University of California, Berkeley, 2013. *Condensed Matter Physics*. His research focuses on the understanding of structure-activity relationships for electrocatalytic materials and the development of efficient electrocatalysts for energy conversion.

Kaden, William, Ph.D., University of Utah, 2010. *Condensed Matter Physics*. Dr. Kaden develops and characterizes novel thin-films and studies surface-confined chemical and electronic processes using surface-science approaches within UHV environments.

Kang, Hyeran, Ph.D., Brown University. Joint appointments in NanoScience Technology Center, Physics Graduate Faculty in Burnett School of Biomedical Sciences. *Biophysics*. Dr. Kang's research focuses on determining molecular mechanisms by which the mechanics of cytoskeletal protein biopolymers are regulated. Her research group integrates multidis-

ciplinary approaches including molecular biophysics with protein biochemistry, molecular biology, polymer physics, and bioengineering techniques.

Lyakh, Arkadiy, Ph.D., University of Florida, 2007. Nanoscience Technology Center. *Condensed Matter Physics, Optics*. Physics of intersubband transitions and carrier transport through multi-layered semiconductor structures, low dimensional semiconductor devices, monolithic sensors, infrared spectroscopy.

Nakajima, Yasuyuki, Ph.D., University of Tokyo, 2007. *Condensed Matter Physics*. Design, crystal growth, and characterization of novel quantum materials, including topological semimetals/insulators, unconventional superconductors, and quantum critical metals. In particular, characterization by utilizing charge/thermal transport and thermodynamic measurements in millikelvin temperature range.

Neupane, Madhab, Ph.D., Boston College, 2010. *Condensed Matter Physics*. Electronic and spin properties of new quantum materials such as correlated topological insulators, three dimensional Dirac, Weyl and nodal semimetals, topological Kondo insulators, topological crystalline insulators, and two-dimensional materials investigated using angle-, spin- and time-resolved photoemission techniques.

Tetard, Laurene, Ph.D., University of Tennessee, 2010. Nanoscience Technology Center. *Biophysics, Nano Science and Technology*. High-resolution microscopy and spectroscopy; physical and chemical surface properties at the nanoscale, with applications on lignocellulosic biomass, cancer cells, photovoltaic systems, proton conductors and polymers.

Vaida, Mihai, Ph.D., Ulm University, 2010. *Condensed Matter Physics*. Ultrafast electron and molecular dynamics, surface science, thin films, 2D materials, photovoltaics, surface chemistry and catalysis.

Research Assistant Professor

Turkowski, Volodymyr, Ph.D., Kiev University, Ukraine, 1998. *Computational Physics, Nano Science and Technology*. Development and application of the theoretical and numerical approaches to study electron-electron and electron-hole correlation effects in different bulk and nanosystems.

Affiliate Professor

Delfyett, Peter J., Ph.D., City University of New York, 1988. The College of Optics and Photonics. *Optics*. Ultrafast Photonics (ultrafast optical physics, devices and signal processing).

Richardson, Martin C., Ph.D., London University, 1967. The College of Optics and Photonics. *Optics, Physics of Beams*. Lasers and plasmas.

Roldan-Cuenya, Beatriz, Ph.D., Gerhard-Mercator Universität, 2001. Ruhr Universitaet, Germany. *Chemical Physics, Nano Science and Technology, Surface Physics*. Solid state and surface physics, nanomagnetism and nanocatalysis.

Shivamoggi, Bhimsen, Ph.D., University of Colorado, 1978. Department of Mathematics. *Nonlinear Dynamics and Complex Systems, Plasma and Fusion*. Mathematical physics, fluid dynamics, plasma physics, stochastic processes, nonlinear dynamics.

Soileau, M. J., Ph.D., University of Southern California, 1979. The College of Optics and Photonics. *Optics*. Lasers, nonlinear optics.

Vodopyanov, Konstantin L., Ph.D., Lebedev Physical Institute, 1983. The College of Optics and Photonics. *Optics*. Mid-IR and THz generation via frequency downconversion, laser spectroscopy, nano-IR spectroscopy, supercontinuum generation in fibers, biomedical applications of lasers, standoff sensing and detection.

Affiliate Assistant Professor

Balaeff, Alexander, Ph.D., University of Illinois, Urbana-Champaign, 2002. Nanoscience Technology Center. *Biophysics*. Biomolecular and biomimetic molecular assemblies.

Potrebko, Peter, Ph.D., University of Manitoba. Senior Medical Physicist, Florida Hospital Orlando Cancer Institute Associate Professor of Radiation Oncology University of Central Florida,College of Medicine. *Medical, Health Physics*. Medical and Health Physics.

Roy, Tania, Ph.D., Vanderbilt University. Joint Appointment with NanoScience Technology Center, Materials Science & Engineering, Electrical & Computer Engineering, and ICAMR. *Electrical Engineering, Materials Science, Metallurgy, Nano Science and Technology*. Semiconductor device physics, solid state physics, next-generation electronics, 2D materials, solar cells.

Zeidan, Omar, Ph.D., University of Tennessee. Chief, Proton Therapy Physics UF Health Cancer Center- Orlando Health (since 2013) Affiliated Clinical Assistant Professor Department of Radiation Oncology College of Medicine, University of Florida (since 2014). *Medical, Health Physics, Nuclear Physics*. Medical and Health Physics.

Instructor

LaMee, Adam, FSU. How to improve teaching and learning in K-16 science with professional collaboration, incorporating current scientific research, and novel performance assessment techniques.

Lecturer

Al Rawi, Ahlam, Ph.D., Kansas State University, 2001. *Biophysics, Computational Physics, Condensed Matter Physics*. Biophysics, computational surface physics and condensed matter physics.

Brueckner, Thomas J., Ph.D., Montana State University, 1997. *Astronomy, Physics and other Science Education*. Physics education research; astronomy.

Cooney, James H., Ph.D., University of Florida, 2004. *Cosmology & String Theory, Physics and other Science Education, Planetary Science*. Planetary Science; Physics education research; cosmology.

Dubey, Archana H., Ph.D., Bhavnagar, 1998. *Computational Physics, Fluids, Rheology*. Ferromagnetic fluids, computational physics.

Flitsiyan, Elena S., Ph.D., University of Moscow, 1975. *Condensed Matter Physics, Nuclear Physics*. Nuclear physics, experimental condensed matter physics.

Montgomery, Michele M., Ph.D., FIT, 2004. *Astrophysics, Planetary Science*. Planetary science; astrophysics.

Velissaris, Christos, Ph.D., University of Rochester, 1995. *High Energy Physics*. Experimental high-energy physics.

Assistant Scientist

Le, Duy, Ph.D., University of Central Florida, 2012. Structural properties, electronic structure, and applications of novel nano-materials with the focus on materials for industrially useful catalysts.

Wu, Yi, Ph.D., University of Central Florida, 2013. *Optics*. Ultrafast laser technique and phenomenon, high flux isolated attosecond pulse generation and characterization.

DEPARTMENTAL RESEARCH SPECIALTIES AND STAFF

Theoretical

Atomic, Molecular, & Optical Physics. The theoretical Atomic, Molecular, and Optical (AMO) physics group is engaged in research directed toward the elucidation of the fundamental details of the structure and dynamics of electrons and positrons interacting within atoms and molecules in the gas phase at thermal and ultra-cold energies. The primary aim of this group is to perform state-of-the-art calculation of (1) photoionization and photo-detachment of electrons from atoms and molecules, (2) electron-atom and electron molecule collisional processes, (3) the collisional processes in molecular plasmas with or without light emitted/absorbed, (4) elementary processes in ultra-cold atomic and molecular gases near the quantum degeneracy using completely ab-initio sophisticated theoretical approach. Argenti, Kokoouline, Saha.

Biophysics. The theoretical and computational Soft Condensed Matter and Biological Physics group engages in both classical and quantum calculations at various length and time scales using high-performance computing systems. There is a strong collaboration with the Biophysics group at the Physics department with several faculty at the College of Medicine. Balaeff, Bhattacharya, Bo Chen.

Chemical Physics. Researchers in chemical physics study chemical processes from the point of view of physics. The focus is on understanding the microscopic factors that control the chemical characteristics of materials at the nanoscale. Size, shape, material, and support dependent properties of nanoparticles, for example, are examined using a range of state-of-art experimental, computational and theoretical techniques. Understanding the effect of the local atomic scale environment is the key towards designing materials for applications such as in solar cells, catalytic convertors, etc. Rahman, Stolbov.

Computational Physics. A variety of computational approaches are developed and used to address a wide array of physical problems. Focus extends from atomic-scale simulation of phenomena at surfaces and in nanomaterials, to heat, mass, and phonon transport phenomena at the nanoscale, to mesoscopic phenomena (DNA translocation through nanopores, self-assembly of amphiphilic peptides), to multiscale modeling, which extend the length and time scales accessible to simulation predictions to make more direct contact with experiment. Balaeff, Bhattacharya, Kara, Le, Rahman, Schelling, Stolbov, Turkowski.

Condensed Matter Physics. The theoretical and computational condensed matter physics group focuses on fundamental physical phenomena, with a strong emphasis in the fields of nanomagnetism, nanotransport, nanocayalysis, energy-related materials, surface science, vibrational dynamics at the nanoscale, superconductivity and semiconductors physics. These investigations will eventually lead to exciting novel applications in current technologies, e.g., catalysis, renewable energies, optoelectronics, medicine, homeland security, as well as potential applications in emerging technologies, e.g., quantum information and computation, coherent terahertz radiation, nanoelectronics, or spintronics and high-sensitivity UV detection. Dubey, Johnson, Kara, Klemm, Leuenberger, Mucciolo, Rahman, Schelling, Stolbov.

Physics and other Science Education. Physics Education Research at UCF is led by two tenure-track assistant professors. Both Dr. Jackie Chini and Dr. Zhongzhou Chen received their Ph.D.s in physics for research in physics education. We study issues relevant to the evolving landscape of higher education in physics and collaborate with colleagues in related disciplines. Dr. Jackie Chini's group examines how to adapt active learning strategies for diverse student populations and institutional contexts. She has received funding through the NSF-WIDER program to study diverse implementations of SCALE-UP across the country and through the NSF-IUSE program to study the efficacy of popular active learning strategies for students with executive function disorders, common among students with ADHD, learning disabilities, autism spectrum disorder and student veterans. Dr. Zhongzhou Chen is interested in combining online education technology with learning science to shape the future of STEM education. Collaborating with the Center for Distributed Learning at UCF, he designs and develops online learning modules based on the concept of deliberate practice. He is also interested in measuring and modeling the fundamental cognitive process behind physics problem solving. Al Rawi, Zhongzhou Chen, Jacquelyn Chini, del Barco, Dubey, Flitsiyan, Rahman.

Quantum Foundations. Research in this area engages in the study of quantum bits made from optical semiconductor quantum dots and explores the physical limits of quantum computation and communications and ways to mitigate the noise problem. Leuenberger, Mucciolo.

Experimental

Atomic, Molecular, & Optical Physics. The current AMO experimental group is focused on far/Terahertz spectroscopy and technology development, in particular, intracavity laser absorption spectroscopy for ultra-trace vapor detection. A large experimental effort is in Attosecond laser pulse generation, characterization and applications. The extremely short XUV pulses are used to probe and control electron dynamics in matter. Overlap between theory and experiment will form a critical component of our research program. Applications of this Attosecond laser pulse source to problems in condensed matter physics are underway. Chang, Richardson.

Biophysics. The experimental Soft Condensed Matter and Biological Physics group involves various spectroscopic studies of proteins under high pressure and other extreme conditions, protein membrane interactions and light scattering studies. One recent technique is solid state NMR. Bo Chen, Kang, Schulte, Tatulain, Tetard.

Condensed Matter Physics. The experimental condensed matter physics group focuses on the examination of many fundamental physical phenomena, with a strong emphasis in the fields of nanomagnetism, nanotransport, nanocatalysis, energy-related materials, surface science, vibrational dynamics at the nanoscale, and semiconductors physics. Chanda, Chernyak, Michael Chini, Chow, del Barco, Flitsiyan, Khondaker, Luo, Lyakh, Nakajima, Neupane, Peale, Roldan-Cuenya, Roy.

Medical, Health Physics. Research in proton accelerators and radiation treatment. Potrebko, Zeidan.

Optics. A variety of topics is studied, from nonlinear optics to attosecond lasers. Chang, Michael Chini, Delfyett, Richardson, Soileau, Vodopyanov.

Planetary Science. The UCF Planetary Sciences Group uses spacecraft data, images from the world's most powerful telescopes, meteorites and moon rocks, and supercomputer calculations to investigate fundamental questions like these: How did our solar system form? What do the surfaces of other worlds tell us about their history? What happens when a comet hits a planet? What's going on in the atmospheres of extrasolar planets? Are there any other planetary systems like ours? Are we alone?. Bennett, Britt, Campins, Colwell, Donoghue, Dove, Fernández, Harrington.

View additional information about this department at www.gradschoolshopper.com. Check out the "Why Choose Us?" section, find out more about the department's culture and get links to social media networks.

UNIVERSITY OF FLORIDA

DEPARTMENT OF PHYSICS

Gainesville, Florida 32611-8440
http://www.phys.ufl.edu/

General University Information
President: W. Kent Fuchs
Dean of Graduate School: Henry T. Frierson
University website: http://www.ufl.edu
School Type: Public
Setting: Urban
Total Faculty: 4,000
Total Graduate Faculty: 2,982
Total number of Students: 50,000
Total number of Graduate Students: 11,766

Department Information
Department Chairman: Prof. Kevin Ingersent, Chair
Department Contact: Pam Marlin, Academic Assistant II
  Total full-time faculty: 49
  Full-Time Graduate Students: 118
  Female Full-Time Graduate Students: 20
  First-Year Graduate Students: 16
  Female First-Year Students: 4
  Total Post Doctorates: 30

Department Address
P.O. Box 118440
Gainesville, FL 32611-8440
Phone: (352) 392-0521 (C)
E-mail: pmarlin@ufl.edu
Website: http://www.phys.ufl.edu/

ADMISSIONS

Admission Contact Information
Address admission inquiries to: Graduate Affairs Office, P.O. Box 118440
Phone: (352) 392-1365
E-mail: webrequests@admissions.ufl.edu
Admissions website: http://www.admissions.ufl.edu/

Application deadlines
Fall admission:
U.S. students: February 1   *Int'l. students*: January 15

Application fee
U.S. students: $30   *Int'l. students*: $30

Admissions information
For Fall of 2018:
  Number of applicants: 226
  Number admitted: 68
  Number enrolled: 16

Admission requirements
Bachelor's degree requirements: Bachelor's degree in Physics is required.
Minimum undergraduate GPA: 3.3

GRE requirements
The GRE is required.

Subjective GRE requirements
The Subjective GRE is recommended.

GRE Physics is strongly recommended, particularly for international students

TOEFL requirements
The TOEFL exam is required for students from non-English-speaking countries.
PBT score: 550
iBT score: 80

Other admissions information
Additional requirements: Admission decisions are based on the entire application file, with emphasis on undergraduate preparation (particularly in physics-related courses), research experience, letters of recommendation, and GRE and Physics GRE scores.
Undergraduate preparation assumed: Applicants are expected to have a solid knowledge at the level of the following textbooks or their equivalents: Griffiths, Introduction to Quantum Mechanics; Griffiths, Introduction to Electrodynamics; Thornton & Marion, Classical Dynamics; Zemansky and Kittel, Thermal Physics.

TUITION

Tuition year 2018–19:
Tuition for in-state residents
  Full-time students: $12,740 annual
Tuition for students employed as research and teaching assistants is paid by the Department. Graduate students are responsible for certain fees each semester.
Credit hours per semester to be considered full-time: 9
Deferred tuition plan: No
Health insurance: Yes, Annual: $2,362.00.
Other academic fees: Graduate students pay fees to cover University services, athletics, and public transportation. Health insurance is provided to full-time Teaching Assistants ans Research Assistants. Others can purchases at the rate of $2,783 per year.
Academic term: Semester
Number of first-year students who received full tuition waivers: 24

Teaching Assistants, Research Assistants, and Fellowships
  Number of first-year
    Teaching Assistants: 24
    Fellowship students: 5
  Average stipend per academic year
    Teaching Assistant: $25,000
    Research Assistant: $25,000
    Fellowship student: $30,000

FINANCIAL AID

Loans
Loans are available for U.S. students.
Loans are available for international students.
GAPSFAS application required: No
FAFSA application required: No

For further information

Address financial aid inquiries to: Graduate Affairs Office, P.O. Box 118440, Department of Physics, Gainesville, FL 32611-8440.

Phone: (352) 392-0181

Financial aid website: http://www.fa.ufl.edu/ufs/

HOUSING

Availability of on-campus housing

Single students: Yes

Married students: Yes

For further information

Address housing inquiries to: Director of Housing.

Housing aid website: http://www.housing.ufl.edu/

Table A—Faculty, Enrollments, and Degrees Granted

| Research Specialty | 2017–18 Faculty | Enrollment Fall 2017–Summer 2018 | | Number of Degrees Granted 2017–18 (2010–18) | | |
		Master's	Doctorate	Master's	Terminal Master's	Doctorate
Astrophysics	4	2	18	2(9)	–	–(14)
Biophysics	2	2	6	2(4)	1(1)	–(5)
Chemical Physics	2	2	16	2(10)	–(1)	1(11)
Condensed Matter Physics	15	5	31	5(31)	–(4)	7(80)
High Energy Physics	13	6	36	6(22)	–(9)	4(37)
Low Temperature Physics	–	–	7	–(3)	–	–(5)
Theoretical Physics	10	1	17	1(5)	–	1(4)
Total	46	18	118	18(84)	1(15)	13(156)
Full-time Grad. Stud.	–	–	118	–	–	–
First-year Grad. Stud.	–	–	16	–	–	–

GRADUATE DEGREE REQUIREMENTS

Master's: Thirty graduate credits in an approved program with satisfactory performance are required. Master's examination is required. A non-thesis option is available. One year of residence is required. There is no foreign language requirement.

Doctorate: Minimum of 90 hours and satisfactory performance in an approved course program are required. Full-time residency for two consecutive semesters is required. There is no foreign language requirement. Preliminary examination, qualifying examination, dissertation, and dissertation examination are required. Teaching experience, residence, a period of concentrated study, and a publishable thesis are required.

Other Degrees: Master of Science in teaching degree requires 36 credits (half in graduate courses) with satisfactory performance in an approved program. Six credits of internship are required. No thesis is required. All candidates for advanced degrees must be registered during the semester in which the degree is awarded.

Thesis: Thesis may be written in absentia.

SPECIAL EQUIPMENT, FACILITIES, OR PROGRAMS

Helium liquefier and Microkelvin Laboratory located on campus; superb computer facilities include a university-operated HiPerGator cluster offering 21,000 compute nodes as well as more specialized clusters within the department. An eight-station electronics laboratory is used for training in analog and digital circuits, instrumentation design, and computer interfacing and programming. A full-service machine shop specializing in all forms of CNC and conventional machining, welding, and soldering is available. An electronics shop is also located in the building, specializing in design, prototype instrumentation, consultation, and repair. Cooperative research programs are conducted at Los Alamos National Laboratory, Oak Ridge National Laboratory, Brookhaven National Laboratory, Fermilab, CERN, and the National High-Magnetic Field Laboratory (NHMFL). The University of Florida is a member of the consortium (UF, FSU, and LANL) responsible for the operation of the National High-Magnetic Field Laboratory.

Table B—Separately Budgeted Research Expenditures by Source of Support

Source of Support	Departmental Research	Physics-related Research Outside Department
Federal government	$7,477,200	
State/local government		
Non-profit organizations	$921,897	
Business and industry	$2,029,249	
Other		
Total	$10,428,346	

Table C—Separately Budgeted Research Expenditures by Research Specialty

Research Specialty	No. of Grants	Expenditures ($)
Astrophysics	13	$2,937,886
Quantum Theory Project	6	$458,958
Condensed Matter Physics	17	$3,885,921
Particles and Fields	19	$2,841,608
Total	55	$10,124,373

FACULTY

Distinguished University Professor

Hebard, Arthur F., Ph.D., Stanford University, 1970. *Applied Physics, Condensed Matter Physics*. Experimental condensed matter physics, solid-state devices.

Mitselmakher, Guenakh, Ph.D., University of Moscow, 1974. *Accelerator, High Energy Physics, Particles and Fields, Relativity & Gravitation*. Experimental high-energy physics.

Ramond, Pierre, Ph.D., Syracuse University, 1969. *Cosmology & String Theory, High Energy Physics, Particles and Fields*. Elementary particle theory.

Sikivie, Pierre, Ph.D., Yale University, 1975. *Astrophysics, High Energy Physics, Particles and Fields*. Elementary particle theory; cosmology.

Tanner, David B., Ph.D., Cornell University, 1972. *Astrophysics, Condensed Matter Physics, Particles and Fields, Relativity & Gravitation*. Experimental condensed matter physics; experimental astrophysics, LIGO.

Will, Clifford, Ph.D., California Institute of Technology, 1971. *Astrophysics, Relativity & Gravitation*. Experimental validation of Einstein's laws.

Professor

Acosta, Darin, Ph.D., University of California, San Diego, 1993. *High Energy Physics, Particles and Fields*. Experimental high-energy physics.

Avery, Paul R., Ph.D., University of Illinois, 1980. *Computational Physics, High Energy Physics, Particles and Fields*. Experimental high-energy physics, data management.

Cheng, Hai Ping, Ph.D., Northwestern University, 1988. *Chemical Physics, Computational Physics, Condensed Matter Physics*. Computational physics; molecules; clusters; nanostructures.

Fry, James N., Ph.D., Princeton University, 1979. *Astrophysics, Cosmology & String Theory*. Theoretical astrophysics; cosmology.

Hagen, Stephen, Ph.D., Princeton University, 1989. Associate Chair. *Biophysics, Condensed Matter Physics*. Experimental condensed matter physics; molecular biophysics; optical spectroscopy.

Hershfield, Selman P., Ph.D., Cornell University, 1989. *Condensed Matter Physics*. Theoretical condensed matter physics.

Hirschfeld, Peter J., Ph.D., Princeton University, 1985. *Condensed Matter Physics*. Theoretical condensed matter physics.

Ingersent, J. Kevin, Ph.D., University of Pennsylvania, 1990. Department Chair. *Condensed Matter Physics*. Theoretical condensed matter physics.

Klimenko, Sergey, Ph.D., Novosibirsk State University, 1993. *Astrophysics, High Energy Physics, Particles and Fields, Relativity & Gravitation*. Theoretical astrophysics.

Korytov, Andrey, Ph.D., Dubna University, 1991. *Accelerator, High Energy Physics, Particles and Fields*. Experimental high-energy physics.

Lee, Yoonseok, Ph.D., Northwestern University, 1997. *Condensed Matter Physics, Low Temperature Physics*. Experimental condensed matter and low-temperature physics.

Müller, Guido, Ph.D., Hannover, 1997. Graduate Coordinator. *Astrophysics, Cosmology & String Theory, Relativity & Gravitation*. Development of gravitational-wave observatories and dark matter detectors.

Maslov, Dmitrii, Ph.D., Landau Institute (Moscow), 1989. *Condensed Matter Physics*. Theoretical condensed matter physics.

Matchev, Konstantin, Ph.D., Johns Hopkins University, 1997. *Accelerator, Cosmology & String Theory, High Energy Physics, Particles and Fields*. Elementary particle theory.

Meisel, Mark W., Ph.D., Northwestern University, 1983. *Biophysics, Condensed Matter Physics, Low Temperature Physics*. Low-temperature physics; experimental condensed-matter physics; biomagnetism.

Muttalib, Khandker A., Ph.D., Princeton University, 1982. *Condensed Matter Physics*. Theoretical condensed matter physics.

Obukhov, Sergei, Ph.D., Landau Institute (Moscow), 1979. *Condensed Matter Physics, Polymer Physics/Science*. Theoretical condensed matter and polymer physics.

Reitze, David, Ph.D., University of Texas, 1990. Presently on leave of absence as Executive Director of the LIGO Laboratory, California Institute of Technology, Pasadena, CA. *Astrophysics, Condensed Matter Physics, Optics, Relativity & Gravitation*. Ultrafast optical probes of solids; gravitational-wave detection.

Rinzler, Andrew, Ph.D., University of Connecticut, 1991. *Applied Physics, Chemical Physics, Condensed Matter Physics*. Experimental condensed matter physics; solid-state devices.

Stanton, Chris J., Ph.D., Cornell University, 1986. *Condensed Matter Physics, Optics*. Theoretical condensed matter physics.

Stewart, Gregory R., Ph.D., Stanford University, 1975. *Chemical Physics, Condensed Matter Physics*. Experimental condensed matter physics.

Sullivan, Neil S., Ph.D., Harvard University, 1972. *Condensed Matter Physics, Cosmology & String Theory, Low Temperature Physics, Particles and Fields*. Experimental condensed matter and low-temperature physics; dark-matter detection.

Takano, Yasumasa, Ph.D., University of Helsinki, 1978. *Condensed Matter Physics, Low Temperature Physics*. Experimental condensed matter and low-temperature physics.

Thorn, Charles B., Ph.D., University of California, Berkeley, 1971. *Cosmology & String Theory, High Energy Physics, Particles and Fields*. Elementary particle theory.

Whiting, Bernard F., Ph.D., University of Melbourne, 1979. *Astrophysics, Relativity & Gravitation*. Theoretical astrophysics.

Woodard, Richard P., Ph.D., Harvard University, 1984. *Cosmology & String Theory, High Energy Physics, Particles and Fields*. Quantum gravity and quantum field theory.

Yelton, John M., Ph.D., University of Oxford, 1981. Chair. *Accelerator, High Energy Physics, Particles and Fields*. Experimental high-energy physics.

Zhang, Xiaoguang, Ph.D., Northwestern University, 1989. *Chemical Physics, Computational Physics, Condensed Matter Physics*. Computational materials physics.

Associate Professor

Biswas, Amlan, Ph.D., University of Bangalore, India, 1999. Undergraduate Coordinator. *Condensed Matter Physics*. Experimental condensed matter physics.

Furic, Ivan, Ph.D., Massachusetts Institute of Technology, 2004. *Accelerator, High Energy Physics, Particles and Fields*.

Matcheva, Katia, Ph.D., Johns Hopkins University, 2000. *Atmosphere, Space Physics, Cosmic Rays, Planetary Science*. Planetary atmospheres.

Ray, Heather, Ph.D., University of Michigan, 2004. *High Energy Physics, Particles and Fields*. Experimental neutrino physics.

Saab, Tarek Khaled, Ph.D., Stanford University, 2002. *Astrophysics*. Experimental astrophysics.

Assistant Professor

Bartos, Imre, Ph.D., Columbia University, 2012. *Astrophysics*. Theoretical and experimental astrophysics.

Blecha, Laura, Ph.D., Harvard University, 2012. *Astrophysics*. Theoretical astrophysics.

Hamlin, James, Ph.D., Washington University, 2007. *Chemical Physics, Condensed Matter Physics*. Experimental condensed matter physics.

Emeritus

Micha, David A., Ph.D., Uppsala University, 1966. *Chemical Physics, Computational Physics*. Chemical physics; theoretical, molecular, and materials sciences.

Professor Emeritus

Adams, E. Dwight, Ph.D., Duke University, 1960. *Low Temperature Physics*. Low-temperature physics.

Dufty, James W., Ph.D., Lehigh University, 1967. *Condensed Matter Physics, Nonlinear Dynamics and Complex Systems, Polymer Physics/Science, Statistical & Thermal Physics*. Nonequilibrium statistical mechanics.

Dunnam, F. Eugene, Ph.D., Louisiana State University, 1958. *Accelerator, Nuclear Physics*. Nuclear physics.

Field, Richard D., Ph.D., University of California, Berkeley, 1971. *Particles and Fields*. Elementary particle theory.

Ihas, Gary G., Ph.D., University of Michigan, 1971. *Condensed Matter Physics, Low Temperature Physics*. Experimental low-temperature physics.

Ipser, James R., Ph.D., California Institute of Technology, 1969. *Astrophysics, Relativity & Gravitation*. Relativistic astrophysics.

Klauder, John R., Ph.D., Princeton University, 1959. *Quantum Foundations, Theoretical Physics*. Mathematical physics.

Kumar, Pradeep, Ph.D., University of California, San Diego, 1973. *Condensed Matter Physics, Low Temperature Physics*. Theoretical condensed matter physics.

Monkhorst, Hendrik J., Ph.D., University of Groningen, 1968. *Chemical Physics, Computational Physics, Plasma and Fu-*

sion. Theoretical chemical physics; neutron-free fusion reactor development.

Ohrn, N. Yngve, Ph.D., Uppsala University, 1963. *Chemical Physics, Computational Physics*. Quantum theory of matter.

Sabin, John R., Ph.D., University of New Hampshire, 1966. *Accelerator, Atomic, Molecular, & Optical Physics, Chemical Physics, Computational Physics*. Ion-beam interaction with solids.

Trickey, Samuel B., Ph.D., Texas A&M University, 1968. *Chemical Physics, Computational Physics, Condensed Matter Physics*. Condensed-matter theory and computation.

Van Rinsvelt, Henri, Ph.D., The Netherlands, 1965. *Accelerator, Condensed Matter Physics*. Condensed Matter Experiment.

Research Professor

Konigsberg, Jacobo, Ph.D., University of California, Los Angeles, 1989. *Accelerator, High Energy Physics, Particles and Fields*. Experimental high-energy physics.

Affiliate Professor

Abernathy, Cammy, Ph.D., Stanford University, 1985. Synthesis of thin-film electronic materials and devices using metal organic chemical vapor deposition and molecular beam epitaxy.

Bartlett, Rodney J., Ph.D., University of Florida, 1971. *Atomic, Molecular, & Optical Physics, Chemical Physics, Computational Physics*. Many-electron theory of atoms, molecules, and solids.

Mareci, Thomas, Ph.D., University of Oxford, 1982. *Biophysics, Medical, Health Physics*. Magnetic resonance imaging (MRI).

Roitberg, Adrian, Ph.D., University of Chicago, 1992. *Biophysics, Chemical Physics, Computational Physics*. Chemical physics; theoretical biophysics.

Shabanov, Sergai, Ph.D., St. Petersburg State University, 1988. *Applied Mathematics, Quantum Foundations*. Mathematical physics.

Affiliate Associate Professor

Bowers, Clifford, Ph.D., California Institute of Technology, 1991. Nuclear magnetic resonance; solid-state NMR.

Tan, Jonathan, Ph.D., University of California, Berkeley, 2001. *Astronomy, Astrophysics*.

Lecturer

Weatherford, Shawn, Ph.D., North Carolina State University, 2011. *Physics and other Science Education*.

Laboratory Director

Deserio, Robert, Ph.D., University of Chicago, 1981. Director of Undergraduate Laboratories. *Physics and other Science Education*. Physics education.

Associate Scientist

Xia, Jian-Sheng, Ph.D., University of Science and Technology of China, 1989. *Low Temperature Physics*. Experimental low-temperature physics.

DEPARTMENTAL RESEARCH SPECIALTIES AND STAFF

Theoretical

Astrophysics. Stellar structure and evolution; variable stars; planetary atmospheres nonlinear dynamics and chaos; high-energy astrophysics; solar neutrinos; general relativity; black holes; gravitational waves; neutron stars; cosmology: early universe. Bartos, Blecha, Fry, Ipser, Klimenko, Sikivie, Tan, Whiting, Will.

Computational Physics. Many-body scattering theory; intermolecular forces; radiation-molecule interactions; propagator methods; density functional theory and local density models; semiempirical molecular orbital methods: electronic structure computation; theory of quantum crystals, molecular crystals, biological molecules, and thin films; theory and application of new computational methods; neutron-free fusion reactor development. Bartlett, Cheng, Micha, Monkhorst, Ohrn, Roitberg, Sabin, Trickey, Zhang.

Condensed Matter Physics. Theory of strongly correlated systems; liquid and solid 3He; high-Tc superconductivity and heavy fermions; glasses; disorder and localization; optical interactions in semiconductors; nonlinear phenomena in condensed matter; polymers and soft condensed matter; plasmas. Dufty, Hershfield, Hirschfeld, Ingersent, Kumar, Maslov, Muttalib, Obukhov, Stanton.

Particles and Fields. Standard Model of strong and electromagnetic interactions; grand unified theories; string unification; superstring theory; particle astrophysics. Acosta, Avery, Field, Konigsberg, Korytov, Matchev, Mitselmakher, Ramond, Ray, Sikivie, Thorn, Woodard, Yelton.

Planetary Science. Modeling of atmospheric phenomena in planets. Matcheva.

Experimental

Biophysics. Protein conformational dynamic and folding; microfluids; in vivo and high-resolution MRI and NMR spectroscopy; bio-optically active processes (Petkova). Hagen, Mareci, Meisel.

Condensed Matter Physics. NMR of solids, liquids, and polymers; NMR imaging; optical properties; quantum magnetic excitations; conducting polymers; organic superconductors; composite materials; thermal and magnetic properties of superconductors; high-temperature superconductors; surface physics; synchrotron radiation; electronic properties of novel materials; ultrafast spectroscopy of novel materials; nonlinear nonequilibrium phenomena; ultrafast spectroscopy of novel materials; high-intensity laser-solid interactions. Biswas, Bowers, Hamlin, Hebard, Lee, Meisel, Reitze, Rinzler, Stewart, Sullivan, Takano, Tanner.

Low Temperature Physics. Properties of macroscopic quantum systems, in particular liquid and solid 3He, solid H2, and electronic and magnetic systems down to 10 μK; thermodynamic, hydrodynamic, magnetic, and transport properties of materials are studied using NMR, ultrasound (P,V,T), and other probes. Adams, Ihas, Lee, Meisel, Sullivan, Takano, Xia.

Particles and Fields. Experimental tests of the standard model and beyond, including searches for cold-dark matter. Acosta, Avery, Bartos, Furic, Konigsberg, Korytov, Mitselmakher, Ray, Saab, Sullivan, Tanner.

Relativity & Gravitation. Ground- and satellite-based gravitational-wave searches. Bartos, Klimenko, Müller, Mitselmakher, Reitze, Tanner.

UNIVERSITY OF SOUTH FLORIDA

DEPARTMENT OF PHYSICS

Tampa, Florida 33620
http://physics.usf.edu/

General University Information
President: Judy L. Genshaft
Dean of Graduate School: Dwayne Smith
University website: http://usf.edu/
School Type: Public
Setting: Urban
Total Faculty: 2,544
Total Graduate Faculty: -
Total number of Students: 50,577
Total number of Graduate Students: 10,810

Department Information
Department Chairman: Prof. David Rabson, Chair
Department Contact: Prof. Inna Ponomareva, Professor and
   Graduate Admissions Director
   Total full-time faculty: 33
   Full-Time Graduate Students: 58
   Female Full-Time Graduate Students: 17
   First-Year Graduate Students: 13
   Female First-Year Students: 4
   Total Post Doctorates: 6

Department Address
4202 E. Fowler Avenue, ISA 2019
Tampa, FL 33620
Phone: (813) 974-2871
Fax: (813) 974-5813
E-mail: phyadmissions@usf.edu
Website: http://physics.usf.edu/

ADMISSIONS

Admission Contact Information
Address admission inquiries to: Director of Graduate Admissions, Prof. Inna Ponomareva, Department of Physics, ISA 2019, University of South Florida, 4202 E. Fowler Ave., Tampa, FL 33620, USA
Phone: 813-974-7286
E-mail: iponomar@usf.edu
Admissions website: http://physics.usf.edu/graduate/

Application deadlines
Fall admission:
U.S. students: February 1   *Int'l. students*: February 1
Spring admission:
U.S. students: September 1   *Int'l. students*: September 1

Application fee
U.S. students: $30   *Int'l. students*: $30
Follow links for the university and departmental on-line applications at http://physics.usf.edu/graduate. During this process, you will be asked to pay a one-time application fee of $30.00 by credit card (Master Card, Visa, or Discover) or e-check.

Admissions information
For Fall of 2018:
   Number of applicants: 104
   Number admitted: 21
   Number enrolled: 9

Admission requirements
Bachelor's degree requirements: Bachelor's degree in Physics or a closely related field (I.e., Mathematics) is required.
Minimum undergraduate GPA: 3.0

GRE requirements
The GRE is required.
There is no GRE cutoff or minimum score. For exceptional candidates GRE could be waived.

Subjective GRE requirements
The Subjective GRE is recommended.
   No cutoff or minimum score requirement.

TOEFL requirements
The TOEFL exam is required for students from non-English-speaking countries.
   PBT score: 550
   iBT score: 79
See http://www.usf.edu/admissions/international/graduate/requirements-deadlines/english-proficiency.aspx for TOEFL alternatives.

Other admissions information
Undergraduate preparation assumed: Applicants' undergraduate preparation will normally include upper-level coursework in classical mechanics, quantum mechanics, electricity and magnetism, and statistical mechanics.

TUITION

Tuition year 2017–18:
Tuition for in-state residents
   Full-time students: $431.43 per credit
   Part-time students: $431.43 per credit
Tuition for out-of-state residents
   Full-time students: $877.17 per credit
   Part-time students: $877.17 per credit
Credit hours per semester to be considered full-time: 9
Deferred tuition plan: Yes
Health insurance: Yes, $2,410.00.
Other academic fees: See http://usfweb2.usf.edu/uco/studentaccounting/Other_Fees.asp
Academic term: Semester
Number of first-year students who received full tuition waivers: 12

Teaching Assistants, Research Assistants, and Fellowships
Number of first-year
   Teaching Assistants: 7
   Research Assistants: 1
   Fellowship students: 1
Average stipend per academic year
   Teaching Assistant: $21,527
   Research Assistant: $21,527
   Fellowship student: $25,000

FINANCIAL AID

Application deadlines
Fall admission:

U.S. students: February 1   *Int'l. students*: February 1
Spring admission:
U.S. students: September 1   *Int'l. students*: September 1

Loans

Loans are available for U.S. students.
Loans are not available for international students.
GAPSFAS application required: Yes
FAFSA application required: Yes

For further information

Address financial aid inquiries to: Director of Financial Aid, SVC 1102, University of South Florida, 4202 E. Fowler Ave., Tampa, FL 33620.
Phone: (813) 974-3700
Financial aid website: http://www.usf.edu/financial-aid

HOUSING

Availability of on-campus housing

Single students: Yes
Married students: Yes
Childcare Assistance: No

For further information

Address housing inquiries to: Housing and Residential Education, RAR 215, University of South Florida, 4202 E. Fowler Ave., Tampa, FL 33620.
Phone: (813) 974-0001
E-mail: housing@usf.edu
Housing aid website: http://www.housing.usf.edu/

Table A—Faculty, Enrollments, and Degrees Granted

Research Specialty	2017–18 Faculty	Enrollment Fall 2017 Mas-ter's	Enrollment Fall 2017 Doc-torate	Number of Degrees Granted 2017–18 (2012–18) Mas-ter's	Number of Degrees Granted 2017–18 (2012–18) Terminal Master's	Number of Degrees Granted 2017–18 (2012–18) Doc-torate
Atomic, Molecular, & Optical Physics	5	–	5	–(10)	–	–(8)
Biophysics	7	1	11	–(5)	–(4)	1(9)
Condensed-Matter and Materials Physics	16	–	23	–(20)	–(7)	3(25)
Medical Physics in Cooperation with the Moffitt Cancer Institute	–	–	5	1(1)	–(1)	1(4)
Other	5	1	16	–	–(1)	1(2)
Total	33	2	47	10(36)	–(13)	16(103)
Full-time Grad. Stud.	–	1	69	–	–	–
First-year Grad. Stud.	–	1	9	–	–	–

GRADUATE DEGREE REQUIREMENTS

Master's: M.S. in Physics: there are two options both requiring one academic year of residence, and no foreign language requirement. (1) Thesis Option: minimum 30 credit hours in an approved program, six of which may be for thesis; final oral exam on the thesis is required. (2) Non-Thesis Option: minimum 30 credit hours in an approved program.

Doctorate: The Department of Physics offers a Ph.D. in applied physics. Research include biophysics, atomic, molecular & optical physics, condensed-matter and materials physics, computational physics, and medical physics. The Industrial Practicum (IP) is a unique feature of our PhD program allowing students to gain first-hand experience in a nonacademic environment, develop relationship with potential future employers, and enhance their career opportunities. Students have completed the IP in industry, in hospitals, and at national laboratories. Average completion is 5 years. Two forms are offered: PhD in Applied Physics and PhD in Applied Physics with Medical Physics concentration. Both require minimum 57 credit hours in an approved program. The detailed distribution is the follows: Core courses-15 Lab/computer training-3 Electives-12 Industrial practicum-3 Dissertation research-24 The concentration in medical physics is accredited by the Committee on the Accreditation of Medical-Physics Education Programs (CAMPEP).

SPECIAL EQUIPMENT, FACILITIES, OR PROGRAMS

Experimental and theoretical research in the Department of Physics is conducted in the following laboratories/programs:

Cellular and Molecular Biophysics Research Laboratory:

The lab is highly interdisciplinary, involving physics, physiology, cell biology, and molecular biology. The structural and functional relationship of membrane proteins, such as ion channels, membrane transporters, and electrogenic pump molecules, as well as their interfaces with external electromagnetic field, are currently studied. One of the projects is to study direct energy transform from inorganic energy to the living system by electrically activating the membrane electrogenic pump molecules, Na/K ATPases. Other projects include the study of percutaneous and targeted drug delivery, understanding the mechanisms underlying electrical injury, and the development of novel techniques for wound healing. The research involves both basic science and its practical application to biology and medicine. The research program is supported by the National Institutes of Health (NIH) since 1994, as well as by many other funding agencies. Our research is conducted and focused on cellular and molecular levels in nanoscales by using broad, state-of-arts techniques, including whole cell/patch clamps, various microscopic imagining systems such as multiple-laser confocal microscope and near field microscope, full line of cellular, and molecular biology technique. (wchen@usf.edu)

Soft Materials Physics Laboratory:
Many mechanical, dynamical and structural properties of materials remain poorly understood for reasons independent of system-specific chemistry. Great advances in understanding these properties can be achieved through coarse-grained and multiscale simulations that are computationally efficient enough to access experimentally accessible spatiotemporal scales yet "chemically" realistic enough to capture the essential physics underlying the properties under study. We have and will continue to concentrate on explaining poorly-understood behaviors of polymeric, colloidal, and nanocomposite systems through coarse-grained modeling and concomitant development of analytic theories. The general theme is to do basic research on topics that are of high practical interest. Current work includes studies of polymer crystallization and polymer-nanocomposite mechanics. Facilities include a 32-core workstation and access to USF's 500-node (5500-core) CIRCE cluster. (rshoy@usf.edu)

Condensed matter/materials physics optical and laser spectroscopy:

This laboratory is currently under development and is designed to apply state-of-the-art optical and laser spectroscopy techniques to study the fundamental properties of advanced materials. Some of the most advanced optical and laser spectroscopy techniques will be available, including multidimensional ultrafast laser spectroscopy possibly spanning a wide spectral range, and single nanostructure photoluminescence and lifetime spectroscopy. The aforementioned optical techniques will be combined to explore the electronic, vibrational, and light-matter interactions in a variety of advanced nanomaterials, correlated-electron materials, and organic/inorganic hybrid materials, used in renewable energy applications for harvesting and storage. Understanding their intrinsic properties will contribute in improving the device performance of solar cells and batteries, important to a renewable-energy future. (karaiskaj@usf.edu)

Digital Holography & Microscopy Laboratory (DHML):

The main theme of our research activities is in the development of novel imaging technologies, with emphasis in holographic and interferographic microscopy. In digital holography (DH), the hologram is recorded by a CCD camera, instead of photographic plates, and the holographic images are calculated numerically using the electromagnetic diffraction theory. This gives direct access to the phase profile of the optical field and leads to a number of powerful imaging techniques that are difficult or impossible in real space holography. Transparent objects, such as many biological cells, thin film structures, and MEMS devices, can be imaged that reveal minute thickness variations with nanometer precision. Optical tomography by digital interference holography (DIH) yields cross-sectional images of biological tissues without actually cutting into them. Cellular motility can be studied by imaging the adhesion layers between a crawling cell and the substrate through the DH of total reflection, important in the study of embryogenesis, neuronal growth, and cancer cell metastasis. Furthermore, we are not only able to image cells and their components but also manipulate them in full three dimensions, using patterns of light produced by holographic optical tweezers (HOT). Cells and organelles can be captured and tracked, coaxed into artificially patterned growth and motion, and operated on with micro manipulation and microsurgery. Students can expect to work on cutting-edge research topics and be trained extensively in advanced optical design and construction, digital image acquisition, computer programming, electronic instrumentation, and cellular and biomedical laboratory procedures. Digital holography is an emerging technology that has been experiencing exponential growth in the last decade, and has potential applications in wide-ranging areas including cellular microscopy, metrology, manufacturing processes and testing, medical imaging and diagnostics, biometry, environmental research, and food science, just to name a few. (mkkim@usf.edu)

Laboratory for Advanced Materials Science and Technology (LAMSAT):

Explores innovations in pulsed laser ablation and plasma processes for the growth of thin films of technologically significant materials, including super hard materials, magnetic materials, superconductors, and compound semiconductors for solar cells. Past NSF- and DOE-sponsored research projects have focused on the application of a dual-laser ablation process discovered in this laboratory to grow large-area, particulate-free films of Cu(InGa)Se2 and ZnO for solar cell applications, and to fabricate diamond and diamond-like carbon structures for MEMS applications. One of the recently funded NSF projects focuses on an hybrid process where chemical self-assembly and physical vapor deposition techniques are combined to grow vertically aligned nano-grained films of superhard materials. Novel optical techniques for high resolution, in-situ plasma imaging, and development of new laser-assisted plasma growth processes are being researched. The research encompasses thin film growth, nanostructures, dynamic optical process diagnostics, thin film analysis, characterization and process modeling leading to the fabrication of single-layer and hetero-structure devices. (pritish@usf.edu, switanach@usf.edu)

Functional Materials Laboratory:

This laboratory is equipped with experimental facilities for studying the electrical and magnetic properties of novel materials. Investigation of the material properties are done over a wide range in temperature (2 K < T < 350 K) and applied magnetic fields up to 7 Tesla. In addition, the frequency-dependent electromagnetic response is probed from DC to 6 GHz. A novel resonant radio-frequency (RF) method has been developed to accurately determine the magnetic anisotropy and switching in materials. Current research projects focus on studies of dynamic magnetic response and high-frequency impedance in nanoparticles, composites, thin films, magnetic semiconductors and multiferroic systems. These technologically important materials are promising candidates as building blocks for the next generation multi-functional device. Other interests include magnetocaloric effect in nanostructured materials, spin polarization studies, and physics of strongly correlated systems. Ongoing research support by NSF, DoD, and DOE. (sharihar@usf.edu)

The Bio-Nano Research Group:

The work of this laboratory is the investigation of the structure/function relationship in biological systems ranging from the single molecule to the multicellular level. Molecular level structures determine the materials properties of the system, which in turn determines the macroscopic biological function. Using the expertise in atomic force microscopy, fluorescence microscopy, rheology, and other techniques found in the laboratory, the physical properties of single molecules and macromolecules are measured, and bulk models are developed and experimentally tested. These models are used to help explain the biology or pathology of systems. Example projects within the lab include investigations of cell surface and extracellular matrix glycoproteins and glycosaminoglycans through single molecule imaging and force spectroscopy. The data from these experiments is used to develop models for the viscoelastic properties of solutions of these biopolymers, which are then tested experimentally. These rheological properties are important for the function of tissues ranging from joint interstitial fluids to lung epithelium and will be used to understand the behaviors observed in these systems. The outcomes of the lab are geared to make significant contributions to biomedicine, and as such require a close collaboration with the Departments of Biology and Chemistry and with the School of Medicine. The work is inherently multidisciplinary, and students develop a broad range of skills from physics, biology, and chemistry. (garrettm@usf.edu)

Novel Materials Laboratory:

The laboratory is designed for the synthesis and characterization (including structural, optical, electrical, thermal, and magnetic) of novel materials for technologically significant applications. The emphasis is on understanding the structure-property relationships of material systems, that is, how crystal structure variations affect the electrical, thermal, optical, magnetic, and mechanical properties of materials. The laboratory applies this understanding towards crystal growth and processing of new and novel materials for varying technologically significant applications. The research focus is on new materials for energy-related technologies. Current materials research includes new semiconductors for electronics and optoelectronics applications, transport properties of "open structured" semiconductors, nanocrystal synthesis and self-assembly approaches, and new magnetic materials. The research is supported by NSF, DOE, ONR, ARO, NASA, and industry. Close collaboration with industry is typical in this interdisciplinary Materials Physics research program that encompasses all aspects of physics and materials science. Students typically acquire a large variety of skill sets and apply this knowledge towards their applied physics research. (gnolas@usf.edu)

Materials Simulations Laboratory (MSL):

Director: Prof. I. I. Oleynik

The research program at MSL focuses on design of new materials and prediction of their structural, electronic, and mechanical properties using first-principles density functional theory and classical molecular dynamics. First-principles based evolutionary search algorithms are applied to design and characterize new materials at high pressures as well as their synthesis pathways upon transformation of precursor materials under compression in diamond anvil cells and/or by shock waves. Using atomic-scale simulation methods, such as density functional theory and classical MD, we investigate structural, electronic and mechanical properties of graphene, boron nitride, metal chalcogenides and other emergent 2D materials. Novel environment-dependent bond-order potentials for covalently bonded materials are being developed by coarse-graining the quantum mechanical electronic structure within a chemically intuitive tight-binding framework, and then implementing environment-dependent screening of interatomic interactions for the physically-correct description of bond breaking and re-making. We study high-strain-rate materials response, condensed phase shock wave and detonation phenomena in large-scale molecular dynamics simulations. (oleynik@usf.edu)

Condensed Matter Theory Research Group:

This group works in condensed-matter theory, with current projects in crystallography, biological data analysis, and magnetic systems. In collaboration with Dr. Benji Fisher, we have reformulated Fourier-space crystallography into the language of cohomology of groups and applied the results to a wider class of structures than previously considered. Continuing work focuses on homological invariants of a new kind and their possible physical implications. In biology, we have been collaborating with Dr. Chun-Min Lo on analysis of electric cell-substrate impedance-sensing experiments. Looking only at statistical signatures of electrical noise, tk;4we can distinguish cancerous from non-cancerous cell cultures of the same type of cell and can detect physiological effects of the toxin cytochalasin-B at lower concentrations than possible with other techniques. Recent work in magnetic systems includes a statistical-mechanical model of helimagnetism in rare-earth heterostructures and a study of the ballistic-to-diffusive crossover in quantum wires. The latter may have applications in quantum computing. (davidra@ewald.cas.usf.edu)

Laboratory of Optical Biophysics:

The overall research focus in our laboratory is on the basic physical principles that govern the phase separation and aggregation of proteins in solution. Depending on the specifics of the protein interactions and solution conditions, proteins can either stay soluble or undergo a variety of phase transitions. These phase transitions include crystallization, liquid-liquid phase separation, precipitation or formation of amyloid fibrils. We are using a variety of optical and spectroscopic techniques to study the thermodynamics and kinetics of these phase separation phenomena of proteins. Our current focus is on the mechanisms governing the self-assembly of a variety proteins into so-called amyloid fibrils. This aggregation process is the molecular hallmark for a large class of protein aggregation diseases, including Alzheimer's disease, Parkinson's disease, and even type-II diabetes. Aside from these biomedical applications, amyloid fibril formation has also been recognized as a unique model for general mechanisms of self-assembly of biomolecules into highly ordered nano- and biomaterials with intriguing mechanical and optical properties. We are pursuing both the biomedical and nano-materials aspects of this assembly process in our current research. (mmuschol@usf.edu)

Computational Soft Matter Laboratory:

Interest of our group lie in the areas of computational bio-physics and mathematical modeling of biological and social systems. In this context, we focus on molecular dynamics simulations, Monte Carlo methods, multiscale modeling based on mean field theory, dynamical systems with an emphasis on Hamiltonian systems, associated numerical methods, and underlying parallel processing issues. Our current focus is on the study of lipid bilayer systems, which form integral components of cellular membranes. These systems are studied using various computational modeling techniques and validated through close interactions with experimentalists. One aspect of our current work involves the study of heterogeneous model membrane systems. We study the interactions between various membrane components such as phospho- and sphingo-lipids, and cholesterol that give rise to stable structures such as "rafts" and caveolae. We intend to develop a multiscale mean filed theory based model into a complete simulation methodology for membrane simulations. The models and methods developed will be used to study the structure and stability of membrane structures such as "raft" and caveolae, which are known to play critical roles in the activation of T-cells in immune response. (pandit@usf.edu)

Computational Condensed Matter Physics and Materials Science Program:

Research interest include the area of theoretical condensed matter physics with a focus on computational nanoscience. The materials of interest include semiconductors, ferroelectrics, ferromagnets, and multiferroics in both bulk and low-dimensional forms. Examples are nanotubes, nanowires, nanodots, and thin films. An exciting feature of such nanoforms is the appearance of new properties and phenomena that do not exist in bulk. The purpose of my research is to identify these novel features, study their fundamental aspects, and explore their new functionalities for future applications in nanoscale devices. An example is utilizing a novel vortex structure that is a unique feature of ferroelectric nanodots in ultrahigh density memory that may increase the current memory capacitance by orders of magnitude. Another research focus is the development of computational techniques that will expand their capabilities beyond existing levels. Examples include the development of first-principle-based techniques for new material forms (nanoscale ferroelectrics and multiferroics) and properties (dielectric loss and tunability). The ultimate research objective is the efficient design of new materials conducted in close collaboration with experimental groups. (iponomar@usf.edu)

Advanced Materials and Devices Theory Group:

Our group is engaged in various problems related to theoretical modeling and description of structural, functional, and nanoscale materials and devices. We pursue two complementary routes - analytical and computational. Analytical techniques based on quantum mechanics, quantum electrodynamics, and many-body theory, are being developed. First principle density functional theory and tight binding models on high-performance supercomputers are being utilized. Currently, we are pursuing problems related to the Casimir effect in nanostructured materials, thermoelectric properties of materials with enhanced cooling and power generation performances, simulations of nanostructured materials properties, and related devices. The projects are funded by various national funding agencies. Our group maintains strong collaborations with experimental teams as well as other theoretical groups from the University of South Florida, other universities and national research laboratories. We are devoted to conducting leading edge research to advance our understanding of complex materials and devices using analytical and computational methods. (lmwoods@usf.edu)

The Nanophysics and Surface Science Laboratory:

In this laboratory, we investigate condensed matter at the atomic scale. The surface of a material is where the action is; at a surface the material interacts with its environment and thus many chemical and physical processes occur at the interface between a solid and a different medium. Our goal is to understand the structural and electronic properties of surfaces and to tune these properties in order for the surface to perform new or improved functions. Currently investigated surface-functional materials are metal oxides for their use as solid state gas sensors and for solar energy conversion. Modification of surfaces with nanoclusters to improve their functionality is one approach to improve and create new functionalities.

Nanoclusters are aggregates of atoms in the realm between molecules and bulk materials. In this size range, condensed matter exhibits new properties, which can be conveniently tuned by controlling their size. In our laboratory, we assemble clusters atom by atom in the gas phase and subsequently place them on a support material. This allows investigating the cluster-support interaction and the cluster-size properties relationship. Most of the sample preparation and characterization is done under ultra high vacuum conditions to ensure the integrity of the samples under investigation. In addition to the in-house measurements, some supplementing photoemission and X-ray absorption studies are performed at synchrotron facilities. (mbatzill@usf.edu)

Soft Semiconductor Materials and Devices Laboratory:

This laboratory studies soft semiconductors with low dimensional electronic structure and are solution processable. Some examples are organic semiconductor, colloidal quantum dots, carbon nanotubes, and perovskites. One research focus is on systematic investigation of correlation between excitonic properties of thin films and electronic responses of pertinent devices. Technical approaches include optical study by linear (absorption, steady state and time-resolved photoluminescence) and various modulation (continuous wave photoinduced absorption, doping induced absorption & Electroabsorption) spectroscopies, and transport measurements using vertical (TOF, CELIV, SCLC, CV) and lateral (FET) device structures. Another major research line is to advance renewable energy technology by development of processing methodologies to integrate multifunctional materials onto soft substrates. One example is the fabrication of transparent and flexible organic solar module by solution-based techniques such as spray and printing. (xjiang@usf.edu)

Solid-State Quantum Optics Laboratory:

This laboratory is equipped with experimental facilities for studying quantum optical phenomena in solid-state nanostructures such as quantum dots, nanocrystals, and impurity centers. The long-term goal of this research is to realize controlled light-matter interactions for use in quantum communication and quantum information science. Optical techniques employed include high-resolution spectroscopy, interferometry, and multi-photon correlation measurements in both ambient and low-temperature (liquid-helium) environments. Novel optical microcavities are being developed to enhance the interactions of light with single quantum emitters and mechanical resonators for harnessing cavity-electrodynamics and cavity-optomechanics phenomena. (mullera@usf.edu)

Quantum Nonlinear Photonics Laboratory:

This laboratory is aimed to experimentally study quantum nonlinear photonics, a broadly defined field that investigates the physics and applications of the nonlinear and quantum aspects of photons and light-matter interaction. In specific, the lab is equipped with facilities to study photonic crystal and other nanophotonics devices on silicon-on-insulator chips and plasmonic nanostructures. Another part of the lab is aimed to develop new concepts of optical technologies that utilize nonclassical nature of light, especially to encode and retrieve information from an optical field in terms of color, amplitude, phase and polarization. (zhiminshi@usf.edu)

Microwave and Ultrafast Terahertz Research Laboratory:

This group focuses on research in theoretical modeling and experimental characterization of photonic structures including metamaterials, surface plasmons and photonic crystals. Numerical modeling and simulation techniques based on the finite element method and the finite-difference time-domain method are used to design functional photonic structures. State-of-the-art microwave and ultrafast terahertz equipments provide the capability of characterizing photonic materials over a wide frequency range. Researchers in this group are devoted to conducting cutting-edge research in both theoretical and experimental aspects of various photonic phenomena. Current research activities include studying nonlinear properties of photonic metamaterials, RF and solar energy harvesting metamaterials and surface plasmons. This group maintains strong collaboration and interaction with several leading research groups from other universities and national laboratories. (jiangfengz@usf.edu)

Astrophysics and Planetary-Science Laboratory:

Our group's main goal is to constrain physical and chemical models of the origins of planetary systems by obtaining and analyzing observations of comets and exoplanets. We perform spectroscopy, interferometry, and imaging at optical, infrared, and millimeter wavelength telescopes and collaborate with leading atmospheric theorists. (mariawomack@gmail.com)

Magnetism and Spin Dynamics Lab:

Our lab, currently under development, focusses on characterization of novel magnetic, multifunctional and strongly correlated materials via in-house techniques (ferromagnetic resonance, magneto-optical Kerr effect) and at national laboratories (electron microscopy and synchrotron-based spectroscopy). While our studies are fundamental in nature, the research has direct relevance to advanced technology for information storage and processing, microwave electronics, green technologies, novel sensors and other devices. (darena@usf.edu)

General Support Facilities:

Include a machine shop to build custom mechanical and vacuum parts and an electronics shop capable of custom design, repair, and fabrication of electronics and computer components.

Table B—Separately Budgeted Research Expenditures by Source of Support

Source of Support	Departmental Research	Physics-related Research Outside Department
Federal government	$2,589,710	
State/local government		
Non-profit organizations		
Business and industry		
Other	$142,603	
Total	$2,732,313	

Table C—Separately Budgeted Research Expenditures by Research Specialty

Research Specialty	No. of Grants	Expenditures ($)
Astrophysics	2	$61,632
Atomic, Molecular, & Optical Physics	7	$573,632
Biophysics	5	$477,597
Condensed Matter Physics	29	$1,619,450
Total	43	$2,732,311

FACULTY

Distinguished University Professor

Nolas, George S., Ph.D., Stevens Institute of Technology, 1994. *Applied Physics, Chemical Physics, Condensed Matter Physics, Energy Sources & Environment, Engineering Physics/Science, Materials Science, Metallurgy, Nano Science and Tech-*

nology. Experimental solid-state, materials, and condensed matter physics.

Professor

Batzill, Matthias, Ph.D., University of Newcastle upon Tyne, UK, 1999. *Applied Physics, Chemical Physics, Condensed Matter Physics, Materials Science, Metallurgy, Nano Science and Technology.* Surface science; gas-surface interactions; structure and electronic properties of metal oxide surfaces; nanoclusters and quantum dots; solid-state gas sensors; photocatalysis and photovoltaic for sustainable and renewable energy.

Chen, Wei, Ph.D., Temple University, 1988. *Biophysics.* Cellular and molecular biophysic; structure and function of membrane proteins; bioenergetics; new technique in synchronization modulation of the electrogenic pump molecules to electrically activate the pump functions, and its biomedical applications.

Kim, Myung K., Ph.D., University of California, Berkeley, 1986. *Applied Physics, Atomic, Molecular, & Optical Physics, Biophysics, Optics.* Digital holography; phase contrast microscopy; optical tomography; biomedical imaging; quantum optics; laser spectroscopy.

Mukherjee, Pritish, Ph.D., State University of New York at Buffalo, 1986. *Applied Physics, Atomic, Molecular, & Optical Physics, Chemical Physics, Condensed Matter Physics, Energy Sources & Environment, Materials Science, Metallurgy, Nano Science and Technology, Optics.* Picosecond lasers and applications; laser-assisted materials growth; nanostructures, thin films, and heterostructures of semi-conductors and oxides.

Oleynik, Ivan I., Ph.D., Russian Academy of Sciences, 1992. *Applied Physics, Chemical Physics, Computational Physics, Condensed Matter Physics, Nano Science and Technology.* Theoretical condensed matter and chemical physics; computational materials science.

Ponomareva, Inna, Ph.D., Russian Academy of Sciences, 2004. Graduate Admission Director. *Applied Physics, Computational Physics, Condensed Matter Physics, Materials Science, Metallurgy, Nano Science and Technology.* Condensed matter physics, numerical quantum chemistry, computational physics, nanoscience, developing and implementation of computational techniques.

Srikanth, Hariharan, Ph.D., Indian Institute of Science, 1993. *Applied Physics, Condensed Matter Physics, Materials Science, Metallurgy, Nano Science and Technology.* Experimental condensed matter; materials sciences.

Witanachchi, Sarath, Ph.D., State University of New York at Buffalo, 1989. *Applied Physics, Atomic, Molecular, & Optical Physics, Chemical Physics, Condensed Matter Physics, Energy Sources & Environment, Materials Science, Metallurgy, Nano Science and Technology, Optics.* Laser ablation, plasma processing, and chemical synthesis of films and nanostructures.

Woods, Lilia, Ph.D., University of Tennessee, 1999. Associate chair. *Applied Physics, Condensed Matter Physics, Materials Science, Metallurgy, Nano Science and Technology.* Theoretical condensed matter physics: theory and computation of nanostructures; dispersive interactions; thermoelectric transport.

Associate Professor

Arena, Dario, Ph.D., Rutgers University, 2000. *Condensed Matter Physics, Solid State Physics.* Condensed matter physics with emphasis on magnetic materials; spintronics; ultrafast dynamics and ferromagnetic resonance; correlated electron systems; experimental design; and data analysis. Experienced spectroscopist (x-ray, photoemission) with strong interest in microscopy.

Jiang, Xiaomei, Ph.D., University of Utah, 2004. *Applied Physics, Atomic, Molecular, & Optical Physics, Chemical Physics, Condensed Matter Physics, Energy Sources & Environment, Materials Science, Metallurgy, Nano Science and Technology, Optics.* Organic electronic materials; fabrication and characterization of light emitting diodes and photovoltaic devices for solar cell applications.

Karaiskaj, Denis, Ph.D., Simon Fraser University, 2002. *Applied Physics, Atomic, Molecular, & Optical Physics, Materials Science, Metallurgy, Nano Science and Technology, Optics.* Two-dimensional spectroscopy on nanostructures, and proteins; optical spectroscopic studies of carbon nanotubes; ultrahigh resolution spectroscopy of semiconductors.

Matthews, Garrett, Ph.D., University of North Carolina, 2001. *Applied Physics, Biophysics, Medical, Health Physics, Nano Science and Technology.* Biological macromolecules and macromolecular biopolymers.

Muller, Andreas, Ph.D., University of Texas, Austin, 2007. *Applied Physics, Atomic, Molecular, & Optical Physics, Optics.* Experimental quantum optics of nanostructures; quantum dots, nanocrystals, impurity centers; cavity quantum electrodynamics and optomechanics for quantum communication and quantum information science.

Muschol, Martin, Ph.D., City University of New York, 1992. *Applied Physics, Atomic, Molecular, & Optical Physics, Biophysics, Medical, Health Physics, Optics.* Neuronal plasticity; advanced optical techniques to probe cellular mechanisms; protein crystallization.

Pandit, Sagar A., Ph.D., University of Pune, India, 1999. *Applied Physics, Biophysics, Computational Physics, Condensed Matter Physics, Statistical & Thermal Physics.* Computational biophysics and mathematical modeling of biological and social systems.

Rabson, David, Ph.D., Cornell University, 1991. Department chair. *Applied Physics, Biophysics, Computational Physics, Condensed Matter Physics, Crystallography, Statistical & Thermal Physics, Theoretical Physics.* Condensed matter theory.

Ullah, Ghanim, Ph.D., Ohio University, 2006. *Applied Physics.* Neuronal disorders; Markov chain models; Calcium dynamics; Cell signaling pathways; Application of control theory to biology.

Zhou, Jiangfeng, Ph.D., Iowa State University, 2008. *Applied Physics, Atomic, Molecular, & Optical Physics, Condensed Matter Physics, Electrical Engineering, Electromagnetism, Optics.* Metamaterials, photonic crystals, plasmonics, numerical electromagnetics, and THz photonics.

Assistant Professor

Gutierrez, Humberto R., Ph.D., Universidade Estadual de Campinas, 2001. *Condensed Matter Physics, Materials Science, Metallurgy, Solid State Physics.* Condensed-matter experiment: synthesis and characterization of nanomaterials including carbon nanomaterials, two-dimensional transition-metal dichalcogenides, semiconductor nanowires and nanoclusters, and metallic and magnetic nanofilaments.

Hoy, Robert S., Ph.D., Johns Hopkins University, 2008. *Applied Physics, Computational Physics, Theoretical Physics.* Soft matter physics; Theoretical and Computational modeling of polymeric, colloidal, and nanocomposite systems; computational method development.

Pan, Jianjun, Ph.D., Carnegie Mellon University, 2009. Structure and function of membrane proteins; interactions between drug molecules and membrane proteins; structure and dynamics of fluid lipid membranes; protein-membrane interactions; drug-lipid composites.

Shi, Zhimin, Ph.D., University of Rochester, 2011. *Applied Physics, Atomic, Molecular, & Optical Physics, Optics, Quantum*

Foundations. Quantum nonlinear photonics, nanophotonics, silicon photonics, photonic crystal, plasmonics, metamaterial. Optical methods utilizing non-classical nature of light.

Voronine, Dmitry, Ph.D., Bowling Green State University, 2004. *Applied Physics, Atomic, Molecular, & Optical Physics, Biophysics, Condensed Matter Physics, Medical, Health Physics.* I apply a variety of techniques in spectroscopy and imaging to biological, atomic, molecular and condensed matter systems, including the development of detectors for minute quantities of poisonous and carcinogenic molecules, and nanometer-scale chemical analysis of single biomolecules, 2D materials, and bacteria.

Research Professor

Womack, Maria P., Ph.D., Arizona State University, 1991. *Astronomy, Astrophysics, Planetary Science.* Observational imaging and spectroscopy of comets and exoplanets at optical, infrared, and mm-wavelengths.

Research Associate Professor

Phan, Manh-Huong, Ph.D., University of Bristol, 2006. *Applied Physics, Condensed Matter Physics, Materials Science, Metallurgy, Nano Science and Technology.* Nanomagnetism and magnetic materials; giant magnetoimpedance (GMI) materials; giant magnetocaloric (GMC) materials; colossal magnetoresistive (CMR) materials; nanoparticles and nanocomposites; multiferroic materials.

Research Assistant Professor

Lisenkov, Sergey, Ph.D., Russian Academy of Sciences, Moscow, 2005. *Applied Physics.* Finite-temperature properties of multiferroic materials; Perovskite superlattices and nanostructures; Electronic and stability properties of nanotubes and fullerenes.

Instructor

Criss, Robert, Ph.D., University of Texas, Dallas, 1993. *Applied Physics, Atomic, Molecular, & Optical Physics, Physics and other Science Education.* Applied VUV-VIS spectroscopy; physics education.

Mackay, Kevin, Ph.D., Queen's University, Belfast, N. Ireland, 2000. *Applied Physics, Astronomy, Astrophysics.* Extra-solar planets, astronomy education, and thin-film magnetic materials.

McCormick, Alexander, Ph.D., University of Maryland, 2015. *Astronomy, Astrophysics.* IR observation of galactic winds in nearby galaxies.

Pradhan, Gauri, Ph.D., University of Pune, 2002. *Biophysics, Statistical & Thermal Physics.* statistical mechanics, game theory, and mathematical modeling applied to primate behaviour.

Woods, Gerald, Ph.D., University of Tennessee, 2001. General Physics Lab Director. *Applied Physics, Condensed Matter Physics, Physics and other Science Education.* Experimental condensed matter.

DEPARTMENTAL RESEARCH SPECIALTIES AND STAFF

Theoretical

Applied Physics. The Ph.D. is in applied physics, interpreted broadly. While our research aims to answer fundamental scientific questions, it also often has practical applications (e.g., new electronic devices) in mind. The research often involves bringing to bear many different branches of physics. Arena, Batzill, Chen, Criss, Gutierrez, Hoy, Jiang, Karaiskaj, Kim, Lisenkov, Mackay, Matthews, McCormick, Mukherjee, Muller, Muschol, Nolas, Oleynik, Pan, Pandit, Phan, Ponomareva, Pradhan, Rabson, Shi, Srikanth, Ullah, Voronine, Witanachchi, Womack, Gerald Woods, Lilia Woods, Zhou.

Biophysics. Theoretical biophysics work in the department includes molecular-dynamics studies of membranes, simulation of calcium channels in cells, and cell-cell signaling in cancer. Chen, Matthews, Muschol, Pan, Pandit, Pradhan, Rabson, Ullah, Voronine.

Condensed Matter Physics. Theoretical work in the department includes both hard and soft condensed-matter physics; example systems include graphene and multiferroics. Arena, Batzill, Gutierrez, Hoy, Jiang, Karaiskaj, Kim, Lisenkov, Mukherjee, Muller, Nolas, Oleynik, Phan, Ponomareva, Rabson, Shi, Srikanth, Ullah, Voronine, Witanachchi, Lilia Woods, Zhou.

Medical, Health Physics. Our Ph.D. in Applied Physics with emphasis in medical physics, offered in collaboration with the Moffitt Cancer Institute on the USF campus, is one of 24 CAMPEP-accredited doctoral programs in medical physics in the United States. After the core coursework in pure and applied physics, as well as electives including radiology, nuclear medicine, and imaging, students undertake dissertation research under the supervision of Moffitt faculty members affiliated with USF Physics. Voronine.

Statistical & Thermal Physics. Stat-Mech research at USF encompasses applications in theoretical biophysics and hard and soft condensed matter. Hoy, Lisenkov, Oleynik, Pandit, Ponomareva, Pradhan, Rabson, Ullah, Lilia Woods.

Experimental

Applied Physics. The Ph.D. is in applied physics, interpreted broadly. While our research aims to answer fundamental scientific questions, it also often has practical applications (e.g., better thermoelectric materials) in mind. The research often involves bringing to bear many different branches of physics. Arena, Batzill, Chen, Gutierrez, Jiang, Karaiskaj, Kim, Matthews, Mukherjee, Muller, Muschol, Nolas, Pan, Phan, Shi, Srikanth, Voronine, Witanachchi, Womack, Zhou.

Astronomy. Multi-wavelength spectroscopy of solar-system bodies and the interstellar medium. Womack.

Astronomy, Astrophysics, Planetary Science. Current observational research focuses on imaging and spectroscopy of comets and exoplanets. Mackay, McCormick, Womack.

Atomic, Molecular, & Optical Physics. Areas of research include digital holographic microscopy, spectroscopy of correlated-electron systems, and metamaterials. Jiang, Karaiskaj, Kim, Muller, Shi, Voronine, Zhou.

Biophysics. Examples of experimental biophysics research in the department include the role of amyloid in Alzheimer's disease and neutron-scattering studies of cell membranes. Chen, Kim, Matthews, Muschol, Pan, Pandit, Ullah, Voronine.

Condensed-Matter and Materials Physics. Research areas include magnetism, graphene, and surface science, and materials for energy applications. Arena, Batzill, Gutierrez, Jiang, Karaiskaj, Lisenkov, Mukherjee, Muller, Nolas, Oleynik, Phan, Ponomareva, Rabson, Srikanth, Voronine, Witanachchi.

Medical, Health Physics. Our Ph.D. in Applied Physics with emphasis in medical physics, offered in collaboration with the Moffitt Cancer Institute on the USF campus, is one of 24 CAMPEP-accredited doctoral programs in medical physics in the United States. After the core coursework in pure and applied physics, as well as electives including radiology, nuclear medicine, and imaging, students undertake dissertation research under the supervision of Moffitt faculty members affiliated with USF Physics. Voronine.

EMORY UNIVERSITY

DEPARTMENT OF PHYSICS

Atlanta, Georgia 30322
http://www.physics.emory.edu/

General University Information
President: Claire E. Sterk
Dean of Graduate School: Lisa Tedesco
University website: http://www.emory.edu
School Type: Private
Setting: Suburban
Total Faculty: 2,945
Total Graduate Faculty: 991
Total number of Students: 14,913
Total number of Graduate Students: 7,103

Department Information
Department Chairman: Prof. Stefan Boettcher, Chair
Department Contact: Barbara Conner, Academic Degree
   Coordinator, Graduate
   Total full-time faculty: 20
   Total number of full-time equivalent positions: 20
   Full-Time Graduate Students: 50
   Female Full-Time Graduate Students: 8
   First-Year Graduate Students: 15
   Female First-Year Students: 3
   Total Post Doctorates: 11

Department Address
400 Dowman Drive, Suite N201
Math and Science Center
Atlanta, GA 30322
Phone: (404) 727-6584
Fax: (404) 727-0873
E-mail: gradphysics@emory.edu
Website: http://www.physics.emory.edu/

ADMISSIONS

Admission Contact Information
Address admission inquiries to: Ms. Barbara Conner; Academic
   Degree Coordinator, Graduate, Department of Physics, Emory
   University, 400 Dowman Dr, Rm N201, Atlanta, GA 30322
Phone: (404) 727-4086
E-mail: barbara.conner@emory.edu
Admissions website: http://www.physics.emory.edu/home/
   academic/graduate/index.html

Application deadlines
Fall admission:
U.S. students: January 15   *Int'l. students*: January 15

Application fee
U.S. students: $75   *Int'l. students*: $75
All applications have to be submitted online at http://www
   .gs.emory.edu/admissions/application.html.

Admissions information
For Fall of 2018:
   Number of applicants: 92
   Number admitted: 31
   Number enrolled: 16

Admission requirements
Bachelor's degree requirements: Bachelor's or higher degree in
   physics or related field is required. For all requirements, see
   http://www.physics.emory.edu/home/academic/graduate/
   application%20information.html.
Minimum undergraduate GPA: 3.0

GRE requirements
The GRE is required.
   Quantitative score: 155
   Verbal score: 153
   Analytical score: 3.0
   Mean GRE score range (25th–75th percentile): 315-330
GRE scores should be supplied online at http://www.gs
   .emory.edu/admissions/application.html at least by February
   15. There is no minimum GRE score. Scores should be competitive with others applying to our program; the suggested
   minimum acceptable scores for admission are verbal 153 (or
   500) and quantitative 155 (or 700). However, these are considered with the strengths of your application as a whole.

Subjective GRE requirements
The Subjective GRE is recommended.
   Mean Advanced GRE score range (25th–75th percentile): N/A
   There is no minimum GRE score. Scores should be com-
   petitive with others applying to our program. Students with
   Physics GRE score of above 650 typically perform better in
   our program.

TOEFL requirements
The TOEFL exam is required for students from non-English-
   speaking countries.
   PBT score: 550
   iBT score: 95
If English is not your first language, you may need to submit
   TOEFL scores.

TUITION

Tuition year 2018–19:
   Full-time students: $62,700 annual
   Part-time students: $62,700 annual
All admitted students receive a full tuition waiver and a stipend.
   More details on stipends and benefits provided can be found
   at http://www.physics.emory.edu/home/academic/graduate/
   index.html
Credit hours per semester to be considered full-time: 9
Deferred tuition plan: No
Health insurance: Available
Other academic fees: Activity and athletic fee (optional). In-
   formation on available facilities can be found at http://
   www.gs.emory.edu/funding/tuition.html
Academic term: Semester
Number of first-year students who received full tuition waivers: 16

Teaching Assistants, Research Assistants, and Fellowships
   Number of first-year
      Teaching Assistants: 8
      Fellowship students: 5
   Average stipend per academic year

Teaching Assistant: $27,000
Research Assistant: $27,000
Fellowship student: $32,000

Stipends are expected to increase in the course of the next year. Admitted students are automatically considered for various graduate school fellowships that range between $2,500 to $5,000 of additional support per year. Details are found at http://www.gs.emory.edu/funding/scholarships/admissions.html

FINANCIAL AID

Loans

Loans are available for U.S. students.
Loans are available for international students.
GAPSFAS application required: No
FAFSA application required: No

For further information

Address financial aid inquiries to: Barbara Conner, Academic Degree Coordinator,Graduate, Department of Physics, Emory University, Atlanta, GA 30322.
Phone: (404) 727-4086
E-mail: barbara.conner@emory.edu
Financial aid website: http://www.physics.emory.edu/home/academic/graduate/index.html

HOUSING

Availability of on-campus housing

Single students: Yes
Married students: Yes
Childcare Assistance: No

For further information

Address housing inquiries to: Barbara Conner, Academic Degree Coordinator,Graduate. Department of Physics, Emory University, Atlanta, GA 30322.
Phone: (404) 727-4086
E-mail: barbara.conner@emory.edu
Housing aid website: http://www.physics.emory.edu/home/academic/graduate/life-in-atlanta.html

Table A—Faculty, Enrollments, and Degrees Granted

Research Specialty	2018–19 Faculty	Enrollment Fall 2018		Number of Degrees Granted 2017–18 (2013–18)		
		Master's	Doctorate	Master's	Terminal Master's	Doctorate
Biophysics	7	–	17	–	1(5)	3(18)
Computational Physics	–	–	1	–	–(2)	–
Condensed Matter Physics	7	–	26	–	1(4)	3(10)
Nonlinear Dynamics and Complex Systems	3	–	8	–	–(2)	–(9)
Total	17	–	52	–	2(11)	6(34)
Full-time Grad. Stud.	–	–	52	–	–	–
First-year Grad. Stud.	–	–	16	–	–	–

GRADUATE DEGREE REQUIREMENTS

Master's: Students are not admitted into the Graduate Program in Physics to pursue the M.S. degree. Students may be offered the M.S. degree, if they leave the Ph.D. program. A thesis and oral defense of research work are required. For complete requirements, see http://www.physics.emory.edu/home/academic/graduate/guide.html#ms_requirements.

Doctorate: Students must complete a total of eight graduate courses (four of which are core required physics topics with a minimum of a B average). Students do two research rotations during their first year to identify a PhD advisor. The qualifier exam in the student's second year involves writing and orally defending a research proposal related to their PhD research. A final dissertation and oral defense are required for graduation. For complete requirements, see http://www.physics.emory.edu/home/academic/graduate/guide.html#phd_requirements.

Other Degrees: We offer a joint degree option with a Ph.D. in Physics and an M.S. in Computer Science; see http://www.physics.emory.edu/home/academic/graduate/guide.html#joint_degree.

Thesis: A thesis is required for Ph.D. and M.S. degrees.

SPECIAL EQUIPMENT, FACILITIES, OR PROGRAMS

For the latest information on our facilities, see http://www.physics.emory.edu/home/facilities/index.html

Research: The Physics Department at Emory University hosts a number of research facilities for material and device preparation and deposition, nanofabrication, characterization, and measurements. Facilities listed as shared departmental equipment are available free of charge to all researchers affiliated with the Physics Department. Facilities located in individual research laboratories are often available to other researchers on a collaborative basis. Other research facilities available in close proximity include the Emory X-ray Crystallography Center, the Nanotechnology Research Center at Georgia Tech, and the Oak Ridge National Laboratory.

Initiatives: The Department participates in the Initiative in Theory and Modeling of Living Systems, which develops program in quantitative biology and biophysics on campus, bringing together about two dozen labs in the field. See http://livingtheory.emory.edu

National Graduate Training Programs: The Department is a member of the International Physics of Living Systems Student Research Network, which allows student exchange with other nodes of the network. See https://pols.rice.edu

Machine Shop: In addition to the basic machining services, the Physics Machine Shop modifies commercial and custom-built research equipment to specification. We assist in the engineering, design, and construction of complex custom apparatuses. No matter what the need, the Machine Shop strives to be the department's one-stop destination for advanced research equipment needs.

Computation: The Technical Team at the Department of Physics provides comprehensive technical support and services in a variety of areas, including software and desktop hardware support. Our department maintains or participates in several clusters for scientific computation, including the Computational Statistical Physics Cluster, The Cherry L. Emerson Center for Scientific Computation, and Emory's High Performance Computing Center.

Education: Our classrooms and educational technologies help to enhance our teaching efforts. The introductory laboratories are kept small to emphasize a personalized approach. Up-to-date instrumentation and computer-based data acquisition prepare students for the challenges of modern science and technology. The advanced laboratories use custom-built experiments that have produced six education-related papers.

Astronomy: The Physics Department houses three major astronomical facilities: A custom-designed planetarium featuring a Zeiss Skymater projector, a 24″ Ritchey-Crietien DFM Casegrain optical telescope, and a 25-foot diameter dish radio telescope. These facilities provide a comprehensive hands-on educational experience encompassing major areas of modern astronomy.

Table B—Separately Budgeted Research Expenditures by Source of Support

Source of Support	Departmental Research	Physics-related Research Outside Department
Federal government	$2,423,000	
State/local government		
Non-profit organizations	$421,000	
Business and industry		
Other		
Total	$2,844,000	

Table C—Separately Budgeted Research Expenditures by Research Specialty

Research Specialty	No. of Grants	Expenditures ($)
Molecular, Systems, and Organismal Biophysics	12	$1,566,000
Condensed Matter incl. Soft Matter	9	$1,278,000
Total	21	$2,844,000

FACULTY

Professor

Berland, Keith M., Ph.D., University of Illinois, 1995. *Biophysics, Optics*. Experimental biophysics. Applications of fluorescence correlation spectroscopy (FCS) in biophysics, of high sensitivity fluorescence measurements in cellular biophysics. Investigation of the role of dynamic processes in biological function, and development and application of novel methods to quantify specific protein-protein interactions in living cells.

Boettcher, Stefan, Ph.D., Washington University, St. Loius, 1993. Department Chair. *Applied Mathematics, Computational Physics, Nonlinear Dynamics and Complex Systems, Statistical & Thermal Physics, Theoretical Physics*. Statistical physics, critical phenomena, computational and theoretical problems in strongly disordered systems, with applications ranging from evolutionary dynamics and amorphous materials to combinatorial optimization.

Finzi, Laura, Ph.D., University of New Mexico, 1990. *Biophysics*. Experimental biophysics. Single-molecule biophysics of transcriptional regulation. Molecular mechanisms of transcriptional regulation using single-molecule techniques, such as the tethered particle motion technique (TPM), magnetic tweezers (MT) and atomic force microscopy (AFM).

Nemenman, Ilya, Ph.D., Princeton University, 2000. Director of Graduate Studies, Winship Distinguished Research Professor. *Biophysics, Computational Physics, Neuroscience/Neuro Physics, Nonlinear Dynamics and Complex Systems, Statistical & Thermal Physics, Theoretical Physics*. Theoretical and statistical physics. Theoretical biophysics, coarse-grained modeling in systems biology and neuroscience, information transduction in biological systems, learning and adaptation in molecular, neural, and evolutionary systems.

Urazhdin, Sergei, Ph.D., Michigan State University, 2002. *Applied Physics, Condensed Matter Physics, Electromagnetism, Materials Science, Metallurgy, Nano Science and Technol-* *ogy, Quantum Foundations, Solid State Physics, Surface Physics*. Experimental condensed matter physics; spintronics, electronic and magnetic properties of surfaces and nanostructures, nonlinear dynamics in nanomagnetic systems, and strongly correlated materials.

Warncke, Kurt, Ph.D., University of Pennsylvania, 1990. *Biophysics, Energy Sources & Environment*. Experimental biophysics. Pulsed-EPR and optical studies of metallocenter- and radical-mediated enzyme and chemical catalyses, with a focus on time-resolve approaches.

Weeks, Eric, Ph.D., University of Texas, Austin, 1997. Samuel Candler Dobbs Professor. *Condensed Matter Physics, Fluids, Rheology, Nonlinear Dynamics and Complex Systems, Optics*. Experimental soft condensed matter. Microscopy of colloidal glasses, nonlinear dynamics, complex fluids, and granular media.

Associate Professor

Roth, Connie, Ph.D., University of Guelph, 2004. Director of Graduate Studies. *Chemical Physics, Condensed Matter Physics, Engineering Physics/Science, Fluids, Rheology, Materials Science, Metallurgy, Mechanics, Nano Science and Technology, Nonlinear Dynamics and Complex Systems, Polymer Physics/Science, Statistical & Thermal Physics, Surface Physics*. Experimental soft condensed matter physics. Polymer materials, glass transition, physical aging, photophysics, miscibility and phase separation; effect of nanoconfinement, surfaces and interfaces, external stresses, electric fields, and nanoparticles.

Assistant Professor

Berman, Gordon J., Ph.D., Cornell University, 2009. Assistant Professor of Biology. *Biophysics, Computational Physics, Mechanics, Medical, Health Physics, Neuroscience/Neuro Physics, Nonlinear Dynamics and Complex Systems, Theoretical Physics*. Theoretical, computational, and data-driven approaches to organism's movements and animal behaviors making connections to neurobiology, genetics, and evolutionary histories.

Burton, Justin C., Ph.D., University of California, Irvine, 2006. *Chemical Physics, Climate/Atmospheric Science, Condensed Matter Physics, Fluids, Rheology, Geophysics, Nonlinear Dynamics and Complex Systems, Statistical & Thermal Physics, Surface Physics*. Experimental condensed matter physics, soft matter physics, non-equilibrium physics, fluid mechanics, jamming and granular physics, geophysics.

Harutyunyan, Hayk, Ph.D., University of Pisa, 2009. *Condensed Matter Physics, Electromagnetism, Engineering Physics/Science, Materials Science, Metallurgy, Nano Science and Technology, Optics, Solid State Physics, Surface Physics*. Experimental condensed matter physics, nanoscience, optics, material physics. Nanophotonic studies of the interaction of light with nanoscale matter including metal plasmonics, graphene photonics and nonlinear optics.

Kim, Minsu, Ph.D., University of Illinois at Urbana-Champaign, 2008. *Biophysics, Nonlinear Dynamics and Complex Systems, Systems Science/Engineering*. Experimental Biophysics. Quantitative systems biology; Single cell microbiology. Advanced biophysical and conventional microbial techniques to characterize biological processes at the molecular and cellular levels. Interdisciplinary research at the intersection of physics, microbiology, synthetic biology, and theoretical biology.

Santos, Luiz, Ph.D., Harvard University, 2012. *Condensed Matter Physics, Strongly Correlated Phenomena, Topological Phases of Matter, Theoretical Physics*. Theoretical condensed matter physics, emergent phenomena in strongly correlated systems, topological excitations and topological field theories. *Condensed Matter Physics, Nonlinear Dynamics and Com-*

plex Systems, Solid State Physics, Theoretical Physics. Condensed Matter Physics, Solid State Physic; strongly correlated systems, and topological phases of matter.

Srivastava, Ajit, Ph.D., Rice University, 2009. *Electromagnetism, Nonlinear Dynamics and Complex Systems, Optics, Quantum Foundations, Solid State Physics, Surface Physics.* Condensed matter physics, quantum optics, strong light-matter interactions, physics of atomically thin 2D materials, role of geometry and topology in low-dimensions, Berry phase and artificial gauge fields, open systems.

Vega, Nic, Ph.D., Boston University, 2013. Assistant Professor of Biology. *Biophysics, Medical, Health Physics.* Experimental Biophysics: The ecology of the microbes and microbial communities that live with eukaryotic hosts, such as the worm C. elegans. PhD 2013, Boston U.

Weissman, Daniel, Ph.D., Stanford University, 2010. *Biophysics, Nonlinear Dynamics and Complex Systems, Statistical & Thermal Physics, Theoretical Physics.* Theoretical physics, evolution, population dynamics, and analysis of genomic data. Build and analyze models of biological populations to predict their future evolution, translation of sequence data into evolutionary predictions.

DEPARTMENTAL RESEARCH SPECIALTIES AND STAFF

Theoretical

Biophysics. Theoretical systems biology. Understanding how biological systems, such as cells, organisms, and populations, learn from their surrounding environment and respond to it ("biological information processing"). Complex phenomena as evolution, sensory processes, animal behavior, human cognition. Berman, Kim, Nemenman, Vega, Weissman.

Computational Physics. Computational biophysics; Simulations of disordered materials and growth processes; Multiscale simulations; Optimization. Berman, Boettcher, Nemenman.

Condensed Matter Physics. Quantum and soft matter materials. Boettcher, Santos, Srivastava.

Nonlinear Dynamics and Complex Systems. Nonlinear dynamics; Complex materials; Criticality, self-organization, and emergence. Berman, Boettcher, Burton, Santos, Srivastava, Weeks, Weissman.

Statistical & Thermal Physics. Glassy and disordered systems; Nonlinear dynamics; Networks and information processing;

Evolutionary processes; Nonequilibrium phenomena; Self-organization and emergence. Berman, Boettcher, Nemenman, Weissman.

Experimental

Biophysics. Molecular biophysics; Cellular biophysics; Experimental systems and populations biophysics. We investigate how structure and dynamics at the molecular and cellular level contributes to the observed function of biological systems (proteins, nucleic acids, biological cells) and bio-inspired artificial systems. We probe spatial scales from bond lengths (0.1 nm) to cells (micrometers), and study dynamics on time scales corresponding to fast collisions of reactants (nanoseconds) to intracellular fluxes (seconds or greater). Berland, Finzi, Kim, Vega, Warncke.

Condensed Matter Physics. Photonics, magnonics, and light-matter interactions; Spintronics, electronic and magnetic properties of surfaces and nanostructures, nonlinear dynamics in nanomagnetic systems, and strongly correlated materials. Optical phenomena of nanoscale materials, quantum optics, strong light-matter interactions, physics of atomically thin 2D materials, role of geometry and topology. Harutyunyan, Roth, Srivastava, Urazhdin.

Fluids, Rheology. Dynamics of fluid and granular flow; Polymers; Friction; Self-organization and pattern formation. Experimental and theoretical studies of far-from-equilibrium systems with complex interactions and emergent behavior over many different length and time scales. Burton, Roth, Weeks.

Materials for Energy. Bio-inspired solar energy conversion; Polymer materials; Photophysics. Harutyunyan, Roth, Srivastava, Warncke.

Nano Science and Technology. Nanomaterials; Surfaces and interfaces; Polymers. Investigates new physical phenomena that emerge in nanoscale systems, at surfaces and interfaces of materials with different physical properties. The overarching goal is to develop fundamental understanding of the effects of confinement, interfaces, the resulting emerging interactions, and strongly nonequilibrium physical states that become possible to achieve only at nanoscale. Burton, Harutyunyan, Roth, Srivastava, Urazhdin.

Soft Matter Physics. Soft matter: fluids, polymers, colloids, granular materials. Glasses and non-equilibrium materials; dynamics and structure. Interfacial interactions and boundary conditions. Burton, Roth, Warncke, Weeks.

View additional information about this department at www.gradschoolshopper.com. Check out the "Why Choose Us?" section, find out more about the department's culture and get links to social media networks.

GEORGIA INSTITUTE OF TECHNOLOGY

SCHOOL OF PHYSICS

Atlanta, Georgia 30332-0430
http://www.physics.gatech.edu

General University Information
President: G. P. Peterson
Dean of Graduate School: Rafael Bras
University website: http://www.gatech.edu
School Type: Public
Setting: Urban
Total Faculty: 1,163
Total Graduate Faculty: 923
Total number of Students: 26,839
Total number of Graduate Students: 11,350

Department Information
Department Chairman: Prof. Pablo Laguna, Chair
Department Contact: James Sowell, Graduate Recruiter
Total full-time faculty: 43
Total number of full-time equivalent positions: 43
Full-Time Graduate Students: 140
Female Full-Time Graduate Students: 32
First-Year Graduate Students: 19
Female First-Year Students: 8
Total Post Doctorates: 23

Department Address
837 State Street
Atlanta, GA 30332-0430
Phone: (404) 894-5200
Fax: (404) 894-9958
E-mail: jim.sowell@physics.gatech.edu
Website: http://www.physics.gatech.edu

ADMISSIONS

Admission Contact Information
Address admission inquiries to: Graduate Recruiter, School of Physics
Phone: (404) 385-1294
E-mail: jim.sowell@physics.gatech.edu
Admissions website: http://www.physics.gatech.edu/graduate-program

Application deadlines
Fall admission:
U.S. students: January 1   *Int'l. students*: January 1

Application fee
U.S. students: $75   *Int'l. students*: $85

Admissions information
For Fall of 2018:
Number of applicants: 260
Number admitted: 48
Number enrolled: 16

Admission requirements
Bachelor's degree requirements: Bachelor's degree in Physics is preferred, with a minimum undergraduate GPA of 3.0 preferred for the M.S. program and 3.5 for the Ph.D. program.
Minimum undergraduate GPA: 3.5

GRE requirements
The GRE is required.
Quantitative score: 155
Verbal score: 153
Analytical score: 3.0

Subjective GRE requirements
The Subjective GRE is recommended.
Minimum accepted Advanced GRE score: 640
GRE Physics test is Required for International Students. It is Optional for US students.

TOEFL requirements
The TOEFL exam is required for students from non-English-speaking countries.
iBT score: 106

Other admissions information
Undergraduate preparation assumed: Classical Mechanics, Thornton & Marion; Electrodynamics, Griffiths; Quantum Mechanics, Griffiths; Thermal Physics, Schroeder.

TUITION

Tuition year 2018–2019:
Tuition for in-state residents
Full-time students: $28,096 annual
Tuition for out-of-state residents
Full-time students: $48,894 annual
Credit hours per semester to be considered full-time: 12
Deferred tuition plan: No
Health insurance: Available at the cost of $664 per year.
Other academic fees: Students employed as Graduate Research or Teaching Assistants pay $25 per semester tuition plus $1100 fee per semester.
Academic term: Semester
Number of first-year students who received full tuition waivers: 15

Teaching Assistants, Research Assistants, and Fellowships
Number of first-year
Teaching Assistants: 15
Average stipend per academic year
Teaching Assistant: $25,068
Research Assistant: $25,068
All Ph.D. students receive financial support either as a Graduate Teaching Assistant or as a Graduate Research Assistant.

FINANCIAL AID

Loans
Loans are not available for U.S. students.
Loans are not available for international students.
GAPSFAS application required: No
FAFSA application required: No

For further information
Address financial aid inquiries to: https://finaid.gatech.edu/contacting-our-office.
Financial aid website: https://finaid.gatech.edu

HOUSING

Availability of on-campus housing
Single students: Yes
Married students: Yes
Childcare Assistance: No

For further information
Address housing inquiries to: Housing Office.
Phone: 404-894-2470
E-mail: information@housing.gatech.edu
Housing aid website: http://www.housing.gatech.edu

Table A—Faculty, Enrollments, and Degrees Granted

Research Specialty	2017–2018 Faculty	Enrollment Fall 2018 Master's	Enrollment Fall 2018 Doctorate	Number of Degrees Granted 2017–18 (2013–18) Master's	Number of Degrees Granted 2017–18 (2013–18) Terminal Master's	Number of Degrees Granted 2017–18 (2013–18) Doctorate
Astrophysics	9	–	18	–	–	5(12)
Atomic, Molecular, & Optical Physics	6	–	22	–	–	–(11)
Biophysics	6	–	23	–	–	–(9)
Condensed Matter Physics	13	–	22	–	–	5(28)
Nonlinear Dynamics and Complex Systems	5	–	18	–	–	2(9)
Soft Matter	4	–	15	–	–	2(3)
Non-specialized	–	3	22	1(3)	–	3(10)
Total	**43**	**3**	**140**	**1(3)**	**–**	**17(82)**
Full-time Grad. Stud.	–	–	140	–	–	–
First-year Grad. Stud.	–	3	16	–	–	–

GRADUATE DEGREE REQUIREMENTS

Master's: Thirty semester hours are required. Thesis is optional; 2.7 GPA is required. One-year residency required. No language requirement.

Doctorate: The number of credit hours is not stipulated except 9 hours in minor with 2.9 GPA required. One-year residency required. No comprehensive examination. Thesis and thesis examination are required.

Thesis: Thesis may be written in absentia.

SPECIAL EQUIPMENT, FACILITIES, OR PROGRAMS

Research programs are described at: http://www.physics.gatech.edu.

Table B—Separately Budgeted Research Expenditures by Source of Support

Source of Support	Departmental Research	Physics-related Research Outside Department
Federal government	$5,366,977	
State/local government	$90,348	
Non-profit organizations	$73,275	
Business and industry		
Other	$33,765	
Total	**$5,564,365**	

Table C—Separately Budgeted Research Expenditures by Research Specialty

Research Specialty	No. of Grants	Expenditures ($)
Astrophysics	19	$1,383,748
Atomic, Molecular, & Optical Physics	8	$689,842
Physics of Living Systems	36	$1,974,894
Condensed Matter Physics	25	$877,978
Nonlinear Dynamics and Complex Systems	12	$450,013
Soft Matter	11	$187,950
Total	**111**	**$5,564,425**

FACULTY

Professor

Cadonati, Laura, Ph.D., Princeton University, 2001. *Astrophysics*. Gravitational wave detection, Gravitational wave astrophysics, Multi-messenger astrophysics.

Chapman, Michael S., Ph.D., Massachusetts Institute of Technology, 1995. *Atomic, Molecular, & Optical Physics*. Experimental quantum optics, Atomic physics.

Conrad, Edward H., Ph.D., University of Wisconsin-Madison, 1983. *Condensed Matter Physics*. Experimental surface physics.

Cvitanović, Predrag, Ph.D., Cornell University, 1973. Glen P. Robinson Chair in Nonlinear Sciences. *Nonlinear Dynamics and Complex Systems*. Nonlinear dynamics.

de Heer, Walter A., Ph.D., University of California, 1984. Regents' Professor. *Condensed Matter Physics*. Experimental condensed matter physics, magnetic and electronic properties of clusters, carbon nanostructures.

Fenton, Flavio, Ph.D., Northeastern University, 1999. *Biophysics*. Nonlinear dynamics, physics of the heart, computational biology, complex systems.

First, Phillip, Ph.D., University of Illinois at Urbana-Champaign, 1988. *Condensed Matter Physics*. Surface and interface physics, materials physics.

Goldman, Daniel I., Ph.D., University of Texas, Austin, 2002. Dunn Professor. *Biophysics*. Experimental biophysics, nonlinear dynamics.

Grigoriev, Roman, Ph.D., California Institute of Technology, 1998. *Nonlinear Dynamics and Complex Systems*. Fluid dynamics, Cardiac arrhythmias, Pattern formation and control.

Kennedy, T. A. Brian, Ph.D., Queen's Belfast University, 1986. Associate Chair for Undergraduate Program. *Atomic, Molecular, & Optical Physics*. Locomotion biomechanics, Robophysics, Soft condensed matter physics.

Laguna, Pablo, Ph.D., University of Texas, Austin, 1987. Chair of the School of Physics. *Astrophysics, Computer Science, Relativity & Gravitation*. Numerical relativity, Gravity wave astrophysics, Computational astrophysics.

Landman, Uzi, Ph.D., Haifa, 1969. F.E. Callaway Chair in Computational Materials Science; Regents' and Institute Professor; Director, Center for Computational Materials Science. *Condensed Matter Physics*. Theoretical condensed matter physics; computational physics.

Sá de Melo, Carlos, Ph.D., Stanford University, 1991. *Condensed Matter Physics*. Theoretical condensed matter physics.

Schatz, Michael F., Ph.D., University of Texas, 1991. Associate Chair for Introductory Physics. *Nonlinear Dynamics and Complex Systems, Statistical & Thermal Physics*. Experimental nonlinear dynamics, fluid dynamics.

Shoemaker, Deirdre, Ph.D., University of Texas, Austin, 1999. Dunn Professor. *Astrophysics*. Gravitational wave astrophysics, Numerical relativity, computational astrophysics.

Silva, Carlos, Ph.D., University of Minnesota, 1983. Professor in School of Chemistry & Biochemistry. *Condensed Matter Physics.*

Trebino, Rick, Ph.D., Stanford University, 1983. Georgia Research-Alliance Scholar Chair. *Atomic, Molecular, & Optical Physics.* Ultrafast optics.

Uzer, Turgay, Ph.D., Harvard University, 1979. Regents' Professor. *Atomic, Molecular, & Optical Physics, Statistical & Thermal Physics.* Theoretical, molecular, and chemical physics, nonlinear dynamics.

Wiesenfeld, Kurt, Ph.D., University of California, Berkeley, 1985. *Nonlinear Dynamics and Complex Systems.* Statistical mechanics, Physics of Living Systems.

Zangwill, Andrew, Ph.D., University of Pennsylvania, 1981. *Condensed Matter Physics.* History of physics.

Associate Professor

Ballantyne, David R., Ph.D., University of Cambridge, 2002. Associate Chair for Graduate Studies. *Astrophysics.* High-energy astrophysics, Active galactic nuclei, Accretion physics.

Bogdanovic, Tamara, Ph.D., Pennsylvania State University, 2006. *Astrophysics.* Black hole astrophysics, Active galactic nuclei, Theoretical and computational astrophysics.

Curtis, Jennifer E., Ph.D., University of Chicago, 2002. Co-Director of Community for Research on Active Surfaces and Interfaces (CRASI). *Biophysics, Fluids, Rheology.* Cell adhesion and migration, Glycobiophysics, Microbial Dynamics.

Davidovic, Dragomir, Ph.D., Johns Hopkins University, 1996. *Condensed Matter Physics.* Mesoscopics and low-temperature physics.

Fernandez de las Nieves, Alberto, Ph.D., University of Granada, 2000. Dunn Family Assistant Professor. *Other.* Soft condensed matter physics.

Gumbart, James, Ph.D., University of Illinois, 2009. *Biophysics.* Molecular dynamics, proteins, and bacteria.

Jiang, Zhigang, Ph.D., Northwestern University, 2005. *Condensed Matter Physics.* Experimental condensed matter physics.

Kim, Harold, Ph.D., Stanford University, 2004. *Biophysics.* Experimental biophysics.

Kindermann, Markus, Ph.D., Universiteit Leiden, 2003. *Condensed Matter Physics.* Nanoscale physics, Two-dimensional materials, Quantum information.

Otte, Nepomuk, Ph.D., Max Planck Institute, 2007. *Astrophysics.* Gamma-ray astrophysics.

Pustilnik, Michael, Ph.D., Bar-Ilan University, 1997. *Condensed Matter Physics, Statistical & Thermal Physics.* Theoretical condensed matter.

Raman, Chandra, Ph.D., University of Michigan, 1997. *Atomic, Molecular, & Optical Physics.* Experimental atomic physics.

Taboada, Ignacio, Ph.D., University of Pennsylvania, 2002. *Astrophysics.* High-energy neutrino astrophysics, Very-high-energy gamma ray astrophysics.

Tan, Shina, Ph.D., University of Chicago, 2006. *Atomic, Molecular, & Optical Physics, Condensed Matter Physics.* Theoretical atomic and condensed matter physics.

Wise, John H., Ph.D., Stanford University, 2007. Dunn Family Associate Professor. *Astrophysics.* Computational astrophysics, Galaxy formation.

Assistant Professor

Li, Gongjie, Ph.D., Harvard University, 2015. *Astrophysics.* Galactic center dynamics, Planetary formation and evolution, Solar System dynamics.

Maldovan, Martin, Ph.D., Massachusetts Institute of Technology. Assistant Professor in School of Chemical & Biomolecular Engineering. *Condensed Matter Physics.* Chemical Physics, Chemical engineering and physics.

Matsumoto, Elisabetta, Ph.D., University of Pennsylvania, 2011. *Other.* Soft condensed matter physics.

Mourigal, Martin, Ph.D., Ecole Polytechnique Federal de Lausanne, 2011. *Condensed Matter Physics.* Quantum materials, Neutron scattering.

Parker, Colin V., Ph.D., Princeton University, 2011. *Atomic, Molecular, & Optical Physics.* Condensed matter physics.

Rocklin, D. Zeb, Ph.D., University of Illinois, Urbana-Champaign, 2013. *Other.* Soft condensed matter physics.

Sponberg, Simon, Ph.D., University of California at Berkeley, 2008. Assistant Professor in School of Biological Sciences. *Biophysics.* Physics of Living Systems.

Yunker, Peter J., Ph.D., University of Pennsylvania, 2012. *Other.* Soft condensed matter physics.

Professor Emeritus

Chou, Mei-Yin, Ph.D., University of California, Berkeley, 1986. *Condensed Matter Physics.*

Gole, James L., Ph.D., Rice University, 1971. *Condensed Matter Physics, Materials Science, Metallurgy.*

Adjunct Faculty

Amini, Jason, Ph.D., University of California, Berkeley, 2006.

Bréchignac, Catherine, Ph.D., University of Paris-Sud, Orsay, 1977. *Atomic, Molecular, & Optical Physics, Condensed Matter Physics, Nano Science and Technology.*

Brown, Kenton, Ph.D., University of Maryland, 2005. Quantum information systems.

Hu, David, Ph.D., Massachusetts Institute of Technology, 2005. *Biophysics.*

Kokkotas, Kostas, Ph.D., Thessalonike, 1988. *Astrophysics, Relativity & Gravitation.* Gravity wave astrophysics.

Orlando, Thomas, Ph.D., Stony Brook University, 1988. *Chemical Physics.* Experimental physical, analytical, and materials chemistry.

Wartell, Roger, Ph.D., University of Rochester, 1971. *Biophysics.* Experimental biophysics.

Weitz, Joshua, Ph.D., Massachusetts Institute of Technology, 2003. *Biophysics.* Theoretical biophysics.

Zhu, Cheng, Ph.D., Columbia University, 1988. *Biophysics.* Biophysics.

Professor of the Practice

Berger, Claire, Ph.D., University Joseph Fourier, Grenoble, 1987. *Condensed Matter Physics.* Experimental condensed matter physics, Graphene.

Senior Research Scientist

Gao, Jianping, Ph.D., Brown University, 1989. *Condensed Matter Physics.* Theoretical condensed matter physics.

Luedtke, William D., Ph.D., Georgia Institute of Technology, 1984. *Condensed Matter Physics.* Theoretical condensed matter physics.

Yannouleas, C., Ph.D., University of Maryland, 1982. *Condensed Matter Physics, Nuclear Physics.* Theoretical condensed matter physics; theoretical nuclear physics.

Research Scientist

Ruan, Wen-Ying, Ph.D., Zhongshan University, 1992. *Condensed Matter Physics.* Theoretical condensed matter physics.

Yoon, Bokwon, Ph.D., University of Paris-Sud, Orsay, 1997. *Condensed Matter Physics.* Theoretical condensed matter physics.

Senior Academic Professional

Scherbakov, Andrew, Ph.D., Georgia Institute of Technology, 1997. *Condensed Matter Physics, Other.* Mesoscopic physics.

Sowell, James, Ph.D., University of Michigan, 1986. *Astronomy.* Stellar astronomy.

Academic Professional

Darnton, Nicholas, Ph.D., Princeton University, 2002. *Astrophysics, Other.* Physics education.

Greco, Edwin, Ph.D., Georgia Institute of Technology, 2008. *Nonlinear Dynamics and Complex Systems, Physics and other Science Education.* Physics education.

Jarrio, Marty, Ph.D., Georgia Institute of Technology, 1996. *Nuclear Physics, Other.* Physics education.

Murray, Eric, Ph.D., Cornell University, 1992. *Materials Science, Metallurgy, Other.* Physics education.

DEPARTMENTAL RESEARCH SPECIALTIES AND STAFF

Theoretical

Astrophysics. General relativity; gravitational wave patterns; gravitational interactions of compact binaries; theoretical and phenomenological astrophysics; galaxy and black hole evolution; high-energy particle astrophysics; accretion disks; numerical relativity; cosmology; gravitating systems; black holes; galaxy and black hole evolution; high-energy particle astrophysics; accretion disks; gravitational physics. Ballantyne, Bogdanovic, Laguna, Li, Shoemaker, Wise.

Atomic, Molecular, & Optical Physics. Three-body recombination; antihydrogen formation; cold collisions; collisional Stark mixing; Rydberg plasmas; classical-quantal correspondences; atomic Fermi gas transport; optical lattices; spin squeezing of atomic ensembles; Bose-Einstein condensate mixtures; quantum fluctuations; spatial solitary waves; nonlinear optical parametric processes; Rydberg atoms; light/matter interactions. Kennedy, Raman, Trebino, Uzer.

Biophysics. Energy transduction; chemiosmosis; noise; protein biosynthesis; energy metabolism; ion channel fluctuations; molecular motors; Hodgkin-Huxley equations; chemomechanical energy conversion; energy driven rectification of Brownian motion; quantum mutations in DNA. Curtis, Fenton, Goldman, Gumbart, Kim, Orlando, Sponberg, Wartell, Weitz, Wiesenfeld, Yunker, Zhu.

Condensed Matter Physics. Nanoscience; phase transitions; mesoscopic physics; quantum interference effects; superconductors in high magnetic fields; Bose-Einstein superconductivity; macroscopic quantum phenomena; ferroelectrics; Sutherland-Calogero models; ferromagnets; spintronics; semiconductor quantum dots. Chou, Fernandez de las Nieves, Kindermann, Landman, Pustilnik, Sá de Melo.

Nonlinear Dynamics and Complex Systems. Molecular fluctuations; chaotic dynamics; quantum chaos; Husimi-Wigner wave packets; Lyapunov exponent; Rydberg states; trajectory analysis; massively coupled oscillators; chemical reaction dynamics; Hamiltonian flows. Cvitanović, Grigoriev, Uzer, Wiesenfeld.

Soft Matter. Fernandez de las Nieves, Matsumoto, Rocklin, Yunker.

Experimental

Astrophysics. Neutrino and gamma-ray astrophysics; gravity wave detection. Ballantyne, Cadonati, Otte, Taboada.

Atomic, Molecular, & Optical Physics. Fundamental properties of ultra-cold condensed gases; atom trapping; multi-atom entanglement; cavity QED; laser Raman and Brillouin scattering; chemical biosensors; photovoltaic devices; quantum memory; ultrafast optics. Chapman, Parker, Raman, Trebino.

Biophysics. Morphogenesis, noise; "g-jitter"; thin organic films; nanotribology; gene expression; biomechanics. Curtis, Fenton, Goldman, Gumbart, Kim, Sponberg, Zhu.

Condensed Matter Physics. Nanoscience; soft matter; scanning tunneling microscopy; high-resolution X-ray scattering; magnetic heterostructures; graphene; Josephson tunneling; molecular clusters; thin-film magnetism; semiconductor nanostructures; atomic force microscopes; friction; nanowires; spintronics; liquid crystals; colloids. Conrad, Davidovic, de Heer, Fernandez de las Nieves, First, Jiang, Mourigal, Yunker.

Nonlinear Dynamics and Complex Systems. Spatiotemporal chaos; control/exploitation of chaos; pattern formation in fluids; weather-in-a-box; spontaneous and manipulated patterns; fluid instabilities; coupled mechanical oscillators; granular matter. Fenton, Goldman, Schatz.

Soft Matter. Fernandez de las Nieves, Matsumoto, Rocklin, Yunker.

View additional information about this department at www.gradschoolshopper.com. *Check out the "Why Choose Us?" section, find out more about the department's culture and get links to social media networks.*

GEORGIA STATE UNIVERSITY

DEPARTMENT OF PHYSICS AND ASTRONOMY

Atlanta, Georgia 30303
http://www.phy-astr.gsu.edu

General University Information
President: Mark P. Becker
Dean of Graduate School: Binghe Wang, Associate Dean for Research and Graduate Studies
University website: http://www.gsu.edu
School Type: Public
Setting: Urban
Total Faculty: 1,886
Total Graduate Faculty: 1,100
Total number of Students: 32,000
Total number of Graduate Students: 8,100

Department Information
Department Chairman: Prof. Sebastien Lepine, Chair
Department Contact: Dr. Sebastien Lepine, Chair
  Total full-time faculty: 31
  Total number of full-time equivalent positions: 31
  Full-Time Graduate Students: 78
  Female Full-Time Graduate Students: 35
  First-Year Graduate Students: 16
  Female First-Year Students: 8
  Total Post Doctorates: 14

Department Address
25 Park Place
Suite 605
Atlanta, GA 30303
Phone: (404) 413-6020
Fax: (404) 413-5481
E-mail: slepine@phy-astr.gsu.edu
Website: http://www.phy-astr.gsu.edu

ADMISSIONS

Admission Contact Information
Address admission inquiries to: Dr. Murad Sarsour, Director of Physics Graduate Program, msar@gsu.edu; Dr. Russel White, Director of Astronomy Graduate Program, white@astro.gsu.edu; Department of Physics and Astronomy, Georgia State University, P.O. Box 5060, Atlanta, GA 30302-5060
Phone: 404-413-6033
E-mail: msar@gsu.edu
Admissions website: http://cas.gsu.edu/graduate-studies/admissions/

Application deadlines
Fall admission:
U.S. students: July 1   *Int'l. students*: February 15

Application fee
U.S. students: $50   *Int'l. students*: $50
Above deadlines are for physics. All astronomy deadlines are 1/15/2019 https://cas.gsu.edu/graduate-services/admissions/graduate-admissions-college-requirements/

Admissions information
For Fall of 2017:
  Number of applicants: 80
  Number admitted: 35
  Number enrolled: 18

Admission requirements
Bachelor's degree requirements: B.S. in Physics or related field.

GRE requirements
The GRE is required.
No set minimum score.

Subjective GRE requirements
The Subjective GRE is recommended.
The Physics GRE is not needed for astronomy. The Physics GRE is recommended for physics. There is no set minimum score.

TOEFL requirements
The TOEFL exam is required for students from non-English-speaking countries.
PBT score: 550
iBT score: 80

Other admissions information
Additional requirements: The GRE general test is required for admission.
  Admission is based on the applicant's undergraduate record, GRE scores and recommendations.
  Georgia State University, a unit of the University System of Georgia, is an equal opportunity/affirmative action educational institution.
Undergraduate preparation assumed: Eisberg and Resnick, Quantum Physics: Griffiths, Introduction to Electrodynamics; Mand1, Statistical Physics; Kreyszig, Advanced Engineering Mathematics; Fowles, Analytic Mechanics.

TUITION

Tuition year 2018–19:
Tuition for in-state residents
  Full-time students: $5,648 per semester
  Part-time students: $694.01 per credit
Tuition for out-of-state residents
  Full-time students: $15,975 per semester
  Part-time students: $1,555.01 per credit
Tuition waived for students with assistantships or fellowships, which are awarded to nearly all full-time Ph.D. students.
Credit hours per semester to be considered full-time: 12
Deferred tuition plan: No
Health insurance: Yes, $1525.00.
Other academic fees: $1,064.00 per semester (not covered by assistantship).
Academic term: Semester
Number of first-year students who received full tuition waivers: 15

Teaching Assistants, Research Assistants, and Fellowships
Number of first-year
  Teaching Assistants: 17
Average stipend per academic year
  Teaching Assistant: $20,000

FINANCIAL AID

Application deadlines
Fall admission:
U.S. students: July 1   *Int'l. students*: February 8

Loans
Loans are available for U.S. students.
Loans are not available for international students.
GAPSFAS application required: No
FAFSA application required: Yes

For further information
Address financial aid inquiries to: Dr. M.Sarsour, Director of
Physics Graduate Program, or Dr. R. White, Director of As-
tronomy Graduate Program; Department of Physics and As-
tronomy, Georgia State University, P.O. Box 5060, Atlanta,
GA 30302-5060.
Phone: 404-413-6033
E-mail: msar@gsu.edu
Financial aid website: http://sfs.gsu.edu/

HOUSING

Availability of on-campus housing
Single students: Yes
Married students: Yes
Childcare Assistance: No

For further information
Address housing inquiries to: University Housing, Georgia State
University, Suite 110, 75 Piedmont Avenue, Atlanta, GA
30303.
Phone: 404-413-1800
E-mail: housing@gsu.edu
Housing aid website: http://myhousing.gsu.edu

Table A—Faculty, Enrollments, and Degrees Granted

Research Specialty	2015–16 Faculty	Enrollment Fall 2015 Master's	Enrollment Fall 2015 Doctorate	Number of Degrees Granted 2015–16 Master's	Number of Degrees Granted 2015–16 Terminal Master's	Number of Degrees Granted 2015–16 Doctorate
Astronomy	10	–	31	–	–	6
Atomic, Molecular, & Optical Physics	1	–	3	–	–	–
Biophysics	1	1	2	–	–	–
Condensed Matter Physics	7	–	28	–	–	2
Neuroscience/Neuro Physics	1	–	5	–	–	2
Nuclear Physics	3	–	6	–	1	2
Physics and other Science Education	2	1	3	–	1	–
Total	25	2	74	–	2	12
Full-time Grad. Stud.	–	2	78	–	–	–
First-year Grad. Stud.	–	2	16	–	–	–

GRADUATE DEGREE REQUIREMENTS

Master's: M.S. students must complete a minimum of 24 semester hours of course work. M.S. students must either complete
an acceptable thesis or complete 6 additional hours of course
work.

Doctorate: The Ph.D. degrees each require a minimum of 71
semester hours (beyond the B.S.). Students must complete and
defend an acceptable dissertation in physics or astronomy.
Qualifying exams are also required.

Thesis: Thesis may not be written in absentia.

SPECIAL EQUIPMENT, FACILITIES, OR PROGRAMS

Research in the department currently is supported by the National
Science Foundation, the Department of Energy, the National Institutes of Health, the Department of Defense, the National Aero-
nautics and Space Administration, the U.S. Army, Navy, and Air-
force.

Research apparatus within the department includes the following:

X- and K-band EPR/ENDOR spectrometers, X-ray diffraction apparatus,apparatus for studies at cryogenic temperatures, several
CO_2 and Nd:YAG lasers, five FTIR spectrometers with accessories for nanosecond time resolved infrared spectroscopy and infrared microscopic imaging, a nanosecond transient absorption
spectrometer, steady-state and time resolved photoluminescence
spectrometer, a nano-infrared imaging system, a Raman spectrometer, a high-resolution absorption spectrometer, a high-
power, frequency agile laser system (200 nm–3000 nm) utilized
in a variety of gas phase and materials characterization techniques, ultrahigh-vacuum surface science apparatus including
high-resolution electron energy loss spectrometer, Auger electron
spectrometer, and low-energy electron diffraction apparatus.

Nuclear researchers use the particle accelerators at Brookhaven
National Laboratories, FermiLab, and CERN's Large Hadron
Collider.

GSU's Center for High Angular Resolution Astronomy
(CHARA) research uses high-spatial resolution imaging techniques to attain image detail beyond that normally obtained with
large telescopes. CHARA's major project is the CHARA Array,
an optical and infrared interferometer at Mount Wilson Observatory in California. The CHARA Array consists of six telescopes
of 1-m aperture that form a Y-shaped figure with baselines from
30 to 330 m. It is currently the premier instrument of its kind
in the world for high angular resolution of stars and their environments.

GSU astronomers also have guaranteed observing time with the
Small and Medium Aperture Research Telescope System at the
Cerro Tololo InterAmerican Observatory in Chile and the Apache
Point Observatory 3.5-meter telescope in New Mexico.

GSU's Hard Labor Creek Observatory (HLCO) is located in a
state park 80 kilometers east of Atlanta. The principal telescopes
at HLCO are new, research-quality 20-inch and 24-inch telescopes.

Department facilities include networks of Linux-based computers
for data analysis and image processing, various PCs and Macs,
and high performance computers for data simulations and theoretical calculations and modeling.

Table B—Separately Budgeted Research Expenditures by Source of Support

Source of Support	Departmental Research	Physics-related Research Outside Department
Federal government	$4,097,862	$2,557,830
State/local government		
Non-profit organizations		
Business and industry		
Other	$52,000	
Total	$4,149,862	$2,557,830

FACULTY

Distinguished University Professor

Crenshaw, D. Michael, Ph.D., Ohio State University, 1985. Chair. *Astronomy, Astrophysics.* Supermassive black holes; active galactic nuclei.

Gies, Douglas R., Ph.D., University of Toronto, 1985. *Astronomy, Astrophysics.* Regents Professor; Be star phenomena; hot stars and stellar wind.

He, Xiaochun, Ph.D., University of Tennessee, 1991. Graduate Director of Physics. *Nuclear Physics, Particles and Fields.* High-energy nuclear physics.

Henry, Todd J., Ph.D., University of Arizona, 1991. *Astronomy, Astrophysics.* Nearby stars; stellar masses and life in the universe.

Manson, Steven T., Ph.D., Columbia University, 1966. Regents Professor. *Atomic, Molecular, & Optical Physics, Theoretical Physics.* Atomic and molecular structure and collisions.

Perera, A. G. Unil, Ph.D., University of Pittsburgh, 1987. Regents Professor. *Condensed Matter Physics, Nano Science and Technology, Optics, Surface Physics.* Condensed matter; semiconductor optoelectonics; nanosensors.

Stockman, Mark I., Ph.D., Novosibirsk, 1989. *Condensed Matter Physics, Nano Science and Technology, Optics, Surface Physics, Theoretical Physics.* Theoretical physics; electronic and optical properties of disordered systems; kinetic and non-linear optical effects in semiconductors. Nanoplasmonics and nano-optics.

Professor

Apalkov, Vadym M., Ph.D., University of Utah, 1995. Condensed matter theory; disordered electronic systems; photonic crystals; quantum cascade lasers.

Dietz, Nikolaus, Ph.D., Technical University, Berlin, 1991. *Optics, Solid State Physics, Surface Physics.* Condensed matter physics.

Hastings, Gary, Ph.D., Imperial College, London (U.K.), 1992. Experimental biophysics; static and time resolved infrared spectroscopies applied to biological systems; experimental physics; energy and electron transfer in photosynthetic organisms.

Jefferies, Stuart M., Ph.D., University of London, 1983. *Astronomy, Astrophysics, Optics, Solar Physics.* Solar Physics, Optics, Instrumentation.

Mani, Ramesh, Ph.D., University of Maryland, 1990. Experimental condensed matter.

Martens, Petrus C., Ph.D., University of Utrecht, 1983. *Astronomy, Astrophysics, Solar Physics.* Solar physics; astroinformatics.

Associate Professor

Bentz, Misty C., Ph.D., Ohio State University, 2007. Active galaxies and quasars; black hole masses.

Dhamala, Mukesh, Ph.D., University of Kansas, 2000. Experimental biophysics; neuroimaging.

Lepine, Sebastien, Ph.D., University of Montreal, 1998. All-sky surveys; low-mass stars and brown dwarfs; galactic structure; extra-solar planets.

Sarsour, Murad, Ph.D., University of Houston, 2002. Experimental nuclear physics. Neutron weak interactions.

Thoms, Brian D., Ph.D., Cornell University, 1992. Physics education research.

White, Russel, Ph.D., University of California, Los Angeles, 1999. Star and planet formation; fundamental stellar properties.

Assistant Professor

Baron, Fabien, Ph.D., University of Paris, 2005. *Astronomy, Astrophysics.* Stellar astrophysics; interferometry.

Connors, Megan, Ph.D., Stony Brook University, 2011. *High Energy Physics, Nuclear Physics.* nuclear physics.

Kozhanov, Alexander, Ph.D., Moscow State University, 2006. Spintronics and Magnetism.

Lei, Sidong, Ph.D., Rice University, 2015. *Condensed Matter Physics, Nano Science and Technology.* Synthesis and characterization of low-dimensional materials.

Pratt, Jane, Ph.D., University of Texas at Austin, 2009. *Astronomy, Astrophysics, Solar Physics.* Computational modeling of magnetic fields in the Sun and other stars, magnetohydrodynamics, massively parellel computing.

Von Korff, Josh, Ph.D., University of California, Berkeley, 2010. Physics education research.

Emeritus

McAlister, Harold A., Ph.D., University of Virginia, 1975. Observational astronomy; binary stars; speckle and long-baseline interferometry.

Miller, H. Richard, Ph.D., University of Florida, 1970. High-energy astrophysics; variability of AGN.

Nave, Carl R., Ph.D., Georgia Institute of Technology, 1966. Experimental physics; molecular structure; magnetic resonance; acoustics.

Wingert, David W., Ph.D., Princeton University, 1974. Observational astronomy; theoretical astrophysics.

Adjunct Faculty

Williams, Michael D., Ph.D., Stanford University, 1987. Professor and Director of the Center of Excellence in Microelectronics and Photonics, Clark Atlanta University. *Condensed Matter Physics.* Materials Physics.

Adjunct Professor

Ferguson, Ian, Ph.D., University of St. Andrews, 1989. Dean, Engineering & Computing, Missouri S&T. *Optics, Solid State Physics, Surface Physics.* Condensed matter physics.

Kloppenborg, Brian, Ph.D., University of Denver, 2012. *Astronomy, Astrophysics.* Optical interferometry of stars and novae; high performance computing; GPU computing.

Raghavan, Deepak, Ph.D., Georgia State University, 2009. Stellar multiplicity.

Ridgway, Steven, Ph.D., Stony Brook University, 1972. Experimental infrared astronomy; high-resolution Fourier transform spectroscopy; imaging.

ten Brummelaar, Theo A., Ph.D., University of Sydney, 1993. Director of the CHARA Array. Optical propagation in a turbulent atmosphere; long-baseline optical stellar interferometry; observational astronomy.

Lecturer

Doluweera, Sumith, Ph.D., University of Cincinnati, 2008. *Physics and other Science Education.*

Evans, J., Ph.D., Georgia State University, 1998. *Physics and other Science Education.*

McGimsey, Ben, Ph.D., University of Florida, 1974. *Physics and other Science Education.*

Wang, Ruli, Ph.D., Georgia State University, 2005. *Physics and other Science Education.*

Research Scientist

Jao, Wei Chun, Ph.D., Georgia State University, 2004. *Astronomy, Astrophysics.* Astronomical measurement techniques, ancient stars.

Sturmann, Judit, Ph.D., Vanderbilt University, 1999. Astronomical instrumentation; optical long-baseline interferometry.

Sturmann, Laszlo, Ph.D., Vanderbilt University, 1997. Astronomical instrumentation; optical long-baseline interferometry.

Turner, Nils H., Ph.D., Georgia State University, 1998. Astronomical instrumentation, optical-long baseline interferometry.

Academic Professional

Wilson, John, Ph.D., Georgia State University, 2004. *Physics and other Science Education.*

DEPARTMENTAL RESEARCH SPECIALTIES AND STAFF

Theoretical

Atomic, Molecular, & Optical Physics. Atomic and molecular structure and collisions. Manson.

Condensed Matter Physics. Electronic and optical properties of disordered systems; kinetic, electrical, and transport phenomena in semiconductor devices, and optical effects in semiconductors, nano-plasmonics, nano-optics. Apalkov, Stockman.

Solar Physics. Computation of solar and stellar magnetic dynamos. Pratt.

Experimental

Astronomy. Active galaxies; quasi-stellar objects; supermassive black holes; galactic astronomy; stellar populations; stellar masses; exoplanets; astrobiology; astroinformatics; hot and cool stars; variable stars; star formation; binary stars; star formation; young stars, Be stars; long-baseline interferometry; solar physics; astroinformatics. Baron, Bentz, Crenshaw, Gies, Henry, Jao, Jefferies, Lepine, Martens, McAlister, McGimsey, Miller, Raghavan, Ridgway, Judit Sturmann, Laszlo Sturmann, ten Brummelaar, Turner, White, Wilson, Wingert.

Biophysics. Solar energy conversion in natural and artificial systems. Photosynthetic protein complexes. Hastings.

Condensed Matter Physics. Defects in solids, acoustical, linear, and nonlinear optical, electrical, and thermal properties of semiconductors; growth of III-N (high-pressure CVD) and waveguided, birefringent heterostructures (OMCVD; real-time growth diagnostics; optoelectronic semiconductor device applications. Dietz, Kozhanov, Lei, Mani, Perera, Thoms.

Neuroscience/Neuro Physics. Neuroimaging of the human brain. Dhamala.

Nuclear Physics. Studies of quark-gluon plasma in heavy-ion collisions at Brookhaven National Labs, proton spin structure. Connors, He, Sarsour.

Physics and other Science Education. Doluweera, Evans, Thoms, Von Korff, Wang, Wilson, Wingert.

Solar Physics. Jefferies, Martens.

View additional information about this department at www.gradschoolshopper.com. Check out the "Why Choose Us?" section, find out more about the department's culture and get links to social media networks.

DEPAUL UNIVERSITY

DEPARTMENT OF PHYSICS

Chicago, Illinois 60614

https://csh.depaul.edu/academics/physics/graduate/physics-ms/Pages/default.aspx

General University Information
President: A. Gabriel Esteban
Dean of Graduate School: NA
University website: http://www.depaul.edu
School Type: Private
Setting: Urban
Total Faculty: 1,842
Total number of Students: 23,110
Total number of Graduate Students: 7,703

Department Information
Department Chairman: Prof. Jesús Pando, Chair
Department Contact: Eric Landahl, Associate Professor & Graduate Director
  Total full-time faculty: 8
  Total number of full-time equivalent positions: 8
  Full-Time Graduate Students: 10
  Female Full-Time Graduate Students: 3
  First-Year Graduate Students: 5
  Female First-Year Students: 1

Department Address
2219 N. Kenmore Avenue
Byrne Hall 211
Chicago, IL 60614
Phone: (773) 325-7330
E-mail: elandahl@depaul.edu
Website: https://csh.depaul.edu/academics/physics/graduate/physics-ms/Pages/default.aspx

ADMISSIONS

Admission Contact Information
Address admission inquiries to: Dr. Eric Landahl, Department of Physics, DePaul University, 2219 N. Kenmore Avenue, Byrne Hall 211, Chicago, IL 60614-3504
Phone: (773) 325-3722
E-mail: elandahl@depaul.edu
Admissions website: http://csh.depaul.edu/departments/physics/Pages/graduate.aspx

Application deadlines
Fall admission:
U.S. students: May 1   *Int'l. students*: May 1

Application fee
U.S. students: $40   *Int'l. students*: $40
No fee waivers are available. All admissions are for Fall.

Admissions information
For Fall of 2018:
  Number of applicants: 18
  Number admitted: 6
  Number enrolled: 6

Admission requirements
Bachelor's degree requirements: Bachelor's degree in Physics, Mathematics, Chemistry, or Engineering is required.
Minimum undergraduate GPA: 2.5

GRE requirements
The GRE is required.
No minimum general GRE score.

Subjective GRE requirements
The Subjective GRE is not required.

TOEFL requirements
The TOEFL exam is required for students from non-English-speaking countries.
  iBT score: 96
A TOEFL minimum score of 96 is a firm requirement.

Other admissions information
Undergraduate preparation assumed: Tipler or Serway, General Physics; Tipler, Modern Physics; Fowles, Mechanics; Griffiths, Electricity and Magnetism; Schroeder, Thermal Physics; Boas, Mathematical Methods in The Physical Sciences; Griffiths, Quantum Mechanics.

TUITION

Tuition year 2017:
  Full-time students: $670 per credit
Credit hours per semester to be considered full-time: 8
Deferred tuition plan: No
Academic term: Quarter
Number of first-year students who received full tuition waivers: 4

Teaching Assistants, Research Assistants, and Fellowships
Number of first-year
  Teaching Assistants: 4
Average stipend per academic year
  Teaching Assistant: $11,500

FINANCIAL AID

Loans
Loans are available for U.S. students.
Loans are not available for international students.
GAPSFAS application required: No
FAFSA application required: Yes

For further information
Address financial aid inquiries to: Financial Aid Office, DePaul Center, Room 9100, 1 E. Jackson Blvd., Chicago, IL 60604-2287.
Phone: (312) 362-8610
E-mail: finaid1@depaul.edu
Financial aid website: http://www.depaul.edu/admission-and-aid/financial-aid/Pages/default.aspx

HOUSING

Availability of on-campus housing
Single students: No
Married students: No

For further information

Address housing inquiries to: Department of Housing Services, Centennial Hall, Suite 301, 2345 N. Shefield Ave., Chicago, IL 60614.

Phone: (773) 325-7196

Housing aid website: http://offices.depaul.edu/housing/Pages/default.aspx

Table A—Faculty, Enrollments, and Degrees Granted

Research Specialty	2017–2018 Faculty	Enrollment Fall 2017		Number of Degrees Granted 2016–17 (2008–16)		
		Mas-ter's	Doc-torate	Mas-ter's	Terminal Master's	Doc-torate
Astrophysics	2	2	–	–	–(7)	–
Biophysics	–	1	–	–	1(4)	–
Condensed Matter Physics	1	2	–	–	1(3)	–
Nonlinear Dynamics and Complex Systems	1	–	–	–	–(1)	–
Nuclear Physics	1	–	–	–	1(4)	–
Optics	1	2	–	–	–	–
Physics and other Science Education	1	1	–	–	–(2)	–
Total	7	8	–	–	3(21)	–
Full-time Grad. Stud.	–	8	–	–	–	–
First-year Grad. Stud.	–	4	–	–	–	–

GRADUATE DEGREE REQUIREMENTS

Master's: Twelve (four quarter hours each) courses, including thesis; minimum 2.75 grade point average on a scale of 4.0; no time residence requirement; no language requirement; oral thesis examination is required. Faculty expertise in astrophysics, biophysics, nonlinear dynamics, complex systems and computational physics, nuclear physics, fluids, laser physics, and condensed matter physics.

Thesis: Thesis may be written in absentia.

SPECIAL EQUIPMENT, FACILITIES, OR PROGRAMS

Ultrafast optics laboratory including a Titanium: Sapphire 20 fs laser oscillator and a Q-switched Nd: YAG laser; high-temperature furnaces (maximum T = 1500 C) with different gas environments; four-point electrical conductivity probe; thermopower setup; hydraulic press (maximum applied load = 11 metric tons).

Our faculty and graduate students are also users of several national scientific user facilities, including Argonne National Laboratory's Advanced Photon Source as well as the National Radio Astronomy Observatory.

Table B—Separately Budgeted Research Expenditures by Source of Support

Source of Support	Departmental Research	Physics-related Research Outside Department
Federal government	$20,000	
State/local government		
Non-profit organizations		
Business and industry		
Other		$40,000
Total	$20,000	$40,000

Table C—Separately Budgeted Research Expenditures by Research Specialty

Research Specialty	No. of Grants	Expenditures ($)
Astrophysics	1	$20,000
Condensed Matter Physics	1	$40,000
Total	2	$60,000

FACULTY

Professor

Beck-Winchatz, Bernhard, Ph.D., University of Washington. *Astronomy*.

Goedde, Christopher G., Ph.D., University of California, Berkeley, 1990. *Computational Physics, Nonlinear Dynamics and Complex Systems*. Nonlinear optics and dynamical systems; computational physics.

Associate Professor

Fischer, Susan M., Ph.D., University of Notre Dame, 1994. *Nuclear Physics, Physics and other Science Education*. Nuclear physics; gamma-ray spectroscopy. Physics education research.

González Avilés, Gabriela, Ph.D., Northwestern University, 2003. *Materials Science, Metallurgy*. Materials science.

Landahl, Eric, Ph.D., University of California, Davis, 2001. Graduate program director. *Accelerator, Biophysics, Condensed Matter Physics, Electrical Engineering, Medical, Health Physics, Optics, Solid State Physics*. Ultrafast physics, including several different areas of application.

Pando, Jesús, Ph.D., University of Arizona, 1997. Department Chair. *Astrophysics*. Astrophysics: cosmology and large-scale structure.

Sarma, Anuj, Ph.D., University of Kentucky, 2000. *Astronomy, Astrophysics*. Astrophysics: star formation and radio astronomy.

Assistant Professor

Kustusch, Mary Bridget, Ph.D., North Carolina State University, 2011. *Physics and other Science Education*. Physics education research.

Emeritus

Milton, John, M.S., Saint Louis University, 1960. Physics education.

Lecturer

Corso, George, Ph.D., Northwestern University, 1975. *Astronomy*. Astronomy.

DEPARTMENTAL RESEARCH SPECIALTIES AND STAFF

Theoretical
Astrophysics. Pando.
Computational Physics. Goedde.
Nonlinear Dynamics and Complex Systems. Goedde.

Experimental
Astronomy. Beck-Winchatz, Corso, Pando, Sarma.
Biophysics. Landahl, Pando.
Materials Science, Metallurgy. González Avilés, Landahl.
Nuclear Physics. Fischer.
Optics. Ultrafast lasers and applications. Time-resolved X-ray diffraction. Landahl.
Physics and other Science Education. Fischer, Kustusch.

ILLINOIS INSTITUTE OF TECHNOLOGY

PHYSICS

Chicago, Illinois 60616
https://science.iit.edu/physics/

General University Information
President: Alan Cramb
Dean of Graduate School: Christopher White
University website: http://www.iit.edu
School Type: Private
Setting: Urban
Total Faculty: 370
Total Graduate Faculty: 370
Total number of Students: 7,164
Total number of Graduate Students: 4,264

Department Information
Department Chairman: Prof. Grant Bunker, Chair
Department Contact: Grant Bunker, Chair
  Total full-time faculty: 20
  Total number of full-time equivalent positions: 20
  Full-Time Graduate Students: 43
  Female Full-Time Graduate Students: 13
  First-Year Graduate Students: 23
  Female First-Year Students: 7
  Total Post Doctorates: 12

Department Address
Robert A. Pritzker Science Center
3105 S. Dearborn St.
Chicago, IL 60616
Phone: 312.567.3579
Fax: 312.567.3494
E-mail: bunker@iit.edu
Website: https://science.iit.edu/physics/

ADMISSIONS

Admission Contact Information
Address admission inquiries to: Office of Graduate and Professional Enrollment, Illinois Institute of Technology, 10 W. 33rd Street, Perlstein Hall, Room 203, Chicago, IL 60616
Phone: (312) 567-3020
E-mail: gradstu@iit.edu
Admissions website: http://www.iit.edu/graduate_admission/

Application deadlines
Fall admission:
U.S. students: September 1   *Int'l. students*: September 1
Spring admission:
U.S. students: October 1   *Int'l. students*: November 1

Application fee
U.S. students: $50   *Int'l. students*: $50
Financial Considerations only apply to those who submit by Jan 31 2018. Professional Master's & Master of Science degrees have a deadline of Aug 1.

Admissions information
For Fall of 2018:
  Number of applicants: 63
  Number admitted: 29
  Number enrolled: 16

Admission requirements
Bachelor's degree requirements: Bachelor's degree in physics or engineering is required.
Minimum undergraduate GPA: 3.0

GRE requirements
The GRE is required.
  Quantitative score: 304
  Verbal score: 304
  Analytical score: 2.5
  Mean GRE score range (25th–75th percentile): 279-335

Subjective GRE requirements
The Subjective GRE is not required.

TOEFL requirements
The TOEFL exam is required for students from non-English-speaking countries.
  PBT score: 523
  iBT score: 70

Other admissions information
Undergraduate preparation assumed: 1–2 years General Physics–Ohanian; 1 year Mechanics–Marion; 1 year Modern Physics–Taylor; 1 year Electricity and Magnetism–Griffiths; Calculus and Differential Equations; 1 year Quantum Mechanics.

TUITION

Tuition year 2018–19:
  Full-time students: $1,530 per credit
  Part-time students: $1,470 per credit
Half tuition for recent grads. Discounted tuition for alumni.
Credit hours per semester to be considered full-time: 9
Deferred tuition plan: Yes
Health insurance: Yes, $1460.00.
Academic term: Semester

Teaching Assistants, Research Assistants, and Fellowships
  Number of first-year
    Teaching Assistants: 5
  Average stipend per academic year
    Teaching Assistant: $1,825

FINANCIAL AID

Application deadlines
Fall admission:
U.S. students: October 1
Spring admission:
U.S. students: October 1

Loans
Loans are available for U.S. students.
Loans are not available for international students.
GAPSFAS application required: No
FAFSA application required: No

For further information
Address financial aid inquiries to: Office of Financial Aid.
Phone: (312) 567-7219
E-mail: finaid@iit.edu
Financial aid website: http://www.iit.edu/financial_aid/

HOUSING

Availability of on-campus housing
Single students: Yes
Married students: Yes
Childcare Assistance: No
For further information
Address housing inquiries to: Residence and Greek Life.
Phone: (312) 567-5075
E-mail: housing@iit.edu
Housing aid website: http://www.iit.edu/housing/

Table A—Faculty, Enrollments, and Degrees Granted

Research Specialty	2017–18 Faculty	Enrollment Fall 2017		Number of Degrees Granted 2016–17 (2012–17)		
		Master's	Doctorate	Master's	Terminal Master's	Doctorate
Accelerator	3	8	14	8(8)	–	1(5)
Biophysics	2	–	3	–	–	–
Condensed Matter Physics	6	3	10	–(23)	–	2(14)
Medical, Health Physics	1	34	–	7(27)	–	–
Particles and Fields	4	2	7	2(4)	–	1(6)
Total	17	47	34	17(62)	–	4(25)
Full-time Grad. Stud.	–	14	29	–	–	–
First-year Grad. Stud.	–	18	3	–	–	–

GRADUATE DEGREE REQUIREMENTS

Master's: 32 semester hours including eight in thesis research (optional); M.S. comprehensive examination: minimum 3.0/4.0 GPA in approved course work; no foreign language requirements; no formal residency requirement.

Doctorate: 84 semester hours including 32 semester hours Ph.D. core courses and at least 32 semester hours in thesis research; passing Ph.D. qualifying and comprehensive examinations and oral thesis defense; minimum of two semesters in full-time resident study.

Other Degrees: Molecular Biochemistry and Biophysics: The department offers interdisciplinary programs leading to M.S. and Ph.D. degrees in molecular biochemistry and biophysics. Professional M.S. degrees. M.S. degrees in Health Physics as well as 4+1 M.S. degrees in Health Physics.

Thesis: Thesis may be written in absentia.

SPECIAL EQUIPMENT, FACILITIES, OR PROGRAMS

Laboratories for experimental research in synchrotron radiation research, super-conduction, condensed matter physics, thin films, and particle physics; campus facilities include x-ray diffraction facility, IIT Academic Computing Center and Galvin Library. Scanning probe microscopy, scanning electron microscopy, and XPS/Auger spectroscopy. Collaborative programs with Fermi National Accelerator Laboratory and Argonne National Laboratory.

Table B—Separately Budgeted Research Expenditures by Source of Support

Source of Support	Departmental Research	Physics-related Research Outside Department
Federal government	$3,150,156	
State/local government		
Non-profit organizations		
Business and industry		
Other		
Total	$3,150,156	

Table C—Separately Budgeted Research Expenditures by Research Specialty

Research Specialty	No. of Grants	Expenditures ($)
Accelerator	3	$781,579
Biophysics	1	$501,444
Condensed Matter Physics	3	$1,482,587
Particles and Fields	4	$384,546
Total	11	$3,150,156

FACULTY

Professor

Betts, Russell, Ph.D., University of Pennsylvania, 1972. Interim Provost, Nuclear Physics. *Condensed Matter Physics, Nuclear Physics*. Nuclear physics.

Bunker, Grant, Ph.D., University of Washington, 1984. Chair. Synchrotron radiation, x-ray spectroscopy, computational biophysics, condensed matter.

Irving, Thomas, Ph.D., University of Guelph, 1989. *Biophysics*. Biophysics of muscle contraction, non-crystalline x-ray diffraction, synchrotron radiation instrumentation.

Kaplan, Daniel, Ph.D., Stony Brook University, 1979. *Particles and Fields*. Experimental elementary particle physics.

Morrison, Timothy, Ph.D., University of Illinois, 1980. *Condensed Matter Physics*. Condensed Matter Physics.

Schieber, Jay, Ph.D., University of Wisconsin-Madison, 1989. Professor of Physics (Joint appointment Chemical Engineering and Applied Math. Kinetic theory of macromolecules, material science, soft condensed matter.

Segre, Carlo U., Ph.D., University of California, San Diego, 1981. *Condensed Matter Physics*. Condensed Matter Physics.

Spentzouris, Linda, Ph.D., Northwestern University, 1996. Accelerator and beam physics.

Sullivan, Zack, Ph.D., University of Illinois, 1998. *High Energy Physics*. Elementary particle theory.

Terry, Jeff, Ph.D., Stanford University, 1997. *Condensed Matter Physics*. Chemical physics with specialization in synchrotron radiation techniques.

White, Chris, Ph.D., University of Minnesota, 1990. *Particles and Fields*. Experimental elementary particle physics.

Zasadzinski, John, Ph.D., Iowa State University, 1979. *Condensed Matter Physics*. Solid state physics.

Associate Professor

Coffey, Liam, Ph.D., University of Chicago, 1985. *Condensed Matter Physics*. Condensed matter theory.

Gidalevitz, David, Ph.D., Weizmann Institute of Science, 1996. Membrane biophysics, biomaterials, biosensors and biomimetric thin films, and polymer films.

Howard, Andrew, Ph.D., University of California, San Diego, 1981. *Biophysics*. Macromolecular crystallography, methods development, synchrotron radiation.

Snopok, Pavel, Ph.D., Michigan State University, 2007. Particle beam physics.

Torun, Yagmur, Ph.D., Stony Brook University, 2000. *Particles and Fields*. Accelerator and experimental high energy physics.

Assistant Professor

Littlejohn, Bryce, Ph.D., University of Wisconsin-Madison, 2012. Experimental neutrino physics, nuclear reactor physics, applied neutrino physics for nuclear non-proliferation.

Wereszczynski, Jeff, Ph.D., University of Michigan, 2008. Biophysics.

Senior Lecturer

Chen, Shih-Yew, Ph.D., University of Illinois, 1978. Director, Professional Master's Health Physics Program. Health Physics, Nuclear Engineering.

Glodowski, Alan, M.S., Creighton University, 1990.

Laurent-Muehleisen, Sally, Ph.D., Pennsylvannia State University, 1996. Associate Chair. *Astrophysics*. Astrophysics.

Shylnov, Yurii, Ph.D., Kharkov State University, 1982.

DEPARTMENTAL RESEARCH SPECIALTIES AND STAFF

Theoretical

Condensed Matter Physics. Transport properties of semiconducting heterostructures and superlattices; transport in semiconductors in strong electric and magnetic fields, high temperature superconductivity. Coffey.

Particles and Fields. Analysis of unified electro-weak theory and quantum chromodynamics; exploring the features of new particles and new interactions high energies; accelerator physics. Sullivan.

Experimental

Accelerator. Neutrino oscillation, neutrino production in nuclear reactors, antineutrino production, muons. Littlejohn, Snopok, Spentzouris, Torun, White.

Biophysics. Protein structural biophysics as studied using synchrotron sources and x-ray laser; photophysics and photobiology at the molecular level; atomic level simulation; membrane structure. Gidalevitz, Wereszczynski.

Condensed Matter Physics. High temperature superconductivity; magnetism, valence phenomena; synchrotron radiation studies of materials; thermal and electrical properties of solids; amorphous alloys; EXAFS and XANES of materials; radiation damage at low temperatures; growth and properties of thin films; Structures of Complex materials using X-ray techniques: diffraction, scattering and spectroscopy. Materials of interest include catalysts, superconductors, oxygen permeable membranes. Bunker, Morrison, Segre, Terry, Zasadzinski.

Particles and Fields. Studies of quantum chromodynamics and production and decay of heavy quarks in experiments at Fermilab. Neutrino oscillations, charm CP violation, meson-antimeson mixing, and rare decays of charm, search for CP violation in hyperon decay. Investigation of techniques for high energy muon colliders and neutrino factories. Kaplan, Littlejohn, White.

View additional information about this department at www.gradschoolshopper.com. Check out the "Why Choose Us?" section, find out more about the department's culture and get links to social media networks.

Find the right graduate school program for you ...

by clicking on "GRE requirements" and sorting by "Minimum GRE Physics."

School name	Department	GRE required	GRE Physics required	Minimum GRE Physics
The Chinese Uni. of Hong Kong	Physics	No	Recommended	850
University of Southern California	Physics & Astronomy	Yes	Required	780
Boston University	Physics	Yes	Required	740
University of California, Berkeley	Physics	Yes	Required	730
Missouri Uni. of Science & Technology	Physics	Yes	Recommended	700

NORTHERN ILLINOIS UNIVERSITY

DEPARTMENT OF PHYSICS

DeKalb, Illinois 60115
http://www.physics.niu.edu/physics/

General University Information

President: Lisa Freeman (Acting President)
Dean of Graduate School: Bradley Bond
University website: http://www.niu.edu
School Type: Public
Setting: Suburban
Total Faculty: 1,177
Total Graduate Faculty: 638
Total number of Students: 18,042
Total number of Graduate Students: 4,319

Department Information

Department Chairman: Prof. Laurence Lurio, Chair
Department Contact: Prof. Philippe Piot, Director of Graduate
  Studies
  Total full-time faculty: 21
  Total number of full-time equivalent positions: 21
  Full-Time Graduate Students: 55
  Female Full-Time Graduate Students: 10
  First-Year Graduate Students: 8
  Total Post Doctorates: 3

Department Address

Physics Department, 202 LaTourette Hall, Normal Road
Northern Illinois University
DeKalb, IL 60115
Phone: (815) 753-1772
Fax: (815) 753-8565
E-mail: physics@niu.edu
Website: http://www.physics.niu.edu/physics/

ADMISSIONS

Admission Contact Information

Address admission inquiries to: The Graduate School, Northern
  Illinois University, 180 Stadium Drive, DeKalb, IL 60115-
  2828, USA
Phone: (815) 753-0395
E-mail: gradsch@niu.edu
Admissions website: http://www.niu.edu/grad/apply/

Application deadlines

Fall admission:
U.S. students: December 15   *Int'l. students*: December 1
Spring admission:
U.S. students: December 10   *Int'l. students*: December 10

Application fee

U.S. students: $60   *Int'l. students*: $60
International application fee can be waived if payment of the fee
  puts a significant financial strain on the applicant.

Admissions information

For Fall of 2018:
  Number of applicants: 61
  Number admitted: 44
  Number enrolled: 8

Admission requirements

Bachelor's degree requirements: Bachelor's degree in Physics
  or a related discipline is required.
Minimum undergraduate GPA: 2.75

GRE requirements

The GRE is required (but no minimum score required).

Subjective GRE requirements

The Subjective GRE is recommended.
GRE Physics is not required, but strongly recommended, especially for international students.

TOEFL requirements

The TOEFL exam is required for students from non-English-
  speaking countries.
  iBT score: 80
TOEFL may be substituted by IELTS, for which the minimum
  acceptable score is 6.5.

Other admissions information

Undergraduate preparation assumed: Mechanics: Taylor; Electricity and Magnetism: Griffiths; Quantum Mechanics: Eis-
  berg/Resnick.

TUITION

Tuition year 2018–19:
Tuition for in-state residents
  Full-time students: $4,464.99 per semester
Tuition for out-of-state residents
  Full-time students: $4,464.99 per semester
Graduate assistantships (TA/RA) include tuition waiver. $357/hour
Credit hours per semester to be considered full-time: 9
Deferred tuition plan: No
Health insurance: Yes, $2,358.00.
Other academic fees: Graduate assistants—$1,233.72/semester
Academic term: Semester
Number of first-year students who received partial tuition waivers: 8

Teaching Assistants, Research Assistants, and Fellowships

Number of first-year
  Teaching Assistants: 6
  Research Assistants: 3
  Fellowship students: 1
Average stipend per academic year
  Teaching Assistant: $15,786.53
  Research Assistant: $18,076.5
  Fellowship student: $18,150
All of the above amounts are for nine months (fall+spring).
  Most students are able to find full support for the summer
  months as RA's and a few as TA's at the same monthly rates.

FINANCIAL AID

Application deadlines

Fall admission:
U.S. students: September 15   *Int'l. students*: September 15
Spring admission:
U.S. students: December 10   *Int'l. students*: December 10

Loans

Loans are available for U.S. students.

Loans are not available for international students.

GAPSFAS application required: No

FAFSA application required: Yes

For further information

Address financial aid inquiries to: Student Financial Aid Office, Swen Parson Hall 245, Northern Illinois University, DeKalb, IL 60115.

Phone: (800) 892-3050

E-mail: finaid@niu.edu

Financial aid website: http://www.niu.edu/fa/

HOUSING

Availability of on-campus housing

Single students: Yes

Married students: Yes

For further information

Address housing inquiries to: Housing & Dining, 101 East Neptune Hall, Northern Illinois University, DeKalb, IL 60115.

Phone: (815) 753-1525

E-mail: housingdining@niu.edu

Housing aid website: http://www.niu.edu/housing/

Table A—Faculty, Enrollments, and Degrees Granted

Research Specialty	2018–19 Faculty	Enrollment Fall 2018		Number of Degrees Granted 2017–18 (2013–18)		
		Master's	Doctorate	Master's	Terminal Master's	Doctorate
Condensed Matter Physics	9	3	12	1(14)	–(9)	1(11)
Cosmology & String Theory	–	–	–	–(2)	–	–(1)
High Energy Physics	7	5	12	1(11)	–(10)	1(9)
Medical, Health Physics	1	–	1	–(3)	–(3)	–
Physics and other Science Education	1	2	–	–(2)	–(4)	–
Physics of Beams	3	–	10	1(10)	–(5)	3(10)
Non-specialized	–	4	6	–	–	–
Total	21	14	41	3(42)	–(30)	5(31)
Full-time Grad. Stud.	–	15	32	–	–	–
First-year Grad. Stud.	–	–	8	–	–	–

GRADUATE DEGREE REQUIREMENTS

Master's: Thirty hours of course work with 24 in physics; thesis required for basic and applied physics specializations.

Doctorate: Students are required to complete 90 semester hours of graduate course work. This includes 15 hours in five out of six core courses covering classical and quantum mechanics, statistical physics, and electromagnetic theory, and twelve hours in two different areas of physics. A minimum of 24 hours dedicated to dissertation research is required. The remaining hours may include additional dissertation work or other graduate course work in physics and related fields. Students entering the program without a master's degree in physics are required to pass a qualifying examination, which is usually taken at the end of the first year. Successful completion of a candidacy examination based on the core courses and other graduate courses is required of all students in the Ph.D. program. Transfer credits for students entering with a master's degree or with graduate coursework from another institution are allowed, pending approval by the Graduate Studies Committee.

Thesis: Thesis may be written in absentia.

SPECIAL EQUIPMENT, FACILITIES, OR PROGRAMS

Students may specialize in five principal areas: condensed matter and materials physics, elementary particles and fields, accelerator physics, medical physics, and physics education.

The Department makes special efforts to accommodate the needs of students, such as employees of nearby industrial government laboratories and teachers employed in the region who wish to gain advanced degrees in physics on either a part-time or full-time basis.

On the departmental faculty are eight condensed matter experimenters and three theorists with whom graduate students may work on their thesis research. In addition there are joint and adjunct professors from both Fermilab and Argonne National Laboratory.

The Physics Department is a member of NIU's Institute for Nano Science, Engineering, and Technology (InSET) and as such faculty and students have access to a class 100 clean room containing a wide array of fabrication and characterization instruments and deposition systems. Some faculty members of the department also base their research programs at Argonne National Laboratory, about a one hour-drive by car from NIU, where they utilize national user facilities such as the Advanced Photon Source, the Electron Microscopy Center, and the Center for Nanomaterials.

Among the faculty working on High Energy (Elementary Particle) Physics are seven experimenters and one theorist, several research scientists and a number of graduate students doing thesis research. At present, the experimenters participate in the ATLAS experiment at the Large Hadron Collider (LHC), CERN (Geneva, Switzerland) as well as the g-2 and the Mu2E experiments at the Fermi National Acceleration Laboratory (40 minutes by car). The group is also active on research and development of particle detection technologies.

Accelerator physics R&D are coordinated through the Northern Illinois Center for Accelerator and Detector Development (NICADD). Current areas include studies of intense and cold electron sources, beam manipulation techniques, nonlinear dynamics, development of advanced diagnostics, and exploration of novel acceleration and radiation source mechanisms.

Both the particles and accelerator groups collaborate closely with nearby Fermilab and Argonne National Lab where they have access to laboratory and computing facilities. They also have their own laboratories at the university.

One faculty member works with a group of graduate students on medical physics, focusing on both diagnostic (proton-computed tomography) and therapeutic (proton therapy) aspects.

One faculty member works closely with graduate students on methods of physics teaching and serves as a supervisor of their student teaching at selected nearby high schools.

Table B—Separately Budgeted Research Expenditures by Source of Support

Source of Support	Departmental Research	Physics-related Research Outside Department
Federal government	$2,756,830	
State/local government		
Non-profit organizations		
Business and industry		
Other		
Total	$2,756,830	

FACULTY

Professor

Blazey, Gerald, Ph.D., University of Minnesota, 1984. Presidential Research Professor. Vice President for Research and Innovative Partnerships. *High Energy Physics.* Elementary Particles, Experiment.

Chakraborty, Dhiman, Ph.D., Stony Brook University, 1994. Presidential Research Professor. *High Energy Physics.* Elementary Particles, Experiment.

Chattopadhyay, Swapan, Ph.D., University of California, Berkeley, 1982. Director of Accelerator Research. Member, Fermilab Directorate Senior Leadership Team. Scientific Associate, CERN. Presidential Research Professor. Accelerator Physics and Engineering, Elementary Particles, Experiment and theory.

Chmaissem, Omar W., Ph.D., University of Grenoble, France, 1992. Presidential Research Professor. *Condensed Matter Physics.* Experiment.

Coutrakon, George, Ph.D., Stony Brook University, 1983. *Medical, Health Physics.* Medical Physics, Experiment.

Dabrowski, Bogdan M., Ph.D., Northwestern University, 1987. Presidential Research Professor. *Condensed Matter Physics, Materials Science, Metallurgy.* Experiment.

Erdelyi, Bela, Ph.D., Michigan State University, 2001. *Nonlinear Dynamics and Complex Systems, Physics of Beams.* Experiment and theory.

Glatz, Andreas, Ph.D., Cologne University, 2004. *Materials Science, Metallurgy, Nonlinear Dynamics and Complex Systems.* Theory.

Hedin, David, Ph.D., University of Wisconsin-Madison, 1980. Board of Trustees Professor. Presidential Research Professor. *High Energy Physics.* Elementary Particles, Experiment.

Lurio, Laurence, Ph.D., Harvard University, 1993. Chair. *Condensed Matter Physics.* Experiment.

Martin, Stephen, Ph.D., University of California, Santa Barbara, 1988. Presidential Research Professor. Presidential Teaching Professor. *Particles and Fields.* Elementary Particles, Theory.

Mini, Susan, Ph.D., Southern Illinois University, 1991. Vice-Provost for Resources and Planning. *Condensed Matter Physics.*

Piot, Philippe, Ph.D., University of Grenoble, 1999. Board of Trustees Professor. Presidential Research Professor. Scientist, Fermi National Accelerator Laboratory. Director of Graduate Studies. *Physics of Beams.* Accelerator Science and Technology, Optics and Lasers, Experiment and Theory.

Thompson, Carol, Ph.D., University of Houston, 1987. Undergraduate Advisor. *Condensed Matter Physics.* Experiment.

Van Veenendaal, Michel, Ph.D., Laboratory of Solid State Physics, RUG, Netherlands, 1994. Presidential Research Professor. Managing Director, Institute of Nano Science, Engineering, and Technology. *Condensed Matter Physics, Nano Science and Technology.* Theory.

Winkler, Roland, Ph.D., University of Regensburg, 1994. *Condensed Matter Physics, Quantum Foundations.* Theory.

Xiao, Zhili, Ph.D., University of Konstanz, 1996. Board of Trustees Professor. Presidential Research Professor. Physicist, Materials Science Division, Argonne National Laboratory. *Condensed Matter Physics, Materials Science, Metallurgy, Nano Science and Technology.* Experiment.

Zutshi, Vishnu, Ph.D., University of Delhi, 1997. Presidential Research Professor. Director of Northern Illinois Center for Accelerator and Detector Development. *High Energy Physics.* Elementary Particles, Physics.

Associate Professor

Brown, Dennis, Ph.D., Stanford University, 1993. *Condensed Matter Physics.* Experiment.

Eads, Michael, Ph.D., Northern Illinois University, 2007. Director of Secondary Educator Licensure. *High Energy Physics.* Physics Teaching, Elementary Particles, Experiment.

Ito, Yasuo, Ph.D., University of Cambridge, 1996. Assistant Chair and Director of Undergraduate Studies. *Condensed Matter Physics, Materials Science, Metallurgy, Nano Science and Technology.* Electron Microscopy and Related Spectroscopy Techniques Experiment.

Assistant Professor

Adelman, Jahred A., Ph.D., The University of Chicago, 2008. Deputy Director of Northern Illinois Center for Accelerator and Detector Development. *High Energy Physics.* Elementary Particles, Experiment.

Emeritus

Albright, Carl H., Ph.D., Princeton University, 1960. *Particles and Fields.* Elementary Particles, Theory.

Fortner, Michael, Ph.D., Brandeis University, 1989. *High Energy Physics.* Elementary Particles, Experiment.

Willis, Suzanne, Ph.D., Yale University, 1979. *Physics and other Science Education.* Physics education.

Research Professor

Syphers, Michael J., Ph.D., University of Illinois at Chicago, 1987. Deputy Director of Northern Illinois Center for Accelerator and Detector Development. *Accelerator, High Energy Physics, Medical, Health Physics, Particles and Fields.* Beam Physics, Large-scale high energy synchrontrons and colliders, Accelerator systems for medical research and therapy.

Adjunct Professor

Alp, Ercan, Ph.D., Southern Illinois University, 1984. *Condensed Matter Physics.* Experiment.

Bhat, Pushpa, Ph.D., Bangalore University, 1982. *High Energy Physics.* Elementary Particles, Experiment.

Khalatyan, Norayr, Ph.D., Yerevan Physics Institute, 1988. *High Energy Physics.* Beam Physics.

Lal, Jyotsana, Ph.D., Boston University, 1991. *Condensed Matter Physics.* Condensed matter systems, x-ray and neutron scattering.

Sen, Tanaji, Ph.D., Stony Brook University, 1986. *Accelerator.* Beam Physics, Theoretical Accelerator Physics.

Stratakis, Diktus, Ph.D., University of Maryland, 2008. *Accelerator, Physics of Beams.* Accelerator Physics.

Welp, Ulrich, Ph.D., University of Konstanz, 1988. *Condensed Matter Physics.* Experiment.

Zaluzec, Nestor, Ph.D., University of Illinois at Urbana-Champaign, 1973. *Condensed Matter Physics.* Experiment.

Zholents, Alexander, Ph.D., Budker Institue of Nuclear Physics of Russian Academy of Science, 1983. Graduate Faculty Scholar. *High Energy Physics.* Accelerator Physics, Theory and Experiment.

Other

Windelborn, Augden, Ph.D., Northern Illinois University, 1983. Assistant Professor Emeritus. *Other.* Physics Education, Distance Learning.

DEPARTMENTAL RESEARCH SPECIALTIES AND STAFF

Theoretical

Condensed Matter Physics. Liquid metals; magnetism and cooperative phenomena; many-body theory; optical properties of solids; electronic structure; multi-particle systems; quantum macrophysics; non-linear dynamics; transport phenomena; non-equilibrium systems; dynamics of disordered elastic systems. Glatz, Van Veenendaal, Winkler.

High Energy Physics. Weak interactions; gauge theory; phenomenology; super-symmetric theories. Albright, Martin.

Physics of Beams. Nonlinear dynamics, Applications of symplectic geometry in, and numerical methods for Hamiltonian dynamics. Chattopadhyay, Erdelyi, Piot, Sen, Syphers, Zholents.

Experimental

Condensed Matter Physics. Mössbauer effect; superconductivity; lattice defects; optical and transport properties of amorphous and crystalline solids; synchrotron radiation; surface physics; magnetic properties of solids; low-temperature physics; X-ray crystallography; materials preparation, polymer physics, biophysics. Alp, Brown, Chmaissem, Dabrowski, Ito, Lurio, Mini, Thompson, Welp, Xiao, Zaluzec.

High Energy Physics. LHC/ATLAS: collider physics at the energy frontier: studies of Higgs boson(s), searches for new massive states, detector design and operations; Fermilab (Mu2E, g-2): searches for rare processes at the intensity frontier; R&D of detector technologies and algorithms; dark matter/energy search; anti-matter physics. Adelman, Bhat, Blazey, Chakraborty, Chattopadhyay, Eads, Hedin, Zutshi.

Physics of Beams. Simulation and operation of high brightness photoinjectors. Electron beam diagnostics. Muon and heavy nuclei accelerators. Charged particle nonlinear beam dynamics and electrodynamics; particle colliders and synchrotron radiation sources; free electron lasers and quantum optics; plasma acceleration. Chattopadhyay, Erdelyi, Piot, Syphers, Zholents.

View additional information about this department at www.gradschoolshopper.com. Check out the "Why Choose Us?" section, find out more about the department's culture and get links to social media networks.

NORTHWESTERN UNIVERSITY

DEPARTMENT OF PHYSICS AND ASTRONOMY

Evanston, Illinois 60208
http://www.physics.northwestern.edu/index.html

General University Information
President: Morton Schapiro
Dean of Graduate School: Theresa Woodruff
University website: http://www.northwestern.edu/
School Type: Private
Setting: Urban
Total Faculty: 2,500
Total Graduate Faculty: 1,000
Total number of Students: 21,403
Total number of Graduate Students: 10,681

Department Information
Department Chairman: Prof. Michael Schmitt, Chair
Department Contact: Bud Robinson, Graduate Assistant
  Total full-time faculty: 39
  Full-Time Graduate Students: 90
  Female Full-Time Graduate Students: 16
  First-Year Graduate Students: 15
  Female First-Year Students: 2
  Total Post Doctorates: 40

Department Address
2145 Sheridan Road
Evanston, IL 60208
Phone: (847) 491-3685
Fax: (847) 491-9982
E-mail: physics-astronomy@northwestern.edu
Website: http://www.physics.northwestern.edu/index.html

ADMISSIONS

Admission Contact Information
Address admission inquiries to: Graduate Admissions Committee, Department of Physics & Astronomy, Northwestern University, Evanston, IL 60208
Phone: (847) 491-3685
E-mail: physics-astronomy@northwestern.edu
Admissions website: http://www.physics.northwestern.edu/graduate/

Application deadlines
Fall admission:
U.S. students: December 31   *Int'l. students*: December 31

Application fee
U.S. students: $95   *Int'l. students*: $95
Students can be admitted at times other than the fall under special conditions.

Admissions information
For Fall of 2017:
  Number of applicants: 445
  Number admitted: 71
  Number enrolled: 33

Admission requirements
Bachelor's degree requirements: Students must have a Bachelor's degree, preferably in Physics, Astronomy, or Mathematics.

GRE requirements
The GRE is required.
  Mean GRE score range (25th–75th percentile): 90%

Subjective GRE requirements
The Subjective GRE is required.

TOEFL requirements
The TOEFL exam is required for students from non-English-speaking countries.
  PBT score: 577
  iBT score: 90

Other admissions information
Additional requirements: Students must submit results of the physics GRE examination and three letters of recommendation. For admission, equal weight is given to GPA, GRE scores, and letters.
Undergraduate preparation assumed: Symon, Mechanics; Reitz and Milford, E & M; Reif, Statistical Mechanics; Zemansky, Thermodynamics; and McGervy, Modern Physics.
  Math preparation should include: Ordinary Differential Equations; Partial Differential Equations; Boundary Value Problems; Complex Variable Theory; Linear Algebra.

TUITION

Tuition year 2017–18:
  Full-time students: $17,413 per quarter
The full cost of tuition is included, if we provide you with financial support.
Credit hours per semester to be considered full-time: 3
Deferred tuition plan:
Health insurance: Available
Other academic fees: About $40 per quarter for using off-campus transportation and the athletic center.
Academic term: Quarter
Number of first-year students who received full tuition waivers: 15

Teaching Assistants, Research Assistants, and Fellowships
Number of first-year
  Fellowship students: 15
Average stipend per academic year
  Teaching Assistant: $32,196
  Research Assistant: $32,196
  Fellowship student: $32,196

FINANCIAL AID

Application deadlines
Fall admission:
U.S. students: December 31   *Int'l. students*: December 31

Loans
Loans are not available for U.S. students.
Loans are not available for international students.
GAPSFAS application required: No
FAFSA application required: Yes

For further information
Address financial aid inquiries to: Graduate Admissions Committee, Department of Physics & Astronomy, Northwestern University, Evanston, IL 60208.
Phone: (847) 491-3685

E-mail: physics-astronomy@northwestern.edu
Financial aid website: http://www.physics.northwestern.edu/graduate/finaid.html

HOUSING

Availability of on-campus housing
Single students: Yes
Married students: Yes

For further information
Address housing inquiries to: Graduate Student Housing Office, 1915 Maple Avenue, Northwestern University, Evanston, IL 60208.
Phone: (847) 491-5127
E-mail: grad-housing@northwestern.edu
Housing aid website: http://www.northwestern.edu/gradhousing/

Table A—Faculty, Enrollments, and Degrees Granted

Research Specialty	2017–18 Faculty	Enrollment Fall 2017 Master's	Enrollment Fall 2017 Doctorate	Number of Degrees Granted 2017–2018 Master's	Number of Degrees Granted 2017–2018 Terminal Master's	Number of Degrees Granted 2017–2018 Doctorate
Astrophysics	11	–	22	2	–	4
Atomic, Molecular, & Optical Physics	3	–	15	1	–	–
Biophysics	3	–	13	–	–	1
Condensed Matter Physics	9	–	27	1	–	2
Particles and Fields	8	–	15	1	–	1
Physics and other Science Education	4	–	–	–	–	–
Non-specialized	–	–	1	–	6	–
Total	**38**	**–**	**93**	**1**	**6**	**8**
Full-time Grad. Stud.	–	–	93	–	–	–
First-year Grad. Stud.	–	–	15	–	–	–

GRADUATE DEGREE REQUIREMENTS

Master's: There are two tracks: a thesis track and an elective track. The thesis track requires 9 graded (ABC) courses and a thesis which is generally written in the Spring and Summer. The elective track requires 13 graded (ABC) courses. The elective track requires study in the Fall of the second year. There is no foreign language requirement.

Doctorate: Minimum of two years of residency is required; 13 quarter courses in physics and/or astronomy are required; "B" average is required. Departmental preliminary examination is required. There is no foreign language requirement. Students receiving a PhD can also receive a Master's degree.

Thesis: Thesis may be written in absentia.

SPECIAL EQUIPMENT, FACILITIES, OR PROGRAMS

We have ties to many research centers at Northwestern, including the Center for Quantum Optics, the Materials Research Center, and the Center for Interdisciplinary Astrophysical Research (CIERA) and the Center for Fundamental Physics. Our faculty also has extensive access to major government research facilities, including Fermilab, CERN, Argonne National Laboratory, the National High-Magnetic Field Laboratory, and many ground-based and space-based astrophysical observatories. We have joint faculty in the Departments of Electrical Engineering, Chemistry, Materials Science, Molecular Biology, and Applied Physics.

Table B—Separately Budgeted Research Expenditures by Source of Support

Source of Support	Departmental Research	Physics-related Research Outside Department
Federal government	$6,366,000	
State/local government		
Non-profit organizations	$1,359,000	
Business and industry	$15,000	
Other		
Total	**$7,740,000**	

Table C—Separately Budgeted Research Expenditures by Research Specialty

Research Specialty	No. of Grants	Expenditures ($)
Astrophysics	33	$1,564,000
Atomic, Molecular, & Optical Physics	11	$1,839,000
Biophysics	11	$576,000
Condensed Matter Physics	18	$2,678,000
Particles and Fields	10	$1,083,000
Total	**83**	**$7,740,000**

FACULTY

Professor

Chandrasekhar, Venkat, Ph.D., Yale University, 1989. Co-Director of Applied Physics. *Applied Physics, Condensed Matter Physics, Nano Science and Technology*. Mesoscopic systems; transport and magnetic properties of small particles.

de Gouvêa, André, Ph.D., University of California, Berkeley, 1999. *Particles and Fields*. Theory of neutrino oscillations; lepton number non-conservation in the Big Bang; dark matter.

Dutta, Pulak, Ph.D., University of Chicago, 1980. Co-Director of Applied Physics. *Applied Physics, Biophysics, Condensed Matter Physics, Fluids, Rheology*. Nanoscale order in soft materials; X-ray scattering studies of self-assembled molecular layers.

Gabrielse, Gerald, Ph.D., University of Chicago, 1980. *Atomic, Molecular, & Optical Physics, Particles and Fields*. Predictions, symmetries and proposed extensions to the standard model. Table-top physics.

Garg, Anupam, Ph.D., Cornell University, 1983. *Applied Physics, Atomic, Molecular, & Optical Physics, Condensed Matter Physics*. Spin tunneling in magnetic molecules; macroscopic quantum phenomena; quantum computing.

Halperin, William, Ph.D., Cornell University, 1974. *Applied Physics, Condensed Matter Physics, Low Temperature Physics*. Low-temperature physics; high-magnetic-field NMR studies of high-Tc superconductors; fluid transport in porous media.

Kalogera, Vassiliki, Ph.D., University of Illinois, 1997. Co-Director of CIERA. *Astrophysics, Relativity & Gravitation*. Gravitational waves; X-ray emission from compact binary objects; coalescence of neutron-star binaries.

Ketterson, John, Ph.D., University of Chicago, 1962. *Applied Physics, Atomic, Molecular, & Optical Physics, Biophysics, Condensed Matter Physics*. Superlattices; conventional and high-Tc super-conductors; organic films; scanning-electron and atomic-force microscopy; nonlinear optics.

Marko, John, Ph.D., Massachusetts Institute of Technology, 1989. Joint appointment with Molecular Biology. *Biophysics, Polymer Physics/Science, Statistical & Thermal Physics*. Applications of statistical mechanics and polymer physics to biophysical problems.

Meyer, David, Ph.D., University of California, Los Angeles, 1984. Co-Director of CIERA. *Astrophysics*. High signal-to-noise spectroscopy of interstellar and extragalactic absorption lines; small-scale structures in diffuse galactic clouds.

Motter, Adilson, Ph.D., UNICAMP (Brazil), 2002. *Biophysics, Statistical & Thermal Physics*. Theory of complex systems; nonlinear phenomena; statistical physics.

Novak, Giles, Ph.D., University of Chicago, 1988. *Astrophysics*. Large-scale galactic magnetic fields; magnetic fields in the vicinity of low-mass protostars; gas turbulence in molecular clouds.

Petriello, Frank, Ph.D., Stanford University, 2003. *Particles and Fields*. Application of perturbative QCD to collider physics; new phenomena at the TeV scale; new calculational techniques for quantum field theory.

Rasio, Frederic, Ph.D., Cornell University, 1991. *Astrophysics, Relativity & Gravitation*. Evolution of dense star clusters; massive black hole formation; coalescing compact binaries; gravity waves; extrasolar planets.

Sauls, James, Ph.D., Stony Brook University, 1980. Director of Graduate Studies. *Applied Physics, Condensed Matter Physics, Low Temperature Physics*. Theory of quantum fluids; strongly correlated metals; systems with disorder; complex symmetry breaking in superfluids and superconductors.

Schmitt, Michael, Ph.D., Harvard University, 1991. *Particles and Fields*. Electroweak behavior in the Standard Model; searches for new elementary particles and new particle interactions; detector technology.

Seth, Kamal, Ph.D., University of Pittsburgh, 1957. *Nuclear Physics, Particles and Fields*. Experimental study of exotic combinations of valence quarks and gluons, glueballs, and charmonium.

Ulmer, Melville, Ph.D., University of Wisconsin-Madison, 1970. *Astrophysics*. Development of X-ray mirrors and ultraviolet detectors; matter distribution in galactic clusters; transient hard X-ray sources.

Velasco, Mayda, Ph.D., Northwestern University, 1995. *Particles and Fields*. Matter-antimatter asymmetry physics beyond the Standard Model; beam instrumentation; multi-TeV electron/positron and gamma/gamma colliders.

Yusef-Zadeh, Farhad, Ph.D., Columbia University, 1986. *Astrophysics*. Study of the black hole Sgr A* at the center of the galaxy; supernova remnant masers; stellar formation within evolved HII regions.

Associate Professor

Figueroa-Feliciano, Enectali, Ph.D., Stanford University, 2001. *Astrophysics, Particles and Fields*. Experimental dark matter and neutrino physics. Design and development of low-temperature detectors to search for dark matter both deep underground and in space, and to study neutrinos from reactors and radioactive sources.

Geraci, Andrew, Stanford University, 2007. *Atomic, Molecular, & Optical Physics*. High-Q resonant sensors for ultrasensitive force and field detection in searches for new physics.

Koch, Jens, Ph.D., Freie Universität, Berlin, 2006. *Applied Physics, Condensed Matter Physics*. Strongly correlated systems; quantum information processing with solid-state devices; theory of quantum transport.

Lithwick, Yoram, Ph.D., California Institute of Technology, 2002. *Astrophysics*. Planet formation; dynamics of planetary systems; accretion disks; MHD turbulence; cosmological halo formation; gamma-ray bursts.

Low, Ian, Ph.D., Carnegie Mellon University, 2000. Joint appointment with Argonne National Laboratory. *Particles and Fields*. Theoretical particle physics: electroweak symmetry breaking; properties of the Higgs boson; aspects of dark matter.

Odom, Brian, Ph.D., Harvard University, 2004. *Applied Physics, Atomic, Molecular, & Optical Physics*. Experiments on mK-trapped molecular ions to investigate changing fundamental constants, parity violation in chiral matter, and quantum effects in chemical reactions below 1 K.

Assistant Professor

Dahl, Eric, Ph.D., Princeton University, 2009. *Particles and Fields*. Experimental astroparticle physics, direct detection of particle dark matter, bubble chamber and other low-background detector development.

Driscoll, Michelle, University of Chicago, 2014. *Biophysics*. Soft-matter physics and fluid dynamics. How structure and patterns emerge in a driven system, and how to use this structure formation as a new way to probe nonequillibrium systems.

Faucher-Giguere, Claude-Andre, Ph.D., Harvard University. *Astrophysics*. Galaxy formation and evolution, including star formation, galaxy-black hole co-evolution, galactic dynamics, and connections with the intergalactic medium and cosmology; Pulsars.

Fong, Wen-fai, Ph.D., Harvard University, 2014. Observations across the electromagnetic spectrum to study explosive transients and their host galaxy environments. Gamma-ray bursts, electromagnetic counterparts to gravitational wave sources, compact object binaries, supernovae, and anything that collides or explodes. *Astronomy, Astrophysics*.

Goswami, Pallab, Ph.D., UCLA, 2008. Developing such theoretical tools for addressing emergent quantum phases and quantum phase transitions in strongly correlated and disordered materials, with an emphasis on underlying topological properties.

Hahn, Kristian, Ph.D., University of Pennsylvania, 2006. *High Energy Physics, Particles and Fields*. Electroweak symmetry breaking; Higgs physics and searches for physics beyond the standard model. Detector data acquisition and trigger. Large-scale computing for physics analysis.

Margutti, Raffaella, Ph.D., University of Milan, 2010. *Astronomy, Astrophysics*. Stellar explosions and stellar tidal disruptions by supermassive black holes.

Stern, Nathaniel, Ph.D., University of California, Santa Barbara, 2008. *Condensed Matter Physics*. Experimental optical condensed-matter physics; nanoscale photonics and magnetism; cavity QED with single atoms and photons; spin dynamics in the solid state.

Tchekovskoy, Alexander, Ph.D., Harvard University, 2010. *Astrophysics*. Black holes and neutron stars interact with their environment. Large-scale numerical simulations as well as algorithm and code development.

Research Associate Professor

Larson, Shane, Ph.D., Montana State University, 1999. *Astronomy, Astrophysics*.

Teaching Professor

Smutko, Michael, Ph.D., University of Chicago, 1998. Joint appointment with Adler Planetarium (Chicago). *Physics and other Science Education*. Physics education.

Teaching Associate Professor

Krusberg, Zosia, Ph.D., University of Chicago, 2011. Physics education.

Rivers, Andrew, Ph.D., New Mexico Institute of Technology, 2000. Joint appointment with College of Arts and Sciences Advising Center. *Physics and other Science Education*. Physics education.

Schmidt, Arthur, Ph.D., University of Notre Dame, 1974. Director of Undergraduate Laboratories. *Physics and other Science Education.* Physics education.

Senior Lecturer

Brown, Deborah, Ph.D., Northwestern University, 1983. *Physics and other Science Education.* Physics education.

DEPARTMENTAL RESEARCH SPECIALTIES AND STAFF

Theoretical

Astrophysics. Neutron stars; formation and dynamics of multiple star systems; stellar atmospheres; Type-I supernovae; dynamics of dense stellar systems; hydrodynamic stellar interactions; X-ray binaries; gravitational waves; planetary formation and dynamics; accretion disks; MHD turbulence; cosmological halo formation; gamma-ray bursts. Faucher-Giguere, Kalogera, Lithwick.

Biophysics. Nonlinear dynamics; chaos; neural networks; statistical physics of biological systems. Motter.

Condensed Matter Physics. Electronic structure of molecules and crystals; electronic, optical, and magnetic structure studies using accurate first principles methods; electronic properties of semiconductors and composite structures; electron-hole liquid at metallic densities and the electron-hole liquid in semiconductors; many-body physics including monomolecular films, chemisorption, and liquid and solid helium. Garg, Goswami, Koch, Sauls.

Particles and Fields. Fundamental interactions of elementary particles; quantum chromodynamics; electroweak symmetry breaking; phenomenology of weak interactions; neutrino oscillations; astrophysical particle theory. de Gouvêa, Low, Petriello, Seth.

Experimental

Astrophysics. Optical/UV observations of interstellar gas/dust and quasar absorption line systems; sub-mm polarimetry of interstellar magnetic fields; radio/IR/X-ray observations of supernova remnants; star formation regions and the Galactic Center; sub-mm/UV/X-ray astronomical instrumentation; gamma-ray bursts. Novak, Smutko, Ulmer, Yusef-Zadeh.

Atomic, Molecular, & Optical Physics. Quantum control of molecular states and processes; tests of astrophysics and fundamental symmetries; trapping and cooling of atoms, anti-atoms, and molecules. Gabrielse, Geraci, Odom.

Biophysics. Applications of statistical mechanics and polymer physics to biophysical problems. Driscoll, Marko.

Condensed Matter Physics. Ultra-low-temperature physics; properties of superfluid helium; magnetic, structural, and superconducting properties of composition modulated alloys; nuclear magnetic resonance; X-ray studies of monolayer and multilayer films; catalysis and properties of small metallic particles; semiconductor superlattices; light scattering. Chandrasekhar, Dutta, Halperin, Ketterson, Stern.

Particles and Fields. Studies of electroweak interactions; spectroscopy of heavy quark states; supersymmetry searches at the 2-TeV pp collider (TeV II) at Fermilab; searches for charmomium states at Fermilab; rare K decay studies (CERN); CMS preparation at CERN. Dahl, Figueroa-Feliciano, Velasco.

View additional information about this department at www.gradschoolshopper.com. Check out the "Why Choose Us?" section, find out more about the department's culture and get links to social media networks.

THE UNIVERSITY OF CHICAGO

DEPARTMENT OF ASTRONOMY AND ASTROPHYSICS

Chicago, Illinois 60637
http://astro.uchicago.edu

General University Information
President: Robert J. Zimmer
Dean of Graduate School: Angela V. Olinto, Dean of the Physical Sciences
University website: http://www.uchicago.edu
School Type: Private
Setting: Urban
Total Faculty: 2,350
Total number of Students: 15,365
Total number of Graduate Students: 9,394

Department Information
Department Chairman: Prof. John E. Carlstrom, Chair
Department Contact: Laticia Rebeles, Student Affairs Administrator
Total full-time faculty: 26
Total number of full-time equivalent positions: 22
Full-Time Graduate Students: 28
Female Full-Time Graduate Students: 10
First-Year Graduate Students: 5
Female First-Year Students: 4
Total Post Doctorates: 9

Department Address
5640 S. Ellis Avenue
5th Floor
Chicago, IL 60637
Phone: (773) 702-9808
E-mail: lrebeles@oddjob.uchicago.edu
Website: http://astro.uchicago.edu

ADMISSIONS

Admission Contact Information
Address admission inquiries to: Department of Astronomy and Astrophysics, 5640 S. Ellis Ave., Chicago, IL 60637
Phone: (773) 702-9808
E-mail: lrebeles@oddjob.uchicago.edu
Admissions website: http://astro.uchicago.edu

Application deadlines
Fall admission:
U.S. students: January 6   *Int'l. students*: January 6

Application fee
U.S. students: $90   *Int'l. students*: $90
Fee waivers are available to applicants who meet certain criteria.
https://physical-sciences.uchicago.edu/page/application-information#Application Fee Waiver

Admissions information
For Fall of 2018:
Number of applicants: 245
Number admitted: 18
Number enrolled: 4

Admission requirements
Bachelor's degree requirements: Bachelor's degree, preferably in physics or another physical science, is required, but others will be considered.

Minimum undergraduate GPA: 3.0

GRE requirements
The GRE is required.

Subjective GRE requirements
The Subjective GRE is recommended.

TOEFL requirements
The TOEFL exam is required for students from non-English-speaking countries.
iBT score: 90

Other admissions information
Additional requirements: Three letters of recommendation and a personal statement.
Undergraduate preparation assumed: If an applicant does not hold a bachelor's degree in physics or another physical science, evidence of a solid foundation in physics and mathematics obtained through coursework or other experiences should be provided to demonstrate that the applicant is prepared for graduate-level work in Astronomy and Astrophysics.

TUITION

Tuition year 2017–2018:
Tuition for in-state residents
   Full-time students: per quarter
   Full-time students: $17,405 per quarter
For advanced graduate students (5th year and beyond) tuition costs are $6,855 per quarter.
Credit hours per semester to be considered full-time: 300
Deferred tuition plan: No
Health insurance: Available at the cost of $3,800 per year.
Other academic fees: Student Life Fee is $388 per quarter during the academic year and $305 in the summer quarter. Lifetime Transcript Fee is $75 (one-time fee).
Academic term: Quarter
Number of first-year students who received full tuition waivers: 4

Teaching Assistants, Research Assistants, and Fellowships
Number of first-year
   Teaching Assistants: 4
Average stipend per academic year
   Teaching Assistant: $32,300
   Research Assistant: $32,300
   Fellowship student: $32,000
All students are supported by either an RA or TA fellowship, or by a fellowship outside of the department.

FINANCIAL AID

Loans
Loans are available for U.S. students.
Loans are available for international students.
GAPSFAS application required: No
FAFSA application required: Yes

For further information
Address financial aid inquiries to: Division of the Physical Sciences, 5640 S. Ellis Ave., Chicago, IL 60637.
Phone: (773) 702-7950
E-mail: eweaston@uchicago.edu

Financial aid website: https://physical-sciences.uchicago.edu/
page/financial-aid

HOUSING

Availability of on-campus housing
Single students: Yes
Married students: Yes

For further information
Address housing inquiries to: UChicagoGRAD, 970 E. 58th St.,
3rd Fl., Chicago, IL 60637.
Phone: (773) 702-3760
Housing aid website: https://grad.uchicago.edu/life-community/
housing

Table A—Faculty, Enrollments, and Degrees Granted

Research Specialty	2017–2018 Faculty	Enrollment Fall 2017		Number of Degrees Granted 2017–2018 (2012–2017)		
		Master's	Doctorate	Master's	Terminal Master's	Doctorate
Astronomy	28	–	31	–	–	6(29)
Total	28	–	–	–	–	6(29)
Full-time Grad. Stud.	–	–	27	–	–	–
First-year Grad. Stud.	–	–	4	–	–	–

GRADUATE DEGREE REQUIREMENTS

Master's: Note: Although not a terminal Master's program, students may receive a Master's degree while studying for the Ph.D. Full-time registration is required. The candidate must complete a required sequence of courses with a 3.0 average and pass the Ph.D. candidacy examinations.

Doctorate: Full-time registration is required. The candidate must complete a required sequence of courses with a 3.0 average, pass the Ph.D. candidacy examinations, submit and defend successfully a thesis, and have the thesis submitted to a recognized journal.

Thesis: Electronic submission of the final thesis to the dissertation office is required of all students.

SPECIAL EQUIPMENT, FACILITIES, OR PROGRAMS

Faculty in the Department of Astronomy and Astrophysics work on a wide range of topics at the frontiers of astrophysics, from understanding the beginning of the Universe to the search for habitable extrasolar planets; from the formation and evolution of the earliest galaxies to modeling the most energetic events in the modern Universe; and from exploring our own solar system to the largest structures of the Universe. The department participates in major facilities that support the programs of our research groups. Many of these projects take advantage of connections with the neighboring national laboratories, Argonne and Fermilab, for both intellectual and technical resources. Research groups have access to leading telescopes worldwide, including the 6.5-m Magellan Telescopes at Las Campanas, Chile; the Dark Energy Survey at Cerro Tololo Inter-American Observatory in Chile; and the South Pole Telescope, with its ongoing development of powerful new imagers for measuring the Cosmic Microwave Background. Departmental researchers also make use of a number of space telescopes (Hubble, Kepler, Chandra, Fermi, and others) and are actively developing new space missions and observational programs for EUSO, JWST, TESS, and SOFIA. Chicago is an active participant in gravitational waves research as a member of LIGO, leading the development of the

Holometer at Fermilab, and studying extreme cosmic particles at the Auger Observatory. We are a founding member of the world's largest optical telescope, the 25-meter Giant Magellan Telescope, which is now under construction in the Chilean Andes with first light expected early in the next decade.

FACULTY

Distinguished University Professor

Freedman, Wendy L., Ph.D., University of Toronto, 1984. *Astronomy, Astrophysics*. Observational cosmology, Hubble constant, dark energy, extragalactic distance scale, supernovae, Cepheids, galaxy evolution, initial mass function; quantum effects on space-time.

Olinto, Angela V., Ph.D., Massachusetts Institute of Technology, 1987. *Astrophysics, Cosmology & String Theory, Particles and Fields*. Particle and nuclear astrophysics; cosmology.

Rosner, Robert, Ph.D., Harvard University, 1976. *Astrophysics, Computational Physics, Plasma and Fusion, Solar Physics*. Fluid and plasma dynamics; solar physics; high-energy astrophysics.

Turner, Michael S., Ph.D., Stanford University, 1978. *Astrophysics, Cosmology & String Theory, Particles and Fields, Relativity & Gravitation*. Cosmology and particle physics; relativistic astrophysics.

Chair Professor

Carlstrom, John E., Ph.D., University of California, Berkeley, 1988. *Astrophysics*. Star formation and cosmology; cosmic microwave background and mm-wave intensity and polarization surveys surveys with the South Pole Telescope; new instrumentation.

Professor

Cattaneo, Fausto, Ph.D., University of Cambridge, 1984. *Astronomy, Astrophysics, Solar Physics*. Solar system astronomy; high-energy and computational astrophysics.

Chen, Hsiao-Wen, Ph.D., Stony Brook University, 1999. Observational extragalactic astronomy.

Frieman, Joshua A., Ph.D., University of Chicago, 1985. *Astrophysics, Cosmology & String Theory*. Cosmology; particle astrophysics.

Gnedin, Nickolay Y., Ph.D., Princeton University, 1996. *Astronomy, Cosmology & String Theory*. Cosmology; galaxy formation; supercomputer simulations.

Harper, Doyal A., Ph.D., Rice University, 1971. Director of Yerkes Observatory. *Astronomy, Astrophysics*. Experimental astrophysics, infrared astronomy, star formation, physics of the interstellar medium.

Hogan, Craig, Ph.D., University of Cambridge, 1980. *Astrophysics*. Dark energy; particle astrophysics.

Holz, Daniel, Ph.D., University of Chicago, 1998. General Relativity; astrophysics; cosmology.

Hooper, Dan, Ph.D., University of Wisconsin-Madison, 2003. *Astrophysics, Cosmology & String Theory, High Energy Physics, Particles and Fields*. Theoretical astrophysics.

Hu, Wayne, Ph.D., University of California, Berkeley, 1995. *Astronomy, Cosmology & String Theory*. Precision cosmology; CMB; galaxy surveys; weak lensing.

Kent, Stephen M., Ph.D., California Institute of Technology, 1980. *Astronomy*. Observational studies of galaxies.

Khokhlov, Alexei, Ph.D., Moscow State University, 1984. *Astrophysics*. Fluid dynamics; supernovae jets; nucleosynthesis; experimental astrophysics.

Kolb, Edward W., Ph.D., University of Texas, 1978. *Astrophysics, Cosmology & String Theory, Particles and Fields*. Particle physics; cosmology; theoretical astrophysics.

Kravtsov, Andrey, Ph.D., New Mexico State University, 1999. Cosmology; structure formation in the universe; numerical simulations.

Kron, Richard G., Ph.D., University of California, Berkeley, 1978. *Astronomy*. Wide-field optical surveys to study both large-scale structure for cosmology and the distribution of stars in the Milky Way.

Meyer, Stephan S., Ph.D., Princeton University, 1979. *Astrophysics, Cosmology & String Theory*. Infrared astrophysics and observational cosmology.

Privitera, Paolo, Ph.D., University of Karlsruhe (Germany), 1993. Astrophysics, Cosmic Rays, Cosmology & String Theory. Dark Matter, Ultra-high-energy cosmic rays.

Associate Professor

Bean, Jacob, Ph.D., University of Texas, 2007. *Astronomy, Astrophysics*. Extra solar planets; properties and physics of low-mass stars; high-precision spectroscopic, photometric, and astrometric methods.

Fabrycky, Daniel, Ph.D., Princeton University, 2007. *Astronomy, Planetary Science*. Formation and evolution of planets; Extrasolar Planets; Exoplanets.

Gladders, Michael, Ph.D., University of Toronto, 2002. *Cosmology & String Theory*. Observational cosmology and instrumentation.

Assistant Professor

Benson, Bradford, Ph.D., Stanford University, 2004. CMB, experimental cosmology, extragalactic astronomy and astrophysics.

Caprioli, Damiano, Ph.D., Scuola Normale Superiore, 2009. High-Energy Astrophysics; Cosmic Rays: Space Physics; Computational Plasma Astrophysics.

Chang, Chiway, Ph.D., Stanford University, 2013. *Astronomy, Astrophysics*. Weak gravitational lensing; large-scale structure; cosmic microwave background; galaxy evolution.

Chang, Clarence L., Ph.D., Stanford University, 2005. *Astronomy, Astrophysics, Condensed Matter Physics, High Energy Physics, Low Temperature Physics, Nuclear Physics, Particles and Fields, Solid State Physics*. Observational cosmology, extragalactic astronomy and astrophysics, superconducting detectors and devices.

Rogers, Leslie, Ph.D., MIT, 2012. *Astronomy, Astrophysics, Planetary Science*. Astrophysics; Astronomy; Planetary Science; Formation, interior structure, and evolution of exoplanets.

Shirokoff, Erik, Ph.D., Berkeley, 2011. Cryogenic detectors operating at millimeter and submm-wavelengths for the study of high-redshift galaxies, the epoch of reionization, and the Cosmic Microwave Background.

Zhuravleva, Irina, Ph.D., Ludwig-Maximilian University and Max Planck Institute for Astrophysics, 2011. *Astrophysics*. High-energy astrophysics; physics of the intra-cluster medium; AGN feedback; turbulence; transport processes; high-resolution X-ray spectroscopy; radiative transfer.

Professor Emeritus

Cudworth, Kyle M., Ph.D., University of California, Santa Cruz, 1974. *Astronomy*. Star clusters.

Hildebrand, Roger H., Ph.D., University of California, Berkeley, 1951. Far infrared and submillimeter astronomy.

Hobbs, Lewis M., Ph.D., University of Wisconsin-Madison, 1966. *Astronomy*. interstellar matter and observational cosmology.

Königl, Arieh, Ph.D., California Institute of Technology, 1980. *Astrophysics*. Theoretical astrophysics. Active galactic nuclei; star and planet formation.

Kibblewhite, E. J., Ph.D., University of Cambridge, 1971. *Optics*. Adaptive optics; high-resolution imaging.

Lamb, Donald Q., Ph.D., University of Rochester, 1974. *Astrophysics*. Compact objects; high-energy astrophysics.

Miller, Richard H., Ph.D., University of Chicago, 1957. *Astronomy*. Numerical experiments and the dynamical evolution of galaxies.

Oka, Takeshi, Ph.D., University of Tokyo, 1960. Laser spectroscopy and interstellar molecules.

Palmer, Patrick E., Ph.D., Harvard University, 1968. *Astronomy*. Radio astronomy and interstellar molecules.

Parker, Eugene N., Ph.D., Caltech, 1951. *Astronomy, Astrophysics, Solar Physics*.

Swerdlow, Noel M., Ph.D., Yale, 1968. *Astronomy, Astrophysics, Other*. Astronomy history and philosophy.

Truran, James W., Ph.D., Yale University, 1965. *Astrophysics*. Nuclear astrophysics; evolution of stars and galaxies; high-energy astrophysics.

Vandervoort, Peter O., Ph.D., University of Chicago, 1960. *Astronomy*. Analytical dynamics of galaxies.

York, Donald G., Ph.D., University of Chicago, 1970. *Cosmology & String Theory*. Interstellar and intergalactic matter; observational cosmology.

DEPARTMENTAL RESEARCH SPECIALTIES AND STAFF

Theoretical

Astrophysics. Research areas include numerical cosmological simulations, gravitational waves, theory and phenomenology of structure formation in the Universe, computational astrophysics, particle and nuclear astrophysics, kinetic theory, experimental physics, dynamics of extrasolar planets and numerical models for the interior, atmosphere, evolution, and formation of small exoplanets. Projects include Dark Energy Survey. Facilities include Large Synoptic Survey Telescope and the Magellan Telescopes. Caprioli, Cattaneo, Fabrycky, Frieman, Gnedin, Hogan, Holz, Hooper, Hu, Khokhlov, Kolb, Kravtsov, Olinto, Privitera, Rogers, Rosner.

Experimental

Astrophysics. Experimental and observational cosmology, Cosmic Microwave Background Radiation anisotropy and polarization, instrumentation and superconducting technology development, expansion rate of the universe, galactic and extragalactic astronomy and astrophysics, planets around low-mass stars and exoplanetary atmospheres. Projects include Dark Energy Survey, South Pole Telescope, Cosmic Microwave Background Stage 4, MAROON-X. Facilities include Magellan Telescopes, Hubble Space Telescope, Spitzer Space Telescope, SOFIA. Benson, Carlstrom, Clarence Chang, Freedman, Gladders, Harper, Kent, Kron, Shirokoff.

View additional information about this department at www.gradschoolshopper.com. Check out the "Why Choose Us?" section, find out more about the department's culture and get links to social media networks.

THE UNIVERSITY OF CHICAGO

DEPARTMENT OF PHYSICS

Chicago, Illinois 60637
http://physics.uchicago.edu/

General University Information
President: Robert J. Zimmer
Dean of Graduate School: N/A
University website: http://uchicago.edu
School Type: Private
Setting: Urban
Total Faculty: 2,168
Total Graduate Faculty: N/A
Total number of Students: 16,016
Total number of Graduate Students: 10,045

Department Information
Department Chairman: Prof. Young-Kee Kim, Chair
Department Contact: Amy Schulz, Graduate Affairs
   Administrator
   Total full-time faculty: 46
   Total number of full-time equivalent positions: 40
   Full-Time Graduate Students: 168
   Female Full-Time Graduate Students: 29
   First-Year Graduate Students: 38
   Female First-Year Students: 10
   Total Post Doctorates: 51

Department Address
5720 S. Ellis Avenue
Chicago, IL 60637
Phone: (773) 702-7007
Fax: (773) 702-2045
E-mail: aschulz@uchicago.edu
Website: http://physics.uchicago.edu/

ADMISSIONS

Admission Contact Information
Address admission inquiries to: Office of Graduate Admissions,
   Department of Physics, University of Chicago, 5720 S. Ellis
   Avenue, Chicago, IL 60637
Phone: (773) 702-7007
E-mail: aschulz@uchicago.edu
Admissions website: https://apply-psd.uchicago.edu/apply/

Application deadlines
Fall admission:
U.S. students: December 15   *Int'l. students*: December 15

Application fee
U.S. students: $90   *Int'l. students*: $90
No mid-year admissions.

Admissions information
For Fall of 2018:
   Number of applicants: 642
   Number admitted: 95
   Number enrolled: 27

Admission requirements
Bachelor's degree requirements: Bachelor's degree in any Physical Science or Engineering is required.

GRE requirements
The GRE is required.
Taking the GRE well in advance of submitting the application
   is strongly recommended so that an applicant can self-report
   the scores before submitting the application. Score verification is done electronically.

Subjective GRE requirements
The Subjective GRE is required.
Taking the October 2018 Physics Subject Test is required.

TOEFL requirements
The TOEFL exam is required for students from non-English-
   speaking countries.
   iBT score: 102
Minimum total score: 102. Minimum scores for the subsections:
   26, 26, 24, and 26 (24 is the minimum required for the Speaking Section). IELTS accepted instead of TOEFL; 7 each area
   is the minimum required.

Other admissions information
Undergraduate preparation assumed: Equivalent of Marion and
   Thornton, Classical Dynamics of Particles and Systems; Reif,
   Statistical and Thermal Physics; Wangsness, Electromagnetic
   Fields: Shankar, Principles of Quantum Mechanics; Eisberg
   and Resnick, Quantum Physics of Atoms, Molecules, Solids,
   Nuclei and Particles; Kittel, Introduction to Solid State Phys-
   ics, 8th ed. Some research experience.

TUITION

Tuition year 2018–2019:
   Full-time students: $17,934 per quarter
Annual tuition charge per academic year is $53,802 (or $17,934
   per quarter for three quarters). In the Summer Quarter regular
   Research Assistants register for a research course, and there-
   fore the 4th quarter tuition becomes due. However, all RAs
   receive full tuition coverage.
Credit hours per semester to be considered full-time: 3
Deferred tuition plan:
Health insurance: Available at the cost of $3,972 per year.
Other academic fees: $388 per quarter student life fee; $60 one-
   time transcript fee.
Academic term: Quarter
Number of first-year students who received full tuition waivers: 38

Teaching Assistants, Research Assistants, and Fellowships
   Number of first-year
      Fellowship students: 9
   Average stipend per academic year
      Teaching Assistant: $24,225
      Research Assistant: $24,225
      Fellowship student: $24,225
   Please note that some students may alternate between RA and
   TA assignments quarterly.

FINANCIAL AID

Application deadlines
Fall admission:

U.S. students: December 15   *Int'l. students*: December 15

Loans

Loans are available for U.S. students.
Loans are available for international students.
GAPSFAS application required: No
FAFSA application required: No

For further information

Address financial aid inquiries to: Graduate Admissions, Department of Physics, University of Chicago, 5720 S. Ellis Ave., Chicago, IL 60637.
Phone: (773) 702-7007
E-mail: aschulz@uchicago.edu
Financial aid website: http://physics.uchicago.edu

HOUSING

Availability of on-campus housing

Single students: Yes
Married students: Yes
Childcare Assistance: Yes

For further information

Address housing inquiries to: Graduate Student Housing Office, 5555 S. Ellis Avenue, Chicago, IL 60637.
Phone: (773) 753-2218
E-mail: rshousing@uchicago.edu
Housing aid website: http://rs.uchicago.edu

Table A—Faculty, Enrollments, and Degrees Granted

Research Specialty	2014–15 Faculty	Enrollment Fall 2014		Number of Degrees Granted 2017–2018 (2008–2018)		
		Master's	Doctorate	Master's	Terminal Master's	Doctorate
Astrophysics	9	–	16	4(4)	–	2(31)
Atomic, Molecular, & Optical Physics	3	–	11	–	–	1(4)
Biophysics	4	–	6	1(1)	–	1(8)
Chemical Physics	–	–	–	–	–	–(6)
Condensed Matter Physics	17	–	55	3(3)	–	6(49)
Nuclear Physics	1	–	4	–	–	–(1)
Particles and Fields	17	–	53	–	–	3(40)
Physics of Beams	2	–	–	–	–	–(1)
Relativity & Gravitation	2	–	4	–	–	–(6)
Non-specialized	–	–	27	10(110)	1(5)	–
Total	55	–	149	18(118)	1(5)	13(145)
Full-time Grad. Stud.	–	–	168	–	–	–
First-year Grad. Stud.	–	–	38	–	–	–

GRADUATE DEGREE REQUIREMENTS

Master's: Although students are not admitted to study for a Master's, they may receive a Master's degree while studying for the Ph.D. For the Master's degree, there is a minimum residence requirement of three-quarters of full-time registration or the equivalent, nine quarter-length courses. In addition, a student must pass nine approved graduate courses and complete the experimental physics requirement, with a GPA of 2.5 or better overall. There is no thesis or foreign language requirement.

Doctorate: There is a minimum residence requirement of nine quarters of full-time registration. The candidate must pass the advanced physics laboratory course or participate in a first-year experimental research experience, and also pass six advanced physics courses. Four of these advanced courses must be selected from course offerings in either three or four general categories associated with active areas of contemporary physics research; the remaining two must be advanced, seminar-type elective courses. Other requirements include convening a first/introductory meeting of the Ph.D. Committee, a pre-oral meeting to discuss the substantive issues of the dissertation, defending the dissertation before the candidate's Ph.D. Committee, and submitting a paper based on the dissertation to a recognized journal. Normally, at the pre-oral meeting, preceding submission of the thesis, the Ph.D. Committee and the student decide whether the paper to be submitted will be a single-authored or multiple-authored paper.

Thesis: Electronic submission of the final thesis to the Dissertation Office is required of all students.

SPECIAL EQUIPMENT, FACILITIES, OR PROGRAMS

The Department of Physics at the University of Chicago offers Ph.D. programs in many areas of physics. Students' formal classwork takes place in the modern lecture halls, classrooms, and instructional laboratories of the Kersten Physics Teaching Center. This building also houses special equipment and support facilities for student experimental projects, departmental administrative offices, and meeting rooms. The Center is situated on the science quadrangle near the John Crerar Science Library, which holds over 1,000,000 volumes and provides modern literature search and data retrieval systems.

Student participation is crucial to virtually all research projects, and both graduate and undergraduate research and training are given high priority. Most of the experimental and theoretical research of Physics faculty and graduate students is carried out within the Enrico Fermi Institute, the James Franck Institute, and the Institute for Biophysical Dynamics. These research institutes provide close interdisciplinary contact, crossing the traditional boundaries between departments.

In the Enrico Fermi Institute, members of the Department of Physics carry out theoretical research in particle theory, string theory, field theory, general relativity, and theoretical astrophysics and cosmology. There are active experimental groups in high-energy physics, nuclear physics, astrophysics and space physics, infrared and optical astronomy, electron and ion microscopy, and atomic physics. Some of this research is conducted at the Fermi National Accelerator Laboratory, at Argonne National Laboratory, and at the European Organization for Nuclear Research (CERN) in Geneva, Switzerland.

Physics faculty in the James Franck Institute study chemical, solid state, condensed matter, and statistical physics. Fields of interest include chaos, chemical kinetics, critical phenomena, high Tc superconductivity, nonlinear dynamics, low temperature, disordered and amorphous systems, the dynamics of glasses, fluid dynamics, surface and interface phenomena, nonlinear and nanoscale optics, unstable and metastable systems, laser cooling and trapping, and polymer physics. Much of the research utilizes specialized facilities operated by the Institute, including a low-temperature laboratory, a materials preparation laboratory, X-ray diffraction and analytical chemistry laboratories, laser equipment, a scanning-tunneling microscope, and extensive shop facilities. Some members of the faculty are involved in research at Argonne National Laboratory.

The Institute for Biophysical Dynamics includes members of both the Physical Sciences and Biological Sciences Divisions, and focuses on the physical basis for molecular and cellular processes. This interface between the physical and biological sciences is an exciting and rapidly developing area, with a bi-directional impact. Research topics include the creation of physical materials by biological self-assembly, the molecular basis of macromolecular interactions and cellular signaling, the derivation of sequence-structure-function relationships by computational means, and structure-function relationships in membranes.

In the areas of chemical, atomic, and biophysics, research toward the doctorate may be done in either the Physics or the Chemistry Department. Facilities are available for research in crystal chemistry, degenerate quantum gases, molecular physics, molecular spectra from infrared to far ultraviolet and Raman spectra, both experimental and theoretical, surface physics, statistical mechanics, radio chemistry, and quantum electronics.

Interdisciplinary research leading to a Ph.D. degree in physics may be carried out under the guidance of faculty committees including members of other departments in the Physical Sciences Division, such as Astronomy and Astrophysics, Chemistry, Computer Science, Geophysical Sciences, Mathematics, or related departments in the Biological Sciences Division.

Table B—Separately Budgeted Research Expenditures by Source of Support

Source of Support	Departmental Research	Physics-related Research Outside Department
Federal government	$18,966,529	$3,059,941
State/local government		
Non-profit organizations	$576,130	
Business and industry	$168,904	
Other	$1,862,120	
Total	$21,573,683	$3,059,941

Table C—Separately Budgeted Research Expenditures by Research Specialty

Research Specialty	No. of Grants	Expenditures ($)
Astrophysics	38	$9,873,604
Atmosphere, Space Physics, Cosmic Rays	9	$349,680
Atomic, Molecular, & Optical Physics	14	$1,000,551
Biophysics	10	$1,128,270
Condensed Matter Physics	43	$1,777,289
Particles and Fields	39	$645,374
Physics of Beams	10	$675,911
Relativity & Gravitation	9	$4,881,198
Solid State Physics	1	$1,192,586
Statistical & Thermal Physics	2	$46,268
Other	1	$2,950
Total	176	$21,573,681

FACULTY

Professor

Blucher, Edward C., Ph.D., Cornell University, 1988. *High Energy Physics, Particles and Fields*. Experimental physics; particle physics.

Carena, Marcela, Ph.D., University of Hamburg, 1989. Scientist, Fermilab. *Particles and Fields*. Theoretical physics; elementary particles.

Carlstrom, John E., Ph.D., University of California, Berkeley, 1988. Professor of Astronomy & Astrophysics. Chairman, Department of Astronomy & Astrophysics. *Astronomy, Astrophysics, Cosmology & String Theory*. Experimental physics and astrophysics; star formation and cosmology; observation and new instrumentation.

Chin, Cheng, Ph.D., Stanford University, 2001. *Atomic, Molecular, & Optical Physics*. Laser cooling; trapping, degenerate quantum gases.

Collar, Juan I., Ph.D., University of South Carolina, 1992. *Astrophysics, Nuclear Physics*. Experimental physics; neutrino and astroparticle physics.

Frisch, Henry, Ph.D., University of California, Berkeley, 1971. *Particles and Fields*. Experimental physics; particle physics.

Gardel, Margaret L., Ph.D., Harvard University, 2004. Director, Materials Research & Engineering Center. *Biophysics, Condensed Matter Physics*. Experimental biophysics.

Guyot-Sionnest, Philippe, Ph.D., University of California, Berkeley, 1987. Professor of Chemistry. Experimental physics; surface physics; nonlinear optical spectroscopy.

Harvey, Jeffrey A., Ph.D., California Institute of Technology, 1981. *Cosmology & String Theory, Particles and Fields*. Theoretical physics; particle physics; quantum field theory; superstring theory.

Holz, Daniel E., Ph.D., University of Chicago, 1998. *Astrophysics, Cosmology & String Theory, Relativity & Gravitation*. General relativity, astrophysics, cosmology.

Isaacs, Eric, Ph.D., Massachusetts Institute of Technology, 1988. Executive Vice President for Research. *Condensed Matter Physics*. Experimental physics; condensed matter physics.

Jaeger, Heinrich M., Ph.D., University of Minnesota, 1987. *Condensed Matter Physics*. Experimental condensed matter physics; mesoscopic physics; high-temperature superconductivity.

Kang, Woowon, Ph.D., Princeton University, 1992. *Condensed Matter Physics*. Experimental condensed matter physics; fractional quantum Hall effect; semiconductor physics.

Kim, Kwang-Je, Ph.D., University of Maryland, 1970. Senior Scientist, Argonne National Laboratory. *Physics of Beams*. Theoretical physics; beam physics.

Kim, Young-Kee, Ph.D., University of Rochester, 1990. Chair, Department of Physics. *Accelerator, High Energy Physics, Particles and Fields*. Experimental elementary particle physics; accelerator physics.

Kutasov, David, Ph.D., Weizmann Institute of Science, 1989. *Cosmology & String Theory, Particles and Fields*. Theoretical physics; quantum field theory; string theory.

Levin, Kathryn, Ph.D., Harvard University, 1970. *Atomic, Molecular, & Optical Physics, Condensed Matter Physics*. Theoretical physics; solid-state physics.

Littlewood, Peter B., Ph.D., University of Cambridge, 1980. *Condensed Matter Physics*. Condensed matter theory.

Martinec, Emil J., Ph.D., Cornell University, 1984. Director, Kadanoff Center for Theoretical Physics. *Cosmology & String Theory, Particles and Fields*. Theoretical physics; string theory; quantum field theory; elementary particles.

Meyer, Stephan S., Ph.D., Princeton University, 1979. Professor of Astronomy & Astrophysics. *Astronomy, Astrophysics, Cosmology & String Theory*. Experimental astrophysics; infrared astrophysics; observational cosmology.

Nagaitsev, Sergei, Ph.D., Indiana University, 1995. Scientist and Head of Accelerator Division at Fermi National Accelerator Laboratory. *Accelerator*.

Nagel, Sidney R., Ph.D., Princeton University, 1974. *Condensed Matter Physics, Fluids, Rheology, Nonlinear Dynamics and Complex Systems*. Experimental physics; condensed matter physics; nonlinear dynamics.

Oreglia, Mark J., Ph.D., Stanford University, 1980. *High Energy Physics, Particles and Fields*. Experimental physics; particle physics.

Privitera, Paolo, Ph.D., Karlsruhe University, 1993. Professor of Astronomy & Astrophysics. *Astronomy, Astrophysics*. Experimental physics; ultrahigh-energy cosmic rays.

Rosner, Robert, Ph.D., Harvard University, 1976. Professor of Astronomy & Astrophysics. *Astrophysics, Fluids, Rheology, Plasma and Fusion*. Theoretical physics; fluid and plasma dynamics; solar physics; high-energy astrophysics.

Savard, Guy, Ph.D., McGill University, 1988. Senior Scientist, Argonne National Laboratory. *Nuclear Physics*. Experimental physics; nuclear physics.

Sethi, Savdeep S., Ph.D., Harvard University, 1996. *Cosmology & String Theory, High Energy Physics, Particles and Fields*. Theoretical physics; quantum field theory; string theory; particle physics.

Shochet, Melvyn J., Ph.D., Princeton University, 1972. *High Energy Physics, Particles and Fields*. Experimental particle physics.

Son, Dam Thanh, Ph.D., Institute for Nuclear Research, Moscow, 1995. Theoretical nuclear physics. *Theoretical Physics*.

Turner, Michael S., Ph.D., Stanford University, 1978. Professor of Astronomy & Astrophysics. Director, Kavli Institute for Cosmological Physics. *Astrophysics, Cosmology & String Theory*. Theoretical astrophysics; particle physics; cosmology.

Vitelli, Vincenzo, Ph.D., Harvard University, 2006. *Condensed Matter Physics*. condensed matter theory, geometrical and topological properties of soft materials.

Wagner, Carlos E. M., Ph.D., Hamburg, 1989. Physicist, Argonne National Laboratory. *High Energy Physics, Particles and Fields*. Theoretical physics; elementary particles; supersymmetric theories.

Wah, Yau W., Ph.D., Yale University, 1983. *High Energy Physics, Particles and Fields*. Experimental physics; particle physics.

Wakely, Scott P., Ph.D., University of Minnesota, 1999. Director, Enrico Fermi Institute. *Astrophysics*. Experimental astroparticle physics, high-energy astrophysics.

Wald, Robert M., Ph.D., Princeton University, 1972. *Relativity & Gravitation*. Theoretical physics; general relativity.

Wang, LianTao, Ph.D., University of Michigan, 2002. *High Energy Physics, Particles and Fields*. Theoretical physics; elementary particles.

Wiegmann, Paul B., Ph.D., Landau Inst., Moscow, 1978. Director, James Franck Institute. *Condensed Matter Physics*. Theoretical physics; condensed matter physics.

Young, Linda, Ph.D., University of California, Berkeley, 1981. Distinguished Fellow, Argonne National Laboratory. *Atomic, Molecular, & Optical Physics*. atomic physics and x-ray physics.

Associate Professor

Irvine, William T., Ph.D., University of California, Santa Barbara, 2006. *Condensed Matter Physics, Electromagnetism*. Experimental soft condensed matter; knotted fields.

Levin, Michael, Ph.D., MIT, 2006. *Condensed Matter Physics*.

Rust, Michael J., Ph.D., Harvard University, 2010. Assistant Professor of Molecular Genetics and Cell Biology. *Biophysics*.

Ryu, Shinsei, Ph.D., University of Tokyo, 2005. *Condensed Matter Physics*. nanoscale physics, strongly correlated systems.

Schuster, David I., Ph.D., Yale University, 2007. *Condensed Matter Physics*. Experimental condensed matter; quantum computing; superconducting circuits.

Simon, Jonathan, Ph.D., Harvard University, 2010. Experimental atomic, molecular, and optical physics.

Zhang, Wendy W., Ph.D., Harvard University, 2001. *Condensed Matter Physics, Fluids, Rheology, Nonlinear Dynamics and Complex Systems*. Condensed matter theory.

Assistant Professor

Grandi, Luca, Ph.D., Universita degli Studi di Pavia, 2005. *Astrophysics*. Experimental physics; dark matter, and astroparticle physics.

Miller, David, Ph.D., Stanford University, 2011. *Particles and Fields*.

Murugan, Arvind, Ph.D., Princeton University, 2009. *Condensed Matter Physics, Theoretical Physics*.

Palmer, Stephanie, Ph.D., Oxford, 2001. Assistant Professor, Dept. of Organismal Biology and Anatomy. *Biophysics*. biophysics and neuroscience.

Schmitz, David, Ph.D., Columbia University, 2008. Experimental particle physics; experimental neutrino physics.

Vieregg, Abigail, Ph.D., UCLA, 2010. *Astrophysics*.

Emeritus

Geroch, Robert P., Ph.D., Princeton University, 1967. *Relativity & Gravitation*. Theoretical physics; general relativity.

Hildebrand, Roger H., Ph.D., University of California, Berkeley, 1951. *Astronomy*. Experimental physics; infrared astronomy.

Levi-Setti, Riccardo, Ph.D., University of Pavia, Italy, 1949. Experimental physics; ion microscopy; secondary ion mass spectrometry; ion-solid interaction.

Mazenko, Gene F., Ph.D., Massachusetts Institute of Technology, 1971. *Condensed Matter Physics, Systems Science/Engineering*. Theoretical physics; statistical physics.

Merritt, Frank S., Ph.D., California Institute of Technology, 1976. *Particles and Fields*. Experimental physics; particle physics.

Rosner, Jonathan L., Ph.D., Princeton University, 1965. *High Energy Physics, Particles and Fields*. Theoretical physics; particle physics; field theory.

Schiffer, John P., Ph.D., Yale University, 1954. Senior Physicist, Argonne National Laboratory. *Nuclear Physics*. Experimental physics; nuclear physics.

Professor Emeritus

Müller, Dietrich, Ph.D., University of Bonn, 1964. *Astrophysics*. Experimental physics; cosmic rays; high-energy astrophysics.

Parker, Eugene N., Ph.D., California Institute of Technology, 1951. *Astrophysics, Plasma and Fusion*. Theoretical physics; astrophysics; plasma physics; space physics.

Pilcher, James E., Ph.D., Princeton University, 1968. *High Energy Physics, Particles and Fields*. Experimental physics; particle physics.

Witten, Thomas A., Ph.D., University of California, San Diego, 1971. *Condensed Matter Physics, Polymer Physics/Science*. Theoretical physics; weakly connected matter.

Senior Lecturer

Gazes, Stuart B., Ph.D., Massachusetts Institute of Technology, 1983. Undergraduate Program Chair. *Nuclear Physics*. Experimental physics; nuclear physics.

Reid, David D., Ph.D., Wayne State University, 1995. Executive Officer. *Atomic, Molecular, & Optical Physics, Physics and other Science Education, Relativity & Gravitation*. Theoretical physics, discrete space-time, electron- and positron-gas scattering; physics pedagogy.

DEPARTMENTAL RESEARCH SPECIALTIES AND STAFF

Theoretical

Astrophysics & Cosmology. Cosmology and early universe particle physics. Big-bang nucleosynthesis. Tests of the Big Bang model. Ultrahigh-energy cosmic-ray processes. Baryogenesis and cosmological phase transitions. Topological defects. Inflationary cosmology. Cosmic microwave background radiation. Dark matter. Formation of structure in the universe. The cosmological constant and dark energy. Aspects of string cosmology. Solar and stellar astrophysics. Astrophysical fluid dynamics. Holz, Parker, Robert Rosner, Turner, Wagner, Wang.

Atomic, Molecular, & Optical Physics. Trapped Fermi and Bose gases. Ionization dynamics. Inner-shell physics of atoms, molecules, and clusters, strong-field and electron-correlation effects. Free-electron lasers. Ultrafast laser-induced phenomena. Electronic many-body theory. Non-Hermiticity in quantum mechanics. Kathryn Levin.

Biophysics. statistical physics, nonequilibrium phenomena, neuroscience. Murugan, Palmer, Witten.

Condensed Matter Physics. Macroscopic dynamics of materials, interfacial singularities, and non-linear processes. Turbulent, chaotic, and stochastic behavior in hydrodynamic and other dynamical systems. Spatial self-organization in polymers, surfactant monolayers, colloids and cell assemblies. Physics of magnetic and superconducting materials (systems) driven by a strong interaction. Physics in low dimensions. Fermi liquid and non-Fermi liquid states in many body systems. High temperature superconductivity. Quantum phase transitions. Phase ordering kinetics and defect dynamics. Non-perturbative phenomena in electronic systems; strongly correlated electronic systems, magnetism. Transition between jammed and fluid states in granular matter, glass-forming liquids, and magnetic flux lattices. Integrable models of statistical mechanics and quantum field theory. Stochastic processes. Irvine, Kathryn Levin, Michael Levin, Littlewood, Mazenko, Murugan, Ryu, Son, Vitelli, Wiegmann, Witten, Zhang.

Particle Physics & String Theory. String theory and unification, duality in gauge theory and string theory, solitons and topological structures, precision electroweak measurements, dark matter candidates, effective field theory, electroweak baryogenesis, low-energy supersymmetry, CP violation, heavy quark physics, confinement in QCD, quantum theory of black holes, large extra dimensions, fermion mass hierarchy, integrable systems. Carena, Harvey, Kutasov, Martinec, Jonathan Rosner, Sethi, Son, Wagner, Wang.

Relativity & Gravitation. Black holes. Asymptotic structure. Gravitational radiation. Mathematical aspects of general relativity. Quantum field theory in curved space-times. Quantum gravitation. Alternative theories. Geroch, Holz, Wald.

Experimental

Accelerator Physics. Investigation of particle and photon beams and their mutual interactions with the goal of developing novel accelerators or radiation devices. Some current topics are production and acceleration of high-brightness electron beams for linear colliders and free electron lasers; beam dynamics in ionization cooling for muon colliders and neutrino factories; self-amplified spontaneous emission for intense, coherent X-rays; miniature IR radiation source via Smith-Purcell process using electron microscope beams. Theoretical and experimental programs at the Enrico Fermi Institute on campus, at the Argonne National Laboratory Advanced Photon Source, and the A0 facility in Fermilab. Kwang-Je Kim, Young-Kee Kim, Nagaitsev.

Astrophysics. Studies of the cosmic microwave background radiation spectrum and anisotropy with ground and space-based detectors. Search for polarization in the cosmic background radiation. Measurements of the Sunyaev-Zel'dovich effect for clusters of galaxies. Measurements of intergalactic radiation fields. High-energy gamma-ray astrophysics with atmospheric Cherenkov telescopes. Development of giant air shower array (Auger Project) for investigation of the highest energy cosmic rays. Development of large detectors for high-energy cosmic rays on space and balloon payloads. Experimental investigations of cosmic ray electrons and of the elemental and isotopic abundances of cosmic-ray nuclei over a wide energy range. Investigations of solar, magnetospheric, and heliospheric phenomena with satellite and deep space missions. Cosmic dust studies. Development of instruments to detect polarization in the far-infrared emission from interstellar clouds. Investigation of the magnetic field structure of dense cloud cores. Airborne and mountain-top polarimetry. Direct

searches for non-baryonic dark matter. Accelerator-based nuclear astrophysics experiments. Carlstrom, Collar, Grandi, Hildebrand, Müller, Meyer, Privitera, Vieregg, Wakely.

Atomic, Molecular, & Optical Physics. Bose-Einstein condensation of molecules and fermionic superfluids. Laser cooling and trapping of atoms. Scalable quantum manipulation and quantum computation. Testing time-reversal symmetry in atoms and nuclei. Chin, Simon, Young.

Biophysics. Cell migration and division, physical aspects of biological organization, mechanical behavior of cells, regulation of cell physiology, nonlinear dynamics, computational biology, time-resolved fluorescence, confocal microscopy, protein-engineering, signal transduction, gene expression, mathematical modeling, large-scale simulations, stochastic and self-assembly processes, elasticity of polymer networks, optical and holographic traps, single-molecule biophysics, nonlinear optics methods, noise and information in intraneuronal pathways and interneuronal communication, homeostatic regulation of single neuronal function and of the function of small neural circuits, design principles of biological networks, biophysics in vivo — quantifying behavior and physiological activity of neurons, high-power computation (grid and parallel computing), biophysics of sleep. Gardel, Rust.

Condensed Matter Physics. Optical and electronic transport in normal and superconducting nanocrystals and arrays. Collective effects at ultra-low temperatures including (fractional) quantum Hall effect, vortex tunneling, metal-insulator transitions, and magnetic quantum critical points. Symmetry-breaking and fluctuations in heavy fermion, organic, and high-Tc superconductors. Nonlinear dynamics and flow properties of granular materials. Scaling behavior of liquid flow and droplet breakup. Mathematical analysis and computer simulation of singularity formation. Universal scaling behavior of relaxation phenomena in supercooled liquids and glasses. Microscopic kinetics and dynamics of phase transitions in colloidal suspensions. Manipulation by dynamic optical holographic traps. Molecular regulation within living cells. Self-assembly and morphology of ultrathin polymer films. Biological properties of the cytoskeleton of eukaryotic cells. The mechanical behavior of cells. Chin, Guyot-Sionnest, Irvine, Isaacs, Jaeger, Kang, Nagel, Schuster, Simon.

Nuclear Physics. Studies of the nuclear many-body system: Nuclear structure and interactions, nuclear reactions in astrophysics, nuclear matter under extreme conditions, precision measurements of critical information to nucleosynthesis along the r- and rp-process paths. Low-energy experiments in fundamental interactions and symmetries, exotic nuclear structure, double beta decay, coherent nuclear scattering. Production, cooling and trapping of rare isotopes, R&D for the Rare Isotope Accelerator (RIA) project. Non-nucleonic degrees of freedom in nuclei and phenomena requiring a quark description. Collar, Savard, Schiffer.

Particles and Fields. Measurements of properties of the top quark. Searches for supersymmetric particles, the Higgs boson, and other new physics. Precision tests of the standard model in W and Z decays. Studies of pp interactions at center-of-mass energies of 1800 GeV. High-precision measurement of CP violation parameters in K decays; high-sensitivity search for rare K decays and for CPT violation. High-precision measurements of hyperon rare decays. High-precision measurements of electroweak interactions at LEP, both near the Z0 and at center-of-mass energies up to 200 GeV. Searches for new physics including the Higgs boson and supersymmetry; precision measurement of Mw. Preparation for the ATLAS experiment at the LHC (high-energy pp interactions at 14 TeV). Research and development on muon colliders and neutrino factories. Use of facilities at Fermi National Accelerator Laboratory and at CERN. Blucher, Frisch, Young-Kee Kim, Merritt, Miller, Nagaitsev, Oreglia, Pilcher, Jonathan Rosner, Schmitz, Shochet, Wah.

UNIVERSITY OF ILLINOIS AT CHICAGO

DEPARTMENT OF PHYSICS

Chicago, Illinois 60607
http://phys.uic.edu/

General University Information
President: Timothy L. Killeen
Dean of Graduate School: Karen J. Colley
University website: http://www.uic.edu
School Type: Public
Setting: Urban
Total Faculty: 1,941
Total Graduate Faculty: 1,589
Total number of Students: 30,539
Total number of Graduate Students: 7,915

Department Information
Department Chairman: Prof. David Hofman, Head
Department Contact: James Nell, Graduate Advisor
  Total full-time faculty: 24
  Full-Time Graduate Students: 86
  Female Full-Time Graduate Students: 23
  First-Year Graduate Students: 12
  Female First-Year Students: 3
  Total Post Doctorates: 8

Department Address
845 West Taylor Street, Room 2236
SES, MC 273
Chicago, IL 60607
Phone: (312) 996-3400
Fax: (312) 996-9016
E-mail: physics@uic.edu
Website: http://phys.uic.edu/

ADMISSIONS

Admission Contact Information
Address admission inquiries to: Graduate Admissions, Department of Physics, MC 273, 845 W. Taylor #2236 SES, Chicago, IL 60607-7059., or FAX: (312) 996-9016
Phone: (312) 996-3400
E-mail: physics@uic.edu
Admissions website: https://grad.uic.edu/admissions

Application deadlines
Fall admission:
U.S. students: March 15   *Int'l. students*: February 15

Application fee
U.S. students: $70   *Int'l. students*: $100
December 15 for consideration for the University Fellowship.

Admissions information
For Fall of 2017:
  Number of applicants: 148
  Number admitted: 43
  Number enrolled: 12

Admission requirements
Bachelor's degree requirements: Bachelor's degree is required. Prior academic work must include at least 20 semester hours of physics, including upper-level undergraduate electrodynamics, quantum mechanics, and classical mechanics.
Minimum undergraduate GPA: 2.75

GRE requirements
The GRE is required.

Subjective GRE requirements
The Subjective GRE is recommended.

TOEFL requirements
The TOEFL exam is required for students from non-English-speaking countries.
  PBT score: 550
  iBT score: 80
Minimum TOEFL subscores: Listening 17 Writing 21 Reading 19 Speaking 20

Other admissions information
Additional requirements: A complete application will include an online application and payment of the application fee (http://www.uic.edu/depts/oar/grad/apply_grad_degree.html); electronic transcripts for previous post-secondary coursework and proof of any degrees earned (if in a language other than English, an electronic certified translated copy is also required); GRE and TOEFL or IELTS scores (minimum acceptable scores: TOEFL paper based 550; computer based statement 213; iBT-80; IELTS 6.5 total); 3 electronic letters of recommendation; an academic statement of purpose; an application for graduate appointment if applying for financial assistance.
Undergraduate preparation assumed: Thornton and Marion - Classical Dynamics; Griffiths - Introduction to Electrodynamics; Gould and Tobochnik - Statistical and Thermal Physics; Griffiths - Introduction to Quantum Mechanics.

TUITION

Tuition year 2018–19:
Tuition for in-state residents
  Full-time students: $5,830 per semester
  Part-time students: $3,887 per semester
Tuition for out-of-state residents
  Full-time students: $11,950 per semester
  Part-time students: $7,967 per semester
Tuition is waived for all students with assistantships.
Credit hours per semester to be considered full-time: 12
Deferred tuition plan: Yes
Health insurance: Available at the cost of $1140 per year.
Other academic fees: Between $1,800-$2,100/semester-dependent on number of credits (figures include the $570/sem. health insurance fee). All fees are waived for students with assistantships except $431 general fee and a portion of $570 health insurance fee.
Academic term: Semester
Number of first-year students who received full tuition waivers: 12

Teaching Assistants, Research Assistants, and Fellowships
Number of first-year
  Teaching Assistants: 12
Average stipend per academic year
  Teaching Assistant: $18,650
  Research Assistant: $18,650

Outstanding physics graduate students have also received graduate college fellowships (http://grad.uic.edu/graduate-college-fellowship-and-award-deadlines).

FINANCIAL AID

Application deadlines
Fall admission:
U.S. students: February 15

Loans
Loans are available for U.S. students.
Loans are not available for international students.
GAPSFAS application required: No
FAFSA application required: Yes

For further information
Address financial aid inquiries to: Graduate Admissions, Department of Physics, M/C 273, 845 W. Taylor #2236 SES, Chicago, IL 60607-7059.
Phone: (312) 996-3400
E-mail: physics@uic.edu
Financial aid website: http://www.uic.edu/depts/financialaid/

HOUSING

Availability of on-campus housing
Single students: Yes
Married students: No
Childcare Assistance: No

For further information
Address housing inquiries to: University of Illinois at Chicago (M/C 579), 818 S. Wolcott St., Chicago, IL 60612.
Phone: (312) 355-6300
E-mail: housing@uic.edu
Housing aid website: http://www.housing.uic.edu

Table A—Faculty, Enrollments, and Degrees Granted

Research Specialty	2016–2017 Faculty	Enrollment Fall 2017		Number of Degrees Granted 2016–17 (2011–17)		
		Master's	Doctorate	Master's	Terminal Master's	Doctorate
Atomic, Molecular, & Optical Physics	–	–	–	–	–	–(5)
Biophysics	4	–	10	1(2)	–(1)	–(9)
Condensed Matter Physics	8	1	32	3(11)	–(3)	3(21)
Energy Sources & Environment	1	–	2	–(2)	–	1(1)
High Energy Heavy Ion Physics	5	–	11	–(4)	–(1)	1(4)
High Energy Particle Physics, Particles and Fields	6	–	9	–	–	1(14)
Non-specialized	–	5	16	–	1(23)	–
Total	24	6	81	4(19)	1(28)	6(54)
Full-time Grad. Stud.	–	6	81	–	–	–
First-year Grad. Stud.	–	–	12	–	–	–

GRADUATE DEGREE REQUIREMENTS

Master's: The general requirement for the Master of Science is satisfactory completion of 32 semester hours of work in courses approved by the department. At least 20 of these hours must be at the 500 level; they must include Physics 501 and 502 (Electrodynamics) and Physics 511 and 512 (Quantum Mechanics), and may not include more than 4 hours of Physics 596 (Individual Study) or more than 8 hours of Physics 598 (Master's Thesis Research).

Doctorate: The minimum requirements for the Ph.D. are: (1) The satisfactory completion of 96 semester hours of course work approved by the department, including at least 36 hours of 500-level courses, exclusive of Physics 596 (Individual Study) and 599 (Thesis Research). These 36 hours must include the sequence Physics 501 and 502 (Electrodynamics), Physics 511 and 512 (Quantum Mechanics), Physics 561 (Statistical Mechanics), at least one complete sequence chosen from among the following: Physics 521 and 522 (Molecular and Laser Physics), Physics 531 and 532 (Solid State Physics), Physics 551 and 552 (Elementary Particle Physics), Physics 513 and 514 (Quantum Field Theory), and five semesters of the Graduate Seminar, Physics 595. (2) Satisfactory performance in a comprehensive qualifying examination consisting of 400-level problems on classical mechanics, electricity and magnetism, quantum mechanics, and thermodynamics and statistical mechanics. This examination may be repeated once but must be passed no later than January of the student's second year in residence. Details on this examination are available from the department office. (3) Satisfactory performance on an oral examination in the general area of the student's doctoral thesis research, which is to be taken within two years after passing the qualifying examination. The examination will normally start with a brief oral report by the student on his or her proposed research. If the performance is only marginally satisfactory, the student may be asked to retake the examination. (4) Satisfactory completion and defense of a doctoral dissertation. (5) Each student is required to serve as a teaching assistant for at least two semesters.

Other Degrees: For physics graduate students interested in science education careers, UIC offers an exciting Masters of Education Degree (MEd) in Instructional Leadership: Science Education (http://www.uic.edu/gcat/EDINLE.shtml). Many physics graduate students who have earned a master's in physics have also earned their MEd degree while at UIC.

Thesis: Thesis may not be written in absentia.

SPECIAL EQUIPMENT, FACILITIES, OR PROGRAMS

Significant onsite research laboratories include the University of Illinois at Chicago (UIC) Research Resources Center, the Microphysics Laboratory, and the Silicon Detector Laboratories for Experimental Particle and Nuclear Physics. These research laboratories contain many notable resources including a new aberration corrected scanning transmission microscope (the UIC JEOL JEM-ARM200CF) located at the Research Resources Center that is the first such instrument in the United States with such a high level of capability. The Microphysics Laboratory has molecular beam epitaxy (MBE), ultrahigh-vacuum growth chambers and surface analytical facilities - as well as helium-3 and dilution refrigerators, an ultrasonic spectrometer, Foner and SQUID magnetometers, a susceptibility balance, a Bruker NMR spectrometer, an atomic force microscopy apparatus, an X-ray diffraction system, an automated adiabatic calorimeter and on-line computer data handling systems with dedicated mini-and microcomputers. The Silicon Detector Laboratories for Experimental Particle and Nuclear Physics has testing equipment and facilities used in the assembly and testing of silicon detectors for large particle and nuclear physics experiments.

Faculty and students are utilizing two major local research laboratories for a wide variety of research; Argonne National Laboratory and Fermilab (located only 22 miles and 35 west of UIC, respectively). Faculty and students are also engaged in materials, laser, and energy research in collaboration with the Pacific Northwest National Laboratory and with the National Renewable Energy Laboratory; use the extensive experimental high-energy particle and nuclear physics facilities of Fermilab, Brookhaven National Laboratory in New York, and CERN in Switzerland; the solid state and the photon source facilities at Argonne National Laboratory and Brookhaven National Laboratory; and the neutron and biophysics related facilities of the NIST Center for Neutron Research, the ISIS facility at the Rutherford Appleton Laboratory in the UK and the ILL (Institut Laue-Langevin) facility in France.

Research is supported by several significant dedicated computer clusters hosted and administered within the department as well as dedicated facilities at the UIC Computer Center including a major UIC Research Computing cluster. UIC is also a major hub of the forefront STARLIGHT advanced research and education high speed network. This high-performance research network is connected to Europe, Asia, and the rest of the world. The UIC Computer Center also hosts campus-wide networks and has wide bandwidth connections to the supercomputer centers at the University of Illinois at Urbana-Champaign and nationwide. Faculty at UIC also hold joint appointments with Argonne National Laboratory which provides additional access to the extensive computing resources available at Argonne.

The Department of Physics research program is supported by a large machine shop with ample equipment and instrument making expertise. The department maintains a sample preparation facility with an arc melter, zone refiner, a spark cutter, X-ray equipment, furnaces, dry boxes, polishing equipment, and other metallurgical instruments.

Table B—Separately Budgeted Research Expenditures by Source of Support

Source of Support	Departmental Research	Physics-related Research Outside Department
Federal government	$3,691,114	
State/local government		
Non-profit organizations		
Business and industry		
Other		
Total	$3,691,114	

Table C—Separately Budgeted Research Expenditures by Research Specialty

Research Specialty	No. of Grants	Expenditures ($)
Biophysics	10	$481,097
Condensed Matter Physics	15	$1,070,231
Energy Sources & Environment	2	$41,409
High Energy Particle Physics, Particles and Fields	11	$1,198,242
High Energy Heavy Ion Physics	6	$900,135
Total	44	$3,691,114

FACULTY

Professor

Ansari, Anjum, Ph.D., University of Illinois at Urbana-Champaign, 1988. *Biophysics*. Biological physics.

Aratyn, Henrik, Ph.D., Copenhagen, N. Bohr Institute, 1984. Associate Dean, College of Liberal Arts and Sciences. *High Energy Physics*. Mathematical physics.

Campuzano, Juan C., Ph.D., University of Wisconsin-Milwaukee, 1978. *Condensed Matter Physics*. Experimental solid-state physics.

Crabtree, George, Ph.D., University of Illinois at Chicago, 1974. *Condensed Matter Physics, Energy Sources & Environment*.

Evdokimov, Olga, Ph.D., Joint Institute for Nuclear Research, Dubna, Russia, 1999. Alternate Director of Undergraduate Studies. *Nuclear Physics*. Experimental high-energy nuclear physics.

Gerber, Cecilia, Ph.D., Universidad de Buenos Aires, 1995. Director of Undergraduate Studies. *High Energy Physics*. Experimental high-energy particle physics.

Grein, Christoph, Ph.D., Princeton University, 1989. Director of Graduate Studies. *Condensed Matter Physics*. Theoretical condensed matter physics.

Hofman, David, Ph.D., Stony Brook University, 1994. Department Head. *Nuclear Physics*. Experimental high-energy nuclear physics.

Klie, Robert F., Ph.D., University of Illinois at Chicago, 2002. *Condensed Matter Physics, Surface Physics*. Atomic-resolution transmission electron microscopy of nanoscale materials systems.

Morr, Dirk, Ph.D., University of Wisconsin-Madison, 1997. *Condensed Matter Physics*. Theoretical condensed matter.

Ogut, Serdar, Ph.D., Yale University, 1995. Alternate Director of Graduate Studies. *Computational Physics, Condensed Matter Physics*. Theoretical condensed matter physics.

Schlossman, Mark, Ph.D., Cornell University, 1987. Associate Department Head. *Biophysics, Condensed Matter Physics*. Experimental soft condensed matter physics, biological physics.

Schroeder, W. Andreas, Ph.D., University of London, Imperial College, 1987. *Condensed Matter Physics*. Ultrafast laser spectroscopy.

Stephanov, Mikhail, Ph.D., University of Oxford, 1994. *Nuclear Physics, Particles and Fields, Theoretical Physics*. Theoretical nuclear and high-energy physics.

Varelas, Nikos, Ph.D., University of Rochester, 1994. Vice Provost for Undergraduate Affairs. *High Energy Physics*. Experimental high-energy particle physics.

Zhou, Huan-Xiang, Ph.D., Drexel University, 1988.

Associate Professor

Cavanaugh, Richard, Ph.D., Florida State University, 1999. *High Energy Physics*. Experimental high-energy particle physics.

Imbo, Tom, Ph.D., University of Texas, 1988. *High Energy Physics, Theoretical Physics, Other*. High-energy theory, mathematical physics, foundations of quantum physics.

Assistant Professor

Khalili-Araghi, Fatemeh, Ph.D., University of Illinois at Urbana-Champaign, 2010. *Biophysics, Computational Physics*. Computational biophysics.

Mills, Corrinne, Ph.D., University of California, Santa Barbara. *High Energy Physics*. Experimental particles physics.

Park, Hyowon, Ph.D., Rutgers University, 2011. *Computational Physics, Condensed Matter Physics*. Theoretical and Computational Condensed Matter and Materials Physics.

Perez-Salas, Ursula, Ph.D., University of Maryland, 2000. *Biophysics*. Biological physics.

Ye, Zhenyu, Ph.D., University of Hamburg, 2006. *Nuclear Physics, Other*. Experimental high-energy nuclear physics, the development of silicon detector technology.

Yee, Ho-Ung, Ph.D., Yale University, 2003. *Nuclear Physics, Theoretical Physics*. Theoretical nuclear and high-energy physics.

Emeritus

Adams, Mark R., Ph.D., Stony Brook University, 1981. *High Energy Physics*. Experimental high-energy particle physics.

Betts, R. Russell, Ph.D., University of Pennsylvania, 1972. *Nuclear Physics*. Nuclear experiment.

Boccara, Nino, Ph.D., 1961. Mathematical physics and modeling.

Bodmer, Arnold, Ph.D., University of Manchester, 1953. Theoretical nuclear physics.

Carhart, Richard, Ph.D., University of Wisconsin-Madison, 1965. Theoretical high-energy physics and environmental physics.

Claus, Helmut, Ph.D., Karlsruhe University, 1965. Experimental solid-state physics.

Faurie, Jean-Pierre, Ph.D., University of Clermont-Ferrand, 1970. Experimental solid-state physics.

Garland, James, Ph.D., University of Chicago, 1966. Theoretical solid-state physics.

Goldberg, Howard, Ph.D., University of California, Berkeley, 1964. Experimental high-energy physics.

Halliwell, Clive, Ph.D., University of Manchester, 1971. *High Energy Physics*. High-energy particle and nuclear physics.

Keung, Wai-Yee, Ph.D., University of Wisconsin-Madison, 1980. *High Energy Physics*. High-energy physics theory and phenomenology.

Licht, Arthur L., Ph.D., University of Maryland, 1963. Theoretical high-energy physics; astrophysics; many-body theory.

McLeod, Donald W., Ph.D., Cornell University, 1962. Experimental high-energy particle and nuclear physics.

McNeil, Edward, Ph.D., University of Illinois at Urbana-Champaign, 1951.

Montano, Pedro, Ph.D., Technion, 1972. Synchrotron radiation science.

Pagnamenta, Antonio, Ph.D., University of Maryland, 1965. Theoretical high-energy physics; microdosimetry; radiation physics.

Rhodes, Charles, Ph.D., Massachusetts Institute of Technology, 1969. *Atomic, Molecular, & Optical Physics*. Laser physics; atomic and molecular physics.

Sharma, Ram R., Ph.D., University of California, Riverside, 1965. Theoretical solid-state physics; biophysics.

Sivananthan, Sivalingham, Ph.D., University of Illinois at Chicago, 1988. Director, Microphysics Laboratory. *Condensed Matter Physics, Materials Science, Metallurgy*. Experimental solid-state physics, material science.

Solomon, Julius, Ph.D., University of California, Berkeley, 1963. Experimental high-energy physics.

Sukhatme, Uday, Ph.D., Massachusetts Institute of Technology, 1971. Theoretical high-energy particle physics.

Research Associate Professor

Chang, Yong, Ph.D., Shanghai Institute of Technical Physics, 1996.

Hahn, Suk-Ryong, Ph.D., Oregon Graduate Institute of Science and Technology, 1993.

Research Assistant Professor

Apanasevich, Leonard, Ph.D., Michigan State University, 2005.

Evdokimov, Anatoly, Institute for Theoretical and Experimental Physics.

Unwin, James, Ph.D., University of Oxford, 2013.

Adjunct Professor

Cho, Michael, Ph.D., Drexel University, 1991.

Dutta, Mitra, Ph.D., University of Cincinnati, 1981.

Kang, TaeWon, Ph.D., Dongguk University, 1982.

Kunde, Gerd, Ph.D., University of Frankfurt, 1994.

Lu, Hui, Ph.D., Beckman Institute, 1999.

Mueller, Mark, Ph.D., Stanford University, 1984.

Norris, James, Ph.D., Washington University, 1968.

Stroscio, Michael, Ph.D., Yale University, 1974.

Visiting Research Assistant Professor

Boguta, John, Ph.D., University of Illinois at Urbana-Champaign, 1968.

Lecturer

Barkan, Adrian, Ph.D., University of Iowa, 1997.

Goeckner, Hans, Ph.D., University of Illinois at Chicago, 1995.

Posdoctoral Research Associate

Basar, Kemal Gokce, Ph.D., University of Connecticut.

Berry, Douglas, Ph.D., University of Notre Dame, 2013.

Jokisaari, Jacob, Ph.D., University of Michigan.

Jung, Kurt, Ph.D., Purdue University, 2016.

Wu, Zhenbin, Ph.D., Baylor University, 2012.

Researcher

Tonjes, Marguerite, Ph.D., Michigan State University.

Other

DeJonghe, Richard, Ph.D., University of Illinois at Chicago, 2013. Visiting Clinical Assistant Professor.

Espinoza, Randall, Ph.D., University of Illinois at Chicago, 2005. Clinical Assistant Professor.

Lefevre, Serguei, Ph.D., Semyonov Institute of Chemical Physics, 1994. Clinical Assistant Professor.

Ugalde, Claudio, Ph.D., University of Notre Dame, 2005. Clinical Assistant Professor.

DEPARTMENTAL RESEARCH SPECIALTIES AND STAFF

Theoretical

Biophysics. Dynamics of nucleic acids, RNA folding, protein-DNA interactions, membrane protein-lipid interactions, structural and dynamics studies in model membranes. Ansari, Khalili-Araghi, Schlossman.

Computational Physics. Multifaceted activities in computational physics which incorporates: high power density plasmas; particle physics; heavy-ion nuclear physics; protein structure and dynamics; materials for energy; ab initio pseudopotential total energy calculations; molecular dynamics simulations. Aratyn, Grein, Khalili-Araghi, Ogut, Park.

Condensed Matter Physics. Metals, semiconductors, and insulators; Density functional electronic structure calculations; cooperative and critical phenomena and phase transitions; Density functional electronic structure calculations; magnetism in disordered systems; structural instabilities; high-Tc superconductivity; surfaces and thin films; ion implantation; thermodynamic and transport properties; optical properties from Raman scattering, ellipsometry, electroreflectance, and photocapacitance; growth by molecular beam epitaxy of II-VI semiconducting epilayers and microstructures such as superlattices and tunneling structures; electronic properties of two-dimensional systems (Shubnikov-Dehaas; Quantum Hall Effect); processing and physics of electronic devices. Grein, Morr, Ogut, Park, Schlossman.

High Energy Physics. Standard model phenomenology, strong and electroweak interactions, Higgs boson and new particle searches, top-quark physics, strings and integrable models, strong and electroweak gauge interactions, CP violation, algebraic and topological aspects of quantum field theory, the foundations of quantum mechanics, quantum information theory, exotic statistics. Aratyn, Imbo, Keung.

Nuclear Physics. Theory of strong interactions (Quantum Chromodynamics) and its applications, such as the physics of neutron stars, heavy-ion collisions, and the quark-gluon plasma. Theory of the tri-critical point in the nuclear phase diagram. Stephanov, Yee.

Experimental

Atomic, Molecular, & Optical Physics. X-ray microimaging and advanced forms of X-ray generation, ultrafast laser spectroscopy. Rhodes, Schroeder.

Biophysics. The primary techniques of X-ray and Neutron Surface Scattering, Laser Temperature-Jump, Single-Molecule FRET, and Fluctuation Correlation Spectroscopy are used to study the following: the dynamics of Nucleic Acids; RNA Folding Protein-DNA Interactions; Membrane Protein-Lipid Interactions; Structure and Dynamics of Lipid-Lipid and Lipid-Cholesterol Interactions in Membranes; Structure and electrostatic interactions at liquid surfaces and interfaces. Ansari, Perez-Salas, Schlossman.

Condensed Matter Physics. Metals, semiconductors, and insulators; Density functional electronic structure calculations; cooperative and critical phenomena and phase transitions; Density functional electronic structure calculations; magnetism in disordered systems; structural instabilities; high-Tc superconductivity; surfaces and thin films; ion implantation; thermodynamic and transport properties; optical properties from Raman scattering, ellipsometry, electroreflectance, and photocapacitance; growth by molecular beam epitaxy of II-VI semiconducting epilayers and microstructures such as superlattices and tunneling structures; electronic properties of two-dimensional systems (Shubnikov-Dehaas; Quantum Hall Effect); processing and physics of electronic devices; Ultrafast laser spectroscopy; Materials for energy; Structure and electrostatic interactions at liquid surfaces and interfaces. Campuzano, Crabtree, Grein, Klie, Park, Schroeder, Sivananthan.

High Energy Physics. Collider physics at the CMS experiment at the Large Hadron Collider in CERN and analysis of data from the D0 Experiment at Fermilab, precision measurements of strong and electroweak interactions, Higgs boson and new particle searches, top-quark physics, searches for new fundamental symmetries in nature and extra dimensions of space, trigger systems development, silicon microstrip tracking detectors; trigger systems and silicon tracker development for CMS detector at CERN LHC. Adams, Cavanaugh, Gerber, Mills, Varelas.

Nuclear Physics. Relativistic heavy ion collision physics, dense nuclear matter, and studies of the quark gluon plasma as measured by the STAR experiment at the Relativistic Heavy Ion Collider (at Brookhaven National Laboratory) and the CMS experiment at the Large Hadron Collider (at CERN, in Geneva Switzerland). Olga Evdokimov, Hofman, Ye.

UNIVERSITY OF ILLINOIS AT URBANA-CHAMPAIGN

DEPARTMENT OF PHYSICS

Urbana, Illinois 61801-3080
http://physics.illinois.edu

General University Information
President: Timothy Killeen
Dean of Graduate School: Wojtek Chodzko-Zajko
University website: http://illinois.edu
School Type: Public
Setting: Urban
Total Faculty: 2,729
Total Graduate Faculty: 2,511
Total number of Students: 48,935
Total number of Graduate Students: 11,613

Department Information
Department Chairman: Prof. Matthias Grosse Perdekamp, Head
Department Contact: Professor S. Lance Cooper, Associate
  Head for Graduate Programs
  Total full-time faculty: 58
  Total number of full-time equivalent positions: 58
  Full-Time Graduate Students: 302
  Female Full-Time Graduate Students: 75
  First-Year Graduate Students: 40
  Female First-Year Students: 14
  Total Post Doctorates: 59

Department Address
Loomis Laboratory of Physics
1110 West Green Street
Urbana, IL 61801-3080
Phone: (217) 333-3645
Fax: (217) 333-4898
E-mail: grad@physics.illinois.edu
Website: http://physics.illinois.edu

ADMISSIONS

Admission Contact Information
Address admission inquiries to: Graduate Office, Department of
  Physics, 1110 W. Green St., Urbana, IL 61801-3080
Phone: (217) 333-3645
E-mail: grad@physics.illinois.edu
Admissions website: http://physics.illinois.edu/admissions/
  graduates/apply.html

Application deadlines
Fall admission:
U.S. students: January 15   *Int'l. students*: January 15

Application fee
U.S. students: $70   *Int'l. students*: $90
The application fee must be paid by a credit card at the time
  an application is submitted online. Payment is valid for only
  one semester and must be submitted before any action is taken
  on an application.

Admissions information
For Fall of 2018:
  Number of applicants: 613
  Number admitted: 149
  Number enrolled: 40

Admission requirements
Bachelor's degree requirements: A bachelor's degree in physics
  or a related field is required. On the last 60 hours of work,
  20 semester hours (30 quarter hours) of intermediate and advanced undergraduate physics are also required.
Minimum undergraduate GPA: 3.0

GRE requirements
The GRE is required.
  Mean GRE score range (25th–75th percentile): 870
  The General Graduate Record Examination (GRE), administered by the Educational Testing Service (ETS), is required.
  The GRE Physics Subject Test is optional. While the application form asks that you provide GRE scores, your official
  score must be sent from ETS directly to the Department of
  Physics by the application deadline (January 15). Please list
  your GRE registration number on your application. The department does not set a minimum GRE score.

Subjective GRE requirements
The Subjective GRE is not required.
No definite minimum score is set for the GRE. The average GRE
  Physics subject score for 2017 admissions was 870.

TOEFL requirements
The TOEFL exam is required for students from non-English-
  speaking countries.
  PBT score: 610
  iBT score: 102
Most students to whom we offer admission are also offered a
  teaching assistantship for financial support. To receive an appointment as a teaching assistant, an international graduate
  student is required to demonstrate proficiency in spoken English. This proficiency can be demonstrated in one of four
  ways: by having a score of 24 or above on the speaking sub-
  section of the Internet Based TOEFL; by having a score of
  8 or above on the speaking sub-section of the IELTS academic
  exam; by having a score of 50 or above on the TSE; or by
  having a score of 5 or above on the locally administered University of Illinois English proficiency interview.

Other admissions information
Additional requirements: Admission to our program is competitive. We have a holistic review process that considers grade-
  point average, research experiences, GRE scores, and potential fit into our research programs. Admissions decisions
  are made by a committee of our senior faculty; please do not
  contact individual professors requesting admission to our program. No informal assessment of your chances for admission
  can be made.
Undergraduate preparation assumed: Although preparation will
  vary, we generally expect one year of upper-division mechanics, one year of electricity and magnetism, one semester of
  optics, one semester of statistical and thermal physics, and
  one year of quantum mechanics. One or two semesters of advanced laboratory courses are also expected.

TUITION

Tuition year 2018–19:
Tuition for in-state residents
  Full-time students: $18,056 annual

Tuition for out-of-state residents
  Full-time students: $34,330 annual
Appointment as a research assistant, teaching assistant, or a fellow provides a full tuition waiver.
Credit hours per semester to be considered full-time: 8
Deferred tuition plan: Yes
Health insurance: Available at the cost of $188 per year.
Other academic fees: A description of fees is posted at http://registrar.illinois.edu/fee-info. Research Assistantships, Teaching Assistantships, and Fellowships include a partial fee waiver.
Academic term: Semester
Number of first-year students who received full tuition waivers: 40

Teaching Assistants, Research Assistants, and Fellowships
  Number of first-year
    Teaching Assistants: 35
    Fellowship students: 5
  Average stipend per academic year
    Teaching Assistant: $23,298
    Research Assistant: $23,298
    Fellowship student: $25,000 The amounts quoted above are for the 11-month calendar year (9-month academic year plus 2-month summer term) for first-year students. Students who have passed their preliminary examination receive an automatic salary increase. The Department of Physics makes every effort to ensure that eligible prospective students are not deterred from attending because of financial constraints, and we are proud of our tradition of providing continuing and adequate support for our students. In case of financial emergencies, short-term loans are available from the University's Office of Student Financial Aid.

FINANCIAL AID

Application deadlines
Fall admission:
U.S. students: January 15   *Int'l. students*: January 15

Loans
Loans are available for U.S. students.
Loans are available for international students.
GAPSFAS application required: No
FAFSA application required: No

For further information
Address financial aid inquiries to: Office of Student Financial Aid.
Phone: (217) 333-0100
E-mail: finaid@illinois.edu
Financial aid website: https://osfa.illinois.edu/

HOUSING

Availability of on-campus housing
  Single students: Yes
  Married students: Yes
  Childcare Assistance: Yes

For further information
Address housing inquiries to: University Housing.
Phone: (217) 333-7111
E-mail: housing@illinois.edu
Housing aid website: http://www.housing.illinois.edu/

GRADUATE DEGREE REQUIREMENTS

Master's: See Academic information on website. Thirty-two hours of satisfactory (GPA 2.75/4.0) graduate course work required. All hours must be at the 400-level or higher. Sixteen of the 32 hours must be in physics, with at least 8 hours of them at the 500-level. At most, 8 hours of individual study may be counted toward the master's degree. At least 16 hours must be in courses meeting on the Urbana-Champaign campus; credit for graduate work taken elsewhere is by petition only. There is no foreign language requirement.

Doctorate: Ninety-six hours of (2.75/4.0 GPA) satisfactory graduate work. Part of these hours must be thesis work. There is no specific residence requirement, but 64 hours must be taken on the Urbana-Champaign campus. The qualifying examination (the "qual") tests the candidate's broad understanding of basic physics and his or her preparation to proceed to thesis research. A student must take and pass the qual by the beginning of the third semester of enrollment in our graduate program. The preliminary examination (the "prelim") reviews the feasibility and appropriateness of a candidate's thesis research proposal. The prelim must be taken within the first two years of joining a research group. The thesis is a comprehensive publication describing the independent research project and its results. The final defense is an oral examination conducted by the candidate's thesis committee and based on the thesis, at which the candidate presents the results of his or her research. There are no foreign language requirements.

Other Degrees: The Medical Scholars Program, which allows students to earn joint M.D./Ph.D. degrees, combines cutting edge research in physics with individualized clinical training in medicine. All graduate and medical training is done at the Urbana-Champaign campus. Only U.S. citizens and permanent residents are eligible for admission.

Thesis: A thesis is required.

SPECIAL EQUIPMENT, FACILITIES, OR PROGRAMS

The Department of Physics offers world-class research facilities in many research areas. For a complete description of physics facilities, please consult our website, http://physics.illinois.edu/research/groups-and-centers/.

Table B—Separately Budgeted Research Expenditures by Source of Support

Source of Support	Departmental Research	Physics-related Research Outside Department
Federal government	$18,504,000	$2,074,000
State/local government	$66,000	
Non-profit organizations	$1,133,000	$87,000
Business and industry	$120,000	
Other	$1,031,000	
Total	$20,854,000	$2,161,000

Table C—Separately Budgeted Research Expenditures by Research Specialty

Research Specialty	No. of Grants	Expenditures ($)
Astrophysics	5	$576,000
Atomic, Molecular, & Optical Physics	17	$4,074,000
Biological Physics	18	$4,641,000
Condensed Matter Physics	41	$4,705,000
High Energy Physics	12	$1,904,000
Low Temperature Physics	16	$1,244,000
Nuclear Physics	5	$3,669,000
Mathematical Physics	2	$41,000
Total	116	$20,854,000

FACULTY

Professor

Abbamonte, Peter, Ph.D., University of Illinois at Urbana-Champaign, 1999. *Condensed Matter Physics.* Experimental condensed matter physics; resonant soft X-ray scattering; electron self-organization; oxide devices; quantum phase transitions; collective excitations.

Aksimentiev, Aleksei, Ph.D., Institute of Physical Chemistry, Warsaw, 1999. Blue Waters Professor. *Biophysics, Computational Physics, Nano Science and Technology.* Theoretical and computational biological physics, molecular mechanics of DNA processing machinery, nanopore systems for single molecule manipulation, DNA nanotechnology, synthetic molecular motors.

Beck, Douglas H., Ph.D., Massachusetts Institute of Technology, 1986. Principal investigator, Nuclear Physics Laboratory. *Nuclear Physics.* Experimental nuclear and particle physics; nucleon structure; fundamental symmetries; electric dipole moments.

Bezryadin, Alexey, Ph.D., J. Fourier Université, 1995. *Condensed Matter Physics, Nano Science and Technology.* Experimental condensed matter physics; nanometer-scale mescopic physics and molecular electronics; quantum phase transitions.

Ceperley, David M., Ph.D., Cornell University, 1976. Founder Professor of Engineering; Blue Waters Professor; Center for Advanced Study Professor of Physics. *Computational Physics, Condensed Matter Physics.* Theoretical condensed matter physics; electronic structure; superfluidity; Monte Carlo methods; physics at high pressure.

Chemla, Yann R., Ph.D., University of California, Berkeley, 2001. Co-Director, Center for the Physics of Living Cells. *Biophysics.* Experimental biological physics; molecular motors; nucleic acid and protein translocases.

Cooper, S. Lance, Ph.D., University of Illinois at Urbana-Champaign, 1988. Associate Head for Graduate Programs. *Condensed Matter Physics.* Experimental condensed matter physics; optical spectroscopy; strongly correlated systems; superconductivity.

Dahmen, Karin A., Ph.D., Cornell University, 1995. *Biophysics, Condensed Matter Physics, Geophysics, Nonlinear Dynamics and Complex Systems.* Theoretical condensed matter physics; nonequilibrium dynamical systems; hysteresis; avalanches; earthquakes; population biology; disorder-induced critical behavior.

DeMarco, Brian, Ph.D., University of Colorado Boulder, 2001. *Atomic, Molecular, & Optical Physics, Condensed Matter Physics, Quantum Foundations.* Experimental atomic, molecular, and optical physics; quantum information science; atomic Bose–Einstein condensates and Fermi gases; optical lattices; strongly correlated systems.

Eckstein, James N., Ph.D., Stanford University, 1978. *Condensed Matter Physics.* Experimental condensed matter physics; atomic layer-by-layer molecular beam epitaxy; colossal magnetoresistance.

El-Khadra, Aida X., Ph.D., University of California, Los Angeles, 1989. *High Energy Physics.* Theoretical high-energy physics; lattice field theory; phenomenology; quark flavor physics.

Fradkin, Eduardo H., Ph.D., Stanford University, 1979. Donald Biggar Willett Professor of Engineering; Director, Institute for Condensed Matter Theory. *Condensed Matter Physics.* Theoretical condensed matter physics; quantum Hall effects; strongly correlated systems; superconductors; critical phenomena; disordered systems; field theory.

Gammie, Charles F., Ph.D., Princeton University, 1992. Professor, Department of Astronomy. *Astrophysics, Computational Physics.* Theoretical and computational astrophysics; star formation; planet formation; relativistic accretion flows.

Giannetta, Russell W., Ph.D., Cornell University, 1980. *Condensed Matter Physics.* Experimental condensed matter physics; superconductivity; magnetic resonance; organic superconductors.

Goldenfeld, Nigel D., Ph.D., University of Cambridge, 1982. Swanlund Chair; Center for Advanced Study Professor of Physics; Director, NASA Institute for Astrobiology; Theme Leader, Institute for Genomic Biology. *Biophysics, Condensed Matter Physics, Statistical & Thermal Physics.* Theoretical condensed matter physics; non-equilibrium statistical physics; multiscale modeling of materials dynamics; pattern formation; physics of living systems; microbial ecology; evolutionary biology; astrobiology; complex biological systems and communities; fluid mechanics and turbulence.

Gollin, George D., Ph.D., Princeton University, 1981. *Physics and other Science Education.* Higher education policy; physics education research.

Grosse Perdekamp, Matthias, Ph.D., University of California, Los Angeles, 1995. Department Head. *Nuclear Physics.* Experimental high-energy nuclear physics; nucleon structure, including spin structure and nuclear effects; spin-dependent hadron fragmentation.

Holder, Gilbert, Ph.D., University of Chicago, 2001. Fortner Chair in Theoretical Astrophysics. *Astrophysics, Computational Physics, Cosmology & String Theory.* Observational and theoretical cosmology, dark matter, early universe.

Kwiat, Paul G., Ph.D., University of California, Berkeley, 1993. Bardeen Chair of Physics and of Electrical and Computer Engineering. *Atomic, Molecular, & Optical Physics, Quantum Foundations.* Experimental quantum optics; optical approaches to quantum information; foundations of quantum mechanics.

Leggett, Anthony J., D.Phil., University of Oxford, 1964. John D. and Catherine T. MacArthur Chair; Center for Advanced Study Professor of Physics; Nobel Laureate in Physics (2003). *Atomic, Molecular, & Optical Physics, Condensed Matter Physics, Low Temperature Physics, Quantum Foundations.* Foundations of quantum mechanics; superfluidity; high-temperature superconductivity; Bose–Einstein condensation; low-temperature properties of glasses; topological quantum computation.

Leigh, Robert G., Ph.D., University of Texas at Austin, 1991. *Condensed Matter Physics, Cosmology & String Theory, High Energy Physics.* Theoretical high-energy physics; quantum field theory, supersymmetric gauge theory; superstring theory.

Madhavan, Vidya, Ph.D., Boston University, 2000. *Condensed Matter Physics.* Experimental condensed matter physics; topological insulators, topological crystalline insulator and topological superconductors, Weyl semi-metals, transition metal dichalcogenides, correlated electron systems, high temperature superconductivity; thin film growth by molecular beam epitaxy (MBE), low-temperature scanning tunneling microscopy (STM), spectroscopy (STS), and spin-polarized STM.

Makins, Naomi C.R., Ph.D., Massachusetts Institute of Technology, 1994. *Nuclear Physics.* Experimental nuclear physics; proton and neutron spin.

Mason, Nadya, Ph.D., Stanford University, 2001. *Condensed Matter Physics, Nano Science and Technology.* Experimental condensed matter physics; quantum properties of nanostructures; superconductivity; quantum phase transitions.

Mestre, Jose, Ph.D., University of Massachusetts, 1979. Professor, Department of Educational Psychology. *Physics and other Science Education.* Physics education research; cognitive processes in learning; role and interaction of language in problem solving; educational technologies.

Mouschovias, Telemachos Ch, Ph.D., University of California, Berkeley, 1975. Professor of Astronomy. *Astrophysics*. Theoretical astrophysics; astrophysical magnetohydrodynamics; astrophysical fluid dynamics; cosmic magnetic fields; star formation; numerical astrophysics.

Nayfeh, Munir H., Ph.D., Stanford University, 1974. *Atomic, Molecular, & Optical Physics, Nano Science and Technology*. Experimental atomic, molecular, and optical physics; laser atomic spectroscopy; silicon nanotechnology.

Oono, Yoshitsugu, Ph.D., Kyushu University, 1976. *Statistical & Thermal Physics*. Nonequilibrium statistical physics/dynamical systems; system reduction/asymptotic analysis, including reduction of large data sets.

Peng, Jen-Chieh, Ph.D., University of Pittsburgh, 1975. *Nuclear Physics*. Experimental medium- and high-energy nuclear physics; parton structures of the nucleons and nuclei; neutrino physics.

Phillips, Philip W., Ph.D., University of Washington, 1982. *Condensed Matter Physics*. Theoretical condensed matter physics; strongly correlated electronic low-dimensional systems; quantum Hall effect; quantum critical phenomena; quantum magnetism.

Pitts, Kevin T., Ph.D., University of Oregon, 1994. Associate Dean for Undergraduate Programs, College of Engineering. *High Energy Physics*. Experimental high-energy physics; heavy quark decays; precision muon physics.

Seidel, H. Edward, Ph.D., Yale University, 1988. Vice President for Economic Development and Innovation, University Administration; Founder Professor, Departments of Physics and of Astronomy. *Astrophysics, Computational Physics, Relativity & Gravitation*. High-performance computing; numerical relativity.

Selen, Mats A., Ph.D., Princeton University, 1989. Associate Head for Undergraduate Programs. *Physics and other Science Education*. Physics education research.

Selvin, Paul R., Ph.D., University of California, Berkeley, 1990. *Biophysics*. Experimental biological physics; structure and dynamics of biological macromolecules; fluorescence microscopy.

Shapiro, Stuart L., Ph.D., Princeton University, 1973. Professor of Astronomy; Senior Research Scientist, NCSA. *Astrophysics, Computational Physics, Relativity & Gravitation*. Theoretical astrophysics and general relativity; physics of black holes and neutron stars; gravitational collapse; generation of gravitational waves; stellar dynamics; magnetohydrodynamics; numerical relativity.

Song, Jun, Ph.D., Massachusetts Institute of Technology, 2001. Founder Professor of Physics. *Biophysics*. Computational biological physics; systems biology; biostatistics; machine learning.

Stelzer, Timothy J., Ph.D., University of Wisconsin-Madison, 1993. *High Energy Physics, Physics and other Science Education*. Physics education research, educational technology, online learning, adaptive learning.

Stone, Michael, Ph.D., University of Cambridge, 1976. *Condensed Matter Physics*. Theoretical condensed matter physics; quantum Hall effect; superconductivity and superfluidity; mathematical physics.

Van Harlingen, Dale J., Ph.D., The Ohio State University, 1977. Donald Biggar Willett Professor of Engineering; Center for Advanced Study Professor of Physics. *Condensed Matter Physics, Low Temperature Physics, Quantum Foundations*. Experimental condensed matter physics; superconductor device physics; unconventional superconductivity; topological materials and devices; quantum information science.

Willenbrock, Scott S., Ph.D., University of Texas at Austin, 1986. *Other*. Energy and the environment; renewable energy; energy efficiency; sustainability.

Wiss, James E., Ph.D., University of California, Berkeley, 1977. *High Energy Physics*. Experimental high-energy physics; photoproduction of charmed mesons; precision study of charmed mesons.

Associate Professor

Hughes, Taylor L., Ph.D., Stanford University, 2009. *Condensed Matter Physics*. Theoretical condensed matter physics; topological insulators/superconductors; use of quantum information/entanglement techniques to characterize quantum condensed matter systems.

Neubauer, Mark, Ph.D., University of Pennsylvania, 2001. *High Energy Physics*. Experimental particle physics; particle astrophysics; neutrino physics; heavy flavor physics; Higgs boson; electroweak diboson physics.

Vishveshwara, Smitha, Ph.D., University of California, Santa Barbara, 2002. *Atomic, Molecular, & Optical Physics, Condensed Matter Physics*. Theoretical condensed matter physics; strongly correlated systems; phase transitions and critical phenomena; disorder and localization physics; superconductivity; quantum Hall systems; Luttinger liquids and edge states; nanophysics; topological systems; cold atom physics.

Assistant Professor

Adshead, Peter, Ph.D., Yale University, 2010. *Astrophysics, Cosmology & String Theory*. Theoretical astrophysics; inflation and early universe cosmology; theoretical cosmology.

Bradlyn, Barry, Ph.D., Yale University, 2015. *Condensed Matter Physics*. Theoretical condensed matter physics; topological insulators and semimetals; quantum Hall effect, geometric response in condensed matter; symmetry.

Clark, Bryan, Ph.D., University of Illinois at Urbana-Champaign, 2009. Blue Waters Professor. *Computational Physics, Condensed Matter Physics*. Computational condensed matter physics; many-body and strongly correlated physics.

Faulkner, Thomas, Ph.D., Massachusetts Institute of Technology, 2009. *Condensed Matter Physics, High Energy Physics*. Theoretical condensed matter physics; high-energy physics and string theory.

Filippini, Jeffrey P., Ph.D., University of California, Berkeley, 2008. *Astrophysics*. Experimental astrophysics and observational cosmology; cosmic microwave background; dark matter; astrophysical and non-accelerator probes of fundamental physics; instrumentation development.

Gadway, Bryce R., Ph.D., Stony Brook University, 2012. *Atomic, Molecular, & Optical Physics, Condensed Matter Physics*. Experimental atomic, molecular, and optical physics; degenerate Bose and Fermi gases; dipolar quantum matter; optical lattices.

Hooberman, Benjamin, Ph.D., University of California, Berkeley, 2009. *High Energy Physics*. Experimental high-energy particle physics; beyond-the-standard-model physics; supersymmetry; weakly interacting massive particles; dark matter.

Kuehn, Seppe, Ph.D., Cornell University, 2007. *Biophysics*. Experimental biological physics; microbial population dynamics in closed ecosystems; phenotypic variation of microbial behavior.

Lorenz, Virginia O., Ph.D., University of Colorado, Boulder, 2007. *Atomic, Molecular, & Optical Physics, Quantum Foundations*. Experimental quantum optics; atomic and molecular spectroscopy; optical magnetometry.

MacDougall, Gregory, Ph.D., McMaster University, 2008. *Condensed Matter Physics*. Experimental condensed matter physics; neutron scattering and muon spin rotation measurements of unconventional superconductors, geometrically frustrated magnets, and multiferroics; single crystal growth of new materials.

Shelton, Jessie, Ph.D., Massachusetts Institute of Technology, 2006. *Astrophysics, High Energy Physics*. Theoretical high-energy physics; particle physics beyond the standard model; dark matter; top quarks; Higgs boson.

Sickles, Anne M., Ph.D., University of New York at Stony Brook, 2005. *Nuclear Physics*. Experimental high-energy nuclear physics; relativistic heavy ion collisions; quark gluon plasma.

Wagner, Lucas K., Ph.D., North Carolina State University, 2006. *Computational Physics, Condensed Matter Physics*. Theoretical and computational condensed matter physics; high-performance computing; quantum Monte Carlo.

Yang, Liang, Ph.D., Harvard University, 2006. *Nuclear Physics*. Experimental low-energy nuclear physics; neutrino physics; low-background detectors; neutrinoless double beta decay; fundamental properties of neutrinos and testing fundamental symmetries.

Professor Emeritus

Debevec, Paul T., Ph.D., Princeton University, 1972. *Energy Sources & Environment, Nuclear Physics*. Experimental nuclear physics; photonuclear interactions; precision muon physics; energy and the environment.

Errede, Steven M., Ph.D., The Ohio State University, 1981. *High Energy Physics*. Experimental high-energy physics; interactions of the electroweak gauge bosons; physics of music.

Gladding, Gary E., Ph.D., Harvard University, 1971. *Physics and other Science Education*. Physics education research.

Nathan, Alan M., Ph.D., Princeton University, 1975. *Nuclear Physics, Other*. Experimental nuclear physics; physics of baseball.

Stack, John D., Ph.D., University of California, Berkeley, 1965. *High Energy Physics*. Theoretical physics.

Thaler, Jon J., Ph.D., Columbia University, 1972. *Astrophysics*. Observational cosmology, focusing on the properties of dark matter and dark energy, as well as neutrino masses and diverse phenomena.

Weaver, Richard L., Ph.D., Cornell University, 1977. *Acoustics, Condensed Matter Physics, Nonlinear Dynamics and Complex Systems*. Condensed matter physics; stochastic waves, disordered and complex structures, quantum chaos, random matrix theory, ultrasonics, structural acoustics.

Weissman, Michael B., Ph.D., University of California, San Diego, 1976. *Condensed Matter Physics*. Experimental condensed matter physics; 1/f noise, spin glasses, amorphous materials.

Wolfe, James P., Ph.D., University of California, Berkeley, 1971. *Condensed Matter Physics, Physics and other Science Education*. Experimental condensed matter physics; imaging and thermodynamics of excitonic matter in semiconductors; the teaching of thermal physics.

Research Professor

Baym, Gordon, Ph.D., Harvard University, 1960. *Astrophysics, Atomic, Molecular, & Optical Physics, Condensed Matter Physics, History & Philosophy of Physics/Science, Nuclear Physics*. Theoretical physics; Bose–Einstein condensation in trapped atomic systems and excitons; superfluid helium; matter under extreme conditions; neutron stars.

Chiang, Tai-Chang, Ph.D., University of California, Berkeley, 1978. *Condensed Matter Physics*. Experimental condensed matter physics; quantum electronic properties of surfaces, single atomic and molecular layers, and thin film structures.

Lamb, Frederick K., Ph.D., University of Oxford, 1970. *Astrophysics*. Theoretical astrophysics; plasma, magnetohydrodynamic, and high-energy processes.

Research Assistant Professor

Riedl, Caroline K., Ph.D., Friedrich-Alexander-Universitaet Erlangen, 2005. *Nuclear Physics*. Experimental nuclear physics; nucleon structure; exclusive processes.

DEPARTMENTAL RESEARCH SPECIALTIES AND STAFF

Theoretical

Astrophysics. Astrophysics at Illinois encompasses problems in star formation, planet formation, stellar dynamics, astrophysical fluid dynamics, the physics of compact objects, and theoretical and observational cosmology. Physics faculty in the astrophysics group work closely with colleagues in the high-energy physics group, the Department of Astronomy, the Department of Chemistry, the National Center for Supercomputing Applications, and the program in Computational Science and Engineering, and many hold joint appointments. Adshead, Baym, Gammie, Holder, Lamb, Mouschovias, Seidel, Shapiro, Shelton.

Atomic, Molecular, & Optical Physics. Theoretical research in ultracold atomic systems focuses on quantum many-body physics and intersections with electronic solids and high-density nuclear matter. Research topics include numerical simulations of lattice gases, the BEC-BCS crossover in Fermi gases, artificial gauge fields and rotating superfluids, and analogs with QCD and nuclear matter. Baym, Ceperley, Fradkin, Leggett, Vishveshwara.

Biological Physics. Theoretical and computational biological physics research at Illinois includes such topics as biomolecular modeling of molecular motors, multiscale modeling of pattern formation, cellular mechanics, multiscale modeling of cells, biocomplexity, and bionanotechnology. Aksimentiev, Dahmen, Goldenfeld, Oono, Song.

Condensed Matter Physics. Theoretical research in condensed matter physics focuses on the collective properties of matter in its solid and liquid forms, the emergence of novel and unusual states, and the behavior of complex systems. Illinois has long been a leader in research on superconductivity, superfluidity, and strongly correlated systems, and it is known for its close and fruitful collaborations of theorists and experimentalists. Every area of modern-day condensed matter physics is represented at Illinois, together with numerous interdisciplinary projects in atomic, molecular and optical physics, quantum information, string theory, materials science, theoretical and applied mechanics, chemistry, biology, and computer science and engineering. Current topics include high-temperature superconductivity, nonequilibrium dynamical systems, pattern formation, Bose–Einstein condensation, quantum phase transitions and quantum critical phenomena, strongly correlated and low-dimensional systems, quantum entanglement, topological insulators and superconductors, and nanoscale physics. Baym, Bradlyn, Ceperley, Clark, Dahmen, Faulkner, Fradkin, Goldenfeld, Hughes, Leggett, Leigh, Oono, Phillips, Stone, Vishveshwara, Wagner, Weaver.

High Energy Physics. Theoretical research in high-energy physics at Illinois covers a very diverse set of topics, including lattice field theory and quark flavor physics, collider phenomenology and simulations, top quark and Higgs physics, as well as quantum field theory, duality, and string theory. There is close collaboration with the high-energy experimental group, as well as the astrophysics and condensed matter theory groups. There are also overlapping interests with the math department in string theory research as well as with the National Center for Supercomputing Applications in computational physics. El-Khadra, Faulkner, Leigh, Shelton, Stack.

Nuclear Physics. Theoretical research in nuclear physics focuses on phase structure of ultrahot and dense hadronic matter; ultrarelativistic heavy ion collisions; hot nuclear matter, pairing in nuclear matter, and equation of state of nuclear matter, with applications to neutron stars; and transport properties of quantum fluids with application to experimental searches for a neutron electric dipole moment. Baym.

Relativity & Gravitation. The Illinois Relativity group focuses on the application of Einstein's theory of general relativity to forefront problems in relativistic astrophysics. The development and application of numerical relativity to tackle problems by computational means are major activities. The merger of binary compact objects (including binary black holes) leading to the generation of gravitational waves and, in some cases, electromagnetic radiation, are areas of great interest. Seidel, Shapiro.

Experimental

Astrophysics. Experimental astrophysics research at Illinois seeks to measure the properties of the universe and its constituents using methods of observational astronomy and experimental physics. Our group pursues a broad range of current problems in cosmology, including measurements of the properties of dark matter and dark energy (which comprise 96% of the universe), astrophysical measurements of neutrino mass, and observational probes of the inflationary epoch. The group's efforts span instrumentation development, data analysis, and observations of the universe at optical, infrared, and millimeter wavelengths. Major current projects include the Dark Energy Survey, the Large Synoptic Survey Telescope, and observations of the cosmic microwave background (CMB) with SPIDER and related instruments. We work in close collaboration with colleagues in the theory group, high-energy physics, the astronomy department, NCSA, and other institutions worldwide. Filippini, Thaler.

Atomic, Molecular, & Optical Physics. Experimental AMO physics at Illinois focuses on three general areas: quantum information science using entangled photons, quantum simulation using ultracold atoms trapped in optical lattices, and optical spectroscopy of atomic and condensed matter dynamics. Current research topics include experimental studies of quantum nonlocality and the development of advanced resources for quantum computation, quantum cryptography, and quantum metrology. We also study cooling, dynamics, and phase transitions in strongly correlated and disordered quantum gases, and we work closely with condensed matter colleagues at Illinois to address outstanding problems in many-body physics and the foundations of quantum mechanics. DeMarco, Gadway, Kwiat, Lorenz.

Biological Physics. Experimental biological physics groups at Illinois use a variety of single-molecule techniques, including single-molecule fluorescence microscopy and spectroscopy, optical trapping, and microfluidics to investigate molecular motors, DNA-protein interactions, gene regulation, intracellular transport, and the structure and dynamics of biological macromolecules. Chemla, Kuehn, Selvin.

Condensed Matter Physics. Condensed matter experiment at Illinois ranges from the design and growth of new materials, to the development of novel methods to elucidate and control quantum phenomena, to the design and construction of ground-breaking new instruments for fundamental physics research. Experimentalists work closely with theorists and across disciplines to address outstanding problems in condensed matter physics. Examples of current projects include imaging electron dynamics in the attosecond regime, detecting nuclear spins with attonewton force sensitivity, engineering solid-state qubits, measuring and controlling the magnetic and superconducting properties of nanodevices and nanostructure arrays, growing epitaxial heterostructures and bulk single crystals of strongly correlated materials, and elucidating the novel phases of magnetic and superconducting materials using neutron, light, and electron spectroscopies. Illinois condensed matter researchers carry out experiments in state-of-the-art facilities at the Frederick Seitz Materials Research Laboratory, the Micro and Nanotechnology Laboratory, the Beckman Institute, and U.S. and international laboratories, as well as in their own well-equipped laboratories. Abbamonte, Bezryadin, Chiang, Cooper, Eckstein, Giannetta, MacDougall, Madhavan, Mason, Nayfeh, Van Harlingen, Weissman, Wolfe.

High Energy Physics. High-energy experiment at Illinois encompasses accelerator-based experiments at the Energy Frontier and the Intensity Frontier. At the former, the group works at the CDF experiment at Fermilab and the ATLAS experiment at the Large Hadron Collider, studying the properties of top and bottom quarks and the Higgs boson, measuring the CKM matrix elements, and searching for rare phenomena and physics beyond the standard model. At the Intensity Frontier, the group is involved in three planned experiments at Fermilab: g–2, which makes precision measurements of the muon g-factor; Mu2e, which will search for the forbidden lepton-number-violating decay of a muon into an electron; and ORKA, which will make a precision measurement of a rare kaon decay. Opportunities exist in all these projects for detector development and operation as well as data analysis. Hooberman, Neubauer, Pitts, Wiss.

Nuclear Physics. The Nuclear Physics Laboratory (NPL) at Illinois focuses on discovery in fundamental nuclear physics using advanced instrumentation and modern data analysis techniques that are developed and built at NPL. The group develops instruments for novel experimental approaches in four main areas of nuclear physics: the precision measurement of the electric dipole moment of the neutron; a broad program studying structure and formation of hadrons; studies of the quark-gluon plasma at RHIC and the LHC; and precision studies of neutrino properties (mass hierarchy, CP-violating phase) and the search for neutrinoless double-beta decay. Recent and current examples of instrumentation developed at Illinois include wire chambers for the COMPASS experiment at CERN, the Drell-Yan muon-trigger scintillator hodoscopes for the SeaQuest experiment at Fermi National Accelerator Laboratory, the W-trigger RPCs for the PHENIX experiment at Brookhaven National Lab, component demonstration for the He-3 system in, and development of NV-diamond magnetic and electric field sensors for the neutron EDM experiment, the electronics upgrade for EXO 200, and PMTs for the Daya Bay neutrino experiment. Beck, Grosse Perdekamp, Makins, Peng, Riedl, Sickles, Yang.

Physics and other Science Education. Physics education research (PER) investigates the learning, understanding, and teaching of physics and the application of physics knowledge. The Illinois PER group has pioneered the application of technology to physics teaching, including development of the i-clicker® student-response system, web-based multimedia learning modules, and a personal, hand-held device that can measure acceleration, spatial orientation, magnetic fields, electrical signals, frequency spectra, and time constants and perform other introductory physics laboratory tasks. Research interests include the role of mathematics and reflection in physics learning, the organization and deployment of physics knowledge by experts and novices, transfer studies, the design and implementation of web-based instruction, curriculum reform, and the evaluation of educational assessments. Experimental techniques and analyses used include eye-tracking, video analysis, student interviews, web-based log data analysis, and analysis of exam data. Gladding, Gollin, Mestre, Selen, Stelzer.

View additional information about this department at www.gradschoolshopper.com. Check out the "Why Choose Us?" section, find out more about the department's culture and get links to social media networks.

INDIANA UNIVERSITY, BLOOMINGTON

DEPARTMENT OF ASTRONOMY

Bloomington, Indiana 47405-7105
http://www.astro.indiana.edu/

General University Information
President: Michael A. McRobbie
Dean of Graduate School: James Wimbush
University website: https://graduate.indiana.edu/index.html
School Type: Public
Setting: Suburban
Total Faculty: 2,804
Total Graduate Faculty: 1,373
Total number of Students: 46,416
Total number of Graduate Students: 9,997

Department Information
Department Chairman: Prof. Caty Pilachowski, Chair
Department Contact: Tiffany Freeman, Senior Office Assistant
  Total full-time faculty: 10
  Total number of full-time equivalent positions: 12
  Full-Time Graduate Students: 18
  Female Full-Time Graduate Students: 6
  First-Year Graduate Students: 4
  Female First-Year Students: 1

Department Address
727 East 3rd Street
Swain West 318
Bloomington, IN 47405-7105
Phone: (812) 855-6911
E-mail: astdept@indiana.edu
Website: http://www.astro.indiana.edu/

ADMISSIONS

Admission Contact Information
Address admission inquiries to: Dr. Katherine Rhode, Graduate
  Advisor, Astronomy Department, Swain Hall West 318, 727
  East Third Street, Bloomington, IN 47405-7105
Phone: (812) 855-6911
E-mail: astdept@indiana.edu
Admissions website: http://www.astro.indiana.edu/admissions-
  .shtml

Application deadlines
Fall admission:
U.S. students: January 15   *Int'l. students*: December 1

Application fee
U.S. students: $60   *Int'l. students*: $65

Admissions information
For Fall of 2018:
  Number of applicants: 58
  Number admitted: 8
  Number enrolled: 4

Admission requirements
Bachelor's degree requirements: A Bachelor's degree in Physics,
  Astronomy, Astrophysics, or a related discipline is required.
Minimum undergraduate GPA: 3.0

GRE requirements
The GRE is required.

Mean GRE score range (25th–75th percentile): V: 480-640,
  Q: 740-800, A: 3.5-4.5

Subjective GRE requirements
The Subjective GRE is not required.
There is no minimum GRE requirement.

TOEFL requirements
The TOEFL exam is required for students from non-English-
  speaking countries.
PBT score: 550
iBT score: 79

Other admissions information
Undergraduate preparation assumed: Physics and math background sufficient to handle the astronomy in the following
  text is assumed: Introduction to Modern Stellar Astrophysics
  by Carroll and Ostlie.

TUITION

Tuition year 2018–19:
Tuition for in-state residents
  Full-time students: $373.17 per credit
Tuition for out-of-state residents
  Full-time students: $1,255.2 per credit
Bloomington campus.
Credit hours per semester to be considered full-time: 8
Deferred tuition plan: No
Health insurance: Available
Other academic fees: Approximately $1000 per semester for a
  full-time student.
Academic term: Semester
Number of first-year students who received full tuition waivers: 4

Teaching Assistants, Research Assistants, and Fellowships
Number of first-year
  Teaching Assistants: 4
Average stipend per academic year
  Teaching Assistant: $26,000
  Research Assistant: $26,000
  Fellowship student: $16,000

FINANCIAL AID

Application deadlines
Fall admission:
U.S. students: March 10   *Int'l. students*: December 1

Loans
Loans are available for U.S. students.
Loans are not available for international students.
GAPSFAS application required: No
FAFSA application required: Yes

For further information
Address financial aid inquiries to: Student Central, Indiana Uni-
  versity, 408 N. Union Street, Bloomington, IN 47405.
Phone: (812) 855-6500
Financial aid website: https://studentcentral.indiana.edu/pay-for-
  college/apply-financial-aid/index.html

HOUSING

Availability of on-campus housing
Single students: Yes
Married students: Yes

For further information
Address housing inquiries to: Halls of Residence, 801 N. Jordan, Bloomington, IN 47405.
Phone: (800) 817-6371
E-mail: housing@indiana.edu
Housing aid website: http://www.rps.indiana.edu/index.cfml

Table A—Faculty, Enrollments, and Degrees Granted

Research Specialty	2017–18 Faculty	Enrollment Fall 2017		Number of Degrees Granted 2017–18 (2013–18)		
		Mas-ter's	Doc-torate	Mas-ter's	Terminal Master's	Doc-torate
Astronomy	10	–	12	2(11)	–(4)	2(15)
Astrophysics	10	–	6	–	–	–
Total	10	–	18	2(11)	–(4)	2(15)
Full-time Grad. Stud.	–	–	18	–	–	–
First-year Grad. Stud.	–	–	4	–	–	–

GRADUATE DEGREE REQUIREMENTS

Master's: The MA degree requires 30 hours with a minimum GPA of 3.0. There is no specific residence requirement. A thesis may be required at the discretion of the faculty. A final oral examination covering work for the degree is also required.

Doctorate: The PhD in Astronomy requires 90 hours with a minimum GPA of 3.0. There is no specific residency requirement, but the student must be continuously enrolled after admission to candidacy. The qualifying examination consists of a written examination (normally after the fourth semester). The requirements for the PhD in Astrophysics include at least four physics courses not required by the PhD in Astronomy. Candidacy is attained by passage of written exams administered by the Physics Department and/or the Astronomy Department.

Thesis: Thesis may be written in absentia.

SPECIAL EQUIPMENT, FACILITIES, OR PROGRAMS

The Department is a partner in the 3.5-m and the 0.9-m WIYN telescopes at Kitt Peak National Observatory near Tuscon, Arizona. Most data for thesis research are obtained at WIYN or with national facilities that provide telescope access for X-ray, UV, optical, infrared, radio, and space applications. Indiana University has superb centralized supercomputing facilities available for student and faculty research, and the department has its own computational systems for data processing and scientific computing. Small local telescopes are available for student training.

Table B—Separately Budgeted Research Expenditures by Source of Support

Source of Support	Departmental Research	Physics-related Research Outside Department
Federal government	$183,619.66	$80,343.7
State/local government		
Non-profit organizations		
Business and industry		
Other		
Total	$183,619.66	$80,343.7

Table C—Separately Budgeted Research Expenditures by Research Specialty

Research Specialty	No. of Grants	Expenditures ($)
Astronomy	12	$183,619.66
Total	12	$183,619.66

FACULTY

Professor

Friel, Eileen D., Ph.D., University of California, Santa Cruz, 1986. *Astronomy, Astrophysics.* Formation and evolution of the Milky Way; galactic chemical evolution; star clusters; stellar evolution and nucleosynthesis; stellar populations.

Lugger, Phyllis M., Ph.D., Harvard University, 1982. *Astronomy, Astrophysics.* Dynamical evolution of globular clusters and other dense stellar systems; X-ray studies of compact binary stars.

Pilachowski, Catherine A., Ph.D., University of Hawaii, 1975. *Astronomy, Astrophysics.* Origin of the elements in the Milky Way; star clusters; stellar evolution; the compositions of stars; stellar populations; stellar seismology.

Salzer, John J., Ph.D., University of Michigan, 1987. *Astronomy, Astrophysics.* Galaxy evolution; active galactic nuclei; starburst galaxies; chemical evolution in galaxies multiwavelength studies of dwarf galaxies; emission-line surveys.

van Zee, Liese, Ph.D., Cornell University, 1996. *Astronomy, Astrophysics.* Galaxy evolution; element enrichment; star formation; extragalactic neutral hydrogen.

Associate Professor

Deliyannis, Constantine P., Ph.D., Yale University, 1990. *Astronomy, Astrophysics.* Stellar evolution; galactic evolution; primordial lithium; Big Bang nucleosynthesis.

Rhode, Katherine, Ph.D., Yale University, 2003. *Astronomy, Astrophysics.* Extragalactic globular cluster systems; galaxy formation; rotation and evolution of solar-type pre-main-sequence stars.

Assistant Professor

Vesperini, Enrico, Ph.D., Scuola Normale Superiore, Pisa, 1994. *Astronomy, Astrophysics.* Theoretical and computational stellar dynamics; dynamical evolution of globular clusters.

Emeritus

Burkhead, Martin S., Ph.D., University of Wisconsin-Madison, 1964. *Astronomy, Astrophysics.* Photoelectric photometry; star clusters; galaxies.

Cohn, Haldan N., Ph.D., Princeton University, 1979. *Astronomy, Astrophysics.* Dynamical evolution of dense stellar systems; high-performance N-body simulations; globular clusters structure and stellar content; X-ray binaries.

Durisen, Richard H., Ph.D., Princeton University, 1972. *Astronomy, Astrophysics.* Star formation; astrophysical fluid dynamics; stellar rotation; planetary rings; complex plasmas.

Honeycutt, R. Kent, Ph.D., Case Western Reserve University, 1968. *Astronomy, Astrophysics.* Stellar astronomy; instrumentation; accretion disks in cataclysmic variables and in other interacting binary stars.

Johnson, Hollis R., Ph.D., University of Colorado, 1960. *Astronomy, Astrophysics.* Model stellar atmospheres: theoretical stellar spectra; ultraviolet spectra of red-giant stars.

Mufson, Stuart L., Ph.D., University of Chicago, 1974. *Astronomy, Astrophysics.* High-energy astrophysics; underground cosmic ray physics; neutrino physics.

Research Professor

Salim, Samir, Ph.D., Ohio State University, 2002. *Astronomy, Astrophysics*. Galaxy evolution; star formation indicators; galaxy bimodality; SED fitting; galaxy surveys; data mining; UV astronomy.

Steiman-Cameron, Thomas Y., Ph.D., Indiana University, 1984. *Astronomy, Astrophysics*. Dynamics of non-planar astrophysics disks; galaxy formation and evolution; structure of galactic halos; spiral structure of the Milky Way; accretion-driven compact X-ray binary stars.

Thornburg, Jonathan, Ph.D., University of British Columbia, 1993. *Astronomy, Astrophysics*. Numerical simulations of gravitational radiation from extreme-mass-ratio binary black hole inspirals/mergers; numerical simulations of binary black hole mergers; gravitational-wave astrophysics.

Visiting Professor

Deibel, Alex T., Ph.D., Michigan State University, 2017. *Astronomy, Astrophysics*. Numerical models of neutron stars; neutron star interiors; nuclear burning on neutron stars and white dwarfs; nuclear astrophysics.

DEPARTMENTAL RESEARCH SPECIALTIES AND STAFF

Theoretical

Theoretical Astrophysics. Dynamical evolution of dense stellar systems; globular clusters; stellar rotation; planetary rings; complex plasma; X-ray studies; high-performance N-body simulations. Cohn, Deibel, Durisen, Lugger, Steiman-Cameron, Vesperini.

Experimental

Observational Astrophysics. Ground-based and space-based multi-wavelength astronomy; imaging and spectroscopy of stars, star clusters, and external galaxies; studies of stellar abundances and evolution, galaxy evolution, and chemical evolution; accretion disks interacting binaries; X-ray binaries; dark energy. Cohn, Deliyannis, Friel, Honeycutt, Lugger, Mufson, Pilachowski, Rhode, Salzer, van Zee.

Observational Astrophysics. Instrumentation; CCD systems; spectrography design; telescope automation. Honeycutt, Pilachowski.

Observational Astrophysics. High-energy particle astrophysics; neutrino and muon astronomy. Mufson.

View additional information about this department at www.gradschoolshopper.com. Check out the "Why Choose Us?" section, find out more about the department's culture and get links to social media networks.

INDIANA UNIVERSITY, BLOOMINGTON

DEPARTMENT OF PHYSICS

Bloomington, Indiana 47405-7105
http://physics.indiana.edu

General University Information
President: Michael A. McRobbie
Dean of Graduate School: James Wimbush
University website: http://graduate.indiana.edu
School Type: Public
Setting: Suburban
Total Faculty: 1,357
Total Graduate Faculty: 1,637
Total number of Students: 46,817
Total number of Graduate Students: 9,955

Department Information
Department Chairman: Prof. David Baxter, Chair
Department Contact: David Baxter, Chair
  Total full-time faculty: 39
  Total number of full-time equivalent positions: 39
  Full-Time Graduate Students: 91
  Female Full-Time Graduate Students: 13
  First-Year Graduate Students: 18
  Female First-Year Students: 4
  Total Post Doctorates: 6

Department Address
727 East Third St.
Bloomington, IN 47405-7105
Phone: (812) 855-1247
Fax: (812) 855-5533
E-mail: gradphys@indiana.edu
Website: http://physics.indiana.edu

ADMISSIONS

Admission Contact Information
Address admission inquiries to: Student Services Coordinator
  Department of Physics, Swain Hall West Room 246, 727 East
  Third St., Bloomington, IN 47405
Phone: (812) 856-7059
E-mail: gradphys@indiana.edu
Admissions website: http://www.indiana.edu/~iubphys/graduate/
  admissions.shtml

Application deadlines
Fall admission:
U.S. students: January 15   *Int'l. students*: December 1

Application fee
U.S. students: $55   *Int'l. students*: $65

Admissions information
For Fall of 2018:
  Number of applicants: 104
  Number admitted: 16
  Number enrolled: 16

Admission requirements
Bachelor's degree requirements: Bachelor's degree in Physics
  or a strong background in Physics included in another degree
  is required.
Minimum undergraduate GPA: 3.0

GRE requirements
The GRE is required.

Subjective GRE requirements
The Subjective GRE is required.

TOEFL requirements
The TOEFL exam is required for students from non-English-
  speaking countries.
  PBT score: 550
  iBT score: 80

TUITION

Tuition year 2018–19:
Tuition for in-state residents
  Full-time students: $4,613.52 per semester
  Part-time students: $384.36 per credit
Tuition for out-of-state residents
  Full-time students: $15,966.12 per semester
  Part-time students: $1,330.51 per credit
Bloomington Campus
Credit hours per semester to be considered full-time: 12
Deferred tuition plan: No
Health insurance: Available at the cost of $3088 per year.
Other academic fees: $1,148 per semester
Academic term: Semester
Number of first-year students who received full tuition waivers: 21

Teaching Assistants, Research Assistants, and Fellowships
Number of first-year
  Teaching Assistants: 12
  Research Assistants: 1
  Fellowship students: 3
Average stipend per academic year
  Teaching Assistant: $22,333
  Research Assistant: $24,000
  Fellowship student: $25,000
When you apply you are automatically considered for fi-
nancial support. In most situations, an offer of acceptance into
our program comes with a teaching or research assistantship.
And all students proceeding successfully through the program
are supported every year.

FINANCIAL AID

Application deadlines
Fall admission:
U.S. students: April 15   *Int'l. students*: April 15
Spring admission:
U.S. students: November 1   *Int'l. students*: November 1

Loans
Loans are available for U.S. students.
Loans are available for international students.
GAPSFAS application required: No
FAFSA application required: Yes

For further information

Address financial aid inquiries to: Student Services Coordinator, Indiana University Physics Department, Swain Hall West Room 246, 727 E. Third St., Bloomington, IN 47405.
Phone: (812) 856-7059
E-mail: gradphys@indiana.edu
Financial aid website: http://www.indiana.edu/~sfa/

HOUSING

Availability of on-campus housing

Single students: Yes
Married students: Yes
Childcare Assistance: No

For further information

Address housing inquiries to: Halls of Residence, 801 N. Jordan, Indiana University, Bloomington, IN 47405.
Phone: (812) 855-1764
E-mail: housing@indiana.edu
Housing aid website: http://www.rps.indiana.edu

Table A—Faculty, Enrollments, and Degrees Granted

Research Specialty	2016–17 Faculty	Enrollment Fall 2017		Number of Degrees Granted 2017–18 (2013–18)		
		Master's	Doctorate	Master's	Terminal Master's	Doctorate
Accelerator	–	7	–	–	–(2)	–
Astrophysics	2	–	1	–	–	–(2)
Biophysics	5	–	7	–	–	–(14)
Chemical Physics	–	–	–	–	–	–
Condensed Matter Physics	9	–	16	–	–	–(9)
Medical, Health Physics	1	2	–	–	1(12)	–
Nuclear Physics	10	–	31	–	–	–(13)
Particles and Fields	10	–	27	–	–	2(11)
Other	–	4	–	8(57)	–(14)	–(1)
Total	37	13	81	8(57)	3(28)	2(50)
Full-time Grad. Stud.	–	13	81	–	–	–
First-year Grad. Stud.	–	3	9	–	–	–

GRADUATE DEGREE REQUIREMENTS

Master's: Master of Science: 30 semester hours, at least 20 in physics, 14 of which must be in courses numbered P501 and higher passed with an average grade of "B" or higher. Physics courses numbered below P501 and passed with a grade of "B−" or lower do not count toward this degree. (Seminar, research, and reading courses may not be counted toward the 14 hour requirement.) Master of Science in Beam Physics and Technology (a national program in collaboration with the U.S. Particle Accelerator School, USPAS): 30 credit hours, including the following: P441 (or equivalent at another institution), P506 (or equivalent), P570, one course at the 500 level or above in laboratory techniques or computational methods, and a master's thesis course (P802). Four advanced courses in beam physics should be chosen from among the special topics courses P571, P671, and P672, with topics to be listed in a syllabus prepared jointly by the I.U. Physics Department and the USPAS. A grade point average of 3.0 or better must be maintained in the courses satisfying the 30 credit-hour requirement. In particular, both P441 and P506 (or equivalents) must be passed with a grade B (3.0) or above. Master's examination is required. Thesis is required. Either an oral defense of the thesis or a written final examination is required and

should take place at Indiana University. The written examination may be substituted for the oral defense only with the permission of the thesis committee. Master of Science in Medical Physics: A total of 40 credit hours of which at least 18 credit hours must be in physics courses numbered 501 or above. Seminars, research, and reading courses may not be counted toward this 18 credit hour requirement. Required courses include: P576 Introduction to Medical Diagnostic Imaging, P572 Radiation Oncology Physics, P526 Principles of Health Physics and Dosimetry, P578 Radiation Biophysics, P683 Practicum in Medical Physics, and one course in scientific ethics. A580 Human Anatomy for Medical Imaging Evaluation, S520 Statistical Methods, and P551 Experiments in Modern Physics are also required if an equivalent course has not been completed previously. Either a research thesis or a written final examination is required.

Doctorate: 90 semester hours in course, reading, and research credits; a minimum of 9 credit hours per semester at the P501 level or above with an average grade of "B" or higher (first-year students are allowed a minimum of 7 credit hours at the P501 level or above); minor requirement can be met either outside of the Department of Physics or within Physics but outside of the student's area of thesis research; written qualifying examination; candidacy seminar; thesis; final oral examination; a minimum of two consecutive semesters in residence. All candidates are required to undertake supervised teaching as an associate instructor for at least one semester. All first-time teaching associate instructors must enroll in a one-hour graduate credit course "Practicum in Physics Laboratory." Associate instructors whose native language is not English are required to take an "Associate Instructor English Examination," which they must pass in order to be qualified to teach. This examination must be passed by the end of the second year of study.

Other Degrees: Ph.D. in Astrophysics: If in residence in the Physics Department, a student must pass specifically designated parts of the qualifying examinations of both departments; thesis; final oral examination. Ph.D. in Chemical Physics: If in residence in the Physics Department, same qualifying examination as above; minor in chemistry with eight hours in designated courses; thesis; final oral examination.

SPECIAL EQUIPMENT, FACILITIES, OR PROGRAMS

The physics department is housed in Swain Hall which has recently be renovated. An extensive machine shop now includes several programmable CNC milling machines and a CNC lathe, numerous other machines, and four full-time machinists. Expertise and high-bay area workshops provide support for assembly of large-scale instrumentation, such as high-energy physics detector assemblies. Capabilities for design and testing of electronics are provided in an Electronics Design Facility, staffed by an experienced electronics engineer and a technician. A 192-node parallel PC cluster is available for research computing. The University provides extensive supercomputing support, including Big Red II, a petaflop scale high-performance parallel computing system, and the Data Capacitor, a high-speed, 5 PB capacity storage facility for large data sets.

Major facilities at CEEM (Center for Exploration of Energy and Matter), located in the Integrated Science and Accelerator Technology (ISAT) Hall, include the Low Energy Neutron Source (LENS). LENS is the first pulsed cold neutron source located at a university, and provides neutron beams for studying large-scale structure in materials and the development of advanced neutron instrumentation. ALPHA is a state-of-the-art facility for measuring radiation effects and is expected to provide brilliant and tunable hard-x-ray beams for materials research. CEEM includes specialized shops and experienced technical and engineering support for design and construction of experimental equipment, cryogenic testing, an assembly area, a 20 mK dilution refrigerator, low-vibration room, polarized 3He laser laboratory, and testing of large or complex detector and electronics systems.

Condensed-matter and low-temperature equipment include two x-ray diffraction systems including SAXS; a multisource high-vacuum sputtering system; a pulsed-laser deposition system; and superconducting solenoids.

The new Nanoscale Characterization Facility in Simon Hall also has a variety of instruments for patterning and characterizing materials on nanometer-length scales, including a JEOL JEM3200FS cryo TEM, SEMs with e-beam lithography capability, a focused ion beam instrument, an XPS instrument, various scanning probe microscopes, confocal microscopes, and various smaller instruments for optical lithography, thin film deposition, thermal gravimetric analysis, reactive ion etching, IR absorption, and other techniques.

Facilities for biophysics research include cell culture and incubation laboratories, a cell sorter, one-photon and two-photon scanning confocal microscopes, instrumentation for multi-electrical array recording and general neurophysics instrumentation, and access to shared core facilities at the Indiana Molecular Biology Institute. The IUB Light Microscopy Imaging Center has a range of microscopes available for users. Systems include an OMX 3D-SIM Super-Resolution system, wide field, deconvolution, and confocal microscopes, all equipped with digital imaging systems.

The Center for Spacetime Symmetries (IUCSS) aims to promote and catalyze scientific progress in theoretical and experimental studies of spacetime and its symmetries, which are central ideas in gravity and particle theories. Studies of spacetime symmetries and their violations offer opportunities to explore foundational aspects of nature. For example, Einstein's theories of special and general relativity are based on spacetime symmetries. IUCSS researchers have proposed that the fundamental theory unifying gravity and quantum physics could lead to tiny violations of the laws of relativity, and many sensitive searches for these effects are underway.

Table B—Separately Budgeted Research Expenditures by Source of Support

Source of Support	Departmental Research	Physics-related Research Outside Department
Federal government	$9,060,647	$1,461,832
State/local government		
Non-profit organizations		
Business and industry		
Other		
Total	$9,060,647	$1,461,832

Table C—Separately Budgeted Research Expenditures by Research Specialty

Research Specialty	No. of Grants	Expenditures ($)
Astrophysics	–	$1,320,207
Biophysics	–	$1,483,591
Condensed Matter Physics	–	$1,563,511
Nuclear Physics	–	$2,957,228
Particles and Fields	–	$1,306,560
Physics of Beams	–	$399,857
Other	–	$33,112
Total	–	$9,064,066

FACULTY

DEPARTMENTAL RESEARCH SPECIALTIES AND STAFF

Theoretical

Astrophysics. Dark matter; neutrinos in astronomical observations; solar neutrinos; supernova neutrinos; dwarf galaxies; galaxies; properties of neutron stars, neutron star crust, and gravitational wave sources.

Biophysics. Intracellular signaling networks; waves in excitable media; non-equilibrium systems; biocomplexity; theoretical neuroscience; information theory.

Condensed Matter Physics. Topological condensed matter systems; fractionalization and exotic quasiparticles; graphene; quantum Hall effect; superconductivity, spin transport, and magnetoresistance; nanoscale systems; soft matter; colloidal and biological materials; electron–phonon interaction in metals; optical and electrical properties of solids; collective excitations; many-body theory; surface electrodynamics; quantum information and computation; correlated electronic materials; many-body physics, strongly correlated systems: high-Tc superconductivity, heavy fermions, materials in high magnetic fields; exotic superconductors; magnetism and spin systems; quantum fluids and solids; ultracold Fermi and Bose gases; topologically quantum ordered systems; quantum statistical mechanics and field theory methods in condensed matter; quantum measurement theory.

High Energy Physics. Phenomenology of elementary particle properties and interactions; quantum chromodynamics and electroweak interactions; lattice gauge field theory; solar neutrinos; grand-unified theories; supersymmetry; gravity and supergravity; superstring theory; CPT and Lorenz symmetry.

Nuclear Physics. Nuclear structure; medium- and high-energy nuclear reactions; quantum chromodynamics; hadron spectra and structure; gluon dynamics; relativistic quantum hadrodynamics; neutron stars and nuclear astrophysics; stellar evolution; neutrino transport.

Experimental

Astrophysics. Magnetic monopoles; antimatter; supernovae; dark matter searches; big bang cosmology; neutrino oscillations; dark energy; solar neutrino. Facilities include an assortment of computers, particle detectors, electronics development equipment, data acquisition systems, and spectrophotometers. Experiments are being performed at Fermi National Laboratory, Superkamiokande, and at a number of balloon launch facilities.

Atomic, Molecular, & Optical Physics.

Biophysics. Experimental and computational neuroscience; multielectrode records in vitro; intracellular and extracellular neural recording in vivo; experimental biocomplexity.

Chemical Physics. Self-assembly and nano-structured materials; optical properties of solids; low-temperature properties of solids; chemisorption and catalysis; confined fluids; nuclear chemistry; x-ray and neutron diffraction.

Condensed Matter Physics. Confined complex and quantum fluids; x-ray and neutron scattering surfactant systems; atomic and electronic transport nanostructures; topological insulators; metal oxides; compositionally modulated thin films; thin film and exotic magnetism and magnetoresistance; metastable systems; surface studies: STM, AFM, EELS; topological insulators; dynamics of electrons in disordered metals and correlated electron systems. Experiments are conducted with a wide variety of in-house equipment (see facilities description) and at national user facilities.

High Energy Physics. Searches for new particles (Higgs bosons, supersymmetric particles, exotics, hybrid systems, glueballs);

heavy quark physics (top, bottom, charm); light quarks; neutrino oscillation; and testing of fundamental symmetries. Detectors used include drift chambers, drift tubes, scintillating fibers, transition radiation detectors, Cerenkov counters, and calorimeters and trigger systems. IU facilities include data acquisition and large-scale data analysis computer clusters, detector construction areas including a high-bay area and large class-10000 clean room, and an electronics design facility. Students work on DØ and MINOS and NOvA at Fermilab, ATLAS at CERN, experiments at Jefferson Laboratory, and in preparations for LBNE for the Linear Collider.

Nuclear Physics. Nucleon structure studies: gluon spin distributions, anti-quark and sea quark contributions to nucleon properties using the STAR detector at BNL RHIC and the Belle detector at KEK; weak interaction studies with slow neutrons: precision measurements of neutron decay and neutron weak interactions at NIST, LANSCE, and SNS; methods for production of ultra-cold neutrons; studies of neutrino properties and interactions at Fermilab and WIPP; fundamental symmetry tests: searches for time-reversal violation via electric dipole moments of the electron and neutron; searches for exotic nucleon spin-dependent couplings, formation and decay of hot nuclei, damped collisions between heavy nuclei, and nuclear fission at MSU, ATLAS, and other laboratories.

View additional information about this department at www.gradschoolshopper.com. Check out the "Why Choose Us?" section, find out more about the department's culture and get links to social media networks.

INDIANA UNIVERSITY — PURDUE UNIVERSITY INDIANAPOLIS

DEPARTMENT OF PHYSICS

Indianapolis, Indiana 46202-3273
http://physics.iupui.edu/

General University Information
President: Michael A. McRobbie
Dean of Graduate School: Sherry F. Queener
University website: http://www.iupui.edu/
School Type: Public
Setting: Urban
Total Faculty: 3,041
Total number of Students: 30,488
Total number of Graduate Students: 8,079

Department Information
Department Chairman: Prof. Andrew Gavrin, Chair
Department Contact: Clair Schaler, Administrative Assistant /
  Graduate Coordinator
  Total full-time faculty: 14
  Total number of full-time equivalent positions: 14
  Full-Time Graduate Students: 24
  Female Full-Time Graduate Students: 2
  First-Year Graduate Students: 5
  Female First-Year Students: 1
  Total Post Doctorates: 1

Department Address
402 N. Blackford St.
LD154
Indianapolis, IN 46202-3273
Phone: (317) 274-6900
Fax: (317) 274-2393
E-mail: physics@iupui.edu
Website: http://physics.iupui.edu/

ADMISSIONS

Admission Contact Information
Address admission inquiries to: Prof. Ricardo Decca, Director
  of Graduate Program, IUPUI Physics Dept., 402 N Blackford
  St., LD 154, Indianapolis, IN 46202
Phone: (317) 274-6900
E-mail: rdecca@iupui.edu
Admissions website: https://physics.iupui.edu/phys/graduate/ap-
  ply

Application deadlines
Fall admission:
U.S. students: March 15   *Int'l. students*: March 3
Spring admission:
U.S. students: November 15   *Int'l. students*: September 15

Application fee
U.S. students: $60   *Int'l. students*: $65
Dates are not hard deadlines; they are recommended dates to have
  applications submitted.

Admissions information
For Fall of 2018:
  Number of applicants: 14
  Number admitted: 6
  Number enrolled: 6

Admission requirements
Bachelor's degree requirements: Bachelor's degree in Physics
  or related areas is required.
Minimum undergraduate GPA: 3.0

GRE requirements
The GRE is required.

Subjective GRE requirements
The Subjective GRE is recommended.

TOEFL requirements
The TOEFL exam is required for students from non-English-
  speaking countries.
  PBT score: 550
  iBT score: 80
Reading-19, Listening-14, Speaking-18, and Writing-18.

Other admissions information
Undergraduate preparation assumed: Symon, Mechanics; Cor-
  son and Lorrain, Electricity and Magnetism; Eisberg and
  Resnick, Quantum Physics; Rief, Thermodynamics.

TUITION

Tuition year 2018–19:
Tuition for in-state residents
  Full-time students: $347.22 per credit
Tuition for out-of-state residents
  Full-time students: $957.66 per credit
Credit hours per semester to be considered full-time: 8
Deferred tuition plan: No
Health insurance: Available at the cost of $3,088 per year.
Other academic fees: Approximately $1,100 for fees.
Academic term: Semester
Number of first-year students who received full tuition waivers: 4

Teaching Assistants, Research Assistants, and Fellowships
Number of first-year
  Teaching Assistants: 4
Average stipend per academic year
  Teaching Assistant: $20,000
  Research Assistant: $20,000
  Fellowship student: $20,000

FINANCIAL AID

Loans
Loans are available for U.S. students.
Loans are not available for international students.
GAPSFAS application required: No
FAFSA application required: No

For further information
Address financial aid inquiries to: Office of Student Financial
  Services.
Phone: 317-274-4162
E-mail: finaid@iupui.edu
Financial aid website: https://studentcentral.iupui.edu/funding/
  index.html

HOUSING

Availability of on-campus housing
Single students: Yes
Married students: Yes
Childcare Assistance: No

For further information
Address housing inquiries to: Division of Student Affairs.
E-mail: commuter@iupui.edu
Housing aid website: https://studentaffairs.iupui.edu/housing/index.html

Table A—Faculty, Enrollments, and Degrees Granted

Research Specialty	2017–18 Faculty	Enrollment Fall 2017 Master's	Enrollment Fall 2017 Doctorate	Number of Degrees Granted 2017–18 Master's	Number of Degrees Granted 2017–18 Terminal Master's	Number of Degrees Granted 2017–18 Doctorate
Atomic, Molecular, & Optical Physics	5	1	8	1	–	–
Biophysics	5	1	5	–	–	2
Condensed Matter Physics	3	–	5	–	–	–
Physics and other Science Education	1	–	4	–	–	–
Total	14	2	22	1	–	2
Full-time Grad. Stud.	–	2	22	–	–	–
First-year Grad. Stud.	–	1	3	–	–	–

GRADUATE DEGREE REQUIREMENTS

Master's: Both thesis and non-thesis master's programs are available. For each program, the student must complete 30 credit hours and maintain a grade point average of 2.7. Twenty-four credit hours must be in physics/biophysics and 6 hours in mathematics. For the thesis master's program, 6 of the 24 hours are satisfied by completing the thesis. All students must pass a qualifying examination early in their program and an oral examination at the completion of their program. The minimum residence requirement is two semesters of full-time work or the equivalent in credits.

Doctorate: Qualified students may pursue the Ph.D. degree at IUPUI in areas in which a program has been arranged with Purdue University-West Lafayette. Students are usually expected to complete an M.S. degree before pursuing the Ph.D. degree. Currently, a Ph.D. program is available in the areas of biological physics, optics, and materials science.

Thesis: Thesis may be written in absentia.

SPECIAL EQUIPMENT, FACILITIES, OR PROGRAMS

The NMR facilities of the department consist of three multinuclear high-resolution FT spectrometers and one solid-state spectrometer. Included among the high-resolution instruments are narrow-bore 500 and 200 MHz spectrometers and a wide-bore 300 MHz spectrometer. The solid-state instrument has broadline and MAS capabilities, operates at 4.2 T, and is home built. An X-band EPR spectrometer is used for biophysics research. Full facilities for the preparation and characterization of biological samples are available. Two optics research laboratories are equipped with argon laser-pumped, CW frequency-doubled Ti-sapphire lasers, diode lasers, and He–Ne lasers, among others. State-of-the-art data-acquisition equipment includes digital oscilloscopes, spectrum analyzers, and computer interfaces. High-finesse optical cavities and high-vacuum systems are used to study atomic behavior in laser fields. A thin-film sputter de-

position system with 4 high-rate magnetron guns, rf and dc excitation, substrate heating to 1000 K, computer-controlled substrate and shutter motions is available. The chamber is cryopumped with background pressure of 10.

Table C—Separately Budgeted Research Expenditures by Research Specialty

Research Specialty	No. of Grants	Expenditures ($)
Biophysics	2	$215,000
Condensed Matter Physics	2	$190,000
Physics and other Science Education	2	$325,968.2
Total	6	$730,968.2

FACULTY

Professor

Decca, Ricardo S., Ph.D., Instituto Balseiro, 1994. Director of Graduate Program. *Condensed Matter Physics, Low Temperature Physics, Materials Science, Metallurgy, Nano Science and Technology*. Condensed matter; scanning probe microscopy; spectroscopy of low dimensional systems; corrections to Newtonian gravity; lipid bilayers.

Ou, Zhe-Yu Jeff, Ph.D., University of Rochester, 1990. *Atomic, Molecular, & Optical Physics, Optics*. Quantum optics; nonlinear optics.

Vemuri, Gautam, Ph.D., Georgia Institute of Technology, 1990. *Atomic, Molecular, & Optical Physics, Nonlinear Dynamics and Complex Systems, Optics*. Nonlinear optics; laser physics.

Wassall, Stephen R., Ph.D., University of Nottingham, 1981. *Biophysics*. Solid-state NMR; biophysics; lipid membranes.

Associate Professor

Cheng, Ruihua, Ph.D., University of Nebraska-Lincoln, 2002. *Condensed Matter Physics, Materials Science, Metallurgy, Nano Science and Technology*. Condensed matter; magnetic nanostructures.

Gavrin, Andrew D., Ph.D., Johns Hopkins University, 1992. Department Chair. *Materials Science, Metallurgy, Physics and other Science Education*. Just-in-Time Teaching; use of technology in education.

Joglekar, Yogesh, Ph.D., Indiana University, 2001. *Condensed Matter Physics, Nano Science and Technology*. Condensed matter; noise spectroscopy; graphene; non-Hermitian quantum mechanics.

Petrache, Horia, Ph.D., Carnegie Mellon University, 1998. *Biophysics*. X-ray scattering; membrane biophysics.

Assistant Professor

Liu, Jing, Ph.D., Purdue University, 2015. *Biophysics, Engineering Physics/Science, Physics and other Science Education*. Single molecule biophysics; optical imagine and microscopy; plasmonics and nano-photonics.

Zhu, Fangqiang, Ph.D., University of Illinois at Urbana-Champaign, 2004. *Biophysics, Computational Physics, Theoretical Physics*. Biomolecular simulation; membrane protein; protein conformation and assembly.

Professor Emeritus

Kemple, Marvin D., Ph.D., University of Illinois, 1971. *Biophysics, Medical, Health Physics*. Biological physics; magnetic resonance and fluorescence.

Senior Lecturer

Woodahl, Brian A., Ph.D., Purdue University, 1999. *Cosmology & String Theory, Particles and Fields*. Physics education; theoretical particle physics.

Lecturer

Rhoads, Edward, Ph.D., University of Minnesota, 2005. *Astronomy*. Astronomy.

Ross, John B., Ph.D., Boston University, 1993. *Physics and other Science Education, Other*. Physics education.

Sengupta, Aparajita P., Ph.D., University of Alabama, Tuscaloosa, 2013. *Astronomy, Physics and other Science Education*. Comparison of galaxy evolution at different stages of cluster evolution.

Associate Scientist

Ray, Bruce D., Ph.D., Indiana University, 1983. *Biophysics*. Biochemistry; isotope labeling; NMR.

DEPARTMENTAL RESEARCH SPECIALTIES AND STAFF

Experimental

Biophysics. Small-angle scattering of membrane systems in solution to determine structure and molecular interactions relevant to biological functions. Petrache, Ray.

Biophysics. Macromolecular structure-function relationships in enzyme-substrate complexes of ATP-utilizing enzymes and alcohol dehydrogenase; internal motions of peptides, proteins, and their complexes; NMR and computer simulations of protein dynamics; broadline deuterium NMR of molecular order and dynamics in membranes; MAS NMR determination of peptide conformation; EPR membrane and cytoplasmic studies of reactive oxygen species and molecular order in model membranes. Kemple, Liu, Petrache, Ray.

Condensed Matter Physics. Spatial and time-resolved spectroscopy in quantum systems; metal-insulator transition in superconductors; correlated electronic systems; Casimir interaction; spin-dependent transport. Cheng, Decca, Petrache.

Condensed Matter Physics. Near-field scanning optical microscopy; atomic force microscopy; probe-sample interaction effect; image analysis and deconvolution; single molecule detection and tracking. Decca.

Materials Science, Metallurgy. Artificially structured materials; ferromagnetic domains and giant magnetoresistive effects in granular metals; domain wall pinning in amorphous alloys; scanning electron microscopy with polarization analysis; fabrication of magnetic nanowires and nanodots. Cheng, Decca.

Optics. Semiconductor lasers; non-linear optics; diode laser and amplifier statistical properties; laser instabilities; chaos and communication; cavity QED; nonlinear optical frequency conversion; photon statistics of nonclassical states; test of EPR nonlocality; multiphoton interference. Ou, Vemuri.

Physics and other Science Education. Just-in-Time-Teaching (JiTT) modulus course design. Gavrin, Liu.

View additional information about this department at www.gradschoolshopper.com. Check out the "Why Choose Us?" section, find out more about the department's culture and get links to social media networks.

PURDUE UNIVERSITY

DEPARTMENT OF PHYSICS AND ASTRONOMY

West Lafayette, Indiana 47907
http://www.physics.purdue.edu

General University Information
President: Mitchell E. Daniels, Jr.
Dean of Graduate School: Linda Mason
University website: http://www.purdue.edu
School Type: Public
Setting: Suburban
Total Faculty: 1,901
Total Graduate Faculty: 1,901
Total number of Students: 41,573
Total number of Graduate Students: 9,626

Department Information
Department Chairman: Prof. John P. Finley, Head
Department Contact: Sandy Formica, Graduate Secretary
  Total full-time faculty: 57
  Full-Time Graduate Students: 150
  Female Full-Time Graduate Students: 25
  First-Year Graduate Students: 36
  Female First-Year Students: 6
  Total Post Doctorates: 25

Department Address
525 Northwestern Avenue
West Lafayette, IN 47907
Phone: (765) 494-3099
Fax: (765) 494-0706
E-mail: physcontacts@purdue.edu
Website: http://www.physics.purdue.edu

ADMISSIONS

Admission Contact Information
Address admission inquiries to: Sandy Formica, Graduate Secretary, Purdue University, Department of Physics and Astronomy, 525 Northwestern Ave, West Lafayette, IN 47907
Phone: (765) 494-3099
E-mail: physcontacts@purdue.edu
Admissions website: https://www.purdue.edu/gradschool/prospective/gradrequirements/westlafayette/phys.html

Application deadlines
Fall admission:
U.S. students: December 15   *Int'l. students*: December 15
Spring admission:
U.S. students: September 1   *Int'l. students*: September 1

Application fee
U.S. students: $60   *Int'l. students*: $75

Admissions information
For Fall of 2018:
  Number of applicants: 270
  Number admitted: 102
  Number enrolled: 36

Admission requirements
Bachelor's degree requirements: Bachelor's degree in Physics is required.
Minimum undergraduate GPA: 3.0

GRE requirements
The GRE is required.
No required minimum

Subjective GRE requirements
The Subjective GRE is required.
No required minimum

TOEFL requirements
The TOEFL exam is required for students from non-English-speaking countries.
  PBT score: 550
  iBT score: 80
Minimum Paper-Delivered Test - no overall score reported With the following minimum section requirements: Reading: 19 Listening: 14 Writing: 18

Other admissions information
Additional requirements: TOEFL (iBT) minimum required individual scores are 18 writing, 18 speaking, 14 listening, and 19 reading.
Undergraduate preparation assumed: A good preparation for entering students includes a sound knowledge of general physics, intermediate level classical mechanics, electricity and magnetism, statistical and thermal physics, quantum mechanics and some introductory atomic, nuclear and condensed matter physics. A corresponding mathematical background includes vector analysis, linear algebra, ordinary differential equations, boundary value problems, and some knowledge of complex analysis. Admitted first year students with deficiencies in any of the above areas can be placed in courses that will supplement the undergraduate program and correct the deficiencies. Strong undergraduate preparation would be provided by adequate study of textbooks at the level of: Marion, Classical Dynamics; Griffiths, Classical Electrodynamics; Kittel & Kroemer, Statistical and Thermal Physics; and Griffiths, Quantum Physics.

TUITION

Tuition year 2018–19:
Tuition for in-state residents
  Full-time students: $4,996 per semester
Tuition for out-of-state residents
  Full-time students: $14,397 per semester
Fees for Teaching Assistantships and Research Assistantships is $392 per semester.
Credit hours per semester to be considered full-time: 9
Deferred tuition plan: Yes
Health insurance: Available at the cost of $529 per year.
Academic term: Semester

Teaching Assistants, Research Assistants, and Fellowships
Average stipend per academic year
  Teaching Assistant: $19,972
  Research Assistant: $20,489
  Fellowship student: $23,403
Nine-month appointment.

FINANCIAL AID

Application deadlines
Fall admission:

U.S. students: March 1   *Int'l. students*: March 1

Loans
Loans are available for U.S. students.
Loans are available for international students.
GAPSFAS application required: No
FAFSA application required: No

For further information
Address financial aid inquiries to: Sandy Formica, Graduate Sec-
retary, Purdue University, Department of Physics and
Astronomy, 525 Northwestern Ave, West Lafayette, IN
47907.
Phone: (765) 494-3099
E-mail: physcontacts@purdue.edu
Financial aid website: http://www.purdue.edu/dfa

HOUSING

Availability of on-campus housing
Single students: Yes
Married students: Yes
Childcare Assistance: No

For further information
Address housing inquiries to: Graduate Housing:
ghapp@purdue.edu, Married and Family Housing:
pvapp@purdue.edu.
E-mail: ghapp@purdue.edu
Housing aid website: http://housing.purdue.edu

Table A—Faculty, Enrollments, and Degrees Granted

Research Specialty	2017–18 Faculty	Enrollment Fall 2017		Number of Degrees Granted 2017–18 (2013–18)		
		Mas-ter's	Doc-torate	Mas-ter's	Terminal Master's	Doc-torate
Accelerator Mass Spectrometry	3	–	–	–	–	–
Applied Physics	1	–	3	–	–	–(1)
Astrophysics	8	–	8	–	–	3(10)
Atomic, Molecular, & Optical Physics	6	–	10	–	–	3(7)
Biophysics	6	–	13	–	1	1(12)
Condensed Matter Physics	13	–	53	–	–	7(33)
Geophysics	1	–	3	–	–	–(4)
Nuclear Physics	4	–	8	–	–	–(6)
Particles and Fields	11	–	13	–	–	2(14)
Physics and other Science Education	3	–	4	–	–	1(3)
Planetary Science	1	–	1	–	–	1(1)
Non-specialized	–	–	32	4(26)	5(18)	–
Total	57	–	148	4(26)	6(19)	17(90)
Full-time Grad. Stud.	–	–	148	–	–	–
First-year Grad. Stud.	–	–	32	–	–	–

GRADUATE DEGREE REQUIREMENTS

Master's: Non-thesis option: completion of a minimum of 30
credit hours with at least 24 hours of approved 500–600 level
courses in physics, including one laboratory course, and 6
credit hours in 500–600 level mathematics courses, which
may be replaced in whole or in part by Methods of Theoretical
Physics I and II: grade in a 500-level physics course must be
A or B, and grade in a 600-level physics or a mathematics course
A, B, or C; minimum graduate grade average of 2.8/4.0; qualifying examination must be taken; written and oral final examinations are given or waived at discretion of student's advisory
committee. More than half of the Purdue credits must be earned
through the Purdue campus where the degree is conferred. Thesis
option: thesis replaces nine credit hours of physics requirement:
final oral examination over thesis is required.

Doctorate: At least 90 hours of credit hours are required for the
Ph.D. plan of study. Core requirements include statistical
physics (one semester), advanced electricity and magnetism
(one semester), quantum mechanics (two semesters), and
three graduate-level specialty courses. A core course need not
be taken at Purdue if its equivalent has been taken previously.
A student entering with a B.S. degree and holding a teaching
assistantship needs about two years to complete all courses.
A master's degree or professional doctoral degree from any
accredited institution may be considered to contribute up to
30 credit hours toward satisfying the 90 credits required for
a Ph.D. degree. An average GPA of 3.0 is required in core
courses. At the start of first semester, students are required
to take a qualifying examination to demonstrate undergraduate knowledge of mechanics at the level of Marion, Classical
Dynamics; of electricity and magnetism at the level of Griffiths, Introduction to Electrodynamics; and of modern physics
at the level of Gasiorowicz, Quantum Physics. Students are
formally admitted to candidacy for the Ph.D. degree only after
they have passed the Ph.D. preliminary examination. The student is eligible to attempt this examination when he or she
has completed the core courses with at least a B average. The
Preliminary Examination Committee of a given student de-
cides on the nature and coverage of that student's examination. The examination may have written and oral portions.
There is no department-wide preliminary examination. After
passing the preliminary examination, students can devote
practically all of their time to the original research that will
serve as the basis for their theses. The research must be of
fully professional character and publishable quality. Completion of the Ph.D. requirements include the completion of
the thesis, passing an oral examination in defense of the thesis,
and preparation of the thesis material for publication.

Other Degrees: Computational Science and Engineering The
Computational Science and Engineering (CS&E) Program at
Purdue provides students with the opportunity to study a specific science or engineering discipline along with computing
in a multi-disciplinary environment. The aim of the program
is to produce a student who has learned how to integrate computing with another scientific or engineering discipline and
is able to make original contributions in both disciplines. The
Physics Department is one of the original departments since
the inception of this program. The participating departments
now number 18 spread over five colleges. Physics CSE students must satisfy both the standard Physics departmental degree requirements and those of the CSE Program. Usually
some of the math and specialty course requirements of the
Physics Department can be met by courses which simulta-
neously contribute toward the satisfaction of the CSE requirements; however, generally, both the number of courses and
grade requirement are higher for the physics students who
elect to specialize in the CSE Program. M.S. graduates should
be well-prepared to join and make significant contributions
to interdisciplinary research teams. Ph.D. graduates are expected to become leaders in research and development at the
forefront of their fields, applying advanced computational
techniques and theory to solve key problems.

Thesis: Thesis may be written in absentia if necessary.

SPECIAL EQUIPMENT, FACILITIES, OR PROGRAMS

Among the major facilities is PRIME Laboratory, a national center for accelerator mass spectrometry (AMS), which is based on an 8-MeV Tandem Van de Graaff accelerator. AMS is an ultrasensitive analytical technique for measuring low levels of long-lived radio nuclides and rare trace elements, and has wide applications to the earth and space sciences, biological sciences, and materials sciences.

The Department has 3,000 sq. ft. of class 10,000 cleanrooms used for assembling and testing detectors for use in high-energy physics experiments. Members of the Purdue Particle Physics Microstructure Development (P3MD) laboratories have built a silicon pixel detector for the CMS experiment at the Large Hadron Collider at CERN near Geneva, Switzerland. The P3MD group is developing silicon pixel sensors for the upgrade of CMS and other future particle physics experiments.

The Physics Department has an Instrument Shop and an Electronics Shop for building scientific apparatus. The Instrument Shop is staffed by professional machinists and features a CNC (Computer Numerical Control) milling machine and CNC lathe. Many undergraduate and graduate students receive training and practical experience in machining and electronics in the Instrument Shop and Electronics Shop. Machining techniques and safety are taught by a professional machinist in the Instrument Shop. Electronics for both research and instruction are designed, built, and repaired in the Electronics Shop, which is staffed by an electrical engineer.

Purdue University has created Discovery Park for interdisciplinary research in both bio- and nano-science. The Birck Nanotechnology Center and the Bindley Bioscience Center are state-of-the-art facilities where Physics faculty, postdoctoral researchers, and graduate students join colleagues from other disciplines in performing ground-breaking research in nanophysics, biophysics, and Sensory Science and Technology. Condensed matter experimentalists make use of synchrotron radiation sources at Argonne National Laboratory and Brookhaven National Laboratory. Physicists in High-Energy Particle and High-Energy Nuclear physics are engaged in experiments at Brookhaven National Laboratory, Fermi National Acceleratory Laboratory, and the CERN Laboratory. Astronomy and astrophysics researchers use facilities at the Whipple telescope at Kitt Peak National Observatory in Arizona, the Hubble Space Telescope, and a variety of other space-based instruments.

Table B—Separately Budgeted Research Expenditures by Source of Support

Source of Support	Departmental Research	Physics-related Research Outside Department
Federal government	$7,892,952	
State/local government		
Non-profit organizations		
Business and industry	$1,722,779	
Other	$130,867	
Total	**$9,746,598**	

Table C—Separately Budgeted Research Expenditures by Research Specialty

Research Specialty	No. of Grants	Expenditures ($)
Applied Physics	3	$116,403
Astrophysics	13	$887,126
Atomic, Molecular, & Optical Physics	9	$645,975
Biophysics	9	$872,845
Condensed Matter Physics	31	$3,810,835
Geophysics	4	$436,295
Nuclear Physics	3	$567,795
Accelerator Mass Spectrometry	9	$829,751
Particles and Fields	9	$1,457,557
Physics and other Science Education	4	$50,141
Planetary Science	4	$71,875
Total	**98**	**$9,746,598**

FACULTY

Distinguished University Professor

Greene, Chris, Ph.D., University of Chicago, 1980. *Atomic, Molecular, & Optical Physics*. Theoretical atomic, molecular, and optical physics. Ultra-cold few-body and many-body quantum systems. Electron-molecule collisions and dissociative recombination. Ultra-fast laser interactions with atoms and molecules. Photofragmentation of atoms and molecules. Novel Rydberg molecules and multi-channel Rydberg atoms.

Melosh, H. J., Ph.D., California Institute of Technology, 1972. University Distinguished Professor, Professor of Earth, Atmospheric, and Planetary Sciences. *Geophysics*. Ramifications of impact cratering; planetary tectonics; the physics of earthquakes and landslides.

Nolte, David D., Ph.D., University of California, Berkeley, 1988. *Biophysics, Condensed Matter Physics, Optics*. The Digital Holography and BioInterferometry group, directed by Professor David D. Nolte, applies the sensitivity of laser interferometry to a broad range of topics that include solid state physics, plasmonics in gold films, graphene, semiconductor physics, biointerferometry in biological physics, protein surface chemistry and holographic imaging of living biological tissues. In all thes areas, the picometer sensitivity of laser interferometry provides unprecidented sensitivity to study the optical properties of materials. For example, the BioCD (Biological Compact Disk) relies on diffraction.

Pyrak-Nolte, Laura, Ph.D., University of California, Berkeley, 1988. *Geophysics*. Wave propagation in fractured and cracked media.

Professor

Barnes, Virgil E., Ph.D., University of Cambridge, 1962. *Particles and Fields*. CDF, pp collisions at the Collider Detector at the Fermilab, including search for supersymmetric (SUSY) particles. Design, construction, and calibration of the CDF Run II scintillating tile-fiber Endplug Calorimeter, including early discovery of wavelength-shifting fiber patterns with excellent response uniformity over the entire scintillating tile, and demonstration of precision calorimeter calibration using moving radioactive sources. Design, construction, and calibration of the CMS Hadron Calorimeters, to probe beyond the Standard Model, including Higgs and SUSY particle searches, with 14 TCDF, pp bar collisions at the Collider Detector at Fermilab, including search for Supersymmetric (SUSY) particles. Design, construction and calibration of the CDF Run II scintillating tile-fiber Endplug Calorimeter, including early discovery of wavelength shifting fiber patterns with excellent response uniformity over the entire scintillating tile, and demonstration of precision calorimeter cal.

Bryan, Lynn, Ph.D., Purdue University, 1997. Professor of Curriculum and Instruction. *Physics and other Science Education.* Science teacher education, physics education; sociocultural influences on teaching and learning, particularly in international and/or rural contexts; evidence-based inquiry and reflection in teacher education; teacher knowledge and beliefs; qualitative research methods.

Caffee, Marc, Ph.D., Washington University, St. Louis, 1986. Director of PRIME Lab. *Geophysics, Other.* Accelerator mass spectrometry; application of stable- and radio-nuclides to problems in the geosciences, including quaternary landform evolution, cosmochronology, hydrology, and atmospheric processes; the development of techniques to enable the measurement of new cosmogenic nuclides.

Carlson, Erica W., Ph.D., University of California, Los Angeles, 2000. *Condensed Matter Physics.* Condensed matter theory of strongly correlated electronic systems; liquid crystalline vortex matter in type II superconductors; theory of high-temperature superconductivity; stripe phases in doped antiferromagnets; granular superconductors; analytic work and Monte Carlo simulations of the XY model; field theoretic calculation of spectral functions in quasi-one-dimensional superconductors; dimensional crossover; anisotropic bipolarons.

Chen, Yong, Ph.D., Princeton University, 2005. Professor of Electrical and Computer Engineering Director of Purdue Quantum Center Associate Director of Research for Birck Nanotechnology Center. *Atomic, Molecular, & Optical Physics, Condensed Matter Physics, Nano Science and Technology.* Experimental condensed matter physics; experimental atomic, molecular, and optical physics; nanoscience; nanotechnology.

Csathy, Gabor, Ph.D., Pennsylvania State University, 2001. Associate Department Head. *Condensed Matter Physics.* Experimental condensed matter physics; new physics in 2-D electrons; BCS-like pairing of composite fermions; non-Abelian statistics and possible applications for quantum computing; solid phases in electronic systems; spin physics in low dimensional semiconductors; spectrally enhanced chemical detection with nanotube transistors.

Cui, Wei, Ph.D., University of Wisconsin-Madison, 1994. *Astrophysics.* Microquasars, active galactic nuclei, gamma-ray bursts, X-ray binaries, and instrumentation for astronomical applications.

Durbin, Stephen M., Ph.D., University of Illinois, 1983. *Biophysics, Condensed Matter Physics.* Experimental condensed matter physics; biophysics; X-ray studies of vibrational modes in biomolecules; X-ray fluorescence imaging; X-ray holographic imaging; Sector Four at the Advanced Photon Source.

Elliott, Daniel S., Ph.D., University of Michigan, 1981. Professor of Electrical and Computer Engineering. *Atomic, Molecular, & Optical Physics.* Experimental atomic, molecular, and optical physics; coherent and quantum optics.

Finley, John P., Ph.D., University of Wisconsin-Madison, 1990. Department Head. *Astrophysics.* Optical, X-ray, and gamma-ray studies of compact objects. The evolution of galactic supernova remnants and their impact on the interstellar medium. The origin of the soft X-ray background. The origin of the cosmic rays.

Fischbach, Ephraim, Ph.D., University of Pennsylvania, 1967. *Particles and Fields.* Theoretical physics; elementary particle theory.

Gutay, Laszlo J., Ph.D., Florida State University, 1964. *Particles and Fields.* Experimental high-energy physics; electroweak physics; W, Z pair production, Higgs, SS particles.

Hirsch, Andrew S., Ph.D., Massachusetts Institute of Technology, 1977. *Nuclear Physics, Physics and other Science Education.* Experimental exploration of the equation of state of nuclear matter. Physics Education Research projects: (1) Making Sense of Global Warming and Climate Change: Model of Student Learning via Collaborative Research; (2) high-energy nuclear physics project (STAR).

Khlebnikov, Sergei, Ph.D., Institute for Nuclear Research of the Academy of Sciences, Moscow, 1988. *Particles and Fields.* Elementary particle theory; cosmology; and quantum field theory.

Koltick, David S., Ph.D., University of Michigan, 1978. *Applied Physics, Nuclear Physics.* Experimental high-energy physics; applied nuclear physics.

Kruczenski, Martin, Ph.D., University of Buenos Aires, 1998. *Particles and Fields.* Theoretical high-energy physics; string theory and its connections to gauge theory; string theory and blackhole physics.

Lister, Matthew L., Ph.D., Boston University, 1999. *Astrophysics.* High-luminosity active galactic nuclei; astrophysical jets and shocks; quasars and BL Lacertae objects; very long baseline interferometry; special relativity.

Love, Sherwin T., Ph.D., Stanford University, 1978. *Particles and Fields.* Quantum field theory and its application to elementary particle physics with focus on aspects of dynamical symmetry breaking, supersymmetric field theories, and the renormalization group.

Lyanda-Geller, Yuli, Ph.D., Ioffe Physico-Technical Institute, 1987. *Atomic, Molecular, & Optical Physics, Condensed Matter Physics.* Mesoscopic physics and interference phenomena; transport and optical phenomena in nanostructures; physics of quantum information.

Lyutikov, Maxim, Ph.D., California Institute of Technology, 1998. *Astrophysics.* Theoretical astrophysics; high-energy astrophysics compact objects; extragalactic astrophysics; cosmic rays; plasma astrophysics.

Manfra, Michael J., Ph.D., Boston University, 1999. Bill and Dee O'Brien Chair Professor of Physics and Astronomy Professor of Electrical and Computer Engineering Professor of Materials Engineering. *Condensed Matter Physics, Nano Science and Technology.* MBE growth of semiconductor nanostructures; transport properties of low-dimensional correlated electron systems.

Miller, David H., Ph.D., Imperial College, London University, 1963. *Particles and Fields.* Discovery physics at the high-energy frontier; physics of quarks.

Muzikar, Paul, Ph.D., Cornell University, 1980. *Condensed Matter Physics, Other.* Various aspects of geochronology form the focus of research. Specific topics include: (1) the use of cosmogenic nuclides such as Be-10 and Al-26 to determine exposure ages, burial ages, and erosion rates; (2) radiocarbon dating in archaeology and the earth sciences; (3) the application of Bayesian statistics to issues in geochronology.

Nakanishi, Hisao, Ph.D., Harvard University, 1980. *Condensed Matter Physics, Statistical & Thermal Physics.* Theoretical physics; condensed matter theory; statistical mechanics.

Neumeister, Norbert, Ph.D., Vienna University of Technology, 1996. *Particles and Fields.* High-energy particle physics; phenomenon of electro-weak symmetry breaking; the origin of the matter antimatter asymmetry in the universe; the search for new physics beyond the established standard model of particle physics.

Rebello, Sanjay, Ph.D., Brown University, 1995. Professor of Curriculum and Instruction. *Physics and other Science Education.* Teacher preparation; Transfer of learning.

Reifenberger, Ronald G., Ph.D., University of Chicago, 1976. *Condensed Matter Physics, Nano Science and Technology.* Condensed matter physics. Nanoscience and nanotechnology. Scanning probe techniques.

Ritchie, Kenneth P., Ph.D., University of British Columbia, 1998. Associate Department Head. *Biophysics.* Experimental biophysics; dynamics of the formation of signaling complexes in the plasma membrane of cells. Diffusion in lipid bilayer membranes with embedded mobile and immobile obstacles. Development of ultra-fast imaging techniques for observing individual molecules in living cells. Single molecule biophysics.

Robicheaux, Francis J., Ph.D., University of Chicago, 1991. *Atomic, Molecular, & Optical Physics*. Time-dependent atomic phenomena; highly excited (Rydberg) atoms; electron scattering; strong fields; ultra-cold plasmas.

Rokhinson, Leonid, Ph.D., Stony Brook University, 1996. *Condensed Matter Physics*. Experimental condensed matter physics; electron transport in mesoscopic systems; spintronics and spin interactions; quantum information processing; molecular electronics; nanofabrication; novel materials and devices.

Savikhin, Sergei, Ph.D., Tartu State University, 1991. *Biophysics*. Experimental biophysics; femtosecond optical studies of artificial and natural biological systems; membrane proteins: structure and function; structure-based computer modeling; exciton kinetics in semiconductors; molecular crystals and biological structures; biomimetic devices; ultra-fast experimental techniques.

Wang, Fuqiang, Ph.D., Columbia University, 1996. *Nuclear Physics*. High-energy nuclear physics, STAR at Brookhaven National Laboratory RHIC.

Xie, Wei, Ph.D., Chinese Academy of Sciences, 1997. *Nuclear Physics*. Experimental high-energy nuclear physics; quark-gluon plasma.

Associate Professor

Giannios, Dimitrios, Ph.D., University of Crete, 2005. *Astrophysics*. Theoretical astrophysics. Relativistic jets; acceleration and composition of ultra-high-energy cosmic rays; the nature of the central engine of gamma-ray bursts; the appearance of compact objects in general relativity and modified theories of gravity.

Haugan, Mark P., Ph.D., Stanford University, 1978. Associate Department Head. *Astrophysics, Physics and other Science Education, Relativity & Gravitation*. Conceptual and empirical foundations of relativity and gravitation physics and physics education research and development.

Jones, Matthew, Ph.D., Carleton University, 1997. *Particles and Fields*. Experimental high-energy physics.

Kaufmann, Birgit, Ph.D., University of Bonn, 1999. Associate Professor of Mathematics. *Condensed Matter Physics*. Condensed matter theory, correlated systems, non-equilibrium phenomena in quantum phase transitions; integrable models and scattering theories; Bethe Ansatz for quantum spin chains; reaction-diffusion systems.

Lang, Rafael F., Ph.D., Max Planck Institut fur Physik, 2008. *Astrophysics, Particles and Fields*. Search for dark matter.

Lifton, Nathaniel A., Ph.D., University of Arizona, 1997. Associate Professor of Earth, Atmospheric, and Planetary Sciences. *Geophysics*. Methods for using in situ cosmogenic nuclides to derive surface exposure ages and/or erosion rates for process-oriented geomorphic studies.

Malis, Oana, Ph.D., Boston University, 1999. *Atomic, Molecular, & Optical Physics, Condensed Matter Physics, Nano Science and Technology*. Structural and optical properties of nanostructured materials.

Molnar, Dénes, Ph.D., Columbia University, 2002. *Nuclear Physics*. Properties of nuclear matter at extreme energy densities, physics of relativistic heavy-ion collisions and the quark-gluon plasma, transport theory.

Peterson, John, Ph.D., Columbia University, 2003. *Astrophysics*. Observational cosmology: studies of dark energy and dark matter; high-resolution X-ray spectroscopy; X-ray emission from clusters of galaxies; cooling flows in clusters of galaxies;

surveys of clusters of galaxies; the Chandra and XMM-Newton X-ray Observatories; optical and X-ray astrophysics instrumentation; weak gravitational lensing of clusters and large-scale structure; optical astrophysics simulation; advanced multivariate Monte Carlo data analysis techniques; the Large Synoptic Survey Telescope (LSST).

Pushkar, Yulia, Ph.D., Freie Universität Berlin, 2003. *Biophysics, Energy Sources & Environment*. Experimental biophysics; energy research.

Rodriguez, Jorge, Ph.D., University of Illinois, 1995. *Biophysics*. Theoretical biophysics; computational electronic structure of active sites in metalloproteins; density functional theory of (bio)molecules; electronic structure and mesoscopic properties of (bio)molecular nanostructures; simulation of biological Mössbauer, EPR, and X-ray spectra; (anti)ferromagnetism in molecular magnets and finite fermion systems.

Assistant Professor

Biswas, Rudro R., Ph.D., Harvard University, 2011. *Condensed Matter Physics*. Theoretical condensed matter physics; geometrical aspects of quantum states of matter; impurities, defects, and disorders in exotic materials.

Hung, Chen-Lung, Ph.D., University of Chicago, 2011. *Atomic, Molecular, & Optical Physics*. Experimental ultra-cold atomic and molecular physics; strongly correlated many-body physics; quantum phase transitions and non-equilibrium dynamics; quantum simulations of condensed matter and gravitational physics; novel atomic trapping and cooling techniques; quantum optics; quantum information and computation.

Iyer-Biswas, Srividya, Ph.D., The Ohio State University, 2009. *Biophysics*. Experimental biophysics; Principles of cellular timekeeping.

Jung, Andreas, Ph.D., University of Heidelberg, 2009. *Particles and Fields*. Experimental high-energy physics; measurement of top quark Yukawa coupling; direct and indirect top quark partner searches; Precision cross-section measurements and dark matter.

Lee, Kyoung-Soo, Ph.D., Johns Hopkins University, 2007. *Astrophysics*. Observational cosmology, galaxy formation, and evolution; star formation and chemical enrichment histories of distant galaxies; cosmic structure formation of dark matter; search for progenitors of galaxy clusters in the young universe.

Li, Tongcang, Ph.D., University of Texas at Austin, 2011. *Atomic, Molecular, & Optical Physics, Nano Science and Technology*. Study the interaction of photons and matter for fundamental physics and broad applications. In particular, researches related to quantum foundations and quantum photonics: spin-optomechanics of levitated nanodiamonds; macroscopic quantum mechanics of living organisms; laser cooling of atoms, molecules, and solids; cold atom nanophotonics and plasmonics; ultra-sensitive optical tweezers.

Milisavljevic, Dan, Ph.D., Dartmouth College, 2011. *Astrophysics*. Time domain astronomy, Three-dimensional supernova reconstruction.

Mugler, Andrew, Ph.D., Columbia University, 2010. *Biophysics*. Dynamic reorganization for dynamic signals; internal vs. external energy in dynamic sensing; inferring environments from sensory network structure; sensing in spatially confined environments.

Zhou, Qi, Ph.D., The Ohio State University. *Atomic, Molecular, & Optical Physics*. Ultra cold atoms with synthetic gauge fields and spin-orbit coupling, Strongly correlated systems in optical lattices, Few- and many-body problems in strongly interacting fermion gas, Quantum dipolar atoms and molecules.

Research Assistant Professor

Srivistava, Brijesh, Ph.D., Indian Institute of Technology, Kanpur, 1975. Experimental high-energy nuclear physics.

Courtesy Professor

Kais, Sabre, Ph.D., Hebrew University of Jerusalem, 1989. Professor of Chemistry. *Condensed Matter Physics.* Theoretical condensed matter physics.

Minton, David, Ph.D., University of Arizona, 2009. Assistant Professor of Earth, Atmospheric, and Planetary Sciences. *Planetary Science.* Orbital dynamics, Planet formation, Planet migration, the Late Heavy Bombardment, Dynamics and structure of small bodies.

Shalaev, Vladimir M., Ph.D., Krasnoyarsk University, 1983. Robert and Anne Burnett Distinguished Professor of Electrical and Computer Engineering. *Electrical Engineering, Nano Science and Technology, Optics.* Fields and optics; biomedical imaging and sensing; communications, networking, signal, and image processing; microelectronics and nanotechnology.

Wasserman, Adam, Ph.D., Rutgers University, 2005. Associate Professor of Chemistry. *Condensed Matter Physics.* Theoretical condensed matter physics.

Courtesy Assistant Professor

Hosseini, Mahdi, Ph.D., Australian National University, 2012. Assistant Professor of Electrical and Computer Engineering. *Atomic, Molecular, & Optical Physics, Nano Science and Technology.* Quantum atom-optics, quantum optomechanics, nano-photonics, quantum optical computation and precision sensing.

DEPARTMENTAL RESEARCH SPECIALTIES AND STAFF

Theoretical

Astrophysics. Cosmology; cosmic microwave background; extra dimensions; experimental tests of general relativity; gravitation; plasma and high-energy astrophysics; pulsars and supernova remnants, active galactic nuclei; gamma-ray bursts; relativistic jets, massive, and supermassive black holes; space plasmas, core-collapse supernovae. Giannios, Lyutikov, Milisavljevic.

Atomic, Molecular, & Optical Physics. Ultra-cold atomic gases; electron-molecule collisions; laser-molecule interactions; time-dependent atomic phenomena; highly excited (Rydberg) atoms; strong fields; antihydrogen; few-body physics. Greene, Robicheaux, Zhou.

Biophysics. Electronic structure in metalloproteins; density functional theory of biomolecules; biomolecular nanostructures; biological Mossbauer, EPR and X-ray spectra simulations; molecular magnetism; cellular computation; molecular clustering; cell-cell communication; cell signaling thermodynamics; biological networks; information theory. Iyer-Biswas, Mugler, Rodriguez, Wasserman.

Condensed Matter Physics. Two-dimensional electron systems, Quantum dots and wires; Quantum Hall effect; Spin-orbit interactions; Spin and charge density waves; high-temperature superconductivity; Ferromagnetism and anti-ferromagnetism; spintronics; quantum fluids; Bose-Einstein condensation; phase transitions; optical phenomena; non-equilibrium dynamics; integrable models; Anderson localization; exotic materials. Biswas, Kais, Kaufmann, Lyanda-Geller, Nakanishi, Wasserman.

Nuclear Physics. Relativistic heavy-ion collisions; Quark-gluon plasma; strong, weak, and electromagnetic interactions in nuclei; Bose-Einstein condensation nuclear fusion and low-energy nuclear reactions. Molnar.

Particles and Fields. Theory and phenomenology of the standard model of elementary particle interactions; aspects of supersymmetry; Neutrino oscillations in astrophysical phenomena; Dynamical symmetry breaking; renormalization group studies; cosmological phase transitions; inflationary models of the early universe; Brane world models; string theory; string/gauge theory duality; tests of general relativity and Newtonian gravity; phenomenology of string-inspired new long-range forces; theory and phenomenology of nuclear decay. Fischbach, Khlebnikov, Kruczenski, Love.

Planetary Science. Ramifications of impact cratering; planetary tectonics; physics of earthquakes and landslides. Melosh, Minton.

Statistical & Thermal Physics. Phase transitions and critical phenomena; phenomenology of first order phase transitions; Ising systems: percolation and other clustering phenomena; quantum percolation and other quantum transport; statistical properties of surfaces and interfaces; scaling in linear and branched polymer chains; kinetics of disorderly growth processes; Brownian motion. Nakanishi.

Experimental

Accelerator Mass Spectrometry. Tandem Van de Graaff accelerator operations; technique development for measuring long-lived radionuclides and other rare particles. applications in physics (neutron transport, trace impurities, cross sections), earth science (dating and tracing processes and events, global change, environment), and biological science (drug metabolism, toxicity). Caffee, Lifton, Muzikar.

Applied Physics. Hazardous material detection; associated particle imaging; neutron activation analysis; gamma-ray detector design; elemental analyses in medical diagnostics. Koltick.

Astrophysics. Studies of ultra-short-period pulsating variable stars, neutron stars, black holes, supernova remnants, interstellar medium, active galactic nuclei, relativistic jets, formation and evolution of galaxies, clusters of galaxies, cosmic background radiation, cosmic rays, dark matter, and dark energy; Satellite-based astronomical observations in infrared, optical, UV, X-ray, and gamma-ray wavelengths; ground-based very-high-energy gamma-ray experiments (VERITAS); radio astronomy and interferometry; optical survey (LSST); direct dark matter search (XENON). Cui, Finley, Lang, Lee, Lister, Peterson.

Atomic, Molecular, & Optical Physics. Bose-Einstein condensates; ultra-cold atoms and molecules; two-pathway coherent control processes; quantum photonics; quantum manipulation of atoms and molecules with lasers; quantum optomechanics; AMO-solid state/nano hybrid quantum systems; precision measurements. Chen, Elliott, Hosseini, Hung, Li, Malis.

Biophysics. Modeling real nervous systems and learning and memory in simple neural systems; vibrational properties of metalloproteins and other biomolecules; Nuclear Resonant Vibrational Spectroscopy of heme proteins; resonant Raman scattering and FTIR of cytochromes and heme compounds. Terahertz time-delay spectroscopy macromolecule vibrations; single molecule spectroscopy of photosynthetic complexes (PS I); live cell, single molecule imaging of membrane molecule dynamics and interactions; cellular timekeeping; signatures of transient dynamics in single cells; sustained biological symmetry breaking. Durbin, Iyer-Biswas, Nolte, Pushkar, Ritchie, Savikhin.

Condensed Matter Physics. Raman scattering and photoluminescence of semiconductors; non-linear optics of semiconductors and their quantum well-structures; graphene and carbon nanotubes; nanoscience, nanomaterials, and nanodevices; metallic surfaces; resistivity of metals; X-ray studies of quasi-crystals; X-ray synchrotron physics; magnetic materials;

quantum transport in GaAs/AlxGa1−xAs microstructures; fractional quantum Hall effect; scanning probe microscopy; Si/SiO2 interface roughness; 2D materials; Topological insulators and related materials. Chen, Csathy, Durbin, Malis, Manfra, Nolte, Reifenberger, Rokhinson, Shalaev.

Geophysics. Rock mechanics and physics of rocks; physical acoustics of heterogeneous materials and discontinuities; volumetric non-destructive imaging of opaque materials; hydrology and percolation physics. Nolte, Pyrak-Nolte.

Nuclear Physics. Relativistic nuclear collisions; quantum chromodynamics; quark-gluon plasma; analysis of Relativistic Heavy Ion Collider (BNL) and Large Hadron Collider (CERN) reaction products. Hirsch, Wang, Xie.

Particles and Fields. Compact Muon Solenoid (CMS) experiment at the Large Hadron Collider; Collider Detector at Fermilab (CDF); Higgs boson particles; Supersymmetric (SUSY) particles; Electroweak interactions; precision measurement of the Standard Model; particle astrophysics; Large Synoptic Survey Telescope; dark matter particles; XENON Dark Matter search. Barnes, Gutay, Jones, Jung, Lang, Miller, Neumeister.

Physics and other Science Education. Science teacher education; sociocultural influences on teaching and learning; Evidence-based inquiry in teacher education; teacher knowledge and beliefs; student attitudes and perceptions of physics. Bryan, Haugan, Hirsch, Rebello.

View additional information about this department at www.gradschoolshopper.com. Check out the "Why Choose Us?" section, find out more about the department's culture and get links to social media networks.

UNIVERSITY OF NOTRE DAME

DEPARTMENT OF PHYSICS

Notre Dame, Indiana 46556-5670
http://physics.nd.edu

General University Information
President: Rev. John I. Jenkins, C.S.C.
Dean of Graduate School: Laura Carlson
University website: http://www.nd.edu/
School Type: Private
Setting: Suburban
Total Faculty: 1,364
Total number of Students: 12,179
Total number of Graduate Students: 2,831

Department Information
Department Chairman: Prof. Peter Garnavich, Chair
Department Contact: Shari Herman, Sr. Admin. Assistant,
   Graduate Student Programs
   Total full-time faculty: 62
   Total number of full-time equivalent positions: 48
   Full-Time Graduate Students: 103
   Female Full-Time Graduate Students: 25
   First-Year Graduate Students: 21
   Female First-Year Students: 7
   Total Post Doctorates: 17

Department Address
225 Nieuwland Science Hall
Notre Dame, IN 46556-5670
Phone: (574) 631-6386
Fax: (574) 631-5952
E-mail: physics@nd.edu
Website: http://physics.nd.edu

ADMISSIONS

Admission Contact Information
Address admission inquiries to: Chair, Graduate Admissions
   Committee, Department of Physics
Phone: (574) 631-6386
E-mail: physics@nd.edu
Admissions website: http://graduateschool.nd.edu/admissions/

Application deadlines
Fall admission:
U.S. students: January 15   *Int'l. students*: January 15

Application fee
U.S. students: $75   *Int'l. students*: $75

Admissions information
For Fall of 2018:
   Number of applicants: 252
   Number admitted: 50
   Number enrolled: 23

Admission requirements
Bachelor's degree requirements: Bachelor's degree in Physics
   is required.
Minimum undergraduate GPA: 3.2

GRE requirements
The GRE is required.

Subjective GRE requirements
The Subjective GRE is required.
   Minimum accepted Advanced GRE score: 600

TOEFL requirements
The TOEFL exam is required for students from non-English-
   speaking countries.
   PBT score: 600
   iBT score: 100
Speaking score should be 23 or over.

Other admissions information
Additional requirements: The GRE physics test is required with
   a score of at least 600.
Undergraduate preparation assumed: Three, three-week course
   offering in the summer prior to beginning: Review of Physics
   A: Mechanics & Thermodynamics; Review of Physics B:
   Electromagnetism; Review of Physics C: Quantum Mechan-
   ics.

TUITION

Tuition year 2017–18:
   Full-time students: $53,218 annual
   Part-time students: $2,930 per credit
Tuition and fees ($250 Technology and $150 Health Center Ac-
   cess Fee) are paid by The Graduate School in most cases.
Credit hours per semester to be considered full-time: 9
Deferred tuition plan: Yes
Health insurance: Yes, University funded.
Other academic fees: $72 Graduate Student Union fee per year;
   $140 parking fee per year (unless TA - then it is paid by the
   Graduate School).
Academic term: Semester
Number of first-year students who received full tuition waivers: 23

Teaching Assistants, Research Assistants, and Fellowships
Number of first-year
   Teaching Assistants: 16
   Research Assistants: 1
   Fellowship students: 4
Average stipend per academic year
   Teaching Assistant: $22,279
   Research Assistant: $22,279
   Fellowship student: $33,000

FINANCIAL AID

Loans
Loans are available for U.S. students.
Loans are available for international students.
GAPSFAS application required: No
FAFSA application required: Yes

For further information
Address financial aid inquiries to: Director, Financial Aid, 115
   Main Building, Notre Dame, IN 46556.
Phone: (574) 631-6436
E-mail: finaid@nd.edu

Financial aid website: http://financialaid.nd.edu/graduate-students/

HOUSING

Availability of on-campus housing
Single students: Yes
Married students: Yes

For further information
Address housing inquiries to: Housing Office, Dean of Students, Residential Life, Notre Dame, IN 46556.
Phone: (574) 631-5878
E-mail: orlh@nd.edu
Housing aid website: http://housing.nd.edu/graduate/

Table A—Faculty, Enrollments, and Degrees Granted

Research Specialty	2017–18 Faculty	Enrollment Fall 2017		Number of Degrees Granted 2016–17 (2012–17)		
		Mas-ter's	Doc-torate	Mas-ter's	Terminal Master's	Doc-torate
Astrophysics	11	–	29	–	–	4(15)
Atomic, Molecular, & Optical Physics	2	–	–	–	–	–
Biophysics	3	–	7	–	–(1)	3(11)
Condensed Matter Physics	10	–	12	–	–	3(24)
High Energy Physics	11	–	18	–	–	2(21)
Nuclear Physics	22	–	48	–	1(1)	8(34)
Total	59	–	114	–	1(18)	12(70)
Full-time Grad. Stud.	–	–	114	–	–	–
First-year Grad. Stud.	–	–	22	–	–	–

GRADUATE DEGREE REQUIREMENTS

Master's: The graduate program in the Department of Physics is research oriented. For that reason, the department does not accept students who plan to terminate their studies with a master's degree. Under certain conditions, a non-research master's program is available. Students must complete 30 credit hours and maintain a grade point average of 3.0. The student must pass a comprehensive oral examination in the major field. Applicants are cautioned that financial aid is normally restricted to students pursuing Ph.D. programs of study. The minimum residence is two successive semesters.

Doctorate: Students must complete 27 credit hours and maintain a grade point average of 3.0. The minimum residency requirement for the Ph.D. degree is full-time status for four consecutive semesters. The student will normally take a sequence of basic courses in a two-year core curriculum, followed by advanced courses and seminars in specialized areas of study. Included in the core curriculum are one semester of mathematical methods in physics, one semester of experimental methods in physics, one semester each of classical mechanics and statistical mechanics, two semesters of quantum mechanics, two semesters of electrodynamics, and one semester of a research-area course (astrophysics, atomic physics, biophysics, condensed-matter physics, elementary particle physics, or nuclear physics), and completion of two semesters of a breadth requirement in physics. Incoming students who have already successfully completed courses equivalent to any of those in the core curriculum will not be expected to take the corresponding core curriculum courses. However, all incoming students are required to take and pass a qualifying examination on undergraduate physics. The student is encouraged to become an active participant in research in the second se-

mester of the first year of his/her graduate work. Prior to admission to candidacy for the Ph.D. degree, the student must pass comprehensive written and oral examinations. There is no foreign language requirement. Approval of the thesis by the research director and three readers and an oral defense of the thesis complete the requirements.

Thesis: Thesis may be written in absentia.

SPECIAL EQUIPMENT, FACILITIES, OR PROGRAMS

JINA-The Joint Institute for Nuclear Astrophysics, http://www.jinaweb.org/

ISNAP-The Institute for Structure and Nuclear Astrophysics, http://isnap.nd.edu/

QuarkNet Center, https://physics.nd.edu/educational-outreach/quarknet-program/

iCeNSA-The Interdisciplinary Center for Network Science and Applications, http://www.icensa.com/

ND REU - Research Experience for Undergraduates at the University of Notre Dame Department of Physics, http://physics.nd.edu/research/reu/

Table B—Separately Budgeted Research Expenditures by Source of Support

Source of Support	Departmental Research	Physics-related Research Outside Department
Federal government	$8,121,869	
State/local government	$2,999,294	
Non-profit organizations	$185,424	
Business and industry	$7,500	
Other		
Total	$11,314,087	

Table C—Separately Budgeted Research Expenditures by Research Specialty

Research Specialty	No. of Grants	Expenditures ($)
Astronomy	14	$1,076,634
Atomic, Molecular, & Optical Physics	1	$19,387
Condensed Matter Physics	11	$1,717.55
High Energy Physics	17	$4,254,153
Nuclear Physics	13	$3,771,868
Physics and other Science Education	5	$474,678
Total	61	$9,598,437.55

FACULTY

Chair Professor

Aprahamian, Ani, Ph.D., Clark University, 1986. Frank M. Freimann Professor of Physics. *Nuclear Physics*. Experimental nuclear physics; gamma-ray spectroscopy; nuclear masses; lifetimes; astrophysics.

Beers, Timothy C., Ph.D., Harvard University, 1983. Notre Dame Professor of Astrophysics. *Astrophysics*. Galactic archeology, the origin and evolution of the elements in the Universe.

Furdyna, Jacek K., Ph.D., Northwestern University, 1960. The Aurora and Thomas Marquez Chair in Information Theory and Computer Technology; Fellow, Nanovic Institute for European Studies; Director, Center for Material Fabrication & Nanotechnology. *Condensed Matter Physics, Materials Science, Metallurgy*. Experimental solid-state physics; man-made materials.

Wiescher, Michael C.F., Ph.D., Universität Münster, 1980. Frank M. Freimann Professor of Physics; Director for the Joint Institute for Nuclear Astrophysics (JINA). *Nuclear Physics*. Experimental nuclear physics; nuclear astrophysics.

Professor

Balsara, Dinshaw S., Ph.D., University of Illinois, 1990. Concurrent Associate Professor, Department of Applied and Computational Mathematics and Statistics. *Astrophysics, Computational Physics*. Theoretical and computational astrophysics.

Bardayan, Dan, Ph.D., Yale University, 1999. *Nuclear Physics*. Explosive nucleosynthesis that occurs in cataclysmic stellar events such as novae, supernovae, and X-ray bursts.

Bunker, Bruce A., Ph.D., University of Washington, 1980. Director, Materials Research Collaborative Access Team (MR-CAT), a multiinstitutional consortium developing and using X-ray beamlines at the Advanced Photon Source, Argonne National Laboratory. *Condensed Matter Physics*. Experimental physics; X-ray, UV, and electron spectroscopy of condensed-matter, and biological/environmental systems.

Collon, Philippe A., Ph.D., Universität Wien, 1999. Associate Chair and Director of Undergraduate Studies. Outreach Coordinator for the Underground Accelerator Collaboration DIANA at the new National Deep Underground Science and Engineering Laboratory (DUSEL). *Nuclear Physics*. Experimental nuclear physics; new techniques, AMS.

Delgado, Antonio, Ph.D., Universidad Autonoma de Madrid, 2001. *Particles and Fields*. The last building block left to be discovered within the Standard Model of Particle Physics; the Higgs boson.

Dobrowolska-Furdyna, Malgorzata, Ph.D., Polish Academy of Sciences, 1979. Associate Dean for Undergraduate Students, College of Science. Rev. John Cardinal O'Hara, C.S.C. Professor of Physics. *Condensed Matter Physics*. Experimental solid-state physics.

Eskildsen, Morten R., Ph.D., University of Copenhagen, 1998. Director of Graduate Admissions. *Condensed Matter Physics*. Studies of superconductivity, especially in the vortices induced in type-II superconductors by an applied magnetic field.

Frauendorf, Stefan G., Ph.D., Technical University Dresden, 1971. *Nuclear Physics*. Theoretical nuclear physics; atomic physics; mesoscopic systems.

Garg, Umesh, Ph.D., Stony Brook University, 1978. Director of the Department of Physics Research Experience for Undergraduates (REU) program. *Nuclear Physics*. Experimental nuclear physics; nuclear structure; giant resonances; gamma-ray spectroscopy; high-spin states.

Garnavich, Peter M., Ph.D., University of Washington, 1991. Chair, Department of Physics. *Astrophysics*. Astrophysics/observational cosmology.

Hildreth, Michael D., Ph.D., Stanford University, 1995. Associate Dean of Research and Graduate Studies, College of Science. *High Energy Physics*. Experimental high-energy elementary particle physics.

Howk, Christopher J., Ph.D., University of Wisconsin-Madison, 1999. *Astrophysics*. Observational astrophysics; interstellar and intergalactic media.

Jankó, Boldizsár, Ph.D., Cornell University, 1996. Director, Institute for Theoretical Sciences. *Condensed Matter Physics*. Theoretical condensed-matter physics.

Jessop, Colin P., Ph.D., Harvard University, 1994. *Particles and Fields*. Experimental high-energy physics.

Kolda, Christopher F., Ph.D., University of Michigan, 1995. Glynn Family Honors Collegiate Professor of Physics. *High Energy Physics*. Theoretical high-energy physics; supersymmetry.

LoSecco, John M., Ph.D., Harvard University, 1976. *Nuclear Physics, Particles and Fields*. Experimental and theoretical physics; high-energy elementary particle physics.

Mathews, Grant J., Ph.D., University of Maryland, 1977. Director, Center for Astrophysics at Notre Dame University (CANDU). *Astrophysics*. Theoretical astrophysics/cosmology; general relativity.

Newman, Kathie E., Ph.D., University of Washington, 1981. *Condensed Matter Physics, Mechanics, Statistical & Thermal Physics*. Theoretical physics; statistical mechanics; semiconductors.

Peaslee, Graham F., Ph.D., SUNY – Stony Brook, 1987. *Accelerator, Nuclear Physics*. Applied nuclear physics.

Rettig, Terrence W., Ph.D., Indiana University, 1976. *Astronomy*. Observational astronomy: comets, solar system formation and T Tauri stars.

Ruchti, Randal C., Ph.D., Michigan State University, 1973. *High Energy Physics*. Experimental physics; high-energy elementary particle physics.

Ruggiero, Steven T., Ph.D., Stanford University, 1981. *Condensed Matter Physics*. Experimental physics; condensed matter and low-temperature physics; superconductivity.

Sapirstein, Jonathan R., Ph.D., Stanford University, 1979. *Atomic, Molecular, & Optical Physics*. Theoretical physics; quantum electrodynamics.

Surman, Rebecca, Ph.D., University of North Carolina, Chapel Hill, 1998. *Astrophysics, Nuclear Physics*. Theoretical nuclear astrophysicist interested in the origins of the heaviest elements.

Tanner, Carol E., Ph.D., University of California, Berkeley, 1985. *Atomic, Molecular, & Optical Physics*. A variety of precision measurements in atomic cesium that are motivated by the study of PNC, fundamental symmetries, and measurements of fundamental constants.

Toroczkai, Zoltan, Ph.D., Virginia Polytechnic Institute and State University (Virginia Tech), 1997. Concurrent Professor, Computer Science, and Engineering. *Biophysics, Condensed Matter Physics*. Theoretical condensed-matter physics; biophysics; complex network theory.

Wayne, Mitchell R., Ph.D., University of California, Los Angeles, 1985. *High Energy Physics*. Experimental high-energy elementary particle physics.

Associate Professor

Caprio, Mark A., Ph.D., Yale University, 2003. Associate Chair and Director of Graduate Studies. *Nuclear Physics*. Nuclear structure theory; many-body physics.

Crepp, Justin R., Ph.D., University of Florida, 2008. *Astronomy*. Developing new technologies and observational techniques to detect faint substellar companions that orbit nearby stars. Design and build instruments that operate at visible and near-infrared wavelengths to directly image and study brown dwarfs and extrasolar planets. Use the Doppler method to measure the radial velocity "wobble" of stars as they gravitationally interact with their planets.

Lannon, Kevin P., Ph.D., University of Illinois, 2003. *High Energy Physics*. Experimental high-energy particle physics.

Ptasinska, Sylwia, Ph.D., Leopold-Franzens-University, 2004. *Biophysics, Condensed Matter Physics*. Experimental studies on electron interaction with molecules and radiation damage to DNA and its component biomolecules.

Assistant Professor

Ahn, Tan, Ph.D., Stony Brook Univresity, 2008. *Nuclear Physics*. The cluster structure of nuclei; the evolution of nuclear structure; and development of active-target techniques and analysis.

Assaf, Badih, Ph.D., Northeastern University, 2014. Frank M. Freimann Assistant Professor of Physics. *Condensed Matter Physics*. Experimental condensed matter.

Brodeur, Maxime, Ph.D., University of British Columbia, 2010. Ortenzio Family Assistant Professorship in Applied Medical and Nuclear Physics. *Nuclear Physics*. Understanding the various aspects of the atomic nucleus, from its birth to its limits of existence passing by its structure and symmetries.

Chilcote, Jeffrey, Ph.D., University of California, Los Angeles, 2014. *Astronomy, Astrophysics*. Astrophysicist whose work centers on building the next generation of astronomical instruments and using those instruments to do cutting-edge research, particularly in the search for exoplanets.

Couder, Manoel, Ph.D., Université Catholique de Louvain, 2004. *Nuclear Physics*. Design, simulate, develop, and optimize new solutions and apply those solutions to real-world measurements of low-energy nuclear reactions of astrophysical interest.

Gomes, Kenjiro K., Ph.D., University of Illinois at Urbana-Champaign, 2008. Frank M. Freimann Assistant Professor of Physics. *Condensed Matter Physics*. Experimental condensed matter physics; scanning tunneling microscope.

Martin, Adam, Ph.D., Boston University, 2007. Tom and Aurora Marquez Assistant Professor of Physics. *High Energy Physics*. Experimental high energy physics.

Simon, Anna M., Ph.D., Jagiellonian University, 2010. *Nuclear Physics*. Nuclear astrophysics, processes leading to production of proton-rich heavy nuclei.

Vural, Dervis C., Ph.D., University of Illinois Urbana-Champaign, 2011. Many body behavior of physical and biological systems in which disorder and strong interactions play and important role.

Emeritus

Berry, H. Gordon, Ph.D., University of Wisconsin-Madison, 1967. *Atomic, Molecular, & Optical Physics*. Experimental atomic physics.

Bigi, Ikaros I., Ph.D., Universität München, 1976. Grace-Rupley II Professor. *High Energy Physics*. Refining the standard model phenomenology for the decays of hadrons carrying the quantum numbers strangeness, charm, and beauty and on electric dipole moments to use them as "indirect" searches for new physics.

Hyder, Anthony K., Ph.D., Air Force Institute of Technology, 1976. *Nuclear Physics*. Experimental physics; space physics; nuclear physics.

Kolata, James J., Ph.D., Michigan State University, 1969. *Nuclear Physics*. Experimental physics; nuclear structure; heavy-ion reactions; radioactive beam physics.

Research Professor

Berg, Georg P., Ph.D., University of Cologne, 1974. *Nuclear Physics*. Nuclear structure and its reaction mechanism mostly using spectrometers exploiting their high-resolution and zero-degree capabilities. –ST. GEORGE recoil separator, a project of JINA funded by the National Science Foundation.

Gorres, Joachim, Ph.D., Universität Münster, 1983. *Nuclear Physics*. Experimental determination of synthesis of elements and the generation of energy in stars with special emphasis on hydrogen burning and on the nucleosynthesis in AGB stars.

Lehner, Nicolas, Ph.D., The Queen's University of Belfast, 2000. *Astrophysics*. Understanding the physical processes that drive and regulate the growth of galaxies.

Research Associate Professor

Liu, Xinyu, Ph.D., University of Notre Dame, 2003. *Condensed Matter Physics*. Experimental condensed matter physics.

Marinelli, Nancy, Ph.D., University of Bari, 1993. *High Energy Physics*. Actively engaged in the experimental program of the LHC (the Large Hadron Collider at CERN).

Robertson, Daniel, Ph.D., University of Notre Dame, 2010. *Nuclear Physics*. Experimental nuclear physics.

Tan, Wanpeng, Ph.D., Michigan State University, 2002. *Nuclear Physics*. Experimental nuclear physics.

Research Assistant Professor

Crass, Jonathan, Ph.D., University of Cambridge, 2014. *Astronomy, Astrophysics*. The design, development and construction of iLocater, a new ultra-precise radial velocity instrument to search for planets around other stars.

O'Malley, Patrick, Ph.D., Rutgers University, 2012. *Nuclear Physics*. Experimental nuclear physics.

Phillips, Lara Arielle, Ph.D., Princeton University, 2003. *Astrophysics*. Astrophysics and cosmology theory; the missing baryon problem.

Placco, Vinicius M., Ph.D., Universidade de Sao Paulo, 2010. *Astrophysics*. The chemical evolution of the Universe, revealed by spectroscopic studies of metal-poor stars.

Professional Specialist

Stech, Edward J., Ph.D., University of Notre Dame, 2004. *Nuclear Physics*. Study nuclear reactions important to the understanding of energy production and the origin of elements in stars and explosive stellar environments.

Assistant Professional Specialist

Kilburn, Micha A., Ph.D., Michigan State University, 2011. Director of Outreach and Education, Joint Institute for Nuclear Astrophysics. *Nuclear Physics*. Experimental nuclear physics.

Mechtenberg, Abigail R., Ph.D., University of Michigan, 2009. Assistant Teaching Professor. *Applied Physics, Physics and other Science Education*. Applied physics, physics education, sustainable development.

Zech, William F., Ph.D., University of Notre Dame, 2010. Director of Advanced Physics Laboratories. *Astrophysics*. Astrophysics.

Concurrent Assistant Professional Specialist

Davis, Keith W., Ph.D., Clemson University, 2007. Director, Digital Visualization Theater. *Astronomy, Astrophysics*. Astrophysics.

Other

LaVerne, Jay A., Ph.D., University of Nebraska, 1981. Concurrent Professional Specialist. *Nuclear Physics*. Radiation effects in condensed phases are due to complex interactions between the transport of energy, the decomposition of medium molecules, and the diffusion and reaction of transient species.

Peng, Jeffrey W., Ph.D., University of Michigan, 1993. Concurrent Associate Professor. *Biophysics*. The Peng Lab works at the interface of the physical and biological sciences to illuminate the role of bio-molecular dynamics in molecular recognition and evolution.

DEPARTMENTAL RESEARCH SPECIALTIES AND STAFF

Theoretical

Astrophysics. Inflationary cosmology; primordial nucleosynthesis; cosmic microwave background; galaxy formation and evolution; large-scale structure; stellar evolution and nucleosynthesis; black holes in a magnetic field; charged black holes; neutron stars; neutron star binaries; gravity waves; gamma-ray bursts; supernovae; numerical relativity. Balsara, Mathews, Phillips, Surman.

Atomic, Molecular, & Optical Physics. Quantum electrodynamics; weak interactions; atomic many-body theory; photoionization and photoexcitation. Sapirstein.

Biophysics. Biological networks; cellular and population dynamics; organogensis and tissue development; epidemics; endosymbiotic evolution. Toroczkai, Vural.

Condensed Matter Physics. Many-body problem; high-temperature superconductivity; superconductivity and magnetism on the nanoscale; tunneling phenomena; metal-metal interfaces; inhomogeneous and layered superconductors; hopping transport; studies of ordering in semiconductors, magnetic semiconductors. Jankó, Newman, Toroczkai, Vural.

Nuclear Physics. Many-body problem; nuclear reactions, few-body problem; boson expansions, structure of nuclei with momentum high angular momentum and exotic proton and neutron numbers. Caprio, Frauendorf, Surman.

Particles and Fields. Formal properties of quantum field theories; supersymmetry, grand unification, spontaneous symmetry breaking, Higgs physics, phenomenology of strong and weak processes, rare decays, and CP violation; lepton dynamics; supergravity; extra dimensions; new particles. Bigi, Delgado, Kolda, Martin.

Statistical & Thermal Physics. Complex networks, phase transitions; critical phenomena in fluids; networks; computer simulations. Newman, Toroczkai.

Experimental

Astrophysics. Spectra and images of comets; stellar nuclear reaction rates; high-redshift supernovae; exoplanets; cosmological parameters. Beers, Chilcote, Crass, Crepp, Davis, Garnavich, Howk, Lehner, Mathews, Phillips, Placco, Rettig, Zech.

Atomic, Molecular, & Optical Physics. Atomic structure; parity violation; tests of fundamental symmetries; excitation mechanisms; radiative decays in neutral and ionized atoms; precision lifetimes. Tanner.

Condensed Matter Physics. Low-temperature physics; superconducting microwave absorption; metal and semiconductor superlattices; magnetism; magnetic resonance; magnetoelastic effects; high-temperature superconductivity; heavy fermion superconductivity; unconventional superconductivity; optical and far-infrared spectroscopy of semiconductors; crystal growth and MBE of semiconductors; magnetostatic effects; layered superconductors; single-electron tunneling; scanning tunneling microscopy and spectroscopy; optical and infrared photoresponse; X-ray absorption spectroscopy and X-ray scattering; neutron scattering. Assaf, Bunker, Dobrowolska-Furdyna, Eskildsen, Furdyna, Gomes, Jankó, Liu, Ptasinska, Ruggiero, Toroczkai.

High Energy Physics. CMS at CERN (Higgs boson properties, supersymmetry, top quark properties, electroweak physics, physics beyond the standard model); Double Chooz (neutrino oscillations); ILC (Beam monitoring, detector R&D); Fermilab D0 experiment (study of the top quark, bottom quark, W boson, and physics beyond the standard model); BaBar experiment at SLAC (CP violation in the b-quark system). Hildreth, Jessop, Lannon, LoSecco, Marinelli, Ruchti, Wayne.

Nuclear Physics. Nuclear structure; reaction energies; electromagnetic transitions; gamma-ray spectroscopy; high-spin states; polarized particles; giant resonances; heavy-ion reactions; radioactive beam studies; nuclear astrophysics. Ahn, Aprahamian, Bardayan, Berg, Brodeur, Collon, Couder, Garg, Gorres, Kolata, LaVerne, O'Malley, Peaslee, Robertson, Simon, Stech, Tan, Wiescher.

View additional information about this department at www.gradschoolshopper.com. Check out the "Why Choose Us?" section, find out more about the department's culture and get links to social media networks.

IOWA STATE UNIVERSITY

DEPARTMENT OF PHYSICS AND ASTRONOMY

Ames, Iowa 50011
http://www.physastro.iastate.edu

General University Information
President: Wendy Wintersteen
Dean of Graduate School: William Graves
University website: http://www.iastate.edu
School Type: Public
Setting: Urban
Total Faculty: 1,973
Total Graduate Faculty: 1,377
Total number of Students: 36,321
Total number of Graduate Students: 4,991

Department Information
Department Chairman: Prof. Frank Krennrich, Chair
Department Contact: Gloria Oberender, Asst to Chair
  Total full-time faculty: 38
  Total number of full-time equivalent positions: 57
  Full-Time Graduate Students: 103
  Female Full-Time Graduate Students: 19
  First-Year Graduate Students: 19
  Female First-Year Students: 5
  Total Post Doctorates: 32

Department Address
Physics 0012
2323 Osborn Drive
Ames, IA 50011
Phone: (515) 294-5441
Fax: (515) 294-6027
E-mail: gloria@iastate.edu
Website: http://www.physastro.iastate.edu

ADMISSIONS

Admission Contact Information
Address admission inquiries to: Iowa State University, Department of Physics and Astronomy, Graduate Admission, 12 Physics Hall, Osborn Drive, Ames, Iowa 50011
Phone: (515) 294-5870
E-mail: physastro@iastate.edu
Admissions website: http://www.admissions.iastate.edu/graduate/

Application deadlines
Fall admission:
U.S. students: January 1   *Int'l. students*: January 1

Application fee
U.S. students: $60   *Int'l. students*: $100
We accept no spring admissions. A limited number of admission fee waivers will be available. See Department website for details (http://www.physastro.iastate.edu/).

Admissions information
For Fall of 2017:
  Number of applicants: 131
  Number admitted: 61
  Number enrolled: 19

Admission requirements
Bachelor's degree requirements: A Bachelor's degree is required.
Minimum undergraduate GPA: 3.0

GRE requirements
The GRE is required.
  Mean GRE score range (25th–75th percentile): 63
Department sets no minimum score for GRE.

Subjective GRE requirements
The Subjective GRE is required.
  Mean Advanced GRE score range (25th–75th percentile): 60
Department sets no minimum score for GRE.

TOEFL requirements
The TOEFL exam is required for students from non-English-speaking countries.
  PBT score: 550
  iBT score: 79

Other admissions information
Additional requirements: The average GRE percentage for 2017 admissions were verbal-62%; quantitative-81%; analytical-31%. The average GRE Physics score for admissions was 60%.
Undergraduate preparation assumed: Saxon, Elementary Quantum Mechanics; Marion, Classical Dynamics; Kittel, Thermal Physics; Lorrain and Corson, Electromagnetic Fields and Waves.

TUITION

Tuition year 2017–2018:
Tuition for in-state residents
  Full-time students: $4,472 per semester
Tuition for out-of-state residents
  Full-time students: $11,328 per semester
  Full-time students: other
  Part-time students: other
Graduate students on 1/4 time or greater assistantships are assessed at the resident rate. In addition, a scholarship of 1/4 tuition is given to students with 1/4-time assistantships, and 1/2 tuition for students with 1/2-time assistantships.
Credit hours per semester to be considered full-time: 12
Deferred tuition plan: Yes
Health insurance: Not available.
Other academic fees: Per semester fees: Activity, services, Building & Rec Fee: $331.95. Health Facility Fee: $8.00. Health Fee: $120.00. Technology Fee Standard: $115.00.
Academic term: Semester
Number of first-year students who received full tuition waivers: 19

Teaching Assistants, Research Assistants, and Fellowships
Number of first-year
  Teaching Assistants: 18
  Research Assistants: 1
Average stipend per academic year
  Teaching Assistant: $18,900
  Research Assistant: $18,900

FINANCIAL AID

Application deadlines
Fall admission:
U.S. students: March 1   *Int'l. students*: March 1

Loans
Loans are available for U.S. students.
Loans are not available for international students.
GAPSFAS application required: No
FAFSA application required: Yes

For further information
Address financial aid inquiries to: Iowa State University, Student Financial Aid Office, 0210 Beardshear Hall, Ames, Iowa 50011.
Phone: (515) 294-2223
E-mail: financialaid@iastate.edu
Financial aid website: http://www.financialaid.iastate.edu

HOUSING

Availability of on-campus housing
Single students: Yes
Married students: Yes

For further information
Address housing inquiries to: Iowa State University, Department of Residence, 2419 Friley Hall, Ames, Iowa 50011.
Phone: (515) 294-2900
E-mail: housing@iastate.edu
Housing aid website: http://www.housing.iastate.edu

Table A—Faculty, Enrollments, and Degrees Granted

Research Specialty	2016–17 Faculty	Enrollment Fall 2017 Master's	Enrollment Fall 2017 Doctorate	Number of Degrees Granted 2016–17 (2012–17) Master's	Number of Degrees Granted 2016–17 (2012–17) Terminal Master's	Number of Degrees Granted 2016–17 (2012–17) Doctorate
Astronomy	6	1	5	–	–	2(5)
Astroparticle Physics	2	–	3	–	–	1(1)
Biophysics	3	–	6	–	–	3(3)
Condensed Matter Physics	20	1	39	1(5)	–(2)	11(32)
High Energy Physics	10	–	10	1(1)	–(1)	3(7)
Nuclear Physics	5	–	19	1(4)	–	2(7)
Non-specialized	–	–	19	2	–	–(3)
Total	46	2	101	5(10)	–(3)	22(58)
Full-time Grad. Stud.	–	2	101	–	–	–
First-year Grad. Stud.	–	–	19	–	–	–

GRADUATE DEGREE REQUIREMENTS

Master's: The Master of Science degree is offered with and without thesis in various areas of physics (applied physics, high-energy, nuclear, condensed matter as examples) and astronomy. The minimum residential requirement is 30 credits, at least 21 of which must be in physics department graduate courses, and 6 of which must be outside the major area. A "B" average (3.0 GPA) must be maintained. There is no foreign language requirement.

Doctorate: The Ph.D. degree in the same areas has a basic requirement of 72 credits, at least one-half of which must be earned at Iowa State University, and 12 of which must be outside the major area. A "B" average (3.0 GPA) must be maintained. There is no foreign language requirement. A qualifying examination

given at the beginning of the student's second year, a preliminary oral examination, and a final thesis defense are the other major requirements.

Other Degrees: Close relationships exist with the Chemistry, Geological and Atmospheric Sciences, Electrical Engineering and Computer Engineering, Materials Science and Engineering, Computer Science, and Mathematics Departments, and joint programs are possible.

Thesis: Thesis may be written in absentia.

SPECIAL EQUIPMENT, FACILITIES, OR PROGRAMS

Five automated ultrasensitive SQUID magnetometers; helium dilution refrigerator millikelvin facility; two rotating anodes and several conventional X-ray diffraction facilities in combination with high- and low-temperature units and a new liquid surface reflectometer; ultra-high vacuum systems for surface physics studies using LEED, RHEED, and STMs; low temperature, high field magneto-optic spectrometer; microelectronics center for thin-film deposition (MBE, e-beam, etc.) and characterization (EELS, X-ray, Auger, ...); magnetic resonance spectrometers with superconducting solenoids for both high- and ultralow-temperature studies; precision spectrometers for neutron scattering and photoemission spectrometry (both carried out at national facilities); high-resolution Ge gamma-ray detectors.

In addition, there are four multi processor Silicon Graphics Computers and many PC-clusters ranging up to 128 processors. The clusters run with Linux and communicate via fast switches and either fast or gigabit-ethernet. Electronics and machine shop support; scanning Auger (600 Å resolution) and atomic resolution electron microscopes are available.

Research facilities are also utilized at the following laboratories: Fermilab (Batavia, IL), CERN (Geneva, Switzerland), BNL (Upton, NY), SRC (Stoughton, WI), ORNL (Oak Ridge, TN), Advanced Photon Source and Intense Pulsed Neutron Source at Argonne National Laboratory (Argonne, IL), Stanford Linear Accelerator (Palo Alto, CA), and VERITAS at Fred Lawrence Whipple Observatory (Amado, AZ).

High-energy physics programs include collaboration on the NOVA experiment, the ANNIE experiment and ATLAS at the CERN LHC Collider. They also include collaboration on long baseline neutrino experiments and atmospheric Cherenkov telescopes (VERITAS, CTA) for the detection of TeV photons.

The Experimental Nuclear Physics group uses the PHENIX experiment at the Relativistic Heavy Ion Collider to study the properties of strongly interacting nuclear matter in nucleus-nucleus collisions (the "Quark-Gluon Plasma") and the partonic structure of hadrons in spin-polarized proton-proton collisions. The group designed and constructed the PHENIX Level-1 trigger system and has expertise in electronics design for particle physics experiments. Major efforts of the group include an electromagnetic preshower detector for the detection of photons at forward angles in PHENIX, as well as upgrades to PHENIX and the evolution of the RHIC program to the future Electron-Ion Collider.

Observational astronomy is pursued over a large range of wavelengths at ISU.

The Gamma-ray astronomy group delivered the focal plane cameras and digital trigger systems for the VERITAS telescopes and is performing TeV photon observations as part of the VERITAS collaboration centered at the Smithsonian's Whipple Observatory.

ISU plays a leading role in using data from NASA's Kepler mission telescope for the study of stellar structure as well as the characterization of extrasolar planetary systems. ISU astronomers have played a key role in the design, execution, and analysis of data from various large-scale observational surveys done with the Spitzer Space Telescope such as GLIMPSE360, SAGE and the calibration of the cosmological distance scale by using variable stars.

Theoretical/computational studies of circumstellar environments, star-formation and evolution, and galaxy evolution are complemented by observations obtained using space-based telescopes such as Spitzer, HST, and Herschel as well as ground-based facilities at national observatories such as the VLA, GBT, KPNO, and CTIO.

Table B—Separately Budgeted Research Expenditures by Source of Support

Source of Support	Departmental Research	Physics-related Research Outside Department
Federal government	$3,350,930	$8,595,749
State/local government		
Non-profit organizations		
Business and industry		
Other	$1,491,758	
Total	**$4,842,688**	**$8,595,749**

Table C—Separately Budgeted Research Expenditures by Research Specialty

Research Specialty	No. of Grants	Expenditures ($)
Astronomy	8	$187,250
Biophysics	10	$663,491
Condensed Matter Physics	17	$9,602,552
High Energy Physics (includes Astroparticle Physics)	13	$1,371,730
Nuclear Physics	7	$1,207,890
Physics and other Science Education	4	$405,525
Total	**59**	**$13,438,438**

FACULTY

Distinguished University Professor

Canfield, Paul C., Ph.D., University of California, Los Angeles, 1990. Distinguished Professor of Liberal Arts & Sciences. *Condensed Matter Physics, Physics and other Science Education*. Experimental physics; design, growth, and characterization of new correlated electron materials.

Goldman, Alan I., Ph.D., Stony Brook University, 1984. *Condensed Matter Physics*. Experimental physics; x-ray and neutron scattering.

Ho, Kai-Ming, Ph.D., University of California, Berkeley, 1978. *Condensed Matter Physics, Theoretical Physics*. Properties of solids and surfaces.

Johnston, David C., Ph.D., University of California, San Diego, 1975. Divisional Associate Editor, Physical Review Letters. *Condensed Matter Physics*. Experimental solid state physics; high-temperature superconductors; low-dimensional antiferromagnets; heavy fermion compounds; novel materials synthesis and measurement.

Soukoulis, Costas M., Ph.D., University of Chicago, 1978. *Condensed Matter Physics, Engineering Physics/Science, Nano Science and Technology*. Development of a theoretical understanding of the property of disordered systems; photonic crystals; metamaterials; random lasers; random magnetic systems; nonlinear systems; amorphous semiconductors.

Chair Professor

Krennrich, Frank, Ph.D., Ludwig Maximilian University, Munich, 1996. *Astrophysics, Particles and Fields*. Experimental particle astrophysics; gamma-ray astronomy.

Professor

Cochran, James H., Ph.D., Stony Brook University, 1993. *High Energy Physics*. Experimental physics. high energy physics.

Evans, James W., Ph.D., University of Adelaide, 1979. Scientist USDOE National Laboratory. *Condensed Matter Physics, Statistical & Thermal Physics, Surface Physics, Theoretical Physics*. Surface science, epitaxial thin film evolution, far-from-equilibrium phenomena.

Furukawa, Yuji, Ph.D., Kobe University, 1995. *Condensed Matter Physics, Low Temperature Physics, Solid State Physics*. Condensed matter physics; low-temperature physics; solid state physics.

Hauptman, John M., Ph.D., University of California, Berkeley, 1974. *High Energy Physics*. Calorimetry; collider detectors.

Kaminski, Adam, Ph.D., University of Illinois at Chicago, 2001. *Condensed Matter Physics*. Experimental condensed matter physics; superconductivity; angle-resolved photoelectron spectroscopy.

Kawaler, Steven D., Ph.D., University of Texas, Austin, 1986. Scientific Editor of 'The Astrophysical Journal'. *Astronomy, Astrophysics*. Stellar astrophysics; asteroseismology.

Lajoie, John, Ph.D., Yale University, 1996. *Nuclear Physics*. Experimental nuclear physics; relativistic heavy-ion physics and nucleon spin.

McQueeney, Robert, Ph.D., University of Pennsylvania, 1996. *Condensed Matter Physics*. Experimental condensed matter physics, neutron scattering.

Ogilvie, Craig A., Ph.D., University of Birmingham, 1987. Assistant Dean of the ISU Graduate College. Morrill Professor. *Nuclear Physics*. Experimental nuclear physics; relativistic heavy-ion physics.

Prell, Soeren, Ph.D., Hamburg University, 1996. *High Energy Physics, Particles and Fields*. High-energy physics, particles and fields.

Prozorov, Ruslan, Ph.D., Bar-Ilan University, 1998. Associate Scientist (US DOE Ames Laboratory). *Condensed Matter Physics, Low Temperature Physics, Nano Science and Technology, Solid State Physics*. Experimental and theoretical condensed matter physics; solid state physics; superconductivity; magnetism; nano-scale physics; bio-magnetism; advanced low-temperature experimental techniques.

Rosati, Marzia, Ph.D., McGill University, 1992. Assistant Department Chair. *Nuclear Physics*. Experimental nuclear physics; relativistic heavy-ion physics.

Schmittmann, Beate, Ph.D., University of Edinburgh, 1984. Dean of the College of Liberal Arts & Sciences at Iowa State University. *Biophysics, Condensed Matter Physics, Mechanics*. Theoretical and computational condensed-matter physics; statistical mechanics; biological physics; complex systems far from equilibrium.

Shinar, Joseph, Ph.D., Hebrew University, 1980. *Applied Physics, Condensed Matter Physics, Electrical Engineering, Engineering Physics/Science, Materials Science, Metallurgy, Optics, Polymer Physics/Science, Solid State Physics, Surface Physics*. Applied physics; optics; condensed matter physics; electrical engineering; engineering physics/science; polymer physics; solid state physics; surface physics; materials science.

Struck, Curtis, Ph.D., Yale University, 1981. *Astronomy, Astrophysics, Nonlinear Dynamics and Complex Systems*. Astronomy; astrophysics; nonlinear dynamics; complex systems.

Travesset, Alex, Ph.D., Universitat de Barcelona, 1997. *Biophysics, Computational Physics, Condensed Matter Physics, Nano*

Science and Technology, Polymer Physics/Science. Soft condensed matter; biophysics; computational physics; polymer physics/science; nano science and technology.

Tringides, Michael, Ph.D., University of Chicago, 1984. *Condensed Matter Physics, Nano Science and Technology, Surface Physics.* Condensed matter physics; nano science and technology; surface science; scanning tunneling microscopy; high-resolution LEED; nanostructure growth and control; surface diffusion.

Tuchin, Kirill, Ph.D., Tel Aviv University, 2001. *High Energy Physics, Nuclear Physics, Particles and Fields, Theoretical Physics.* Nuclear physics; high energy physics, particles, and fields; theoretical physics.

Vary, James P., Ph.D., Yale University, 1970. *Computational Physics, Nuclear Physics, Theoretical Physics.* Nuclear physics; computational physics; theoretical physics.

Wang, Jigang, Ph.D., Rice University, 2006. *Condensed Matter Physics, Optics, Quantum Foundations.* Experimental condensed matter; ultrafast laser spectroscopy; quantum processes and collective phenomena in correlated electrons and nanostructures; spectroscopy; nonlinear optics.

Whisnant, Kerry L., Ph.D., University of Wisconsin-Madison, 1982. Dept. Undergraduate Advising Coordinator. *High Energy Physics, Theoretical Physics.* Theoretical high energy physics; neutrino physics; neutrino mass and mixing.

Associate Professor

Chen, Chunhui, Ph.D., University of Pennsylvania, 2003. *High Energy Physics, Particles and Fields.* Experimental high energy physics, particles, and fields.

Kerton, Charles, Ph.D., University of Toronto, 2000. *Astronomy, Astrophysics.* Astronomy; astrophysics; star formation; interstellar medium.

Marengo, Massimo, Ph.D., SISSA/ISAS, 2000. *Astrophysics, Planetary Science.* Stellar astrophysics; extrasolar planets.

Sánchez, Mayly, Ph.D., Tufts University, 2003. *High Energy Physics.* Experimental neutrino physics.

Sivasankar, Sanjeevi, Ph.D., University of Illinois at Urbana-Champaign, 2001. *Biophysics, Nano Science and Technology.* Biophysics; nano science/technology; single molecule biophysics; molecular biotechnology.

Weinstein, Amanda, Ph.D., Stanford University, 2005. *Astrophysics, High Energy Physics, Particles and Fields.* Experimental particle astrophysics.

Assistant Professor

Fei, Zhe, Ph.D., University of California, 2014. *Condensed Matter Physics, Nano Science and Technology.* Light-matter interactions, nanoscale structures, nanophotonics, plasmonics, spectroscopy.

Flint, Rebecca, Ph.D., Rutgers University, 2010. *Condensed Matter Physics, Theoretical Physics.* Condensed matter physics; theoretical physics.

Orth, Peter P., Ph.D., Yale University, 2011. *Condensed Matter Physics, Quantum Foundations, Theoretical Physics.* Theoretical condensed matter physics, strongly correlated quantum materials.

Wang, Xuefeng, Ph.D., Purdue University, 2009. *Biophysics, Mechanics.* Cell mechanics, biophysics.

Wetstein, Matthew, Ph.D., University of Maryland, 2009. *High Energy Physics, Particles and Fields.* Particle physics.

Emeritus

Anderson, E. Walter, Ph.D., Columbia University, 1965. *High Energy Physics.* High energy physics.

Borsa, Ferdinando, Ph.D., Pavia, 1961. *Condensed Matter Physics.* Experimental condensed matter; nuclear magnetic resonance; phase transitions.

Carter-Lewis, David, Ph.D., Michigan, 1974. *Astronomy, Astrophysics.* Experimental particle astrophysics; gamma-ray astronomy.

Crawley, H. Bert, Ph.D., Iowa State, 1966. *High Energy Physics.* Experimental high energy physics.

Finnemore, Douglas, Ph.D., Illinois, 1962. Distinguished Emeritus Professor. *Condensed Matter Physics, Low Temperature Physics.* Experimental physics; superconductivity and very low temperature phenomena.

Firestone, Alex, Ph.D., Yale, 1966. Experimental physics; high energy. *High Energy Physics.* High energy physics.

Harmon, Bruce N., Ph.D., Northwestern University, 1973. Distinguished Emeritus Professor. *Condensed Matter Physics.* Computational materials science.

Hill, John C., Ph.D., Purdue University, 1967. *Nuclear Physics.* Relativistic heavy-ion physics and spin physics.

Hodges, Laurent, Ph.D., Harvard, 1966. *Energy Sources & Environment.* Energy and environmental physics.

Lassila, Kenneth, Ph.D., Yale, 1961. *High Energy Physics, Theoretical Physics.* Theoretical physics, high energy.

Luban, Marshall, Ph.D., University of Chicago, 1962. *Condensed Matter Physics.* Molecular magnetism; statistical physics.

Lynch, David, Ph.D., Illinois, 1958. Distinguished Emeritus Professor. *Condensed Matter Physics, Optics, Solid State Physics, Surface Physics.* Condensed matter physics; optics; solid state physics; surface physics.

Peterson, Francis, Ph.D., Cornell, 1968. *Physics and other Science Education.* Physics education.

Pursey, Derek, Ph.D., Glasgow, 1952. *Nonlinear Dynamics and Complex Systems, Quantum Foundations, Theoretical Physics.* Theoretical physics; super-symmetric quantum mechanics; foundations of quantum theory; nonlinear physics.

Qiu, Jianwei, Ph.D., Columbia, 1987. *High Energy Physics, Nuclear Physics, Theoretical Physics.* Theoretical physics; quantum chromodynamics high energy and nuclear physics.

Rosenberg, Eli I., Ph.D., University of Illinois, 1971. *High Energy Physics.* Experimental physics; high energy physics.

Ross, Dennis, Ph.D., Stanford, 1968. *Relativity & Gravitation, Theoretical Physics.* Theoretical physics; general relativity; foundations of physics.

Stanford, John, Ph.D., Maryland, 1965. *Atmosphere, Space Physics, Cosmic Rays.* Theoretical and experimental atmospheric physics.

Swenson, Clayton, Ph.D., Oxford, 1949. Distinguished Emeritus Professor. *Low Temperature Physics.* Experimental physics; thermodynamic properties at low temperatures.

Williams, Stanley, Ph.D., Rensselaer, 1962. *Theoretical Physics.* Theoretical physics; quark structure of the nucleus.

Willson, Lee Anne, Ph.D., University of Michigan, 1973. Vice President, American Astronomical Society. University Emeritus Professor. *Astronomy.* Mass loss; stellar winds; stellar evolution with mass loss.

Wohn, Fred, Ph.D., Indiana, 1967. *Other.* Experimental physics; relativistic heavy-ion physics.

Young, Bing-Lin, Ph.D., Minnesota, 1966. *High Energy Physics, Theoretical Physics.* Theoretical high energy physics.

Research Professor

Maris, Pieter, Ph.D., Groningen, 1993. *Particles and Fields, Theoretical Physics.* Theoretical nuclear and particle physics; strongly interaction quantum many-particle and many-field systems.

Adjunct Professor

Biswas, Rana, Ph.D., Cornell University, 1984. *Condensed Matter Physics.* Condensed matter physics; electronic and structural properties of solids and surfaces; photonics; plasmonics.

Bud'ko, Sergey L., Ph.D., University of Moscow, 1986. Thermodynamic and transport properties of materials in multi-extreme conditions.

Vaknin, David, Ph.D., Hebrew University, 1987. *Condensed Matter Physics.* Experimental physics; condensed-matter physics; neutron; X-ray scattering; superconductivity-magnetism.

Adjunct Associate Professor

Koschny, Thomas, Ph.D., University of Leipzig, 2001. *Condensed Matter Physics, Theoretical Physics.* Theoretical physics; condensed-matter physics.

Levin, Evgenii (Eugene), Ph.D., Lviv State University, 1980. *Condensed Matter Physics.* Experimental condensed-matter physics.

Tanatar, Makariy, Ph.D., Ukrainian Academy of Science, 1980. *Condensed Matter Physics.* Experimental condensed matter; transport phenomena.

Adjunct Assistant Professor

Kreyssig, Andreas, Ph.D., Dresden, 2001. *Condensed Matter Physics, Solid State Physics.* Experimental physics; condensed matter; solid state; magnetism; crystal structure; excitations; electronic correlations; x-ray scattering; neutron scattering.

Affiliate Professor

Johnson, Duane, Ph.D., Cincinnati, 1985. *Condensed Matter Physics.* Condensed matter theory; materials physics; electronic-structure methods; computational materials science; thermodynamics and multi-scale modeling.

Senior Lecturer

Atwood, David, Ph.D., McGill University, 1989. *High Energy Physics, Theoretical Physics.*

Fretwell, Helen, Ph.D., University of Bristol, 1993. Lecturer in Physics. *Physics and other Science Education.* Physics education.

Herrera-Siklody, Paula, Ph.D., Universitat de Barcelona, 1999. Laboratory Supervisor. *Physics and other Science Education.* Physics education.

Lecturer

Adhikari, Lekha N., Ph.D., New Mexico State Univ., 2014. *Nuclear Physics, Theoretical Physics.* Nuclear Theoretical Physics.

Scientist

Krumnack, Nils, Ph.D., Hamburg, 2004. *High Energy Physics.* High energy physics.

DEPARTMENTAL RESEARCH SPECIALTIES AND STAFF

Theoretical

Astronomy. Stellar evolution, stellar winds, and mass loss; pulsating and variable stars. Galaxy formation and evolution, galaxy collisions, and star formation; and population evolution in galaxies. Kawaler, Kerton, Krennrich, Marengo, Struck.

Condensed Matter Physics. Superconducting vortex pinning; superconducting-normal proximity effects; Josephson junction arrays; electron-phonon interactions; magnetism. Biswas, Evans, Flint, Ho, Soukoulis, Vaknin.

Condensed Matter Physics. Photoemission; surface properties; optical properties; magnetic properties, electronic structure, lattice dynamics, critical phenomena; localization in disordered and quasiperiodic solids; spin glasses; quantum nanostructures; quantum computing photonic band gaps, many body theory, and simulations. Biswas, Flint, Furukawa, Goldman, Ho, Orth, Soukoulis, Jigang Wang.

High Energy Physics. Phenomenology of the standard model and extensions; neutrino mass and oscillations; quantum chromodynamics; dynamical symmetry breaking and chiral perturbation theory. Atwood, Chen, Cochran, Prell, Whisnant.

Nuclear Physics. Quark and gluon interactions in nuclei; relativistic heavy-ion and intermediate energy interactions; high-energy reactions of leptons and hadrons with nuclei; nuclear structure. Adhikari, Lajoie, Ogilvie, Rosati, Vary.

Experimental

Astronomy. Radio, infrared, and optical studies of galaxies; image processing techniques; studies of galaxy clusters at high redshift; photoelectric stellar radial velocity measurements; multi-wavelength spectroscopy and photometry of variable stars; stellar seismology; identification and study of TeV gamma-ray sources. Kawaler, Kerton, Krennrich, Marengo, Weinstein, Wetstein.

Astrophysics. Astroparticle physics; gamma-ray astronomy; dark matter; supernova remnants; active galaxies; cosmic infrared background. Krennrich, Weinstein, Wetstein.

Condensed Matter Physics. Optical properties; photoemission; neutron scattering; X-ray diffraction; magnetism; thermodynamic measurements; electrical properties; nuclear magnetic resonance; surface studies; thin films; transport properties; new materials design and growth; anisotropic superconductors; X-ray scattering studies of surfaces. Bud'ko, Canfield, Evans, Fei, Flint, Furukawa, Goldman, Johnston, Kaminski, Kreyssig, Prozorov, Shinar, Tringides, Vaknin, Jigang Wang.

Condensed Matter Physics. Superconducting materials; magneto-optic devices; amorphous material devices; semiconductors. Biswas, Bud'ko, Canfield, Tringides, Jigang Wang.

Energy Sources & Environment. Energy conservation; solar energy; radon in homes. Shinar.

High Energy Physics. pp interactions at the LHC; searches for dark matter, heavy neutrinos, fourth-generation quarks; studies of the Higgs boson, W and Z bosons and the top quark, CP violation; long baseline neutrino experiments; collider experiments at CERN, SLAC, and Fermilab; Indirect dark matter searches with VERITAS, axion-like particle searches in gamma-ray spectra. Chen, Cochran, Hauptman, Krennrich, Prell, Sánchez, Weinstein, Wetstein.

Nuclear Physics. Search for quark-gluon plasma and strange quark matter with RHIC collider and AGS accelerator; studies of nuclear matter under extreme conditions of density and temperature using the PHENIX detector; studies of electromagnetic dissociation at the CERN-SPS. Adhikari, Lajoie, Ogilvie, Rosati, Vary.

THE UNIVERSITY OF IOWA

DEPARTMENT OF PHYSICS AND ASTRONOMY

Iowa City, Iowa 52242
http://www.physics.uiowa.edu

General University Information
President: Bruce Harreld
Dean of Graduate School: John C. Keller
University website: http://www.uiowa.edu
School Type: Public
Setting: Urban
Total Faculty: 3,044
Total Graduate Faculty: 1,506
Total number of Students: 33,564
Total number of Graduate Students: 5,816

Department Information
Department Chairman: Prof. Frederick Skiff, Chair
Department Contact: Frederick Skiff, Professor & Chair
  Total full-time faculty: 31
  Total number of full-time equivalent positions: 31
  Full-Time Graduate Students: 61
  Female Full-Time Graduate Students: 10
  First-Year Graduate Students: 14
  Female First-Year Students: 1
  Total Post Doctorates: 9

Department Address
203 Van Allen Hall
30 N. Dubuque Street
Iowa City, IA 52242
Phone: (319) 335-1686
Fax: (319) 335-1753
E-mail: physics-astronomy@uiowa.edu
Website: http://www.physics.uiowa.edu

ADMISSIONS

Admission Contact Information
Address admission inquiries to: Dean of Admissions, 107 Calvin
  Hall, The University of Iowa, Iowa City, IA 52242-1396
Phone: (319) 335-3847
E-mail: gradmail@uiowa.edu
Admissions website: http://www.uiowa.edu/admissions/index
  .html

Application deadlines
Fall admission:
U.S. students: January 15   *Int'l. students*: January 15
Spring admission:
U.S. students: January 15   *Int'l. students*: January 15

Application fee
U.S. students: $60   *Int'l. students*: $100
If you apply online, the $60 application fee ($100 for interna-
  tional students) is payable by Discover, MasterCard, or Visa.
  If you cannot pay by credit card, you may download and print
  an application and pay the fee by cheque or money order in
  U.S. currency made payable to "The University of Iowa."

Admissions information
For Fall of 2018:
  Number of applicants: 96
  Number admitted: 35

Number enrolled: 14

Admission requirements
Bachelor's degree requirements: Bachelor's degree in Physics
  and/or astronomy is required with a minimum undergraduate
  GPA of "B.".
Minimum undergraduate GPA: 3.0

GRE requirements
The GRE is required.

Subjective GRE requirements
The Subjective GRE is recommended.
GRE Physics is not required, but highly recommended. Students
  with a GRE Physics subject test score of 630 and higher are
  exempted from taking the Ph.D. Qualifying Exam 50% of our
  offers of admission had GRE subject scores greater than 700.

TOEFL requirements
The TOEFL exam is required for students from non-English-
  speaking countries.
  PBT score: 550
  iBT score: 100
Normally scores under 100 do not pass the on-campus English proficiency exam required for graduate teaching assistantships.

Other admissions information
Additional requirements: The minimum acceptable score is not
  specifically stated.
Undergraduate preparation assumed: Griffiths, Quantum Mechanics; Griffiths, Introduction to Electrodynamics; Fowles
  and Cassiday, Analytical Mechanics; Reif, Statistical and
  Thermal Physics.

TUITION

Tuition year 2018–19:
Tuition for in-state residents
  Full-time students: $5,571 per semester
  Part-time students: $820.75 per credit
Tuition for out-of-state residents
  Full-time students: $15,041 per semester
  Part-time students: $820.75 per credit
Tuition noted is for graduate program tuition
Credit hours per semester to be considered full-time: 9
Deferred tuition plan: Yes
Health insurance: Yes, $19-$29.50/month, depending on plan.
Other academic fees: Technology Fee (FT) $156.50 Health Fee
  (FT) $118.50 Student Activity Fee (FT) $36.00 Student Ser-
  vices Fee (FT) $38.50 Student Union Fee (FT) $62.00 Build-
  ing Fee (FT) $61.50 Arts & Cultural Events Fee (FT) $13.00
  Recreation Fee (FT) $146.00 Professional Enhancement (FT)
  $40.00
Academic term: Semester
Number of first-year students who received full tuition waivers: 13

Teaching Assistants, Research Assistants, and Fellowships
  Number of first-year
    Teaching Assistants: 13
    Research Assistants: 2
    Fellowship students: 1

Average stipend per academic year
Teaching Assistant: $19,236
Research Assistant: $19,236
Fellowship student: $19,650
Average Fellowship Stipend (by fiscal year) $25,150

FINANCIAL AID

Application deadlines
Fall admission:
U.S. students: September 1   *Int'l. students*: September 1
Spring admission:
U.S. students: September 1   *Int'l. students*: September 1

Loans
Loans are available for U.S. students.
Loans are not available for international students.
GAPSFAS application required: No
FAFSA application required: Yes

For further information
Address financial aid inquiries to: The University of Iowa, Office of Student Financial Aid, 208 Calvin Hall, Iowa City, IA 52242-1315.
Phone: (319) 335-1450
E-mail: financial-aid@uiowa.edu
Financial aid website: http://grad.admissions.uiowa.edu/finances

HOUSING

Availability of on-campus housing
Single students: Yes
Married students: Yes
Childcare Assistance: Yes

For further information
Address housing inquiries to: University Housing & Dining, 4141 Burge Hall, Iowa City, IA 52242.
Phone: (319) 335-3009
E-mail: housing@uiowa.edu
Housing aid website: https://uiowa.edu/homepage/housing-information

GRADUATE DEGREE REQUIREMENTS

Master's: Thirty hours of coursework and research with a grade point average of at least 3.00 and an oral final examination are required. Thesis or critical essay options are available. No foreign language requirement is specified. The residence requirement may be fulfilled by completing a minimum of 24 semester hours under the auspices of The University of Iowa.

Doctorate: A minimum of 72 hours of coursework and research with a grade point average of at least 3.00, a qualifying examination, comprehensive examination, participation in advanced seminars, and original research are required for the Ph.D. A candidate for the degree will not be recommended until he/she has written the dissertation in proper form for formal publication and has submitted it, with the approval of the research advisor, for publication to a standard scientific journal of wide distribution. There is no specific foreign language requirement. Beyond the first 24 semester hours of graduate work, the residence requirement may be fulfilled by either: (1) enrollment as a full-time student (nine semester hours minimum) in each of two semesters or (2) enrollment for a minimum of six semester hours in each of three semesters during which time the student holds at least a one-third-time assistantship certified by the Department as contributing to the student's doctoral program.

Thesis: Thesis may be written in absentia.

SPECIAL EQUIPMENT, FACILITIES, OR PROGRAMS

Comprehensive facilities for design, construction, and testing of instruments for space flight, and for the decoding, analysis, and display of flight data; automated 37-cm optical telescope at remote dark site, 3.0- and 4.5-m radio telescopes for instrumentation development; steady-state magnetized plasma devices (gas discharges and Q-machines) with 1-10 kG magnetic fields; a wide array of gas discharges and diagnostics for the study of plasmas containing charged dust grains; compact medical cyclotron for production of radionuclides; molecular-beam epitaxy machines for growth of state-of-the-art III-V semiconductor quantum wells, superlattices, quantum dots, and optoelectronic devices; a large computer cluster for analysis of high-energy nuclear data with direct connections to Fermilab and CERN; a state-of-the-art computer-controlled photomultiplier test station for high-energy and nuclear physics detectors; facilities for testing and calibration of space-based X-ray astronomical spectrometers and polarimeters; local medium-scale computing facilities for high performance and high throughput computing tasks; and a large number of continuous-wave and pulsed (including ultrafast) lasers for spectroscopy.

Table A—Faculty, Enrollments, and Degrees Granted

Research Specialty	2017–18 Faculty	Enrollment Fall 2017 Master's	Enrollment Fall 2017 Doctorate	Number of Degrees Granted 2017–18 (2013–18) Master's	Number of Degrees Granted 2017–18 (2013–18) Terminal Master's	Number of Degrees Granted 2017–18 (2013–18) Doctorate
Astronomy	7	1	6	–	–(2)	2(9)
Atmosphere, Space Physics, Cosmic Rays	7	1	8	–	–(4)	1(11)
Atomic, Molecular, & Optical Physics	–	–	–	–	–(1)	–(9)
Condensed Matter Physics	6	1	10	–	–	5(5)
Medical, Health Physics	3	–	–	–	–	–(1)
Nuclear Physics	2	–	9	–	–	–
Particles and Fields	6	–	15	1(4)	–(1)	6(19)
Plasma and Fusion	5	–	15	–	1(1)	2(6)
Non-specialized	–	–	–	–	–	–
Total	31	3	63	1(5)	3(11)	18(56)
Full-time Grad. Stud.	–	1	58	–	–	–
First-year Grad. Stud.	–	1	10	–	–	–

Table B—Separately Budgeted Research Expenditures by Source of Support

Source of Support	Departmental Research	Physics-related Research Outside Department
Federal government	$14,270,996	
State/local government	$1,302,096	
Non-profit organizations	$169,312	
Business and industry		
Other		
Total	$15,742,404	

Table C—Separately Budgeted Research Expenditures by Research Specialty

Research Specialty	No. of Grants	Expenditures ($)
Astronomy	27	$1,093,847
Atmosphere, Space Physics, Cosmic Rays	45	$10,208,075
Condensed Matter Physics	31	$1,518,034
Nuclear Physics	4	$11,905
Particles and Fields	21	$934,795
Plasma and Fusion	23	$1,466,483
Other	6	$509,265
Total	157	$15,742,404

FACULTY

Professor

Andersen, David R., Ph.D., Purdue University, 1986. Primary appointment in Electrical and Computer Engineering. *Condensed Matter Physics, Electrical Engineering, Materials Science, Metallurgy, Optics.* Nonlinear optics; quantum electronics; solid state; embedded systems.

Boggess, Thomas F., Ph.D., North Texas State University, 1982. Additional appointment in Electrical and Computer Engineering. *Applied Physics, Condensed Matter Physics, Electrical Engineering, Nano Science and Technology.* Nonlinear optics; ultrafast spectroscopy of semiconductor heterostructures.

Elcock, Adrian H., D.Phil., Oxford University, 1994. Primary appointment in Biochemistry. *Nonlinear Dynamics and Complex Systems.* Statistic mechanics, protein folding.

Flatté, Michael E., Ph.D., University of California, Santa Barbara, 1992. Director of Optical Science Technology Center. *Applied Physics, Condensed Matter Physics, Materials Science, Metallurgy, Nano Science and Technology.* Condensed-matter physics; materials theory.

Goree, John A., Ph.D., Princeton University, 1985. *Condensed Matter Physics, Plasma and Fusion.* Experimental plasma physics; biomedical applications of plasmas; soft condensed matter physics.

Gurnett, Donald A., Ph.D., University of Iowa, 1965. *Atmosphere, Space Physics, Cosmic Rays.* Experimental space plasma physics.

Hichwa, Richard, Ph.D., University of Wisconsin-Madison, 1981. Primary appointment in Department of Radiology. *Medical, Health Physics.* Medical physics.

Kaaret, Philip E., Ph.D., Princeton University, 1989. *Astronomy, Astrophysics.* X-ray and gamma-ray astronomy and instrumentation; black hole binaries; jet ejection from black holes.

Kleiber, Paul D., Ph.D., University of Colorado, 1981. *Atmosphere, Space Physics, Cosmic Rays, Atomic, Molecular, & Optical Physics.* Atmospheric physics; chemical physics.

Kletzing, Craig A., Ph.D., University of California, San Diego, 1989. *Atmosphere, Space Physics, Cosmic Rays.* Experimental space plasma physics; laboratory plasma physics.

Mallik, Usha, Ph.D., City University of New York, 1978. *Particles and Fields.* Experimental elementary particle physics.

Merlino, Robert L., Ph.D., University of Maryland, 1980. *Plasma and Fusion.* Experimental plasma physics.

Meurice, Yannick, Ph.D., UCL Louvain-la-Neuve, 1985. *Particles and Fields, Theoretical Physics.* Theoretical elementary particle physics; lattice gauge theory; optical lattices.

Mutel, Robert L., Ph.D., University of Colorado, 1975. *Astronomy, Astrophysics, Atmosphere, Space Physics, Cosmic Rays.* Radio astronomy; space physics; plasma astrophysics.

Onel, Yasar, Ph.D., University of London, 1975. *Nuclear Physics, Particles and Fields.* Experimental elementary particle physics; nuclear physics.

Polyzou, Wayne N., Ph.D., University of Maryland, 1979. *Nuclear Physics, Theoretical Physics.* Nuclear, particle, and mathematical physics. Research involves formulating mathematical models of physical systems, development of theoretical frameworks that are consistent with special relativity and quantum mechanics, and developing computational methods that can be used in strongly interacting theories.

Prineas, John P., Ph.D., University of Arizona, 2000. *Applied Physics, Condensed Matter Physics, Electrical Engineering, Materials Science, Metallurgy, Nano Science and Technology, Optics.* Experimental semiconductor physics; growth and fabrication; spectroscopy; microscopy; semiconductor nanostructures; optoelectronics and photonics; III–V MBE growth; nonlinear optics.

Reno, Mary Hall, Ph.D., Stanford University, 1985. *Particles and Fields, Theoretical Physics.* Theoretical elementary particle physics; astroparticle physics.

Rodgers, Vincent G. J., Ph.D., Syracuse University, 1985. *Particles and Fields, Theoretical Physics.* Theoretical particle physics; string theory.

Scudder, Jack D., Ph.D., University of Maryland, 1975. *Atmosphere, Space Physics, Cosmic Rays, Plasma and Fusion.* Space plasma physics.

Skiff, Frederick N., Ph.D., Princeton University, 1985. Departmental Chair. *Plasma and Fusion.* Laser spectroscopy; plasma physics.

Spangler, Steven R., Ph.D., University of Iowa, 1975. *Astronomy, Astrophysics, Atmosphere, Space Physics, Cosmic Rays, Plasma and Fusion.* Radio astronomy; plasma astrophysics; space plasma physics.

Wohlgenannt, Markus, Ph.D., University of Utah, 2000. *Condensed Matter Physics.* Experimental polymer physics.

Associate Professor

Baalrud, Scott D., Ph.D., University of Wisconsin-Madison, 2010. *Plasma and Fusion, Theoretical Physics.* Basic and applied theoretical plasma physics.

Gayley, Kenneth G., Ph.D., University of California, San Diego, 1990. *Astronomy, Astrophysics.* Radiative transfer; radiation hydrodynamics; spectral line diagnostics.

Halekas, Jasper S., Ph.D., University of California, Berkeley, 2003. *Astronomy, Astrophysics, Atmosphere, Space Physics, Cosmic Rays.* Experimental space physics.

Howes, Gregory G., Ph.D., University of California, Los Angeles, 2004. *Computational Physics, Plasma and Fusion.* Theoretical and computational plasma physics.

Lang, Cornelia C., Ph.D., University of California, Los Angeles, 2000. Departmental Associate Chair. *Astronomy, Astrophysics.* Radio astronomy; X-ray astronomy; observational study of interstellar medium and galactic center.

Nachtman, Jane M., Ph.D., University of Wisconsin-Madison, 1997. *Particles and Fields.* Experimental elementary particle physics.

Pryor, Craig, Ph.D., University of California, Santa Barbara, 1990. *Computational Physics, Condensed Matter Physics, Materials Science, Metallurgy, Nano Science and Technology, Theoretical Physics.* Theoretical condensed matter; semiconductor nanostructures.

Sunderland, John J., Ph.D., University of Wisconsin-Madison, 1990. Primary appointment in Department of Radiology; Director of PET Imaging. *Medical, Health Physics.* Medical physics.

Assistant Professor

DeRoo, Casey, Ph.D., University of Iowa, 2016. *Astronomy.* Astronomy.

Fu, Hai, Ph.D., University of Hawaii, 2008. *Astronomy, Astrophysics.* Extragalactic astronomy.

Jaynes, Allison N., Ph.D., University of New Hampshire, 2013. *Atmosphere, Space Physics, Cosmic Rays.* Experimental space plasma physics.

Miles, David M., Ph.D., University of Alberta, 2017. *Atmosphere, Space Physics, Cosmic Rays.* Experimental space plasma physics.

Toor, Fatima, Ph.D., Princeton University, 2009. Primary appointment in Electrical and Computer Engineering. *Condensed Matter Physics, Electrical Engineering, Electromagnetism, Materials Science, Metallurgy, Nano Science and Technology, Optics, Quantum Foundations.* Experimental semiconductor optoelectronics; electromagnetic design; nanofabrication; spectroscopy; microscopy; semiconductor nanostructures; optoelectronics and photonics, optical system design.

Emeritus

Klink, William H., Ph.D., Johns Hopkins University, 1964. Theoretical nuclear physics; mathematical physics.

Knorr, Georg, Ph.D., Ludwig Maximilian University, Munich, 1963. Theoretical plasma physics.

Lonngren, Karl E., Ph.D., University of Wisconsin-Madison, 1964. Experimental plasma physics.

McCliment, Edward R., Ph.D., University of Illinois, 1962. Elementary particle physics.

Neff, John S., Ph.D., University of Wisconsin-Madison, 1961. Observational optical astronomy.

Newsom, Charles R., Ph.D., University of Texas, 1980. *Particles and Fields.* Experimental elementary particle physics.

Payne, Gerald L., Ph.D., University of California, San Diego, 1967. *Nuclear Physics.* Theoretical nuclear physics.

Schweitzer, John W., Ph.D., University of Cincinnati, 1966. Theoretical and experimental solid-state physics.

DEPARTMENTAL RESEARCH SPECIALTIES AND STAFF

Theoretical

Astrophysics. Radiation-driven winds from hot stars; plasma waves and turbulence in the interplanetary and interstellar media; physics of nonthermal radio sources. Gayley, Howes, Mutel, Spangler.

Atmosphere, Space Physics, Cosmic Rays. Physics of space magneto-plasmas and their kinetic properties; analytical and numerical solution of MHD, Vlasov, and Fokker-Planck equations; magnetic reconnection and plasma turbulence in the magnetotail; the solar corona and the solar wind. Howes, Scudder.

Atomic, Molecular, & Optical Physics. Gauge interactions on optical lattices. Meurice.

Condensed Matter Physics. Strong correlation problems and magnetic properties of materials; electrical, magnetic, and optical properties of nanostructures; spintronics; quantum computation. Flatté, Pryor, Schweitzer.

Mathematical Physics. Coherent states in semiconductors; carrier dynamics in semiconductor lasers and detectors; nonlinear propagation phenomena. Andersen, Flatté, Pryor.

Nuclear Physics. Numerical and theoretical studies of reactions, structure, and electroweak Properties of few hadron and few quark systems using relativistic and nonrelativistic quantum mechanics and quantum field theory. Klink, Payne, Polyzou.

Other. Mathematical methods with emphasis on group theory, operator algebras, infinite dimensional Lie algebras, and nonlinear dynamics; Yang Mill and Chern Simons theories. Klink, Meurice, Polyzou, Rodgers.

Other. Biomolecular simulations; Brownian and molecular dynamics simulations of biological macromolecules. Elcock.

Particles and Fields. Particle phenomenology of colliders and neutrino detectors; astroparticle physics and dark matter; renormalization group methods; lattice gauge theory; heavy flavor physics; gauge/gravity duals; superstrings. Meurice, Reno, Rodgers.

Plasma and Fusion. Basic plasma physics; theoretical and computational studies of space; astrophysics; laboratory plasmas; turbulence in kinetic plasmas; development and implementation of high-performance gyrokinetic codes for first-principles simulation of kinetic plasmas; strongly coupled plasmas; high-energy-density plasmas; magnetic reconnection; sheaths; double layers; plasma-based electron sources. Baalrud, Howes.

Relativity & Gravitation. Superstring theory; string theory; gauge/gravity duality; supergravity; conformal field theory; cosmology; representations of diffeomorphisms. Klink, Rodgers.

Experimental

Astronomy. Radio, X-ray, and gamma-ray astronomy; very-long-baseline radio astronomy; interstellar radio scintillation; studies of the galactic center; radio continuum observations of galactic and extragalactic sources; radio-imaging spectroscopy; X-ray and gamma-ray observations of black holes, neutron stars, and the interstellar medium; jet ejection from black holes; plasma astrophysics, including radiation hydrodynamics, and astrophysical turbulence; X-ray and gamma-ray astronomical instrumentation; X-ray sounding rocket payloads; high-resolution X-ray spectroscopy. DeRoo, Fu, Gayley, Halekas, Jaynes, Kaaret, Lang, Miles, Mutel, Spangler.

Atmosphere, Space Physics, Cosmic Rays. Space plasmas and atmospheric physics; collisionless magnetic reconnection; energetic particles and waves in the radiation belts; electric and magnetic fields; plasma instabilities; wave phenomena and radio emissions at earth, in planetary magnetospheres, and in the interplanetary medium; auroral phenomena and magnetosphere-ionsphere coupling, including global imaging; chemistry and physics of atmospheric dust. Gurnett, Halekas, Kleiber, Kletzing, Scudder.

Condensed Matter Physics. MBE growth and fabrication of III–V semiconductor nanomaterials and devices; synthesis and applications of organic semiconductors; electrical transport and magnetic properties of layered ternary transition metal sulfides; ultrafast optical and electronic properties of semiconductor quantum wells and superlattices; optical measurements of high-speed carrier dynamics, including transport, recombination, energy relaxation, and scattering in semiconductor structures and devices; soft condensed matter, including structure and waves in Coulomb crystals and 2D and 3D experiments under laboratory and microgravity conditions. Boggess, Prineas, Schweitzer, Toor, Wohlgenannt.

Medical, Health Physics. Design of radiation detector systems for medical applications and nuclear medicine imaging; development of processing methodologies for analysis of medical images; development of high-speed electronics, associated hardware and application software for PET imaging devices; fabrication of nuclear targets and automated radiochemistry synthesis systems to produce PET radiopharmaceuticals. Hichwa, Sunderland.

Nuclear Physics. Study of Pb + Pb at 1000 TeV with CMS/LHC at CERN. Breakup of excited nuclei into large fragments using large national accelerators in the United States and Europe. Onel.

Other. Remotely controlled imaging telescope linked to regent's institutions. Mutel.

Other. Development of ultrafast optical sources and their use in spectroscopy of bulk and microstructure semiconductors; nonlinear optical properties of solid-state materials; coherent processes in semiconductors; semiconductor lasers, detectors, and other photonic devices. Andersen, Boggess, Prineas, Wohlgenannt.

Particle Physics. Higgs, SUSY, and beyond the Standard Model searches at Fermilab, CMS/LHC, and ATLAS/LHC; Liquid Argon Calorimeter Upgrade; study of charm baryons at Fermilab; quartz fiber Cherenkov calorimetry development for collider physics at Iowa-HEP laboratory; silicon pixel and microstrip detector development at Fermilab and silicon pixel study in ATLAS/LHC; digital calorimetry, Compton polarimeter, and Particle Flow Algorithm development for a high-energy e+e– linear collider. Mallik, Nachtman, Onel.

Plasma and Fusion. Plasma waves and instabilities; nonlinear particle dynamics; negative ion plasmas; dusty plasma; interdisciplinary study of strongly coupled Coulomb crystal structure and dynamics; laboratory simulation of space and astrophysical plasmas; microgravity experiments; technological topics, including biomedical applications of plasmas, laser scattering and laser-induced fluorescence diagnostics of plasmas, plasma source for plasma processing, and particulate contamination in plasma processing. Goree, Kletzing, Lonngren, Merlino, Skiff.

View additional information about this department at www.gradschoolshopper.com. Check out the "Why Choose Us?" section, find out more about the department's culture and get links to social media networks.

KANSAS STATE UNIVERSITY

DEPARTMENT OF PHYSICS

Manhattan, Kansas 66506-2601
http://www.phys.ksu.edu

General University Information
President: Richard B. Myers
Dean of Graduate School: Carol Shanklin
University website: http://www.k-state.edu/
School Type: Public
Setting: Rural
Total Faculty: 1,437
Total Graduate Faculty: 1,215
Total number of Students: 21,400
Total number of Graduate Students: 4,000

Department Information
Department Chairman: Prof. Brett DePaola, Head
Department Contact: Michael O'Shea, Professor
  Total full-time faculty: 30
  Total number of full-time equivalent positions: 30
  Full-Time Graduate Students: 64
  Female Full-Time Graduate Students: 17
  First-Year Graduate Students: 12
  Female First-Year Students: 4
  Total Post Doctorates: 18

Department Address
1228 N. 17th
116 Cardwell Hall
Manhattan, KS 66506-2601
Phone: (785) 532-1612
Fax: (785) 532-6806
E-mail: graduate@phys.ksu.edu
Website: http://www.phys.ksu.edu

ADMISSIONS

Admission Contact Information
Address admission inquiries to: Graduate Secretary, Department
  of Physics, Kansas State University, 1228 N. 17th Street, 116
  Cardwell Hall, Manhattan, KS 66506-2601
Phone: (785) 532-1612
E-mail: graduate@phys.ksu.edu
Admissions website: http://www.phys.ksu.edu

Application deadlines
Fall admission:
U.S. students: January 8   *Int'l. students*: January 8

Application fee
U.S. students: $65   *Int'l. students*: $75

Admissions information
For Fall of 2018:
  Number of applicants: 126
  Number admitted: 25
  Number enrolled: 12

Admission requirements
Bachelor's degree requirements: Bachelor's degree in Physics
  is required.
Minimum undergraduate GPA: 3.0 0 0 0.0 No minimum score
  is set.

Subjective GRE requirements
The Subjective GRE is not required.

TOEFL requirements
The TOEFL exam is required for students from non-English-
  speaking countries.
PBT score: 550
iBT score: 79
The IELTS and Pearson Test of English are also accepted. See
  http://www.k-state.edu/grad/admissions/application-process/
  international/index.html#English-Proficiency-Requirements
  for minimum scores.

Other admissions information
Additional requirements: Candidates with engineering or mathematics degrees will also be considered.
Undergraduate preparation assumed: Mechanics (3 to 6 hours);
  Physics Lab (6 hours); Electricity and Magnetism (3 to 6
  hours); Modern Physics (3 hours); Quantum Mechanics (3
  hours); Mathematics through Differential Equations and Vector Analysis.

TUITION

Tuition year 2018–19:
Tuition for in-state residents
  Full-time students: $2,515.2 per semester
  Part-time students: $419.2 per credit
Tuition for out-of-state residents
  Full-time students: $5,677.2 per semester
  Part-time students: $946.2 per credit
Graduate assistants pay resident fees; tuition is waived for gradu-
  ate and research teaching assistants. Students pay campus
  privilege fees and course enhancement fees.
Credit hours per semester to be considered full-time: 6
Deferred tuition plan: Yes
Health insurance: Available at the cost of $354 per year.
Other academic fees: Campus privilege and health insurance fees
  paid out-of-pocket by graduate assistants are $1442 during
  the academic year based on 12 credit hours. Summer campus
  fees for a typical 3 credit hour enrollment would be $183.
  Health insurance for summer is $71.
Academic term: Semester
Number of first-year students who received full tuition waivers: 12

Teaching Assistants, Research Assistants, and Fellowships
Number of first-year
  Teaching Assistants: 8
  Research Assistants: 1
  Fellowship students: 3
Average stipend per academic year
  Teaching Assistant: $18,000
  Research Assistant: $18,000
  Fellowship student: $23,000
Figures listed above are 9 month academic salaries and do
  not include 6 bi-weekly pay periods of salary for RAs or 4
  weeks for TAs in the summer.

FINANCIAL AID

Application deadlines
Fall admission:
U.S. students: March 1

Loans
Loans are available for U.S. students.
Loans are not available for international students.
GAPSFAS application required: No
FAFSA application required: Yes

For further information
Address financial aid inquiries to: Office of Student Financial
Assistance, 104 Fairchild Hall, Kansas State University, Man-
hattan, KS 66506-1104.
Phone: (785) 532-6420
E-mail: finaid@k-state.edu
Financial aid website: http://www.k-state.edu/sfa/

HOUSING

Availability of on-campus housing
Single students: Yes
Married students: Yes
Childcare Assistance: Yes

For further information
Address housing inquiries to: Department of Housing & Dining
Services, Kansas State University, 1531 Mid Campus Dr.
North, 104 Pitmann Building, Manhattan, KS 66506.
Phone: (785) 532-6453
E-mail: housing@k-state.edu
Housing aid website: http://housing.k-state.edu/

Table A—Faculty, Enrollments, and Degrees Granted

Research Specialty	2017–18 Faculty	Enrollment Fall 2017 Mas-ter's	Enrollment Fall 2017 Doc-torate	Number of Degrees Granted 2017–18 (2013–18) Mas-ter's	Number of Degrees Granted 2017–18 (2013–18) Terminal Master's	Number of Degrees Granted 2017–18 (2013–18) Doc-torate
Atomic, Molecular, & Optical Physics	11	–	24	–	–(5)	3(10)
Condensed Matter Physics	7	–	13	–	1(4)	4(4)
Cosmology & Particle Astrophysics	2	2	4	1(2)	1(1)	–(2)
High Energy Physics	5	–	7	–	–	1(7)
Physics and other Science Education	2	1	6	–(1)	–(1)	–(7)
Other	2	1	2	–	1(1)	–
Total	**28**	**4**	**56**	**–(2)**	**1(15)**	**5(34)**
Full-time Grad. Stud.	–	4	56	–	–	–
First-year Grad. Stud.	–	–	10	–	–	–

GRADUATE DEGREE REQUIREMENTS

Master's: Thirty graduate credits in approved program with satisfactory performance and ″B″ average in coursework are required. Thesis is required for which up to six credits may
be earned. Examination over thesis and one academic year
of residence are also required.

Doctorate: Ninety graduate credits in approved program of study
with satisfactory performance with a ″B″ average in coursework is required. Preliminary examination in area of specialization and related fields is required. Dissertation for
which 30 credits may be earned, oral examination, and one
full year of residency are also required.

Thesis: Thesis may be written in absentia.

SPECIAL EQUIPMENT, FACILITIES, OR PROGRAMS

Ultrafast Ti:Sapphire laser systems for studies of the interaction
of high-intensity ultrafast electromagnetic pulses with matter, Cr:
Forsterite and fiber lasers for studies of optical frequency standards, and a 30-keV ECR ion source for ion research in atomic,
molecular, and optical physics. Linux computer clusters are available for large-scale computational studies. State-of-the-art laser
laboratories equipped with argon ion, Nd:YAG, and dye lasers
and Raman, Fabry-Perot, and correlation spectrometers.

Laboratories for the study of soft condensed matter include extensive static and dynamic light scattering facilities; a broad array
of microscopies including atomic force, fluorescence, Raman,
and reflection interference contrast; surface ellipsometry and wetting apparatus; and a synthetic chemistry lab.

Table B—Separately Budgeted Research Expenditures by Source of Support

Source of Support	Departmental Research	Physics-related Research Outside Department
Federal government	$5,694,471	
State/local government		
Non-profit organizations		
Business and industry		
Other		
Total	**$5,694,471**	

Table C—Separately Budgeted Research Expenditures by Research Specialty

Research Specialty	No. of Grants	Expenditures ($)
Atomic, Molecular, & Optical Physics	–	$4,278,605
Condensed Matter Physics	–	$221,130
with Cosmology	–	$974,286
Physics and other Science Education	–	$220,450
Total	**–**	**$5,694,471**

FACULTY

Distinguished University Professor

Ben-Itzhak, Itzik, Ph.D., Technion, Haifa, 1986. *Atomic, Molecular, & Optical Physics*. Experimental AMO physics; imaging dissociation and ionization of molecular ions by ultrashort intense laser pulses; imaging fragmentation of
molecular-ion beams induced by slow collisions with atomic
targets.

Esry, Brett D., Ph.D., University of Colorado Boulder, 1997.
Atomic, Molecular, & Optical Physics. Theoretical atomic
physics; intense laser-molecule and laser atom interactions;
few-body physics.

Lin, Chii-Dong, Ph.D., University of Chicago, 1974. *Atomic,
Molecular, & Optical Physics*. Theoretical studies of laser-
molecule interactions; attosecond physics; few-body physics;
atomic collisions; dynamic chemical imaging.

Ratra, Bharat, Ph.D., Stanford University, 1986. *Cosmology &
String Theory*. Cosmology; astroparticle physics; particle theory.

Sorensen, Christopher M., Ph.D., University of Colorado, 1976.
Condensed Matter Physics. Experimental condensed matter
physics.

Professor

Bolton, Timothy, Ph.D., Massachusetts Institute of Technology, 1988. *High Energy Physics*. Experimental high-energy physics.

Chakrabarti, Amitabha, Ph.D., University of Minnesota, 1987. Dean of College of Arts & Sciences. *Condensed Matter Physics*. Theoretical and computational studies in soft-condensed matter and biological physics including self-assembly of nanoparticles, colloids, proteins, and aerosols.

Corwin, Kristan, Ph.D., University of Colorado Boulder, 1999. Associate Dean of College of Arts and Sciences. *Atomic, Molecular, & Optical Physics*. Experimental atomic physics; optical frequency metrology; ultrafast optics; laser development.

DePaola, Brett D., Ph.D., University of Texas, Dallas, 1984. Department Head. *Atomic, Molecular, & Optical Physics*. Experimental atomic physics; crossed beams; laser-beam interactins.

Flanders, Bret, Ph.D., University of Chicago, 1999. *Biophysics, Condensed Matter Physics*. Soft-matter nanotechnology and biological physics.

Horton-Smith, Glenn, Ph.D., Stanford University, 1998. *High Energy Physics*. Experimental neutrino physics.

Law, Bruce M., Ph.D., University of Victoria, 1985. *Condensed Matter Physics*. Condensed matter interfaces; nonequilibrium liquids.

Maravin, Yurii, Ph.D., Southern Methodist University, 2002. *High Energy Physics*. Experimental high-energy physics.

O'Shea, Michael, Ph.D., University of Sussex, 1981. Associate Department Head and Graduate Advisor. *Condensed Matter Physics*. Experimental condensed matter physics.

Thumm, Uwe, Ph.D., University of Freiburg, 1989. *Atomic, Molecular, & Optical Physics*. Theoretical atomic, molecular, optical, and surface physics. Numerical modeling of electronic excitation, electron-transfer, and fragmentation processes in interactions of intense light in the IR to XUV spectral range with atoms, ions, molecules, clusters, nanostructures, and solid surfaces.

Wysin, Gary M., Ph.D., Cornell University, 1985. *Condensed Matter Physics*. Condensed matter theory; nonlinear magnetic excitations; magnetic vortices; electromagnetics.

Associate Professor

Berg, Matthew J., Ph.D., Kansas State University, 2008. *Applied Physics, Other*. Electromagnetism; atomic, molecular & optical physics; optics; holography.

Ivanov, Andrew G., Ph.D., University of Rochester, 2004. *High Energy Physics*. Experimental high-energy research aimed at pursuing searches for new phenomena at the Large Hadron Collider (LHC).

Kumarappan, Vinod, Ph.D., Tata Institute of Fundamental Research, 2002. *Atomic, Molecular, & Optical Physics*. Strong field alignment and orientation of molecules; experimental atomic, molecular, and optical physics.

Rudenko, Artem A., Ph.D., Moscow Institute of Physics & Technology, 2002. *Atomic, Molecular, & Optical Physics*. Experimental atomic, molecular, and optical physics; ultrafast laser and free electron laser interactions with atoms and molecules; 3D imaging of fragmentation processes.

Sayre, Eleanor, Ph.D., University of Maine, 2007. *Physics and other Science Education*. Student identity development in STEM; interplay between physics and math understanding; cognitive and cultural models of learning; faculty development in research-based teaching and assessment; qualitative, quantitative, and mixed-methods research; and evidence-based curriculum development.

Schmit, Jeremy D., Ph.D., University of California, Santa Barbara, 2005. *Biophysics, Condensed Matter Physics*. Theoretical soft-matter physics and biological physics; protein phase behavior, self-assembly, and fibril formation; drug formulation.

Washburn, Brian R., Ph.D., Georgia Institute of Technology, 2002. *Atomic, Molecular, & Optical Physics*. Nonlinear fiber optics; ultrafast optics; laser development; optical frequency combs; metrology.

Assistant Professor

Blaga, Cosmin, Ph.D., Stony Brook University, 2009. *Atomic, Molecular, & Optical Physics*. Experimental atomic, molecular and optical physics; ultrafast, strong-field laser-matter interactions; nonlinear optics.

Greenman, Loren, Ph.D., University of Chicago, 2011. *Atomic, Molecular, & Optical Physics, Chemical Physics, Computational Physics, Theoretical Physics*. Theoretical atomic, molecular, and optical physics.

Kaadze, Ketino, Ph.D., Kansas State University, 2010. *High Energy Physics*. Experimental high-energy particle physics.

Laverty, James (J.T.) T., Ph.D., Michigan State University, 2013. *Physics and other Science Education*. Particles and fields; high energy physics.

Rolles, Daniel, Ph.D., Technische Universität Berlin, 2005. *Atomic, Molecular, & Optical Physics*. Experimental atomic, molecular and optical physics; ultrafast X-ray science.

Samushia, Lado, Ph.D., Kansas State University, 2009. *Cosmology & String Theory*. Dark energy; models of gravity; large-scale structure of the Universe; galaxy clustering; galaxy surveys (DESI, EUCLID, LSST); observational tests of cosmological models; astrostatistics.

Research Professor

Carnes, Kevin D., Ph.D., Purdue University, 1984. *Atomic, Molecular, & Optical Physics, Nuclear Physics*. Experimental atomic, molecular, and optical physics; accelerator physics; computer controls.

Research Assistant Professor

Fehrenbach, Charles, Ph.D., University of Michigan, 1993. *Atomic, Molecular, & Optical Physics*. Experimental atomic, molecular, and optical physics.

Kemppinen, Osku, Ph.D., Aalto University, 2016. *Applied Physics, Other*. Electromagnetism; atomic, molecular & optical physics; optics; holography.

Nepal, Arjun, Ph.D., Kansas State University, 2015. *Condensed Matter Physics*. Experimental condensed matter physics.

DEPARTMENTAL RESEARCH SPECIALTIES AND STAFF

Theoretical

Atomic, Molecular, & Optical Physics. Interaction of intense femtosecond and attosecond light pulses with atoms, molecules, and surfaces. The group seeks to resolve in time and space the motion of electrons and nuclei during the fragmentation of molecules by intense, ultrashort laser light pulses. To this end, they work closely with the AMO experimentalists in the department and across the world, proposing new experiments and more efficient ways to generate the laser pulses themselves as well as helping to interpret experiments. Esry, Greenman, Lin, Thumm.

Condensed Matter Physics. Studies of magnetic models with pinned magnetic vortices; influence of impurity-pinned magnetic vortices on dynamic correlations; dipolar effects on pinned magnetic vortices; optical cavities; Monte Carlo simulations of phase transitions in XY-symmetry magnets with vacancies; theory for stability of singly-charged and doubly-charged vortices pinned on vacancies; development of projection quantum Monte Carlo schemes to calculate dynamic modes at fixed momentum for magnetic models. Wysin.

Cosmology & Particle Astrophysics. Dark energy; dark matter; classical cosmological tests; cosmic microwave background anisotropies; inflation; cosmological magnetic fields; developing models for the large-scale matter and radiation distributions in the universe. Testing these models by comparing their predictions to observational data, including the anisotropy in the cosmic microwave background radiation, and the mass correlation function; cosmological gravitational waves; large-scale structure. Ratra, Samushia.

Soft Condensed Matter and Biological Physics. Aggregation and self-assembly of colloids and proteins; protein crystallization; liquid mixtures including polymers, liquid crystals, aerosols, colloids, nanoparticles; protein phase behavior; amyloid fibril formation; drug formulations. Chakrabarti, Schmit.

Experimental

Atomic, Molecular, & Optical Physics. Harmonic generation, AMO ultrafast, and attosecond science; collisions with MOT targets; collisions between molecular ions and atomic laser interactions with nano-structures and fast ion beams; laser metrology; fiber laser development; nonlinear fiber optics. Ben-Itzhak, Blaga, Carnes, Corwin, Fehrenbach, Kumarappan, Rolles, Rudenko, Washburn.

High Energy Physics. Energy frontier and intensity frontier physics; searches for new phenomena using the CMS detector at the CERN Large Hadron Collider; measurements of neutrino interactions using the MicroBooNE detector at Fermilab; searches for new physics at the Fermilab Mu2e experiment; development of next-generation pixel detectors, new instrumentation and algorithms for calorimetry, and advanced methods in detector and physics simulation; research in new directions for neutrino physics and collider physics. Bolton, Horton-Smith, Ivanov, Kaadze, Maravin.

Physics and other Science Education. Student identity development in STEM; interplay between physics and math understanding; cognitive and cultural models of learning; faculty development in research-based teaching and assessment; qualitative, quantitative, and mixed-methods research; and evidence-based curriculum development. Laverty, Sayre.

Soft Condensed Matter and Biological Physics. Soft-matter nanotechnology and biophysics; nano-electronic devices fabricated to measure electromechanical properties at selected sites on living cells; Liquid surface physics, thin films, surface and interfacial forces; Nanoparticle synthesis and solution behavior, light scattering by irregular particles, aerosols and gels. Berg, Flanders, Law, Sorensen.

View additional information about this department at www.gradschoolshopper.com. Check out the "Why Choose Us?" section, find out more about the department's culture and get links to social media networks.

UNIVERSITY OF KANSAS

DEPARTMENT OF PHYSICS AND ASTRONOMY

Lawrence, Kansas 66045
http://physics.ku.edu

General University Information
Chancellor: Douglas Girod
Dean of Graduate School: Michael Roberts
University website: http://ku.edu
School Type: Public
Setting: Suburban
Total Faculty: 1,600
Total Graduate Faculty: unknown
Total number of Students: 26,866
Total number of Graduate Students: 9,127

Department Information
Department Chairman: Prof. Hume A. Feldman, Chair
Department Contact: Joel Sauerwein, Graduate Coordinator
  Total full-time faculty: 26
  Total number of full-time equivalent positions: 26
  Full-Time Graduate Students: 52
  Female Full-Time Graduate Students: 12
  First-Year Graduate Students: 13
  Female First-Year Students: 5
  Total Post Doctorates: 12

Department Address
1251 Wescoe Hall Dr,
Malott Hall, Room 1082
Lawrence, KS 66045
Phone: (785) 864-1225
Fax: (785) 864-5262
E-mail: physics@ku.edu
Website: http://physics.ku.edu

ADMISSIONS

Admission Contact Information
Address admission inquiries to: Graduate Admissions, University of Kansas, Department of Physics and Astronomy, Malott Hall, 1251 Wescoe Hall Drive, Room 1082, Lawrence, Kansas 66045
Phone: (785) 864-1225
E-mail: physics@ku.edu
Admissions website: http://graduate.ku.edu/ku-graduate-application

Application deadlines
Fall admission:
U.S. students: December 31   *Int'l. students*: December 31
Spring admission:
U.S. students: October 1   *Int'l. students*: October 1

Application fee
U.S. students: $65   *Int'l. students*: $85
*International applicants not in possession of a U.S. Visa should apply earlier.

Admissions information
For Fall of 2018:
  Number of applicants: 73
  Number admitted: 33

Number enrolled: 13

Admission requirements
Bachelor's degree requirements: A Bachelor's degree in Physics, Astronomy, or a related field is desired.
Minimum undergraduate GPA: 3.0

GRE requirements
The GRE is not required.
GRE General Scores: A scanned version of score report is acceptable for review. GRE Code for KU: 6871

Subjective GRE requirements
The Subjective GRE is not required.
The exam is not required for admission; however, a Ph.D. student who sends in an original copy of a Physics GRE score of 650 or higher before enrollment will be excused from the Department's undergraduate certification process. A scanned version of score report is acceptable for review. However, an official score report is required before an admission can be offered. GRE code for KU: 6871

TOEFL requirements
The TOEFL exam is required for students from non-English-speaking countries.
PBT TOEFL Test Score Requirements: -Regular Admission: A minimum score of 53 in each section is required for admission. -Regular Admission with GTA (Graduate Teaching Assistant): A minimum score of 53 in each section plus must score at least a 50 on the KU SPEAK Test conducted by the Applied English Center. iBT TOEFL Test Score Requirements: -Regular Admission: A minimum score of 20 in each section (Reading, Listening, Writing, Speaking) is required. -Regular Admission with GTA (Graduate Teaching Assistant): A minimum score of 20 in Reading, Listening, Writing AND a score of 22 in the Speaking section. IELTS Test Score Requirements: -Regular Admission: A minimum overall score of 6.0, with no individual section having a score below 5.5. -Regular Admission with GTA: A minimum overall score 6.0 with no part score below 5.5, AND a score of 8.0 in the Speaking section. TOEFL Code for KU: 6871

Other admissions information
Additional requirements: International student applicants must take a TOEFL or an IELTS test with a speaking component/speaking score in order to be considered for a Graduate Teaching Assistantship (GTA) position.
Undergraduate preparation assumed: Mechanics (at the level of the textbook by Marion and Thornton), Electrodynamics (level of D. J. Griffiths), Quantum Mechanics (level of Liboff), Laboratory (level of Melissinos or Brophy); at least two courses in mathematics beyond elementary calculus.

TUITION

Tuition year 2018–19:
Tuition for in-state residents
  Full-time students: $415.95 per credit
  Part-time students: $415.95 per credit
Tuition for out-of-state residents

Full-time students: $969.05 per credit
Part-time students: $969.05 per credit
Fees include a $10/credit hour technology fee.
Credit hours per semester to be considered full-time: 9
Deferred tuition plan:
Health insurance: Available.
Other academic fees: There are also some additional miscellaneous campus fees of approximately $458/semester.
Academic term: Semester
Number of first-year students who received full tuition waivers: 8

Teaching Assistants, Research Assistants, and Fellowships

Number of first-year
 Teaching Assistants: 8
 Research Assistants: 1
 Fellowship students: 3
Average stipend per academic year
 Teaching Assistant: $18,200
 Research Assistant: $18,200
 Fellowship student: $32,000
Fellowships are dependent on funding being provided to the department from the College or University. Research Assistantships are dependent upon the level of research support available via faculty grants, combined with the number of present graduate students already being supported via RAs.

FINANCIAL AID

Application deadlines
Fall admission:
U.S. students: December 31   *Int'l. students*: December 31
Spring admission:
U.S. students: November 13   *Int'l. students*: November 13

Loans
Loans are not available for U.S. students.
Loans are not available for international students.
GAPSFAS application required: No
FAFSA application required: No

For further information
Address financial aid inquiries to: Graduate Admissions, University of Kansas, Department of Physics and Astronomy, 1251 Wescoe Hall Drive, Malott Hall, Room 1082, Lawrence, KS 66045.
Phone: (785) 864-1225
E-mail: physics@ku.edu
Financial aid website: http://physics.ku.edu/

HOUSING

Availability of on-campus housing
Single students: Yes
Married students: Yes
Childcare Assistance: No

For further information
Address housing inquiries to: KU Dept. of Student Housing, 422 West 11th St., Ste. DSH, Lawrence, KS 66045-3312.
Phone: (785) 864-4560
E-mail: housing@ku.edu
Housing aid website: http://housing.ku.edu/

Table A—Faculty, Enrollments, and Degrees Granted

Research Specialty	2017–18 Faculty	Enrollment Fall 2017		Number of Degrees Granted 2017–18 (2013–18)		
		Master's	Doctorate	Master's	Terminal Master's	Doctorate
	–	–	–	–	–	–
Total	26	–	–	2(24)	–	7(23)
Full-time Grad. Stud.	–	9	50	–	–	–
First-year Grad. Stud.	–	–	10	–	–	–

GRADUATE DEGREE REQUIREMENTS

Master's: Thirty hours of advanced courses and at least two hours of Master's research with satisfactory progress; no foreign language requirement; better than a B average required and a general examination in physics required. Thirty hours of resident study is required, but up to six of these may be transferred from another accredited university.

Doctorate: Thirty-three hours of advanced lecture courses; course work should average better than a B; students with a cumulative average grade less than B will be placed on probation; three full academic years of residency are required, two semesters normally consecutive and excluding summer session subsequent to the first year of graduate study must be spent at the University of Kansas; no foreign language requirement; demonstrated skill in computer programming related to the student's field of study is required; undergraduate certification by the graduate committee and a comprehensive exam are required; a dissertation showing the results of original research is required.

Other Degrees: Computational Physics and Astronomy (M.S.).

Thesis: Thesis may be written in absentia.

SPECIAL EQUIPMENT, FACILITIES, OR PROGRAMS

The campus Computer Center has a supercomputer system and several high-end Compaq Alpha servers (UNIX and Open VMS). The Department of Physics & Astronomy has recently purchased a node for research data on the KU Community Cluster project. Stored data is accessible within the KU network or remotely via the KU Anywhere virtual private network (VPN). In addition, the campus computer network has high-speed redundant connections to the Internet and is in the process of converting to nearly all-wireless via the Wireless First initiative. The University is a member of Internet 2 (consisting of more than 120 universities), which provides the latest network connection technology.

Condensed matter physics facilities include an advanced materials research lab, a quantum electronics lab, and a semiconductor laser optics lab. These labs are well equipped with thin film deposition systems, a new scanning electron microscope, a unique UHV multi-probe scanning microscopy system, an X-ray diffractometer, SQUID magnetometers, a 6-mK dilution refrigerator, microwave synthesizers and a vector network analyzer, a Nd:YAG laser, and an optical parametric oscillator. A clean room with photo- and electron beam lithography, as well as wafer processing tools is also available for micro- and nano-fabrication of solid state devices and circuits. Professionally staffed machine shop including CNC and Kern Precision mills, and 3D printer.

High-energy and nuclear physics groups utilize experimental facilities at various universities and national and international laboratories as part of collaborative experiments. These groups are particularly active in the CMS experiment at CERN.

The Department shares with San Diego State University access to a new 1.25-m reflecting telescope located at Mt. Laguna Observatory in southern California. This research-quality instrument is located at an excellent site and is equipped with a CCD imager and a variety of filters. Observing is done remotely from on-campus.

The Astrobiophysics Working Group sponsors collaborations among the departments of Physics and Astronomy, Ecology and Evolutionary Biology, Geology, and the Biodiversity Research Center. This group has a large allocation of supercomputer time at the NSF Teragrid.

Table B—Separately Budgeted Research Expenditures by Source of Support

Source of Support	Departmental Research	Physics-related Research Outside Department
Federal government	$2,593,634.12	
State/local government	$4,787.32	
Non-profit organizations	$139,227.16	
Business and industry	$114,844.73	
Other	$370,040.13	
Total	$3,222,533.46	

FACULTY

Distinguished University Professor

Bean, Alice L., Ph.D., Carnegie Mellon University, 1987. *High Energy Physics*. Experimental physics; elementary particle physics.

Royon, Christophe, Ph.D., University of Orsay - Paris XI/CEA Saclay, 1994. *Nuclear Physics*. Experimental nuclear physics.

Wu, Judy Z., Ph.D., University of Houston, 1993. *Condensed Matter Physics, Energy Sources & Environment*. Experimental condensed matter physics; fabrication, characterization, and application of thin films and nanowires.

Professor

Baringer, Philip S., Ph.D., Indiana University, 1985. *High Energy Physics*. Experimental physics; elementary particle physics.

Besson, David Z., Ph.D., Rutgers University, 1986. *High Energy Physics*. Experimental physics; elementary particle physics.

Cravens, Thomas E., Ph.D., Harvard University, 1975. *Atmosphere, Space Physics, Cosmic Rays*. Experimental, theoretical physics; astrophysics; space physics; plasma physics.

Feldman, Hume A., Ph.D., Stony Brook University, 1989. Department Chair. *Astrophysics*. Astrophysics and cosmology; computational physics; particle Astrophysics.

Han, Siyuan, Ph.D., Iowa State University, 1986. *Condensed Matter Physics*. Experimental condensed matter physics; physics and application of Josephson junctions and SQUIDs; mesoscopic physics; quantum computing.

Medvedev, Mikhail V., Ph.D., University of California, San Diego, 1996. *Atmosphere, Space Physics, Cosmic Rays*. Theoretical astrophysics; space physics; plasma physics; nonlinear dynamics; astrobiology.

Murray, Michael J., Ph.D., University of Pittsburgh, 1989. *Nuclear Physics*. Experimental nuclear physics, Astrobiophysics.

Ralston, John P., Ph.D., University of Oregon, 1980. *Astrophysics, High Energy Physics, Particles and Fields*. Theoretical physics; elementary particle physics; particle astrophysics.

Rudnick, Gregory H., Ph.D., University of Arizona, 2001. Director of Graduate Studies. *Astronomy, Astrophysics*. Astronomy; galaxy evolution; galaxy formation.

Sanders, Stephen J., Ph.D., Yale University, 1977. *Nuclear Physics*. Experimental nuclear physics.

Shandarin, Sergei F., Ph.D., Moscow Physical Technical Institute, 1975. Astrophysics and cosmology; nonlinear dynamics; computational physics.

Shi, Jicong, Ph.D., University of Houston, 1991. *Nonlinear Dynamics and Complex Systems, Physics of Beams*. Theoretical physics; nonlinear dynamics; beam dynamics; accelerator physics; computational physics.

Twarog, Bruce A., Ph.D., Yale University, 1980. *Astronomy, Astrophysics*. Stellar nucleosynthesis; chemical evolution of galaxies; stellar photometry; high resolution stellar spectroscopy.

Wilson, Graham W., Ph.D., University of Lancaster, 1989. Director of Undergraduate Studies. *High Energy Physics*. Experimental physics; elementary particle physics.

Zhao, Hui, Ph.D., Northern Jiaotong University, 2000. *Condensed Matter Physics*. Experimental condensed matter physics.

Associate Professor

Chan, Wai-Lun, Ph.D., Brown University, 2007. *Condensed Matter Physics, Materials Science, Metallurgy*. Renewable energy.

Fischer, Christopher J., Ph.D., University of Michigan, 2000. Associate Chair Director of Engineering Physics. *Biophysics*. Biophysics, Astrophysics.

Kong, Kyoungchul (K.C.), Ph.D., University of Florida, 2006. Graduate Student Advisor. *High Energy Physics, Particles and Fields*. Theoretical physics; elementary particle physics.

Assistant Professor

Kirkpatrick, Allison, Ph.D., University of Massachusetts, Amherst, 2016. *Astronomy*. Galaxies, black holes.

Lewis, Ian M., Ph.D., University of Wisconsin-Madison, 2011. *Astrophysics, High Energy Physics, Particles and Fields, Theoretical Physics*. Theoretical physics; elementary particle physics; particle astrophysics.

Rogan, Christopher S., Ph.D., California Institute of Technology, 2013. *High Energy Physics, Particles and Fields*. Experimental physics; elementary particle physics.

Tapia Takaki, Daniel, Ph.D., University of Birmingham, 2008. *Nuclear Physics*. Heavy-ion physics.

Emeritus

Anthony-Twarog, Barbara J., Ph.D., Yale University, 1981. *Astronomy, Astrophysics*. Stellar evolution in open star clusters; CCD and photoelectric photometry; globular clusters; high resolution stellar spectroscopy.

Armstrong, Thomas P., Ph.D., University of Iowa, 1966. *Atmosphere, Space Physics, Cosmic Rays*. Experimental, theoretical physics; astrophysics; space physics; plasma physics.

Bearse, Robert C., Ph.D., Rice University, 1964. *Nuclear Physics*. Nuclear physics; materials control and accounting; nuclear safeguards; computer database applications.

Davis, Robin E. P., Ph.D., University of Oxford, 1962. *High Energy Physics*. Experimental physics; elementary particle physics.

Eagleman, Joe R., Ph.D., University of Missouri, 1963. *Other*. Atmospheric science.

Hawley, Steven A., Ph.D., University of California, Santa Cruz, 1977. *Astronomy, Astrophysics*. Observational astronomy; spectrophotometry of H II regions and planetary nebulae; astrobiology; human spaceflight.

Kwak, Nowhan, Ph.D., Tufts University, 1962. *High Energy Physics*. Experimental physics; elementary particle physics.

McKay, Douglas W., Ph.D., Northwestern University, 1968. Theoretical physics; elementary particle physics; particle astrophysics.

Melott, Adrian L., Ph.D., University of Texas, Austin, 1981. *Astrophysics, Geophysics, Other*. Astrobiophysics.

Munczek, Herman J., Ph.D., University of Buenos Aires, 1958. *Particles and Fields*. Theoretical physics; elementary particle physics.

Sapp, Richard C., Ph.D., Ohio State University, 1955. *Condensed Matter Physics*. Experimental physics; solid state and low-temperature; low-temperature magnetism.

Shawl, Stephen J., Ph.D., University of Texas, Austin, 1972. *Astronomy*. Observational astronomy; stellar astronomy; polarization; globular clusters; astronomy education.

Wong, Kai-Wai, Ph.D., Northwestern University, 1962. *Condensed Matter Physics*. Theoretical physics; many-body theory; superconductivity; liquid helium.

DEPARTMENTAL RESEARCH SPECIALTIES AND STAFF

Theoretical

Astrophysics. Dark matter; γ-ray bursts; particle astrophysics. Feldman, Medvedev, Melott, Ralston, Shandarin.

Atmosphere, Space Physics, Cosmic Rays. Space probes; trapped particles; solar wind; radiation belts. Cravens, Medvedev.

Cosmology. Large-scale structure. Feldman, Shandarin.

Particles and Fields. Symmetry properties and dynamics of elementary particles. Kong, Lewis, Ralston.

Experimental

Astrobiophysics.. Fischer, Melott, Murray.

Astronomy. Stellar astronomy; nebular astrophysics; galaxy evolution; polarization. Anthony-Twarog, Hawley, Kirkpatrick, Rudnick, Twarog.

Astrophysics. Space plasma physics, neutrino detection. Besson, Cravens, Medvedev, Melott, Shandarin.

Biophysics. Kinetics and thermodynamics of protein-protein and protein-nucleic acid interactions. Fischer.

Condensed Matter Physics. Quantum tunneling and coherence, superconducting and single electron devices, high-temperature superconductivity, electronic structure, semiconductors. Chan, Han, Wu, Zhao.

High Energy Physics. astrophysics research with ANITA in Antarctica; study of proton-proton collisions with the CMS experiment at the CERN LHC; research and development work on a future linear electron-positron collider. Baringer, Bean, Besson, Kong, Lewis, Ralston, Rogan, Wilson.

Nuclear Physics. Heavy-ion reactions at CERN, and nuclear structure. Collaborations with the CMS and ALICE experiments at CERN. Murray, Royon, Sanders, Tapia Takaki.

View additional information about this department at www.gradschoolshopper.com. Check out the "Why Choose Us?" section, find out more about the department's culture and get links to social media networks.

UNIVERSITY OF KENTUCKY

DEPARTMENT OF PHYSICS AND ASTRONOMY

Lexington, Kentucky 40506-0055
http://pa.as.uky.edu

General University Information
President: Eli Capilouto
Dean of Graduate School: Brian Jackson
University website: http://www.uky.edu
School Type: Public
Setting: Urban
Total Faculty: 2,291
Total Graduate Faculty: 1,221
Total number of Students: 30,131
Total number of Graduate Students: 7,207

Department Information
Department Chairman: Prof. Al Shapere, Chair
Department Contact: Prof. Christopher Crawford, Director of
    Graduate Studies
    Total full-time faculty: 30
    Total number of full-time equivalent positions: 30
    Full-Time Graduate Students: 93
    Female Full-Time Graduate Students: 22
    First-Year Graduate Students: 13
    Female First-Year Students: 2
    Total Post Doctorates: 11

Department Address
177 Chemistry-Physics Building
505 Rose Street
Lexington, KY 40506-0055
Phone: (859) 257-2504
Fax: (859) 323-2846
E-mail: physics@pa.uky.edu
Website: http://pa.as.uky.edu

ADMISSIONS

Admission Contact Information
Address admission inquiries to: Graduate Admissions Commit-
    tee, Department of Physics and Astronomy, University of
    Kentucky, 177 Chemistry-Physics Building, 505 Rose Street,
    Lexington, KY 40506-0055
Phone: (859) 257-6722
E-mail: gradapp@pa.uky.edu
Admissions website: http://www.pa.uky.edu/grad

Application deadlines
Fall admission:
U.S. students: February 1   *Int'l. students*: February 1

Application fee
U.S. students: $65   *Int'l. students*: $75

Admissions information
For Fall of 2017:
    Number of applicants: 144
    Number admitted: 36
    Number enrolled: 17

Admission requirements
Bachelor's degree requirements: A Bachelor's degree in Physics,
    Astronomy, or a related field is required.
Minimum undergraduate GPA: 2.75

GRE requirements
The GRE is required.
There is no official minimum score requirement for the General
    GRE Exam.

Subjective GRE requirements
The Subjective GRE is recommended.
    There is no official minimum score requirement for the GRE
    Physics Exam.

TOEFL requirements
The TOEFL exam is required for students from non-English-
    speaking countries.
    PBT score: 550
    iBT score: 79
The University of Kentucky requires a minimum TOEFL score
    of 213 computer-based (550 paper-based, iBT 79) or a min-
    imum IELTS score of 6.5 for all international students whose
    first language is not English. Submitted scores must be no
    more than two years old. International students who receive
    college degrees from US universities and universities in other
    designated English-speaking countries may be exempted from
    taking the TOEFL test. For example, if you obtain an M.S.
    degree from a US University you do not need the TOEFL.

Other admissions information
Undergraduate preparation assumed: The Department recom-
    mends one semester of advanced undergraduate mechanics,
    two semesters of advanced undergraduate electricity and mag-
    netism, two semesters of advanced undergraduate quantum
    physics, and at least one semester of laboratory at the junior
    or senior level. Substantial variations in preparation can be
    accommodated.

TUITION

Tuition year 2018–19:
Tuition for in-state residents
    Full-time students: $6,526 per semester
Tuition for out-of-state residents
    Full-time students: $15,682 per semester
Nearly all admitted graduate students are offered a Teaching As-
    sistantship or Fellowship, both of which include a stipend in
    addition to a full-tuition scholarship.
Credit hours per semester to be considered full-time: 9
Deferred tuition plan: No
Health insurance: Available at the cost of $2,265 per year.
Academic term: Semester
Number of first-year students who received full tuition waivers: 14

Teaching Assistants, Research Assistants, and Fellowships
Number of first-year
    Teaching Assistants: 18
    Fellowship students: 7
Average stipend per academic year
    Teaching Assistant: $20,000
    Research Assistant: $20,000
    Fellowship student: $22,500
In addition, $3000 summer support is provided to eligible students.

FINANCIAL AID

Application deadlines
Fall admission:
U.S. students: February 1   *Int'l. students*: February 1

Loans
Loans are available for U.S. students.
Loans are not available for international students.
GAPSFAS application required: No
FAFSA application required: No

For further information
Address financial aid inquiries to: Office of Student Financial Aid, 128 Funkhouser Building, University of Kentucky, Lexington, KY 40506-0054.
Phone: (859) 257-3172
Financial aid website: http://www.uky.edu/financialaid/

HOUSING

Availability of on-campus housing
Single students: Yes
Married students: Yes

For further information
Address housing inquiries to: 300 Alumni Drive Apartment 156, Lexington, KY 40503. Fax: (859) 323-1900.
Phone: (859) 257-3721
E-mail: ukapthousing@email.uky.edu
Housing aid website: http://www.uky.edu/housing/graduate/about

Table A—Faculty, Enrollments, and Degrees Granted

Research Specialty	2015–16 Faculty	Enrollment Fall 2014 Master's	Enrollment Fall 2014 Doctorate	Number of Degrees Granted 2014–15 (2008–13) Master's	Number of Degrees Granted 2014–15 (2008–13) Terminal Master's	Number of Degrees Granted 2014–15 (2008–13) Doctorate
Astronomy	5	–	5	1(8)	1(3)	2(6)
Atomic, Molecular, & Optical Physics	2	–	5	–	–	–(1)
Condensed Matter Physics	9	–	10	3(10)	–	4(10)
Nuclear Physics	7	–	11	3(11)	3(3)	3(8)
Particles and Fields	7	–	5	–(3)	–	–(5)
Non-specialized	–	–	36	–(1)	2(12)	–(1)
Total	30	–	72	7(33)	2(18)	9(31)
Full-time Grad. Stud.	–	–	72	–	–	–
First-year Grad. Stud.	–	–	14	–	–	–

GRADUATE DEGREE REQUIREMENTS

Master's: PLAN A: 24 semester hours of graduate credit with satisfactory performance and a thesis. PLAN B: Same as Plan A except six hours of course work at the advanced level is substituted for the thesis. Minimum GPA of 3.0 for both plans.

Doctorate: Minimum GPA of 3.0 in approved course program, as determined by student's advisory committee. Students must pass the GRE Physics Subject Test with a score at the 50th percentile or above and also pass 6 graduate core physics courses with GPA of 3.0 or higher. 36 credit hours and two-year full-time residency before and one-year full-time residency after qualification exam.

Thesis: Written thesis required for Ph.D. degree.

SPECIAL EQUIPMENT, FACILITIES, OR PROGRAMS

On Campus: 6.5 MV van de Graaff accelerator, Center for Advanced Materials, Liquid Helium Liquefier, MacAdam Student Observatory, Center for Computational Sciences. Users at ORNL, LANL, NIST, Fermilab, PSI, TRIUMF, Lund, HIGS, RHIC, NRAO, JLab/CEBAF.

Table B—Separately Budgeted Research Expenditures by Source of Support

Source of Support	Departmental Research	Physics-related Research Outside Department
Federal government	$1,750,752	$4,782,069
State/local government		
Non-profit organizations		
Business and industry		
Other	$618,066	
Total	**$2,368,818**	**$4,782,069**

FACULTY

Professor

Brill, Joseph W., Ph.D., Stanford University, 1978. *Condensed Matter Physics*. Experimental condensed matter physics.

Cavagnero, Michael, Ph.D., University of Chicago, 1983. *Atomic, Molecular, & Optical Physics*. Theoretical atomic physics.

Das, Sumit R., Ph.D., University of Chicago, 1983. *Particles and Fields*. Theoretical particle physics; string theory.

DeLong, Lance E., Ph.D., University of California, San Diego, 1977. *Condensed Matter Physics*. Experimental condensed matter physics.

Draper, Terrence, Ph.D., University of California, Los Angeles, 1984. *Particles and Fields*. Theoretical particle physics.

Eides, Michael I., Ph.D., Leningrad State University, 1977. *Particles and Fields*. Theoretical particle physics.

Ferland, Gary J., Ph.D., University of Texas, 1978. *Astrophysics*. Theoretical astrophysics.

Gardner, Susan V., Ph.D., Massachusetts Institute of Technology, 1988. *Nuclear Physics, Particles and Fields*. Astrophysics and Cosmology, Theoretical nuclear and particle physics.

Gorringe, Tim P., Ph.D., University of Birmingham, 1984. *Nuclear Physics*. Experimental nuclear physics.

Korsch, Wolfgang, Ph.D., University of Marburg, 1990. *Nuclear Physics*. Experimental nuclear physics.

Kovash, Michael A., Ph.D., Ohio State University, 1978. *Nuclear Physics*. Experimental nuclear physics.

Liu, Keh-Fei, Ph.D., Stony Brook University, 1975. *Particles and Fields*. Theoretical nuclear and particle physics.

Martin, Nicholas L. S., Ph.D., University of Oxford, 1977. *Atomic, Molecular, & Optical Physics*. Experimental atomic and molecular physics.

Murthy, Ganpathy, Ph.D., Yale University, 1987. *Condensed Matter Physics*. Theoretical condensed matter physics.

Ng, Kwok-Wai, Ph.D., Iowa State University, 1986. *Condensed Matter Physics*. Experimental condensed matter physics.

Plaster, Brad, Ph.D., Massachusetts Institute of Technology, 2004. Associate Department Chair. *Nuclear Physics*. Experimental nuclear physics.

Shapere, Alfred D., Ph.D., University of California, Santa Barbara, 1988. Department Chair. *Particles and Fields*. Theoretical physics.

Shlosman, Isaac, Ph.D., Tel-Aviv University, 1986. *Astrophysics*. Theoretical astrophysics, numerical simulations.

Straley, Joseph P., Ph.D., Cornell University, 1970. *Condensed Matter Physics, Physics and other Science Education*. Theoretical condensed matter physics; physics education.

Troland, Thomas H., Ph.D., University of California, Berkeley, 1980. *Astronomy*. Observational astronomy.

Associate Professor

Crawford, Christopher, Ph.D., Massachusetts Institute of Technology, 2005. Director of Graduate Studies. *Nuclear Physics*. Experimental nuclear physics.

Fatemi, Renee, Ph.D., University of Virginia, 2002. Director of Undergraduate Studies. *Nuclear Physics*. Experimental nuclear physics.

Hill, Richard J., Ph.D., Cornell University, 2002. *Particles and Fields*. Theoretical nuclear/particle physics.

Kaul, Ribhu, Ph.D., Duke University, 2006. *Condensed Matter Physics*. Theoretical condensed matter physics.

Seo, Sung, Ph.D., Seoul National University, 2007. *Condensed Matter Physics*. Experimental condensed matter physics.

Strachan, Douglas, Ph.D., University of Maryland, 2002. *Condensed Matter Physics*. Experimental condensed matter physics.

Wilhelm, Ronald, Ph.D., Michigan State University, 1995. *Astronomy*. Observational astronomy.

Assistant Professor

Dymarsky, Anatoly, Ph.D., Princeton University, 2007. *Particles and Fields*. theoretical high energy physics, cosmology, quantum field theory and string theory.

Yan, Renbin, Ph.D., University of California, Berkeley, 2007. *Astrophysics*. Observational astronomy.

Emeritus

Christopher, John E., Ph.D., University of Virginia, 1967. *Physics and other Science Education*. Physics education.

Elitzur, Moshe, Ph.D., Weizmann Institute of Science, 1971. *Astrophysics*. Theoretical astrophysics.

Li, Bing An, Ph.D., Chinese Academy of Sciences, 1968. *Particles and Fields*. Theoretical particle physics.

McEllistrem, Marcus T., Ph.D., University of Wisconsin-Madison, 1956. *Nuclear Physics*. Experimental nuclear physics.

DEPARTMENTAL RESEARCH SPECIALTIES AND STAFF

Theoretical

Theoretical Astrophysics. Interstellar masers; radiation transport; cosmology; stellar dynamics; high-z radio-galaxies; active galactic nuclei; cataclysmic variable stars; accretion disks; red giant atmospheres. Elitzur, Ferland, Shlosman.

Theoretical Atomic Physics. Few-body states of atoms and molecules. Collective effects in atoms, molecules and ultra-cold gases. Cold and ultra-cold dipolar gases. Elementary collision processes in atomic and molecular physics. Cavagnero.

Theoretical Condensed Matter Physics. Structure and electronic properties of clusters, defects, and surfaces; catalysis; statistical mechanisms of phase transitions; Josephson networks; quantum dots; quantum Hall effect; tunneling; superconductivity; mesoscopic systems, quantum Monte-Carlo, exact diagonalization, quantum criticality, nanophysics. Kaul, Murthy, Straley.

Theoretical Particle Physics. Lattice QCD; particle phenomenology; string theory; quantum gravity; fundamental symmetries; particle cosmology. Das, Draper, Dymarsky, Eides, Gardner, Hill, Li, Liu, Shapere.

Experimental

Experimental Atomic Physics. Electron impact excitation and ionization of atoms. (e,2e) Spectroscopy of autoionizing levels. Non-dipole photoelectron studies on autoionizing levels. Laser assisted electron scattering. Martin.

Experimental Condensed Matter Physics. Physical properties of new and novel materials; organic metals, magnetic oxides, heavy fermion systems, charge density wave systems, superconducting materials; scanning tunneling electron microscopy, patterned thin films. Brill, DeLong, Ng, Seo, Strachan.

Experimental Nuclear Physics. Tests of fundamental symmetries, neutron beta-decay, muon capture, muon anomalous magnetic moment g-2, neutron electric dipole moment, radium electric dipole moment, nucleon electromagnetic structure, nucleon spin structure, hadronic weak interactions. Crawford, Fatemi, Gorringe, Korsch, Kovash, McEllistrem, Plaster.

Observational Astronomy. Observational radio astronomy; interstellar material and star formation; interstellar magnetic fields; kinematics of ancient stars; active galactic nuclei; galaxy formation and evolution. Troland, Wilhelm, Yan.

View additional information about this department at www.gradschoolshopper.com. Check out the "Why Choose Us?" section, find out more about the department's culture and get links to social media networks.

UNIVERSITY OF MAINE

DEPARTMENT OF PHYSICS AND ASTRONOMY

Orono, Maine 04469-5709
http://www.physics.umaine.edu/

General University Information

President: Joan Ferrini-Mundy
Dean of Graduate School: Kody Varahramyan
University website: http://www.umaine.edu
School Type: Public
Setting: Suburban
Total Faculty: 851
Total Graduate Faculty: 715
Total number of Students: 11,040
Total number of Graduate Students: 1,961

Department Information

Department Chairman: Prof. John R. Thompson, Chair
Department Contact: James McClymer, Associate Professor
  Total full-time faculty: 17
  Total number of full-time equivalent positions: 11
  Full-Time Graduate Students: 26
  Female Full-Time Graduate Students: 6
  First-Year Graduate Students: 5
  Female First-Year Students: 2
  Total Post Doctorates: 1

Department Address

5709 Bennett Hall
Orono, ME 04469-5709
Phone: (207) 581-1039
Fax: (207) 581-3410
E-mail: physics@maine.edu
Website: http://www.physics.umaine.edu/

ADMISSIONS

Admission Contact Information

Address admission inquiries to: Dr. James McClymer, University of Maine, Department of Physics and Astronomy, 5709 Bennett Hall, Orono, ME 04469-5709
Phone: (207) 581-1034
E-mail: mcclymer@maine.edu
Admissions website: http://www.umaine.edu/graduate/admissions/

Application deadlines

Fall admission:
U.S. students: January 15   *Int'l. students*: January 15

Application fee

U.S. students: $65   *Int'l. students*: $65
Application review begins in mid-February and continues until programs are filled. Early application is recommended if financial assistance is required.

Admissions information

For Fall of 2017:
  Number of applicants: 38
  Number admitted: 5
  Number enrolled: 5

Admission requirements

Bachelor's degree requirements: Bachelor's degree in Physics is normally required.
Minimum undergraduate GPA: 3.0

GRE requirements

The GRE is required.
  Quantitative score: 150
  Verbal score: 145
  Analytical score: 3.0
  Mean GRE score range (25th–75th percentile): 170-230

Subjective GRE requirements

The Subjective GRE is recommended.
  Minimum accepted Advanced GRE score: 450
  Mean Advanced GRE score range (25th–75th percentile): 450-800

TOEFL requirements

The TOEFL exam is required for students from non-English-speaking countries.
  PBT score: 450
  iBT score: 92

Other admissions information

Additional requirements: No minimum score for admission is required.
Undergraduate preparation assumed: Modern Physics: Krane, Modern Physics, 3rd Ed. Mechanics: Fowles and Cassiday, Analytical Mechanics; Electricity and Magnetism: Griffiths, Introduction to Electrodynamics; Mathematics: Paul, Differential Equations for Mathematics, Science, and Engineering.

TUITION

Tuition year 2018–19:
Tuition for in-state residents
  Full-time students: $439 per credit
  Part-time students: $439 per credit
Tuition for out-of-state residents
  Full-time students: $1,430 per credit
  Part-time students: $1,430 per credit
Credit hours per semester to be considered full-time: 6
Deferred tuition plan: Yes
Health insurance: Yes, $2,668/year.
Other academic fees: $1,204/year (activity fee, communication fee, unified fee, recreation center fee).
Academic term: Semester
Number of first-year students who received full tuition waivers: 6

Teaching Assistants, Research Assistants, and Fellowships

Number of first-year
  Teaching Assistants: 5
Average stipend per academic year
  Teaching Assistant: $16,050
  Research Assistant: $17,000
Average 12-month stipends: $21,400 for TA, $22,500 for RA.

FINANCIAL AID

Loans

Loans are available for U.S. students.
Loans are available for international students.
GAPSFAS application required: No
FAFSA application required: Yes

For further information

Address financial aid inquiries to: Student Financial Aid, 5781 Wingate Hall, Orono, ME 04469-5781.
Phone: (207)581-1324
E-mail: umfinaid@maine.edu
Financial aid website: http://www.umaine.edu/stuaid/graduate-students/

HOUSING

Availability of on-campus housing

Single students: Yes
Married students: Yes

For further information

Address housing inquiries to: Housing Services, 103L Hilltop, Orono, ME 04469-5734.
Phone: (207) 581-4580
E-mail: um.housing@maine.edu
Housing aid website: http://umaine.edu/graduate/housing

Table A—Faculty, Enrollments, and Degrees Granted

Research Specialty	2017–18 Faculty	Enrollment Fall 2017		Number of Degrees Granted 2017–18 (2013–18)		
		Master's	Doctorate	Master's	Terminal Master's	Doctorate
Astronomy	2	–	–	–	–	–
Astrophysics	2	2	5	–	2(1)	–(3)
Biophysics	2	2	3	1(1)	–	–(4)
Chemical Physics	3	–	–	–	–(1)	–
Condensed Matter Physics	3	–	4	–	–(1)	–(2)
Energy Sources & Environment	1	–	1	–(1)	1(3)	–
Engineering Physics/Science	3	1	–	–	–(3)	–
Fluids, Rheology	1	–	–	–	–	–
Geophysics	1	–	–	–	–	–(3)
Marine Science/Oceanography	1	–	–	–	–	–(1)
Materials Science, Metallurgy	3	–	3	–(1)	–	–
Nano Science and Technology	3	–	–	–(1)	–	–(1)
Nuclear Physics	1	–	–	–	–	–
Physics and other Science Education	5	–	5	–(1)	–	2(5)
Relativity & Gravitation	1	–	–	–	–	–
Statistical & Thermal Physics	2	–	–	–	–	–
Non-specialized	–	–	–	–	–	–
Total	13	5	21	1(5)	1(8)	2(19)
Full-time Grad. Stud.	–	5	21	–	–	–
First-year Grad. Stud.	–	–	6	–	–	–

GRADUATE DEGREE REQUIREMENTS

Master's: 30 graduate (semester) credits, with 24 devoted to courses in physics and allied fields; courses must be passed with a minimum grade of "B-"; at least 12 hours of coursework must be taken while a full-time student in residence. There are no foreign language or computer language requirements. A Graduate Written Examination is required. A thesis is required. A minimum GPA of 3.0 (B) must be obtained.

Doctorate: 30 graduate (semester) credits in courses required; courses must be passed with a minimum grade of "B-". Residence requirement satisfied by registering for a full program of study for two consecutive years following the baccalaureate, or for one year following the award of a Master's degree; no foreign language required, no computer language required; a comprehensive examination required; thesis required. A minimum GPA of 3.0 (B) must be obtained.

Other Degrees: Other programs: Through cooperative efforts of faculty in the Departments of Physics, Chemistry, Earth Sciences, Electrical and Computer Engineering, and Biochemistry, students may work for an M.S. or Ph.D. degree in Physics with a concentration in applied physics, materials science, quaternary studies, and biophysics. M.E. in engineering (engineering physics) requirements are the same as for the M.S. in physics except that nine hours of the 30 must be selected from engineering courses. A non-thesis option for the M.E. in engineering is available with 36 course hours required. A minimum GPA of 3.0 (B) must be obtained.

Thesis: Thesis may be written in absentia with permission.

SPECIAL EQUIPMENT, FACILITIES, OR PROGRAMS

The Laboratory for Surface Science and Technology (LASST) unites researchers from the Departments of Chemistry, Physics, Electrical and Computer Engineering, and Chemical and Biological Engineering in many projects spanning aspects of surface and interface science, thin films, sensors, microsystems, and nanotechnology. Current facilities include thin film synthesis, electron and optical spectroscopies, scanning probe microscopies, X-ray and electron diffraction, focused ion beam-scanning electron microscopy, fluorescence microscopy, device fabrication (Class-1000 clean room with photolithography, metallization, wet and dry etch, PECVD, sputtering, mask generation, and packaging), and sensor testing (gas delivery systems, electrical and microwave test equipment, and data acquisition/integrated electronic test suites).

The Physics Education Research Laboratory has facilities and equipment for conducting research on the learning and teaching of physics including a classroom intended for curricular activities based on physics education research (PER) and dedicated clinical interview space to ensure the anonymity and privacy of students participating in our research work (as required by our institutional review board for testing with human subjects).

Astronomy/Astrophysics: The Emera Astronomy Center consists of two observatories, a planetarium, and multi-purpose classroom space. The Jordan Observatory houses a PlaneWave CDK20 (20 inch) telescope on a German Equatorial Mount with an Apogee Aspen CG16M CCD camera with 7 slot filter wheel forimaging and photometry. The telescope and dome both can be remotely controlled. Additionally thefacility has an historic Alvin Clark refractor (8 inch) housed in a roll-off roof observatory for visual observations.The Jordan Planetarium is a 10 meter 4K digital planetarium with 50 seats which can show a variety of astronomy and science visualizations, real time astronomical data, and full-dome films.The planetarium conducts regular public programs, school programs, and numerous special events. The facility has a multipurpose classroom housing a number of interactive displays and is used for astronomy labs and other university courses.

A Linux/PC workstation network is available for astronomical research data reduction and analysis, either from observations at our UMaine facility or at national or international observatories

The Radon Measurement Laboratory contains a liquid scintillation counter, 3 HP Ge detectors, X-ray fluorescence, Wrenn detectors, and a portable NaI spectrometer interfaced to a Digidart portable multichannel analyzer.

Biophysics and Optics: Three laboratories include a super-resolution localization microscopy facility and four F-PALM microscopes, image processing computer cluster, tunable femtosecond pulsed Ti:Sapphire laser and optical parametric oscillator (OPO), cell culture facilities, polymerase chain reaction (PCR) thermal cycler, and other equipment for molecular biology, confocal and two-photon laser-scanning microscopes, fluorescence correlation and cross-correlation microscope, fluorimeter, spectrophotometer, Krypton-Argon and Argon ion lasers, numerous diode lasers spanning visible wavelengths from 400-700 nm, and optical tweezer.

Table B—Separately Budgeted Research Expenditures by Source of Support

Source of Support	Departmental Research	Physics-related Research Outside Department
Federal government	$1,365,810	
State/local government		
Non-profit organizations		
Business and industry		
Other		
Total	**$1,365,810**	

Table C—Separately Budgeted Research Expenditures by Research Specialty

Research Specialty	No. of Grants	Expenditures ($)
Biophysics	3	$ 209,367
Energy Sources & Environment	2	$ 32,000
Physics and other Science Education	3	$ 171,000
Surface Physics	3	$ 953,443
Total	**11**	**$1,365,810**

FACULTY

Professor

Astumian, R. D., Ph.D., University of Texas, Arlington, 1983. *Biophysics, Condensed Matter Physics.* Theoretical condensed-matter physics; biophysics of molecular motors and pumps.

Batuski, David J., Ph.D., New Mexico State University, 1986. *Astronomy, Astrophysics.* Observational cosmology; large-scale structure in the universe; weak gravitational lensing studies of dark matter in superclusters of galaxies; dynamics of superclusters; radio sources in galaxy clusters.

Comins, Neil F., Ph.D., University College, Cardiff, 1978. *Astronomy, Astrophysics, Cosmology & String Theory, Physics and other Science Education, Relativity & Gravitation.* Observational and theoretical astrophysics; galactic evolution and stability; stellar systems; general relativity; astronomy education.

Hess, C. Thomas, Ph.D., Ohio University, 1967. *Biophysics, Geophysics, Medical, Health Physics, Nuclear Physics.* Environmental nuclear physics; health physics; radioactivity studies.

Hess, Samuel T., Ph.D., Cornell University, 2002. *Biophysics.* Experimental and theoretical biophysics; super-resolution fluorescence microscopy and spectroscopy; function and lateral organization of biomembranes; influenza virus infection; single-molecule fluorescence photophysics.

Lad, Robert J., Ph.D., Cornell University, 1986. *Condensed Matter Physics, Nano Science and Technology.* Surface physics; thin films; sensor technology; materials science; ceramics; electronic materials; photovoltaics; material characterization.

McKay, Susan R., Ph.D., Massachusetts Institute of Technology, 1987. *Nonlinear Dynamics and Complex Systems.* Theoretical condensed-matter physics; nonlinear systems and transitions to chaos; phase transitions and critical phenomena; spin glasses; amorphous magnetism; quenched disorder; pattern formation; systems far from equilibrium; applications of network theory.

Thompson, John R., Ph.D., Brown University, 1998. *Physics and other Science Education.* Research interest: Physics Education. Research on teaching and learning, curriculum development and assessment, primarily at the upper division (thermal physics, electricity and magnetism, and quantum mechanics). Student use of mathematics, mathematical methods, and mathematical reasoning in physics (e.g., differentials, derivatives, and integrals in single variable, multivariable, and vector calculus); analysis via specific difficulties, symbolic forms, and conceptual blending.

Wittmann, Michael C., Ph.D., University of Maryland, 1998. *Physics and other Science Education.* Physics education. Research on teaching and learning. Learning theory development, curriculum development and evaluation, use of mathematics in physics, and teacher knowledge of student thinking, both at the college and the K-12 level, in particular middle school. Student and teacher understanding of energy and accelerated motion in middle school and in high school.

Associate Professor

McClymer, James P., Ph.D., University of Delaware, 1986. *Optics, Other.* Digital imaging and light scattering from equilibrium and nonequilibrium transitions in liquid crystals and complex fluids.

Meulenberg, Robert W., Ph.D., University of California, Santa Barbara, 2002. *Condensed Matter Physics, Materials Science, Metallurgy, Nano Science and Technology.* Experimental condensed-matter physics: electronic structure of nanoscale materials; surface and interfacial physics of nanostructures; magnetic materials; applications of synchrotron radiation to materials science.

Stetzer, MacKenzie R., Ph.D., University of Pennsylvania, 2000. *Physics and other Science Education.* Physics education: research on teaching and learning, curriculum development and assessment. Student understanding of analog electronics in physics and engineering. Troubleshooting in electronics. The development of student reasoning skills and metacognitive skills in physics and the application of findings and theories from cognitive science to student reasoning in physics.

Assistant Professor

Yu, Liping, Ph.D., North Carolina State University, 2009. *Materials Science, Metallurgy, Nano Science and Technology.* Inverse materials design; defects in solids; semiconductor physics; energy materials (e.g., photovoltaics, catalysts, batteries, supercapacitors); flexible 2D electronics; surface and interface physics and chemistry; application of density functional theory and high-throughput computation.

Emeritus

Kleban, Peter H., Ph.D., Brandeis University, 1970. *Statistical & Thermal Physics.*

263

Unertl, William N., Ph.D., University of Wisconsin-Madison, 1973. *Surface Physics.*

DEPARTMENTAL RESEARCH SPECIALTIES AND STAFF

Theoretical

Biophysics. Polyelectrolyte microgels and microcapsules are microscopic gel particles that are swollen in a solvent. Composed of porous, elastic networks of cross-linked polymers, microgels are soft colloids that can encapsulate dye molecules or drugs. Their sensitive response to environmental conditions (e.g., temperature and pH) and influence on flow properties suit microgels to widespread applications in the chemical, pharmaceutical, food, and consumer care industries. We model microgels and microcapsules using molecular simulations and Poisson-Boltzmann theory. Lipid membranes surround all living cells, forming a barrier that ensures integrity and function. We are interested in understanding the physical properties of membranes and relating them to biological functions. Among the interesting questions are how different lipids influence the lateral organization of a lipid bilayer and what the role of membrane-associated proteins is. Some of our work also addresses bending of lipid membranes and electrostatic interactions between the lipid bilayer and adsorbed macroions.

Electronic Structure of Nanoparticles from First Principles. The ability to control properties of nanomaterials via size, shape, composition, surface structure, and self-assembly has opened new degrees of freedom inaccessible in conventional device design. At the same time, computational studies of nanostructures have become an attractive alternative to actual experiments, since the ability to explore the vast set of all possible configurations experimentally is limited. In recent years, advances in ab initio electronic structure techniques, such as Density Functional Theory, combined with new computational capabilities have enabled accurate calculations for atomistic models of nanoparticles. The results of these studies often serve as a unique source of insight into nanomaterial properties. We study properties of photoexcited semiconductor nanoparticles, such as quantum dots, nanowires, nanofilms, and carbon nanotubes. This requires description of electrons, photons, and atomic vibrations (phonons), all of which are interacting quantum mechanical particles. In our work methods of modern quantum field theory, which have been mostly used in theoretical nuclear and particle physics, are combined with advanced computational electronic structure capabilities.

Materials Theory and Design. The key, technology-enabling materials have historically often been discovered through intuition-driven trial-and-error experiments or through lucky accidents. Moving a material after initial discovery to the market ,can take 20 or more years. Our research is focused on designing and creating new materials with tailored properties, aiming to significantly accelerate the pace of discovery and deployment of advanced material systems. We use quantum mechanical first-principles methods of computational electronic-structure and defect theory, which have provided extremely powerful tools for predicting the electronic, structural, and defect properties of materials. We seek to understand the physical properties of condensed matter and materials, identify the rational structure-property relationships, and discover new materials for experimental realization. Our research covers a broad range of material classes, including but not limited to, complex oxides and their interfaces for next-generation electronics, 2D flexible electronics, photovoltaic materials, transparent conductors, heterogeneous catalysts, and batteries and super-capacitors. Yu.

Physics Education Research. We use theories and frameworks drawn from a variety of research areas, including cognitive science and science education as well as disciplined-based education research (e.g., physics and mathematics). Recent investigations have employed dual-process theories of reasoning and decision-making, analysis based on student difficulties, epistemic games, symbolic forms, the resource framework, and gesture analysis and embodied cognition. These frameworks serve as analytical lenses through which we may gain insight into student thinking. In some cases, the knowledge generated is used to guide the development of instructional approaches as well as student-centered instructional resources.

Experimental

Biophysics of Influenza Virus. Influenza virus continues to cause significant illness in humans. Development of new vaccines takes time, and many of the circulating strains are resistant to available drugs. New strategies for identifying anti-viral targets are needed. The viral glycoprotein hemagglutinin (HA) catalyzes membrane fusion, which is crucial for viral entry, and the clustering of HA is necessary for fusion to occur. We recently discovered an association between HA and several host cell actin binding proteins (ABPs) and actin itself in the absence of other viral components. However, the mechanism for this interaction is unknown. We are using FPALM to examine the nanoscale interactions between HA and the actin cytoskeleton under perturbations of HA, lipid microenvironment, and cell signaling. Results obtained will help determine the mechanism for influenza interactions with host cell actin, improve understanding of membrane cell biology, and identify new host cell targets for anti-viral therapies. Samuel Hess.

Hyperspectral Remote Sensing Physics. We have pioneered the development of aircraft- and spacecraft-based imaging Fourier transform spectrometers for a wide range of remote sensing applications. Current research is focused on development of tomographic hyperspectral systems, and on application of hyperspectral remote sensing to the transportation infrastructure, particularly applications involving Unmanned Aircraft Systems (UAS). C. Hess, Samuel Hess.

Liquid Crystals and Complex Fluids. Static and dynamic light scattering in liquid crystals and complex fluids, phase transitions. McClymer.

Physics and other Science Education. Physics Education Research. We investigate the learning and teaching of physics, as well as related topics, from a disciplinary perspective. These include empirical studies of conceptual understanding and student reasoning approaches, development and assessment of instructional materials, identification of both specific student difficulties and productive student resources while learning physics, teacher knowledge of student thinking about physics and physical science, and student metacognitive and reasoning skills in a variety of instructional environments, including upper-division laboratories. One emphasis of our research group is a focus at the upper division and in interdisciplinary studies, including the use and understanding of mathematics in physics as well as the teaching and learning of electronics in both physics and engineering. Another emphasis is the study of K-12 teachers, their knowledge of content and students' ideas, and their use of formative assessment during classroom interactions with students. Data come from free-response written items, surveys, individual and multi-subject interviews, and classroom video. Stetzer, Thompson, Wittmann.

Super-Resolution Microscopy. Diffraction limits resolution in optical microscopy, but much of biology occurs at the molecular level. The development of localization-based super-resolution microscopy has broken the diffraction limit, resulting in a Nobel Prize in Chemistry in 2014. Our invention, fluorescence photoactivation localization microscopy (FPALM; S.T. Hess et al. Biophysical Journal, 2006) uses a combination of photophysics and fluorescence to sequentially activate sparse subsets of individual molecules (initially in a dark state), image them, determine their positions (localization), convert them back to a dark state, and repeat. Recent development of a combined super-resolution imaging and single molecule spectroscopy instrument (Mlodzianoski et al., PLoS One, 2016) has enabled us to measure emission spectra from individual fluorescent particles while also localizing their positions, to distinguish three different fluorescent proteins within a cell, and to observe changes in the emission spectrum of a single molecule over time. This capability has led to the discovery of spectral wandering in a variety of photoactivatable fluorescent proteins and organic fluorophores we have examined, and suggests a host of new super-resolution imaging methodologies based on changes in single molecule emission spectra. Samuel Hess.

Thin Film and Sensor Technology. A variety of thin film materials (metal alloys, oxides, borides, nitrides, and oxynitrides) are being developed for application as thin film components in chemical, biological, and physical sensors and MEMS devices. Film synthesis is being carried out using e-beam evaporation, magnetron sputtering, plasma-assisted epitaxy, atomic layer deposition, and other methods to yield thin film nanocomposite structures and novel multilayer films. Film properties are characterized including nanostructure, nanomorphology, chemical composition, electrical response, chemical reactivity, and friction, hardness and wear to optimize the performance of materials and devices. Recent interests focus on thin film sensor materials that can operate in harsh environments up to 1500oC and oxidizing and reducing gases up to 600 psi. Lad.

View additional information about this department at www.gradschoolshopper.com. Check out the "Why Choose Us?" section, find out more about the department's culture and get links to social media networks.

UNIVERSITY OF MARYLAND

DEPARTMENT OF ASTRONOMY

College Park, Maryland 20742-2421
http://www.astro.umd.edu

General University Information
President: Wallace D. Loh
Dean of Graduate School: Dr. Steve Fetter
University website: https://www.umd.edu/
School Type: Public
Setting: Suburban
Total Faculty: 4,610
Total Graduate Faculty: 2,052
Total number of Students: 40,521
Total number of Graduate Students: 10,653

Department Information
Department Chairman: Prof. Andrew Harris, Chair
Department Contact: Ms. MaryAnn Phillips, Coordinator
  Total full-time faculty: 117
  Total number of full-time equivalent positions: 15
  Full-Time Graduate Students: 42
  Female Full-Time Graduate Students: 17
  First-Year Graduate Students: 10
  Female First-Year Students: 2
  Total Post Doctorates: 21

Department Address
PSC 1113
College Park, MD 20742-2421
Phone: (301) 405-1505
Fax: (301) 314-9067
E-mail: astr-grad@astro.umd.edu
Website: http://www.astro.umd.edu

ADMISSIONS

Admission Contact Information
Address admission inquiries to: Graduate Entrance Committee,
  c/o MaryAnn Phillips, Dept. of Astronomy, University of
  Maryland, College Park, MD 20742-2421
Phone: (301) 405-1505
E-mail: astr-grad@deans.umd.edu
Admissions website: http://www.astro.umd.edu/graduate/
  admissions.html

Application deadlines
Fall admission:
U.S. students: December 15   *Int'l. students*: December 15

Application fee
U.S. students: $75   *Int'l. students*: $75
Applicants are strongly encouraged to have all their materials
submitted by December 15, when the Admissions Committee
begins considering applications. Applications received after
that date may be considered if openings remain. Also, note
that the Department of Astronomy accepts applications for
the Ph.D. program only. (Admitted students typically receive
an M.S. degree after their second year.)

Admissions information
For Fall of 2018:
  Number of applicants: 151
  Number admitted: 17

  Number enrolled: 10

Admission requirements
Bachelor's degree requirements: An undergraduate degree in a
related field (normally Astronomy or Physics) is required.
Minimum undergraduate GPA: 3.0

GRE requirements
The GRE is required.
Please contact astr-grad@deans.umd.edu to discuss exceptions.

Subjective GRE requirements
The Subjective GRE is required.
Please contact astr-grad@deans.umd.edu to discuss exceptions.

TOEFL requirements
The TOEFL exam is required for students from non-English-
speaking countries.
  PBT score: 575
  iBT score: 84
Students with low scores may be required by the Graduate School
to enroll in a language program. For details and the most current information, see https://gradschool.umd.edu/admissions/
english-language-proficiency-requirements.

Other admissions information
Additional requirements: The Department of Astronomy eval-
uates applicants on their course grades, GRE scores, personal
statements, research experience, and letters of recommendation.
  Students from non-English speaking countries are required to
demonstrate proficiency in English via the TOEFL or IELTS
exams.
Undergraduate preparation assumed: Students who enter the
graduate program are normally expected to have strong backgrounds in astronomy, physics, and mathematics. A student
with deficiencies in one of these areas may be admitted but
will be expected to remedy such deficiencies as soon as possible.

TUITION
Tuition year 2018–19:
Tuition for in-state residents
  Full-time students: $717 per credit
Tuition for out-of-state residents
  Full-time students: $1,548 per credit
The Department guarantees funding (with tuition waivers) for
a minimum of 6 years, assuming adequate progress toward
the degree. Students in teaching or research assistant positions
or on full fellowships receive 10 credits of tuition remission
per semester, which covers the normal courseload.
Credit hours per semester to be considered full-time: 8
Deferred tuition plan: No
Health insurance: Yes, Varies; 80% subsidized.
Other academic fees: Semester fees are listed at https://
bursar.umd.edu/Tuitionfees.html. (Click on 'Graduate Students'.)
Academic term: Semester
Number of first-year students who received full tuition waivers: 10

Teaching Assistants, Research Assistants, and Fellowships

Number of first-year
Teaching Assistants: 10
Average stipend per academic year
Teaching Assistant: $29,000
Research Assistant: $30,000
Fellowship student: $35,000

The listed values are 12-month stipends. TA/RA stipends rise from $28k to $31.6k as students progress through the program. The stipends also increase when the university receives COLAs or merit raises.

FINANCIAL AID

Loans

Loans are not available for U.S. students.
Loans are not available for international students.
GAPSFAS application required: No
FAFSA application required: No

For further information

Address financial aid inquiries to: Ms. MaryAnn Phillips, Dept. of Astronomy, University of Maryland, College Park, MD 20742-2421.
Phone: (301) 405-1505
E-mail: astr-grad@deans.umd.edu
Financial aid website: https://www.financialaid.umd.edu/

HOUSING

Availability of on-campus housing

Single students: No
Married students: No

For further information

Address housing inquiries to: Off-Campus Housing, Department of Resident Life, University of Maryland, College Park, MD 20742.
Phone: (301) 314-3645
E-mail: och@umd.edu
Housing aid website: http://www.och.umd.edu/och/InfoForHS-GenInfo.aspx

Table A—Faculty, Enrollments, and Degrees Granted

Research Specialty	2018–19 Faculty	Enrollment Fall 2018 Master's	Enrollment Fall 2018 Doctorate	Number of Degrees Granted 2017–18 (2013–18) Master's	Number of Degrees Granted 2017–18 (2013–18) Terminal Master's	Number of Degrees Granted 2017–18 (2013–18) Doctorate
Astronomy	18	–	39	5(28)	–(3)	4(30)
Total	18	–	39	5(28)	–(3)	4(30)
Full-time Grad. Stud.	–	–	39	–	–	–
First-year Grad. Stud.	–	–	10	–	–	–

GRADUATE DEGREE REQUIREMENTS

Master's: Students must complete 30 credits (including at least six graduate Astronomy courses) with a minimum GPA of 3.0. A 2nd-year research project with a written report is also required.

Doctorate: Students must complete six graduate Astronomy courses and two more graduate courses in Astronomy or supporting areas (normally during the first two years). A minimum GPA of 3.0 is required. Students also complete a research project (normally in the 2nd year) and pass a thesis proposal defense (normally in the 3rd year) prior to admission to candidacy. After admission to candidacy, students must com-plete a minimum of 12 credits of doctoral research, a dissertation, and pass a dissertation defense. (Admission to candidacy must occur within four years of admission to the program, and the remaining requirements must be completed no less than one or more than four years after admission to candidacy.).

SPECIAL EQUIPMENT, FACILITIES, OR PROGRAMS

Graduate students observe with some of the largest telescopes in the United States and around the world, as well as a wide range of space telescopes covering the electromagnetic spectrum from gamma-rays to the sub-millimeter. The Department has guaranteed access to the 4.3-meter Discovery Channel Telescope through a partnership with Lowell Observatory. We have joined Caltech and other partners in the Zwicky Transient Facility, a time-domain survey at Palomar Observatory for studying rare and exotic transient phenomena. Our planetary science team is heavily involved with space missions visiting solar system bodies, such as NASA's Deep Impact and Rosetta missions to study comets. Complementing its observational program, the Department has a strong theory group, and there is also an important emphasis on the design and building of powerful new instruments.

An extensive department network provides seamless access to software and hardware on a variety of UNIX and LINUX platforms. The computational astrophysics group maintains and upgrades a cluster for computation-intensive science projects. The department also has privileged access to three larger university clusters maintained by the university, including the world-class 'DeepThought2' and 'MARCC/Bluecrab,' which have been invaluable to our students in completing computationally intensive thesis projects. Finally, the department has a new visualization laboratory for state-of-the-art simulations and displays of large data sets.

Many of our students conduct cutting-edge research and instrumentation projects with distinguished scientists at the nearby NASA Goddard Space Flight Center. The university's scientific partnership with Goddard has been further strengthened via the creation of the Joint Space Science Institute (JSI), which supports collaboration between the Departments of Astronomy and Physics and Goddard scientists on topics such as black hole physics, high-energy astrophysics, and cosmology.

The Department has established a partnership with Pontificia Universidad Catolica de Chile (PUC), one of the top two institutions for astronomy in Chile. UMD and PUC signed an agreement that enables astronomy graduate students at both institutions to participate in a joint Ph.D. program starting in their third year. These students split their time between both locations and conduct their thesis research under the supervision of UMD and PUC co-advisors. UMD students gain improved access to Chilean observatories, which include many of the best telescopes in the world.

The department is located in two adjoining buildings, including the new Physical Sciences Complex (PSC). The PSC is an architectural masterpiece, and all 1st and 2nd year graduate students have windowed offices there.

Table B—Separately Budgeted Research Expenditures by Source of Support

Source of Support	Departmental Research	Physics-related Research Outside Department
Federal government	$30,200,000	
State/local government		
Non-profit organizations		
Business and industry		
Other		
Total	$30,200,000	

Table C—Separately Budgeted Research Expenditures by Research Specialty

Research Specialty	No. of Grants	Expenditures ($)
Astronomy	180	$30,200,000
Total	180	$30,200,000

FACULTY

Professor

Bolatto, Alberto D., Ph.D., Boston University, 2000. *Astronomy*. Extragalactic astronomy; IR and radio astronomy.

Deming, L. Drake, Ph.D., University of Illinois, 1976. *Astronomy, Planetary Science*. Extrasolar planets; supernovae.

Hamilton, Douglas P., Ph.D., Cornell University, 1994. *Astrophysics, Planetary Science*. Solar system dynamics; solar system origins.

Harris, Andrew I., Ph.D., University of California, Berkeley, 1986. Department Chair. *Astronomy*. Extragalactic astrophysics; radio astronomy; instrumentation.

Miller, M. Coleman, Ph.D., California Institute of Technology, 1990. Graduate Director. *Astrophysics, Relativity & Gravitation*. Theoretical modeling of neutron stars and black holes; gravitational lensing.

Mundy, Lee G., Ph.D., University of Texas, 1984. Director, Laboratory for Millimeter-wave Astronomy; Director, Center for Research and Exploration in Space Science and Technology. *Astronomy*. Millimeter-wave and IR astronomy; star and planet formation; interstellar matter; astrobiology.

Mushotzky, Richard, Ph.D., University of California, San Diego, 1976. *Astronomy, High Energy Physics*. High-energy astrophysics; X-ray astronomy; extragalactic astronomy.

Papadopoulos, Konstantinos, Ph.D., University of Maryland, 1968. *Atmosphere, Space Physics, Cosmic Rays*. Space plasma physics; Earth's radiation belts.

Richardson, Derek, Ph.D., University of Cambridge, 1994. *Astrophysics, Computational Physics, Planetary Science*. Asteroid evolution; granular dynamics; computational astrophysics.

Sunshine, Jessica, Ph.D., University of California, San Diego, 1993. *Astronomy, Planetary Science*. Comets; asteroids; space missions.

Veilleux, Sylvain, Ph.D., University of California, Santa Cruz, 1989. Director, Discovery Channel Telescope Partnership. *Astronomy*. Extragalactic astronomy; AGNs; formation and evolution of galaxies.

Vogel, Stuart, Ph.D., University of California, Berkeley, 1983. *Astronomy*. Millimeter-wave astronomy; interstellar medium; extragalactic astronomy.

Associate Professor

Ricotti, Massimo, Ph.D., University of Colorado, 2001. *Astrophysics, Computational Physics, Cosmology & String Theory*. Theoretical cosmology; galaxy formation; computational astrophysics.

Assistant Professor

Gezari, Suvi, Ph.D., Columbia University, 2005. *Astronomy*. Time domain astrophysics; supermassive black holes and AGNs; supernovae.

Kempton, Eliza, Ph.D., Harvard University, 2009. *Astrophysics, Planetary Science*. Extrasolar planets.

Emeritus

Earl, James A., Ph.D., Massachusetts Institute of Technology, 1957. *Atmosphere, Space Physics, Cosmic Rays*. Cosmic rays.

Harrington, J. Patrick, Ph.D., Ohio State University, 1967. *Astrophysics*. Planetary nebulae; interstellar matter; stellar atmospheres.

Leventhal, Marvin, Ph.D., Brown University, 1964. *Astronomy*. Gamma-ray astronomy.

DEPARTMENTAL RESEARCH SPECIALTIES AND STAFF

Theoretical

Atmospheric & Space Physics. Space plasma physics; terrestrial radiation belts. Papadopoulos.

Computational Astrophysics - Simulations of asteroid evolution. Richardson.

Computational Astrophysics - Simulations of cosmological halo evolution. Ricotti.

Cosmology and Galaxy Formation. Ricotti.

High Energy Astrophysics. Black holes; neutron stars; gravitational radiation. Miller.

Planetary Science. Solar system dynamics: rings, asteroids, collisions; solar system origins (Hamilton, Richardson); extrasolar planets (Kempton). Hamilton, Kempton, Richardson.

Relativity & Gravitation. Black hole astrophysics. Miller.

Experimental

Extragalactic Astronomy. Optical, infrared, radio, and X-ray observations. Active galactic nuclei; jets; time-domain astronomy; starbursts; star formation; galactic winds; intergalactic medium; galaxy clusters; dark matter; cosmology. Bolatto, Gezari, Mushotzky, Veilleux.

Millimeter-Wave Astronomy. Star formation; interstellar medium; galactic structure, dynamics, and evolution; protostellar disks; active galactic nuclei; instrumentation. Bolatto, Harris, Mundy, Vogel.

Planetary Science. Comets; asteroids; solar system space missions (Sunshine); extrasolar planets (Deming). Deming, Sunshine.

UNIVERSITY OF MARYLAND, BALTIMORE COUNTY

ATMOSPHERIC PHYSICS GRADUATE PROGRAM

Baltimore, Maryland 21250
http://physics.umbc.edu

General University Information
President: Freeman A. Hrabowski
Dean of Graduate School: Janet C. Rutledge
University website: http://www.umbc.edu
School Type: Public
Setting: Suburban
Total Faculty: 825
Total Graduate Faculty: 527
Total number of Students: 13,839
Total number of Graduate Students: 2,596

Department Information
Department Chairman: Prof. L. Michael Hayden, Chair
Department Contact: Jennifer Salmi, Business Services
Specialist
Total full-time faculty: 23
Total number of full-time equivalent positions: 23
Full-Time Graduate Students: 41
Female Full-Time Graduate Students: 0
First-Year Graduate Students: 12
Female First-Year Students: 1
Total Post Doctorates: 5

Department Address
1000 Hilltop Circle
Physics Building, Room 220
Baltimore, MD 21250
Phone: (410) 455-2513
Fax: (410) 455-1072
E-mail: jen.salmi@umbc.edu
Website: http://physics.umbc.edu

ADMISSIONS

Admission Contact Information
Address admission inquiries to: Dr. Laszlo Takacs, Graduate Admissions Coordinator, Deptartment of Physics
Phone: (410) 455-2513
E-mail: takacs@umbc.edu
Admissions website: http://physics.umbc.edu

Application deadlines
Fall admission:
U.S. students: January 1   *Int'l. students*: January 1
Spring admission:
U.S. students: November 1   *Int'l. students*: May 1

Application fee
U.S. students: $50   *Int'l. students*: $50

Admissions information
For Fall of 2017:
Number of applicants: 18
Number admitted: 8
Number enrolled: 3

Admission requirements
Bachelor's degree requirements: Bachelor's degree in Physics, Atmospheric Sciences, Chemistry, Math, Engineering, or related field is required.

Minimum undergraduate GPA: 3.0

GRE requirements
The GRE is required.
Quantitative score: 150

Subjective GRE requirements
The Subjective GRE is not required.

TOEFL requirements
The TOEFL exam is required for students from non-English-speaking countries.
PBT score: 550
iBT score: 90

Other admissions information
Additional requirements: Letters of recommendation, undergraduate transcripts, personal statement.
Undergraduate preparation assumed: Young and Freedman. University Physics; Reif, Thermal Physics; Marion, Newtonian Dynamics; Tippler and Llewellyn, Introduction to Modern Physics; Griffiths, Introduction to Electrodynamics.

TUITION

Tuition year 2016–17:
Tuition for in-state residents
Full-time students: $621 per credit
Tuition for out-of-state residents
Full-time students: $1,047 per credit
Credit hours per semester to be considered full-time: 9
Deferred tuition plan:
Health insurance: Available
Other academic fees: $132/credit.
Academic term: Semester
Number of first-year students who received full tuition waivers: 4

Teaching Assistants, Research Assistants, and Fellowships
Number of first-year
Teaching Assistants: 14
Average stipend per academic year
Teaching Assistant: $23,700
Research Assistant: $27,000
Fellowship student: $29,000

FINANCIAL AID

Application deadlines
Fall admission:
U.S. students: April 15   *Int'l. students*: April 15
Spring admission:
U.S. students: November 1

Loans
Loans are available for U.S. students.
Loans are available for international students.
GAPSFAS application required: No
FAFSA application required: No

For further information
Address financial aid inquiries to: Dr. Laszlo Takacs, Graduate Admissions Coordinator, Department of Physics.
Phone: (410) 4552513
E-mail: takacs@umbc.edu
Financial aid website: http://www.umbc.edu/financialaid/

HOUSING

Availability of on-campus housing
Single students: Yes
Married students: No

For further information
Address housing inquiries to: Office of Residential Life.
Housing aid website: http://www.umbc.edu/reslife/

Table A—Faculty, Enrollments, and Degrees Granted

Research Specialty	2016–17 Faculty	Enrollment Fall 2017 Master's	Enrollment Fall 2017 Doctorate	Number of Degrees Granted 2015–16 (2000–16) Master's	Terminal Master's	Doctorate
Atmospheric Physics	5	–	17	2(10)	2(9)	2(8)
Total	5	–	17	2(10)	2(9)	2(8)
Full-time Grad. Stud.	–	–	17	–	–	–
First-year Grad. Stud.	–	–	4	–	–	–

GRADUATE DEGREE REQUIREMENTS

Master's: The M.S. degree is designed to prepare the graduate for immediate entry into the workforce as a practicing professional or as an entry into a doctoral program. This degree program is designed to offer students maximum flexibility, with many of the course requirements being electives. The minimum requirement for the master's degree is a total of 30 credit hours, of which 18 credit hours must be taken at the 600 level or higher. Students are encouraged to choose the thesis option, although a non-thesis option is available. All students must pass two ATPH core courses: PHYS 621: Atmospheric Physics I and PHYS 622: Atmospheric Physics II with a minimum grade of "B-". Additional 600-level or higher credits may be specialized ATPH courses or general physics courses. The specialized ATPH courses include PHYS 721: Radiative Transfer and PHYS 731 Atmospheric Dynamics, PHYS 722: Remote Sensing of the Earth's Atmosphere; PHYS 627 Atmospheric Measurement; PHYS 732: Computational Fluid Dynamics; and PHYS 741: Inverse Methods and Data Analysis. The general physics courses include courses in the areas of Electromagnetism; Statistical Mechanics; Classical Mechanics; Quantum Mechanics; Mathematical Physics; Computational Physics and Optics. In addition, all students also are required to take PHYS 698: Physics Seminar for two semesters. In addition to the master's core curriculum, students selecting the thesis option must complete a further six credit hours of course work approved by a faculty advisor and six credit hours of PHYS 799: Master's Thesis Research. Approval of the graduate program director is required if the thesis research is not performed under the direction of a faculty member within the UMBC physics department. Students selecting the non-thesis option must complete a further 12 credit hours of lecture course work approved by a faculty advisor, write a scholarly paper as part of an elective course and pass a written comprehensive examination. At least six of these additional 12 credits will be courses offered by the physics department, unless approved by the graduate

program advisor in advance. The Qualifying Examination for ATPH students will be offered twice a year, one in late August and the other in January. The Qualifying Examination includes a written and an oral component and is designed to evaluate the student's level of knowledge in the areas taught in the first year of the ATPH physics program as well as the student's abilities to perform research.

Doctorate: The minimum requirement for the Ph.D. is 46 credit hours, with a minimum of 27 credit hours of lecture courses at the 600-level or higher and 12 credit hours of doctoral research (PHYS 899). The graduate program director must approve all coursework. All students must pass two ATPH core courses: PHYS 621: Atmospheric Physics I and PHYS 622: Atmospheric Physics II with a minimum grade of "B-". All students must also take the PHYS 640: Computational Physics. Additional 600-level or higher credits may be specialized ATPH courses or general physics courses. The specialized ATPH courses include PHYS 721: Radiative Transfer and PHYS 731 Atmospheric Dynamics, PHYS 722: Remote Sensing of the Earth's Atmosphere; PHYS 627 Atmospheric Measurement; PHYS 732: Computational Fluid Dynamics; and PHYS 741: Inverse Methods and Data Analysis. The general physics courses include courses in the areas of Electromagnetism; Statistical Mechanics; Classical Mechanics; Quantum Mechanics; Mathematical Physics and Optics. In addition, all students also are required to take PHYS 698: Physics Seminar for three semesters; PHYS 690: Professional Techniques in Physics; and a minimum of 18 credit hours of PHYS 899: Doctoral Thesis Research. To be admitted to candidacy for the doctoral degree, students first must complete the Ph.D. core curriculum (PHYS621 & PHYS622) with a minimum grade of "B-" and then pass the ATPH qualifying examination. The qualifying examination for ATPH students will be offered twice a year, one in late August and the other in January. The examination includes a written and an oral component and is designed to evaluate the student's level of knowledge in the areas taught in the first year of the ATPH physics program as well as the student's abilities to perform research. Students must pass the entire qualifying examination by the beginning of their 4th semester. Students who fail to do so will not be admitted to candidacy for the Ph.D. degree. A prospective doctoral student must select a faculty advisor to supervise the dissertation research. Usually dissertation research is performed under the direction of a tenure-track faculty member of the UMBC department of physics. After selecting an advisor, students should begin acquiring the necessary background knowledge and skills to conduct research and develop a research plan. By the beginning of the 3rd year, a prospective doctoral student, in consultation with their advisor, should form a preliminary committee consisting of the advisor and two other faculty members from the UMBC Department of Physics. At least two of the members of this committee must be tenure-track faculty. The preliminary committee is charged with determining whether the student should be admitted to candidacy for the doctoral degree. A recommendation to this effect must be made to the full physics faculty by the start of the 4th year. The full faculty then will vote whether to recommend to the Graduate School that the student be admitted to candidacy for the doctoral degree. Immediately after it has been formed, the preliminary committee will meet with the student to discuss the proposed research project and progress to date. The committee will inform the student of any actions he or she must perform satisfactorily for the committee to make a positive recommendation to the faculty. In formulating its recommendation, the committee may gather and consider any relevant information concerning the student's potential for performing research at the doctoral level. This information should include, but is not limited to, the student's overall graduate record, a written research proposal and an oral presentation of the proposed research project. After admission to candidacy and completion of the research, the student will be required to write and defend a dissertation before a committee constituted in accordance with Graduate School regulations. This research should be of a quality suitable for publication in a refereed physics journal. The chair of this committee must be a regular member of the graduate faculty and a tenure-track faculty member in the Department of Physics.

Thesis: Thesis may be written in absentia.

SPECIAL EQUIPMENT, FACILITIES, OR PROGRAMS

There are close relationships between UMBC and several other research institutions in the Baltimore-Washington area. Formal cooperative agreements are in place between the UMBC and NASA Goddard Space Flight Center (GSFC) in the form of the Joint Center for Earth Systems and Technology (JCET) http://jcet. umbc.edu, the Center for Research and Exploration in Space Science and Technology (CRESST) http://cresst.umd.edu/, and the Goddard Planetary Heliophysics Institute (GPHI) http://gphi. umbc.edu. UMBC also hosts the Center for Advanced Studies in Photonics Research (CASPR) http://www.umbc.edu/caspr/.

Table B—Separately Budgeted Research Expenditures by Source of Support

Source of Support	Departmental Research	Physics-related Research Outside Department
Federal government	$4,453,938	$256,851
State/local government		
Non-profit organizations		
Business and industry		
Other		
Total	$4,453,938	$256,851

Table C—Separately Budgeted Research Expenditures by Research Specialty

Research Specialty	No. of Grants	Expenditures ($)
Atmospheric Physics	19	$2,322,350
Total	19	$2,322,350

FACULTY

Professor

Demoz, Belay, Ph.D., University of Nevada-Reno, 1992. *Climate/Atmospheric Science.* Atmospheric Physics and Chemistry, Meteorological Observations.

Franson, James D., Ph.D., California Institute of Technology, 1977. Quantum optics and quantum computing.

Gougousi, Theodosia, Ph.D., University of Pittsburg, 1996. Nanoscience, interfaces.

Hayden, L. Michael, Ph.D., University of California, Davis, 1987. Department Chair. Nonlinear optical properties of polymers; electro-optic techniques; photonic devices.

Johnson, Anthony, Ph.D., City College of New York, 1981. *Optics.* Ultra-fast optical and optoelectronic phenomena.

Martins, Vanderlei J., Ph.D., University of Sao Paulo, 1999. Aerosol and Cloud Physics; radiative transfer; optics, satellite remote sensing; instrumentation development for laboratory, field, aircraft, and satellite measurements.

Pittman, Thomas, Ph.D., University of Maryland, Baltimore County, 1996. Graduate Program Director – Physics. Quantum optics and quantum computing.

Rous, Philip, Ph.D., Imperial College of Science and Technology, University of London, 1986. Provost and Senior Vice President for Academic Affairs. *Condensed Matter Physics.*

Shih, Yanhua, Ph.D., University of Maryland, 1987. Quantum optics; laser physics; nonlinear optics.

Turner, T. Jane, Ph.D., University of Leicester, 1988. Extragalactic astrophysics; x-ray astronomy.

Associate Professor

Georganopoulos, Markos, Ph.D., University of Thessaloniki, 1989. Broad-band synchrotron emission from relativistic flows in active galaxies, galactic microquasars and gamma-ray bursts.

George, Ian M., Ph.D., University of Leicester, 1988. Director of the Center for Space Science and Technology. Astrophysics; x-ray astronomy.

Henriksen, Mark J., Ph.D., University of Maryland, 1986. Astrophysics; X-ray astronomy.

Hoban, Susan, Ph.D., University of Maryland, College Park, 1989. Scientific information systems; digital library technologies and information technologies for science, technology, engineering and mathematics (STEM) education.

Kramer, Ivan, Ph.D., University of California, Berkeley, 1967. Mathematical modeling.

Sparling, Lynn C., University of Texas, Austin, 1987. Atmospheric physics; modeling.

Takacs, Laszlo, Ph.D., Eotvos University, 1978. Director of UMBC Nano-Imaging Center, Chair of Graduate Admissions Committee. Amorphous and metastable crystalline alloys; energy-dispersive X-ray diffraction; magnetic susceptibility.

Worchesky, Terrance L., Ph.D., Georgetown University, 1984. Associate Departmental Chair Undergraduate Program Director. Optical properties of semiconductors; photonics.

Zhang, Zhibo, Ph.D., Texas A&M University, 2008. Graduate Program Director–Atmospheric Physics. *Climate/Atmospheric Science.* Satellite-based remote sensing; cloud and aerosol micro-physical and optical properties; radiative transfer; aerosol-cloud-precipitation-radiation interactions; atmospheric physics.

Assistant Professor

Deffner, Sebastian, Ph.D., University of Augsburg, 2011. *Quantum Foundations, Theoretical Physics.* My research concerns all topics of Quantum Thermodynamics. As a theoretical physicist, I employ tools from Statistical Physics, Open Quantum Dynamics, Quantum Information Theory, Quantum Optics, Condensed Matter Theory and Optimal Control Theory to investigate the nonequilibrium properties of nanosystems operating far from thermal equilibrium.

Kestner, Jason, Ph.D., University of Michigan, 2009. Condensed matter theory, quantum information theory.

Meyer, Eileen, Ph.D., Rice University, 2012. *Astrophysics.*

Pelton, Matthew, Ph.D., Stanford University, 2002.

Zhai, Pengwang, Ph.D., Texa A&M University, 2006. *Climate/Atmospheric Science.* Light scattering; radiative transfer; remote sensing; aerosols and clouds.

Emeritus

Hoff, Raymond M., Ph.D., Simon Fraser University, 1975. Atmospheric physics; lidar, air quality, satellite remote sensing.

Melfi, Harvey, Ph.D., College of William and Mary, 1970. Atmospheric lidar; remote sensing.

Rasera, Robert L., Ph.D., Purdue University, 1965. Perturbed gamma-ray angular correlation spectroscopy.

Reno, Robert C., Ph.D., Brandeis University, 1970. Hyperfine interactions in solids; electron microscopy; neutron diffraction measurement.

Rubin, Morton H., Ph.D., Princeton University, 1964. Theoretical physics; quantum optics.

Research Professor

Remer, Lorraine A., Ph.D., University of California, Davis, 1991. *Climate/Atmospheric Science.* Aerosol and cloud remote sensing. Cloud-aerosol-precipitation-climate interactions.

Strow, L. Larrabee, Ph.D., University of Maryland, 1981. High-resolution infrared molecular spectroscopy; atmospheric radiative transfer.

Research Associate Professor

Davis, David, Ph.D., University of Maryland, College Park, 1994. Galaxy clusters, X-ray astronomy.

Kundu, Prasun, Ph.D., University of Rochester, 1981. Satellite and ground-based remote sensing.

McCann, Kevin J., Ph.D., Georgia Institute of Technology, 1974. Lidar and atmospheric aerosols.

Olson, William, Ph.D., University of Wisconsin-Madison, 1987. Remote sensing of precipitation.

Varnai, Tamas, Ph.D., McGill University, 1996. Cloud physics and radiation transfer.

Research Assistant Professor

De Souza-Machado, Sergio, Ph.D., University of Maryland, College Park, 1996. Infrared remote sensing, radiation transfer, spectroscopy, plasma physics.

Johnson, Benjamin, Ph.D., University of Wisconsin-Madison, 2007. *Climate/Atmospheric Science.* Precipitation cloud modeling, radiative transfer, and remote sensing.

Yuan, Tianle, Ph.D., University of Maryland College Park, 2008. *Climate/Atmospheric Science.* Aerosol-cloud-precipitation interactions; remote sensing.

Lecturer

Anderson, Eric, Ph.D., Arizona State University, 1993. Physics education.

DEPARTMENTAL RESEARCH SPECIALTIES AND STAFF

Theoretical

air quality. study the impact of atmospheric pollutions, such as ozone, aerosols and smoke on air quality and public health. Demoz, Remer, Sparling.

Atmospheric Physics. Atmospheric dynamics; hurricane; radiative transfer; aerosol-cloud-precipitation interactions; cloud physics; remote sensing. De Souza-Machado, Demoz, Hoff, Benjamin Johnson, Kundu, Martins, Melfi, Olson, Remer, Sparling, Strow, Varnai, Yuan, Zhai, Zhang.

Climate Change/Global Warming. Study the physics underlying climate change and global warming. De Souza-Machado, Demoz, Hoban, Hoff, Martins, Remer, Sparling, Strow, Yuan, Zhai, Zhang.

Remote Sensing. Satellite-based remote sensing of aerosol and cloud properties, ocean color, temperature and water vapor and trace gases. De Souza-Machado, Demoz, Martins, Strow, Varnai, Yuan, Zhai, Zhang.

Experimental

Atmospheric Physics. Aerosol and cloud properties; atmospheric dynamics; remote sensing measurements; LIDAR; aerosol-cloud-precipitation interactions; air pollution; atmospheric radiative transfer; optics instrumentation. De Souza-Machado, Demoz, Hoff, Benjamin Johnson, Kundu, Martins, Remer, Sparling, Strow, Varnai, Yuan, Zhang.

Remote Sensing Instrumentation. Develop in situ, airborne, ground-based and satellite-based instruments for observing atmosphere. Demoz, Hoff, Strow, Zhai, Zhang.

View additional information about this department at www.gradschoolshopper.com. Check out the "Why Choose Us?" section, find out more about the department's culture and get links to social media networks.

UNIVERSITY OF MARYLAND, BALTIMORE COUNTY

PHYSICS GRADUATE PROGRAM

Baltimore, Maryland 21250
http://physics.umbc.edu/

General University Information
President: Freeman A. Hrabowski
Dean of Graduate School: Janet C. Rutledge
University website: http://www.umbc.edu/
School Type: Public
Setting: Suburban
Total Faculty: 838
Total Graduate Faculty: 546
Total number of Students: 13,662
Total number of Graduate Students: 2,428

Department Information
Department Chairman: Prof. L. Michael Hayden, Chair
Department Contact: Jennifer Salmi, Programs Specialist
 Total full-time faculty: 22
 Total number of full-time equivalent positions: 22
 Full-Time Graduate Students: 32
 Female Full-Time Graduate Students: 6
 First-Year Graduate Students: 9
 Female First-Year Students: 2
 Total Post Doctorates: 5

ADMISSIONS

Admission Contact Information
Address admission inquiries to: Dr. Laszlo Takacs, Graduate Admissions Coordinator, Department of Physics
Phone: (410) 455-2513
E-mail: takacs@umbc.edu
Admissions website: http://physics.umbc.edu/

Application deadlines
Fall admission:
U.S. students: January 1   *Int'l. students*: January 1

Application fee
U.S. students: $50   *Int'l. students*: $50

Admissions information
For Fall of 2018:
 Number of applicants: 59
 Number admitted: 17
 Number enrolled: 9

Admission requirements
Bachelor's degree requirements: Bachelor's degree in Physics, Chemistry, Math, or Engineering is required.
Minimum undergraduate GPA: 3.0

GRE requirements
The GRE is required.

Subjective GRE requirements
The Subjective GRE is recommended.

TOEFL requirements
The TOEFL exam is required for students from non-English-speaking countries.
 PBT score: 550
 iBT score: 80

Other admissions information
Additional requirements: Letters of recommendation, undergraduate transcripts, and personal statement.

Undergraduate preparation assumed: Thermal and Statistical Physics (Mandl); Classical Mechanics (Taylor); Modern Physics (Thornton & Rex); Introduction to Electrodynamics (Griffiths); Introduction to Quantum Mechanics (Griffiths).

TUITION
Tuition year 2018–19:
Tuition for in-state residents
 Full-time students: $640 per credit
Tuition for out-of-state residents
 Full-time students: $1,099 per credit
Credit hours per semester to be considered full-time: 9
Deferred tuition plan: No
Health insurance: Available
Other academic fees: $136/credit.
Academic term: Semester
Number of first-year students who received full tuition waivers: 9

Teaching Assistants, Research Assistants, and Fellowships
 Number of first-year
 Teaching Assistants: 9
 Average stipend per academic year
 Teaching Assistant: $26,000
 Research Assistant: $28,000
 Fellowship student: $31,000

FINANCIAL AID

Application deadlines
Fall admission:
U.S. students: April 15   *Int'l. students*: April 15

Loans
Loans are available for U.S. students.
Loans are available for international students.
GAPSFAS application required: No
FAFSA application required: No

For further information
Address financial aid inquiries to: Dr. Laszlo Takacs, Graduate Admissions Coordinator, Department of Physics.
Phone: (410)-455-2513
E-mail: takacs@umbc.edu
Financial aid website: http://www.umbc.edu/financialaid/

HOUSING

Availability of on-campus housing
 Single students: Yes
 Married students: No

For further information
Address housing inquiries to: Office of Residential Life.
Housing aid website: http://www.umbc.edu/reslife/

Table A—Faculty, Enrollments, and Degrees Granted

Research Specialty	2018–19 Faculty	Enrollment Fall 2018 Master's	Enrollment Fall 2018 Doctorate	Number of Degrees Granted 2017–18 (2013–2018) Master's	Number of Degrees Granted 2017–18 (2013–2018) Terminal Master's	Number of Degrees Granted 2017–18 (2013–2018) Doctorate
Astrophysics	5	–	7	1(3)	2(3)	1(7)
Atmospheric Physics	5	–	1	–	–	–
Condensed Matter Physics	7	–	14	2(5)	–(4)	1(8)
Quantum Optics and Quantum Information	5	–	10	1(5)	1(3)	–(7)
Total	**22**	**–**	**32**	**4(13)**	**3(10)**	**2(22)**
Full-time Grad. Stud.	–	–	31	–	–	–
First-year Grad. Stud.	–	–	9	–	–	–

GRADUATE DEGREE REQUIREMENTS

Master's: Completion of 30 credit hours of coursework, including required core courses in quantum mechanics and mathematical physics. Overall competence must be demonstrated by an oral thesis defense (thesis option) or a written comprehensive examination (non-thesis option). For thesis option, six hours of the required 30 credit hours are for thesis research.

Doctorate: Completion of a core curriculum consisting of quantum mechanics I & II, statistical mechanics, mathematical physics, classical mechanics, and electromagnetic theory I & II. In addition, students are required to take physics seminar, and a minimum of 3 graduate elective courses. Students are required to pass a written examination in order to qualify for candidacy for the Ph.D. degree. Upon completion of the doctoral research, students are required to write and defend a dissertation before a committee constituted in accordance with the graduate school regulations.

Thesis: Thesis may be written in absentia.

SPECIAL EQUIPMENT, FACILITIES, OR PROGRAMS

There are close working relationships between UMBC and several other research institutions in the Baltimore-Washington area. Formal cooperative agreements are in place between UMBC and the NASA Goddard Space Flight Center (GSFC) in the form of the Joint Center for Earth Systems Technology (JCET) [http://jcet.umbc.edu/] and the Center for Research and Exploration in Space Science and Technology (CRESST) [http://cresst.umd.edu/]. UMBC also hosts the Center for Advanced Studies in Photonics Research (CASPR) [http://www.umbc.edu/caspr/]. The Physics Department also houses the new state-of-the-art UMBC Nano Imaging Center (NIC) .

Table B—Separately Budgeted Research Expenditures by Source of Support

Source of Support	Departmental Research	Physics-related Research Outside Department
Federal government	$1,737,844	
State/local government		
Non-profit organizations		
Business and industry		
Other		
Total	**$1,737,844**	

Table C—Separately Budgeted Research Expenditures by Research Specialty

Research Specialty	No. of Grants	Expenditures ($)
Astrophysics	22	$621,139
Condensed Matter Physics	4	$383,392
Quantum Optics and Quantum Information	7	$733,313
Total	**33**	**$1,737,844**

FACULTY

Professor

Demoz, Belay, Ph.D., University of Nevada and DRI, 1992. Director, JCET. *Climate/Atmospheric Science.* Atmospheric physics and chemistry; meteorological observations.

Franson, James D., Ph.D., California Institute of Technology, 1977. Quantum optics and quantum computing.

Gougousi, Theodosia, Ph.D., University of Pittsburgh, 1996. Nanoscience; interfaces.

Hayden, L. Michael, Ph.D., University of California, Davis, 1987. Nonlinear optical properties of polymers; electro-optic techniques; photonic devices.

Johnson, Anthony M., Ph.D., City College of New York, 1981. Director, JCET. Nonlinear optics; ultrafast optics; optoelectronics; ultrashort pulse propagation.

Martins, Vanderlei, Ph.D., University of São Paolo, 1999. Radiative effects of biomass burning and bio-aerosols.

Pittman, Todd B., Ph.D., University of Maryland, Baltimore County, 1996. Quantum optics and quantum computing.

Shih, Yanhua, Ph.D., University of Maryland, 1987. Quantum optics; laser physics; nonlinear optics.

Turner, T. Jane, Ph.D., University of Leicester, 1988. Extragalactic astrophysics; x-ray astronomy.

Associate Professor

Georganopoulos, Markos, Ph.D., Boston University, 1999. Broad-band synchrotron emission from relativistic flows in active galaxies, galactic microquasars, and gamma-ray bursts.

George, Ian M., Ph.D., University of Leicester, 1988. Astrophysics; x-ray astronomy.

Henriksen, Mark J., Ph.D., University of Maryland, 1986. Astrophysics; X-ray astronomy.

Sparling, Lynn C., Ph.D., University of Texas, Austin, 1987. Atmospheric physics; modeling.

Takacs, Laszlo, Ph.D., Eotvos University, 1978. Amorphous and metastable crystalline alloys; energy-dispersive X-ray diffraction; magnetic susceptibility.

Worchesky, Terrance L., Ph.D., Georgetown University, 1984. Optical properties of semiconductors; photonics.

Zhang, Zhibo, Ph.D., Texas A&M University, 2008. Remote sensing; aerosol-cloud-precipitation interactions; atmospheric physics.

Assistant Professor

Ataca, Can, Ph.D., Bilkent University, 2012. Computational physics, nanophysics, condensed matter physics.

Deffner, Sebastian, Ph.D., University of Augsburg, 2011. Quantum thermodynamics, quantum information theory, condensed matter theory.

Kestner, Jason, Ph.D., University of Michigan, 2009. Condensed matter theory; quantum information theory.

Meyer, Eileen T., Ph.D., Rice University, 2012. *Astrophysics.* Galaxy formation; HST imaging.

Pelton, Matthew, Ph.D., Stanford, 2002. Optical studies of nanomaterials; nanophotonics.

Zhai, Pengwang, Ph.D., Texas A&M University, 2006. *Atmosphere, Space Physics, Cosmic Rays.* Atmospheric physics.

Emeritus

Hoff, Raymond M., Ph.D., Simon Fraser University, 1975. Atmospheric physics; LIDAR.

Kramer, Ivan, Ph.D., University of California, Berkeley, 1967. Mathematical modeling.

McCann, Kevin J., Ph.D., Georgia Institute of Technology, 1974. LIDAR and atmospheric aerosols.

Melfi, Harvey, Ph.D., College of William and Mary, 1970. Atmospheric LIDAR; remote sensing.

Reno, Robert C., Ph.D., Brandeis University, 1970. Hyperfine interactions in solids; electron microscopy; neutron diffraction measurement.

Rous, Philip J., Ph.D., Imperial College of Science and Technology, 1986. Theoretical physics: surfaces, interfaces, and nanostructures.

Rubin, Morton H., Ph.D., Princeton University, 1964. Theoretical physics; quantum optics.

Summers, Geoffrey P., Ph.D., University of Oxford, 1970. Radiation effects in semiconductors; defects in solids.

Wu, En-Shinn, Ph.D., Cornell, 1972. Optical studies of macromolecules.

Research Professor

Strow, L. Larrabee, Ph.D., University of Maryland, 1981. High-resolution infrared molecular spectroscopy; atmospheric radiative transfer.

Research Associate Professor

Peter, Kuchunov, Ph.D., University of Texas Health Science Center at San Antonio, 2001. MRI; quantitative imaging; imaging genetics.

Adjunct Professor

Fitelson, Michael, Ph.D., Pennsylvania State University, 1966. Advanced technologies.

Krotkov, Nickolay, Ph.D., Shirshov Institute, Russian Academy of Sciences, 1990. Atmospheric physics.

Kuchner, Marc, Ph.D., California Institute of Technology, 2000. Astrophysics.

Affiliate Professor

Remer, Lorraine, Ph.D., University of California, Davis, 1991. Climate change; remote sensing.

Affiliate Associate Professor

Davis, David, Ph.D., University of Maryland, College Park, 1994. Galaxy clusters; X-ray astronomy.

Hoban, Susan, Ph.D., University of Maryland, 1989. Planetary science; comets; dust in the solar system; STEM education.

Olson, William, Ph.D., University of Wisconsin-Madison, 1987. Remote sensing of precipitation.

Pottschmidt, Katja, Ph.D., Universitaet Tuebingen, 2002. High-energy astrophysics; accreting X-ray binary stars.

Varnai, Tamas, Ph.D., McGill University, 1996. Cloud physics and radiation transfer.

Yuan, Tianle, Ph.D., University of Maryland, College Park, 2008. Atmospheric and oceanic sciences.

Affiliate Assistant Professor

De Souza-Machado, Sergio, Ph.D., University of Maryland, College Park, 1996. Infrared remote sensing and radiation transfer.

Engel, Don, Ph.D., University of Pennsylvania, 2005. Computational physics; molecular biophysics; statistical artificial intelligence.

Johnson, Benjamin, Ph.D., University of Wisconsin-Madison, 2007. Cloud modeling, radiative transfer, cloud microphysics.

Lecturer

Anderson, Eric, Ph.D., Arizona State University, 1993. Physics education.

Cui, Lili, Ph.D., Kansas State University, 2006. Physics education.

Goolsby-Cole, Cody, Ph.D., University of Massachusetts, 2017. Physics education, theoretical physics.

DEPARTMENTAL RESEARCH SPECIALTIES AND STAFF

Theoretical

Astrophysics. High-energy astrophysics; active galactic nuclei; relativistic jets; quasars, X-ray astronomy. Davis, Georganopoulos, George, Henriksen, Hoban, Kuchner, Meyer, Pottschmidt, Turner.

Atmospheric Physics. De Souza-Machado, Demoz, Engel, Hoban, Benjamin Johnson, Martins, Olson, Remer, Sparling, Strow, Varnai, Yuan, Zhai, Zhang.

Condensed Matter Physics. Semiconductor quantum dots; cold atoms; theoretical physics. Ataca, Deffner, Kestner.

Quantum Optics and Quantum Information. Quantum foundations; entanglement; non-classical states; quantum imaging; photonic qubits; spin qubits; quantum information theory; quantum thermodynamics. . . Deffner, Franson, Kestner, Shih.

Experimental

Astrophysics. X-ray astronomy; active galaxies; extragalactic astrophysics. Davis, Georganopoulos, George, Henriksen, Meyer, Pottschmidt, Turner.

Atmospheric Physics. De Souza-Machado, Demoz, Hoff, Martins, Remer, Strow, Zhai, Zhang.

Condensed Matter Physics. Thin films; surfaces and interfaces; atomic layer deposition; polymer physics; mechanical alloying; semi-conductors; optical studies of nanomaterials. Gougousi, Hayden, Anthony Johnson, Pelton, Takacs, Worchesky.

Quantum Optics and Quantum Information. Photonic quantum information; quantum imaging; entanglement; single photon physics; quantum foundations. Franson, Pelton, Pittman, Shih.

BOSTON COLLEGE

DEPARTMENT OF PHYSICS

Chestnut Hill, Massachusetts 02467-3811
http://www.bc.edu/physics

General University Information
President: Fr. William P. Leahy, S.J.
Dean of Graduate School: Gregory Kalscheur, S.J.
University website: http://www.bc.edu
School Type: Private
Setting: Suburban
Total Faculty: 821
Total number of Students: 14,400
Total number of Graduate Students: 4,600

Department Information
Department Chairman: Prof. Michael J. Graf, Chair
Department Contact: Jane Carter, Associate Director,
   Administrative & Student Services
   Total full-time faculty: 17
   Total number of full-time equivalent positions: 24
   Full-Time Graduate Students: 46
   Female Full-Time Graduate Students: 9
   First-Year Graduate Students: 8
   Female First-Year Students: 3
   Total Post Doctorates: 5

Department Address
140 Commonwealth Avenue
Higgins 335
Chestnut Hill, MA 02467-3811
Phone: +1 617 552 3575
Fax: +1 617 552 8478
E-mail: physics@bc.edu
Website: http://www.bc.edu/physics

ADMISSIONS

Admission Contact Information
Address admission inquiries to: Admissions, Morrissey Graduate
   School of Arts and Sciences, Boston College, 140 Com-
   monwealth Avenue, Chestnut Hill, MA 02467
Phone: +1 617 552 3268
E-mail: gsasinfo@bc.edu
Admissions website: http://www.bc.edu/gsas

Application deadlines
Fall admission:
U.S. students: January 1   *Int'l. students*: January 1

Application fee
U.S. students: $75   *Int'l. students*: $75

Admissions information
For Fall of 2018:
   Number of applicants: 51
   Number admitted: 15
   Number enrolled: 8

Admission requirements
Bachelor's degree requirements: A bachelor's degree is required.

GRE requirements
The GRE is required.

Subjective GRE requirements
The Subjective GRE is required.

TOEFL requirements
The TOEFL exam is required for students from non-English-
speaking countries.

Other admissions information
Additional requirements: A statement of purpose, three letters
   of recommendation, and official transcripts are required.
Undergraduate preparation assumed: Reif, Fundamentals of Statistical and Thermal Physics; Lorrain and Corson, Electromagnetic Fields and Waves (2nd ed.); Symon, Mechanics;
   Rosenberg, The Solid State; Eisberg, Modern Physics.

TUITION

Tuition year 2018–19:
   Full-time students: per credit
Deferred tuition plan: No
Health insurance: Available
Academic term: Semester

Teaching Assistants, Research Assistants, and Fellowships
   Number of first-year
      Teaching Assistants: 8
   Average stipend per academic year
      Teaching Assistant: $30,000
      Research Assistant: $30,000

FINANCIAL AID

Loans
Loans are not available for U.S. students.
Loans are not available for international students.
GAPSFAS application required: No
FAFSA application required: No

For further information
Address financial aid inquiries to: Admissions, Morrissey Graduate College of Arts and Sciences.

HOUSING

Availability of on-campus housing
   Single students: No
   Married students: No

Table A—Faculty, Enrollments, and Degrees Granted

Research Specialty	2018–19 Faculty	Enrollment Fall 2018		Number of Degrees Granted 2017–18		
		Mas-ter's	Doc-torate	Mas-ter's	Terminal Master's	Doc-torate
Condensed Matter Physics	17	–	46	5	–	7
Total	17	–	46	–	8	45
Full-time Grad. Stud.	–	–	46	–	–	–
First-year Grad. Stud.	–	–	8	–	–	–

GRADUATE DEGREE REQUIREMENTS

Doctorate: For a doctorate degree, the following are required: (1) pass comprehensive exam, including general and special field; (2) thesis with oral defense; (3) course requirements, including advanced quantum mechanics, electromagnetic theory, and statistical physics; and (4) a distributional requirement of electives in four distinct areas of the graduate curriculum. One year of residency is required. There is no language requirement. All requirements must be completed within eight consecutive years.

SPECIAL EQUIPMENT, FACILITIES, OR PROGRAMS

The Physics Department has significant research facilities avaiable, including state-of-the-art materials characterization and micro/nanofabrication facilities, low-temperature/high magnetic field, metamaterial, nanophotonics, photovoltaics, STM, and thermoelectric and optical spectroscopy research laboratories.

In addition, the Physics Department has established ties to many outside facilities, including Los Alamos, Brookhaven, and Argonne National Laboratories, NASA, and the National High Magnetic Field Laboratory.

FACULTY

Chair Professor

Graf, Michael J., Ph.D., Brown University, 1987. Experimental condensed matter physics at low temperatures.

Professor

Bedell, Kevin S., Ph.D., Stony Brook University, 1979. *Condensed Matter Physics, Solid State Physics.* Theoretical condensed matter physics.

Broido, David A., Ph.D., University of California, San Diego, 1985. Theoretical condensed matter physics.

Di Bartolo, Baldassare, Ph.D., Massachusetts Institute of Technology, 1964. Solid state spectroscopy; flash photolysis of gases and liquids.

Kempa, Krzysztof, Ph.D., University of Wroclaw, 1980. Theoretical condensed matter physics.

Naughton, Michael J., Ph.D., Boston University, 1986. *Applied Physics, Biophysics, Computational Physics, Condensed Matter Physics, Electromagnetism, Energy Sources & Environment, Engineering Physics/Science, Low Temperature Physics, Materials Science, Metallurgy, Medical, Health Physics, Nano Science and Technology, Neuroscience/Neuro Physics, Optics, Solar Physics, Solid State Physics.*

Wang, Ziqiang, Ph.D., Columbia University, 1989. Theoretical condensed matter physics.

Associate Professor

Burch, Kenneth, Ph.D., UCSD, 2006. Spectroscopic studies of novel solids, interfaces and nano-materials. Materials of interest include: Topological Insulators, Unconventional Superconductors, Spin/Valleytronics, thermoelectrics and 2D atomic crystals.

Engelbrecht, Jan R., Ph.D., University of Illinois at Urbana-Champaign, 1993. Theoretical condensed matter physics; biological physics.

Opeil, Cyril P., Ph.D., Boston College, 2004. Experimental condensed matter physics.

Ran, Ying, Ph.D., Massachusetts Institute of Technology, 2007. Theoretical condensed matter physics; correlated electrons.

Assistant Professor

Tafti, Fazel, Ph.D., University of Toronto, 2011. *Condensed Matter Physics, Solid State Physics.* Material Synthesis, Electrical and Thermal Transport Measurements, High Pressure and High Field Experiments.

Zeljkovic, Ilija, Ph.D., Harvard University, 2013. *Condensed Matter Physics.* Atomic-scale spectroscopic characterization of quantum materials (topological insulators, high-temperature superconductors, transition metal dichalcogenides) using scanning tunneling microscopy (STM); Layer-by-layer material synthesis utilizing molecular beam epitaxy (MBE); Manipulation of electronic properties via strain, electrostatic gating and magnetic field.

Zhou, Brian, Ph.D., Princeton University, 2014. *Condensed Matter Physics.* Dr. Zhou is an experimental condensed matter physicist investigating atomic-scale defect centers in diamond for quantum information processing and nanoscale sensing. In his research, Dr. Zhou uses the nitrogen-vacancy center to demonstrate novel quantum dynamics and to probe magnetism and light-matter interactions in condensed matter systems.

Research Professor

Bakshi, Pradip, Ph.D., Harvard University, 1962. Mathematical physics; theoretical plasma physics; quantum field theory.

Herczynski, Andrzej, Ph.D., Lehigh University, 1987. Fluid dynamics.

Kalman, Gabor, Israel Inst. of Tech., 1961. Theoretical plasma physics; many-body physics; astrophysics.

Scientist

Shepard, Stephen, Framingham State College. Integrated Sciences Nanofabrication Clean Room Facility Manager.

DEPARTMENTAL RESEARCH SPECIALTIES AND STAFF

Theoretical

Condensed Matter Physics. Electronic, optical, magnetic and transport properties of nanoscale systems; thermoelectrics; strongly correlated electron systems; superconductivity; heavy fermion systems; Fermi liquid theory; electromagnetic response of metals; surfaces; topological insulators. Bakshi, Bedell, Broido, Di Bartolo, Engelbrecht, Herczynski, Kalman, Kempa, Ran, Wang, Zeljkovic.

History & Philosophy of Physics/Science. Selected topics in the foundations of physics and in the history and philosophy of science.

Nano Science and Technology. Applied / integrated nanoscale physics at the interface of biology, chemistry and neuroscience. Broido, Burch, Engelbrecht, Kempa.

Plasma and Fusion. Strongly coupled plasmas. Bakshi, Kalman.

Experimental

Condensed Matter Physics. Electronic, optical, magnetic, and transport properties of nanoscale systems; photovoltaics; nanophotonics; thermoelectrics; strongly correlated electron systems; superconductivity; heavy fermion systems; Fermi liquid theory; topological insulators; low-temperature physics; heavy-fermion systems; molecular organic conductors; physics in strong magnetic fields; neutron scattering; high-resolution STM and STS; fluorescence spectroscopy; nanoscale manipulation of light; nanomaterials for energy; metamaterials. Burch, Di Bartolo, Graf, Naughton, Opeil, Zeljkovic.

Nano Science and Technology. Applied / integrated nanoscale physics at the interface of biology, chemistry and neuroscience, and energy science. Burch, Naughton, Opeil.

Optics. Near and far-field nanophotonics, plasmonics, photovoltaics, Raman, ARPES. Burch, Di Bartolo, Naughton.

BOSTON UNIVERSITY

DEPARTMENT OF PHYSICS

Boston, Massachusetts 02215
http://physics.bu.edu

General University Information
President: Robert A. Brown
Dean of Graduate School: Ann Cudd
University website: http://www.bu.edu
School Type: Private
Setting: Urban
Total Faculty: 3,870
Total Graduate Faculty: Unavailable
Total number of Students: 33,617
Total number of Graduate Students: 14,662

Department Information
Department Chairman: Prof. Andrei Ruckenstein, Chair
Department Contact: Mirtha Cabello, Graduate Program
  Coordinator
  Total full-time faculty: 43
  Total number of full-time equivalent positions: 43
  Full-Time Graduate Students: 91
  Female Full-Time Graduate Students: 12
  First-Year Graduate Students: 28
  Female First-Year Students: 3
  Total Post Doctorates: 17

Department Address
590 Commonwealth Avenue
Room 255
Boston, MA 02215
Phone: (617) 353-2623
Fax: (617) 353-9393
E-mail: cabello@bu.edu
Website: http://physics.bu.edu

ADMISSIONS

Admission Contact Information
Address admission inquiries to: Graduate Admissions, Boston
  University, Physics Department, 590 Commonwealth Ave-
  nue, Boston, MA 02215
Phone: (617) 353-2623
E-mail: cabello@bu.edu
Admissions website: http://physics.bu.edu

Application deadlines
Fall admission:
U.S. students: January 13   *Int'l. students*: January 13

Application fee
U.S. students: $95   *Int'l. students*: $95

Admissions information
For Fall of 2018:
  Number of applicants: 381
  Number admitted: 93
  Number enrolled: 28

Admission requirements
Bachelor's degree requirements: Bachelor's degree in Physics
  or astronomy is required.

GRE requirements
The GRE is required.
  Mean GRE score range (25th–75th percentile): 60th - 75th
The average scores of the entering class are: *Quantitative score*:
  165/88%; *Verbal score*: 155/66%; *subject in physics score*:
  849/77%.

Subjective GRE requirements
The Subjective GRE is required.

TOEFL requirements
The TOEFL exam is required for students from non-English-
  speaking countries.
  PBT score: 600
  iBT score: 84
**Minimum scores by section (iBT): Reading section: 21; Listen-
  ing section: 21; Speaking section: 21; Writing section: 21.

Other admissions information
Additional requirements: Exceptional candidates from other
  fields will be considered.
Undergraduate preparation assumed: Students are expected to
  have taken junior/senior-level courses in classical mechanics
  (at the level of Marion & Thornton or equivalent), electromagnetism (Griffiths), quantum or modern physics (Liboff or Griffiths), and statistical/thermal physics (Kittel or Reif).

TUITION
Tuition year 2018–19:
  Full-time students: $53,572 annual
A tuition and fees scholarship and medical insurance coverage
  is awarded to teaching fellows, research assistants, and non-
  service fellows.
Credit hours per semester to be considered full-time: 12
Deferred tuition plan: No
Health insurance: Yes, Scholarship/waiver.
Other academic fees: Mandatory fees are covered with the teach-
  ing/research non-service fellowships.
Academic term: Semester
Number of first-year students who received full tuition waivers: 28

Teaching Assistants, Research Assistants, and Fellowships
Number of first-year
  Teaching Assistants: 27
  Research Assistants: 1
Average stipend per academic year
  Teaching Assistant: $33,990
  Research Assistant: $33,990
  Fellowship student: $33,990

FINANCIAL AID

Application deadlines
Fall admission:
U.S. students: January 13   *Int'l. students*: January 13

Loans

Loans are available for U.S. students.

Loans are not available for international students.

GAPSFAS application required: Yes

FAFSA application required: Yes

For further information

Address financial aid inquiries to: Graduate School, Financial Aid Office, 705 Commonwealth Avenue, Room 112, Boston, MA 02215.

Phone: (617) 353-2696

E-mail: grs@bu.edu

Financial aid website: http://www.bu.edu/cas/students/graduate/financial-aid/

HOUSING

Availability of on-campus housing

Single students: Yes

Married students: Yes

Childcare Assistance: No

For further information

Address housing inquiries to: Boston University Real Estate, 19 Deerfield Street, Boston, MA 02215.

Phone: (617) 353-4101

E-mail: rental@bu.edu

Housing aid website: http://www.bu.edu/realestate

Table A—Faculty, Enrollments, and Degrees Granted

Research Specialty	2018–19 Faculty	Enrollment Fall 2017 Master's	Enrollment Fall 2017 Doctorate	Number of Degrees Granted 2017–18 (2013–18) Master's	Number of Degrees Granted 2017–18 (2013–18) Terminal Master's	Number of Degrees Granted 2017–18 (2013–18) Doctorate
Biophysics	5	–	7	–(7)	–(4)	2(6)
Computational Physics	1	–	–	–	–	–(1)
Condensed Matter Physics	14	–	39	2(15)	–(3)	6(26)
High Energy Physics	11	–	17	2(13)	–(5)	3(14)
Particles and Fields	7	–	4	–(1)	–(1)	–
Statistical & Thermal Physics	2	–	8	1(3)	–(1)	3(26)
Other	3	–	–	–	–	–
Total	43	–	75	5(39)	–(14)	14(73)
Full-time Grad. Stud.	–	–	75	–	–	–
First-year Grad. Stud.	–	–	9	–	–	–

GRADUATE DEGREE REQUIREMENTS

Master's: Eight semester courses (32 credits) are required, including Advanced Lab, Mathematical Physics, Statistical Physics and Thermodynamics I, Electrodynamics I, Mathematical Methods, Quantum Mechanics I and II and one elective course. All students must complete a "Scholarly Methods in Physics" course. Each student must satisfy a residency requirement of a minimum of two consecutive regular semesters of full-time graduate study at Boston University.

Doctorate: Eight semester courses (32 credits) beyond those used to fulfill the Master's degree requirements. These must include Advanced Lab, if not already taken to fulfill Master's requirements and at least five lecture courses numbered between 500 and 850. Up to three non-lecture courses may count toward the total of eight courses, but no more than one directed study course and one seminar course. The five lecture courses must include at least two distribution courses from the category outside the student's area of specialization. (Cat-

egory I includes elementary particle and mathematical physics and Category II includes biological physics and condensed matter physics.) Passing grade on the preliminary oral exam; interim progress report, prospectus, a departmental seminar; a dissertation and a PhD defense. Each student must satisfy a residency requirement of a minimum of two consecutive regular semesters of full-time graduate study at Boston University.

Other Degrees: Interdisciplinary Ph.D. is also available with many other departments, including Astronomy, Mathematics, Biology, Chemistry, and with departments in the College of Engineering and the Photonics Center.

Thesis: Dissertation may be written in absentia.

SPECIAL EQUIPMENT, FACILITIES, OR PROGRAMS

The Scientific Instrument Facility employs three experimental machinists, one Senior Experimental Machinist, Welder, Student Shop Instructor, and an Operations Manager who runs the facility. The facility houses a Wire EDM Machine, a variety of CNC Lathes and 4/5 Axis CNC Milling machines, CMM, Microhights, tools interfaced to a state-of-the-art CAD/CAM (SOLIDWORK and MASTERCAM) system, as well as manual lathes, milling machines, and grinders, high-vacuum welding equipment, helium leak detection and precision measurement equipment. It is capable of assisting with practically any scientific hardware needs. The facility also has expertise for fabrication and assembly of complex parts.

The Electronics Design Facility provides complete electronics design and assembly capabilities for research instrumentation. The facility is equipped with extensive CAD tools for analog and digital circuit design and simulation and PCB layout. Facility engineers have extensive experience in low-noise and high-speed circuit design, programmable logic, fiber-optic links, and controlled-impedance PCB design.

In-house research laboratories include central facilities, as well as individual group laboratories. Central facilities available in Physics, Photonics, and Materials Science and Engineering include STEM, SEM, and AFM microscopy, X-ray diffraction, small-angle X-ray scattering, focused ion beam (FIB), vapor-phase deposition, spectroscopy, and submicron UV photolithography and electron-beam lithographic nano-fabrication facilities. Individual research laboratories include the UHV elastic and inelastic He surface scattering laboratory; the electronic-structure laboratory using high-resolution electron and photon spectroscopies; the materials diffraction X-ray scattering laboratory; the low-temperature scanning-optical-microscopy laboratory; the MBE laboratory for growing wide-band-gap semiconductors; and the nano-optics laboratory with near-field solid immersion and subcellular florescent microscopies. They also include the nano-scale transport laboratory with He3 and dilution refrigerator; the low-temperature, high-frequency, and high-magnetic field facilities; molecular biophysics and polymer laboratories, electron, atomic force, confocal, and near-field scanning probe microscopies, and Fourier transform infrared, Raman, UV-visible and ultrafast laser spectroscopy laboratories.

An extensive network of computational facilities supports the research activities of the Department. There are Linux clusters, Windows and Mac computers available to departmental faculty, staff, and students. Additional Linux servers and workstations, as well as many Windows and Mac computers are available to research groups.

For computationally intensive applications, students have access to a large-scale Linux cluster supported through the Center for Computational Science and the Office of Information Services & Technology. This shared Linux cluster has 3700 Intel and

AMD CPU cores, 103,996 NVIDIA GPU Cuda cores, more than 22 TB of main memory and nearly 2 PB of disk. The nodes are interconnected with a variety of fabrics including QDR & FDR Infiniband, 10 GigE and GigE. The cluster is composed of nearly equal portions of fully shared resources, available on a fair-share basis to all faculty-sponsored research groups, and buy-in resources, funded by researchers for their own priority use. Excess buy-in capacity is returned to the shared pool for general use.

The large-scale computational resources are housed at the Massachusetts Green High-Performance Computing Center (MGH-PCC). The MGHPCC is a state-of-the-art data center built by a collaboration of universities, industry, and the Massachusetts state government. The five university partners, Boston University, Harvard, MIT, Northeastern and University of Massachusetts, have equal shares of the facility. The data center, located in Holyoke, Massachusetts, takes advantage of the abundant source of clean renewable energy from Holyoke Gas and Electric's hydroelectric power plant on the Connecticut River. This project has created a world-class, high performance computing center with an emphasis on green, sustainable computing and unprecedented opportunities for collaboration between research, government, and business in Massachusetts. The computing infrastructure in the MGHPCC facility includes 33,000 sq. ft. of computer room space optimized for high-performance computing systems, a 19 MW power feed, and a high-efficiency cooling plant that can support up to 10 MW of computing load.

A vast and diverse array of optical fiber connections to the NoX, Metro Ring and commercial ISPs provide multiple Gb/s of bandwidth and connectivity to the Internet, Internet2, and international research networks. Two pairs of 10 Gb/s fiber optic links connect the MGFHPCC data center to the campus. The Departmental Computer Facility supports a wide range of software applications for physics data collection, analysis, simulation, and visualization.

Table B—Separately Budgeted Research Expenditures by Source of Support

Source of Support	Departmental Research	Physics-related Research Outside Department
Federal government	$5,153,940.29	
State/local government		
Non-profit organizations	$1,014,074.63	
Business and industry	$271,795.64	
Other		
Total	$6,439,810.56	

Table C—Separately Budgeted Research Expenditures by Research Specialty

Research Specialty	No. of Grants	Expenditures ($)
Biophysics	11	$753,066.44
Condensed Matter Physics	17	$1,490,730.04
Particles and Fields	34	$3,812,186.18
Physics and other Science Education	8	$233,521.45
Statistical & Thermal Physics	4	$150,306.45
Total	74	$6,439,810.56

FACULTY

Professor

Ahlen, Steven P., Ph.D., University of California, Berkeley, 1976. *Astrophysics, Particles and Fields*. Experimental particle physics and astrophysics.

Bishop, David, Ph.D., Cornell University, 1978. Professor of Physics and ECE. Head of the BU Division of Materials Science and Engineering. *Condensed Matter Physics, Nano Science and Technology*. Condensed matter experimental including superconductivity, magnetic vortices, MEMS devices for optical networks, single atom MBE.

Butler, John M., Ph.D., Stanford University, 1986. *Astrophysics, High Energy Physics*. Experimental particle physics and astrophysics.

Campbell, David, Ph.D., University of Cambridge, 1970. *Condensed Matter Physics, Quantum Foundations, Theoretical Physics*. Quantum condensed matter theory. Nonlinear phenomena.

Carey, Robert, Ph.D., Harvard University, 1989. Director of Undergraduate Studies. Experimental particle physics and high-precision measurements.

Chamon, Claudio, Ph.D., Massachusetts Institute of Technology, 1996. *Condensed Matter Physics, Quantum Foundations, Theoretical Physics*. Quantum condensed matter theory.

Cohen, Andrew G., Ph.D., Harvard University, 1986. *Particles and Fields, Theoretical Physics*. Theoretical particle physics.

El-Batanouny, Maged, Ph.D., University of California, Davis, 1978. Director of Graduate Studies. *Condensed Matter Physics*. Experimental condensed matter physics.

Erramilli, Shyamsunder, Ph.D., University of Illinois, 1986. *Biophysics*. Biological physics.

Katz, Emanuel, Ph.D., Massachusetts Institute of Technology, 2001. Theoretical particle physics.

Kearns, Edwards, Ph.D., Harvard University, 1990. *Astrophysics, Particles and Fields*. Experimental particle physics and astrophysics.

Klein, William, Ph.D., Temple University, 1972. *Statistical & Thermal Physics*. Statistical physics.

Lane, Kenneth D., Ph.D., Johns Hopkins University, 1970. Theoretical particle physics.

Ludwig, Karl F., Ph.D., Stanford University, 1986. Chair of Department. Experimental condensed matter physics.

Miller, James P., Ph.D., Carnegie Mellon University, 1975. *Particles and Fields*. Experimental particle physics and high-precision measurements.

Mohanty, Pritiraj, Ph.D., University of Maryland, College Park, 1998. Experimental condensed matter physics.

Pi, So-Young, Ph.D., Stony Brook University, 1974. *Particles and Fields*. Theoretical particle physics.

Polkovnikov, Anatoli, Ph.D., Yale University, 2003. Quantum condensed matter theory.

Rebbi, Claudio, Ph.D., International University College of Turin, 1967. Theoretical particle physics.

Roberts, B. Lee, Ph.D., College of William and Mary, 1974. Experimental particle physics and high-precision measurements.

Rohlf, James, Ph.D., California Institute of Technology, 1980. *High Energy Physics*. Experimental particle physics and astrophysics.

Rothschild, Kenneth, Ph.D., Massachusetts Institute of Technology, 1974. Experimental biological physics.

Ruckenstein, Andrei, Ph.D., Cornell University, 1984. *Condensed Matter Physics*.

Sandvik, Anders, Ph.D., University of California, Santa Barbara, 1993. *Condensed Matter Physics*. Computational quantum condensed matter physics.

Schmaltz, Martin, Ph.D., University of California, San Diego, 1995. Theoretical particle physics.

Smith, Kevin, Ph.D., Yale University, 1988. *Condensed Matter Physics*. Experimental condensed matter physics.

Stanley, H. Eugene, Ph.D., Harvard University, 1967. Director, Center for Polymer Studies. Statistical physics.

Sulak, Lawrence, Ph.D., Princeton University, 1971. Experimental particle physics and astrophysics.

Tsui, Ophelia, Ph.D., Princeton University, 1996. *Condensed Matter Physics*. Biological physics; experimental condensed matter physics.

Associate Professor

Mehta, Pankaj, Ph.D., Rutgers University, 2006. *Statistical & Thermal Physics*. Biological physics; Statistical physics.

Assistant Professor

Chandran, Anushya, Ph.D., Princeton University, 2013. *Condensed Matter Physics*. Condensed Matter Theory.

Demiragli, Zeynep, Ph.D., Brown University, 2015. Particle Physics Experiment, High Energy Experiment.

Fitzpatrick, Andrew L., Ph.D., Harvard University, 2008. High Energy Theory.

Grant, Christopher, Ph.D., The University of Alabama, 2012. Neutrino.

Hu, Wanzheng, Ph.D., Institute of Physics, Chinese Academy of Sciences, 2010. Condense Matter Experiment.

Kamenetska, Maria, Ph.D., Columbia University, 2012. Condensed Matter Experiment, Biological Physics, Biochemistry.

Korolev, Kiril, Ph.D., Moscow Institute of Physics and Technology (MIPT), 2010. *Biophysics, Statistical & Thermal Physics*. Biological physics; Statistical physics.

Laumann, Christopher, Ph.D., Princeton University, 2010. *Condensed Matter Physics*. Condensed Matter Theory.

Suarez, Indara, Ph.D., Texas A&M University, 2014. Particle Physics Experiment, High Energy Experiment.

Sushkov, Alexander O., Ph.D., University of California, Berkeley, 2006. *Condensed Matter Physics*. Experimental Condensed Matter Physics; Precision Particle Physics.

Emeritus

Bansil, Rama, Ph.D., University of Rochester, 1974. *Biophysics, Condensed Matter Physics*. Experimental condensed matter physics and biological physics.

Booth, Edward C., Ph.D., Johns Hopkins University, 1955. Biological physics.

Corinaldesi, Ernesto, Ph.D., The University of Manchester, 1951. Quantum mechanics.

Edmonds, Jr., Dean S., Ph.D., Massachusetts Institute of Technology, 1958. Electronics and instrumentation.

Glashow, Sheldon, Ph.D., Harvard University, 1958. *Theoretical Physics*. Theoretical particle physics.

Goldberg, Bennett B., Ph.D., Brown University, 1987. *Nano Science and Technology*. Experimental condensed matter physics.

Redner, Sidney, Ph.D., Massachusetts Institute of Technology, 1977. *Statistical & Thermal Physics*. Statistical physics.

Skocpol, William, Ph.D., Harvrd University, 1974. *Condensed Matter Physics*.

Stone, James L., Ph.D., University of Michigan, 1977. Experimental particle physics and astrophysics.

Whitaker, J. Scott, Ph.D., University of California, Berkeley, 1976. Experimental particle physics and astrophysics.

Willis, Charles R., Syracuse University, 1957. Biophysics; nonlinear physics; statistical physics.

Zimmerman, George O., Yale University, 1963. Low-temperature physics; magnetism.

Professor Emeritus

Teich, Malvin C., Ph.D., Cornell University, 1966. Joint Appointment with the College of Engineering. Quantum optics and imaging.

Research Faculty

Hong, Mi Kyung, Ph.D., University of Illinois, 1988. *Biophysics*. Experimental biophysics.

Ivanov, Plamen, Ph.D., Boston University, 1998. *Biophysics, Polymer Physics/Science, Statistical & Thermal Physics*. Statistical physics; physiologic dynamics and neural control; network physiology; nonlinear dynamics and coupling; excitable media; disordered systems; phase transitions in physical and biological systems econophysics.

Krapivsky, Paul, Ph.D., Moscow Physical Technical Institute, 1991. *Condensed Matter Physics*. Theoretical condensed matter physics.

Shank, James, Ph.D., University of California, Berkeley, 1988. *High Energy Physics*.

Youssef, Saul, Ph.D., Carnegie Mellon University, 1992. *High Energy Physics*.

Adjunct Professor

Averitt, Richard, Ph.D., Rice University, 1998. *Condensed Matter Physics*.

Affiliate Professor

Ünlü, M. Selim, Ph.D., University of Illinois, 1997. Joint Appointment with the College of Engineering. Near-field Optical Microscopy and Spectroscopy.

Bigio, Irving, Ph.D., University of Michigan, 1974. Joint Appointment with the College of Engineering. *Biophysics*. Biomedical and biological physics.

Brower, Richard, Ph.D., University of California, Berkeley, 1969. Joint Appointment with the College of Engineering. *Theoretical Physics*. Theoretical particle physics.

Cheng, Ji-Xin, Ph.D., University of Science and Technology of China, 1998. Molecular spectroscopic imaging technologies Label-free microscopy Medical Photonics Neurophotonics Cancer metabolism Photonics for infectious diseases.

Coker, David, Ph.D., Australian National University. Joint Appointment with the Chemistry. *Condensed Matter Physics*.

Cui, Qiang, Ph.D., Emory University, 1997. Developing computational techniques and theoretical models for complex systems, Simulation of complex molecular machines in bioenergy transduction, Interfacing biology and material science.

DeLisi, Charles, Ph.D., New York University, 1969. Joint Appointment with the College of Engineering. Biological physics.

Giles, Roscoe, Ph.D., Stanford University, 1975. Joint Appointment with the College of Engineering. Advanced computer architectures; distributed and parallel computing; computational science.

Moustakas, Theodore, Ph.D., Columbia University, 1974. Joint Appointment with the College of Engineering. Synthetic novel materials.

Sergienko, Alexander, Ph.D., Moscow State University, 1987. Joint Appointment with the College of Engineering. Correlation spectroscopy.

Swan, Anna, Ph.D., Boston University, 1993. Joint Appointment with the College of Engineering. Experimental condensed matter physics.

White, Alice, Ph.D., Harvard University. Chair of Mechanical Engineering. Joint Appointment with the College of Engineering. *Condensed Matter Physics*. Experimental condensed matter physics.

Affiliate Associate Professor

Garik, Peter, Ph.D., Cornell University. Joint Appointment with the School of Education. Physics Education.

Meller, Amit, Ph.D., Weizmann Institute of Science. Joint Appointment with the College of Engineering. *Biophysics*. Experimental biophysics.

Mertz, Jerome, Ph.D., University of California, Santa Barbara, 1991. Joint Appointment with the College of Engineering. Biological Physics.

Segre, Daniel, Ph.D., Weizmann Institute of Science. Joint Appointment with the College of Engineering. *Biophysics*. Theoretical biophysics.

Affiliate Assistant Professor

Brown, Keith, Ph.D., Harvard University. Joint Appointment with the College of Engineering. *Condensed Matter Physics*. Experimental condensed matter physics.

Bunch, Scott, Ph.D., Cornell University. Joint Appointment with the College of Engineering. *Condensed Matter Physics*. Experimental condensed matter physics.

Sgro, Allyson, Ph.D., University of Washington, 2011. Experimental condensed matter and biological physics. Biomedical Engineering: Systems biology, quantitative biology, collective behavior, cell signaling, tissue assembly, fluorescence microscopy, microfluidics, methods development.

Sharifzadeh, Sahar, Ph.D., Princeton University, 2009. Joint Appointment with the College of Engineering. *Condensed Matter Physics*. Theoretical condensed matter physics.

Senior Lecturer

Duffy, Andrew, Ph.D., Queen's University at Kingston, 1995. Physics Education Research.

Jariwala, Manher, Ph.D., University of Maryland, 2004. Academic Scheduling Advisor. Physics Education Research.

DEPARTMENTAL RESEARCH SPECIALTIES AND STAFF

Theoretical

Condensed Matter Physics. Strongly interacting electron systems. Low-dimensional quantum magnetism and quantum antiferromagnets. High-temperature and organic superconductors and heavy electron systems. Fractional quantum Hall effect. Surface physics; solitons on surfaces. Structural and vibrational properties of adsorbed atomic layers. Equilibrium and nonequilibrium properties of interacting many particle atomic systems. Quantum Monte Carlo algorithms. Graphene. Bose-Einstein condensates in optical lattices. Quantum adiabatic algorithm. Quantum quenches. Four postdoctoral fellows. Campbell, Chamon, Chandran, Coker, El-Batanouny, Goldberg, Hu, Ivanov, Kamenetska, Klein, Krapivsky, Laumann, Ludwig, Mehta, Polkovnikov, Redner, Ruckenstein, Sandvik, Sgro, Sharifzadeh, Skocpol, Stanley, Sushkov, Swan, Teich, White, Willis, Zimmerman.

Particles and Fields. Physical origin of electroweak and flavor symmetry breaking, including theoretical and phenomenological studies of technicolor, little Higgs, extra dimensions and supersymmetry. Quantum chromodynamics. Collider phenomenology. Numerical simulations of lattice gauge theories. Fundamental studies of quantum field theory. Theoretical astrophysics and cosmology; dark matter, inflation, baryogenesis, and the formation of large scale structure. Seven postdoctoral fellows. Brower, Cohen, Fitzpatrick, Glashow, Grant, Katz, Lane, Pi, Rebbi, Schmaltz, Shank, Youssef.

Statistical & Thermal Physics. Kinetics of phase transitions and coarsening processes. Chemical reactions, stochastic processes, and the role of spatial fluctuations. Structure of heterogeneous networks; the dynamics, resilience, and failure mechanism of networks. Population biology models. Theoretical biology; collective biological behavior; biological computation and environmental response. Fluctuation dynamics, nonlinearity, and complexity in physiological systems. Neural control and coupling of organ systems. Network physiology. Dynamics of social systems. Econophysics. Mechanisms of nucleation and spinodal decomposition. Physics of disordered media; percolation models of disordered materials. Fractals and multifractals. Hydrogen-bonded network formation in liquid water. Dynamics of earthquake faults. Dynamics of materials damage mechanisms. Acceleration algorithms for Monte Carlo simulations. First-passage processes and their applications. Stochastic transport processes. Theoretical studies of polymers. Two postdoctoral fellows. Brower, Campbell, Chamon, Giles, Ivanov, Klein, Korolev, Krapivsky, Laumann, Mehta, Polkovnikov, Redner, Sandvik, Stanley.

Experimental

Astrophysics. Atmospheric and solar neutrino studies and neutrino astrophysics with the Super-K experiment. Dark matter searches. Two postdoctoral fellows. Grant, Kearns, Stone, Sulak, Sushkov, Whitaker.

Biophysics. Energy transduction, ion transport, and signal receptor studies of microbial and vertebrate rhodopsins and their complexes by FTIR, resonance Raman spectroscopy and their bioengineering for optogenetics. Biomembrane technology and molecular electronics. Structure and electrical properties of membranes. Ultrafast vibrational spectroscopy, STM, AFM imaging of macromolecular assemblies, membrane surfaces, and protein-lipid interactions. Gelation of mucin and mucus. Novel Fluorescent Imaging for subcellular microscopy. Dynamics of DNA. Signaling and Information Processing in Biochemicals networks. One postdoctoral fellow. Bansil, Bigio, Cheng, Cui, DeLisi, Erramilli, Goldberg, Ivanov, Kamenetska, Korolev, Mehta, Meller, Mertz, Rothschild, Ruckenstein, Segre, Sgro, Tsui.

Condensed Matter Physics. Mesoscopic phenomena; quantum transport and quantum coherence phenomena in nanostructures. Advanced electronic materials. Nano-optics and spectroscopy of quantum dots, photonic bandgap systems, and carbon nanotubes. Single molecule spectroscopy and subcellular imaging. Studies of structural phase transitions in thin-film semiconductors. Synchrotron X-ray scattering studies of kinetics of nucleation, spinodal decomposition, and phase transitions. Growth of artificially structured materials using molecular beam epitaxy, sputtering, and chemical vapor deposition. Properties of high-Tc superconductor-normal interfaces. X-ray emission and photoemission studies of wide-band-gap semiconductors, organic superconductors, and low-dimensional transition metal oxides. Terahertz spectroscopy and time-integrated and time-resolved optical spectroscopy of correlated electron materials. Investigation of the structural, dynamical, and magnetic properties of solid surfaces using neutral helium and metastable He beam scattering. Current interest is focused on the surfaces of topological insulators and multi-ferroics. High-resolution photoemission and X-ray emission studies of metals, semiconductors, and oxides. Superconductivity, magnetic vortices, MEMS devices for optical networks, single-atom MBE. Four postdoctoral fellows. Averitt, Bansil, Bishop, Brown, Bunch, El-Batanouny, Erramilli, Goldberg, Hong, Hu, Kamenetska, Ludwig, Mohanty, Moustakas, Rothschild, Sergienko, Smith, Sushkov, Swan, Tsui, White, Zimmerman.

High Energy Physics. Studies of the Higgs boson and electroweak symmetry breaking, W and Z bosons, top quarks, rare b quark decays and searches for new physics beyond the standard model at the CERN LHC. Study of neutrino properties using long baseline neutrino oscillation. Study of grand unified theories using proton decay. Precision measurements of the anomalous part of the muon magnetic dipole moment. Precision measurement of the muon lifetime and the Fermi constant. New limit on muon to electron conversion. New limit on the electric dipole moment of the muon and neutron. Precision measurement of muon capture on hydrogen and determination of the pseudoscalar coupling constant. Precision measurement of muon capture on deuterium. Eight postdoctoral fellows. Ahlen, Booth, Butler, Carey, Demiragli, Grant, Kearns, Miller, Roberts, Rohlf, Suarez, Sulak.

Polymer Physics/Science. X-ray, light-scattering, rheology and microscopy studies of the structure, dynamics, and phase separations of gels, block copolymers, polymer nanocomposites, polymer thin films, and interfaces. Two postdoctoral fellows. Bansil, Rothschild, Stanley, Tsui.

Surface Physics. Investigation of the structural, dynamical, and magnetic properties of solid surfaces using neutral helium and metastable helium beam scattering. Current interest is focused on the surfaces of topological insulators and multiferroics. High-resolution photoemission studies of metals, semiconductors, and oxides. Two postdoctoral fellows. Cui, El-Batanouny, Ludwig, Smith.

View additional information about this department at www.gradschoolshopper.com. Check out the "Why Choose Us?" section, find out more about the department's culture and get links to social media networks.

CLARK UNIVERSITY

DEPARTMENT OF PHYSICS

Worcester, Massachusetts 01610
http://physics.clarku.edu

General University Information
President: David Angel
Dean of Graduate School: Yuko Aoyama
University website: http://clarku.edu
School Type: Private
Setting: Urban
Total Faculty: 201
Total Graduate Faculty: 201
Total number of Students: 3,153
Total number of Graduate Students: 913

Department Information
Department Chairman: Prof. Arshad Kudrolli, Chair
Department Contact: Sujata Davis, Office Manager
  Total full-time faculty: 6
  Total number of full-time equivalent positions: 6
  Full-Time Graduate Students: 11
  Female Full-Time Graduate Students: 1
  First-Year Graduate Students: 2
  Female First-Year Students: 1
  Total Post Doctorates: 1

Department Address
950 Main Street
Worcester, MA 01610
Phone: (508) 793-7169
Fax: (508) 793-8861
E-mail: physics@clarku.edu
Website: http://physics.clarku.edu

ADMISSIONS

Admission Contact Information
Address admission inquiries to: Graduate Admissions Office,
  Clark University, 950 Main Street, Worcester, MA 01610
Phone: (508) 793-7373
E-mail: gradadmissions@clarku.edu
Admissions website: http://www.clarku.edu/graduate

Application deadlines
Fall admission:
U.S. students: February 1   *Int'l. students*: February 1

Application fee
U.S. students: $75   *Int'l. students*: $75

Admissions information
For Fall of 2018:
  Number of applicants: 28
  Number admitted: 4
  Number enrolled: 2

Admission requirements
Bachelor's degree requirements: A Bachelor's degree in Physics,
  Chemistry, Mathematics, or Engineering, with a minimum un-
  dergraduate GPA of "B-" is required.
Minimum undergraduate GPA: 2.7

GRE requirements
The GRE is recommended but not required.

The GRE is strongly recommended. There is no set minimum
score for the GRE; each case is judged individually.

Subjective GRE requirements
The Subjective GRE is recommended.
The GRE Advanced is strongly recommended. There is no set minimum score for the GRE Advanced; each case is judged individually.

TOEFL requirements
The TOEFL exam is required for students from non-English-
speaking countries.
Students from non-English-speaking countries are required to
demonstrate proficiency in English via the TOEFL exam.

Other admissions information
Additional requirements: The GRE and GRE Advanced are
strongly recommended. There are no set minimum scores for
GRE or GRE Advanced; each case is judged individually. Students from non-English-speaking countries are required to
demonstrate proficiency in English via the TOEFL exam.

TUITION

Tuition year 2018–19:
  Full-time students: $45,380 annual
  Part-time students: $5,672.5 per credit
Credit hours per semester to be considered full-time: 9
Deferred tuition plan: No
Health insurance: Available at the cost of $1,647 per year.
Other academic fees: Health and accident insurance is required but is
  waived on evidence of other insurance. Graduate students are
  charged a $100 Graduate Enrollment Fee, in the semester they begin
  their graduate program. This is a one-time only fee.
Academic term: Semester
Number of first-year students who received full tuition waivers: 2

Teaching Assistants, Research Assistants, and Fellowships
Number of first-year
  Teaching Assistants: 2
Average stipend per academic year
  Teaching Assistant: $15,346
  Research Assistant: $16,442
Support is normally provided over a twelve month period to
all eligible students. The 12 month TA stipend is $21,000.
The 12 month RA stipend is $22,500.

LED;&-3QFINANCIAL AID

Loans
Loans are not available for U.S. students.
Loans are not available for international students.
GAPSFAS application required: No
FAFSA application required: No

For further information
Address financial aid inquiries to: Department of Physics, Clark
University, 950 Main Street, Worcester, MA 01610.
Phone: (508) 793-7169
E-mail: physics@clarku.edu

Financial aid website: http://www.clarku.edu/graduate-admissions/financial-aid/scholarships-assistantships.cfm

HOUSING

Availability of on-campus housing
Single students: Yes
Married students: No

For further information
Address housing inquiries to: Department of Physics, Clark University, 950 Main Street, Worcester, MA 01610.
Phone: (508) 793-7169
E-mail: physics@clarku.edu
Housing aid website: http://www.clarku.edu/offices/housing/

Table A—Faculty, Enrollments, and Degrees Granted

Research Specialty	2017–18 Faculty	Enrollment Fall 2017		Number of Degrees Granted 2017–18 (2013–2018)		
		Master's	Doctorate	Master's	Terminal Master's	Doctorate
Condensed Matter Physics	7	1	10	–	–	2(5)
Physics and other Science Education	1	–	–	–	–	–
Statistical & Thermal Physics	1	–	–	–	–	–
Total	9	1	10	–	–	2(5)
Full-time Grad. Stud.	–	1	10	–	–	–
First-year Grad. Stud.	–	1	2	–	–	–

GRADUATE DEGREE REQUIREMENTS

Master's: Eight total courses are required, two of which may be transferred and one may be for thesis. A thesis (or Ph.D. candidacy) is required. There is no language requirement. Teaching experience is required.

Doctorate: One year in residence beyond the master's degree (eight courses) is required; three area qualification examinations and thesis proposal examination, teaching experience, and dissertation are also required.

Thesis: Thesis may be written in absentia.

SPECIAL EQUIPMENT, FACILITIES, OR PROGRAMS

The Department stresses research experience at the earliest possible time and requires all students to enroll in a research rotation during their first semester. Through research rotations, students can work directly with several faculty members on specific research projects and find a research group/project best suited to their interests. This allows dissertation work to begin substantially earlier than is usually the case in graduate programs. Clark's size affords a uniquely close association between faculty and students.

Table B—Separately Budgeted Research Expenditures by Source of Support

Source of Support	Departmental Research	Physics-related Research Outside Department
Federal government	$344,300	
State/local government		
Non-profit organizations	$46,100	
Business and industry	$10,000	
Other	$102,925	
Total	**$503,325**	

Table C—Separately Budgeted Research Expenditures by Research Specialty

Research Specialty	No. of Grants	Expenditures ($)
Condensed Matter Physics	6	$503,325
Total	6	$503,325

FACULTY

Professor

Agosta, Charles C., Ph.D., Duke University, 1986. *Applied Physics, Astronomy, Computational Physics, Condensed Matter Physics, Energy Sources & Environment, Low Temperature Physics, Nano Science and Technology, Statistical & Thermal Physics*. Properties of organic superconductors and other materials in high, pulsed magnetic fields; Renewable energy DC microgrids.

Kudrolli, Arshad, Ph.D., Northeastern University, 1995. *Applied Physics, Condensed Matter Physics, Engineering Physics/Science, Fluids, Rheology, Geophysics, Mechanics, Nonlinear Dynamics and Complex Systems, Statistical & Thermal Physics*. Experimental nonlinear physics; granular matter and soft condensed matter; self-assembly.

Associate Professor

Boyer, Michael, Ph.D., Massachusetts Institute of Technology, 2008. *Condensed Matter Physics, Low Temperature Physics*. Experimental condensed matter physics; correlated electron systems; low-dimensional materials; low-energy electron induced reactions; scanning tunneling microscopy, Astrochemistry.

Capogrosso Sansone, Barbara, Ph.D., University of Massachusetts, Amherst, 2008. *Atomic, Molecular, & Optical Physics, Computational Physics, Condensed Matter Physics*. Strongly correlated many-body systems, phase transitions, ultracold atoms and polar molecules, superfluidity, development of quantum Monte Carlo algorithms.

Mukhopadhyay, Ranjan, Ph.D., California Institute of Technology, 1998. *Biophysics, Computational Physics, Condensed Matter Physics, Statistical & Thermal Physics, Theoretical Physics*. Theoretical and computational biophysics; soft condensed matter physics; self-organization.

Assistant Professor

Petroff, Alexander P., Ph.D., Massachusetts Institute of Technology, 2011. *Applied Physics, Biophysics, Condensed Matter Physics, Engineering Physics/Science, Geophysics, Mechanics, Nonlinear Dynamics and Complex Systems, Statistical & Thermal Physics*. Complex microbial ecosystems, active matter, experimental biophysics, Earth Science.

Emeritus

Blatt, S. Leslie, Ph.D., Stanford University, 1965. *Astronomy, Nuclear Physics, Optics, Physics and other Science Education*. Experimental nuclear physics; college/pre-college curriculum development and teacher education.

Gould, Harvey A., Ph.D., University of California, Berkeley, 1966. *Computational Physics, Condensed Matter Physics, Statistical & Thermal Physics*. Statistical physics; computer simulation; phase transitions.

Kohin, Roger P., Ph.D., University of Maryland, 1961. *Condensed Matter Physics*. Experimental condensed matter physics; electron spin resonance studies.

Landee, Christopher P., Ph.D., University of Michigan, 1975. *Condensed Matter Physics*. Experimental condensed matter physics; quantum magnetism; magnetochemistry.

DEPARTMENTAL RESEARCH SPECIALTIES AND STAFF

Theoretical

Atomic, Molecular, & Optical Physics. Capogrosso Sansone.

Biophysics. Physical mechanisms underlying molecular and cellular processes; membranes; biopolymers; mechanical, biomechanical, and genetic networks. Mukhopadhyay.

Computational Physics. Agosta, Capogrosso Sansone, Gould, Mukhopadhyay.

Condensed Matter Physics. Soft matter, including polymers, liquid crystals, and gels; complex and disordered systems. Capogrosso Sansone, Gould, Mukhopadhyay.

Statistical & Thermal Physics. Computer simulation; phase transitions. Gould, Mukhopadhyay.

Experimental

Astrochemistry. Radiolysis and photolysis of cosmic ice analogs. Boyer.

Biophysics. Dynamics of complex microbial ecosystems. Petroff.

Condensed Matter Physics. Magnetism; low-dimensional conductors; organic superconductors; pulsed magnetic fields; scanning tunneling microscopy; active soft matter. Agosta, Boyer, Kudrolli, Landee, Petroff.

Energy Sources & Environment. Risk assessment; energy policy. Agosta.

Nonlinear Dynamics and Complex Systems. Granular matter; pattern formation; soft matter. Kudrolli, Petroff.

Physics and other Science Education. Teaching methods in science. Blatt.

View additional information about this department at www.gradschoolshopper.com. Check out the "Why Choose Us?" section, find out more about the department's culture and get links to social media networks.

HARVARD UNIVERSITY

DEPARTMENT OF PHYSICS

Cambridge, Massachusetts 02138
http://www.physics.harvard.edu

General University Information
President: Lawrence Bacow
Dean of Graduate School: Emma Dench
University website: http://www.harvard.edu
School Type: Private
Setting: Urban
Total Faculty: 2,400
Total Graduate Faculty: 2,400
Total number of Students: 21,000
Total number of Graduate Students: 14,500

Department Information
Department Chairman: Prof. Subir Sachdev, Chair
Department Contact: Lisa Cacciabaudo, Graduate Program
  Administrator
  Total full-time faculty: 35
  Total number of full-time equivalent positions: 41
  Full-Time Graduate Students: 234
  Female Full-Time Graduate Students: 72
  First-Year Graduate Students: 38
  Female First-Year Students: 13
  Total Post Doctorates: 116

Department Address
17 Oxford St.
Jefferson Physical Lab, Room 370
Cambridge, MA 02138
Phone: (617) 495-4327
Fax: (617) 495-0416
E-mail: gradinfo@physics.harvard.edu
Website: http://www.physics.harvard.edu

ADMISSIONS

Admission Contact Information
Address admission inquiries to: Graduate School of Arts and Sciences,
  Harvard University, Office of Admissions, Holyoke Center, 3rd
  Floor, 1350 Massachusetts Avenue, Cambridge, MA 02138
Phone: (617) 496-6100
E-mail: admiss@fas.harvard.edu
Admissions website: http://www.gsas.harvard.edu/prospective_
  students/admissions_overview.php

Application deadlines
Fall admission:
U.S. students: December 15   *Int'l. students*: December 15

Application fee
U.S. students: $105   *Int'l. students*: $105
All applicants to the Department of Physics are required to submit, in addition to the Abstract of Courses, a list of their four
  most advanced courses in physics and their two most advanced courses in mathematics, indicating textbooks (and au-
  thors) used in each course.

Admissions information
For Fall of 2018:
  Number of applicants: 628
  Number admitted: 74
  Number enrolled: 38

Admission requirements
Bachelor's degree requirements: A Bachelor's degree (or equivalent) is required.

GRE requirements
The GRE is required.
We do not have a minimum GRE score

Subjective GRE requirements
The Subjective GRE is required.
We do not have a minimum Physics GRE score

TOEFL requirements
The TOEFL exam is required for students from non-English-
  speaking countries.
  iBT score: 80

Other admissions information
Undergraduate preparation assumed: The only specific requirements
  for admission are those stipulated by the Graduate School of Arts
  and Sciences. An undergraduate degree in physics is preferred but
  not assumed. Applicants with an undergraduate degree in engineering, mathematics, or chemistry have ideally taken introductory
  and intermediate physics courses.

TUITION

Tuition year 2018–19:
  Full-time students: $50,926 annual
Note: All physics graduate students either receive a fellowship
  that covers tuition, fees, health insurance, and stipend an-
  nually, or their funding is paid through a Research Assistant
  appointment or a Teaching Fellow appointment.
Credit hours per semester to be considered full-time: 4
Deferred tuition plan: No
Health insurance: Yes, included in tuition.
Other academic fees: Grad student council fee of $25/year
Academic term: Semester
Number of first-year students who received full tuition waivers: 38

Teaching Assistants, Research Assistants, and Fellowships
  Number of first-year
    Fellowship students: 38
  Average stipend per academic year
    Teaching Assistant: $30,690
    Research Assistant: $30,690
    Fellowship student: $30,690

FINANCIAL AID

Loans
Loans are not available for U.S. students.
Loans are not available for international students.
GAPSFAS application required: No
FAFSA application required: No

For further information
Address financial aid inquiries to: Tracey Newman.
Phone: (617) 495-5396
E-mail: gsasfinaid@fas.harvard.edu

Financial aid website: https://gsas.harvard.edu/financial-support/funding-aid

HOUSING

Availability of on-campus housing
Single students: Yes
Married students: Yes
Childcare Assistance: No

For further information
Address housing inquiries to: Ashley Skipwith, Housing Coordinator, Patty Collyer, Housing Assistant, Dudley House B2.
Phone: (617) 495-5060
E-mail: gsashous@fas.harvard.edu
Housing aid website: https://gsas.harvard.edu/student-life/housing-dining

Table A—Faculty, Enrollments, and Degrees Granted

Research Specialty	2017–18 Faculty	Enrollment Fall 2018 Master's	Enrollment Fall 2018 Doctorate	Number of Degrees Granted 2017–2018 Master's	Number of Degrees Granted 2017–2018 Terminal Master's	Number of Degrees Granted 2017–2018 Doctorate
Acoustics	1	–	–	–	–	–
Applied Mathematics	3	–	1	–	–	–
Applied Physics	17	–	1	–	–	1
Astronomy	1	–	–	–	–	–
Astrophysics	7	–	12	1	–	3
Atomic, Molecular, & Optical Physics	13	–	80	4	–	5
Biophysics	17	–	21	–	1	2
Chemical Physics	7	–	9	1	–	–
Computational Physics	2	–	5	–	–	1
Condensed Matter Physics	20	–	50	–	–	6
Cosmology & String Theory	6	–	30	–	–	3
Electrical Engineering	1	–	–	–	–	–
Electromagnetism	2	–	–	–	–	1
Energy Sources & Environment	1	–	–	–	–	–
Fluids, Rheology	1	–	–	–	–	–
High Energy Physics	7	–	14	–	–	2
History & Philosophy of Physics/Science	2	–	–	–	–	–
Low Temperature Physics	3	–	–	–	–	–
Materials Science, Metallurgy	2	–	1	–	–	–
Medical, Health Physics	3	–	–	–	–	–
Nano Science and Technology	2	–	–	–	–	–
Nonlinear Dynamics and Complex Systems	3	–	–	–	–	–
Nuclear Physics	2	–	–	–	–	–
Optics	4	–	–	–	–	–
Particles and Fields	6	–	7	1	–	4
Physics and other Science Education	5	–	–	–	–	–
Polymer Physics/Science	1	–	–	–	–	–
Relativity & Gravitation	5	–	–	–	–	–
Statistical & Thermal Physics	6	–	–	–	–	–
Other	–	–	3	–	5	1
Total	**66**	**–**	**234**	**7**	**6**	**29**
Full-time Grad. Stud.	–	–	234	–	–	–
First-year Grad. Stud.	–	–	38	–	–	–

GRADUATE DEGREE REQUIREMENTS

Master's: The Department of Physics does not admit students whose sole purpose is to study for the master of arts degree. However, the A.M. degree is frequently taken by students who continue on for the Ph.D. degree. For those who do not attain the doctorate, the A.M. degree attests to the completion of a full year's study beyond the bachelor's degree, including 8 graduate courses.

Doctorate: Each student is required to demonstrate proficiency in a broad range of fields of physics by obtaining honor grades ("B-" or better) in at least eight half-courses (a minimum of four core courses and an additional four elective courses). Qualifying oral examination for Ph.D. candidacy thesis, and final oral examination thereon. No language requirement; laboratory experience is required for students not submitting experimental theses.

Thesis: The final examination, or thesis defense, includes a talk given by the thesis student defending the thesis. If the coursework does not indicate a wide proficiency in the field of the dissertation, the examination may be extended to test this proficiency as well.

SPECIAL EQUIPMENT, FACILITIES, OR PROGRAMS

Electronic Instrument Design Laboratory:

The Laboratory provides work space, tools, parts, and technical assistance for Physics/SEAS students and faculty who need to design and build custom electronic instruments. The Laboratory staff can assist with schematic and circuit board design, help order parts, provide soldering/assembly instruction, and help debug circuits. Alternatively, we can start from your specifications and develop fully custom instrumentation to meet your needs.

Physics/SEAS Instructional Instrument Laboratory:

The Machine Shop is set up to be primarily a teaching shop. We have a state-of-the-art facility, complete with computerized machine tools and full arc welding capabilities.

Biophysics (Ph.D.-Track Program): The primary objective of the program is to educate and train individuals with background in physical or quantitative science, especially chemistry, physics, computer science, or mathematics, to apply the concepts and methods of the physical sciences to the solution of biological problems.

Center for Nanoscale Systems (CNS): The Center's scientific focus is on how nanoscale components can be integrated into large and complex interacting systems. It brings together the disciplines of chemistry, physics, engineering, materials science, geology, biology, and medicine.

The Center for the Fundamental Laws of Nature:

This interdisciplinary theoretical research center aims to advance our basic knowledge of the universe through the interactive collaboration of physicists, mathematicians, and cosmologists.

The Center for Ultracold Atoms (CUA):

A joint venture with MIT, the CUA encompasses experimental and theoretical research in the following areas:

- Bose-Einstein condensates: development of new methods for manipulating and probing condensed atomic gases, ultracold interactions, and collision dynamics.

- Atom optics: atom interferometry, atom waveguides, surface physics and quantum reflection, many body physics in lower dimensions.

- Cryogenic Sources for BEC: creation of large condensates of alkalis and other atoms, sympathetic cooling, novel condensates, creation of intense hydrogen sources, and optical techniques for ultracold hydrogen.

Engineering and Physical Biology Program (EPB) (Ph.D.-Track Program):

A joint venture between Physics, Engineering, Chemistry, and Biology that focuses on determining how basic physical principles govern and explain biological processes.

Harvard-Smithsonian Center for Astrophysics (CfA):

The Center for Astrophysics combines the resources and research facilities of the Harvard College Observatory and the Smithsonian Astrophysical Observatory to study the basic physical processes that determine the nature and evolution of the universe. Some of its pioneering achievements include:

- Development of instrumentation for orbiting observatories in space.

- Ground-based gamma-ray astronomy.

- The application of computers to problems of theoretical. astrophysics, particularly stellar atmospheres.

The Institute for Quantum Science and Engineering (IQSE):

The mission of the IQSE is to foster cross-disciplinary research and education in new areas at the intersection of nanoscience, atomic physics, device engineering and computer science, that in various ways seeks to apply principles of quantum mechanics to advanced technologies.

Institute for Theoretical Atomic and Molecular Physics (ITAMP):

The Institute for Theoretical Atomic, Molecular and Optical Physics was established in November 1988 at the Harvard-Smithsonian Center for Astrophysics in order to address the critical shortage of theorists in atomic and molecular physics at major universities throughout the nation.

Laboratory for Particle Physics and Cosmology (LPPC):

The Laboratory for Particle Physics and Cosmology carries out forefront programs in high-energy physics research and provides first-rate educational opportunities for students. LPPC's experimental programs are carried out at the major accelerator centers throughout the world and address important questions both within and beyond the Standard Model.

Materials Research Science and Engineering Center (MRSEC):

The Materials Research and Engineering Center is the focus of Harvard's long tradition of interdisciplinary materials research.

Nanoscale Science Engineering Center (NSEC):

The Nanoscale Science and Engineering Center is a collaborative effort that combines "top down" and "bottom up" approaches to construct novel electronic and magnetic devices with nanoscale sizes and understand their behavior, including quantum phenomena.

Several collaborations and projects are also being carried out by Physics Department faculty and graduate students at centers outside of Cambridge: the Fermi National Accelerator Laboratory; the CERN in Geneva; the Stanford Linear Accelerator Center; the Soudan Mines in Northern Minnesota; and the National Institute of Standards and Technology.

Table B—Separately Budgeted Research Expenditures by Source of Support

Source of Support	Departmental Research	Physics-related Research Outside Department
Federal government	$19,134,919	
State/local government		
Non-profit organizations	$4,173,115	
Business and industry		
Other	$2,076,645	
Total	**$25,384,679**	

Table C—Separately Budgeted Research Expenditures by Research Specialty

Research Specialty	No. of Grants	Expenditures ($)
Astrophysics	7	$1,004,521
Atomic, Molecular, & Optical Physics	37	$12,012,460
Biophysics	7	$1,015,582
Condensed Matter Physics	51	$6,398,853
Cosmology & String Theory	8	$859,177
High Energy Physics	8	$1,142,982
Particles and Fields	6	$1,078,896
Total	**124**	**$23,512,471**

FACULTY

Distinguished University Professor

Galison, Peter, Ph.D., Harvard University, 1983. Director, Collection of Historical Scientific Instruments. *History & Philosophy of Physics/Science*. History of 20th century physics; particle physics.

Shapiro, Irwin I., Ph.D., Harvard University, 1955. *Astrophysics, Relativity & Gravitation*. Astrophysics; observational tests of general relativity.

Chair Professor

Sachdev, Subir, Ph.D., Harvard University, 1985. *Condensed Matter Physics*. Condensed matter theory: quantum phase transitions, etc.

Professor

Brenner, Michael P., Ph.D., University of Chicago, 1994. *Applied Mathematics, Applied Physics, Biophysics*. Theoretical modeling in physical sciences and engineering, breaking of fluid droplets, sonoluminescence, the sedimentation of small particles, electrospinning, developing algorithms to accelerates imulations of global pollution, understanding the limitations of self assembly and pattern formation.

Cohen, Adam, Ph.D., University of Cambridge, 2003. *Biophysics, Chemical Physics*. Experimental physical chemistry.

Demler, Eugene, Ph.D., Stanford University, 1998. *Atomic, Molecular, & Optical Physics, Condensed Matter Physics*. Theoretical condensed matter physics.

Desai, Michael, Ph.D., Harvard University, 2006. *Biophysics, Nonlinear Dynamics and Complex Systems, Statistical & Thermal Physics*. Studies of genetic variation to develop methods to infer the evolutionary history of populations from the variation observed in sequence data. Primary focus on natural selection in asexual populations such as microbes and viruses.

Doyle, John M., Ph.D., Massachusetts Institute of Technology, 1991. *Atomic, Molecular, & Optical Physics*. Quantum science and particle physics; cold molecules; search for electron EDM.

Finkbeiner, Douglas, Ph.D., University of California, Berkeley, 1999. *Astrophysics*. Astroparticle physics; interstellar medium; large-scale astronomical surveys.

Franklin, Melissa, Ph.D., Stanford University, 1982. Chair, Department of Physics. *High Energy Physics*. Experimental high-energy physics.

Gabrielse, Gerald, Ph.D., University of Chicago, 1980. *Atomic, Molecular, & Optical Physics, High Energy Physics*. Experimental atomic, optical, plasma, and elementary particle physics.

Georgi, Howard M., Ph.D., Yale University, 1971. *Particles and Fields*. Field theory and particle physics.

Golovchenko, Jene A., Ph.D., Rensselaer Polytechnic Institute, 1972. *Applied Physics, Atomic, Molecular, & Optical Physics, Biophysics, Condensed Matter Physics, Electromagnetism, Materials Science, Metallurgy*. Condensed matter systems.

Greiner, Markus, Ph.D., Ludwig Maximilians, 2003. *Atomic, Molecular, & Optical Physics*. Bose-Einstein condensation; optical lattices; quantum simulation; quantum magnetism; quantum gas microscopy.

Halperin, Bertrand I., Ph.D., University of California, Berkeley, 1965. *Condensed Matter Physics*. Condensed matter theory, especially properties of electrons and spins in nanoscale systems, electron systems in strong magnetic fields, effects of disorder and electron-electron interactions.

Hau, Lene Vestergaard, Ph.D., Aarhus, 1991. *Applied Physics, Atomic, Molecular, & Optical Physics, Biophysics*. Experimental atomic physics; Bose-Einstein condensation; nonlinear optics.

Heller, Eric J., Ph.D., Harvard University, 1973. *Acoustics, Applied Physics, Atomic, Molecular, & Optical Physics, Chemical Physics, Computational Physics, Condensed Matter Physics, Nonlinear Dynamics and Complex Systems*. Theory of electrons in two dimensions and imaging by scanning probe microscopy. Semiclassical methods for scattering theory, decoherence, quantum chaos. Wave propagation in random media. Molecular spectroscopy and photochemistry. Ultracold collisions of atoms and molecules. Random matrix and semiclassical approaches to statistical physics.

Hoffman, Jennifer, Ph.D., University of California, Berkeley, 2003. *Condensed Matter Physics*. Scanning probe microscopies of exotic electron materials. Scanning tunneling microscopy, force microscopy studies of correlated electron systems, superconductors, and topological materials.

Huth, John, Ph.D., University of California, Berkeley, 1985. *High Energy Physics*. Experimental high-energy physics.

Jaffe, Arthur M., Ph.D., Princeton University, 1966. *Particles and Fields*. Foundations of theoretical physics: fundamental investigation of quantum theory, relativity, and statistical physics, as well as other possible physical views of nature.

Kaxiras, Efthimios, Ph.D., Massachusetts Institute of Technology, 1987. *Applied Physics, Chemical Physics, Computational Physics, Condensed Matter Physics*. Condensed matter theory.

Kim, Philip, Ph.D., Harvard University, 1999. *Condensed Matter Physics*. Experimental investigation of quantum transport phenomena in low dimensional material systems.

Kovac, John M., Ph.D., University of Chicago, 2004. *Astrophysics*. observations of the cosmic microwave background (CMB).

Lukin, Mikhail, Ph.D., Texas A&M University, 1998. *Atomic, Molecular, & Optical Physics, Condensed Matter Physics*. Quantum optics; quantum information science; many-body quantum dynamics.

Mahadevan, L., Ph.D., Stanford University, 1995. *Applied Mathematics, Applied Physics, Biophysics*. Applied math and biophysics.

Manoharan, Vinothan, Ph.D., University of California, Santa Barbara, 2004. *Applied Physics, Biophysics, Condensed Matter Physics, Fluids, Rheology, Optics, Statistical & Thermal Physics*. Light scattering, optical microscopy, spectroscopy, synthesis, and other experimental techniques to understand the physics of self-organization.

Mazur, Eric, Ph.D., Leiden University, 1982. *Applied Physics, Biophysics, Materials Science, Metallurgy, Optics, Physics and other Science Education*. Interaction of short laser pulses with matter.

Morii, Masahiro, Ph.D., University of Tokyo, 1994. *High Energy Physics*. Experimental high-energy physics.

Murray, Cherry, Ph.D., Massachusetts Institute of Technology, 1978. Dean, School of Engineering and Applied Sciences. *Applied Physics*. Light scattering.

Narayanamurti, Venkatesh, Ph.D., Cornell University, 1965. *Applied Physics, Condensed Matter Physics*. Science and Technology Policy; experimental condensed matter physics.

Nelson, David R., Ph.D., Cornell University, 1975. *Applied Mathematics, Applied Physics, Biophysics, Chemical Physics, Condensed Matter Physics, Polymer Physics/Science, Statistical & Thermal Physics*. Statistical physics and condensed matter theory.

Park, Hongkun, Ph.D., Stanford University, 1996. *Atomic, Molecular, & Optical Physics, Biophysics, Condensed Matter Physics*. Experimental optical physics; condensed matter physics and biophysics; quantum optoplasmonics; quantum information science; nano-bio interfaces for cell-circuit studies; brain-machine interfacing.

Prentiss, Mara, Ph.D., Massachusetts Institute of Technology, 1986. *Biophysics*. Biologically inspired strategies for self-assembly; roles of mechanical force in biological systems; single-molecule force experiments.

Randall, Lisa, Ph.D., Harvard University, 1987. *Cosmology & String Theory, Particles and Fields, Relativity & Gravitation*. Field theory; the Standard Model and beyond.

Samuel, Aravinthan, Ph.D., Harvard University, 1999. *Biophysics*. Biophysics, neurobiology, and animal behavior.

Schwartz, Matthew, Ph.D., Princeton University, 2003. *Particles and Fields*. Cosmology, particles, and fields. Theoretical particle physics and cosmology with connections to experimental data.

Silvera, Isaac F., Ph.D., University of California, Berkeley, 1965. *Condensed Matter Physics, Low Temperature Physics*. High-pressure and low-temperature physics: electrons in liquid helium, in particular multi-electron bubbles; high pressure: properties of hydrogen under pressure to multi- megabar pressures, aimed at metallization of hydrogen; nEDM-measurement of the electric dipole moment of the neutron.

Strominger, Andrew, Ph.D., Massachusetts Institute of Technology, 1982. *Cosmology & String Theory, Relativity & Gravitation*. String theory, black holes and topological strings, 2D quantum field theory.

Stubbs, Christopher, Ph.D., University of Washington, 1988. *Astronomy, Astrophysics, Relativity & Gravitation*. Experimental physics at the interface between particle physics, cosmology, and gravitation.

Vafa, Cumrun, Ph.D., Princeton University, 1985. *Cosmology & String Theory*. String theory; interplay between geometry and physics, including applications to QFTs and black holes.

Vishwanath, Ashvin, Ph.D., Princeton University, 2001. *Condensed Matter Physics*. condensed matter physics, topological phases, quantum phase transitions, magnetism and superconductivity.

Weitz, David, Ph.D., Harvard University, 1978. *Applied Physics, Biophysics, Condensed Matter Physics*. Soft condensed matter physics, biophysics, and biotechnology.

Westervelt, Robert M., Ph.D., University of California, Berkeley, 1977. *Applied Physics, Condensed Matter Physics, Low Temperature Physics, Medical, Health Physics, Nano Science and Technology.* Experimental condensed matter physics: Cooled Scanning Probe Microscope imaging of electron motion in nanostructures; Biophysics: programmable Integrated Circuit Microfluidic chips for biomedicine.

Wu, Tai Tsun, Ph.D., Harvard University, 1956. *High Energy Physics, Statistical & Thermal Physics.* Electromagnetism; high-energy physics; statistical and thermal physics; quantum information processing.

Yacoby, Amir, Ph.D., Weizmann Institute of Science, 1994. *Condensed Matter Physics.* Experimental condensed matter physics; quantum computing; strongly correlated electrons; graphene; scan probe techniques; NV centers in diamond.

Yau, Shing-Tung, Ph.D., University of California, Berkeley, 1971. *Relativity & Gravitation.* differential geometry, especially in geometric analysis, interface between geometry and theoretical physics.

Yin, Xi, Ph.D., Harvard University, 2006. *Cosmology & String Theory.* String theory.

Zhuang, Xiaowei, Ph.D., University of California, Berkeley, 1996. *Biophysics.* Biophysics and Bioimaging. Single-molecule spectroscopy; super-resolution imaging; single-molecule biophysics; cellular biophysics.

Associate Professor

Levine, Erel, Ph.D., Weizmann Institute of Science, 2005. *Biophysics, Nonlinear Dynamics and Complex Systems, Statistical & Thermal Physics.* Collective dynamics in biological systems; multiscale approaches to gene regulation; statistical and information physics of embryonic and post-embryonic development.

Reece, Matthew, Ph.D., Cornell University, 2008. *Particles and Fields.* Physics beyond the Standard Model.

Assistant Professor

Dvorkin, Cora, Ph.D., University of Chicago, 2011. *Astrophysics.* "Data driven" cosmology: predictions from fundamental physics which can be tested with cosmological data.

Guenette, Roxanne, Ph.D., McGill University, 2010. *High Energy Physics, Particles and Fields.* neutrino physics (oscillation physics, cross-section measurements, sterile neutrinos) noble liquid detectors research and development of particle detectors.

Jafferis, Daniel L., Ph.D., Harvard University, 2007. *Cosmology & String Theory.* Quantum field theory, string theory, and quantum gravity.

Mundy, Julia, Ph.D., Cornell University, 2014. *Condensed Matter Physics.* Prof. Mundy's research combines thin film deposition with advanced characterization techniques to design, synthesize and probe novel quantum materials at the atomic-scale.

Ni, Kang-Kuen, Ph.D., University of Colorado, Boulder, 2009. *Atomic, Molecular, & Optical Physics, Chemical Physics.* Ultra-cold atoms.

Emeritus

Glauber, Roy J., Ph.D., Harvard University, 1949. *Atomic, Molecular, & Optical Physics, Electromagnetism, Nuclear Physics, Optics, Particles and Fields, Statistical & Thermal Physics.* Theoretical physics.

Holton, Gerald, Ph.D., Harvard University, 1948. *History & Philosophy of Physics/Science.* Experimental physics; history of 19th and 20th century physics.

Horowitz, Paul, Ph.D., Harvard University, 1970. *Astrophysics, Electrical Engineering.* Experimental astrophysics.

Professor Emeritus

Berg, Howard C., Ph.D., Harvard University, 1964. *Biophysics.* Biophysics; motile behavior of bacteria.

Feldman, Gary, Ph.D., Harvard University, 1971. *High Energy Physics.* Experimental high-energy physics.

Pershan, Peter S., Ph.D., Harvard University, 1960. *Chemical Physics, Condensed Matter Physics.* Experimental chemical physics; experimental condensed matter physics.

Senior Lecturer / Research Associate

Walsworth, Ronald, Ph.D., Harvard University, 1991. *Applied Physics, Astrophysics, Atomic, Molecular, & Optical Physics, Biophysics, Condensed Matter Physics, Low Temperature Physics, Medical, Health Physics, Nano Science and Technology, Optics.* Precision measurement tools, laser frequency combs, nanoscale magnetometry, etc.

Lecturer

Barandes, Jacob A., Ph.D., Harvard University, 2011. Associate Director of Graduate Studies, Director of Graduate Studies for FAS Science. *Cosmology & String Theory, Physics and other Science Education, Theoretical Physics.* String theory.

Hayes, Thomas, Other, Harvard University, 1969. Instructional Laboratory Associate in Physics. *Applied Physics, Physics and other Science Education.* Laboratory electronics, device physics, etc.

McCarty, Logan, Ph.D., Harvard University, 2007. Director of Physical Sciences Education. *Applied Physics, Chemical Physics, Physics and other Science Education.* Science education, etc.

Morin, David, Ph.D., Harvard University, 1996. Associate Director of Undergraduate Studies. *Applied Physics, Physics and other Science Education.* Classical mechanics, special relativity, etc.

Senior Research Fellow

Yelin, Susanne, Ph.D., Ludwig-Maximilians University, 1998. Senior Research Fellow. *Atomic, Molecular, & Optical Physics.* Quantum optics; quantum information science; cold molecules.

DEPARTMENTAL RESEARCH SPECIALTIES AND STAFF

Theoretical

Acoustics. Heller.

Applied Mathematics. Brenner, Mahadevan, Nelson.

Applied Physics. Brenner, Heller, Kaxiras, Nelson.

Astrophysics. Dvorkin, Finkbeiner, Reece, Shapiro.

Atomic, Molecular, & Optical Physics. Demler, Glauber, Heller.

Biophysics. Brenner, Desai, Levine, Mahadevan, Nelson.

Chemical Physics. Heller, Kaxiras, Nelson.

Computational Physics. The development of multiscale methods to couple disparate spatial and temporal scales for the study of complex physical phenomena, and the application of such methods to problems related to energy conversion and energy storage systems. Heller, Kaxiras.

Condensed Matter Physics. Demler, Halperin, Heller, Kaxiras, Nelson, Sachdev, Vishwanath.

Cosmology & String Theory. Studying the nature of time in de-Sitter space and exploring models of quantum gravity. Barandes, Jafferis, Randall, Strominger, Vafa, Yin.

Electromagnetism. Glauber.

Energy Sources & Environment.

High Energy Physics. Wu.

History & Philosophy of Physics/Science. Galison, Holton.

Nonlinear Dynamics and Complex Systems. Desai, Heller, Levine.

Nuclear Physics. Glauber.

Optics. Glauber, Jaffe, Randall, Reece, Schwartz.

Particles and Fields. Theoretical particle physics and cosmology with connections to experimental data from the Large Hadron Collider. Understanding Jets at The Large Hadron Collider and studying effective field theories and the study of unparticles. Barandes, Georgi, Schwartz.

Polymer Physics/Science. Nelson.

Relativity & Gravitation. Randall, Shapiro, Strominger, Yau.

Statistical & Thermal Physics. Desai, Glauber, Levine, Nelson, Wu.

Experimental

Applied Physics. Golovchenko, Hau, Manoharan, Mazur, Murray, Narayanamurti, Walsworth, Weitz, Westervelt.

Astrophysics. The experimental astrophysics effort includes microwave background polarization measurements to constrain the physics of inflation, observations designed to better determine the nature of dark energy, dark matter searches using indirect detection techniques and precision tests of gravity in astrophysical systems. Additional projects include efforts to improve the precision of astronomical measurements and detector development for LSST. Horowitz, Kovac, Stubbs, Walsworth.

Atomic, Molecular, & Optical Physics. Ultracold molecules, physics in the quantum regime, advanced cold molecule electron electric dipole moment search, cold atom interferometry for inertial sensing, the production and study of antiprotons and cold antihydrogen, monlinear optics and ultrashort laser pulses, quantum optical techniques for solid-state quantum information processing. Quantum sensing, quantum optics, strongly correlated quantum gas with single site addressability. Doyle, Gabrielse, Golovchenko, Greiner, Hau, Lukin, Mazur, Ni, Park, Walsworth.

Biophysics. Biophysical approaches to complex navigational behaviors in larval Drosophila melanogaster, subcellular surgery, coherent molecular profiling using nano-structured environments illegitimate recombination by drug resistance elements. Berg, Desai, Golovchenko, Levine, Manoharan, Mazur, Park, Prentiss, Samuel, Walsworth, Weitz, Westervelt, Zhuang.

Chemical Physics. Cohen, Ni, Pershan.

Condensed Matter Physics. Mesoscopic quantum phenomena at the interface between micro and macro scales, Bulk Magnetometry, and Quantum Information Processing (QIP) focusing on Diamond characterization and quantum physics. Interaction of ultrashort laser pulses with matter, novel semiconductor materials, light scattering, optical microscopy, spectroscopy, synthesis and other experimental techniques to understand the physics of self-organization. Multi-Qubit Systems based on electron spins in coupled quantum dots, development of novel quantum devices using nitrogen vacancy centers in diamond, development of solid-state topological quantum computing, spin-resolved imaging of correlated electron systems including cuprates and pnictides, metallization of hydrogen. Golovchenko, Hoffman, Kim, Lukin, Manoharan, Mundy, Narayanamurti, Nelson, Park, Pershan, Silvera, Walsworth, Weitz, Westervelt, Yacoby.

Electrical Engineering. Horowitz.

Electromagnetism. Golovchenko.

Energy Sources & Environment.

Fluids, Rheology. Manoharan.

High Energy Physics. Collider physics with the ATLAS experiment at the Large Hadron Collider. Neutrino physics with the MINOS and NOVA experiments. Feldman, Franklin, Gabrielse, Guenette, Huth, Morii.

Low Temperature Physics. Study of multi-electron bubbles in superfluid helium, hydrogen at low temperature, measurement of the electric dipole moment. Halperin, Heller, Hoffman, Silvera, Walsworth, Westervelt.

Materials Science, Metallurgy. Golovchenko, Mazur.

Medical, Health Physics. Walsworth, Westervelt.

Nano Science and Technology. Walsworth, Westervelt.

Nonlinear Dynamics and Complex Systems. Desai, Levine.

Nuclear Physics.

Optics. Manoharan, Mazur, Walsworth.

Physics and other Science Education. Barandes, Mazur, Morin.

Relativity & Gravitation. Stubbs.

Statistical & Thermal Physics. Desai, Levine, Manoharan.

View additional information about this department at www.gradschoolshopper.com. Check out the "Why Choose Us?" section, find out more about the department's culture and get links to social media networks.

MASSACHUSETTS INSTITUTE OF TECHNOLOGY

DEPARTMENT OF EARTH, ATMOSPHERIC, AND PLANETARY SCIENCES

Cambridge, Massachusetts 02139
http://eapsweb.mit.edu

General University Information

President: L. Rafael Reif
Dean of Graduate School: Senior Associate Dean, Blanche Staton
University website: http://web.mit.edu
School Type: Private
Setting: Urban
Total Faculty: 1,872
Total Graduate Faculty: 1,036
Total number of Students: 11,376
Total number of Graduate Students: 6,696

Department Information

Department Chairman: Prof. Robert van der Hilst, Head
Department Contact: Megan Jordan, Academic Program Administrator
  Total full-time faculty: 39
  Total number of full-time equivalent positions: 39
  Full-Time Graduate Students: 140
  Female Full-Time Graduate Students: 69
  First-Year Graduate Students: 26
  Female First-Year Students: 14
  Total Post Doctorates: 64

Department Address

54-912
77 Massachusetts Avenue
Cambridge, MA 02139
Phone: (617) 253-3381
Fax: (617) 253-8298
E-mail: eaps-admissions@mit.edu
Website: http://eapsweb.mit.edu

ADMISSIONS

Admission Contact Information

Address admission inquiries to: Education Office, Department of Earth, Atmospheric, and Planetary Sciences, Room 54-912, MIT, 77 Massachusetts Avenue, Cambridge, MA 02139
Phone: (617) 253-3381
E-mail: eaps-admissions@mit.edu
Admissions website: http://eapsweb.mit.edu/graduate-admissions

Application deadlines

Fall admission:
U.S. students: January 5   *Int'l. students*: January 5
Spring admission:
U.S. students: November 5   *Int'l. students*: November 5

Application fee

U.S. students: $75   *Int'l. students*: $75

Admissions information

For Fall of 2018:
  Number of applicants: 216
  Number admitted: 31
  Number enrolled: 20

Admission requirements

Bachelor's degree requirements: A strong undergraduate emphasis in math and science is necessary. We have no minimum GPA requirement. All applications are reviewed.

GRE requirements

The GRE is required.
We set no minimum scores for the GRE and Advanced GRE tests. All applications are reviewed.

Subjective GRE requirements

The Subjective GRE is required.
GRE Physics or Chemistry subject test is required only for applicants to our Planetary Sciences program.

TOEFL requirements

The TOEFL exam is required for students from non-English-speaking countries.
  PBT score: 577
  iBT score: 100

Other admissions information

Additional requirements: IELTS is the preferred examination, rather than the TOEFL, and 7.0 is the minimum acceptable score. The GRE subject test in chemistry or physics is required for the planetary science program.
Undergraduate preparation assumed: An undergraduate degree should have strong emphasis on math and science. Specific preparation will depend on the area of study chosen.

TUITION

Tuition year 2017–18:
  Full-time students: $25,760 per semester
  Part-time students: $800 per credit
(12 units/course) Definition of "tuition waiver": all incoming doctoral students have their tuition fully paid through a fellowship or research assistantship.
Credit hours per semester to be considered full-time: 36
Deferred tuition plan:
Health insurance: Available at the cost of $3144 per year.
Other academic fees: $312 student life fee.
Academic term: Semester
Number of first-year students who received full tuition waivers: 14

Teaching Assistants, Research Assistants, and Fellowships

Number of first-year
  Fellowship students: 19
Average stipend per academic year
  Teaching Assistant: $29,367
  Research Assistant: $28,683
  Fellowship student: $28,683
All students accepted into our doctoral programs are provided with support that includes tuition, a stipend, and health insurance. These stipend number reflect a 9 month academic year. Students also commonly received stipends over the summer

FINANCIAL AID

Loans

Loans are available for U.S. students.
Loans are not available for international students.
GAPSFAS application required: Yes
FAFSA application required: No

For further information

Address financial aid inquiries to: Student Financial Services, MIT Room 11-320, 77 Massachusetts Avenue, Cambridge, MA 02139.
Phone: (617) 253-4971
E-mail: sfs@mit.edu
Financial aid website: http://web.mit.edu/sfs/financial_aid/index.html

HOUSING

Availability of on-campus housing

Single students: Yes
Married students: Yes
Childcare Assistance: No

For further information

Address housing inquiries to: Graduate Housing Office, MIT Room W59-200, 77 Massachusetts Avenue, Cambridge, MA 02139.
Phone: (617) 253-5148
E-mail: graduatehousing@mit.edu
Housing aid website: http://housing.mit.edu/graduatefamily/graduate_family_housing

Table A—Faculty, Enrollments, and Degrees Granted

Research Specialty	2017–18 Faculty	Enrollment Fall 2017		Number of Degrees Granted 2016–17		
		Master's	Doctorate	Master's	Terminal Master's	Doctorate
Climate/Atmospheric Science	12	1	27	–	–	7
Geology/Geochemistry/ Geobiology	12	1	20	–	–	4
Geophysics	10	3	10	–	3	2
Marine Science/ Oceanography	9	–	71	–	–	22
Planetary Science	9	2	10	–	1	3
Total	39	6	–	–	4	38
Full-time Grad. Stud.	–	6	138	–	–	–
First-year Grad. Stud.	–	4	26	–	–	–

GRADUATE DEGREE REQUIREMENTS

Master's: Sixty-six units of total credit, which include 42 units within a subject area. A thesis is required.
Doctorate: Completion of the departmental program, passing the qualifying examination, and a thesis are required.
Thesis: Required for all students.

SPECIAL EQUIPMENT, FACILITIES, OR PROGRAMS

Students have access to the Magellan telescopes at Las Campanas Observatory. Students in the MIT/WHOI Joint Program have access to the extensive oceanographic research facilities of the Woods Hole Oceanographic Institution. The Department gives students access to excellent computer and laboratory facilities. Students may also participate in a variety of field camps: geological, geophysical, astronomical, and oceanographic.

Table B—Separately Budgeted Research Expenditures by Source of Support

Source of Support	Departmental Research	Physics-related Research Outside Department
Federal government	$13,874,100	
State/local government	$520,279	
Non-profit organizations	$1,387,410	
Business and industry	$1,384,410	
Other	$173,426	
Total	$17,339,625	

Table C—Separately Budgeted Research Expenditures by Research Specialty

Research Specialty	No. of Grants	Expenditures ($)
Astronomy	2	$151,612
Climate/Atmospheric Science	27	$6,466,790
Geology/Geochemistry/Geobiology	33	$4,209,096
Geophysics	24	$2,745,759
Marine Science/Oceanography	2	$459,367
Planetary Science	21	$3,310,001
Total	109	$17,342,625

FACULTY

Professor

Binzel, Richard P., Ph.D., University of Texas, 1986. *Astronomy*. Planetary astronomy; collisional evolution of asteroids; physical parameters and surface features of the Pluto-Charon system.

Boyle, Edward A., Ph.D., Massachusetts Institute of Technology, 1976. *Geology/Geochemistry, Marine Science/Oceanography*. Paleoceanography and paleoclimatology; variability of the chemical composition of seawater; trace element chemistry of seawater, rivers, and estuaries.

Emanuel, Kerry A., Ph.D., Massachusetts Institute of Technology, 1981. *Climate/Atmospheric Science*. Relationship between cumulus convection and large-scale circulations; parametric representation of convection in large-scale weather forecast and climate models; the Hadley circulation; mesoscale dynamics of fronts and cyclones; tropical cyclone dynamics.

Ferrari, Raffaele, Ph.D., Scripps Institution of Oceanography, 2001. *Climate/Atmospheric Science, Marine Science/Oceanography*. Turbulence in the ocean and atmosphere using a combination of theory, models, and observations; role of the ocean on climate and on biological productivity.

Flierl, Glenn R., Ph.D., Harvard University, 1975. *Climate/Atmospheric Science*. Impacts of oceanic eddies upon the distribution of tracers and on the biology of the sea, including both transport and alterations in the reaction terms.

Follows, Michael, Ph.D., University of East Anglia, 1990. *Climate/Atmospheric Science, Marine Science/Oceanography*. Biogeochemical cycles of carbon and nutrients in the ocean. Use of numerical models to understand the combination of physical transport, chemical and biological processes that determine the distributions and fluxes of these elements in the ocean.

Grove, Timothy L., Ph.D., Harvard University, 1976. *Geology/Geochemistry, Planetary Science*. Igneous petrology;

magma generation processes in island arc-continental settings and mid-ocean ridges; crystal growth and nucleation; phase transitions in minerals; diffusion in crystalline solids and silicate melts; thermal histories of geologic materials.

Hager, Bradford H., Ph.D., Harvard University, 1978. *Geophysics*. Physics of geologic processes; numerical modeling of mantle convection in terrestrial planets; numerical modeling of crustal deformation; GPS geodesy.

Herring, Thomas A., Ph.D., Massachusetts Institute of Technology, 1983. *Geophysics*. Techniques of space geodesy, including very long baseline interferometry and the use of the Global Positioning System; surface deformations related to plate tectonics and plate boundary zones; effects of whole-Earth dynamics on the nutation series.

Marshall, John C., Ph.D., Imperial College, 1980. *Climate/Atmospheric Science, Marine Science/Oceanography*. Dynamics and causes of the general circulation of the atmosphere and ocean; thermocline theory; geostrophic eddies; global-scale ocean modeling.

Morgan, Dale, Ph.D., Massachusetts Institute of Technology, 1981. *Geophysics*. Rock physics; geoelectromagnetism; inverse methods; applied seismology; environmental geophysics.

Prinn, Ronald G., Ph.D., Massachusetts Institute of Technology, 1971. *Climate/Atmospheric Science, Planetary Science*. Chemical-dynamical models of the atmosphere; measurement and modeling of the long-lived gases involved in the greenhouse effect and ozone depletion; atmospheric chemistry of carbon and sulfur compounds; integrated global system modelling that couples atmospheric, oceanic, and terrestrial physics, chemistry, and biology.

Rizzoli, Paola M., Ph.D., Scripps Institution of Oceanography, 1978. *Climate/Atmospheric Science, Marine Science/Oceanography*. Numerical modeling of the ocean general circulation with specific emphasis on the tropical Atlantic ocean, tropical/subtropical interactions, tropical instability waves, and coupled ocean-atmosphere modes; assimilation of oceanographic data into ocean numerical models through ensemble approaches and optimal design of fixed and adaptive observational arrays; physical-biochemical modeling of the Black Sea ecosystem.

Rothman, Daniel H., Ph.D., Stanford University, 1986. *Climate/Atmospheric Science, Geology/Geochemistry, Geophysics*. Dynamical organization of the past and present environment, including coevolution of life and the physical environment; dynamics of the carbon cycle; geological fluid mechanics; geomorphology.

Royden, Leigh H., Ph.D., Massachusetts Institute of Technology, 1982. *Geology/Geochemistry, Geophysics*. Regional geology and geophysics; plate tectonics; thermal effects of continental deformation; mechanics of large-scale continental deformation; lithospheric flexure; continental extensions and sedimentary basin formation; uplift and erosion in mountain belts.

Seager, Sara, Ph.D., Harvard University, 1999. *Astronomy, Atmosphere, Space Physics, Cosmic Rays, Planetary Science*. Finding and characterizing earth-like exoplanets; theoretical models of atmospheres, interiors, and biosignatures of all kinds of exoplanets; astrobiology.

Solomon, Susan, Ph.D., University of California, Berkeley, 1981. *Climate/Atmospheric Science*. Atmospheric chemistry and transport in the stratosphere and troposphere; climate change and its coupling to chemistry; comparative studies of environment and society.

Summons, Roger, Ph.D., University of New South Wales, 1972. *Climate/Atmospheric Science, Geology/Geochemistry*. Lipid chemistry of microbes; early biotic and environmental evolution; extinction and radiation events in earth history; biogeochemical fossils; petroleum; astrobiology.

van der Hilst, Robert D., Ph.D., Utrecht University, 1990. *Geophysics*. Seismic tomography; studies of the earth's structure with emphasis on mantle beneath convergent plate boundaries; tectonic evolution of subduction systems; mantle dynamics; structure and evolution of continental lithosphere; field studies with portable seismometers.

Weiss, Benjamin P., Ph.D., California Institute of Technology, 2003. *Geology/Geochemistry, Geophysics, Planetary Science*. Paleomagnetic studies of rocks from Mars, the moon, asteroids, and the earth; dynamo evolution, planetary histories and interiors; use and development of new magnetometry techniques.

Wisdom, Jack, Ph.D., California Institute of Technology, 1981. *Planetary Science*. Solar system dynamics; long-term evolution of the orbits and spins of the planets and natural satellites; qualitative behavior of dynamical systems; chaotic behavior.

Zuber, Maria T., Ph.D., Brown University, 1986. *Geophysics, Planetary Science*. Theoretical modeling of geophysical processes; analysis of altimetry, gravity, and tectonics to determine the structure and dynamics of the earth and solid planets; development and implementation of spacecraft laser and radio-tracking experiments.

Associate Professor

Bosak, Tanja, Ph.D., California Institute of Technology, 2004. *Geology/Geochemistry*. Microbial sediments throughout geologic time as indicators of biological processes and environmental conditions; morphological and chemical biosignatures; early earth; astrobiology.

Cahoy, Kerri, Ph.D., Stanford University, 2008. *Climate/Atmospheric Science, Planetary Science*. Planetary atmospheres; exoplanet atmospheres with optical direct imaging instruments (coronagraphs) onboard spacecraft; solar system planets with spacecraft radio occultation; Earth with GNSS radio occultation.

Cziczo, Daniel J., Ph.D., University of Chicago, 1999. *Climate/Atmospheric Science*. Chemical composition of atmospheric aerosols with an emphasis on their effect on cloud formation mechanisms, the Earth's radiative budget, and meteoritic debris and launch vehicle emissions in the atmosphere.

Heald, Colette L., Ph.D., Harvard University, 2005. *Climate/Atmospheric Science*. Atmospheric chemistry and composition; biosphere-atmosphere interactions; global modeling; satellite observations.

Jagoutz, Oliver, Ph.D., ETH Zurich, 2004. *Geology/Geochemistry*. Field-related studies of igneous processes; crust mantle interaction; formation and evolution of the oceanic and continental lithosphere.

Juanes, Ruben, Ph.D., University of California, Berkeley, 2003. *Energy Sources & Environment, Geology/Geochemistry, Geophysics*. Physics of multiphase flow in porous media; application of theoretical, computational and experimental research to energy and environment-driven geophysical problems, such as petroleum recovery, carbon sequestration, methane hydrates, and water infiltration in soil.

McGee, David, Ph.D., Columbia University, 2009. *Climate/Atmospheric Science, Geology/Geochemistry*. Reconstruction of past climates using cave, lake, and marine deposits; U-Th dating of cave and lacustrine carbonates; U-series investigations of marine sediments; constant flux proxies; records of past atmospheric circulation and hydrology.

O'Gorman, Paul, Ph.D., California Institute of Technology, 2004. *Climate/Atmospheric Science*. Large-scale circulation of the atmosphere; interactions of moisture and baroclinic eddies; effect of climate change on the hydrological cycle; turbulence closure theories.

Ono, Shuhei, Ph.D., Pennsylvania State University, 2001. *Geology/Geochemistry*. Isotope biogeochemistry of sulfur and oxygen, water-rock-microbe interactions, seafloor hydrothermal deposits, deep biosphere, and global sulfur cycles.

Perron, J. Taylor, Ph.D., University of California, Berkeley, 2006. *Geology/Geochemistry, Planetary Science*. Measurement and modeling of physical processes that shape the surfaces of planets; river networks; biotic effects on landscape evolution; volatile cycling on Mars and Titan.

Selin, Noelle Eckley, Ph.D., Harvard University, 2007. *Climate/Atmospheric Science*. Atmospheric chemistry modeling; biogeochemical cycling of mercury (Hg); air pollution/climate interactions; air pollution health impacts; science-policy interactions.

Assistant Professor

Babbin, Andrew R., Ph.D., Princeton University, 2014. *Climate/Atmospheric Science, Geology/Geochemistry*. His research incorporates elements from field observations, numerical modeling and laboratory experiments to understand the environment and the fundamental controls on marine biogeochemistry.

Bergmann, Kristin, Ph.D., California Institute of Technology, 2014. *Geology/Geochemistry*. Marine carbonate deposition through time and how that informs our understanding of Earth's past climate and seawater chemistry. Sedimentological observations to inform petrography and sequence stratigraphy.Use of carbonate clumped isotope thermometry and a variety of microanalytical techniques to probe the temperature and fluid composition of depositional environments and diagenetic events. Currently working in Svalbard, Oman, the Basin and Range and the mid-continent on the Neoproterozoic through end-Orodovician glaciation.

Cronin, Timothy W., Ph.D., Massachusetts Institute of Technology, 2014. *Climate/Atmospheric Science*. Cold air formation in warmer climates; self-aggregation of convection; diurnal cycle and island rainfall; boundary layer sensitivity; details about radiative-convective equilibrium; tropical cyclones in odd environments; Hadley circulation and eddies.

Fournier, Gregory, Ph.D., University of Connecticut, 2009. *Other*. Reconstructing events in the history of life has a long tradition in the geological and paleontological sciences. However, only with the recent advent of extensive genomic sequencing has molecular biology been able to look backward in time in the same way, using the record of events preserved within the genomes of existing organisms. My research attempts to integrate these methods in order to investigate important questions in evolution: reconstructing ancestral protein sequences and determining the functional roles of proteins existing in organisms early in the history of life.

Minchew, Brent, Ph.D., California Institute of Technology, 2016. *Geophysics*. Dynamics of extant glaciers, with an emphasis on the mechanics of glacier beds, ice-ocean interactions, and ice rheology.

Pĕc, Matĕj, Ph.D., University of Basel, 2012. *Geology/Geochemistry*. Experimental rock deformation; structural geology; igneous petrology.

DEPARTMENTAL RESEARCH SPECIALTIES AND STAFF

Theoretical

Climate/Atmospheric Science. Dynamics of the atmosphere and ocean; climate dynamics and modeling; theory of monsoons; coupled ocean-atmosphere models; chemical dynamical models of the atmosphere; inverse methods applied to global trace gas cycles; climatic effects of changes in carbon dioxide concentrations and solar constant; dynamics of planetary atmospheres; data assimilation and adaptive sampling; predictability and ensemble forecasting; mesoscale dynamics of fronts and cyclones; dynamics of tropical intraseasonal oscillations and tropical cyclones; modeling planetary atmospheres. Boyle, Cronin, Cziczo, Emanuel, Ferrari, Flierl, Follows, Heald, Marshall, McGee, O'Gorman, Prinn, Rizzoli, Rothman, Seager, Selin, Solomon, Summons.

Geophysics. Numerical models of nonlinear dynamical systems; fluid dynamics; theoretical models of rock physics; numerical methods for seismology; mantle dynamics; geodesy. Hager, Herring, Juanes, Morgan, Rothman, Royden, van der Hilst, Weiss, Zuber.

Marine Science/Oceanography. Dynamics of thermohaline circulation of the ocean, numerical modeling of ocean-climate interactions, and analysis of oceanic data; modeling of the physics, chemistry, and biology of strongly nonlinear eddies and meandering jets; interactions between waves and vortices. Boyle, Emanuel, Ferrari, Flierl, Follows, Marshall, Rizzoli, Rothman.

Planetary Science. Numerical experiments and theoretical studies of geophysical fluid dynamics; origins and evolution of planetary jet-stream wind profiles; solar system dynamics; long-term evolution of orbits and spins of planets and satellites; chaotic behavior; dynamics of planetary rings; planetary history, planetary gravity, and magnetic fields; geochemical and geophysical studies of meteorites, atmospheres, and interiors of exoplanets. Binzel, Cahoy, Cziczo, Grove, Perron, Prinn, Seager, Weiss, Wisdom, Zuber.

Experimental

Climate/Atmospheric Science. Ocean general circulation, paleo-oceanography, and paleo-climatology; abrupt climate change; development and application of trace element, organic geochemical, and stable isotopic techniques in oceanography and paleoclimatology; decadal-to-millennial scale climate change; origin of organic-rich sediment sequences in the marine environment; marine nitrogen cycle; acoustic tomography; hydrometeorology and hydroclimatology; global measurements of radiatively and chemically important trace gases; climate diagnostic studies; El Niño Southern Oscillation phenomenon; diagnostic studies of the general circulation; satellite observations of planetary atmospheres. Boyle, Cronin, Cziczo, Emanuel, Ferrari, Flierl, Follows, Heald, Marshall, McGee, O'Gorman, Prinn, Rizzoli, Rothman, Seager, Selin, Solomon, Summons.

Geology/Geochemistry. Rift magmatism, origin, and evolution of continental lithosphere using radiogenic isotopes, earth history, active tectonics, structural geology, metamorphic and igneous petrology, geochronology, and numerical simulations of depositional systems; magma generation processes in arcs, ocean ridges, ocean islands, and large igneous processes; mineralogy of the mantle and mantle processes controlling mantle geochemistry; mechanics and thermal effects of continental deformation, sediment transport by currents and waves, interpretation of ancient sedimentary environments, process geomorphology, debris-flow rheology, tectonic geomorphology, environmental monitoring of natural terrestrial and marine ecosystems, and the role of climate in the evolution of orogenic systems; petroleum systems; lipids of cultured microbes and microbial consortia; molecular signatures of hydrothermal ecosystems; signals of biochemical change through time. Babbin, Bergmann, Bosak, Boyle, Fournier, Grove, Jagoutz, McGee, Ono, Pĕc, Perron, Rothman, Royden, Summons, Weiss.

Geophysics. Application of rock mechanics to tectonic problems; mantle dynamics; numerical modeling of solid-state convection; space geodesy; plate tectonics; seismology; geodetic observation of surface deformation; thermal structure of oceanic lithosphere in the vicinity of hot-spot volcanoes; rock physics; environmental geophysics; seismic tomography for characterization of the earth's crust and petroleum reservoirs; tectonic evolution of subduction systems; structure and evolution of continental lithospheres. Hager, Herring, Juanes, Minchew, Morgan, Pĕc, Rothman, Royden, van der Hilst, Weiss, Zuber.

Marine Science/Oceanography. Numerical modeling of ocean general circulation; paleo-oceanography and paleo-climatology; trace element geochemistry; acoustic tomography. Boyle, Ferrari, Flierl, Follows, Marshall, Rizzoli.

Planetary Science. Collisional of asteroids; planetary atmospheric dynamics; Kuiper belt; stellar occultations at optical and infrared wavelengths; geodesy; radar and radio studies of physical properties of planets; the Pluto-Charon system; origins and evolution of eddy features (e.g., Jupiter's Great Red Spot); models of planetary lithosphere deformation and the physics of volcanism; development and implementation of space-based laser ranging systems; planetary paleomagnetism and geomagnetism; astrobiology and planetary history; extrasolar planets. Binzel, Cahoy, Cziczo, Grove, Perron, Prinn, Seager, Weiss, Wisdom, Zuber.

View additional information about this department at www.gradschoolshopper.com. Check out the "Why Choose Us?" section, find out more about the department's culture and get links to social media networks.

MASSACHUSETTS INSTITUTE OF TECHNOLOGY

DEPARTMENT OF PHYSICS

Cambridge, Massachusetts 02139
http://web.mit.edu/physics/index.html

General University Information
President: L. Rafael Reif
Dean of Graduate School: Cynthia Barnhart, Chancellor
University website: http://web.mit.edu
School Type: Private
Setting: Urban
Total Faculty: 1,047
Total Graduate Faculty: 1,047
Total number of Students: 11,466
Total number of Graduate Students: 6,916

Department Information
Department Chairman: Prof. Peter Fisher, Head
Department Contact: Matthew Cubstead, Administrative
  Officer
  Total full-time faculty: 78
  Total number of full-time equivalent positions: 78
  Full-Time Graduate Students: 253
  Female Full-Time Graduate Students: 56
  First-Year Graduate Students: 44
  Female First-Year Students: 11
  Total Post Doctorates: 97

ADMISSIONS

Admission Contact Information
Address admission inquiries to: Graduate Admissions Officer,
  Department of Physics, Room 4-315
Phone: (617) 253-9703
E-mail: physics-grad@mit.edu
Admissions website: http://web.mit.edu/physics/prospective/
  graduate/index.html

Application deadlines
Fall admission:
U.S. students: December 15   *Int'l. students*: December 15

Application fee
U.S. students: $75   *Int'l. students*: $75

Admissions information
For Fall of 2018:
  Number of applicants: 932
  Number admitted: 87
  Number enrolled: 42

Admission requirements
Bachelor's degree requirements: Bachelor's degree in Physics
  is required.

GRE requirements
The GRE is required.

Subjective GRE requirements
The Subjective GRE is required.

TOEFL requirements
Students from non-English speaking countries are required to
  demonstrate proficiency in English via the IELTS exam or
  the TOEFL exam.

Other admissions information
Undergraduate preparation assumed: Reif, Fundamentals of Statistical and Thermal Physics: Marion, Classical Dynamics,
  and Classical Electromagnetic Radiation; Griffiths, Quantum
  Mechanics.

TUITION

Tuition year 2018–19:
  Full-time students: $51,520 annual
  Part-time students: $800 per credit
(12 units/course) Definition of 'tuition waivers': all incoming
  students have their tuition fully paid through a fellowship,
  research assistantship, or teaching assistantship.
Credit hours per semester to be considered full-time: 36
Deferred tuition plan: No
Health insurance: Available at the cost of $3,144 per year.
Other academic fees: Student Life Fee $312
Academic term: Semester
Number of first-year students who received full tuition waivers: 44

Teaching Assistants, Research Assistants, and Fellowships
Number of first-year
  Teaching Assistants: 1
  Research Assistants: 9
  Fellowship students: 34
Average stipend per academic year
  Teaching Assistant: $39,156
  Research Assistant: $39,156
  Fellowship student: $39,156

FINANCIAL AID

Application deadlines
Fall admission:
U.S. students: December 15   *Int'l. students*: December 15

Loans
Loans are not available for U.S. students.
Loans are not available for international students.
GAPSFAS application required: No
FAFSA application required: No

For further information
Address financial aid inquiries to: Graduate Admissions Officer,
  Department of Physics, Room 4-315.
Phone: (617) 253-9703
E-mail: physics-grad@mit.edu
Financial aid website: http://web.mit.edu/physics/prospective/
  graduate/funding.html

HOUSING

Availability of on-campus housing
Single students: Yes
Married students: Yes
Childcare Assistance: No

For further information

Address housing inquiries to: MIT Housing Office, W59-200, 77 Massachusetts Ave., Cambridge MA 02139.

Phone: (617) 253-5148

E-mail: graduatehousing@mit.edu

Housing aid website: http://housing.mit.edu/graduatefamily/graduate_family_housing

Table A—Faculty, Enrollments, and Degrees Granted

Research Specialty	2018–19 Faculty	Enrollment Fall 2017		Number of Degrees Granted 2017–18 (2014–18)		
		Master's	Doctorate	Master's	Terminal Master's	Doctorate
Astrophysics	19	–	29	–(3)	–(1)	4(20)
Atomic, Molecular, & Optical Physics	5	–	38	–(1)	–(1)	6(20)
Biophysics	7	–	30	–	–	2(10)
Condensed Matter Physics	13	–	55	–	1(2)	5(41)
Nuclear Physics	7	1	46	–	–(2)	6(29)
Particles and Fields	23	–	29	–	–	6(29)
Plasma and Fusion	1	–	15	–(1)	–(1)	1(14)
Quantum Information and Quantum Computing	4	–	15	–	–	4(6)
Total	79	1	257	–(5)	1(7)	34(169)
Full-time Grad. Stud.	–	1	257	–	–	–
First-year Grad. Stud.	–	1	41	–	–	–

GRADUATE DEGREE REQUIREMENTS

Master's: Approximately six graduate level courses in physics are required. A "B−" average must be maintained. Thesis required. Residence: one semester. There are no foreign language or comprehensive exam requirements.

Doctorate: Two academic years of full-time graduate work (including thesis) are required for the Ph.D. degree. Two courses are required inside, and two outside, the candidate's doctoral specialty. A "B−" average must be maintained. A general Doctoral examination consisting of one written exam and one oral exam must be passed in the second or third year of graduate work. Original research, demonstrated through a thesis is required. The thesis and oral defense of the thesis complete the requirements for the doctorate.

Thesis: Thesis may be written in absentia (with special permission only).

Table B—Separately Budgeted Research Expenditures by Source of Support

Source of Support	Departmental Research	Physics-related Research Outside Department
Federal government	$99,124,485	
State/local government	$19,836	
Non-profit organizations	$2,853,835	
Business and industry	$547,481	
Other	$998,226	
Total	**$103,543,863**	

Table C—Separately Budgeted Research Expenditures by Research Specialty

Research Specialty	No. of Grants	Expenditures ($)
Astrophysics	–	$37,293,793
Atomic, Molecular, & Optical Physics	–	$9,069,252
Condensed Matter Physics	–	$11,303,485
Nuclear Physics	–	$21,432,033
Plasma and Fusion	–	$22,097,430
Other	–	$2,347,870
Total	**–**	**$103,543,863**

FACULTY

Professor

Ashoori, Raymond, Ph.D., Cornell University, 1990. *Condensed Matter Physics*. Experimental and Condensed Matter Physics.

Belcher, John W., Ph.D., California Institute of Technology, 1970. *Astrophysics, Plasma and Fusion*. Theoretical Physics; Solar Plasma.

Bertschinger, Edmund W., Ph.D., Princeton University, 1984. *Astrophysics*. Theoretical Physics; Astrophysics.

Canizares, Claude, Ph.D., Harvard University, 1972. *Astronomy, Astrophysics*. Experimental Physics; X-ray Astronomy.

Chakrabarty, Deepto, Ph.D., California Institute of Technology, 1996. Division Head, Astrophysics. *Astronomy, Astrophysics*. Experimental Physics; Compact Objects.

Chakraborty, Arup, Ph.D., University of Delaware, 1988. *Engineering Physics/Science*. Chemical Engineering, Physics of Living Systems.

Chen, Min, Ph.D., University of California, Berkeley, 1969. *Particles and Fields*. Experimental Physics; High Energy.

Chuang, Isaac, Ph.D., Stanford University, 1997. *Atomic, Molecular, & Optical Physics, Computational Physics*. Experimental Physics; Quantum Computation.

Conrad, Janet, Ph.D., Harvard University, 1993. *Particles and Fields*. Experimental Physics; High Energy.

Fisher, Peter H., Ph.D., California Institute of Technology, 1988. Department Head. *Particles and Fields*. Experimental Physics; High Energy.

Formaggio, Joseph, Ph.D., Columbia University, 2001. Division Head, Experimental Nuclear and Particle Physics. *Particles and Fields*. Experimental Physics; High Energy.

Gedik, Nuh, Ph.D., University of California, Berkeley, 2004. *Condensed Matter Physics, Optics*. Experimental Condensed Matter Physics.

Guth, Alan J., Ph.D., Massachusetts Institute of Technology, 1972. *Astronomy, Particles and Fields*. Theoretical Physics; Elementary Particle Physics; Cosmology.

Hewitt, Jacqueline, Ph.D., Massachusetts Institute of Technology, 1986. Director, Kavli Institute for Astrophysics and Space Research. *Astrophysics*. Experimental Physics; Gravitational Lenses.

Hughes, Scott, Ph.D., California Institute of Technology, 1998. *Astrophysics, Relativity & Gravitation*. Theoretical Physics; Gravitational Physics.

Jaffe, Robert, Ph.D., Stanford University, 1972. *Particles and Fields*. Theoretical Physics; Elementary Particles.

Jarillo-Herrero, Pablo D., Ph.D., Delft University of Technology, 2005. *Condensed Matter Physics*. Experimental Condensed Matter Physics.

Joannopoulos, John, Ph.D., University of California, Berkeley, 1974. *Condensed Matter Physics, Nano Science and Technology*. Theoretical Physics; Solid State, Nanotechnology.

Johnson, Stephen, Ph.D., Massachusetts Institute of Technology, 2001. *Applied Mathematics, Computational Physics, Electromagnetism.* Applied Mathematics.

Kaiser, David, Ph.D., Harvard University, 2000. *Astronomy, Particles and Fields.* Theoretical Physics; Elementary Particle Physics; Cosmology.

Kardar, Mehran, Ph.D., Massachusetts Institute of Technology, 1986. *Biophysics, Condensed Matter Physics.* Condensed Matter Theory, Biophysics.

Ketterle, Wolfgang, Ph.D., Ludwig-Maximilian University of Munich, 1986. *Atomic, Molecular, & Optical Physics.* Experimental Physics; Atomic.

Levitov, Leonid, Ph.D., Moscow, Physical Technical Institute, 1989. *Condensed Matter Physics.* Condensed Matter Theory.

Liu, Hong, Ph.D., Case Western Reserve University, 1997. *Particles and Fields.* Theoretical Particle Physics; String Theory.

Lloyd, Seth, Ph.D., Rockefeller University, 1988. *Computational Physics.* Quantum Information and Computing.

Mavalvala, Nergis, Ph.D., Massachusetts Institute of Technology, 1997. Associate Department Head. *Astrophysics, Relativity & Gravitation.* Astrophysics; Gravity.

Milner, Richard, Ph.D., California Institute of Technology, 1984. *Nuclear Physics.* Experimental Nuclear Physics.

Paus, Christoph M.E., Ph.D., III Phys. Institut RWTH Aachen, 1996. *Particles and Fields.* Experimental Physics; High Energy.

Pritchard, David E., Ph.D., Harvard University, 1968. *Atomic, Molecular, & Optical Physics.* Experimental Physics; Atomic.

Rajagopal, Krishna, Ph.D., Princeton University, 1993. Dean for Digital Learning. *Nuclear Physics, Particles and Fields.* Theoretical Nuclear and Particle Physics.

Redwine, Robert, Ph.D., Northwestern University, 1973. *Nuclear Physics.* Experimental Physics; Nuclear Structure.

Roland, Gunther, Ph.D., University of Frankfurt, 1993. *Nuclear Physics.* Experimental Physics; Relativistic Heavy Ion.

Seager, Sara, Ph.D., Harvard University, 1999. *Astrophysics, Atmosphere, Space Physics, Cosmic Rays.* Theoretical Physics; Astrophysics.

Simcoe, Robert, Ph.D., California Institute of Technology, 2003. *Astronomy, Astrophysics, Optics.* Experimental Physics; Optical.

Soljacic, Marin, Ph.D., Princeton University, 2000. *Condensed Matter Physics, Optics.* Theoretical Physics; Nonlinear Optics.

Stewart, Iain, Ph.D., California Institute of Technology, 1999. *Nuclear Physics, Particles and Fields.* Theoretical Nuclear Physics.

Taylor, Washington, Ph.D., University of California, Berkeley, 1993. Division Head, Theoretical Nuclear and Particle Physics. *Particles and Fields.* Theoretical Physics; String Theory.

Tegmark, Max, Ph.D., University of California, Berkeley, 1994. *Astronomy, Astrophysics.* Theoretical Physics; Cosmology.

Ting, Samuel C. C., Ph.D., University of Michigan, 1962. *High Energy Physics, Particles and Fields.* Experimental Physics; High Energy.

Todadri, Senthil, Ph.D., Yale University, 1997. *Condensed Matter Physics.* Condensed Matter Theory.

Vuletic, Vladan, Ph.D., University of Munich, 1997. *Atomic, Molecular, & Optical Physics, Low Temperature Physics.* Experimental Physics; Atomic.

Wen, Xiao-Gang, Ph.D., Princeton University, 1987. *Condensed Matter Physics.* Condensed Matter Theory.

Wilczek, Frank, Ph.D., Princeton University, 1974. *Particles and Fields.* Theoretical Particle Physics.

Wyslouch, Boleslaw, Ph.D., Massachusetts Institute of Technology, 1987. Director, Laboratory for Nuclear Science. *Nuclear Physics, Particles and Fields.* Experimental Nuclear Physics; High Energy.

Zwiebach, Barton, Ph.D., California Institute of Technology, 1983. *Particles and Fields.* Theoretical; Elementary Particle Theory.

Zwierlein, Martin, Ph.D., Massachusetts Institute of Technology, 2007. Division Head, Atomic, Biological, Condensed Matter, and Plasma Physics. *Atomic, Molecular, & Optical Physics.* Experimental Physics; Atomic.

Associate Professor

Detmold, William, Ph.D., University of Adelaide, 2002. *Nuclear Physics, Particles and Fields.* Theoretical Nuclear Physics: Lattice QCD.

England, Jeremy L., Ph.D., Stanford University, 2009. *Biophysics.* Theoretical Biophysics and Statistical Physics.

Evans, Matthew, Ph.D., California Institute of Technology, 2002. *Astrophysics, Relativity & Gravitation.* Astrophysics; Gravity.

Frebel, Anna L., Ph.D., Australian National University, 2006. *Astronomy.* Astrophysics.

Fu, Liang, Ph.D., University of Pennsylvania, 2009. *Condensed Matter Physics.* Theoretical Condensed Matter Physics.

Gore, Jeff, Ph.D., University of California, Berkeley, 2005. *Biophysics.* Experimental Biophysics.

Harrow, Aram, Ph.D., Massachusetts Institute of Technology, 2005. *Computational Physics, Theoretical Physics.* Quantum Information and Computing.

Klute, Markus, Ph.D., University of Bonn, 2004. *Particles and Fields.* Experimental Physics; High Energy.

Lee, Yen-Jie, Ph.D., Massachusetts Institute of Technology, 2011. *Nuclear Physics.* Heavy Ion Physics; QCD.

Loureiro, Nuno, Ph.D., Imperial College London, 2005. *Nuclear Engineering, Plasma and Fusion.* Plasma and Fusion; Nuclear Engineering.

Mirny, Leonid, Ph.D., Harvard University, 1998. *Biophysics, Computational Physics, Medical, Health Physics.* Health Sciences.

Thaler, Jesse, Ph.D., Harvard University, 2004. *Particles and Fields.* Theoretical Physics; Elementary Particles.

Vogelsberger, Mark, Ph.D., University of Munich, 2009. *Astrophysics, Theoretical Physics.* Theoretical Physics; Astrophysics.

Weinberg, Nevin N., Ph.D., California Institute of Technology, 2005. *Astrophysics.* Theoretical Astrophysics.

Williams, Michael, Ph.D., Carnegie Mellon University, 2007. *Nuclear Physics, Particles and Fields.* Experimental Nuclear Physics.

Assistant Professor

Checkelsky, Joseph, Ph.D., Princeton, 2010. *Condensed Matter Physics.* Experimental and Condensed Matter Physics.

Cisse, Ibrahim, Ph.D., University of Illinois, Urbana-Champaign, 2009. *Biophysics.* Biological Physics.

Comin, Riccardo, Ph.D., University of British Columbia, 2013. *Condensed Matter Physics, Solid State Physics.* Condensed Matter Physics. Sold State Physics.

Crossfield, Ian, Ph.D., UCLA, 2012. *Astrophysics, Atmosphere, Space Physics, Cosmic Rays.* Astrophysics; exoplanets.

Fakhri, Nikta, Ph.D., Rice University, 2010. *Biophysics.* Experimental Biophysics.

Harlow, Daniel, Ph.D., Stanford University, 2012. *Astrophysics, Theoretical Physics.* Quantum Field Theory; Astrophysics.

Harris, Philip, Ph.D., Massachusetts Institute of Technology, 2011. *Particles and Fields.* Experimental Physics; High Energy.

Hen, Or, Ph.D., Tel-Aviv University, 2016. *Nuclear Physics, Particles and Fields.* Experimental Nuclear Physics.

Ju, Long, Ph.D., University of California, Berkeley, 2015. *Condensed Matter Physics, Optics*. Experimental Condensed Matter Physics; Optics.

Masui, Kiyoshi, Ph.D., University of Toronto, 2013. *Astrophysics*. Astrophysics; Cosmology.

McDonald, Michael, Ph.D., University of Maryland, 2011. *Astronomy, Astrophysics*. Astrophysics.

Metlitski, Max, Ph.D., Harvard University, 2011. *Condensed Matter Physics*. Theoretical Condensed Matter Theory.

Perez, Kerstin, Ph.D., California Institute of Technology, 2011. *Astrophysics, Particles and Fields*. Experimental Particle Physics; Astrophysics.

Shanahan, Phiala, Ph.D., University of Adelaide, 2015. *Particles and Fields, Theoretical Physics*. Theoretical Nuclear and Particle Physics.

Slatyer, Tracy, Ph.D., Harvard University, 2010. *Astrophysics, Particles and Fields*. Experimental Nuclear Physics; Particle and Fields; Cosmology; Astrophysics.

Vitale, Salvatore, Ph.D., Pierre et Marie Curie University, 2010. *Astrophysics, Relativity & Gravitation*. Astrophysics; Gravity.

Winslow, Lindley, Ph.D., University of California, Berkeley, 2008. *Nuclear Physics*. Experimental Nuclear Physics.

DEPARTMENTAL RESEARCH SPECIALTIES AND STAFF

Theoretical

Astrophysics. Belcher, Bertschinger, Hughes, Seager, Tegmark, Vogelsberger, Weinberg.

Atomic, Molecular, & Optical Physics. Johnson.

Biophysics. Chakraborty, Cisse, England, Kardar.

Condensed Matter Physics. Fu, Joannopoulos, Kardar, Levitov, Metlitski, Soljacic, Todadri, Wen.

Nuclear Physics. Detmold, Rajagopal, Stewart, Todadri, Wen.

Particles and Fields. Guth, Jaffe, Kaiser, Liu, Rajagopal, Shanahan, Stewart, Taylor, Thaler, Wilczek, Zwiebach.

Plasma and Fusion. Belcher.

Quantum Information and Quantum Computing. Chuang, Harlow, Harrow, Lloyd.

Experimental

Astrophysics. Canizares, Chakrabarty, Crossfield, Frebel, Hewitt, Masui, Mavalvala, McDonald, Simcoe, Vitale.

Atomic, Molecular, & Optical Physics. Chuang, Ketterle, Pritchard, Vuletic, Zwierlein.

Biophysics. Chakraborty, Fakhri, Gore, Mirny.

Condensed Matter Physics. Ashoori, Checkelsky, Comin, Gedik, Jarillo-Herrero, Ju.

Nuclear Physics. Milner, Redwine, Roland, Slatyer, Williams, Wyslouch.

Particles and Fields. Chen, Conrad, Fisher, Formaggio, Harris, Hen, Klute, Paus, Perez, Ting, Winslow, Wyslouch.

Plasma and Fusion. Loureiro.

View additional information about this department at www.gradschoolshopper.com. Check out the "Why Choose Us?" section, find out more about the department's culture and get links to social media networks.

NORTHEASTERN UNIVERSITY

DEPARTMENT OF PHYSICS

Boston, Massachusetts 02115
http://cos.northeastern.edu/physics

General University Information
President: Joseph E. Aoun
Dean of Graduate School: Kenneth W. Henderson
University website: http://www.northeastern.edu/
School Type: Private
Setting: Urban
Total Faculty: 2,829
Total number of Students: 35,635
Total number of Graduate Students: 15,713

Department Information
Department Chairman: Prof. Mark Williams, Chair
Department Contact: Meni Wanunu, Professor and Graduate Program Director
  Total full-time faculty: 36
  Total number of full-time equivalent positions: 53
  Full-Time Graduate Students: 81
  Female Full-Time Graduate Students: 0
  First-Year Graduate Students: 15
  Female First-Year Students: 5
  Total Post Doctorates: 28

Department Address
111 Dana Research Center
360 Huntington Avenue
Boston, MA 02115
Phone: (617) 373-4240
Fax: (617) 373-2943
E-mail: gradphysics@northeastern.edu
Website: http://cos.northeastern.edu/physics

ADMISSIONS

Admission Contact Information
Address admission inquiries to: Graduate Coordinator, Physics Department, Northeastern University, 360 Huntington Ave, 111 DA, Boston, MA 02115
Phone: (617) 373-4240
E-mail: gradphysics@northeastern.edu
Admissions website: https://cos.northeastern.edu/physics/academics/graduate/admissions-and-financial-aid/

Application deadlines
Fall admission:
U.S. students: January 1   *Int'l. students*: January 1

Application fee
U.S. students: $75   *Int'l. students*: $75
The priority deadline for Ph.D. programs is January 1.

Admissions information
For Fall of 2018:
  Number of applicants: 170
  Number admitted: 58
  Number enrolled: 27

Admission requirements
Bachelor's degree requirements: A Bachelor's degree in Physics or a related field is required.

GRE requirements
The GRE is required.
We do not have minimum GRE score requirements.

Subjective GRE requirements
The Subjective GRE is recommended.
GRE Physics is strongly recommended but not required.

TOEFL requirements
The TOEFL exam is required for students from non-English-speaking countries.
  iBT score: 86

Other admissions information
Additional requirements: The GRE General is required and Physics Subject Test is strongly recommended for admission to the Ph.D. program. The minimum acceptable score suggested for admission is not specified.
Undergraduate preparation assumed: Although preparation will vary, a strong background in differential and integral calculus and differential equations is expected. Courses using Classical Mechanics (Marion), Electromagnetic Theory (Hayt and Buck), and Modern Physics (Serway) are assumed. It is also desirable, but not required, to have studied complex variables and linear algebra and to have an undergraduate background in most of the following areas: statistical physics and thermodynamics (Sears), optics (Hecht), solid-state physics (Kittel), and quantum mechanics (Griffiths).

TUITION

Tuition year 2018–2019:
  Full-time students: $1,503 per credit
Credit hours per semester to be considered full-time: 8
Deferred tuition plan: Yes
Health insurance: Available at the cost of $2,159 per year.
Other academic fees: Full health insurance coverage provided for all graduate assistants. Additional fees include International Student, University Health Center, Student Activity, Campus Recreation and Student Center Fee
Academic term: Semester
Number of first-year students who received full tuition waivers: 18

Teaching Assistants, Research Assistants, and Fellowships
Number of first-year
  Teaching Assistants: 18
Average stipend per academic year
  Teaching Assistant: $23,886
  Research Assistant: $23,886
Average stipend is per "eight month" academic year, and the stipend includes full tuition coverage. Most students receive an additional equivalent four month summer stipend. Stipend rates are for 2018–2019.

FINANCIAL AID

Application deadlines
Fall admission:
U.S. students: March 1   *Int'l. students*: March 1

Loans

Loans are available for U.S. students.

Loans are not available for international students.

GAPSFAS application required: No

FAFSA application required: Yes

For further information

Address financial aid inquiries to: Student Financial Services, 360 Huntington Ave, 354 Richards Hall, Boston, MA 02115.

Phone: (617) 373-5899

E-mail: sfs@northeastern.edu

Financial aid website: http://studentfinance.northeastern.edu

HOUSING

Availability of on-campus housing

Single students: Yes

Married students: No

For further information

Address housing inquiries to: Housing and Residential Life, 360 Huntington Ave, 4 Speare Commons, Boston, MA 02115.

Phone: (617) 373-2814

E-mail: housing@northeastern.edu

Housing aid website: https://www.northeastern.edu/housing/

Table A—Faculty, Enrollments, and Degrees Granted

Research Specialty	2017–18 Faculty	Enrollment Fall 2017 Master's	Enrollment Fall 2017 Doctorate	Number of Degrees Granted 2017–18 (2013–18) Master's	Number of Degrees Granted 2017–18 (2013–18) Terminal Master's	Number of Degrees Granted 2017–18 (2013–18) Doctorate
Biophysics	6	–	17	–	–	3(11)
Condensed Matter Physics	5	–	16	–	–	3(6)
Medical, Health Physics	1	–	1	–	–	–
Nano Science and Technology	6	–	7	–	–	1(6)
Network Science	3	–	7	–	–	1(3)
Particles and Fields	8	–	16	–	–	–(12)
Plasma and Fusion	1	–	2	–	–	–(1)
Non-specialized	6	2	14	6(18)	2(13)	–
Total	36	–	80	6(18)	2(13)	8(39)
Full-time Grad. Stud.	–	2	80	–	–	–
First-year Grad. Stud.	–	2	14	–	–	–

GRADUATE DEGREE REQUIREMENTS

Master's: Thirty-two semester hours, of which 24 are in specific courses, and a minimum grade average of B are required. Time in residence is not stipulated. Foreign languages and comprehensive and/or qualifying examination are not required. Some options include a standard M.S. with/without an M.S. thesis or an M.S. with a concentration in applied physics, engineering physics, chemical physics, biophysics, materials physics, mathematical physics, or computational physics.

Doctorate: Forty-two semester hours and a minimum grade average of B are required. Time in residence is one year after the qualifying examination. Foreign languages are not required. A qualifying examination is required after completion of one year of graduate courses. A thesis is required. M.S. degree may be earned while qualifying for Ph.D. degree.

SPECIAL EQUIPMENT, FACILITIES, OR PROGRAMS

Northeastern University is located in the Back Bay section of Boston, close to the Museum of Fine Arts, the Conservatory of Music, Symphony Hall, and historic Copley Square. It is an exciting, vibrant place to pursue graduate studies, because Greater Boston is home to more universities and research facilities than any other area in the world.

Thesis research can be undertaken in any one of the department's research specialities or in interdisciplinary areas, such as materials physics, mathematical physics, chemical physics, molecular biophysics, or applied engineering physics. An additional option allows cooperative research to be done at high-technology industrial, government, national or international laboratories, and at medical research institutions in the Boston area.

The department is housed in the Dana Research Center, with some optics, biological physics, and condensed matter physics laboratories also located in the Egan Research Center and the new ISEC building. There are ample modern research laboratories, department and student machine shops, an electronics shop, a high-resolution electron microscope, conference and seminar rooms, and faculty and graduate student offices. The Egan Center provides a direct interface with materials researchers in chemistry and engineering. Numerous computational facilities are available on campus, including the Physics Department Computer Center in the Dana Research Center, and the newly developed Massachusetts Green High Performance Computational Center near Holyoke, Massachusetts (www.mghpcc.org).

In addition to the research they do at campus facilities, faculty members and graduate students also work at research centers located in the United States and Europe. High-energy physics experiments are under way at Fermilab (Batavia, Illinois) and CERN (Geneva, Switzerland). Astroparticle physics research is performed at the Pierre Auger Observatory in Argentina. Some groups use the synchrotron facilities at Brookhaven National Laboratory (Long Island, New York) and Argonne National Laboratory (Argonne, Illinois), and many faculty members have flourishing collaborations with scientists in Europe, Asia, and South America.

Table B—Separately Budgeted Research Expenditures by Source of Support

Source of Support	Departmental Research	Physics-related Research Outside Department
Federal government	$11,259,402	
State/local government		
Non-profit organizations	$3,226,986	
Business and industry	$592,179	
Other	$84,000	
Total	$15,162,567	

Table C—Separately Budgeted Research Expenditures by Research Specialty

Research Specialty	No. of Grants	Expenditures ($)
Experimental biological and medical physics	18	$3,598,674
Condensed Matter Theory	9	$1,464,968
Experimental Nanophysics	18	$1,696,133
Network Science	26	$7,104,015
Particles and Fields	9	$1,298,777
Total	80	$15,162,567

FACULTY

Professor

Bansil, Arun, Ph.D., Harvard University, 1974. *Condensed Matter Physics*. Theoretical condensed matter physics.

Barabási, Albert-László, Ph.D., Boston University, 1994. Network Science.

Champion, Paul M., Ph.D., University of Illinois at Urbana-Champaign, 1975. *Biophysics*. Experimental biological physics.

Heiman, Donald, Ph.D., University of California, Irvine, 1975. Experimental nanophysics.

Karma, Alain S., Ph.D., University of California, Santa Barbara, 1985. Theoretical condensed matter and biological physics.

Kravchenko, Sergey, Ph.D., Institute of Solid State Physics, Chernogolovka, 1988. Experimental nanophysics.

Markiewicz, Robert S., Ph.D., University of California, Berkeley, 1975. Theoretical condensed matter physics.

Nath, Pran, Ph.D., Stanford University, 1964. Theoretical particle physics.

Sridhar, Srinivas, Ph.D., California Institute of Technology, 1983. Experimental nanophysics.

Taylor, Tomasz, Ph.D., Warsaw University, 1981. Theoretical particle physics.

Vespignani, Alessandro, Ph.D., University of Rome, 1994. Network Science.

Williams, Mark C., Ph.D., University of Minnesota, 1998. Experimental biological physics.

Wood, Darien, Ph.D., University of California, Berkeley, 1987. Experimental particle physics.

Associate Professor

Alverson, George O., Ph.D., University of Illinois at Urbana-Champaign, 1979. *Particles and Fields*. Experimental particle physics.

Barberis, Emanuela, Ph.D., University of California, Santa Cruz, 1996. Experimental particle physics.

Feiguin, Adrian E., Ph.D., Facultad de Ciencias Exactas e Ingenieria. Universidad Nacional de Rosario, 2000. Theoretical condensed matter physics.

Israeloff, Nathan, Ph.D., University of Illinois at Urbana-Champaign, 1991. Experimental nanophysics.

Kar, Swastik, Ph.D., Indian Institute of Science, 2004. Experimental nanophysics.

Krioukov, Dmitri, Ph.D., Old Dominion University, 1998. Network Science.

Menon, Latika, Ph.D., Tata Institute of Fundamental Research, 1997. Experimental nanophysics.

Nelson, Brent, Ph.D., University of California, Berkeley, 2001. College of Science Associate Dean for Undergraduate Affairs. Theoretical particle physics.

Sage, J. Timothy, Ph.D., University of Illinois at Urbana-Champaign, 1986. Experimental biological physics.

Stepanyants, Armen, Ph.D., University of Rhode Island, 1999. Theoretical condensed matter and biological physics.

Swain, John D., Ph.D., University of Toronto, 1990. Experimental particle physics.

Wanunu, Meni, Ph.D., Weizmann Institute of Science, 2005. *Biophysics, Nano Science and Technology*. Experimental biological physics.

Whitford, Paul C., Ph.D., University of California, San Diego, 2009. Theoretical condensed matter and biological physics.

Assistant Professor

Bi, Dapeng Max, Ph.D., Brandeis University, 2012. *Biophysics, Condensed Matter Physics*. Theoretical condensed matter and biological physics.

Halverson, James, Ph.D., University of Pennsylvania, 2012. *Particles and Fields*. Theoretical particle physics.

Orimoto, Toyoko J., Ph.D., University of California, Berkeley, 2006. Experimental particle physics.

Spring, Bryan, Ph.D., University of Illinois at Urbana-Champaign, 2008. *Biophysics*. Experimental biomedical physics.

Venkatachalam, Vivek, Ph.D., Harvard University, 2012. Experimental Biological Physics.

Emeritus

Aaron, Ronald, Ph.D., University of Pennsylvania, 1961. Medical physics.

Argyres, Petros N., Ph.D., University of California, Berkeley, 1954. Condensed matter theory.

José, Jorge V., National University of Mexico, 1976. Theoretical Condensed Matter Physics.

Lowndes, Robert P., Ph.D., University of London, 1966. Condensed matter physics.

Perry, Clive H., Ph.D., University of London, 1960. Condensed matter experimental physics.

Shiffman, Carl A., Ph.D., University of Oxford, 1956. Medical physics.

Sokoloff, Jeffrey B., Ph.D., Massachusetts Institute of Technology, 1967. Theoretical condensed matter physics.

Srivastava, Yogendra, Ph.D., Indiana University, 1964. Condensed matter theory.

Vaughn, Michael T., Ph.D., Purdue University, 1960. Elementary particle theory.

von Goeler, Eberhard, Ph.D., University of Illinois, 1961. High-energy experimental physics.

Wu, Fa-Yueh, Ph.D., Washington University, 1963. Condensed matter theory.

Distinguished Adjunct Professor

Kotliar, Gabriel, Ph.D., Princeton University, 1983. Condensed Matter Physics.

Adjunct Professor

Das, Tanmoy, Ph.D., Northeastern, 2009. Theoretical condensed matter physics.

Farmelo, Graham, Ph.D., University of Liverpool, 1977. High-energy experimental physics.

Gongora-Trevino, Maria Araceli, Ph.D., University of Oxford, 1984. Condensed matter physics.

Lindroos, Matti, Ph.D., Tampere University of Technology, Finland, 1979. Condensed matter theory.

Lu, Wentao, Ph.D., Northeastern University, 2001. Electron microscopy facility manager.

Mijnarends, Peter, Ph.D., Delft University of Technology, 1969. Condensed matter theory.

Adjunct Assistant Professor

Lin, Hsin, Ph.D., Northeastern University, 2008. Condensed matter physics.

Affiliate Professor

Nieminen, Juoko, Ph.D., Tampere University of Technology, 1989. Condensed matter physics.

Affiliate Associate Professor

Wang, Dashun, Ph.D., Northeastern University, 2013. Network Science.

Affiliate Assistant Professor

Sharma, Amitabh, Ph.D., Institute of Genomics and Integrative Biology, CSIR, 2008. Network science.

Sinatra, Roberta, Ph.D., University of Catania, 2012. Network science.

Szell, Michael, Ph.D., University of Vienna, 2012. Network science.

Other

Wray, Andrew, Ph.D., Princeton University, 2010. Adjunct Research Scientist. Experimental condensed matter physics.

DEPARTMENTAL RESEARCH SPECIALTIES AND STAFF

Theoretical

Condensed Matter Theory. The group performs research on diverse topics that span forefront areas of hard/soft condensed matter physics and emerging areas at the intersection of physics and other disciplines. Specific research areas include the electronic structure and spectroscopy of high-temperature superconductors and other complex materials, nanotribology atomic-scale friction in crystalline and polymeric materials, theoretical/computational materials science, cardiac nonlinear dynamics, and theoretical/computational neuroscience. Bansil, Barabási, Bi, Feiguin, José, Karma, Sokoloff, Stepanyants, Vespignani, Whitford, Wu.

High Energy Theory. The faculty and students in the theoretical particle physics group are actively exploring questions concerning supersymmetry SUSY, and more specifically its local extension to supergravity SUGRA, with a view to understanding the connection between the universe at very large and very small scales. This leads to the study of supersymmetry and supergravity, possible extra dimensions beyond the usual four, and related exotic phenomena, such as mini-black holes, which may be produced at accelerators or by ultra-high-energy cosmic rays. Our formal investigations in superstring theory and M-theory are also conducted with the purpose of making connections between fundamental theory and experiment. The elementary particle theory group at NU initiated the PASCOS and SUSY series of conferences, which have become major conferences in high-energy physics. Halverson, Nath, Nelson, Srivastava, Taylor.

Network Science. Complex network research is not a single discipline; it is highly interdisciplinary, seeking the answers to some fundamental questions about living, adaptable, and changeable systems. Several of the main disciplines are "network theory" involving the research areas of computer science, network science, and graph theory. Another is "network science (NS)" attempting to research engineered networks, information networks, biological networks, semantic networks, and social networks, whereas "dynamic network analysis (DNA)" will use traditional social network analysis, link analysis and multi-agent systems involving large amounts of electronic data. We should also add "complex adaptive systems," which is grounded in modern chemistry, biological views on adaption, expatriation, and evolution. In all of these and more network-related areas, the study of emergence and self-organization are fundamental. Although academic disciplines are hugely diverse in complex network research, here in the Department of Physics, disciplines in statistical analysis involving physics, mathematics, and computational analysis (data mining) are its primary focus. Barabási, Krioukov, Vespignani.

Experimental

Experimental Biological and Medical Physics. The group performs research on multiple levels from molecules to cells to tissue Research programs include single molecule DNA-protein interactions, nanoscale biophysical interaction measurements, vibrational dynamics of biomolecules, femtosecond protein dynamics, and biomedical optics. Aaron, Champion, Israeloff, Sage, Shiffman, Spring, Venkatachalam, Wanunu, Williams.

Experimental Nanophysics. The faculty is actively pursuing research at the frontiers of nanoscience. The thrust areas in nanophysics include the following: left-handed metamaterials for photonic crystals, nanomedicine, spintronics, mesoscopic physics, low-dimensional electronic systems, nanomagnetism, and quantum chaos. Research is aimed at the synthesis of nanoscale materials and devices, as well as fundamental materials issues. Heiman, Israeloff, Kar, Kravchenko, Menon, Sridhar.

Experimental Particle Physics. The Experimental Particle Physics group concentrates its efforts on the following activities: CMS and the Pierre Auger Observatory. Compact Muon Solenoid at LHC (Alverson, Barberis, Orimoto, Wood): The CMS detector recently resumed operations at the Large Hadron Collider (LHC), located near Geneva, Switzerland. The LHC is currently colliding protons at 13 TeV, the highest energy available in the world. At Northeastern, we are supporting the end cap muon detector and the electromagnetic calorimeter, are studying the newly-found Higgs boson, and are searching for leptoquarks (exotic particles with properties of both leptons and quarks), Dark Matter, massive new gauge bosons (Stueckelberg Z-primes), and other new physics. Postdoctoral fellows include Dr. Andreas Massironi, Dr. David Morse, and Dr. Daniele Trocino. Pierre Auger Observatory (Swain): The Pierre Auger Observatory makes use of the one accelerator bigger than the LHC-the one that gives us cosmic rays from intergalactic space. Currently taking data with a fully instrumented detector covering 3000 square kilometers. Alverson, Barberis, Orimoto, Swain, Wood.

View additional information about this department at www.gradschoolshopper.com. Check out the "Why Choose Us?" section, find out more about the department's culture and get links to social media networks.

UNIVERSITY OF MASSACHUSETTS, AMHERST

DEPARTMENT OF PHYSICS

Amherst, Massachusetts 01003
http://www.physics.umass.edu

General University Information
Chancellor: Kumble R. Subbaswamy
Dean of Graduate School: Barbara Krauthamer
University website: http://www.umass.edu/
School Type: Public
Setting: Rural
Total Faculty: 1,563
Total Graduate Faculty: 1,475
Total number of Students: 30,340
Total number of Graduate Students: 6,952

Department Information
Department Chairman: Prof. Narayanan Menon, Head
Department Contact: Katie Bryant, Graduate Program
  Manager
  Total full-time faculty: 29
  Total number of full-time equivalent positions: 29
  Full-Time Graduate Students: 100
  Female Full-Time Graduate Students: 22
  First-Year Graduate Students: 23
  Female First-Year Students: 3
  Total Post Doctorates: 18

Department Address
710 N. Pleasant
Amherst, MA 01003
Phone: (413) 545-2548
Fax: (413) 545-0648
E-mail: gradmiss@physics.umass.edu
Website: http://www.physics.umass.edu

ADMISSIONS

Admission Contact Information
Address admission inquiries to: Graduate Student Service Center,
  534 Goodell Building, University of Massachusetts, 140
  Hicks Way, Amherst, MA 01003-9333
Phone: (413) 545-0722
E-mail: gradadm@grad.umass.edu
Admissions website: http://umass.edu/gradschool

Application deadlines
Fall admission:
U.S. students: January 15   *Int'l. students*: January 15

Application fee
U.S. students: $75   *Int'l. students*: $75
Please see website (www.umass.edu/gradschool/admissions)

Admissions information
For Fall of 2018:
  Number of applicants: 179
  Number admitted: 54
  Number enrolled: 17

Admission requirements
Bachelor's degree requirements: Bachelor's degree in Physics
  or a related area is required.
Minimum undergraduate GPA: 3.0

GRE requirements
The GRE is required.
  GRE Exam is required for Ph.D. applicants; optional for MS
  applicants.

Subjective GRE requirements
The Subjective GRE is required.
GRE Exam is required for Ph.D. applicants; optional for MS ap-
  plicants.

TOEFL requirements
The TOEFL exam is required for students from non-English-
  speaking countries.
  PBT score: 577
  iBT score: 90

Other admissions information
Undergraduate preparation assumed: Marion, Classical Mechanics; Marion, Electricity and Magnetism; Eisberg, Fundamentals of Modern Physics; Jenkins and White, Fundamentals of Optics; Reif, Statistical Mechanics.

TUITION

Tuition year 2018–2019:
Tuition for in-state residents
  Full-time students: per credit
  Part-time students: per credit
Tuition for out-of-state residents
  Full-time students: per credit
  Part-time students: per credit
Tuition and most fees are waived for PHD students with Teaching
  Assistantship/Research Assistantship appointment. For up-
  dated tuition and fees, please see website (http://umass.edu/
  bursar).
Credit hours per semester to be considered full-time: 9
Deferred tuition plan: No
Health insurance: Available at the cost of $2710 per year.
Other academic fees: First year entering fee, $357 (one-time-only
  fee)plus Service fee, graduate senate fee. Health Insurance
  Family Plan,$8,424 per year. For PHD students with an assis-
  tantship, tuition and most fees are waived.
Academic term: Semester
Number of first-year students who received full tuition waivers: 15

Teaching Assistants, Research Assistants, and Fellowships
  Number of first-year
    Teaching Assistants: 16
    Fellowship students: 4
  Average stipend per academic year
    Teaching Assistant: $20,862
    Research Assistant: $28,548

FINANCIAL AID

Application deadlines
Fall admission:
U.S. students: January 15   *Int'l. students*: January 15

Loans

Loans are available for U.S. students.

Loans are not available for international students.

GAPSFAS application required: No

FAFSA application required: No

For further information

Address financial aid inquiries to: Financial Aid Services, 243 Whitmore Admin. Building, 181 Presidents Dr., Amherst, MA 01003.

Phone: (413) 577-0555

E-mail: finaid@finaid.umass.edu

Financial aid website: http://www.umass.edu/umfa/

HOUSING

Availability of on-campus housing

Single students: Yes

Married students: Yes

Childcare Assistance: No

For further information

Address housing inquiries to: Residential Life Student Services, 235 Whitmore Administration Building, 181 Presidents Drive, Amherst, MA 01003-9393.

Phone: (413) 545-2100

E-mail: Living@umass.edu

Housing aid website: http://www.umass.edu/living/grad, http://www.umocss.org/

Table A—Faculty, Enrollments, and Degrees Granted

Research Specialty	2017–2018 Faculty	Enrollment Fall 2017 Master's	Enrollment Fall 2017 Doctorate	Number of Degrees Granted 2017–2018 (2013–18) Master's	Number of Degrees Granted 2017–2018 (2013–18) Terminal Master's	Number of Degrees Granted 2017–2018 (2013–18) Doctorate
Biophysics	2	–	11	–	–	–(5)
Condensed Matter Physics	11	–	30	1(1)	–(1)	6(13)
Nuclear Physics	4	–	7	2(3)	–(1)	1(2)
Particles and Fields	9	–	17	2(1)	–(2)	1(13)
Polymer Physics/Science	–	–	3	–	–	–(6)
Statistical & Thermal Physics	2	–	5	–	–	2(4)
Non-specialized	–	–	–	–(8)	–(6)	–
Total	28	–	73	5(18)	–(10)	10(43)
Full-time Grad. Stud.	–	–	73	–	–	–
First-year Grad. Stud.	–	–	15	–	–	–

GRADUATE DEGREE REQUIREMENTS

Master's: The M.S. program in Physics is course-based with no thesis or research requirements. The requirements that must be satisfied are described below and can be completed within two years, under normal circumstances. The requirements for the M.S. degree in Physics consist of the following: ● Minimum of 30 graduate credits taken (course number 500 or higher); ● At least 12 credits shall be at 600-level or higher; ● At least 21 of the credits must be in physics; ● At least half of the total credits must be for a letter grade, and the GPA must be at least 3.0; ● Independent Study credits are allowed; ● A maximum of 6 credits of graduate-level coursework taken at another institution can be transferred to the UMass M.S. program.

Doctorate: Six core physics graduate courses are required. Qualification through the core courses, thesis proposal, disserta-

tion, and dissertation examination are required. There is no language requirement. Three research area courses are required, at least one of which must be outside of the dissertation research area.

Thesis: Thesis/dissertation may be written in absentia.

FACULTY

Professor

Candela, Donald, Ph.D., Harvard University, 1983. Experimental low-temperature physics; condensed matter physics.

Dallapiccola, Carlo, Ph.D., University of Colorado, 1993. Graduate Program Director. Experimental High Energy Physics.

Dinsmore, Anthony D., Ph.D., University of Pennsylvania, 1997. Experimental condensed matter physics.

Goldner, Lori, Ph.D., Cornell University, 1984. Biological physics.

Hallock, Robert B., Ph.D., Stanford University, 1969. Experimental low-temperature physics; condensed matter physics.

Menon, Narayanan, Ph.D., University of Chicago, 1995. Department Head. Experimental condensed matter physics.

Miskimen, Rory A., Ph.D., Massachusetts Institute of Technology, 1983. Experimental nuclear physics.

Prokofiev, Nikolay, Ph.D., Kurchatov, 1987. Theoretical condensed matter physics; computational physics.

Ramsey-Musolf, Michael J., Ph.D., Princeton, 1989. Theoretical high energy physics.

Sorbo, Lorenzo, Ph.D., (SISSA/ISAS) of Trieste, 2001. Theoretical high-energy physics.

Svistunov, Boris V., Ph.D., Kurchatov, 1990. Theoretical condensed matter physics; computational physics.

Traschen, Jennie, Ph.D., Harvard University, 1984. Theoretical high-energy physics; relativity; gravitation.

Tuominen, Mark, Ph.D., University of Minnesota, 1990. Experimental condensed matter physics.

Willocq, Stéphane, Ph.D., Tufts University, 1992. Experimental high-energy physics.

Associate Professor

Blaylock, Guy, Ph.D., University of Illinois, 1986. Experimental high-energy physics.

Brau, Benjamin, Ph.D., Massachusetts Institute of Technology, 2002. Experimental high-energy physics.

Davidovitch, Benjamin, Ph.D., Weizmann Institute of Science, 2001. Theoretical condensed matter physics.

Kawall, David, Ph.D., Stanford University, 1996. Experimental nuclear, particle and atomic physics.

Pocar, Andrea, Ph.D., Princeton University, 2003. Experimental neutrino physics.

Ross, Jennifer, Ph.D., University of California, Santa Barbara, 2004. Experimental biological physics.

Santangelo, Christian, Ph.D., University of California, Santa Barbara, 2004. Theoretical condensed matter physics.

Assistant Professor

Coelho Lopes de Sa, Rafael, Ph.D., Stony Brook, 2013. Experimental High Energy Physics.

Draper, Patrick, Ph.D., University of Chicago, 2011. *Theoretical Physics*. Theoretical high-energy physics.

Hertel, Scott, Ph.D., Massachusetts Institute of Technology, 2012. Experimental dark matter physics.

Martinez Outschoorn, Verena, Ph.D., Harvard University, 2011. Experimental High Energy Physics.

Sedrakyan, Tigran, Ph.D., Yerevan Physics Institute, 2002. Theoretical Condensed Matter.

Vasseur, Romain, Ph.D., Ecole Normale Superieure, 2013. Theoretical Physics.

Wang, Chen, Ph.D., Cornell University, 2012. Experimental condensed matter physics.

Yan, Jun, Ph.D., Columbia, 2009. Experimental condensed matter. Nanoscience and Technology.

Lecturer

Bourgeois, Paul, Ph.D., University of Massachusetts, 2005. Director of Physics Teaching Laboratories. Experimental nuclear physics.

Dujovne, Irene, Ph.D., Columbia University, 2004. Experimental Condensed Matter Physics.

Hatch, Heath, Other, University of Northern British Columbia, 1998.

Kastor, David, Ph.D., University of Chicago, 1988. Associate Department Head. Theoretical high-energy physics; relativity; gravitation.

Stevens, Jason, Other, University of Massachusetts Amherst, 1994.

Tewari, Shubha, Ph.D., University of California, Los Angeles, 1993. Theoretical condensed matter physics.

Toggerson, Brokk, Ph.D., University of California Irvine, 2012.

DEPARTMENTAL RESEARCH SPECIALTIES AND STAFF

Theoretical

Condensed Matter Physics. Complex and disordered systems; phase transitions, dynamics, and transport; computational methods and computational complexity; classical and quantum Monte Carlo methods; polymers, liquid crystals, and poly-electrolytes; transport of biological macromolecules through membranes; quantum fluids and solids: Bose-Einstein condensation and kinetic theory; quantum dissipation and decoherence: tunneling, qubits, nanomagnets, and low-dimensional conductors and elasticity and geometry of thin structures. Davidovitch, Prokofiev, Santangelo, Sedrakyan, Svistunov.

Particles and Fields. Gauge theories; CP violation; heavy-quark physics; structure of weak interactions; physics beyond the Standard Model; gravitation; string theory; cosmology, inflation, baryogenesis, dark matter, collider phenomenology; Higgs physics; supersymmetry. Draper, Kastor, Ramsey-Musolf, Sorbo, Traschen.

Theoretical Nuclear Physics. Fundamental symmetry tests, hadronic structure. Ramsey-Musolf.

Experimental

Biophysics. Molecular and cellular biological physics: molecular forces in biological environments; biopolymers such as RNA, DNA, proteins; self-assembly of supramolecular assemblies such as cytoskeletal filaments; intracellular organization; aggregation kinetics; membrane biophysics; cellular motility; molecular motors; cellular machineries; ion channels, transport, and nerve excitation; electrophysiology; advanced single molecule imaging, fluorescence imaging, optical trapping and instrumentation. Dinsmore, Goldner, Ross, Tuominen.

Experimental Particles and Fields. At the LHC at CERN: search for physics beyond the Standard Model. Brau, Coelho Lopes de Sa, Dallapiccola, Martinez Outschoorn, Willocq.

Low Temperature Physics. Quantum fluids and solids: superconductivity, spin-polarized systems, 3He-4He mixtures, weak-binding systems, helium films, and solid helium; phase transitions: wetting, 2D effects, restricted geometry, quenched disorder, localization, and nanostructures; NMR; microbalance; thermal techniques; high field/temperature ratio; superconducting quantum circuits. Candela, Hallock, Tuominen, Wang.

Nano Science and Technology. Thin film and nanostructures: device fabrication, electron-beam lithography, time-resolved optical spectroscopy, single electron devices, superconductivity, mesoscopic quantum phenomena, plasmonics, liquid and solid helium, superfluidity, physics in two dimensions, and liquid helium mixtures; magnetic and transport properties of nanostructure; electrical and optical properties of semiconductors, and solid functional nanostructures, photonic crystal devices, and networks, electrical and optical properties of atomically thin two dimensional crystal. Candela, Dinsmore, Hallock, Tuominen, Wang, Yan.

Nuclear, Neutrino and Dark Matter Physics. Studies of the structure of hadrons, Standard Model tests through measurements of magnetic and electric dipole moments in leptons and nuclei, studies of solar neutrinos, searches for neutrinoless double beta decay, and particle dark matter. Hertel, Kawall, Miskimen, Pocar.

Soft Condensed Matter Physics. Complex and disordered systems: fluids in porous media; diffusion and dispersion in random media; avalanche phenomena; flow and rheology of granular materials; glass transitions; fluid-solid interfacial phenomena; active matter; liquid crystals; polymers and macromolecules; complex fluids; chemical self-assembly; polymer nanostructures; molecular-scale devices; x-ray imaging; optical microscopy; light scattering. Candela, Dinsmore, Menon, Ross, Tuominen.

View additional information about this department at www.gradschoolshopper.com. Check out the "Why Choose Us?" section, find out more about the department's culture and get links to social media networks.

UNIVERSITY OF MASSACHUSETTS, LOWELL

DEPARTMENT OF PHYSICS AND APPLIED PHYSICS

Lowell, Massachusetts 01854
http://www.uml.edu/physics

General University Information
Chancellor: Jacqueline Moloney
Dean of Graduate School: Steve Tello
University website: http://www.uml.edu
School Type: Public
Setting: Urban
Total Faculty: 1,112
Total Graduate Faculty: N/A
Total number of Students: 18,316
Total number of Graduate Students: 3,777

Department Information
Department Chairman: Prof. Robert H. Giles, Chair
Department Contact: Robert H. Giles, Department Chair
  Total full-time faculty: 31
  Total number of full-time equivalent positions: 31
  Full-Time Graduate Students: 68
  Female Full-Time Graduate Students: 20
  First-Year Graduate Students: 16
  Female First-Year Students: 7
  Total Post Doctorates: 6

Department Address
1 University Ave.
Lowell, MA 01854
Phone: (978) 934-3780
Fax: (978) 934-3068
E-mail: Robert_Giles@uml.edu
Website: http://www.uml.edu/physics

ADMISSIONS

Admission Contact Information
Address admission inquiries to: Prof. Viktor A. Podolskiy, Physics Graduate Coordinator, Dept of Physics and Applied Physics, U. Massachusetts Lowell, Lowell MA 01854
Phone: (978) 934-3398
E-mail: Viktor_Podolskiy@uml.edu
Admissions website: http://www.uml.edu/grad

Application deadlines
Fall admission:
U.S. students: January 15   *Int'l. students*: January 15
Spring admission:
U.S. students: November 15   *Int'l. students*: November 15

Application fee
U.S. students: $50   *Int'l. students*: $50
Ph.D. applications are only considered for the Fall, other than in exceptional situations. M.S. application deadline for the Fall is March 15/2019.

Admissions information
For Fall of 2018:
  Number of applicants: 79
  Number admitted: 29

Admission requirements
Bachelor's degree requirements: Bachelor's degree in Physics or related area is required.
Minimum undergraduate GPA: 3.0

GRE requirements
The GRE is required.
No set minimum score

Subjective GRE requirements
The Subjective GRE is required.
Physics GRE required for Ph.D. applicants but not for M.S. applicants. No set minimum score.

TOEFL requirements
The TOEFL exam is required for students from non-English-speaking countries.
PBT score: 550
iBT score: 79

Other admissions information
Undergraduate preparation assumed: Taylor, Mechanics; Wangsness or Griffiths, Electromagnetism; Liboff, Quantum Mechanics; Mandl, Statistical Mechanics.

TUITION

Tuition year 2017–18:
Tuition for in-state residents
  Full-time students: $15,040 annual
  Part-time students: $835.54 per credit
Tuition for out-of-state residents
  Full-time students: $26,820 annual
  Part-time students: $1,490 per credit
The above numbers include fees. Tuition and fees are fully waived for TA/RA appointments, which apply to ALL students in the Ph.D. program throughout their graduate career.
Credit hours per semester to be considered full-time: 9
Deferred tuition plan: Yes
Health insurance: Available at the cost of $1,568 per year.
Other academic fees: The health insurance is for the 2018–19 academic year. TA/RA compensation package covers 80% of health insurance fees.
Academic term: Semester
Number of first-year students who received full tuition waivers: 9

Teaching Assistants, Research Assistants, and Fellowships
Number of first-year
  Teaching Assistants: 9
Average stipend per academic year
  Teaching Assistant: $25,000
  Research Assistant: $25,000
TA/RA reserved for students in the Ph.D. program, which include full tuition and fees waiver and 80% of health insurance costs. MS students are not eligible for TA/RA appointments. For PhD candidates, the 12-month TA/RA stipend is $25,000, which includes research funding outside the academic year.

FINANCIAL AID

Application deadlines
Fall admission:
U.S. students: January 15   *Int'l. students*: January 15

Loans
Loans are available for U.S. students.
Loans are not available for international students.
GAPSFAS application required: No
FAFSA application required: No

For further information
Address financial aid inquiries to: Prof. Viktor Podolskiy, Physics Graduate Coordinator, Dept. of Physics and Applied Physics, 1 University Ave, University of Massachusetts Lowell, Lowell, MA, 01854.
Phone: (978) 934-3398
E-mail: Viktor_Podolskiy@uml.edu
Financial aid website: https://www.uml.edu/Sciences/physics/Programs-of-Study/Graduate-Program.aspx

HOUSING

Availability of on-campus housing
Single students: Yes
Married students: No

For further information
Address housing inquiries to: Office of Residence Life, 1 University Ave, University of Massachusetts Lowell, Lowell, MA, 01854.
Phone: (978) 934-5160
E-mail: ResLife@uml.edu
Housing aid website: http://www.uml.edu/student-services/reslife/housing

Table A—Faculty, Enrollments, and Degrees Granted

Research Specialty	2017–18 Faculty	Enrollment Fall 2017		Number of Degrees Granted 2017–18 (2013–18)		
		Master's	Doctorate	Master's	Terminal Master's	Doctorate
Applied Physics	5	1	2	1	1	–
Astrophysics	3	–	8	1	1	1
Atmosphere, Space Physics, Cosmic Rays	2	1	4	–	–	–
Biophysics	3	–	1	–	–	1
Condensed Matter Physics	2	1	1	–	–	–
Materials Science, Metallurgy	5	–	–	–	–	–
Medical, Health Physics	4	9	15	10	9	–
Nano Science and Technology	3	1	6	1	1	1
Nuclear Physics	3	3	7	1	1	–
Optics	3	–	–	–	–	–
Particles and Fields	1	–	–	–	–	–
Physics and other Science Education	3	–	–	–	–	–
Polymer Physics/Science	2	–	1	–	–	–
Quantum Foundations	1	–	2	–	–	–
Relativity & Gravitation	1	1	2	1	1	–
Non-specialized	–	1	1	–	–	–
Non-specialized	–	–	–	–	–	–
Total	24	18	50	15(99)	14(66)	3(42)
Full-time Grad. Stud.	–	18	50	–	–	–
First-year Grad. Stud.	–	11	9	–	–	–

GRADUATE DEGREE REQUIREMENTS

Master's: Thirty graduate credits with a "B" average are required. There is no foreign language requirement. There is no qualifying or comprehensive examination required. One year of residence is required. Thesis or project is required.

Doctorate: Sixty graduate credits with a "B" average are required. Comprehensive written and oral examinations are required; a two-semester research project or master's thesis is required. One-year residence is required. Dissertation is required.

SPECIAL EQUIPMENT, FACILITIES, OR PROGRAMS

Located in the historic industrial city of Lowell, 25 miles northwest of Boston, our campus is nestled in a sharp bend in the Merrimack River. We have an exceptional research footprint in physics and applied physics. Our department was recently ranked 51st in the nation in research expenditures.

Our astronomy and astrophysics research includes: the development of instruments used on suborbital sounding rockets to study the structure of galaxies and interstellar media; the investigation of atmospheres and environments of planets and exoplanets; multi-wavelength observations (infra-red, optical and X-ray) of X-ray binaries; and time-domain survey of X-ray pulsars.

The Center for Advanced Materials is a multidisciplinary facility for the design, synthesis, characterization, and intelligent processing of advanced materials in the areas of organic polymers, ceramics, biomaterials, composites, semiconductors and electro-optic materials.

The Photonics Laboratory forms a core of design and fabrication facilities to support various university initiatives requiring innovative semiconductor-based photonic and electronic device technologies, which primarily apply semiconductor, dielectric, and metallic nanomaterials for new robust photonic devices for defense, medical, and commercial applications. Equipment includes three molecular beam epitaxy machines and concomitant lithography and epilayer characterization facilities.

The Submillimeter-Wave Technology Laboratory is a leader in terahertz transmitter and receiver technologies, pioneering the design and fabrication of broadband solid-state multiplier sources, ultra-stable optically pumped lasers, and laser/microwave hybrid systems. The research team builds and maintains a variety of high-performance solid-state and laser-based measurement systems to generate terahertz frequency radiation, resulting in the development of a wide range of materials characterization techniques and high-resolution imaging systems for industry, defense, and medical applications.

The Biomedical Terahertz Technology Center focuses on developing biomedical imaging for cancer diagnosis using non-ionizing terahertz radiation.

The Radiation Laboratory with a 1-MW research reactor, an intense Cobalt-60 gamma source, and a 5.5-MV Van de Graaff accelerator, is a unique interdisciplinary facility for nuclear science and technology research. The experimental nuclear physics group carries out fundamental research on nuclear structure and nuclear astrophysics, with experiments at national heavy-ion accelerator facilities with high-resolution detector arrays, as well as detector development with industry, for nuclear science, advanced nuclear energy R&D, medical imaging, and homeland security applications. Applied nuclear research includes materials studies, fast neutron and fission spectroscopy, as well as radiation damage and recovery.

The Multiscale Electromagnetics Group combines theoretical and computational physics, supporting investigations in nano- and micro-structured composites, meta-materials, device design optimization, photonics, plasmonics, and imaging.

The Advanced Biophotonics Laboratory provides fundamental expertise on the structural and functional characterization of pathology for exploratory efforts in medical and bioengineering applications. Integrating multiple optical imaging and spectroscopic approaches, researchers monitor biochemical and physiological processes in real time on a variety of spatially different scales.

The Laboratory for Nano-science and Laser Applications has a femtosecond pulsed laser facility to study light-matter interactions for investigation of material structures and chemical reactions at the molecular level. The laser technology is also used to facilitate the manufacture of micro- and nano-structure materials. Applications include opto-electronics such as high-efficiency photo-detectors and solar cells, as well as in bio-medical research such as micro/nano tunnels for low-friction fluidity.

Space physics research at the UMass Lowell Center for Atmospheric Research include solar wind-magnetosphere interaction modeling, magnetosphere-ionosphere-thermosphere coupling theory, plasmasphere sounding and modeling, plasmasphere depletion and refilling processes, ionosphere sounding and modeling, radiation belt wave-particle interactions, antenna-plasma interaction, antenna radiation theory and experiments, whistler mode wave propagation, and ionospheric coupling.

The Medical Physics program is CAMPEP accredited. The Health Physics program is ABET accredited and has a separate Professional Science Master's program in Radiological Science and Protection. Research efforts include aerosol transport, dosimetry, medical imaging, diagnostics and therapeutics with nanoparticles, and research on radiation mitigating drugs.

Theory and Computation in Soft Matter and Dynamic Systems include applications in polymers, interfacial phenomena of electrolytes, and biological ensembles.

Research in quantum engineering and quantum computing lies at the interface of theory and experiment, and encompasses aspects of high-fidelity quantum information processing in low-dimensional systems.

Theoretical research in cosmology and general relativity focuses on using detailed measurements the cosmic microwave background and large scale structures in the universe to probe the physics of inflation, dark energy and dark matter.

Table B—Separately Budgeted Research Expenditures by Source of Support

Source of Support	Departmental Research	Physics-related Research Outside Department
Federal government	$7,233,602	
State/local government		
Non-profit organizations		
Business and industry	$1,106,387	
Other		
Total	$8,339,989	

Table C—Separately Budgeted Research Expenditures by Research Specialty

Research Specialty	No. of Grants	Expenditures ($)
Applied Physics	–	$5,444,730
Astronomy	–	$115,818
Astrophysics	–	$1,105,964
Atmosphere, Space Physics, Cosmic Rays	–	$547,361
Medical, Health Physics	–	$128,271
Nano Science and Technology	–	$130,154
Nuclear Physics	–	$397,292
Optics	–	$381,486
Polymer Physics/Science	–	$88,913
Total	**–**	**$8,339,989**

FACULTY

Professor

Chakrabarti, Supriya, Ph.D., University of California, Berkeley, 1982. Space experiments, hyperspectral imaging, LIDAR. *Astronomy, Astrophysics.*

Chowdhury, Partha, Ph.D., Stony Brook University, 1979. *Nuclear Physics.* Nuclear structure, advanced radiation detection, applied nuclear science.

Giles, Robert, Ph.D., University of Massachusetts, Lowell, 1986. *Applied Physics, Biophysics, Materials Science, Metallurgy, Optics.* Terahertz laser physics.

Kumar, Jayant, Ph.D., Rutgers University, 1983. *Biophysics, Condensed Matter Physics, Materials Science, Metallurgy, Optics, Polymer Physics/Science.* Optical and electronic properties of materials, spectroscopy, devices.

Mittler, Arthur, Ph.D., University of Kentucky, 1970. *Physics and other Science Education.*

Podolskiy, Viktor, Ph.D., New Mexico State University, 2002. *Computational Physics, Condensed Matter Physics, Materials Science, Metallurgy, Optics.* Photonics, plasmonics, nanoscience, metamaterials.

Sajo, Erno, University of Massachusetts, Lowell, 1990. *Medical, Health Physics, Nuclear Engineering.* Radiological science, aerosol science.

Sebastian, Kunnat J., Ph.D., University of Maryland, 1969. *Atomic, Molecular, & Optical Physics, Particles and Fields.* Theoretical atomic and particle physics.

Song, Paul, Ph.D., University of California, Los Angeles, 1991. *Atmosphere, Space Physics, Cosmic Rays.* Geophysics, space plasma physics.

Associate Professor

Shen, Mengyan, Ph.D., University of Science and Technology of China, 1990. *Applied Physics, Nano Science and Technology, Optics.* Femtosecond laser physics.

Tries, Mark A., Ph.D., University of Massachusetts, Lowell, 1999. *Medical, Health Physics.* Radiological science and protection.

Yaroslavsky, Anna, Ph.D., Saratov State University, 1999. *Biophysics, Medical, Health Physics, Optics.* Medical imaging, confocal microscopy, multispectral imaging.

Assistant Professor

Agarwal, Nishant, Ph.D., Cornell University, 2011. *Cosmology & String Theory, Relativity & Gravitation.* Theoretical cosmology, general relativity, dark energy, dark matter.

Bender, Peter C., Ph.D., Florida State University, 2011. *Nuclear Physics.* Nuclear structure, nuclear astrophysics, advanced radiation detection.

Cohen, Ofer, Ph.D., University of Michigan, 2008. *Astrophysics, Atmosphere, Space Physics, Cosmic Rays, Computational*

Physics, Planetary Science, Plasma and Fusion, Solar Physics. Simulations of solar and stellar atmospheres, space weather, plasma physics, planetary science, exoplanets.

Cook, Timothy A., Ph.D., University of Colorado, 1991. *Astronomy, Astrophysics.* Visible and UV instrumentation, sounding rockets, small satellites, tomography.

Guo, Wei, Ph.D., Brown University, 2008. *Applied Physics, Materials Science, Metallurgy, Optics, Solid State Physics.* Photonics and optoelectronics; nanomaterial growth.

Jandel, Marian, Ph.D., Slovak Academy of Sciences, 2003. *Medical, Health Physics, Nuclear Physics.* Neutron physics, medical isotopes, fission, multi-detector arrays.

Kamal, Archana, Ph.D., Yale University, 2013. *Optics, Quantum Foundations.* Quantum information, quantum computing, strongly-interacting quantum systems.

Laycock, Silas, Ph.D., University of Southampton, 2002. *Astronomy, Astrophysics, Physics and other Science Education.* Neutron stars and black holes in X-ray binaries, pulsars, multi-wavelength astronomy, time-domain astrophysics.

Ngwa, Wilfred F., Ph.D., University of Leipzig, 2004. *Biophysics, Medical, Health Physics.* Nanoparticles.

Qian, Xifeng, Ph.D., University of Massachusetts Lowell, 2009. *Materials Science, Metallurgy, Nano Science and Technology, Solid State Physics.* Photonic devices, epi-growth, nanofabrication.

Rogers, Andrew, Ph.D., Michigan State, 2009. *Nuclear Physics.* Nuclear structure, nuclear astrophysics.

Zwanikken, Johannes (Jos), Ph.D., Utrecht University, 2009. *Biophysics, Computational Physics, Condensed Matter Physics, Polymer Physics/Science, Theoretical Physics.* Theory and computation in Soft Matter and Dynamic Systems, with applications in polymers, interfacial phenomena of electrolytes, and biological ensembles.

Emeritus

Altman, Albert, Ph.D., University of Maryland, 1962. *Physics and other Science Education.* Physics education.

Egan, James J., Ph.D., University of Kentucky, 1969. *Nuclear Physics.* Neutron scattering.

Goodhue, William D., Ph.D., University of Massachusetts, Lowell, 1982. *Applied Physics, Condensed Matter Physics, Materials Science, Metallurgy, Optics.* Photonics and optoelectronics; molecular beam epitaxy.

Hardy, F. Raymond, M.S., University of Massachusetts, Lowell, 1962. *Physics and other Science Education.*

Kannenberg, Lloyd C., Ph.D., Northeastern University, 1966. *Relativity & Gravitation.*

Karakashian, Aram S., Ph.D., University of Maryland, 1970. *Condensed Matter Physics, Optics.* Theoretical/computational solid-state physics/optics.

Kegel, Gunter H. R., Ph.D., Massachusetts Institute of Technology, 1961. *Accelerator, Materials Science, Metallurgy, Nuclear Physics, Physics of Beams.* Neutron physics.

Lister, Christopher J., Ph.D., University of Liverpool, 1977. *Nuclear Physics.* Nuclear structure, detector development and instrumentation, applied nuclear science.

Pullen, David J., University of Oxford, 1963. *Nuclear Physics, Physics and other Science Education.*

Schier, Walter, Ph.D., University of Notre Dame, 1964. *Nuclear Physics.* Neutron detection.

Stimets, Richard W., Ph.D., Massachusetts Institute of Technology, 1969. *Astronomy, Condensed Matter Physics, Optics.* Image processing.

Waldman, Jerry, Ph.D., Massachusetts Institute of Technology, 1970. *Applied Physics, Materials Science, Metallurgy, Optics.* Experimental laser physics.

Wilner, Martin, Ph.D., Massachusetts Institute of Technology, 1964. *Optics, Solid State Physics, Theoretical Physics.*

Research Associate Professor

Gatesman, Andrew, Ph.D., University of Massachusetts, Lowell, 1993. *Engineering Physics/Science, Optics, Systems Science/Engineering.* Radar signatures; IR, submillimeter, and millimeter wave optical systems.

Adjunct Faculty

Bobek, Leo, M.S., University of Massachusetts, Lowell, 1989. *Medical, Health Physics, Nuclear Engineering.* Reactor operations.

Coulombe, Michael, M.S., University of Massachusetts, Lowell, 1989. *Systems Science/Engineering.* Microwave systems; terahertz physics.

DeMartinis, Guy B., Ph.D., University of Massachusetts, Lowell, 2008. *Applied Physics.* Terahertz technology.

Finn, Susanna, Ph.D., Boston University, 2012. *Astronomy, Astrophysics.*

Goyette, Thomas M., Ph.D., Duke University, 1990. *Applied Physics, Optics.* Laser systems; terahertz spectroscopy.

Li, Lian, Ph.D., University of Massachusetts, Lowell, 1993. *Optics, Polymer Physics/Science.* Nonlinear optics.

Menyhart, Gabor, M.S., University of Kentucky, 2002. *Medical, Health Physics.*

Montesalvo, Mary, M.S., University of Massachusetts, Lowell, 1985. *Medical, Health Physics.* Radiation dosimetry.

Morse, Christopher, Ph.D., Michigan State University, 2015. *Nuclear Physics.*

Mosurkal, Ravi, Ph.D., University of Hyderabad, 1998. *Polymer Physics/Science.* Polymer physics.

Pretorius, P. Hendrik, Ph.D., University of Orange Free State, 1994. *Biophysics, Medical, Health Physics.*

Regan, Thomas, M.S., University of Massachusetts, Lowell, 1994. *Nuclear Engineering, Nuclear Physics.* Nuclear engineering; neutron radiography.

Rivard, Mark, Ph.D., Wayne State University, 1998. *Medical, Health Physics.* Medical physics.

Seco, Joao, Ph.D., University of London, 2001. *Medical, Health Physics.* Radiation oncology.

Sivjee, Abbas H., Ph.D., Johns Hopkins University, 1970. *Astronomy, Astrophysics.*

Snay, Steven, M.S., University of Massachusetts, Lowell, 2007. *Medical, Health Physics.* Radiological science.

Sullivan, Nancy L. B., Ph.D., University of Massachusetts, Lowell, 1993. *Physics and other Science Education.* Physics education.

Weintraub, Sheri M., M.S., University of Cincinnati, 1999. *Medical, Health Physics.* Radiation oncology.

Wong, Eric T., Other, Rutgers Medical School, 1989. M.D., Neuro-oncology.

Visiting Lecturer

Joseph, Cecil, Ph.D., University of Massachusetts, Lowell, 2010. *Applied Physics, Biophysics, Physics and other Science Education.* Biophysics; medical applications.

Narayan, Chandrika, Ph.D., University of Massachusetts, Lowell, 1992. *Applied Physics, Materials Science, Metallurgy, Physics and other Science Education.* Materials physics; accelerator applications.

Lecturer

Danylov, Andriy, Ph.D., University of Massachusetts, Lowell, 2010. *Materials Science, Metallurgy, Optics, Physics and other Science Education.* Submillimeter wave technology.

Lepeshkin, Nikolay, Ph.D., New Mexico State University, 2001. *Optics.* Physics education.

DEPARTMENTAL RESEARCH SPECIALTIES AND STAFF

Theoretical

metamaterials. plasmonics, metamaterials, metasurfaces. Podolskiy.

Optics. Quantum optics; dielectric waveguides;surface plamons; spectroscopy; imaging. Danylov, Kamal, Podolskiy.

Particles and Fields. Sebastian.

Plasma Physics. Simulations of solar and stellar atmospheres, magnetospheres, space physics and exoplanets. Cohen.

Quantum Information. Quantum engineering, quantum computing, strongly interacting quantum systems. Kamal.

Relativity & Gravitation. Cosmology, dark energy, dark matter, simulations. Agarwal.

Soft Condensed Matter. Theory and Computation in Soft Matter and Dynamic Systems, with applications in polymers, interfacial phenomena of electrolytes, and biological ensembles. Zwanikken.

Experimental

Applied Physics. Advanced detector development; gamma ray imaging; neutron detection; fast neutron spectroscopy; nuclear instrumentation; decay heat and cross-section measurements; proton microbeams; medical isotopes. Bender, Chowdhury, Jandel, Kumar, Lister, Rogers, Schier.

Applied Physics. Development of coherent sources, receivers; novel imaging systems at THz frequencies. DeMartinis, Giles, Goyette, Joseph, Waldman.

Applied Physics. Materials tunable visible, infrared and far-infrared lasers; opto-electronic materials and devices; image processing; surface plasmons; polymers and biological materials. Danylov, DeMartinis, Gatesman, Giles, Goyette, Guo, Joseph, Kumar, Li, Qian, Shen, Waldman.

Astronomy. X-ray binaries; galactic formation and structure: suborbital sounding rockets for astronomical observation; development of novel instruments and data analysis techniques; UV imaging and spectroscopy; exoplanet observations. Chakrabarti, Cook, Laycock.

Atmosphere, Space Physics, Cosmic Rays. Solar wind-magnetosphere-ionosphere interactions. Song.

Medical, Health Physics. Dosimetry; shielding; biological effects of radiation; radon monitoring studies; radiation safety and control; aerosol physics;biophotonics;medical isotopes. Jandel, Ngwa, Pretorius, Rivard, Sajo, Seco, Tries, Weintraub, Wong, Yaroslavsky.

Nano Science and Technology. Femtosecond laser surface interactions. Shen.

Nuclear Physics. Nuclear structure; nuclear astrophysics; spectroscopy of nuclei far from stability; heavy-ion reactions; nuclear isomers; superheavy nuclei. Bender, Chowdhury, Lister, Rogers.

Optics. Gatesman, Giles, Guo, Kumar, Waldman, Yaroslavsky.

View additional information about this department at www.gradschoolshopper.com. Check out the "Why Choose Us?" section, find out more about the department's culture and get links to social media networks.

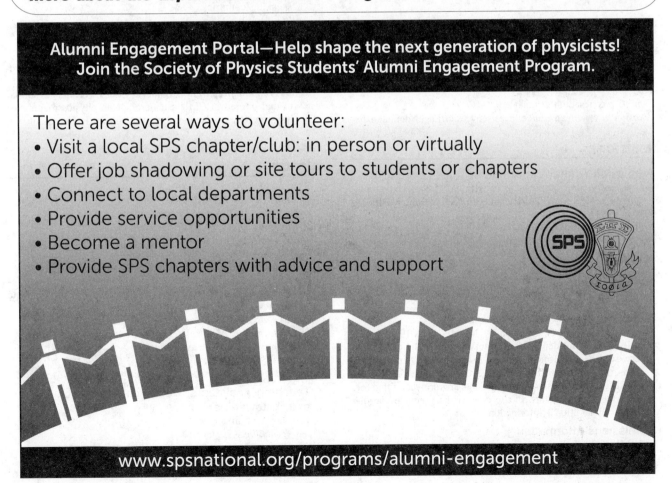

CENTRAL MICHIGAN UNIVERSITY

DEPARTMENT OF PHYSICS

Mt. Pleasant, Michigan 48859
www.cmich.edu/colleges/se/physics/Pages/default.aspx

General University Information
President: George Ross
Dean of Graduate School: David Ash
University website: http://www.cmich.edu
School Type: Public
Setting: Rural
Total Faculty: 1,017
Total Graduate Faculty: 650
Total number of Students: 23,335
Total number of Graduate Students: 6,157

Department Information
Department Chairman: Prof. Christopher Tycner, Chair
Department Contact: Juan Peralta, Graduate Coordinator
  Total full-time faculty: 14
  Total number of full-time equivalent positions: 17
  Full-Time Graduate Students: 15
  Female Full-Time Graduate Students: 2
  First-Year Graduate Students: 6
  Female First-Year Students: 2
  Total Post Doctorates: 5

Department Address
Dow Science 203
201 E Ottawa Court
Mt. Pleasant, MI 48859
Phone: (989) 774-3321
Fax: (989) 774-2697
E-mail: physicsadmit@cmich.edu
Website: www.cmich.edu/colleges/se/physics/Pages/default.aspx

ADMISSIONS

Admission Contact Information
Address admission inquiries to: Central Michigan University, Graduate Recruiting, 260 Ronan Hall, Mt. Pleasant, MI 48859
Phone: (989) 774-4444
E-mail: apply@cmich.edu
Admissions website: https://apply.cmich.edu

Application deadlines
Fall admission:
U.S. students: March 15   *Int'l. students*: March 15

Application fee
U.S. students: $60   *Int'l. students*: $60
Applications should be received by March 15, 2019. All applicants are considered for assistantship unless indicated otherwise. The department expects to offer a PhD in Physics soon, in addition to the existing PhD degree in Science of Advanced Materials program. Students are rarely admitted for a spring semester start. Please contact the graduate coordinator for additional information.

Admissions information
For Fall of 2018:
  Number of applicants: 33
  Number admitted: 5
  Number enrolled: 5

Admission requirements
Bachelor's degree requirements: Bachelor's degree in Physics or a closely related discipline from an accredited Science or Engineering program.
Minimum undergraduate GPA: 2.7

GRE requirements
The GRE is recommended but not required.
  Mean GRE score range (25th–75th percentile): 50th-60th percentile
  GRE scores are not required but recommended for all applicants, but especially for those seeking a graduate assistantship.

Subjective GRE requirements
The Subjective GRE is recommended.
  Mean Advanced GRE score range (25th–75th percentile): 40th-60th percentile
  A Physics GRE score is not required but recommended for applicants seeking a graduate assistantship.

TOEFL requirements
The TOEFL exam is required for students from non-English-speaking countries.
  PBT score: 550
  iBT score: 79

Other admissions information
Additional requirements: Three letters of recommendation are requested for applicants seeking an assistantship.
Undergraduate preparation assumed: Coursework that is similar to that offered in CMU's undergraduate physics major. See https://www.cmich.edu/colleges/se/physics/Pages/default.aspx.

TUITION

Tuition year 2018–19:
Tuition for in-state residents
  Full-time students: $575 per credit
  Part-time students: $575 per credit
Tuition for out-of-state residents
  Full-time students: $850 per credit
  Part-time students: $850 per credit
All students receiving graduate assistantships receive tuition remission that covers all the required classes in the graduate Physics program.
Credit hours per semester to be considered full-time: 6
Deferred tuition plan:
Health insurance: Not available.
Academic term: Semester
Number of first-year students who received full tuition waivers: 6

Teaching Assistants, Research Assistants, and Fellowships
Number of first-year
  Teaching Assistants: 6
  Research Assistants: 2
Average stipend per academic year
  Teaching Assistant: $13,750
  Research Assistant: $13,750

Fellowship student: $13,750

Majority (more than 90%) of graduate students receive full or partial RA support during the summer that provides an additional $6,875 in support for the summer for a total for calendar year of up to $20,625. Doctoral assistantships are $25,875 per calendar year.

FINANCIAL AID

Application deadlines
Fall admission:
U.S. students: March 15   *Int'l. students*: March 15

Loans
Loans are available for U.S. students.
Loans are not available for international students.
GAPSFAS application required: No
FAFSA application required: Yes

For further information
Address financial aid inquiries to: CMU Office of Scholarships and Financial Aid, Student Service Court, Mount Pleasant, MI 48859.
Phone: (989) 774-3674
E-mail: CMUOSFA@cmich.edu
Financial aid website: https://www.cmich.edu/ess/OSFA/Pages/Graduate-Students.aspx

HOUSING

Availability of on-campus housing
Single students: Yes
Married students: Yes
Childcare Assistance: No

For further information
Address housing inquiries to: Residence Life, Ronan Hall Room 270, Central Michigan University, Mount Pleasant, MI 48859.
Phone: (989) 774-3111
E-mail: reslife@cmich.edu
Housing aid website: http://www.reslife.cmich.edu

Table A—Faculty, Enrollments, and Degrees Granted

Research Specialty	2017–18 Faculty	Enrollment Fall 2016 Master's	Enrollment Fall 2016 Doctorate	Number of Degrees Granted 2016–17 Master's	Number of Degrees Granted 2016–17 Terminal Master's	Number of Degrees Granted 2016–17 Doctorate
Astronomy	2	2	–	–	–	–
Condensed Matter Physics	6	6	2	–	–	–
Materials Science, Metallurgy	1	2	2	–	–	–
Nuclear Physics	5	8	1	–	–	–
Total	14	18	5	10	3	–
Full-time Grad. Stud.	–	18	5	–	–	–
First-year Grad. Stud.	–	4	1	–	–	–

GRADUATE DEGREE REQUIREMENTS

Master's: A total of 30 credit hours are required, plus a Thesis. Equivalently, Thesis work can be replaced by 6 credit hours of elective courses plus a small research project.

Other Degrees: The Department of Physics participates in an interdisciplinary PhD program in the Science of Advanced Materials (SAM). See https://www.cmich.edu/colleges/se/sam/Pages/default.aspx for details. Students may begin with the M.S. in Physics and enter the SAM Ph.D. program after earning the M.S. degree.

Thesis: A written Thesis is required, along with an oral thesis defense for graduation under the Thesis option.

SPECIAL EQUIPMENT, FACILITIES, OR PROGRAMS

The department of Physics operates X-ray crystallography laboratory, astronomical observatory, polymer physics laboratory, and three experimental nuclear physics laboratories. Faculty and students also access computational resources at the High Performance Computer Center at Michigan State University and the National Superconducting Cyclotron Laboratory.

Table B—Separately Budgeted Research Expenditures by Source of Support

Source of Support	Departmental Research	Physics-related Research Outside Department
Federal government	$2,138,800	
State/local government		
Non-profit organizations		
Business and industry		
Other		
Total	$2,138,800	

Table C—Separately Budgeted Research Expenditures by Research Specialty

Research Specialty	No. of Grants	Expenditures ($)
Astrophysics	1	$60,000
Condensed Matter Physics	6	$500,000
Nuclear Physics	3	$300,000
Total	10	$860,000

FACULTY

Professor

Finck, Joseph E., Ph.D., Michigan State University, 1982. *Nuclear Physics*. Experimental nuclear physics; properties of neutron-rich nuclei near the neutron drip-line; MoNA and LISA neutron detectors.

Fornari, Marco, Ph.D., University of Trieste, 1998. *Condensed Matter Physics*. Electronic structure, thermo-electric materials, ferro- and piezo-electric materials; physics education.

Horoi, Mihai, Ph.D., Institute of Atomic Physics, Bucharest, 1990. *Nuclear Physics*. Theoretical nuclear physics; nuclear shell structure; medical physics.

Jackson, Koblar A., Ph.D., University of Wisconsin-Madison, 1989. *Chemical Physics, Condensed Matter Physics*. Density functional theory-based methods for studying the properties of materials; theory of atomic clusters; chemical physics.

Peralta, Juan E., Ph.D., University of Buenos Aires, 2002. Graduate Coordinator. *Chemical Physics, Condensed Matter Physics*. Magnetic phenomena in molecules and nanomaterials from first-principles; novel theoretical and computational methods for understanding the chemical and physical properties of new materials.

Petkov, Valeri G., Ph.D., University of Sofia, 1991. *Condensed Matter Physics*. X-ray diffraction of materials.

Tycner, Christopher, Ph.D., University of Toronto, 2004. *Astronomy, Astrophysics*. Study of circumstellar disks of hot stars using a variety of ground-based instruments, including long-baseline optical interferometry and spectroscopy.

Williams, Glen, Ph.D., University of Michigan, 1983. *Astrophysics*. Studies of hydrodynamics and radiation transfer in accretion disks of Cataclysmic Variable stars.

Associate Professor

Barone, Veronica, Ph.D., University of Buenos Aires, 2003. *Chemical Physics, Condensed Matter Physics, Energy Sources & Environment*. Electronic structure calculations based on density functional theory with applications in energy storage, electronic devices, and characterization methods; Computational Materials science. Publication info: https://scholar.google.com/citations?user=MYs9tMUAAAAJ&hl=en&oi=ao

Mellinger, Axel P., Ph.D., Technical University Munich, 1995. *Condensed Matter Physics, Polymer Physics/Science*. Ferroelectret polymers and dielectric nanocomposites: new concepts for piezoelectric sensors and actuators; non-destructive 3D space-charge and polarization tomography; energy harvesting.

Perdikakis, Georgios, Ph.D., National Technical University of Athens, 2006. *Nuclear Physics*. Experimental nuclear physics and nuclear astrophysics, stellar nucleosynthesis, stellar energy production, nuclear structure and reactions, physics with rare isotopes.

Redshaw, Matthew, Ph.D., Florida State University, 2007. *Atomic, Molecular, & Optical Physics, Nuclear Physics*. Precision mass measurements using ions confined in a Penning trap; atomic mass measurements on stable and short-lived isotopes with applications in nuclear physics and nuclear astrophysics, neutrino physics, atomic physics, chemistry and metrology.

Assistant Professor

Estrade, Alfredo, Ph.D., Michigan State University, 2010. *Nuclear Engineering, Nuclear Physics*. Nuclear physics and astrophysics: experiments with radioactive ion beams, r-process nucleosynthesis and X-ray bursts in neutron stars, nuclear structure of unstable isotopes.

Yang, Junjie, Ph.D., Tsinghua University, 2010. *Condensed Matter Physics, Crystallography, Solid State Physics*. Single crystal growth and Neutron Scattering.

DEPARTMENTAL RESEARCH SPECIALTIES AND STAFF

Theoretical

Computational electronic structure. Electronic structure theory of molecules and clusters. Magnetic and electric properties of low-dimensional systems. Barone, Jackson, Peralta.

Computational materials physics. Electronic structure of materials using first-principles techniques. Barone, Fornari, Jackson, Peralta.

Nuclear structure physics. Spectroscopy and nuclear structure; shell model calculations. Estrade, Horoi, Perdikakis.

Physics of circumstellar disks. Observational studies of disks using optical interferometry; computational modeling of radiative transfer in disks. Tycner, Williams.

Rare isotope physics. High-precision mass determinations; transfer reactions. Horoi.

Experimental

Astrophysics. Nuclear Astrophysics. Estrade, Perdikakis.

Condensed Matter Physics. Single crystal growth and characterization. Petkov, Yang.

Materials characterization. X-ray characterization of materials; nanoparticles; disordered materials; rheology and polymer physics. Mellinger, Petkov.

Quantum Materials. Bulk single crystal growth of quantum materials, such as multiferroics, topological insulators, new superconductors and frustrated magnets. Yang.

Rare isotope physics. High-precision mass determinations; transfer reactions. Finck, Perdikakis, Redshaw.

View additional information about this department at www.gradschoolshopper.com. Check out the "Why Choose Us?" section, find out more about the department's culture and get links to social media networks.

EASTERN MICHIGAN UNIVERSITY

DEPARTMENT OF PHYSICS AND ASTRONOMY

Ypsilanti, Michigan 48197
http://www.emich.edu/physics

General University Information
President: James M. Smith
Dean of Graduate School: Wade Tornquist (interim)
University website: http://www.emich.edu
School Type: Public
Setting: Suburban
Total Faculty: 957
Total number of Students: 24,287
Total number of Graduate Students: 5,627

Department Information
Department Chairman: Prof. Alexandria Oakes, Head
Department Contact: J. Marshall Thomsen, Advisor
  Total full-time faculty: 11
  Total number of full-time equivalent positions: 13
  Full-Time Graduate Students: 10
  Female Full-Time Graduate Students: 1
  First-Year Graduate Students: 5
  Female First-Year Students: 1

Department Address
Physics and Astronomy
Ypsilanti, MI 48197
Phone: (734) 487-8794
E-mail: jthomsen@emich.edu
Website: http://www.emich.edu/physics

ADMISSIONS

Admission Contact Information
Address admission inquiries to: Office of Admissions, 401 Pierce
  Hall, Ypsilanti, MI 48197
Phone: (800) 468-6368
E-mail: graduate.admissions@emich.edu
Admissions website: http://www.emich.edu/graduate/admissions

Application deadlines
Fall admission:
U.S. students: March 15   *Int'l. students*: February 15

Application fee
U.S. students: $45   *Int'l. students*: $45

Admissions information
For Fall of 2018:
  Number of applicants: 12
  Number admitted: 9
  Number enrolled: 6

Admission requirements
Bachelor's degree requirements: A Bachelor's degree in Physics
  is required.
Minimum undergraduate GPA: 2.7

GRE requirements
The GRE is not required.

Subjective GRE requirements
The Subjective GRE is not required.

TOEFL requirements
The TOEFL exam is required for students from non-English-
  speaking countries.
  PBT score: 550
  iBT score: 85

Other admissions information
Additional requirements: Conditional admission may be granted
  to those without a standard undergraduate preparation in physics. A physics education degree, which includes a minor in
  physics and status as an in-service or prospective teacher, is
  available. A physical science degree, which includes a minor
  in a science with not less than 30 semester-hours in science
  and mathematics and status as an in-service or prospective
  teacher is also available. Students from non-English-speaking
  countries are required to demonstrate proficiency in English
  via the ELI exam; the minimum acceptable score for admission is 85 (admission with lower scores, but requiring special English courses, may be granted).

TUITION

Tuition year 2017–18:
Tuition for in-state residents
  Full-time students: $712 per credit
Tuition for out-of-state residents
  Full-time students: $1,268 per credit
Credit hours per semester to be considered full-time: 6
Deferred tuition plan:
Health insurance: Yes, see website.
Other academic fees: $50/credit.
Academic term: Semester
Number of first-year students who received full tuition waivers: 4

Teaching Assistants, Research Assistants, and Fellowships
  Number of first-year
    Teaching Assistants: 4
  Average stipend per academic year
    Teaching Assistant: $10,000

FINANCIAL AID

Application deadlines
Fall admission:
U.S. students: February 15   *Int'l. students*: February 15

Loans
Loans are available for U.S. students.
Loans are not available for international students.
GAPSFAS application required: No
FAFSA application required: No

For further information
Address financial aid inquiries to: Graduate Assistantships: Grad-
  uate School, Other: Director of Financial Aid.
Phone: (734) 487-0042
E-mail: graduate_school@emich.edu
Financial aid website: http://www.emich.edu/graduate/
  financial_assistance/

HOUSING

Availability of on-campus housing
Single students: Yes
Married students: Yes

For further information
Address housing inquiries to: EMU Housing, Ypsilanti, MI 48197.
Phone: (734) 487-1300
E-mail: housing@emich.edu
Housing aid website: http://www.emich.edu/residencelife

Table A—Faculty, Enrollments, and Degrees Granted

Research Specialty	2016–17 Faculty	Enrollment Fall 2016		Number of Degrees Granted 2015–16 (2011–16)		
		Master's	Doctorate	Master's	Terminal Master's	Doctorate
Physics and other Science Education	11	7	–	2(8)	–	–
Non-specialized	–	13	–	6(35)	–	–
Other	2	7	–	4(11)	–	–
Total	13	27	–	11(54)	–	–
Full-time Grad. Stud.	–	10	–	–	–	–
First-year Grad. Stud.	–	11	–	–	–	–

GRADUATE DEGREE REQUIREMENTS

Master's: Master's degree in physics: A "B" average in 30 semester hours of graduate credits on an advisor-approved program is required. There are no language requirements. Eighteen hours of program must be taken on campus. An oral examination and a written research report/thesis are required. Master's degree in physics education: The requirements are as specified for the Physics Master's program, except that the program emphasizes courses beneficial to secondary school teachers. Master's degree in physical science: A program for middle school science teachers. A "B" average in 30 semester hours of approved graduate credits. Eighteen hours of the program must be taken on campus. There are no language, oral examination, or thesis requirements.

Thesis: Thesis may be written in absentia.

SPECIAL EQUIPMENT, FACILITIES, OR PROGRAMS

The Department has among its facilities an observatory, workstations, a staffed machine shop, a plasma physics laboratory, a thin film and surface science laboratory, and a modern optics laboratory.

Table B—Separately Budgeted Research Expenditures by Source of Support

Source of Support	Departmental Research	Physics-related Research Outside Department
Federal government	$1,402,000	
State/local government		
Non-profit organizations		
Business and industry	$60,000	
Other	$31,000	
Total	$1,493,000	

Table C—Separately Budgeted Research Expenditures by Research Specialty

Research Specialty	No. of Grants	Expenditures ($)
Atmosphere, Space Physics, Cosmic Rays	4	$431,000
Nano Science and Technology	3	$486,000
Physics and other Science Education	2	$555,000
Total	9	$1,472,000

FACULTY

Professor
Behringer, Ernest, Ph.D., Cornell University, 1994. *Condensed Matter Physics, Optics*. Optical tweezers.
Carroll, James, Ph.D., West Virginia University, 1997. Assoc. Provost and Assoc. V. P. for Administration. Plasma physics.
Jacobs, Diane A., Ph.D., University of Texas, Austin, 1984. *Condensed Matter Physics, Plasma and Fusion*. Plasma experiments.
Koehn, Patrick, Ph.D., University of Michigan, 2002. Space physics.
Oakes, Alexandria, Ph.D., Lehigh University, 1986. Department Head. *Acoustics, Mechanics*.
Sharma, Natthi, Ph.D., Ohio University, 1982. *Atomic, Molecular, & Optical Physics, Condensed Matter Physics*.
Sheerin, James P., Ph.D., University of Michigan, 1980. *Atmosphere, Space Physics, Cosmic Rays, Nonlinear Dynamics and Complex Systems, Plasma and Fusion*. Active Space Experiments.
Thomsen, Marshall, Ph.D., Michigan State University, 1984. *Condensed Matter Physics, Theoretical Physics*.
Wylo, Bonnie, Other, University of Michigan, 1993. Ed.D. *Physics and other Science Education*.

Associate Professor
Kubitskey, Beth, Ph.D., University of Michigan, 2006. Assoc. Dean for Students and Curriculum College of Education. *Physics and other Science Education*. Teacher education.
Pawlowski, David J., Ph.D., University of Michigan, 2009. *Atmosphere, Space Physics, Cosmic Rays*. Planetary Atmospheres.

Assistant Professor
Paradis, Eric G., Ph.D., University of Michigan, 2013. *Atomic, Molecular, & Optical Physics*.
Skuza, Jonathan R., Ph.D., College of William and Mary, 2011. *Condensed Matter Physics, Nano Science and Technology, Surface Physics*.

DEPARTMENTAL RESEARCH SPECIALTIES AND STAFF

Theoretical
Acoustics. Oakes.
Atmosphere, Space Physics, Cosmic Rays. Koehn, Pawlowski, Sheerin.
Computational Physics. Pawlowski, Sheerin, Thomsen.
Condensed Matter Physics. Sharma, Thomsen.
Electromagnetism. Sharma.
Mechanics. Oakes.
Optics. Sharma.
Plasma and Fusion. Koehn, Pawlowski, Sheerin.

Experimental
Atmosphere, Space Physics, Cosmic Rays. Koehn, Sheerin.
Atomic, Molecular, & Optical Physics. Behringer, Paradis.
Condensed Matter Physics. Behringer, Jacobs, Skuza, Thomsen.

Fluids, Rheology. Jacobs.
Nonlinear Dynamics and Complex Systems. Jacobs, Sheerin.
Optics. Behringer, Paradis, Sharma, Thomsen.

Physics and other Science Education. Kubitskey, Wylo.
Plasma and Fusion. Carroll, Jacobs, Sheerin.
Surface Physics. Skuza.

View additional information about this department at www.gradschoolshopper.com. Check out the "Why Choose Us?" section, find out more about the department's culture and get links to social media networks.

MICHIGAN TECHNOLOGICAL UNIVERSITY

DEPARTMENT OF PHYSICS

Houghton, Michigan 49931-1295
http://www.phy.mtu.edu

General University Information
President: Richard J. Koubek
Dean of Graduate School: Pushpalatha Murthy
University website: http://www.mtu.edu
School Type: Public
Setting: Rural
Total Faculty: 477
Total Graduate Faculty: 715
Total number of Students: 7,319
Total number of Graduate Students: 1,402

Department Information
Department Chairman: Prof. Ravindra Pandey, Chair
Department Contact: Andrea S. Lappi, Departmental
 Coordinator
 Total full-time faculty: 19
 Total number of full-time equivalent positions: 19
 Full-Time Graduate Students: 44
 Female Full-Time Graduate Students: 13
 First-Year Graduate Students: 13
 Female First-Year Students: 7
 Total Post Doctorates: 2

Department Address
1400 Townsend Drive
Houghton, MI 49931-1295
Phone: (906) 487-2086
Fax: (906) 487-2933
E-mail: physics@mtu.edu
Website: http://www.phy.mtu.edu

ADMISSIONS

Admission Contact Information
Address admission inquiries to: Dean of Graduate School, 1400
 Townsend Dr., Houghton, MI 49931-1295
Admissions website: http://www.mtu.edu/gradschool

Application deadlines
Fall admission:
U.S. students: February 1   *Int'l. students*: February 1

Application fee
There is no application fee required.

Admissions information
For Fall of 2018:
 Number of applicants: 136
 Number admitted: 39
 Number enrolled: 6

Admission requirements
Bachelor's degree requirements: A Bachelor's degree in Physics
 is usually required; however, degree recipients in related areas
 often apply and are accepted.
Minimum undergraduate GPA: 3.0

GRE requirements
The GRE is required.
 Quantitative score: 720
 Analytical score: 3.0

Subjective GRE requirements
The Subjective GRE is not required.

TOEFL requirements
The TOEFL exam is required for students from non-English-
 speaking countries.
 PBT score: 570
 iBT score: 88
IELTS = Band of 6.5 or better.

Other admissions information
Undergraduate preparation assumed: Taylor, Classical Mechanics; Eisberg and Resnick, Quantum Physics; Griffiths, Introduction to Electrodynamics.

TUITION

Tuition year 2017–18:
Tuition for in-state residents
 Full-time students: $8,550 per semester
Tuition for out-of-state residents
 Full-time students: $8,550 per semester
Laboratory fees required in curriculum; student-voted fee of
 $124/year.
Credit hours per semester to be considered full-time: 9
Deferred tuition plan:
Health insurance: Available at the cost of $627 per year.
Other academic fees: International student surcharge of $250/se-
 mester, if applicable.
Academic term: Semester

Teaching Assistants, Research Assistants, and Fellowships
Number of first-year
 Teaching Assistants: 6
 Research Assistants: 1
Average stipend per academic year
 Teaching Assistant: $15,766
 Research Assistant: $16,487
 Fellowship student: $17,186
Finishing fellowships awarded by the graduate school in re-
 cipient's defending semester.

FINANCIAL AID

Loans
Loans are available for U.S. students.
Loans are not available for international students.
GAPSFAS application required: No
FAFSA application required: Yes

For further information
Address financial aid inquiries to: Graduate Studies Chair, Physics Department/MTU, 1400 Townsend Dr. Houghton, MI
 49931-1295.
E-mail: physics@mtu.edu

Financial aid website: http://www.mtu.edu/finaid

HOUSING

Availability of on-campus housing
Single students: Yes
Married students: Yes

For further information
Address housing inquiries to: Director of Housing, 1400 Townsend Dr., Houghton, MI 49931-1295.
Housing aid website: http://www.mtu.edu/housing

Table A—Faculty, Enrollments, and Degrees Granted

Research Specialty	2017–18 Faculty	Enrollment Fall 2017		Number of Degrees Granted 2017–18 (2013–17)		
		Master's	Doctorate	Master's	Terminal Master's	Doctorate
Astronomy	1	–	3	–	–(1)	–
Astrophysics	3	3	3	–	3	–(4)
Atmosphere, Space Physics, Cosmic Rays	4	1	12	1(3)	1(4)	–
Atomic, Molecular, & Optical Physics	3	4	4	1	–(3)	1(2)
Biophysics	–	–	–	–	–	–
Condensed Matter Physics	5	2	6	–	–	–(5)
Materials Science, Metallurgy	3	–	6	–	–(2)	1(5)
Total	**19**	**10**	**34**	**2(3)**	**4(10)**	**2(16)**
Full-time Grad. Stud.	–	4	27	–	–	–
First-year Grad. Stud.	–	6	7	–	–	–

GRADUATE DEGREE REQUIREMENTS

Master's: All Physics graduate degree requirements include six core courses (15 credits) and two to three elective courses. M.S. degrees have a coursework option, project report option, and a thesis option.

Doctorate: Ph.D. in Physics and Applied Physics requires 30 course and/or research credits beyond the M.S. degree or 60 course/research credits beyond the Bachelor's degree, passing a written qualifying examination and dissertation proposal, performing research, and presenting final oral dissertation.

SPECIAL EQUIPMENT, FACILITIES, OR PROGRAMS

The department maintains a machine shop with a full-time machinist. Research laboratories include atmospheric physics; atomic and molecular laser spectroscopy; cloud physics; environmental optics; integrated photonics and materials integration; materials physics synthesis and characterization; nuclear magnetic resonance; quantum optics; and computational physics. For details, see http://www.mtu.edu/physics/research-facilities/research-labs/

Additionally, physics houses the Elizabeth and Richard Henes Center for Quantum Phenomena, which supports a variety of initiatives for physics students including scientific colloquia, funding for travel to professional conferences and research institutions, and research awards for outstanding graduate students. Other university facilities include microfabrication X-ray diffraction; electron, scanning probe, and optical microscopy; focused ion beam system; a state-of-the-art parallel computing facility; and an excellent library.

Table B—Separately Budgeted Research Expenditures by Source of Support

Source of Support	Departmental Research	Physics-related Research Outside Department
Federal government	$1,193,569	
State/local government	$1,140	
Non-profit organizations		
Business and industry		
Other	$1,217,738	
Total	**$2,412,447**	

Table C—Separately Budgeted Research Expenditures by Research Specialty

Research Specialty	No. of Grants	Expenditures ($)
Astronomy	1	$65,896
Astrophysics	2	$157,241
Atmosphere, Space Physics, Cosmic Rays	12	$597,850
Atomic, Molecular, & Optical Physics	1	$66,759
Condensed Matter Physics	2	$85,658
Materials Science, Metallurgy	7	$220,165
Total	**25**	**$1,193,569**

FACULTY

Professor

Borysow, Jacek I., Ph.D., University of Texas, Austin, 1986. Laser spectroscopy.

Cantrell, Will, Ph.D., University of Alaska, 1999. *Atmosphere, Space Physics, Cosmic Rays*. Atmospheric sciences.

Fick, Brian E., Ph.D., Virginia Polytechnic Institute and State University (Virginia Tech), 1985. Experimental astro-particle physics.

Huentemeyer, Petra, Ph.D., University of Hamburg, Germany, 2001. *Astrophysics*. Particle astrophysics.

Jaszczak, John A., Ph.D., Ohio State University, 1989. Computational solid-state physics; nanotechnology education.

Kostinski, Alexander, Ph.D., University of Illinois at Chicago, 1984. Radar meteorology; polarization optics; atmospheric physics.

Levy, Miguel, Ph.D., City University of New York, 1988. Surface physics.

Mazzoleni, Claudio, Ph.D., University of Nevada, 2003. *Atmosphere, Space Physics, Cosmic Rays*. Atmospheric physics.

Moran, Peter D., Ph.D., University of Wisconsin-Madison. *Atomic, Molecular, & Optical Physics, Condensed Matter Physics, Materials Science, Metallurgy*. Materials physics; device fabrication and characterization.

Nemiroff, Robert J., Ph.D., University of Pennsylvania, 1987. Astronomy; astrophysics.

Nitz, David, Ph.D., University of Rochester, 1978. High-energy astrophysics.

Pandey, Ravindra, Ph.D., University of Manitoba, Canada, 1987. Materials theory.

Pati, Ranjit, Ph.D., University at Albany, State University of New York, 1998. *Condensed Matter Physics*. Theoretical condensed-matter physics; materials science.

Perger, Warren F., Ph.D., Colorado State University, 1987. Computational atomic and condensed-matter physics.

Shaw, Raymond, Ph.D., Pennsylvania State University, 1998. *Atmosphere, Space Physics, Cosmic Rays*. Atmospheric sciences.

Suits, Bryan, Ph.D., University of Illinois, 1981. *Atomic, Molecular, & Optical Physics, Condensed Matter Physics*. Experimental condensed-matter physics; NMR.

Yap, Yoke Khin, Ph.D., Osaka University, 1999. *Condensed Matter Physics, Nano Science and Technology.* Materials science; materials and laser physics.

Associate Professor

El-Ganainy, Ramy, Ph.D., University of Central Florida, 2009. *Optics.* Photonics; quantum optics.

Weidman, Robert S., Ph.D., University of Illinois, 1980. *Condensed Matter Physics.* Theoretical condensed-matter physics; electronic structure.

Assistant Professor

Nakamura, Issei, Ph.D., McMaster University, 2010. *Applied Physics, Chemical Physics, Computational Physics, Condensed Matter Physics, Polymer Physics/Science, Statistical & Thermal Physics.* Soft-matter theory and simulation.

Suh, Jae Yong, Ph.D., Vanderbilt University, 2007. *Optics.* Nanoscale photonics; quantum optics; plasmonics.

DEPARTMENTAL RESEARCH SPECIALTIES AND STAFF

Theoretical

Astronomy. All-sky monitoring and gamma-ray burst detection. Nemiroff.

Astrophysics. Gravitational lensing; high-energy astrophysics; close binary stars; cosmology; cosmic rays. Fick, Huentemeyer, Nemiroff, Nitz.

Atmospheric Physics. Satellite meteorology; optics; digital image processing; cloud precipitation and nucleation. Kostinski.

Atomic, Molecular, Optical, and Condensed Matter Physics. Electronic structure of metals and oxides; photonics; biological molecules; point defects; surfaces; metal-insulator transitions; atomistic simulations of materials; relativistic and correlation effects in atomic structure. El-Ganainy, Jaszczak, Nakamura, Pandey, Pati, Perger.

Experimental

Astrophysics. High-energy cosmic rays; Pierre Auger Observatory; HAWC gamma-rays. Fick, Huentemeyer, Nitz.

Atmospheric Physics. Optics; digital image processing; cloud precipitation and nucleation; climate; air quality. Cantrell, Mazzoleni, Shaw.

Atomic, Molecular, Optical, and Condensed Matter Physics. Laser spectroscopy; quantum optics. Borysow, Suh.

Materials Physics. Photonic, magnetic, and nano-materials. Levy, Moran, Suh, Suits, Yap.

View additional information about this department at www.gradschoolshopper.com. Check out the "Why Choose Us?" section, find out more about the department's culture and get links to social media networks.

OAKLAND UNIVERSITY

DEPARTMENT OF PHYSICS

Rochester, Michigan 48309-4479
http://www.oakland.edu/physics

General University Information

President: Ora Hirsch Pescovitz, M.D.
Dean of Graduate School: Claudia Petrescu, Dean of Graduate Education
University website: http://www.oakland.edu
School Type: Public
Setting: Suburban
Total Faculty: 608
Total Graduate Faculty: 608
Total number of Students: 19,333
Total number of Graduate Students: 3,432

Department Information

Department Chairman: Prof. Andrei Slavin, Chair
Department Contact: Carol Searight, Administrative Secretary
Total full-time faculty: 15
Total number of full-time equivalent positions: 15
Full-Time Graduate Students: 14
Female Full-Time Graduate Students: 5
First-Year Graduate Students: 3
Female First-Year Students: 2
Total Post Doctorates: 1

Department Address

Mathematics and Science Center, Room 190
146 Library Drive
Rochester, MI 48309-4479
Phone: (248) 370-3416
E-mail: searight@oakland.edu
Website: http://www.oakland.edu/physics

ADMISSIONS

Admission Contact Information

Address admission inquiries to: Graduate Study and Lifelong Learning, O'Dowd Hall, Room 520, 586 Pioneer Drive, Rochester, MI 48309-4482
Phone: (248) 370-2700
E-mail: gradinfo@oakland.edu
Admissions website: http://www.oakland.edu/grad

Application deadlines

Fall admission:
U.S. students: April 15   *Int'l. students*: May 1
Spring admission:
U.S. students: November 15   *Int'l. students*: September 1

Application fee

There is no application fee required.

Admissions information

For Fall of 2017:
Number of applicants: 45
Number admitted: 4
Number enrolled: 3

Admission requirements

Bachelor's degree requirements: A Bachelor's degree in Physics is required with no minimum undergraduate GPA specified.

GRE requirements

The GRE is required.

Subjective GRE requirements

The Subjective GRE is recommended.

TOEFL requirements

The TOEFL exam is required for students from non-English-speaking countries.
PBT score: 550
iBT score: 79

Other admissions information

Additional requirements: The GRE is required, and the GRE Advanced is recommended, for the Ph.D. program only. Foreign students must meet minimum acceptable score for TOEFL or have a baccalaureate or more advanced degree from an institution in the United States.
Undergraduate preparation assumed: Fowles, Analytical Mechanics; Reitz and Milford, Electromagnetic Theory; Tipler, Modern Physics; Jenkins and White, Optics; Saxon, Elementary Quantum Mechanics.

TUITION

Tuition year 2017–18:
Tuition for in-state residents
  Full-time students: $706.25 per credit
  Part-time students: $706.25 per credit
Tuition for out-of-state residents
  Full-time students: $1,027 per credit
  Part-time students: $1,027 per credit
Credit hours per semester to be considered full-time: 8
Deferred tuition plan:
Health insurance: Yes, $1,860.00, for international students only.
Other academic fees: No other academic fees.
Academic term: Semester
Number of first-year students who received full tuition waivers: 2

Teaching Assistants, Research Assistants, and Fellowships

Number of first-year
  Teaching Assistants: 2
Average stipend per academic year
  Teaching Assistant: $14,000
  Research Assistant: $14,000
  Fellowship student: $14,000
Average TA stipend for M.S. students is $8,000/year. Additional support is often available by teaching in the summer.

FINANCIAL AID

Application deadlines

Fall admission:
U.S. students: October 1
Spring admission:
U.S. students: October 1

Loans

Loans are available for U.S. students.
Loans are not available for international students.
GAPSFAS application required: No
FAFSA application required: Yes

For further information

Address financial aid inquiries to: Student Financial Services, North Foundation Hall, Room 120, 318 Meadow Brook Road, Rochester, MI 48309-4454.
Phone: (248) 370-2550
E-mail: finservices@oakland.edu
Financial aid website: http://www.oakland.edu/financialservices

HOUSING

Availability of on-campus housing
Single students: Yes
Married students: Yes

For further information

Address housing inquiries to: University Housing, Hamlin Hall, Room 448, 550 Meadow Brook Road, Rochester, MI 48309-4452.
Phone: (248) 370-3570
E-mail: housing@oakland.edu
Housing aid website: http://www.oakland.edu/housing/

Table A—Faculty, Enrollments, and Degrees Granted

Research Specialty	2017–18 Faculty	Enrollment Fall 2017 Master's	Enrollment Fall 2017 Doctorate	Number of Degrees Granted 2016–17 (2012–17) Master's	Number of Degrees Granted 2016–17 (2012–17) Terminal Master's	Number of Degrees Granted 2016–17 (2012–17) Doctorate
Applied Physics	2	3	–	–	1(10)	–
Astrophysics	1	–	–	–	–	–
Condensed Matter Physics	8	–	–	–	–	–
Medical, Health Physics	4	–	11	–	–	4(11)
Total	15	3	11	–	1(10)	4(11)
Full-time Grad. Stud.	–	3	11	–	–	–
First-year Grad. Stud.	–	1	2	–	–	–

GRADUATE DEGREE REQUIREMENTS

Master's: Thirty-six credits of graduate courses including four credits of PHY 6730 (Quantum Mechanics), one credit of PHY 6940 (Seminar), 23 credits of additional 4000–5000–6000-level courses approved by the department, eight credits of research, including a thesis or a critical essay. No foreign language requirements.

Doctorate: Biomedical Sciences-Medical Physics. Eighty semester hours of graduate credit including at least 20 hours of dissertation research, grade point average of 3.0 or higher, three full-time equivalent semesters (at least eight credits/semester) in residence, qualifying examination, and dissertation.

Thesis: Thesis may be written in absentia.

SPECIAL EQUIPMENT, FACILITIES, OR PROGRAMS

Research facilities in the high-pressure optics laboratory include Raman spectrometers with single- or multi-channel detectors, facilities for photoluminescence studies in the visible and infrared regions, argon ion and Ti: sapphire lasers, high-pressure cells capable of generating 10 GPa, and closed cycle helium refrigerators.

Research facilities in the condensed matter physics laboratories include a Faraday Magnetometer, an AC susceptometer, a ferromagnetic resonance spectrometer at x-band, a Scanning Probe Microscope, a Scanning Microwave Microscope, Vector Network Analyzers (1kHz-110 GHz), a Philips x-ray diffractometer, and facilities for thin film deposition and fullerene preparation.

Research facilities in the NMR microscopy laboratory include a Bruker AVANCE III HD 300 NMR spectrometer with a 7-Tesla/89-mm bore superconducting magnet and micro-imaging accessories, PerkinElmer Spotlight 300 Fourier-transform infra-

red microscope, Leica polarized light microscope, Skyscan 1174 micro-CT scanner, and EnduraTEC 3200 mechanical testing system. The department also has microwave device facilities in the frequency range from 100 kHz to 70 GHz. Supporting facilities include electronics and mechanical workshops staffed by experienced technical personnel. Most research laboratories are located in the modern Mathematics and Science Center on campus.

The Physics Department recently installed two modern computer clusters, the newest one, funded through the NSF Major Research Instrumentation program, is composed of 24 nodes containing two AMD Opteron 6136 "Magny-Cours", running at 2.4 GHz, with eight cores and 64 gigabytes RAM each, for a total of 384 cores and more than 1.5 terabytes of RAM. In addition, the two head nodes combined provide 18 terabytes of hard disk space. Both clusters are located in modern computer rooms at the Oakland Information Technology Center.

Among research facilities in neighboring hospitals available to medical physics students are a 3.0-Tesla whole-body NMR system and two 7.0-Telsa/20-cm horizontal bore magnet NMR systems for imaging and in vivo spectroscopy, a 7-channel SQUID magnetometer, a 148-channel whole-head SQUID neuromagnetometer, a Zeiss LSM 510 two photon microscope, Leica LMD6000 laser microdissection system, Philips EM208 Transmission Electron Microscope, a nuclear medicine laboratory, radiology and CT scanning facilities, advanced modalities cancer therapy laboratory (including radiotherapy), diagnostic ultrasonic equipment, a laser surgery laboratory, and major hospital medical libraries.

Table B—Separately Budgeted Research Expenditures by Source of Support

Source of Support	Departmental Research	Physics-related Research Outside Department
Federal government	$1,063,184	
State/local government		
Non-profit organizations		
Business and industry		
Other	$413,326	
Total	$1,476,510	

Table C—Separately Budgeted Research Expenditures by Research Specialty

Research Specialty	No. of Grants	Expenditures ($)
Condensed Matter Physics	7	$901,805
Medical, Health Physics	4	$574,705
Total	11	$1,476,510

FACULTY

Distinguished University Professor

Chopp, Michael, Ph.D., New York University, 1975. *Biomedical Physics*. My research efforts include basic and applied research into the development of neurorestorative therapies for the treatment of neurological diseases and injury, e.g. stroke, traumatic brain injury, multiple sclerosis, and peripheral neuropathy. These treatments are designed to remodel the central and peripheral nervous systems to enhance neurological recovery resulting from a neurological disease or injury. In addition, my laboratory seeks to develop therapies for the treatment of brain tumors. Our studies range from research into fundamental molecular mechanisms of therapeutic action, to preclinical and clinical studies, using a vast array of biological and physical methods.

Slavin, Andrei, Ph.D., Leningrad Technical University, 1977. *Applied Physics, Condensed Matter Physics, Materials Science, Metallurgy, Nano Science and Technology, Nonlinear Dynamics and Complex Systems.* The main focus of my research is magnetic excitations in finite-size samples, spin waves, non-linear spin waves, Bose-Einstein condensation of magnons; microwave signal processing using spin waves; and spin-torque oscillators.

Srinivasan, Gopalan, Ph.D., Indian Institute of Technology, 1980. *Condensed Matter Physics, Materials Science, Metallurgy.* Current research projects are on the physics of composite multiferroics and applications for useful technologies. The primary focus is on the nature of magnetoelectric interactions in ferromagnetic piezoelectric composites. Studies involve measurements over 1 Hz–110 GHz in layered and nanocomposites. Applications-related efforts are on magnetic field sensors, microwave and millimeter devices, and miniature antennas.

Xia, Yang, Ph.D., Massey University, 1992. *Applied Physics, Biophysics, Fluids, Rheology, Mechanics, Medical, Health Physics, Polymer Physics/Science, Magnetic Resonance Imaging (MRI), Nuclear Magnetic Resonance (NMR).* Concentrating research in the degradation of articular cartilage, which is a hallmark of clinical joint diseases, such as osteoarthritis. Uses multidisciplinary imaging techniques to study cartilage, including microscopic magnetic resonance imaging, polarized light microscopy, Fourier-transform infrared imaging, and microscopic X-ray tomography. Aims to resolve subtle changes in the physical, biological, chemical, and morphological properties of cartilage at the early stage of the cartilage degradation non-destructively.

Professor

Elder, Ken, Ph.D., University of Toronto, 1989. *Condensed Matter Physics, Materials Science, Metallurgy, Statistical & Thermal Physics.* The main focus of my research is on understanding the formation of complex spatial morphologies that form in nature. This research has included studies of spinodal decomposition, eutectic solidification, order/disorder transitions, Rayleigh-Benard convection, and the absorption of liquids by random media. Recently, I developed, in collaboration with others, the "Phase Field Crystal" method of modeling elastic and plastic deformation in polycrystalline systems.

Garfinkle, David, Ph.D., University of Chicago, 1985. *Relativity & Gravitation.* I do research in general relativity, especially black holes, gravitational collapse, and singularities. My methods are mostly numerical. I also have interests in cosmology.

Roth, Bradley, Ph.D., Vanderbilt University, 1987. *Biophysics, Medical, Health Physics.* Theoretical and numerical modeling of bioelectric and biomagnetic phenomena.

Associate Professor

Khain, Evgeniy, Ph.D., Hebrew University of Jerusalem, 2005. *Condensed Matter Physics, Materials Science, Metallurgy, Nonlinear Dynamics and Complex Systems, Statistical & Thermal Physics, Other.* Other specialty: Biological physics. Modeling of collective cell behavior in biological systems (growth of malignant brain tumors and wound healing). Population dynamics (mathematical biology). Statistical physics far from equilibrium. Pattern formation and non-linear dynamics. Driven granular gases, instabilities in granular flows.

Rojo, Alberto, Ph.D., Instituto Balseiro, Bariloche, 1990. *Condensed Matter Physics.*

Wang, Yuejian, Ph.D., Texas Christian University, 2006. Other specialty: High-pressure physics. *Applied Physics, Nano Science and Technology.* My research focuses on the investigations of the new structures, properties, and applications of materials with various crystal sizes under high pressures by using diamond anvil cells integrated with synchrotron X-ray, Raman, micro-photographic techniques. Our high-pressure research group also synthesizes novel materials with unique properties for practical application.

Assistant Professor

Zhang, Wei, Ph.D., University of Washington, 2013. *Applied Physics, Condensed Matter Physics, Materials Science, Metallurgy, Nano Science and Technology.* My research studies the properties of quantum-mechanical effects of condensed matter such as the novel magnetic textures and spin-orbit effects, to seek potential optimization of low-power, high-capability future electronics devices.

Emeritus

Liboff, Abraham R., Ph.D., New York University, 1964. *Biophysics, Medical, Health Physics.*

Tepley, Norman, Ph.D., Massachusetts Institute of Technology, 1963. *Low Temperature Physics, Medical, Health Physics.*

Research Associate Professor

Tyberkevych, Vasyl, Ph.D., University of Kyiv, 2001. *Applied Physics, Condensed Matter Physics, Materials Science, Metallurgy, Nano Science and Technology.* Static and dynamic properties of magnetic nano-dot arrays (ground states, multi-stability, dynamic excitations, parametric processes, etc.); dynamic phenomena induced by a spin-polarized current in magnetic nanostructures (magnetization switching, persistent microwave oscillations, etc.); spin waves in micro- and nano-sized magnetic particles and films (spin wave spectra, non-linear spin wave interactions, etc.); practical applications of spin waves for microwave signal processing (isolators and circulators, passive and active delay lines, filters, oscillators, etc.).

Adjunct Professor

Chen, Jieli, Other, Tianjin Medical University, 1985. *Medical, Health Physics.*

Chetty, Indrin J., Ph.D., UCLA, 1999.

Ding, Xuanfeng, Ph.D., Wake Forest University, 2012.

Ewing, James R., Ph.D., Oakland University, 1992. *Medical, Health Physics.*

Gerhart, Grant R., Ph.D., Wayne State University, 1972. *Condensed Matter Physics.*

Glide-Hurst, Carrie K., Ph.D., Wayne State University, 2007.

Guerrero, Thomas, Other, University of California, 1997.

Jiang, Quan, Ph.D., Oakland University, 1991. *Medical, Health Physics.*

Shumaker, Bryan, Other, Michigan State University, 1974.

Soltanian-Zadeh, Hamid, Ph.D., University of Michigan, 1992. *Medical, Health Physics.*

Venkatesan, Srinivasan, Ph.D., University of London, 1974.

Venkateswaran, Uma Devi, Ph.D., University of Missouri (Columbia), 1985.

Wilson, George D., Ph.D., University of Liverpool, 1980. *Medical, Health Physics.*

Yan, Di, Ph.D., Washington University, 1990. *Medical, Health Physics.*

Zhong, Hualiang, Ph.D., University of Western Ontario, 2000.

Adjunct Associate Professor

Bidthanapally, Rao, Ph.D., Indian Institute of Technology, Bombay, India, 1985.

Castoldi, Kapila Clara, Ph.D., University of Milan, Italy, 1976. *Particles and Fields.*

Knight, Robert A., Ph.D., Oakland University, 1991. *Medical, Health Physics.*

Liang, Jian, Ph.D., Zhejiang University, 1994. *Medical, Health Physics.*

McDermott, Patrick N., Ph.D., University of Rochester, 1985. *Medical, Health Physics.*

Adjunct Assistant Professor

Bowyer, Susan, Ph.D., Oakland University, 1998. *Medical, Health Physics.*

Buller, Benjamin, Ph.D., Oakland University, 2010. *Medical, Health Physics.*

Castillo, Edward, Ph.D., Rice University, 2007.

Ionascu, Dan, Ph.D., Northeastern University, 2005. *Medical, Health Physics.*

Jenrow, Kenneth, Ph.D., Oakland University, 1995. *Medical, Health Physics.*

Qian, Chunqi, Ph.D., University of California, Berkeley, 2007.

Surdutovich, Eugene, Ph.D., Wayne State University, 1998. *Atomic, Molecular, & Optical Physics, Biophysics, Medical, Health Physics.* I do theoretical research in physics related to ion-beam cancer therapy. My methods are mostly analytical, but I also use molecular dynamics simulations.

DEPARTMENTAL RESEARCH SPECIALTIES AND STAFF

Theoretical

Applied Physics. Slavin, Tyberkevych.

Atomic, Molecular, & Optical Physics. Surdutovich.

Biological Physics. Khain.

Biophysics. Roth, Surdutovich.

Condensed Matter Physics. Elder, Khain, Rojo, Slavin, Srinivasan, Tyberkevych.

Materials Science, Metallurgy. Elder, Khain, Slavin, Srinivasan, Tyberkevych.

Medical, Health Physics. Roth, Surdutovich.

Nano Science and Technology. Slavin, Tyberkevych.

Nonlinear Dynamics and Complex Systems. Khain, Slavin.

Relativity & Gravitation. Garfinkle.

Statistical & Thermal Physics. Elder, Khain.

Experimental

Applied Physics. Wang, Xia, Zhang.

Biomedical Physics. Chopp.

Biophysics. Liboff, Xia.

Condensed Matter Physics. Zhang.

Fluids, Rheology. Xia.

High-pressure Physics. Wang.

Low Temperature Physics. Tepley.

Magnetic Resonance Imaging (MRI). Xia.

Materials Science, Metallurgy. Zhang.

Mechanics. Xia.

Medical, Health Physics. Liboff, Tepley, Xia.

Nano Science and Technology. Wang, Zhang.

Nuclear Magnetic Resonance (NMR). Xia.

Particles and Fields. Castoldi.

Polymer Physics/Science. Xia.

View additional information about this department at www.gradschoolshopper.com. Check out the "Why Choose Us?" section, find out more about the department's culture and get links to social media networks.

WAYNE STATE UNIVERSITY

DEPARTMENT OF PHYSICS AND ASTRONOMY

Detroit, Michigan 48201
http://physics.clas.wayne.edu

General University Information
President: M. Roy Wilson, M.D., M.S.
Dean of Graduate School: Ambika Mather, Dean
University website: http://wayne.edu
School Type: Public
Setting: Urban
Total Faculty: 2,511
Total Graduate Faculty: 918
Total number of Students: 27,089
Total number of Graduate Students: 7,710

Department Information
Department Chairman: Prof. David A. Cinabro, Chair
Department Contact: David A. Cinabro, PhD, Chair
  Total full-time faculty: 28
  Total number of full-time equivalent positions: 28
  Full-Time Graduate Students: 56
  Female Full-Time Graduate Students: 7
  First-Year Graduate Students: 7
  Female First-Year Students: 2
  Total Post Doctorates: 9

Department Address
666 West Hancock
Suite # 135 Physics Research Building
Detroit, MI 48201
Phone: (313) 577-2720 (C)
Fax: (313) 577-3932
E-mail: cinabro@wayne.edu
Website: http://physics.clas.wayne.edu

ADMISSIONS

Admission Contact Information
Address admission inquiries to: Dr. Claude Pruneau, Chairman,
  Graduate Admissions Committee, Dept. of Physics, Wayne
  State University, Detroit, MI 48201
Phone: (313) 577-2775
E-mail: pruneau@physics.wayne.edu
Admissions website: http://physics.clas.wayne.edu

Application deadlines
Fall admission:
U.S. students: June 1   *Int'l. students*: May 1
Spring admission:
U.S. students: February 1   *Int'l. students*: January 1

Application fee
U.S. students: $50   *Int'l. students*: $50
Wayne State is tri-Semester; Fall Semester(Begins in August)
Spring/Summer Semester(Begins in May) Deadlines for Winter Semester; Winter Admission(Begins in January).

Admissions information
For Fall of 2018:
  Number of applicants: 81
  Number admitted: 10
  Number enrolled: 7

Admission requirements
Bachelor's degree requirements: Bachelor's degree in Physics
  or related fields is required.
Minimum undergraduate GPA: 3.0

GRE requirements
The GRE is required.
  Quantitative score: 700

Subjective GRE requirements
The Subjective GRE is recommended.
  Minimum accepted Advanced GRE score: 700
  Mean Advanced GRE score range (25th–75th percentile): 50

TOEFL requirements
The TOEFL exam is required for students from non-English-
  speaking countries.
  PBT score: 550
  iBT score: 79
550 or higher on paper-based test.

Other admissions information
Additional requirements: A GPA below 3.0 would require a probationary admission.
Undergraduate preparation assumed: J.R. Taylor, Classical Mechanics; D.J. Griffith, Introduction to Quantum Mechanics; Reitz, Milford and Christy Foundations of Electromagnetic Theory; A.H. Carter, Classical and Statistical Thermodynamics.

TUITION

Tuition year 2018–19:
Tuition for in-state residents
  Full-time students: $690.36 per credit
  Part-time students: $690.36 per credit
Tuition for out-of-state residents
  Full-time students: $1,435.42 per credit
  Part-time students: $1,435.42 per credit
Credit hours per semester to be considered full-time: 8
Deferred tuition plan: No
Health insurance: Not available.
Other academic fees: Registration Fee: $297.29.
Academic term: Semester

Teaching Assistants, Research Assistants, and Fellowships
Number of first-year
  Teaching Assistants: 7
Average stipend per academic year
  Teaching Assistant: $19,560
  Research Assistant: $19,560
  Fellowship student: $19,560
Assistantships/Fellowships, include Tuition Assistance, Medical and Dental benefits with co-pay.

FINANCIAL AID

Application deadlines
Fall admission:
U.S. students: June 30
Spring admission:

U.S. students: June 30

Loans

Loans are available for U.S. students.
Loans are not available for international students.
GAPSFAS application required: Yes
FAFSA application required: Yes

For further information

Address financial aid inquiries to: Wayne State University, Office of Student Financial Aid, The Welcome Center, 42 W. Warren Avenue, P.O. Box 2340, Detroit, MI 48202-0340; also; The Graduate School; gradschool.wayne.edu/funding.
Phone: (313) 577-2100
E-mail: studentservices@wayne.edu
Financial aid website: http://finaid.wayne.edu

HOUSING

Availability of on-campus housing

Single students: Yes
Married students: Yes
Childcare Assistance: No

For further information

Address housing inquiries to: Wayne State University, Director, Housing & Residential Life, 5221 Gullen Mall, 582 Student Center Bldg., Detroit, MI 48202.
Phone: (313) 577-2116
E-mail: housing@wayne.edu
Housing aid website: http://www.housing.wayne.edu

Table A—Faculty, Enrollments, and Degrees Granted

Research Specialty	2017–18 Faculty	Enrollment Fall 2017 Master's	Enrollment Fall 2017 Doctorate	Number of Degrees Granted 2017–2018 (2013–18) Master's	Number of Degrees Granted 2017–2018 (2013–18) Terminal Master's	Number of Degrees Granted 2017–2018 (2013–18) Doctorate
Applied Physics	–	–	–	–	–	–
Astrophysics	1	–	3	–(2)	–(3)	1(3)
Atomic, Molecular, & Optical Physics	1	–	–	–(7)	–(4)	–(3)
Biophysics	3	2	8	2(6)	–	1(4)
Condensed Matter Physics	9	–	11	2(62)	1(16)	4(43)
Low Temperature Physics	–	–	–	–	–	–
Materials Science, Metallurgy	–	–	–	–	–	–
Nuclear Physics	6	3	8	1(10)	–(7)	3(10)
Optics	–	–	–	–	–	–
Particles and Fields	7	–	16	–(15)	–(7)	3(19)
Physics and other Science Education	–	6	7	–	–	–
Total	27	11	53	5(102)	1(37)	12(82)
Full-time Grad. Stud.	–	6	58	–	–	–
First-year Grad. Stud.	–	2	7	–	–	–

GRADUATE DEGREE REQUIREMENTS

Master's: The Master degree is offered with (M.S.) and without (M.A.) thesis in various areas of physics. Requirements for the M.S. degree are 24 credits of course work at the 5000 level or above plus an eight-credit thesis, while the M.A. degree requires 29 credits of course work at the 5000 level or above plus a three-credit essay. Both degrees require at least nine credits at the 7000 level or above with at least half of the course work in physics. Students must maintain a 3.0 GPA and must complete their degree within six years. A final oral exam over the thesis or essay is required of all students.

Doctorate: The Ph.D. degree has a basic requirement of 90 credits, which include 30 dissertation credits. Courses at the graduate level in mathematical physics, mechanics and dynamics, quantum mechanics, electromagnetic theory, and statistical mechanics are required for all students as well as certain other courses depending on the area of concentration. A written Ph.D. qualifying exam usually taken after the end of the student's first year, a preliminary oral exam, and a final dissertation defense are the other major requirements. A 3.0 GPA must also be maintained. There is a seven-year time limit for completion of the degree.

Thesis: Thesis may be written in absentia.

SPECIAL EQUIPMENT, FACILITIES, OR PROGRAMS

The department has numerous well-equipped research laboratories with concentrated efforts in the areas of high-energy nuclear and particle physics, applied physics, biophysics, and condensed matter physics.

The relativistic heavy-ion group participates in two major international collaborations: the STAR experiment at the Relativistic Heavy-Ion Collider (RHIC) at Brookhaven National Laboratory NY, and the ALICE experiment at the Large Hadron Collider (LHC) at CERN in Switzerland. The group is a leader in using jets to probe the quark-gluon plasma and studying the nature of QCD phase transitions. On campus the group is part of the construction effort for the tracking system upgrade to ALICE.

The nuclear theory group is exploring a range of topics related to these experimental results, including the hydrodynamics of the quark-gluon plasma.

The experimental particle physics groups are part of the CMS collaboration at CERN, and the Belle II collaboration at KEK (Japan) and have set up facilities on campus for the design and development of electronic systems for the particle detectors and accelerators. They also have a leadership role in a future high energy electron-positron linear collider.

The particle theory group works on understanding the fundamental properties of elementary particles, including phenomenology of quantum chromodynamics in heavy quark systems, studies of CP-violation and Dark Matter.

The astrophysics group studies accreting systems such as neutron stars and black holes with x-rays.

Research programs in condensed matter physics have extensive materials characterization and synthesis facilities available for investigating problems ranging from superconductivity to magnetism to semiconductors to pattern formation to nano-confined fluids. There is a strong emphasis on nanotechnology, with research projects including studies on carbon nano-tubes and graphene, two-dimensional electron gas, nano-particles, and thin films. The materials characterization tools available include systems for electrical, dielectric, thermodynamic, and optical studies, all of which can be performed under a range of temperatures and magnetic fields. Some specialized measurements available for these studies include micro Raman spectroscopy, atomic force spectroscopy, X-ray photoemission spectroscopy, and fluorescence correlation spectroscopy. The condensed matter theory group uses state-of-the-art computer facilities along with analytical calculations to investigate the dynamics of systems far from equilibrium, pattern formation, and positron interactions with biologically relevant molecules.

The biophysics group is interested in applying techniques from Physics to solve problems in medicine and biology. Active projects in the biophysics group include studies of molecular motors, such as myosin, protein-binding interactions using atomic force microscopy, and cancer detection using Raman spectroscopy, structure of biologically active molecules with neutron scattering, and the structure and functionality of membranes.

Information about the graduate program and other research activities in the department is also available at http://physics.clas.wayne.edu.

Table B—Separately Budgeted Research Expenditures by Source of Support

Source of Support	Departmental Research	Physics-related Research Outside Department
Federal government	$8,531,056	
State/local government		
Non-profit organizations	$165,000	
Business and industry		
Other	$189,500	
Total	$8,885,556	

Table C—Separately Budgeted Research Expenditures by Research Specialty

Research Specialty	No. of Grants	Expenditures ($)
Astrophysics	6	$775,596
Biophysics	4	$1,442,795
Condensed Matter Physics	2	$507,748
Nuclear Physics	6	$1,643,040
Particles and Fields	11	$4,516,377
Other	–	
Total	29	$8,885,556

FACULTY

Professor

Bonvicini, Giovanni, Ph.D., Universita di Bologna, 1981. *Astrophysics, High Energy Physics, Particles and Fields.* Experimental high-energy particle, CLEO, astrophysics.

Cinabro, David A., Ph.D., University of Wisconsin-Madison, 1991. Chair of the Department. *Astrophysics, High Energy Physics, Particles and Fields.* Astrophysics; high-energy physics; particles and fields; experimental high-energy particle physics; heavy flavor physics in e+e- collisions at Belle observational astrophysics; supernova cosomology.

Gavin, Sean, Ph.D., University of Illinois, 1987. *Nuclear Physics, Theoretical Physics.* Theoretical nuclear; relativistic heavy-ion physics; quark gluon plasma theory; QCD phenomenology.

Harr, Robert F., Ph.D., University of California, Berkeley, 1990. *High Energy Physics, Particles and Fields.* High-energy physics, particles, and fields; experimental high-energy particle physics; searches for new particles through rare decays and CP violation at CMS.

Hoffmann, Peter M., Ph.D., Johns Hopkins University, 1999. *Condensed Matter Physics, Nano Science and Technology.* Experimental soft condensed matter physics; biophysics; nanomechanics; atomic force microscopy studies of interatomic and intermolecular forces.

Huang, Zhi-Feng, Ph.D., Tsinghua University, 1997. *Condensed Matter Physics, Nano Science and Technology, Theoretical Physics.* Theoretical condensed matter physics; nonequilibrium and nonlinear phenomena in complex dynamical systems; nanostructures and defect dynamics in strained thin films; mesophase dynamics of block copolymer films; nonlinear pattern formation and defect chaos.

Karchin, Paul E., Ph.D., Cornell University, 1982. *Particles and Fields.* Particles and fields; experimental particle physics; CMS experiment; lepton and quark substructure; muon detection detector develop; electronics.

Nadgorny, Boris E., Ph.D., Stony Brook University, 1996. *Condensed Matter Physics.* Experimental condensed matter physics, superconductivity, magnetism and spintronics materials, transport, tunneling and percolation effects.

Naik, Ratna, Ph.D., West Virginia University, 1982. Associate Dean for Academic Personnel and Faculty Affairs, College of Liberal Arts and Sciences. *Condensed Matter Physics.* Experimental condensed matter physics; materials science, magnetism, and magnetic materials; magnetic nanoparticles; sensor materials.

Petrov, Alexey A., Ph.D., University of Massachusetts, Amherst, 1997. *Astrophysics, Particles and Fields.* Theoretical particle physics; heavy quark physics; CP violation; QCD; LHC phenomenology; effective field theories; theoretical particle astrophysics: dark matter.

Pruneau, Claude A., Ph.D., Universite Laval, Quebec, 1987. *High Energy Physics, Nuclear Physics.* Experimental nuclear physics; RHIC (relativistic heavy-ion collisions), LHC (Cern); quark gluon plasma.

Voloshin, Sergei A., Ph.D., Moscow Engineering & Physics Institute, 1980. *High Energy Physics, Nuclear Physics.* Experimental nuclear physics; RHIC (relativistic heavy-ion collisions); phenomenology of multiparticle production.

Wadehra, Jogindra M., Ph.D., New York University, 1977. Associate Department Chair and Department Graduate Advisor. *Astrophysics, Atomic, Molecular, & Optical Physics, Theoretical Physics.* Theoretical atomic and molecular physics; astrophysics; the scattering of positrons (antiparticles of electrons) and electrons from various atoms and molecules.

Associate Professor

Cackett, Edward M., Ph.D., University of St. Andrews, 2006. *Astronomy, Astrophysics.* Observational Astrophysics; compact objects (neutron stars and black holes), accretion across the mass scale; from neutron stars and black holes in X-ray binaries to Active Galactic Nuclei (AGN).

Chu, Xiang-Qiang, Ph.D., Massachusetts Institute of Technology, 2010. *Biophysics.* Experimental biophysics; probing the structure and dynamics of biomolecules, nanomaterials; protein structures and dynamics using neutron and x-ray scattering.

Huang, Jian, Ph.D., Michigan State University, 2001. *Condensed Matter Physics, Low Temperature Physics, Nano Science and Technology.* Experimental condensed matter physics; interaction-driven phenomena in strongly correlated 1D and 2D systems (i.e. quantum Wigner Solids); quantum Hall effects; quantum charge and spin effects in mesoscopic and nano systems; semiconductor physics; low temperature (mK) techniques and quantum transport; nanofabrication and nanomaterials (graphene, VO2, MoS2).

Llope, William J., Ph.D., State University of New York-Stony Brook, 1992. *Nuclear Physics.* Experimental high-energy nuclear physics; development of detector hardware and data software analyzing large experiments; study of the QCD phase diagram via fluctuation observables.

Majumder, Abhijit, Ph.D., McGill University, Montreal, 2002. *Nuclear Physics, Theoretical Physics.* Theoretical nuclear physics; study of extended systems of QCD matter; perturbative QCD calculations; lattice QCD simulations.

Mukhopadhyay, Ashis, Ph.D., Kansas State University, 2000. *Condensed Matter Physics.* Experimental soft condensed matter physics; materials science.

Padmanabhan, Karur R., Ph.D., University of Poona, 1975. *Condensed Matter Physics.* Experimental condensed matter physics; materials science, materials modification; ion-solid interaction and ion channeling.

Paz, Gil, Ph.D., Cornell University, 2006. *High Energy Physics, Particles and Fields, Theoretical Physics.* Theoretical particle physics; QCD; effective field theories; supersymmetry.

Putschke, Joern H., Ph.D., Technical University of Munich, 2004. *High Energy Physics, Nuclear Physics.* Experimental high-energy nuclear physics; RHIC (relativistic heavy-ion collisions).

Sakamoto, Takeshi, Ph.D., Kanazawa University, 2001. *Biophysics, Medical, Health Physics.* Experimental biophysics: mechanisms of myosin-dependent motility, protein-protein interactions, actin-myosin interactions and visualization using single-molecule imaging techniques in vitro and in vivo.

Zhou, Zhixian, Ph.D., Florida State University, 2004. *Condensed Matter Physics, Nano Science and Technology.* Experimental condensed matter physics: Individual nanoscale materials and single organic molecules: synthesis and characterization, nanoscale device fabrication, electrical transport measurements.

Assistant Professor

Kelly, Christopher V., Ph.D., University of Michigan-Ann Arbor, 2009. *Biophysics.* Experimental biophysics; subdiffraction-limited optics and biological membranes; spectroscopy.

Matos Abiague, Alex, Ph.D., Martin-Luther-Universitat Halle-Wittenberg, 2004. *Computational Physics, Condensed Matter Physics, Theoretical Physics.* Theoretical condensed matter and computational physics.

Shah, Nausheen R., Ph.D., University of Chicago, 2009. *High Energy Physics, Particles and Fields.* Theoretical studies of the Higgs and dark matter lamp posts for physics at the weak scale.

Shen, Chun, Ph.D., The Ohio State University, 2014. *Nuclear Physics, Theoretical Physics.* Theoretical Nuclear Physics - Precision fluid dynamical modelling of quark-gluon plasma at finite baryon density; Jet and electromagnetic tomography in strongly-coupled systems; Rapid thermalization and out-of-equilibrium physics of many-body QCD; Gluon saturation and 3D imaging of nucleus at high energy.

DEPARTMENTAL RESEARCH SPECIALTIES AND STAFF

Theoretical

Atomic, Molecular, & Optical Physics. Studying the scattering of positrons (antiparticles of electrons) and electrons from various atoms and molecules. Wadehra.

Computational Nuclear Physics-Interdisciplinary. Distributed and high performance computing applications to simulations of nuclear collisions; Monte Carlo simulation, Algorithms, Data Science, Bayesian Statistical analysis, Heterogeneous Computation Architectures. Majumder, Putschke.

Condensed Matter Physics. Material structures and growth; multiple-scale modeling; non-equilibrium phenomena in complex systems; spintronics; topological phases of matter; two-dimensional materials. Zhi-Feng Huang, Matos Abiague.

Nuclear Physics. QCD phenomenology; relativistic heavy-ion collisions; quark gluon plasma; extended systems of QCD matter at all temperatures and densities that are experimentally accessible; Jet & electromagnetic tomography in strongly-coupled systems; Gluon saturation and 3D imaging of nucleus at high energy. Gavin, Majumder, Shen.

Particles and Fields. Heavy quark physics, CP violation, electroweak physics, and QCD phenomenology; Higgs, dark matter, and beyond the Standard Model phenomenology and model building. Paz, Petrov, Shah.

Plasma and Fusion. Production and diagnostics of negative ion beams. Wadehra.

Experimental

Astrophysics. Accretion onto neutron stars and black holes in X-ray Binaries & Active Galactic Nuclei (AGN), Relativistic Fe Lines in neutron star los-mass X-ray binaries, observational probes of the neutron star equation of state (neutron star radii and masses). Cackett.

Biophysics. Molecular Motor. Single molecule imaging studies with Total Internal Reflection Fluorescent (TIRF)microscopy. Measuring single-/multiple-power stroke of molecular motor by using Optical tweezers, Traction force microscopy for cancer research. Molecular and cellular imaging, protein dynamics using neutron and X-ray scattering. Biological Physics - Subdiffraction-limited optics and biological membranes by using nanoscale engineering and biophysical techniques. Single-molecule and live cell atomic force microscopy. Chu, Hoffmann, Kelly, Sakamoto.

Condensed Matter Physics. Atomic force and scanning tunneling microscopy of surfaces; Magnetic materials and device applications; Conventional and high-temperature superconductivity; Andreev reflection; Electron and Josephson tunneling; Spin transport and spin polarization; Spintronics; Ion channeling; Thin-film and materials research; Surface studies and modification; Energy storage and generation materials; Calorimetric and ultrasonic properties; Raman spectroscopy; Soft matter physics, polymers and nano-confined liquids. Hoffmann, Jian Huang, Mukhopadhyay, Nadgorny, Naik, Padmanabhan, Zhou.

Nuclear Physics. High energy nuclear collisions, quark-gluon plasma, strongly interacting matter at extreme temperatures and densities. Llope, Pruneau, Putschke, Voloshin.

Particles and Fields. Exotic searches and precision measurements at LHC/CMS; Micro-pattern gas and silicon micro-strip detector development, heavy quark physics at KEK/BELLE; Electron beamstrahlung detector development. Bonvicini, Cinabro, Harr, Karchin.

View additional information about this department at www.gradschoolshopper.com. Check out the "Why Choose Us?" section, find out more about the department's culture and get links to social media networks.

WESTERN MICHIGAN UNIVERSITY

DEPARTMENT OF PHYSICS

Kalamazoo, Michigan 49008-5252
http://wmich.edu/physics

General University Information
President: Edward B. Montgomery
Dean of Graduate School: Susan Stapleton
University website: http://www.wmich.edu/
School Type: Public
Setting: Suburban
Total Faculty: 924
Total Graduate Faculty: 1,153
Total number of Students: 22,894
Total number of Graduate Students: 4,958

Department Information
Department Chairman: Prof. Paul Pancella, Chair
Department Contact: Lori Krum, Administrative Assistant II
  Total full-time faculty: 14
  Total number of full-time equivalent positions: 14
  Full-Time Graduate Students: 24
  Female Full-Time Graduate Students: 10
  First-Year Graduate Students: 4
  Female First-Year Students: 3
  Total Post Doctorates: 2

Department Address
1903 W Michigan Avenue
Kalamazoo, MI 49008-5252
Phone: (269) 387-4940
Fax: (269) 387-4939
E-mail: physics-department@wmich.edu
Website: http://wmich.edu/physics

ADMISSIONS

Admission Contact Information
Address admission inquiries to: Graduate Advisor, Department
  of Physics, 1903 W Michigan Avenue, Kalamazoo, MI
  49008-5252
Phone: (269) 387-4940
E-mail: physics-department@wmich.edu
Admissions website: http://www.wmich.edu/admissions/

Application deadlines
Fall admission:
U.S. students: February 15   *Int'l. students*: February 15

Application fee
U.S. students: $50   *Int'l. students*: $100
For full consideration for an assistantship, a completed file is
  needed by February 15.

Admissions information
For Fall of 2018:
  Number of applicants: 30
  Number admitted: 21
  Number enrolled: 7

Admission requirements
Bachelor's degree requirements: Bachelor's degree in Physics
  or related discipline is required.
Minimum undergraduate GPA: 3.0

GRE requirements
The GRE is required.
  Quantitative score: 155
  Verbal score: 138
  Analytical score: 3.0
For doctoral applicants, a minimum score at the 65 percentile
  level is required on the quantitative portion of the exam.

Subjective GRE requirements
The Subjective GRE is recommended.
  Preference in admission is given to applicants who have taken
  and scored well on the GRE Physics exam.

TOEFL requirements
The TOEFL exam is required for students from non-English-
  speaking countries.
  PBT score: 550
  iBT score: 80

Other admissions information
Undergraduate preparation assumed: Halliday and Resnick,
  Fundamentals of Physics; Sprott, Introduction to Modern
  Electronics; Fowles, Analytical Mechanics; Christy, Reitz,
  and Milford, Electricity, and Magnetism; Eisberg and
  Resnick, Quantum Physics; Meyer-Arendt, Introduction to
  Classical and Modern Optics; Sears, Thermodynamics, Ki-
  netic Theory, and Statistical Thermodynamics.

TUITION

Tuition year 2017–18:
Tuition for in-state residents
  Full-time students: $596.25 per credit
  Part-time students: $596.25 per credit
Tuition for out-of-state residents
  Full-time students: $1,204.17 per credit
  Part-time students: $1,204.17 per credit
Doctoral associates with candidacy, doctoral graduate assistants,
  and master's graduate assistants can receive up to 24 credit
  hours of tuition waiver.
Credit hours per semester to be considered full-time: 6
Deferred tuition plan: Yes
Health insurance: Not available.
Other academic fees: $411.50/semester enrollment fee (5 or more
  credit hours); $42/semester student assessment fee; $8/semes-
  ter sustainability fee; $25 international student fee/semester;
  $300 one-time records initiation fee.
Academic term: Semester
Number of first-year students who received full tuition waivers: 6

Teaching Assistants, Research Assistants, and Fellowships
Number of first-year
  Teaching Assistants: 6
Average stipend per academic year
  Teaching Assistant: $14,364
  Research Assistant: $14,972
  Fellowship student: $12,498
Summer TA and RA assistantships are available.

FINANCIAL AID

Application deadlines

Fall admission:

U.S. students: February 15   *Int'l. students*: February 15

Loans

Loans are available for U.S. students.

Loans are not available for international students.

GAPSFAS application required: No

FAFSA application required: Yes

For further information

Address financial aid inquiries to: WMU Student Financial Aid, 1903 W Michigan Avenue, Kalamazoo, MI 49008-5337.

Phone: (269) 387-6000

E-mail: finaid-info@wmich.edu

Financial aid website: http://www.wmich.edu/finaid/

HOUSING

Availability of on-campus housing

Single students: Yes

Married students: Yes

Childcare Assistance: No

For further information

Address housing inquiries to: WMU Residence Life, 1903 W Michigan Avenue, Kalamazoo, MI 49008-5312.

Phone: (269) 387-4735

E-mail: wmu-housing@wmich.edu

Housing aid website: http://www.wmich.edu/housing/

Table A—Faculty, Enrollments, and Degrees Granted

Research Specialty	2017–18 Faculty	Enrollment Fall 2017 Master's	Enrollment Fall 2017 Doctorate	Number of Degrees Granted 2017–18 (2013–18) Master's	Number of Degrees Granted 2017–18 (2013–18) Terminal Master's	Number of Degrees Granted 2017–18 (2013–18) Doctorate
Astronomy	2	–	1	–	–(1)	–(1)
Atomic, Molecular, & Optical Physics	3	–	3	–(1)	–(1)	–(5)
Condensed Matter Physics	5	1	7	1(4)	–	–(4)
Nuclear Physics	4	–	7	–	–	–(1)
Physics and other Science Education	2	1	–	–	–	–
Non-specialized	–	2	2	–	2(14)	–
Total	16	4	20	1(5)	2(16)	–(11)
Full-time Grad. Stud.	–	4	20	–	–	–
First-year Grad. Stud.	–	2	2	–	–	–

GRADUATE DEGREE REQUIREMENTS

Master's: Thirty semester hours of graduate credit with a GPA of 3.0/4.0 or better are required. Students may transfer only six hours from another institution. There is no residency requirement. Eighteen hours of coursework required in Mathematical Physics, Classical Mechanics, Electricity and Magnetism, Quantum Mechanics, Statistical Mechanics and Research Seminar. In addition, six hours in physics, mathematics, computer science, or other departments chosen with the consent of the graduate advisor are required. Successful completion of Mathematical Physics, Quantum Mechanics I, Classical Mechanics and Electricity and Magnetism I with a GPA of 3.0 or better or satisfactory completion of a master's thesis (six credit hours) is also required.

Doctorate: Sixty semester hours of graduate credit with a GPA of 3.0 or better are required. Successful completion of Mathematical Physics, Quantum Mechanics I, Classical Mechanics and Electricity and Magnetism I with a GPA of 3.0 is required.

Thesis: Thesis may not be written in absentia.

SPECIAL EQUIPMENT, FACILITIES, OR PROGRAMS

A 12-MV tandem Van de Graaff accelerator with the associated equipment and electronics and support staff is used for atomic, nuclear, and applied research. A well-equipped instrument shop and electronic shops with technical support staff are available. A computer laboratory is reserved for physics graduate students. The department has ready access to the University alpha-cluster and Sun systems. A superconducting NMR spectrometer and scanning electron microscopes are also available at the university.

Table B—Separately Budgeted Research Expenditures by Source of Support

Source of Support	Departmental Research	Physics-related Research Outside Department
Federal government	$427,210	
State/local government		
Non-profit organizations		
Business and industry		
Other		
Total	$427,210	

Table C—Separately Budgeted Research Expenditures by Research Specialty

Research Specialty	No. of Grants	Expenditures ($)
Astronomy	4	$107,638
Atomic, Molecular, & Optical Physics	3	$149,855
Condensed Matter Physics	3	$8,121
Nuclear Physics	4	$106,868
Physics and other Science Education	2	$54,728
Total	16	$427,210

FACULTY

Chair Professor

Pancella, Paul V., Ph.D., Rice University, 1987. *Nuclear Physics*. Experimental nuclear physics; efficient transportation.

Professor

Burns, Clement, Ph.D., University of California, San Diego, 1993. *Condensed Matter Physics*. Studies of materials with highly correlated electrons, creation and testing of novel solar cell materials, and x-ray synchrotron radiation instrumentation development.

Chung, Sung G., Ph.D., University of Tokyo, 1981. *Condensed Matter Physics*. Many-body method, electronic structure calculations, and nano-physics.

Gorczyca, Thomas, Ph.D., University of Colorado, 1990. *Atomic, Molecular, & Optical Physics*. Theoretical atomic physics focusing on the fundamental interactions between electrons, photons and atomic ions in atmospheric and plasma environments.

Henderson, Charles, Ph.D., University of Minnesota, 2002. Director of the Mallinson Institute for Science Education. *Physics and other Science Education*. Physics education research, change in higher education, and discipline-based education research.

Korista, Kirk, Ph.D., The Ohio State University, 1990. Graduate Advisor. *Astronomy*. Spectroscopy and numerical simulations of photoionized gaseous nebulae.

McGurn, Arthur R., Ph.D., University of California, Santa Barbara, 1975. *Condensed Matter Physics*. Photonic crystals, meta-materials and negative refraction, nonlinear dynamics-soliton, chaos.

Paulius, Lisa, Ph.D., University of California, San Diego, 1993. *Condensed Matter Physics*. Vortex dynamics in high temperature superconductors.

Tanis, John A., Ph.D., New York University, 1976. *Atomic, Molecular, & Optical Physics*. Experimental accelerator-based atomic and molecular collision physics; transmission of electrons through micro- and nano-capillaries.

Associate Professor

Bautista, Manuel, Ph.D., Ohio State University, 1997. *Astronomy*. Atomic physics and atomic data for astrophysics; modeling of astronomical plasmas; active galactic nuclei.

Famiano, Michael, Ph.D., The Ohio State University, 2001. *Nuclear Physics*. Stellar nucleosynthesis, nuclear astrophysics, and nuclear equation-of-state.

Kayani, Asghar, Ph.D., Ohio University, 2003. *Condensed Matter Physics*. Surfaces, interface and thin film analysis; properties and synthesis of nano structure/particles; high and low energy ion-surface interactions.

Litvinova, Elena, Ph.D., Joint Institute for Nuclear Research, 2003. *Nuclear Physics*. Relativistic nuclear many-body problem; exotic nuclear systems; nuclear astrophysics.

Rosenthal, Alvin S., Ph.D., University of Colorado, 1978. *Optics*. Theoretical quantum and non-linear optics.

Schuster, David, Ph.D., University of Witwatersrand, 1972. *Physics and other Science Education*.

Assistant Professor

Chajecki, Zbigniew, Ph.D., The Ohio State University, 2009. *Nuclear Physics*. Equation of state of nuclear matter, neutron stars, nuclear fission of exotic nuclei, and astrophysical r-process.

DEPARTMENTAL RESEARCH SPECIALTIES AND STAFF

Theoretical

Astronomy. Atomic data and spectral models for astrophysics; numerical simulations of spectra of photoionized gaseous nebulae. Bautista, Korista.

Atomic, Molecular, & Optical Physics. Electron-ion collisions; ion-atom collisions; many-body theory; R-matrix theory; atomic photoionization; photodetachment; dielectronic recombinations; non-linear optics. Gorczyca, Rosenthal.

Condensed Matter Physics. Photonic crystals; Anderson localization; scattering of light by the localized surface polaritons of disordered media; inelastic neutron scattering from mixed Ising systems; computer simulations of the dynamics of Heisenberg magnetic alloys; fractions; nano-electronics; spintronics; quantum computing; superconductor-insulator transition; metal-insulator transition; novel many-body techniques. Chung, McGurn.

Nuclear Physics. The nuclear many-body problem, structure of exotic nuclei, and nuclear astrophysics. Litvinova.

Experimental

Astronomy. Acquisition and interpretation of spectroscopic data from active galactic nuclei, high-redshift quasars, and galactic emission line sources. Bautista, Korista.

Atomic, Molecular, & Optical Physics. Studies of mechanisms of electronic excitation, ionization, and charge-changing are investigated for collisions of ions with atomic and molecular targets. These investigations include strongly correlated electron systems that have applications to photon interactions with atomic and molecular targets. Tanis.

Condensed Matter Physics. Studies of highly correlated electron systems, including high-temperature superconductor parent compounds; inelastic X-ray scattering instrument development and measurements; research on the properties of materials for new types of solar cells; electrical and magnetic properties of high-temperature superconductors; flux vortex dynamics; surfaces and interface analysis; high-energy ion-surface interactions and bulk disorder; low-energy ion-surface interactions and near surface disorder; multi-layered and composite, nano-structured, oxidation and wear resistant, optical and decorative, and sensor thin films; physical properties of novel condensed matter materials; properties of nano structures/particles; ion beam analysis of materials; development of solid oxide fuel cells and hydrogen storage materials. Burns, Kayani, Paulius.

Nuclear Physics. Equation of state of nuclear matter; symmetry energy in nuclei; pion production; structure of neutron stars; fission of exotic nuclei; clustering phenomena in light nuclei; medium effects on nucleon properties and two-nucleon force; light nuclei near the neutron dripline. Chajecki, Famiano, Pancella.

Physics and other Science Education. Curriculum design, evaluation, and assessment; change in higher education teaching practices, cognitive aspects of the teaching and learning of science, such as conceptual understanding, problem solving, and epistemology; teacher beliefs and teacher professional development. Henderson, Schuster.

View additional information about this department at www.gradschoolshopper.com. Check out the "Why Choose Us?" section, find out more about the department's culture and get links to social media networks.

UNIVERSITY OF MINNESOTA, DULUTH

DEPARTMENT OF PHYSICS AND ASTRONOMY

Duluth, Minnesota 55812-3009
http://www.d.umn.edu/physics

General University Information
Chancellor: Lendley Black
Dean of Graduate School: Scott Lanyon
University website: http://www.d.umn.edu/
School Type: Public
Setting: Urban
Total Faculty: 607
Total Graduate Faculty: 428
Total number of Students: 11,168
Total number of Graduate Students: 669

Department Information
Department Chairman: Prof. Jay Austin, Head
Department Contact: Alec Habig, Director of Graduate Studies
  Total full-time faculty: 13
  Total number of full-time equivalent positions: 13
  Full-Time Graduate Students: 16
  Female Full-Time Graduate Students: 5
  First-Year Graduate Students: 8
  Female First-Year Students: 9
  Total Post Doctorates: 3

Department Address
371 Marshall W. Alworth Hall
1023 University Dr
Duluth, MN 55812-3009
Phone: 218-726-7214
E-mail: umdphys@d.umn.edu
Website: http://www.d.umn.edu/physics

ADMISSIONS

Admission Contact Information
Address admission inquiries to: Director of Graduate Studies, Physics and Astronomy Department 371 MWAH, University of Minnesota Duluth, 1023 University Drive, Duluth, MN 55812
Phone: (218) 726-7096
E-mail: ahabig@d.umn.edu
Admissions website: http://www.d.umn.edu/physics/grad/index.html

Application deadlines
Fall admission:
U.S. students: June 15   *Int'l. students*: May 15

Application fee
U.S. students: $75   *Int'l. students*: $95
Decisions about assistantships start 1 April and are usually completed by early May. Late applications will be considered up until the last assistantship. If you are considering a late application, please inquire.

Admissions information
For Fall of 2017:
  Number of applicants: 25
  Number admitted: 11
  Number enrolled: 7

Admission requirements
Bachelor's degree requirements: Bachelor's degree in Physics or the equivalent is expected.
Minimum undergraduate GPA: 2.5

GRE requirements
The GRE is recommended but not required.
  Mean GRE score range (25th–75th percentile): 157-164
  Range is for GRE-Q only, not GRE-V. We do not enforce a minimum.

Subjective GRE requirements
The Subjective GRE is not required.
The GRE physics test, while not required, is very helpful when calibrating transcripts from different schools.

TOEFL requirements
The TOEFL exam is required for students from non-English-speaking countries.
PBT score: 550
iBT score: 79
Most accepted international students have a TOEFL considerably above this minimum score. Some international students who will TA will be required to take a listening and speaking course.

Other admissions information
Undergraduate preparation assumed: Taylor, Classical Mechanics; Griffiths, Introduction to Electrodynamics; Schroeder, Thermal Physics; Griffiths, Quantum Mechanics.

TUITION

Tuition year 2017–18:
Tuition for in-state residents
  Full-time students: $8,120.04 annual
  Part-time students: $1,353.34 per credit
Tuition for out-of-state residents
  Full-time students: $12,560.04 annual
  Part-time students: $2,093.34 per credit
Tuition is waived for half-time assistants (up to 14 credits).
Credit hours per semester to be considered full-time: 6
Deferred tuition plan:
Health insurance: Yes, $2000 ($242 with assistantship).
Other academic fees: Transportation $15 Student Services: $294.16 Capital Improvement: $6.05 Collegiate Fee: $276 Athletics Fee $84 Total $675.21 per semester International student fee is an additional $152/semester
Academic term: Semester
Number of first-year students who received full tuition waivers: 8

Teaching Assistants, Research Assistants, and Fellowships
Number of first-year
  Teaching Assistants: 8
  Fellowship students: 3
Average stipend per academic year
  Teaching Assistant: $15,490
  Research Assistant: $15,490
  Fellowship student: $5,000

Fellowships available to exceptional applicants that augment the stipend or provide research support for the summer before your first semester. Summer support is available to students after their first year in the form of TA, stipend.

FINANCIAL AID

Application deadlines
Fall admission:
U.S. students: April 20   *Int'l. students*: April 20

Loans
Loans are available for U.S. students.
Loans are not available for international students.
GAPSFAS application required: No
FAFSA application required: No

For further information
Address financial aid inquiries to: Director of Graduate Studies, Physics and Astronomy, University of Minnesota Duluth, 1023 University Dr. MWAH 371, Duluth, MN 55812.
Phone: (218) 726-7214
E-mail: ahabig@d.umn.edu
Financial aid website: http://www.d.umn.edu/onestop/student-finances/financial-aid/

HOUSING

Availability of on-campus housing
Single students: No
Married students: No

For further information
Address housing inquiries to: Housing Office, University of Minnesota Duluth, 149 Lake Superior Hall, Duluth, MN 55812.
Phone: (218) 726-8178
E-mail: umdhouse@d.umn.edu
Housing aid website: http://www.d.umn.edu/housing

Table A—Faculty, Enrollments, and Degrees Granted

Research Specialty	2017–2018 Faculty	Enrollment Spring 2018 Mas-ter's	Enrollment Spring 2018 Doc-torate	Number of Degrees Granted 2016–17 (2009–15) Mas-ter's	Number of Degrees Granted 2016–17 (2009–15) Terminal Master's	Number of Degrees Granted 2016–17 (2009–15) Doc-torate
Astrophysics	1	3	–	–(2)	–	–
Condensed Matter Physics	1	2	–	1(8)	–	–
Cosmology & String Theory	1	2	–	1(3)	–	–
High Energy Physics	2	5	–	1(6)	–	–
Marine Science/ Oceanography	3	2	–	1(4)	–	–
Particles and Fields	2	1	–	2(3)	–	–
Relativity & Gravitation	2	2	–	–(3)	–	–
Total	**12**	**17**	**–**	**7(29)**	**–**	**–**
Full-time Grad. Stud.	–	17	–	–	–	–
First-year Grad. Stud.	–	8	–	–	–	–

GRADUATE DEGREE REQUIREMENTS

Master's: There are two programs of study that are planned with faculty advisors to suit the needs and interests of students. A grade point average of 2.8 must be maintained (on a scale of 4.0), with no "D"s in required courses. All students complete a common 14 semester credit core in classical and quantum physics, a choice among three methods courses, six cred-

its in related fields, and a final examination. Plan A requires a master's thesis. Plan B requires 10 additional credits in approved electives and preparation of one or more papers.
Other Degrees: For students with exceptional motivation, there is a possibility to complete M.S. degrees in two disciplines in three years. Some interdisciplinary research options joint with faculty in other departments, biophysics, medical physics, electrical engineering, and mathematics – please inquire.
Thesis: Thesis may be written in absentia.

SPECIAL EQUIPMENT, FACILITIES, OR PROGRAMS

There are opportunities in physical limnology and oceanography through Large Lakes Observatory plus well-funded multidisciplinary Natural Resources Research Institute. Participation in Fermilab-based NOvA, MINERvA and DUNE neutrino experiments. Students can use the Minnesota Supercomputing Center and Fermilab grid-computing resources for their work. There are excellent opportunities for interdisciplinary M.S. thesis projects, recently students have worked with optoelectronic and semiconductor design and fabrication; multiple projects in biophysics; and mathematics; please inquire about current opportunities.

The program features upper-level methods courses and a focus on early research opportunities.

Other equipment available in the department: Lasers and vacuum UV facilities; scanning probe microscopes; low-temperature facility; facilities for vacuum deposition of materials. A planetarium is the centerpiece of outreach and education efforts.

Table B—Separately Budgeted Research Expenditures by Source of Support

Source of Support	Departmental Research	Physics-related Research Outside Department
Federal government	$348,496	$340,909
State/local government		
Non-profit organizations	$17,317	
Business and industry		
Other		
Total	**$365,813**	**$340,909**

Table C—Separately Budgeted Research Expenditures by Research Specialty

Research Specialty	No. of Grants	Expenditures ($)
Cosmology & String Theory	2	$17,317
High Energy Physics	3	$348,496
Marine Science/Oceanography	8	$340,909
Total	**13**	**$706,722**

FACULTY

Professor

Austin, Jay, Ph.D., Massachusetts Institute of Technology and Woods Hole Oceanographic Institution, 1999. Department Head. *Climate/Atmospheric Science, Marine Science/Oceanography*. Physical limnology and oceanography.

Gran, Richard, Ph.D., University of Minnesota, 2002. *High Energy Physics, Nuclear Physics*. Neutrino oscillations and neutrino cross sections. Active on MINERvA neutrino interaction experiment, and DUNE next generation ocillation experiment.

Habig, Alec, Ph.D., Indiana University, 1996. Director of graduate Studies. *Astrophysics, High Energy Physics*. Currently working on the MINOS, NOvA, and DUNE long-baseline neutrino oscillation experiments, and the HALO and SNEWS supernovae neutrino projects.

Hiller, John R., Ph.D., University of Maryland, 1980. *Computational Physics, Particles and Fields, Theoretical Physics.* Theoretical particle physics, computational QCD.

Katsev, Serguei, Ph.D., University of Ottawa, 2002. *Marine Science/Oceanography.* Coupling of physical and biogeochemical processes in sediments and water columns of stratified lakes. Large modern lakes as model systems for ancient oceans. Reaction-transport modeling.

Seigar, Marc S., Ph.D., Liverpool John Moores U, 1998. Associate Dean. *Astrophysics.* Structure and dynamics of disk galaxies; star formation in galaxies; dark matter in galaxies; the nature of dark matter; observational cosmology.

Associate Professor

Vanchurin, Vitaly, Ph.D., Tufts University, 2005. *Cosmology & String Theory.* Cosmic strings; quantum cosmology; cosmic inflation; dark energy.

Assistant Professor

Chabysheva, Sophia, Ph.D., Southern Methodist University, 2009. *Particles and Fields, Theoretical Physics.* Theoretical particle physics, nonperturbative quantum field theory, quantum mechanics in curved spacetime.

Kelly, Samuel M., Ph.D., Oregon State U, 2012. *Marine Science/Oceanography.* Physical oceanography, coastal oceanography, internal wave dynamics.

Maps, Jonathan, Ph.D., University of Massachusetts, 1982. *Condensed Matter Physics, Solid State Physics.* Solid-state physics.

Todhunter, Audrey, Ph.D., Tufts, 2016. *Cosmology & String Theory.* Cosmology, quantum cosmology, gravitation.

West, Eric, Ph.D., Syracuse University, 2011. *Relativity & Gravitation.* Relativity and gravitation, black holes, gravitational waves, celestial mechanics.

Emeritus

Jordan, Thomas F., Ph.D., University of Rochester, 1962. *Quantum Foundations, Relativity & Gravitation, Theoretical Physics.* General relativity and quantum foundations.

DEPARTMENTAL RESEARCH SPECIALTIES AND STAFF

Theoretical

Cosmology & String Theory. Cosmology; quantum cosmology, general relativity; string theory; cosmic strings; cosmic inflation. Vanchurin, West.

Marine Science/Oceanography. Dynamics of large- and meso-scale circulation; numerical modeling of coastal shelves, estuaries, and large lakes; coupling between sediment and water column; sediment early diagenesis. Austin, Katsev, Kelly.

Particles and Fields. Elementary particles; quark model calculations; non-perturbative quantum field theory. Chabysheva, Hiller.

Quantum Foundations. Non-linear quantum dynamics. Jordan.

Relativity & Gravitation. black holes, gravitational waves, celestial mechanics. West.

Experimental

Astrophysics. Neutrino astrophysics; stellar development. Structure and dynamics of disk galaxies, star formation in galaxies, dark matter in galaxies, the nature of dark matter, observational cosmology. Habig, Seigar.

Condensed Matter Physics. Scanning probe microscopy; surface states and excitons in alkali halides; resonance Raman spectroscopy; opto-electronic materials; device physics. Maps.

High Energy Physics. High-energy neutrino oscillations and neutrino cross-sections. Gran, Habig.

Marine Science/Oceanography. Observations of the circulation dynamics of large lakes, estuaries, and coastal shelves. Austin, Katsev, Kelly.

View additional information about this department at www.gradschoolshopper.com. Check out the "Why Choose Us?" section, find out more about the department's culture and get links to social media networks.

MISSISSIPPI STATE UNIVERSITY

DEPARTMENT OF PHYSICS AND ASTRONOMY

Mississippi State, Mississippi 39762-5167
http://physics.msstate.edu

General University Information
President: Mark E. Keenum
Dean of Graduate School: Brien Henry, Interim
University website: http://www.msstate.edu
School Type: Public
Setting: Rural
Total Faculty: 1,410
Total Graduate Faculty: 1,004
Total number of Students: 21,883
Total number of Graduate Students: 3,571

Department Information
Department Chairman: Prof. Mark A. Novotny, Head
Department Contact: Henk F. Arnoldus, Professor of Physics
  Total full-time faculty: 16
  Total number of full-time equivalent positions: 20
  Full-Time Graduate Students: 46
  Female Full-Time Graduate Students: 16
  First-Year Graduate Students: 9
  Female First-Year Students: 4
  Total Post Doctorates: 2

Department Address
355 Lee Boulevard
Hilbun Hall, Room 125
Mississippi State, MS 39762-5167
Phone: (662) 325-2806
Fax: (662) 325-8898
E-mail: hfa1@msstate.edu
Website: http://physics.msstate.edu

ADMISSIONS

Admission Contact Information
Address admission inquiries to: Mississippi State University, Office of Graduate School, P.O. Box G, Mississippi State, MS 39762-5507
Phone: (662) 325-7400
Admissions website: http://www.grad.msstate.edu

Application deadlines
Fall admission:
U.S. students: February 1   *Int'l. students*: February 1
Spring admission:
U.S. students: September 1   *Int'l. students*: September 1

Application fee
U.S. students: $60   *Int'l. students*: $80

Admissions information
For Fall of 2017:
  Number of applicants: 61
  Number admitted: 13
  Number enrolled: 9

Admission requirements
Bachelor's degree requirements: Bachelor's degree in Physics or a closely related field is required.
Minimum undergraduate GPA: 2.75

GRE requirements
The GRE is recommended but not required.

Subjective GRE requirements
The Subjective GRE is recommended.

TOEFL requirements
The TOEFL exam is required for students from non-English-speaking countries.
  PBT score: 525
  iBT score: 69

Other admissions information
Additional requirements: Students from non-English-speaking countries are required to demonstrate proficiency in English via the TOEFL exam or IELTS examination. A minimum acceptable TOEFL score for admission is 525 (or 69 for iBT). The minimum acceptable IELTS score for admission is 6.0.
Undergraduate preparation assumed: Undergraduate major in physics or a closely related field; deficiencies may be corrected by additional coursework.

TUITION

Tuition year 2018–19:
Tuition for in-state residents
  Full-time students: $4,325 other
  Part-time students: $480.62 per credit
Tuition for out-of-state residents
  Full-time students: $11,625 per semester
  Part-time students: $1,291.87 per credit
Out-of-state portion of tuition is waived for teaching assistantship holders, and 71% is waived of the in-state portion. Research assistantship holders receive 100% tuition waiver.
Credit hours per semester to be considered full-time: 12
Deferred tuition plan: Yes
Health insurance: Yes, $1738.00.
Other academic fees: $100 international student charge/semester; $50 capital improvement charge/semester
Academic term: Semester
Number of first-year students who received full tuition waivers: 1
Number of first-year students who received partial tuition waivers: 8

Teaching Assistants, Research Assistants, and Fellowships
Number of first-year
  Teaching Assistants: 5
  Research Assistants: 1
Average stipend per academic year
  Teaching Assistant: $13,950
  Research Assistant: $15,397
TA students are eligible for up to $1,500 for summer support for the first year.

FINANCIAL AID

Application deadlines
Fall admission:
U.S. students: February 1   *Int'l. students*: February 1
Spring admission:
U.S. students: September 1   *Int'l. students*: September 1

Loans

Loans are available for U.S. students.
Loans are not available for international students.
GAPSFAS application required: No
FAFSA application required: No

For further information

Address financial aid inquiries to: Mississippi State University,
Student Financial Aid, Box 6035, Mississippi State, MS
39762-6035.
Phone: (662) 325-2450
E-mail: financialaid@saffairs.msstate.edu
Financial aid website: http://www.sfa.msstate.edu

HOUSING

Availability of on-campus housing

Single students: Yes
Married students: No

For further information

Address housing inquiries to: Housing and Residence Life, Box
9502, Mississippi State, MS 39762.
Phone: (662) 325-3555
E-mail: housing@saffairs.msstate.edu
Housing aid website: http://www.housing.msstate.edu

Table A—Faculty, Enrollments, and Degrees Granted

Research Specialty	2017–18 Faculty	Enrollment Fall 2017 Master's	Enrollment Fall 2017 Doctorate	Number of Degrees Granted 2017–18 (2012–18) Master's	Terminal Master's	Doctorate
Astrophysics	2	3	1	1(2)	–	–(1)
Atomic, Molecular, Plasma, & Optical Physics	4	8	13	3(13)	–	1(4)
Computational Physics	8	1	9	3(9)	–	2(6)
Condensed Matter Physics	4	–	3	–(2)	–	–(1)
Nuclear Physics	10	1	15	2(8)	–	–(6)
Physics and other Science Education	4	–	–	–	–	–
Total	36	8	41	9(34)	–	7(24)
Full-time Grad. Stud.	–	6	40	–	–	–
First-year Grad. Stud.	–	1	8	–	–	–

GRADUATE DEGREE REQUIREMENTS

Master's: A total of 30 credit hours of graduate courses is required with a minimum average grade of B. The residence requirement is a minimum of 30 weeks. For the thesis option, six credit hours of thesis research are required, and a total of 24 hours of graduate courses, as is an oral examination on the thesis. For the non-thesis option, written qualifying examinations on the physics core courses and an oral examination are required.

Doctorate: At least three academic years beyond the bachelor's degree are necessary. The minimum number of course credit hours is 24, and the total minimum number of credit hours is 54. A written preliminary examination is required for admission to candidacy after completion of academic coursework. A minimum of 20 credit hours of research for the dissertation must be scheduled. An oral defense of the dissertation is required.

Thesis: Thesis may be written in absentia.

SPECIAL EQUIPMENT, FACILITIES, OR PROGRAMS

Faculty and graduate students in the Department of Physics and Astronomy are involved in research at the Center for Advanced Vehicular Systems (CAVS), the Center for Computational Sciences (CCS), the High Performance Computing Collaboratory (HPC2), and the Institute for Clean Energy Technology (ICET), all located on the Mississippi State University campus.

Table B—Separately Budgeted Research Expenditures by Source of Support

Source of Support	Departmental Research	Physics-related Research Outside Department
Federal government	$1,343,138	$130,161
State/local government	$29,293	$114,593
Non-profit organizations		
Business and industry		
Other		
Total	$1,372,431	$244,754

Table C—Separately Budgeted Research Expenditures by Research Specialty

Research Specialty	No. of Grants	Expenditures ($)
Astrophysics	2	$252,470
Atomic, Molecular, Plasma, & Optical Physics	6	$346,440
Computational Physics	1	$2,500
Condensed Matter Physics	1	$88,398
Nuclear Physics	11	$738,226
Physics and other Science Education	2	$189,151
Total	23	$1,617,185

FACULTY

Professor

Afanasjev, Anatoli, Ph.D., Latvian Academy of Sciences, 1993. *Computational Physics, Nuclear Physics, Theoretical Physics*. Covariant (relativistic) density functional theory and its development and application to nuclei at normal and extreme conditions; rotating nuclei; nuclear fission; the crust of neutron stars.

Arnoldus, Hendrik F., Ph.D., Eindhoven University of Technology, The Netherlands, 1985. Graduate Coordinator. *Atomic, Molecular, & Optical Physics, Electromagnetism*. Theoretical optics with emphasis on near-field and nanoscale optics at interfaces.

Clay, R. Torsten, Ph.D., University of Illinois, 1999. Undergraduate Coordinator. *Computational Physics, Condensed Matter Physics*. Theoretical condensed matter physics; electronic and magnetic properties of strongly correlated materials; computational methods for strongly correlated systems.

Dunne, James A., Ph.D., American University, 1995. *Nuclear Physics*. Experimental medium energy nuclear physics; nucleon structure.

Dutta, Dipangkar, Ph.D., Northwestern University, 1999. *Accelerator, Nuclear Physics, Particles and Fields*. Medium-energy nuclear physics; precision measurement of the fundamental properties of nucleons.

Kim, Seong-Gon, Ph.D., Michigan State University, 1994. Director for the Center for Computational Sciences (CCS). *Computational Physics, Condensed Matter Physics, Nano Science and Technology*. Application of first principles computational techniques of condensed matter physics and materials science to the study of the electronic and structural properties of nanostructures, semiconductors, and metals.

Novotny, Mark A., Ph.D., Stanford University, 1978. Department Head of Physics and Astronomy. *Chemical Physics, Computational Physics, Condensed Matter Physics, Nano Science and Technology, Statistical & Thermal Physics.* Computational physics approaches to understanding the time dependence of classical and quantum models for materials and quantum computing.

Tanner, Angelle M., Ph.D., University of California, Los Angeles, 2004. *Astronomy.* Exoplanets.

Wang, Chuji, Ph.D., University of Science and Technology of China, 1998. *Atomic, Molecular, & Optical Physics, Biophysics, Engineering Physics/Science, Medical, Health Physics.* Develop and apply measuring, monitoring, and sensing technologies to address real problems in energy, environment, and biomedical engineering.

Winger, Jeffry A., Ph.D., Iowa State University, 1987. *Nuclear Physics.* Decay spectroscopy of neutron-rich nuclei; evolution of single-particle energies; application of nuclear physics to nuclear energy.

Ye, Jinwu, Ph.D., Yale University, 1993. *Atomic, Molecular, & Optical Physics, Computational Physics, Condensed Matter Physics.* Quantum systems both optical and condensed matter.

Associate Professor

Pierce, Donna M., Ph.D., University of Maryland, 2006. *Astronomy, Astrophysics, Planetary Science.* Planetary astronomy; chemical composition of comets.

Rupak, Gautam Lan Tai Moong, Ph.D., University of Washington, 2000. *Astrophysics, Atmosphere, Space Physics, Cosmic Rays, Computational Physics, Nuclear Physics, Theoretical Physics.* Nuclear structure and reactions using QCD and effective field theory.

Assistant Professor

Crider, Benjamin P., Ph.D., University of Kentucky, 2014. *Astrophysics, Nuclear Physics.* My research focuses on low-energy nuclear structure studies of shape coexistence using fast-timing techniques for measuring the half-lives of nuclear states and high-energy-resolution detector arrays for gamma-ray branching ratio measurements. These results enable the determination of transition strengths that can be compared to theoretical calculations, providing direct feedback to the validity of the models.

El Fassi, Lamiaa, Ph.D., Mohammed V University, 2008. *High Energy Physics, Nuclear Physics, Particles and Fields.* Medium-energy nuclear physics; precision measurement of the fundamental properties of nucleons.

Gombojav, Ariunbold, Ph.D., Texas A&M, 2011. *Applied Physics, Atomic, Molecular, & Optical Physics, Biophysics, Optics.* Experimental Optics.

Adjunct Professor

Gaskell, David, Ph.D., Oregon State University, 2001. *Nuclear Physics.* Medium-energy nuclear physics.

McIntyre, Dustin L., Ph.D., West Virginia University, 2007. *Atomic, Molecular, & Optical Physics.* Applications of laser spectroscopy.

Park, Brent K., Ph.D., Ohio University, 1991. Associate Laboratory Director at Oak Ridge National Laboratory. *Nuclear Physics.* Physics of national security issues.

Rykaczewski, Krzysztof P., Ph.D., Warsaw University, 1983. *Nuclear Physics.* Decay spectroscopy for low-energy nuclear structure.

Singh, J. P., Ph.D., Banares Hindu University, 1980. *Applied Physics, Atomic, Molecular, & Optical Physics.* Applications of laser spectroscopy.

Instructor

Lung, Florin D., Ph.D., Clemson University, 2011. *Physics and other Science Education.* Physics education.

Solomon, Lazarus, Ph.D., Mississippi State University, 2010. *Computational Physics, Engineering Physics/Science, Nano Science and Technology, Solid State Physics, Theoretical Physics.* Computational physics.

Worthy, Mark C., M.S., University of Alabama in Huntsville, 1994. *Applied Physics, Electromagnetism, Physics and other Science Education.* Physics education.

DEPARTMENTAL RESEARCH SPECIALTIES AND STAFF

Theoretical

Atomic, Molecular, Plasma, & Optical Physics. Computational modeling of electromagnetic scattering from complex single-particle and multiparticle systems and analytical investigations in fundamental electromagnetic theory and interactions with matter: (1) study of energy flow patterns in electromagnetic radiation fields at nanoscale (subwavelength) levels; (2) study of the quantum nature of electromagnetic radiation, including coherent states, squeezed states, correlations, photon counting statistics, and interactions with quantum phases of matter. Arnoldus, Ye.

Computational Physics. Computational methods to study a diverse range of physics topics; algorithm development and large-scale computational facilities at MSU are used to study the specific research specialization; research also involves collaborative efforts with many disciplines, including engineering, chemistry, mathematics, and computer science. Afanasjev, Clay, Kim, Novotny, Park, Rupak, Solomon, Ye.

Condensed Matter Physics. Theoretical and computational condensed matter physics and materials science: (1) electronic and magnetic properties of strongly correlated materials; (2) computational methods for strongly correlated systems; (3) electronic and structural properties of nanostructures, semiconductors, and metals; and (4) time dependence of classical and quantum models for materials. Clay, Kim, Novotny, Ye.

Nuclear Physics. Theoretical and computational studies: (1) understanding nuclear structure and reactions in a manner that is consistent with quantum chromodynamics using effective field theory to construct the low energy nuclear theory; (2) properties of light nuclei and the properties of dense nuclear matter in an astrophysical context, such as neutron stars; and (3) use of relativistic mean field theory to understand the structure of medium- to heavy-mass nuclei. Afanasjev, Dunne, Dutta, El Fassi, Rupak, Winger.

Experimental

Astrophysics. Planetary astronomy focused on the study of asteroids and comets, particularly the study of cometary atmospheres. Searches to discover exoplanets. Pierce, Tanner.

Atomic, Molecular, Plasma, & Optical Physics. Multidisciplinary research involving physics, chemistry, and optical engineering to develop and apply measuring, monitoring, and sensing technologies to address problems in energy, environment, and biomedical engineering; laser diagnostics in plasma and combustion, especially plasma-assisted combustion; time-domain fiber-optic sensor and sensor network for multifunction (physical, chemical, and biological) monitoring and sensing; cavity ring-down instrumentation for trace elements, isotopes, and volatile organic compounds; breath biomarkers for noninvasive disease diagnostics and metabolic status monitoring; in situ classification of airborne small particles. Arnoldus, Gombojav, McIntyre, Singh, Wang.

Nuclear Physics. Low-energy nuclear physics (LENP) group studies both high-spin states (including triaxial super deformation) produced in fusion evaporation reactions and lower spin structures fed by various decay processes (including half-lives, delayed-neutron probabilities, shell closures, etc.); medium-energy physics (MEP) group conducts high-precision measurements that probe the fundamental nature of quarks inside atomic nuclei and precision tests of fundamental symmetries and the standard model and is also involved in building novel detectors, systems, and targets for the experimental program at the Thomas Jefferson National Accelerator Facility (JLab); research is performed at Argonne National Laboratory, JLab, Oak Ridge National Laboratory, and the National Superconducting Cyclotron Laboratory. Afanasjev, Crider, Dunne, Dutta, El Fassi, Gaskell, Rykaczewski, Winger.

View additional information about this department at www.gradschoolshopper.com. Check out the "Why Choose Us?" section, find out more about the department's culture and get links to social media networks.

THE UNIVERSITY OF MISSISSIPPI

DEPARTMENT OF PHYSICS AND ASTRONOMY

University, Mississippi 38677
http://physics.olemiss.edu/

General University Information
Chancellor: Jeffrey Vitter
Dean of Graduate School: Christy Wyandt (Interim)
University website: http://www.olemiss.edu
School Type: Public
Setting: Suburban
Total Faculty: 1,095
Total Graduate Faculty: 583
Total number of Students: 21,260
Total number of Graduate Students: 2,040

Department Information
Department Chairman: Dr. Luca Bombelli, Chair
Department Contact: Ginger Dykes, Operations Coordinator
Total full-time faculty: 17
Total number of full-time equivalent positions: 18
Full-Time Graduate Students: 43
Female Full-Time Graduate Students: 8
First-Year Graduate Students: 7
Female First-Year Students: 1
Total Post Doctorates: 6

Department Address
108 Lewis Hall
P.O.Box 1848
University, MS 38677
Phone: (662) 915-7046
Fax: (662) 915-5045
E-mail: physics@phy.olemiss.edu
Website: http://physics.olemiss.edu/

ADMISSIONS

Admission Contact Information
Address admission inquiries to: The University of Mississippi, Graduate School, P.O. Box 1848, University, MS 38677
Phone: (662) 915-7474
E-mail: gschool@olemiss.edu
Admissions website: http://gradschool.olemiss.edu/

Application deadlines
Fall admission:
U.S. students: January 15   *Int'l. students*: January 15
Spring admission:
U.S. students: September 15   *Int'l. students*: September 15

Application fee
U.S. students: $50   *Int'l. students*: $50

Admissions information
For Fall of 2018:
Number of applicants: 77
Number admitted: 13
Number enrolled: 6

Admission requirements
Bachelor's degree requirements: Bachelor's degree in physics is required.
Minimum undergraduate GPA: 3.0

GRE requirements
The GRE is required.
Quantitative score: 155

Subjective GRE requirements
The Subjective GRE is recommended.
The GRE Physics Subject Test is optional. But if available, a score from the Physics Subject Test should be sent.

TOEFL requirements
The TOEFL exam is required for students from non-English-speaking countries.
PBT score: 550
iBT score: 79
Minimum accepted computer based exam (CB): 213

Other admissions information
Additional requirements: In addition to test scores, applicants should submit official undergraduate transcripts, two letters of recommendation, and a brief statement of purpose.
Undergraduate preparation assumed: Competitive GRE scores and an undergraduate GPA equivalent to a B or higher.

TUITION

Tuition year 2018–19:
Tuition for in-state residents
Full-time students: $8,550 annual
Part-time students: $475 per credit
Tuition for out-of-state residents
Full-time students: $24,502.5 annual
Part-time students: $1,361.25 per credit
None of our graduate students pay out of pocket for tuition. This is an estimated cost of attendance and will be finalized in July 2018.
Credit hours per semester to be considered full-time: 9
Deferred tuition plan: No
Health insurance: Yes, $1,809.00.
Other academic fees: Premium may be adjusted for additional coverage (spouse and/or child/dependent)
Academic term: Semester
Number of first-year students who received full tuition waivers: 9

Teaching Assistants, Research Assistants, and Fellowships
Number of first-year
Teaching Assistants: 9
Research Assistants: 1
Fellowship students: 1
Average stipend per academic year
Teaching Assistant: $16,000
Research Assistant: $16,000
Fellowship student: $16,000
The stipends quoted are for the nine-month academic year. Students who carry out research or teaching duties during the summer receive an additional $4000.

FINANCIAL AID

Application deadlines
Fall admission:

U.S. students: April 1   *Int'l. students*: April 1
Spring admission:
U.S. students: October 1   *Int'l. students*: October 1

Loans
Loans are available for U.S. students.
Loans are not available for international students.
GAPSFAS application required: No
FAFSA application required: Yes

For further information
Address financial aid inquiries to: Financial Aid Office, P.O. Box 1848, University, MS 38677.
Phone: (800) 891-4596
E-mail: finaid@olemiss.edu
Financial aid website: http://finaid.olemiss.edu/

HOUSING

Availability of on-campus housing
Single students: Yes
Married students: No
Childcare Assistance: No

For further information
Address housing inquiries to: Student Housing Office, P.O. Box 1848, University, MS 38677.
Phone: (662) 915-7328
E-mail: housing@olemiss.edu
Housing aid website: http://studenthousing.olemiss.edu/

Table A—Faculty, Enrollments, and Degrees Granted

Research Specialty	2018–19 Faculty	Enrollment Fall 2017 Master's	Enrollment Fall 2017 Doctorate	Number of Degrees Granted 2017–2018 (2013–18) Master's	Number of Degrees Granted 2017–2018 (2013–18) Terminal Master's	Number of Degrees Granted 2017–2018 (2013–18) Doctorate
Acoustics	5	–	–	3(4)	–	–(1)
Atmosphere, Space Physics, Cosmic Rays	1	–	–	1(1)	–	1
Condensed Matter Physics	1	–	–	–	–	–
High Energy Physics	6	–	–	–(2)	–	1(4)
Relativity & Gravitation	3	–	–	2(8)	–	2(4)
Other	–	–	–	–(3)	–	2(3)
Total	16	–	–	6(18)	–	6(12)
Full-time Grad. Stud.	–	–	–	–	–	–
First-year Grad. Stud.	–	–	–	–	–	–

GRADUATE DEGREE REQUIREMENTS

Master's: A Master of Arts degree requires 30 credit hours of suitable graduate course work. A Master of Science degree requires 24 hours of suitable graduate course work and 6 hours of thesis research. The degree program must be completed within six years.

Doctorate: A Ph.D. degree requires three years of study (54 credit hours), a minimum of two years (36 hours) of graduate study at the University of Mississippi, and a minimum of one year full-time graduate work beyond the Master's degree in continuous residence. An average grade of B or above is required for all course work. Successful completion of a comprehensive examination (written and oral) and dissertation prospectus defense are required. The preparation and defense of a dissertation are required. A foreign language is not required.

Thesis: Thesis may be written in absentia.

SPECIAL EQUIPMENT, FACILITIES, OR PROGRAMS

The Department of Physics and Astronomy is housed primarily in Lewis Hall with some faculty and physics graduate students having offices and research space in the Jamie Whitten National Center for Physical Acoustics nearby on campus. The Department has labs for electronics, optics, and modern physics. The department also uses Kennon Observatory adjacent to Lewis Hall and has a variety of telescopes used in astronomy laboratories. These include a portable 25-inch Dobsonian telescope, a 15-inch refracting telescope (mounted in the large dome of Kennon Observatory), and a 17-inch Plane Wave Corrected Dall Kirkham (CDK) telescope on a Paramount ME mount and outfitted with a CCD camera is mounted in the small dome. Additional 8-inch and 12-inch portable telescopes are also used for astronomy lab courses.

The Lewis Hall Research Wing has eight large laboratory rooms used for research in atmospheric physics, condensed matter physics, gravitational theory, and high-energy physics. The Research Wing also houses the department's machine shop, which is equipped with a large computer-controlled lathe, three computer-controlled mills, and a computer-controlled measuring machine. Facilities of the high-energy physics group in the Lewis Hall Research Wing include a modern LINUX parallel-computing farm. This Linux farm is used for DØ, LHC and Muon Collider simulations. Data-acquisition systems of the high-energy physics group are used in the development and testing of detectors for future high-energy physics experiments. The high-energy physics group also has a large-sample Perkin Elmer spectrophotometer.

The Jamie Whitten National Center for Physical Acoustics, a few minutes' walk from Lewis Hall, contains the technical and support facilities of a world-class research program. This facility includes a high-bay laboratory, an anechoic chamber, and a large open bay with subsonic and supersonic wind tunnels.

Table B—Separately Budgeted Research Expenditures by Source of Support

Source of Support	Departmental Research	Physics-related Research Outside Department
Federal government	$1,130,845	$2,841,153
State/local government		
Non-profit organizations		
Business and industry		
Other		
Total	$1,130,845	$2,841,153

Table C—Separately Budgeted Research Expenditures by Research Specialty

Research Specialty	No. of Grants	Expenditures ($)
Acoustics	12	$2,841,153
Astrophysics	1	$92,000
Atmosphere, Space Physics, Cosmic Rays	1	$209,000
High Energy Physics	5	$711,938
Theoretical Physics	2	$95,000
Other	3	$22,907
Total	24	$3,971,998

FACULTY

Chair Professor
Bombelli, Luca, Ph.D., Syracuse University, 1987. *Relativity & Gravitation*. General relativity and quantum gravity.

Professor

Cavaglià, Marco, Ph.D., International School for Advanced Studies of Trieste, 1996. *Astrophysics, Relativity & Gravitation.* Astrophysics.

Cremaldi, Lucien, Ph.D., Northwestern University, 1983. *High Energy Physics.* Particle physics.

Gladden, Joseph, Ph.D., Pennsylvania State University. Interim Vice Chancellor for Research. *Acoustics, Condensed Matter Physics.*

Kroeger, Robert S., Ph.D., University of Pittsburgh, 1986. *High Energy Physics.* High-energy physics.

Marshall, Thomas, Ph.D., New Mexico Institute of Mining and Tech., 1981. *Atmosphere, Space Physics, Cosmic Rays.* Atmospheric physics.

Ostrovskii, Igor, Ph.D., KSU, Kiev, 1982. *Condensed Matter Physics.* Acoustics.

Quinn, Breese, Ph.D., University of Chicago, 2000. *High Energy Physics, Particles and Fields.*

Summers, Donald J., Ph.D., University of California, Santa Barbara, 1984. *High Energy Physics.* High-energy physics.

Associate Professor

Beach, Kevin, Ph.D., Massachusetts Institute of Technology, 2004. Graduate Program Coordinator. *Computational Physics, Condensed Matter Physics.*

Datta, Alakabha, Ph.D., University of Hawaii, 1995. *High Energy Physics, Particles and Fields.* Particle theory.

Labuda, Cecille, Ph.D., University of Mississippi, 2008. Undergraduate Program Coordinator. *Acoustics.*

Mobley, Joel, Ph.D., Washington University, 1998. *Acoustics, Biophysics.*

Assistant Professor

Bennett, Jake, Ph.D., Indiana University - Bloomington, 2014. *High Energy Physics.* Belle II.

Stein, Leo, Ph.D., MA Institute of Technology, 2012. General relativity, gravitation and astrophysical phenomena.

Zhang, Likun, Ph.D., Washington State University, 2012. *Acoustics, Fluids, Rheology.*

Research Associate Professor

Stolzenburg, Maribeth, Ph.D., University of Oklahoma, 1996. Atmospheric physics.

Waxler, Roger, Ph.D., Columbia University, 1986. *Acoustics.* Acoustics.

Research Assistant Professor

Dooley, Katherine, Ph.D., University of Florida, 2011. *Optics, Relativity & Gravitation.*

Hickey, Craig, Ph.D., University of Alberta, 1994. *Geophysics.* Geophysics.

Lu, Zhiqu, Ph.D., Université de Pau et des Pays de l'Adour, 1998. Acoustic thermal-physics.

Torma, Tibor, Ph.D., UMass, 1996. *Particles and Fields.* Particle physics.

Adjunct Professor

Aranchuk, Vyacheslav, Ph.D., Minsk, 1989. Engineering Science.

Berti, Emanuele, Ph.D., University of Rome La Sapienza, 2001. *Astrophysics, Relativity & Gravitation.*

Cardoso, Victor, Ph.D., CENTRA/IST, 2003. *Astrophysics, Relativity & Gravitation.*

Godang, Romulus, Ph.D., Virginia Polytechnic Institute and State University (Virginia Tech), 2000. HEP.

Keppens, Veerle, Ph.D., Katholieke Universiteit Leuven, 1995. *Acoustics, Solid State Physics.* Solid state acoustics.

Prather, Wayne, Ph.D., University of Mississippi, 1999. *Acoustics.* Acoustics.

Visiting Assistant Professor

Meyer, Jennifer, Ph.D., MA Institute of Technology, 2011. *Geophysics, Planetary Science.*

Xiao, Bin, Ph.D., North Carolina State University, 2016.

Instructor

Hill, James, M.A., Bowling Green State University, 1969. *Astronomy.*

Perera, Lalith, Ph.D., University of Cincinnati, 1995. *Astronomy, High Energy Physics.*

DEPARTMENTAL RESEARCH SPECIALTIES AND STAFF

Theoretical

Condensed Matter Physics. Beach.
Particles and Fields. Datta.
Relativity & Gravitation. Bombelli, Cardoso, Cavaglià, Stein.

Experimental

Acoustics. Aranchuk, Gladden, Hickey, Keppens, Labuda, Lu, Mobley, Prather, Waxler, Zhang.
Atmospheric electricity, thunderstorm electrification. Marshall, Stolzenburg.
Condensed Matter Physics. Gladden, Keppens, Ostrovskii.
High Energy Physics. Bennett, Cremaldi, Kroeger, Quinn, Summers.

View additional information about this department at www.gradschoolshopper.com. Check out the "Why Choose Us?" section, find out more about the department's culture and get links to social media networks.

MISSOURI UNIVERSITY OF SCIENCE AND TECHNOLOGY

DEPARTMENT OF PHYSICS

Rolla, Missouri 65409
http://physics.mst.edu

General University Information
Chancellor: Christoper G. Maples
Dean of Graduate School: Stephen P. Roberts
University website: http://mst.edu
School Type: Public
Setting: Rural
Total Faculty: 372
Total Graduate Faculty: 307
Total number of Students: 8,884
Total number of Graduate Students: 1,964

Department Information
Department Chairman: Prof. S. Thomas Vojta, Chair
Department Contact: Thomas Vojta, Chairman
   Total full-time faculty: 17
   Total number of full-time equivalent positions: 19
   Full-Time Graduate Students: 37
   Female Full-Time Graduate Students: 7
   First-Year Graduate Students: 12
   Female First-Year Students: 3
   Total Post Doctorates: 5

Department Address
1315 N. Pine Street
Rolla, MO 65409
Phone: (573) 341-4781
Fax: (573) 341-4715
E-mail: physics@mst.edu
Website: http://physics.mst.edu

ADMISSIONS

Admission Contact Information
Address admission inquiries to: Director of Admissions, 106
   Parker Hall, 300 W. 13th Street
Phone: (573) 341-4165
E-mail: graduate-admissions@mst.edu
Admissions website: http://futurestudents.mst.edu

Application deadlines
Fall admission:
U.S. students: September 1   *Int'l. students*: September 1
Spring admission:
U.S. students: December 15   *Int'l. students*: November 15

Application fee
U.S. students: $50   *Int'l. students*: $50

Admissions information
For Fall of 2018:
   Number of applicants: 53
   Number admitted: 16
   Number enrolled: 16

Admission requirements
Bachelor's degree requirements: A Bachelor's degree in Physics
   is required.
Minimum undergraduate GPA: 3.0

GRE requirements
The GRE is required.
   Quantitative score: 700
   Analytical score: 3.0
   Mean GRE score range (25th–75th percentile): 70

Subjective GRE requirements
The Subjective GRE is recommended.
   Minimum accepted Advanced GRE score: 700
   Mean Advanced GRE score range (25th–75th percentile): 70th

TOEFL requirements
The TOEFL exam is required for students from non-English-
   speaking countries.
   PBT score: 570
   iBT score: 80

Other admissions information
Additional requirements: The minimum acceptable score sug-
   gested for admission is 1100 (verbal plus quantitative).
   No minimum acceptable score is used.
Undergraduate preparation assumed: General Physics, Halliday;
   Fundamentals of Physics; Modern Physics, Thornton; Modern
   Physics for Scientists and Engineers; Mechanics, Marion;
   Classical Dynamics of Particles and Systems; Thermodynam-
   ics, Reif; Fundamentals of Statistical and Thermal Physics;
   Electricity and Magnetism, Griffiths; Introduction to Elec-
   trodynamics; Quantum Mechanics, Liboff; Introduction to
   Quantum Mechanics.

TUITION
Tuition year 2018–2019:
Tuition for in-state residents
   Full-time students: $5,947 per semester
   Part-time students: $746.78 per credit
Tuition for out-of-state residents
   Full-time students: $13,109 per semester
   Part-time students: $1,532.4 per credit
Out-of-state fees are waived for Graduate Assistants, Graduate
   Teaching and Research Assistants
Credit hours per semester to be considered full-time: 9
Deferred tuition plan: Yes
Health insurance: Yes, $2907.00.
Academic term: Semester
Number of first-year students who received full tuition waivers: 12

Teaching Assistants, Research Assistants, and Fellowships
Number of first-year
   Teaching Assistants: 1
   Research Assistants: 2
Average stipend per academic year
   Teaching Assistant: $18,545.67
   Research Assistant: $18,545.67
   1 student received the Chancellor's Distinguished Fellowship

FINANCIAL AID

Application deadlines
Fall admission:

U.S. students: September 1   *Int'l. students*: September 1
Spring admission:
U.S. students: September 1   *Int'l. students*: September 1

Loans

Loans are available for U.S. students.
Loans are available for international students.
GAPSFAS application required: Yes
FAFSA application required: Yes

For further information

Address financial aid inquiries to: Student Financial Assistance, G1 Parker Hall, 300 W. 13th Street, Rolla, MO 65409.
Phone: (573) 341-4282
E-mail: sfa@mst.edu
Financial aid website: http://sfa.mst.edu

HOUSING

Availability of on-campus housing
Single students: Yes
Married students: Yes

For further information

Address housing inquiries to: Office of Residential Life, 205 W. 12th Street, Rolla, MO 65409.
Phone: (573) 341-4218
E-mail: reslife@mst.edu
Housing aid website: http://reslife.mst.edu

Table A—Faculty, Enrollments, and Degrees Granted

Research Specialty	2017–18 Faculty	Enrollment Fall 2017 Master's	Enrollment Fall 2017 Doctorate	Degrees Master's	Degrees Terminal Master's	Degrees Doctorate
Astrophysics	–	–	5	–	–	–(1)
Atomic, Molecular, & Optical Physics	7	–	8	–(7)	–(3)	3(6)
Biophysics	–	–	3	–	–	1(2)
Condensed Matter Physics	8	–	12	–(3)	–(1)	3(9)
Optics	–	–	–	–	–	–
Physics and other Science Education	1	–	–	–	–(2)	–
Polymer Physics/Science	1	–	–	–	–(1)	–(2)
Statistical & Thermal Physics	1	–	1	–	–(1)	–
Non-specialized	–	–	9	1(1)	–(5)	1
Other	1	–	–	–	–	–(1)
Total	19	–	38	1(11)	–(13)	8(21)
Full-time Grad. Stud.	–	–	38	–	–	–
First-year Grad. Stud.	–	–	12	–	–	–

GRADUATE DEGREE REQUIREMENTS

Master's: Thirty graduate credit hours for a master's degree with thesis and 30 graduate credit hours for a non-thesis master's degree in an approved program with satisfactory performance are required. A thesis exam and a B average are required. There are no residence or language requirements.

Doctorate: A minimum of 72 hours with satisfactory performance is required. There is a residency requirement of three years (six semesters; those with a master's degree from the University of Minnesota, Rochester or other institution is two years, four semesters). A Ph.D. qualifying exam, dissertation, and dissertation exam are required. The language requirement

includes passing an examination or an equivalent of one-year collegiate-level course work with a grade of B or better, with an overall requirement of B grades or better.
Thesis: Thesis may be written in absentia.

SPECIAL EQUIPMENT, FACILITIES, OR PROGRAMS

The Cloud and Aerosol Sciences Laboratory provides a wide range of special instrumentation for the study of atmospheric physics, including an assortment of aerosol generators, direct Aitken nuclei counters, condensation nuclei counters, diffusion cloud chambers, and expansion cloud chambers suitable for low-temperature applications. A major mobile laboratory facility is available for the characterization of gas turbine and rocket engine exhaust emissions and is suitable for ground test, airborne, and altitude chamber venues.

The Graduate Center for Materials Research provides accessibility to electron spectroscopy for chemical analysis, auger spectrometers, an scanning electron microscope, an automatic X-ray spectrometer, mass spectrometers, etc.

The Physics Department itself provides access to an ion energy loss spectrometer, an ion implantation accelerator system, electron spin resonance, a full range of lasers, and general research equipment.

Table B—Separately Budgeted Research Expenditures by Source of Support

Source of Support	Departmental Research	Physics-related Research Outside Department
Federal government	$993,981.28	$118,256.99
State/local government	$60,945.22	
Non-profit organizations		
Business and industry		
Other		$21,626.86
Total	$1,054,926.5	$139,883.85

Table C—Separately Budgeted Research Expenditures by Research Specialty

Research Specialty	No. of Grants	Expenditures ($)
Atomic, Molecular, & Optical Physics	13	$850,069.51
Condensed Matter Physics	7	$310,945.98
Physics and other Science Education	4	$12,168
Other	1	$21,626.86
Total	25	$1,194,810.35

FACULTY

Professor

Madison, Don H., Ph.D., Florida State University, 1972. *Atomic, Molecular, & Optical Physics*. Electron-atom and ion-atom scattering; theoretical physics.

Parris, Paul E., Ph.D., University of Rochester, 1984. *Condensed Matter Physics, Polymer Physics/Science, Statistical & Thermal Physics*. Electron transport in disordered solids; theoretical physics.

Peacher, Jerry L., Ph.D., Indiana University, 1965. *Atomic, Molecular, & Optical Physics*. Atomic collisions; scattering; theoretical physics.

Schulz, Michael, Ph.D., University of Heidelberg, 1984. *Atomic, Molecular, & Optical Physics*. Ion-atom collisions; electron correlation; experimental physics.

Vojta, S. Thomas, Ph.D., University of Chemnitz, 1994. *Condensed Matter Physics*. Correlated electrons; quantum phase transitions; theoretical physics.

Waddill, G. Daniel, Ph.D., Indiana University, 1987. Chairman of the Department. *Condensed Matter Physics*. Characterization of metallic surfaces and interfaces by X-ray and ultraviolet photoelectron spectroscopy; experimental physics.

Wilemski, Gerald, Ph.D., Yale University, 1972. *Statistical & Thermal Physics, Other*. Nucleation theory; theoretical physics.

Associate Professor

Medvedeva, Julia E., Ph.D., Institute of Metal Physics, Russian Academy of Science, 2002. *Condensed Matter Physics*. Density functional theory; theoretical physics.

Story, J. Greg, Ph.D., University of Southern California, 1989. *Atomic, Molecular, & Optical Physics*. Studies of Rydberg atom properties; experimental physics.

Assistant Professor

Chernatynskiy, Aleksandr, Ph.D., University of Louisville, 2005. Thermal transport and other materials properties in the extreme environments at the fundamental level, as well as in industrial applications, such as nuclear energy, geophysics and others.

Fischer, Daniel, Ph.D., Heidelberg University, 2003. Interactions of single excited and polarized atoms or ultra-cold and quantum-degenerate ensembles of atoms with intense femtosecond laser pulses. Furnishes a laser lab for advanced light sources that allow to cool, trap, manipulate, and ionize lithium atoms with an unprecedented level of control.

Hor, Yew San, Ph.D., Rutgers University, 2004. *Condensed Matter Physics*. Growth and characterization of novel bulk and nanostructured materials; experimental physics.

Jentschura, Ulrich, Ph.D., University of Technology, Dresden, 1999. *Atomic, Molecular, & Optical Physics*. Quantum electrodynamic bound-state calculations; relativistic quantum dynamic processes in laser fields; analysis of high-precision experiments; theoretical physics.

Kurter, Cihan, Ph.D., Illinois Institute of Technology, 2009. *Condensed Matter Physics, Physics and other Science Education*. Topological insulators/superconductors; superconducting terahertz sources and detection techniques; superconducting nanostructures and Josephson devices and RF and microwave metamaterials; metamaterial-based EIT.

Yamilov, Alexey, Ph.D., City University of New York, 2001. *Condensed Matter Physics*. Mesoscopic phenomena in light propagation; photonics; theoretical physics.

Teaching Associate Professor

Vojta, Agnes, Ph.D., Technische Universitat, 1994.

Teaching Assistant Professor

Musser, James, Ph.D., Texas A&M University, 2005.

DEPARTMENTAL RESEARCH SPECIALTIES AND STAFF

Theoretical

Atomic, Molecular, & Optical Physics. Atomic collisions; scattering; primary ionization. Fischer, Jentschura, Madison, Parris, Peacher, Schulz, Story.

Condensed Matter Physics. Electron transport in disordered solids; surface phenomena; electronic polymers; density functional theory; mesoscopic phenomena in light propagation; photonics; correlated electrons and quantum phase transitions. Chernatynskiy, Hor, Medvedeva, S. Vojta, Waddill, Wilemski, Yamilov.

Other. Cloud and Aerosol Sciences Laboratory; homomolecular and heteromolecular nucleation studies; properties of water clusters; surface nucleation; simulation of initial stages of cloud formation; condensational drop growth/evaporation; aerosol dynamics; neutron scattering by aerosols; density functional theory of inhomogeneous fluids. Wilemski.

Physics and other Science Education.

Experimental

Atomic, Molecular, & Optical Physics. Ion-atom and electron collisions; heavy-ion impact excitation; energy-loss spectrometry; lifetimes; photoionization; electron impact; recoil ion momentum spectroscopy; electron spectroscopy; quantum electronics; Penning reactions; lasers; crossed-beam molecular scattering. Fischer, Jentschura, Madison, Schulz, Story.

Condensed Matter Physics. Ion implantation; electron spin resonance; magnetism; ferroelectricity; surfaces; superconductivity; electronic ceramics. Chernatynskiy, Hor, Kurter, Medvedeva, Waddill, Wilemski, Yamilov.

Other. Cloud and Aerosol Sciences Laboratory; fundamental studies of aerosol generation, measurement of physical and chemical properties, and evolution in the atmosphere; current emphasis on the exhaust emissions from jet and rocket engines, with measurement campaigns conducted in situ with airborne facilities, in ground-based facilities in engine test stands, combustor rigs, altitude chambers, and in laboratory combustion facilities; the laboratory has an interdisciplinary flavor with strong interactions with chemistry and engineering. Wilemski.

Physics and other Science Education. Development of traditional and nontraditional learning experiences; production of audiovisual aids.

Physics and other Science Education.

View additional information about this department at www.gradschoolshopper.com. Check out the "Why Choose Us?" section, find out more about the department's culture and get links to social media networks.

UNIVERSITY OF MISSOURI

DEPARTMENT OF PHYSICS AND ASTRONOMY

Columbia, Missouri 65211
http://physics.missouri.edu/

General University Information
President: Mun Y. Choi
Dean of Graduate School: Jenni Hart
University website: http://www.missouri.edu
School Type: Public
Setting: Urban
Total Faculty: 2,184
Total Graduate Faculty: 1,850
Total number of Students: 33,266
Total number of Graduate Students: 7,150

Department Information
Department Chairman: Prof. Sashi Satpathy, Chair
Department Contact: Paul F. Miceli, Director of Graduate
  Studies
  Total full-time faculty: 30
  Total number of full-time equivalent positions: 26
  Full-Time Graduate Students: 48
  Female Full-Time Graduate Students: 8
  First-Year Graduate Students: 9
  Female First-Year Students: 1
  Total Post Doctorates: 12

Department Address
223 Physics Building
Columbia, MO 65211
Phone: (573) 882-3335
Fax: (573) 882-4195
E-mail: umcasphysics@missouri.edu
Website: http://physics.missouri.edu/

ADMISSIONS

Admission Contact Information
Address admission inquiries to: Office of Graduate Studies, University of Missouri, 210 Jesse Hall, Columbia, MO 65211
Phone: (800) 877-6312
E-mail: gradadmin@missouri.edu
Admissions website: http://gradstudies.missouri.edu/admissions/

Application deadlines
Fall admission:
U.S. students: March 1   *Int'l. students*: March 1
Spring admission:
U.S. students: October 1   *Int'l. students*: October 1

Application fee
U.S. students: $65   *Int'l. students*: $90

Admissions information
For Fall of 2018:
  Number of applicants: 70
  Number admitted: 12
  Number enrolled: 8

Admission requirements
Bachelor's degree requirements: A Bachelor's degree in Physics or related fields is required.
Minimum undergraduate GPA: 3.0

GRE requirements
The GRE is required.
  Quantitative score: 155
  Verbal score: 146
  Analytical score: 3.0
  Mean GRE score range (25th–75th percentile): 300-320

Subjective GRE requirements
The Subjective GRE is recommended.
  Minimum accepted Advanced GRE score: 500
  Mean Advanced GRE score range (25th–75th percentile): 500-800

TOEFL requirements
The TOEFL exam is required for students from non-English-speaking countries.
  PBT score: 550
  iBT score: 80

Other admissions information
Additional requirements: The minimum acceptable scores suggested for admission are as follows: verbal, 146; quantitative, 155. The average GRE scores for admission are as follows: verbal, 150; quantitative, 160. The IELTS test with a minimum score of 6.5 is an acceptable alternative to the TOEFL.

TUITION

Tuition year 2017–18:
Tuition for in-state residents
  Full-time students: $352.6 per credit
  Part-time students: $352.6 per credit
Tuition for out-of-state residents
  Full-time students: $965.5 per credit
  Part-time students: $965.5 per credit
Credit hours per semester to be considered full-time: 9
Deferred tuition plan: Yes
Health insurance: Yes, Depends on choice of coverage.
Other academic fees: Recreational facility fee, $73.17 per semester (enrolled 6+ hours); activity fee, $16.66 per credit hour (maximum $99.96); health fee, $83.40 per semester (enrolled 6+ hours); information technology fee, $13.20 per credit hour.
Academic term: Semester
Number of first-year students who received full tuition waivers: 10

Teaching Assistants, Research Assistants, and Fellowships
Number of first-year
  Teaching Assistants: 9
  Research Assistants: 5
  Fellowship students: 10
Average stipend per academic year
  Teaching Assistant: $18,000
  Research Assistant: $22,000
  Fellowship student: $21,000
TA students are eligible for up to $3,000 summer fellowship support.

FINANCIAL AID

Application deadlines
Fall admission:
U.S. students: March 1   *Int'l. students*: March 1
Spring admission:
U.S. students: October 1   *Int'l. students*: October 1

Loans
Loans are available for U.S. students.
Loans are not available for international students.
GAPSFAS application required: Yes
FAFSA application required: Yes

For further information
Address financial aid inquiries to: University of Missouri-Columbia, Office of Student Financial Aid, 11 Jesse Hall, Columbia, MO 65211.
Phone: (573) 882-7506
E-mail: finaidinfo@missouri.edu
Financial aid website: http://financialaid.missouri.edu/

HOUSING

Availability of on-campus housing
Single students: Yes
Married students: Yes

For further information
Address housing inquiries to: Department of Residential Life, University of Missouri, 0780 Defoe-Graham Hall, 901 Hitt Street, Columbia, MO 65211.
Phone: (573) 882-7275
E-mail: reslife@missouri.edu
Housing aid website: http://reslife.missouri.edu/

Table A—Faculty, Enrollments, and Degrees Granted

Research Specialty	2018–19 Faculty	Enrollment Fall 2016 Master's	Enrollment Fall 2016 Doctorate	Number of Degrees Granted 2016–17 (2012–17) Master's	Number of Degrees Granted 2016–17 (2012–17) Terminal Master's	Number of Degrees Granted 2016–17 (2012–17) Doctorate
Astronomy	5	1	10	1(4)	1(4)	1(2)
Biophysics	4	–	12	2(6)	–(1)	3(10)
Condensed Matter Physics	12	2	24	2(9)	1(3)	4(19)
Energy Sources & Environment	2	–	4	1(4)	–	1(5)
Nano Science and Technology	5	–	–	–	–(3)	–
Optics	1	–	2	–(2)	–	1(2)
Physics and other Science Education	3	–	–	–	–	–
Relativity & Gravitation	1	–	1	–	–	–
Total	**26**	**3**	**51**	**6(25)**	**2(11)**	**9(37)**
Full-time Grad. Stud.	–	3	51	–	–	–
First-year Grad. Stud.	–	1	9	–	–	–

GRADUATE DEGREE REQUIREMENTS

Master's: A master's degree requires completion of 30 credit hours beyond the bachelor's degree (at least 15 hours of those must be 8000-level courses) with a grade of 3.0 (B) or better. Completion of the departmental qualifying examination at the M.S. pass level or a written thesis is required. There are no foreign language or computing requirements.

Doctorate: A doctorate degree requires completion of a minimum of 18 hours beyond the master's degree with a grade of 3.0 (B) or better and completion of the department qualifying examination at the Ph.D. pass level. The degree candidate must also meet the residency requirements. A student is required to have taken a minimum of three full years of graduate work beyond the bachelor's degree. To be an official candidate, the student must pass the comprehensive examination for the Ph.D., which is based on graduate coursework in the department. A dissertation is required.

SPECIAL EQUIPMENT, FACILITIES, OR PROGRAMS

The University of Missouri Research Reactor at Columbia provides a unique opportunity for neutron scattering research. The thermal neutron flux at the beam port is 2×10^{14} neutrons/cm^{2}s, the highest of any university in the United States. Current projects/programs include studies of neutron and X-ray scattering, critical phenomena, surface and interfaces, lattice and liquid dynamics, magnetic materials, optoelectronics, theoretical, computational, and experimental biological physics, biomedical imaging and optics, theory of gravity and relativistic astrophysics, spintronics, and condensed matter theory.

Table B—Separately Budgeted Research Expenditures by Source of Support

Source of Support	Departmental Research	Physics-related Research Outside Department
Federal government	$2,197,587	
State/local government	$205,870	
Non-profit organizations	$2,275	
Business and industry		
Other		
Total	**$2,405,732**	

Table C—Separately Budgeted Research Expenditures by Research Specialty

Research Specialty	No. of Grants	Expenditures ($)
Astronomy	4	$130,887
Biophysics	3	$421,640
Condensed Matter Physics	8	$483,357
Physics and other Science Education	7	$1,318,398
Total	**22**	**$2,354,282**

FACULTY

Professor

Chandrasekhar, Meera, Ph.D., Brown University, 1976. Curators' Distinguished Teaching Professor. *Condensed Matter Physics*. Optical spectroscopy of semiconductors and superconductors with an emphasis on high-pressure studies.

Chen, Shi-Jie, Ph.D., University of California, San Diego, 1994. *Biophysics*. Theoretical and computational biophysics.

Gangopadhyay, Shubhra, Ph.D., Indian Institute of Technology, Kharagpur, 1982. Professor of Electrical Engineering (joint appointment). *Condensed Matter Physics, Electrical Engineering, Nano Science and Technology*. Nanotechnology.

Godwin, Linda, Ph.D., University of Missouri, 1980. *Astronomy*. Astronomy; space science.

Guha, Suchi, Ph.D., Arizona State University, 1996. *Condensed Matter Physics*. Experimental condensed matter physics; light scattering and organic optoelectronics.

Hawthorne, M. Frederick, Ph.D., University of California, Los Angeles, 1953. Professor of Radiology and Director of Nanomedicine (joint position); Member of the National Academy of Sciences. *Medical, Health Physics, Nano Science and Technology.* Nanomedicine.

Katti, Kattesh, Ph.D., Indian Institute of Science, Bangalore, 1984. Director, University of Missouri Cancer Nanotechnology Platform; Curator's Distinguished Professor of Radiology and Physics (joint position). *Medical, Health Physics, Nano Science and Technology.* Development of site-specific radiopharmaceuticals; chemotherapeutic agents for cancer therapy; chemical and biomedical aspects of optical materials.

Kopeikin, Sergei, Ph.D., Space Research Institute of the Russian Academy of Science, Moscow, 1986. *Astrophysics, Relativity & Gravitation.* General relativity and cosmology; theoretical and experimental gravity.

Kosztin, Ioan, Ph.D., University of Illinois at Urbana-Champaign, 1997. *Biophysics.* Theoretical and computational biological physics.

Li, Aigen, Ph.D., Leiden University, 1998. *Astronomy, Astrophysics.* Theoretical astrophysics.

Miceli, Paul, Ph.D., University of Illinois at Urbana-Champaign, 1987. Director of Graduate Studies. *Condensed Matter Physics.* Surfaces and interfaces of condensed matter investigated by X-ray and neutron scattering.

Pfeifer, Peter, Ph.D., ETH Zurich Swiss Federal Institute of Technology, 1980. Department Chair. *Condensed Matter Physics, Energy Sources & Environment.* Surface physics; fractals and quantum dynamics; porous media; energy storage.

Satpathy, Sashi, Ph.D., University of Illinois at Urbana-Champaign, 1982. *Condensed Matter Physics.* Theoretical condensed matter physics; electronic structure and magnetism in solids.

Singh, David J., Ph.D., University of Ottawa, 1985. *Computational Physics, Condensed Matter Physics, Materials Science, Metallurgy, Solid State Physics, Theoretical Physics.* Electronic structure calculations, superconductivity and spin fluctuation models, thermoelectric materials, magnetism and functional oxides.

Speck, Angela, Ph.D., University College London, 1998. Director of Astronomy. *Astronomy, Astrophysics.* Astronomy, including stellar evolution, astromineralogy, and dust around evolved stars, galactic chemical evolution, and meteoritics.

Ullrich, Carsten, Ph.D., University of Wuerzburg, 1995. *Condensed Matter Physics.* Condensed matter theory; density-functional theory.

Vignale, Giovanni, Ph.D., Northwestern University, 1984. *Condensed Matter Physics.* Condensed matter theory.

Wexler, Carlos, Ph.D., University of Washington, 1997. *Condensed Matter Physics, Energy Sources & Environment.* Condensed matter theory.

Yu, Ping, Ph.D., Hong Kong University of Science and Technology, 1998. *Biophysics, Condensed Matter Physics, Optics.* Optoelectronics and biomedical imaging.

Zou, Xiaoqin, Ph.D., University of California, San Diego, 1993. *Biophysics.* Theoretical and computational biophysics.

Associate Professor

King, Gavin, Ph.D., Harvard University, 2004. *Biophysics.* Single-molecule biophysics; atomic force microscopy.

Montfrooij, Wouter, Ph.D., University of Delft, 1990. *Condensed Matter Physics.* Phase transitions in condensed matter; neutron scattering.

Yan, Haojing, Ph.D., Arizona State University, 2003. *Astronomy, Astrophysics.* Astrophysics; early galaxy formation.

Assistant Professor

Bian, Guang, Ph.D., University of Illinois at Urbana-Champaign, 2012. *Condensed Matter Physics.* Fabrication and spectro-

scopic characterization of low-dimensional quantum systems and novel topological/functional materials.

Guo, Yicheng, Ph.D., University of Massachusetts, 2012. *Astronomy.* Galaxy formation and evolution.

Singh, Deepak, Ph.D., University of Massachusetts, Amherst, 2006. *Condensed Matter Physics.* Nanoengineered materials; geometrically frustrated magnetic materials.

Teaching Professor

Kosztin, Dorina, Ph.D., University of Illinois at Urbana-Champaign, 1998. Director of Undergraduate Studies. *Biophysics.* Theoretical biophysics.

Teaching Associate Professor

Zhang, Yun, Ph.D., University of California, San Diego, 1999. *Condensed Matter Physics.* Experimental condensed matter physics.

Teaching Assistant Professor

Bompadre, Silvia, Ph.D., University of Washington, 1998. *Biophysics.* Biological physics; transmembrane proteins.

King, Karen, Ph.D., Dartmouth College, 2003. *Biophysics, Physics and other Science Education.* Medical imaging and biomechanical modeling; physics and engineering education.

DEPARTMENTAL RESEARCH SPECIALTIES AND STAFF

Theoretical

Biophysics. Molecular modeling transport through membranes; RNA folding and assembly; computational drug design. Chen, Karen King, Ioan Kosztin, Zou.

Condensed Matter Physics. Electronic structure of materials, magnetic devices, and spintronics; quantum many-body theory; density-functional theory; transport and optical excitations in semiconductors; quantum and classical statistical mechanics; fractals and phase transitions. Pfeifer, Satpathy, David Singh, Ullrich, Vignale, Wexler.

Cosmology & String Theory. Origin and fate of the universe; gravitational radiation; post-Newtonian gravity; black holes. Kopeikin.

Experimental

Astronomy. Cosmic dust; planetary and star formation and evolution; galactic chemical evolution; origin of molecules; early galaxy formation; science of space exploration. Godwin, Guo, Li, Speck, Yan.

Biophysics. Cellular biomechanics; physical mechanisms of cell and developmental biology; organ printing and tissue engineering; single-molecule atomic force microscopy; transmembrane proteins. Bompadre, Gavin King, Yu.

Condensed Matter Physics. Organic displays and photovoltaics; Raman scattering; ZnO-based optoelectronics; dielectrics; high-pressure optical spectroscopy; magnetic fractals; quantum phase transitions; organic thin films; neutron and x-ray scattering; epitaxial growth; alternative fuel research; hydrogen storage; surface science; geometrically frustrated magnetic systems; topological materials. Bian, Chandrasekhar, Gangopadhyay, Guha, Miceli, Montfrooij, Pfeifer, Deepak Singh, Yu.

Medical, Health Physics. Nanomedicine; drug delivery; cancer research. Hawthorne, Katti.

Optics. Biomedical imaging; nonlinear optics. Chandrasekhar, Yu.

Physics and other Science Education. Writing-to-learn strategies; formative assessment tools; inquiry-based teaching methodologies. Karen King.

WASHINGTON UNIVERSITY

DEPARTMENT OF PHYSICS

St. Louis, Missouri 63130
http://physics.wustl.edu/

General University Information
Chancellor: Mark S. Wrighton, Chancellor
Dean of Graduate School: William Tate
University website: http://www.wustl.edu
School Type: Private
Setting: Suburban
Total Faculty: 3,759
Total number of Students: 14,385
Total number of Graduate Students: 7,009

Department Information
Department Chairman: Prof. Mark G. Alford, Chair
Department Contact: Sarah Akin, Administrative Assistant
   Total full-time faculty: 31
   Total number of full-time equivalent positions: 23
   Full-Time Graduate Students: 83
   Female Full-Time Graduate Students: 19
   First-Year Graduate Students: 12
   Female First-Year Students: 4
   Total Post Doctorates: 7

Department Address
1 Brookings Drive
St. Louis, MO 63130
Phone: (314) 935-6250
Fax: (314) 935-6219
E-mail: sarahj@wustl.edu
Website: http://physics.wustl.edu/

ADMISSIONS

Admission Contact Information
Address admission inquiries to: Sarah Akin, Washington University, Department of Physics, One Brookings Drive, CB 1105, St. Louis, MO 63130-4899
Phone: (314) 935-6250
E-mail: sarahj@wustl.edu
Admissions website: https://www.applyweb.com/wustl/index.ftl

Application deadlines
Fall admission:
U.S. students: December 15   *Int'l. students*: December 15

Application fee
U.S. students: $45   *Int'l. students*: $45

Admissions information
For Fall of 2018:
   Number of applicants: 97
   Number admitted: 30
   Number enrolled: 12

Admission requirements
Bachelor's degree requirements: Bachelor's degree is required.

GRE requirements
The GRE is required.
   The average GRE percentile score for those who were offered admission for 2017–18 were verbal-68%; quantitative-89%; analytic writing-41%; and physics -79%.

Subjective GRE requirements
The Subjective GRE is recommended.
   Mean Advanced GRE score range (25th–75th percentile): N/A

TOEFL requirements
The TOEFL exam is required for students from non-English-speaking countries.
   PBT score: 577
   iBT score: 90
The GRE /TOEFL Institution Code for Washington University in St. Louis Graduate School is 6929.

Other admissions information
Undergraduate preparation assumed: Mechanics: Marion, Classical Dynamics of Particles and Systems; Electromagnetic Theory: Lorrain and Corson, Electromagnetic Fields and Waves; Statistical Physics: Reif, Statistical and Thermal Physics; Quantum Mechanics: Griffiths, Introduction to Quantum Mechanics; Mathematics: through the level of Advanced Calculus and Differential Equations.

TUITION

Tuition year 2018–19:
Tuition for in-state residents
   Full-time students: annual
   Part-time students: per credit
Tuition for out-of-state residents
   Full-time students: annual
   Part-time students: per credit
   Full-time students: $52,400 annual
   Part-time students: $2,183 per credit
Credit hours per semester to be considered full-time: 9
Deferred tuition plan: No
Health insurance: Yes, $1817.5.
Other academic fees: For complete description of fees go to: https://graduateschool.wustl.edu/funding-support
Academic term: Semester
Number of first-year students who received full tuition waivers: 12

Teaching Assistants, Research Assistants, and Fellowships
Average stipend per academic year
   Fellowship student: $23,360 Students who are admitted to graduate study for the Ph.D. in Physics at Washington University generally receive a complete financial support package including a tuition scholarship that pays full tuition, together with a stipend. Such financial support is guaranteed by the department for the first five years for students who are making satisfactory progress towards the Ph.D. degree. Thus, graduate study in Physics generally does not require additional student loans, working part-time, or any other outside means of support. Washington University does not have TA's. Each graduate student is required to serve as an Assistant in Instruction for at least two semesters.

FINANCIAL AID

Loans
Loans are not available for U.S. students.
Loans are not available for international students.
GAPSFAS application required: No
FAFSA application required: No

HOUSING

Availability of on-campus housing
Single students: No
Married students: No
Childcare Assistance: Yes

For further information
Address housing inquiries to: Off-Campus Housing, Box 1016.
Phone: (314) 935-9511
E-mail: quadrangle@wustl.edu
Housing aid website: https://quadrangle.wustl.edu

Table A—Faculty, Enrollments, and Degrees Granted

Research Specialty	2017–18 Faculty	Enrollment Fall 2018 Master's	Enrollment Fall 2018 Doctorate	Number of Degrees Granted 2017–18 (2013–18) Master's	Number of Degrees Granted 2017–18 (2013–18) Terminal Master's	Number of Degrees Granted 2017–18 (2013–18) Doctorate
Astrophysics	5	–	–	–	–	2(12)
Biophysics	3	–	–	–	–	5(15)
Condensed Matter Physics	3	–	–	–	–	5(19)
High Energy Physics	1	–	–	–	–	–
Neuroscience/Neuro Physics	1	–	–	–	–	–(6)
Nuclear Physics	4	–	–	–	–	–(5)
Particles and Fields	2	–	–	–	–	4(6)
Non-specialized	–	2	12	–	–(4)	–
Total	23	–	–	–	–(4)	13(73)
Full-time Grad. Stud.	–	–	93	–	–	–
First-year Grad. Stud.	–	–	14	–	–	–

GRADUATE DEGREE REQUIREMENTS

Master's: New Masters Degree program AY 2018 36 semester hours of course credits, of which at least 30 semester hours must either be in the classroom or in seminar courses at the 400 level or higher. The student must maintain an overall grade average of B (GPA 3.0). Among the student's coursework there must be at least 12 semester-hours of the "core" courses required for Ph.D. qualification, passed with an average grade of B (GPA 3.0).

Doctorate: Students must complete 36 units of courses, maintaining an average grade of "B" (GPA 3.0), including at least 36 units of "academic credit". Once the academic credit is completed, the remaining units up to a total of 72 can include more lecture courses. Students must also pass the Ph.D. qualification procedure before they can formally join a research group; this is normally completed before the start of the third year. 18 semester-hours of core courses must be passed to qualify. There are also teaching requirements, a thesis requirement ("doctoral dissertation"), and students must pass an oral thesis defense examination.

Thesis: Thesis may be written in absentia.

FACULTY

Professor
Alford, Mark G., Ph.D., Harvard University, 1990. Department Chairman. *Nuclear Physics, Particles and Fields*. Nuclear and quark matter; neutron stars.

Buckley, James H., Ph.D., University of Chicago, 1994. *Astrophysics, Atmosphere, Space Physics, Cosmic Rays*. High-energy particle astrophysics; gamma-ray astronomy; semiconductor detector development.

Carlsson, Anders E., Ph.D., Harvard University, 1981. *Biophysics*. Generation and control of forces in cells.

Cowsik, Ramanath, Ph.D., Bombay University, 1968. Director, McDonnell Center for the Space Sciences. *Astrophysics, Particles and Fields, Relativity & Gravitation*. Astroparticle physics, cosmology, dark matter, and experimental gravitation.

Dickhoff, Willem H., Ph.D., Free University of Amsterdam, 1981. *Astrophysics, Nuclear Physics*. Nuclear reactions, nuclear structure, Rare isotopes, Nuclear and neutron matter, Superfluidity in neutron stars.

Israel, Martin H., Ph.D., California Institute of Technology, 1968. *Astrophysics*. Particle Astrophysics.

Katz, Jonathan I., Ph.D., Cornell University, 1973. *Astrophysics*. Historical Climatology and Theories of Fast Radio Bursts.

Kelton, Kenneth F., Ph.D., Harvard University, 1983. Arthur Holly Compton Professor of Arts & Sciences; Professor of Materials Science. *Condensed Matter Physics, Materials Science, Metallurgy*. Nucleation in liquids and glasses, liquid and glass structure, metallic glass formation, the connection between structure and dynamics in metallic liquids.

Krawczynski, Henric, Ph.D., Hamburg University, 1997. *Astrophysics*. Experimental and theoretical high-energy astrophysics; X-ray astronomy, general relativity, black holes, radiative transfer, X-ray polarimetry, semiconductor detector development; low-temperature detectors.

Nussinov, Zohar, Ph.D., University of California, Los Angeles, 2000. *Condensed Matter Physics*. Topological quantum order & structure of glasses.

Ogilvie, Michael C., Ph.D., Brown University, 1980. *Particles and Fields, Theoretical Physics*. Lattice gauge theory; QCD; phase transitions.

Wessel, Ralf, Ph.D., University of Cambridge, 1992. *Neuroscience/Neuro Physics*. Neural circuits dynamic and computation.

Associate Professor
Ferrer, Francesc, Ph.D., Universitat Autónoma de Barcelona, 2001. *Particles and Fields, Theoretical Physics*. Cosmology beyond the standard model.

Murch, Kater, University of California, Berkeley, 2008. *Atomic, Molecular, & Optical Physics, Condensed Matter Physics*. Conducts research at the interface of Atomic, Molecular, and Optical (AMO) and condensed matter physics. Quantum optics and atomic physics with superconducting circuits.

Seidel, Alexander, Ph.D., Massachusetts Institute of Technology, 2003. *Condensed Matter Physics*. Strongly correlated electronic systems.

Yang, Li, Ph.D., Georgia Institute of Technology, 2006. *Computational Physics, Condensed Matter Physics, Solid State Physics*. Many-electron effects, electronic and optical properties, and design of new materials for applications.

Assistant Professor
Dev, Bhupal, Ph.D., University of Maryland, 2012. *High Energy Physics*. Beyond Standard Model Physics, Astroparticle Physics and Cosmology.

Henriksen, Erik, Ph.D., Columbia University, 2008. *Condensed Matter Physics*. Graphene, atomically thin materials, quantum Hall effects, quantum spin liquids.

Mukherji, Shankar, Ph.D., Massachusetts Institute of Technology/Harvard Medical School, 2010. *Biophysics*. Systems cell biology.

Ogliore, Ryan, Ph.D., California Institute of Technology, 2007. *Astrophysics, Planetary Science*. Formation & evolution of the solar system.

Pastore, Saori, Ph.D., Old Dominion University, 2010. *Nuclear Physics*. Nuclear Structure and Reactions. Many-body nuclear theory. Electroweak decays and properties of Nuclei. Electrons and Neutrinos' Interactions with Nuclei.

Piarulli, Maria, Ph.D., Old Dominion University, 2015. *Nuclear Physics*. Nuclear interactions, Nuclear structure and reactions, Many-body nuclear theory, Electroweak properties of light nuclei, Neutron matter.

Tikhonov, Mikhail, Ph.D., Princeton University, 2014. *Biophysics, Statistical & Thermal Physics*. Microbial ecology; Quantitative evolution; Microbiome.

Research Professor

Amari, Sachiko, Ph.D., Kobe University, Kobe, Japan, 1986. *Astrophysics, Planetary Science*. Cosmochemistry.

Binns, W. Robert, Ph.D., Colorado State University, 1969. *Astrophysics, Atmosphere, Space Physics, Cosmic Rays*. Experimental measurements of the composition of cosmic ray nuclei, Production of elements and isotopes in supernova, Production of elements and isotopes in Binary Neutron Star Mergers.

Meshik, Alex P., Ph.D., Vernadsky Institute, Moscow, 1988. *Astrophysics*. Solar system origin & evolution.

Nowak, Michael A., Ph.D., Stanford Univeristy, 1992. *Astronomy*. High energy astrophysics; multi-wavelength studies of black holes, neutron stars, inter-stellar and inter-galactic media.

Research Associate Professor

Pradivtseva, Olga, Ph.D., Vernadsky Institute, Russian Academy of Sciences, 1994. *Astrophysics*. Evolution and chronology of the early solar system.

Research Assistant Professor

Bugaev, Viatcheslav, Ph.D., Altai State University, 2002. *Astrophysics, Atmosphere, Space Physics, Cosmic Rays, Particles and Fields*. Astrophysics of supernova remnants; Observation of Ultra-high-energy Cosmic Rays; Simulations for the LUX-Zeplin, a direct Dark Matter detection experiment.

Liu, Nan, Ph.D., University of Chicago, 2014. *Astrophysics, Planetary Science*. Stellar evolution and nucleosynthesis, the origin and evolution of the solar system.

Rauch, Brian, Ph.D., Washington University in St. Louis, 2008. *Astrophysics*. High-energy experimental astroparticle physics, with a particular focus in Ultra-Heavy Cosmic Ray Observations.

Senior Lecturer

Hynes, Kathryn, Ph.D., Washington University, 2010. *Astrophysics, Physics and other Science Education*.

Lecturer

Errando, Manel, Ph.D., Universitat Autonoma de Barcelona, 2009. *Astrophysics*.

DEPARTMENTAL RESEARCH SPECIALTIES AND STAFF

Theoretical

Astrophysics. Ultradense matter, neutron stars, and quark stars; superfluidity and color superconductivity in compact stars; high-energy astrophysics and astroparticle physics; black holes and their jets. Alford, Cowsik, Dickhoff, Ferrer, Katz.

Biophysics. Force generation in biological systems; self-assembly of biopolymer networks; neural networks; computational neuroscience; nonlinear dynamics. Microbial ecology; quantitative evolution; microbiome. Carlsson, Tikhonov, Wessel.

Computational Physics. Parallel computation; simulation; numerical analysis; first-principles calculations. Yang.

Condensed Matter Physics. Quantum fluids; strongly correlated electron systems; metal-insulator transitions; non-Fermi liquids; quantum criticality; superconductivity; spin systems; quantum Hall effect; one-dimensional and two-dimensional materials; soft condensed matter; magnetism; topological order; amorphous and complex ordered structures; glass transition; electronic structure; orbital order; statistical mechanics; mesoscopic physics; optimization and network problems; cold atom physics; excitonic effects. Nussinov, Seidel, Yang.

High Energy Physics. Physics beyond the standard model; dark matter cosmology. Dev, Ferrer.

Nuclear Physics. Many-body theory of nuclear matter and finite nuclei. Ultradense matter, neutron stars, and quark stars; superfluidity and color superconductivity in compact stars. Alford, Dickhoff.

Particles and Fields. Quantum chromodynamics; non-Abelian gauge theories and confinement; quark matter; color superconductivity; PT-symmetric theories; semiclassical approximations. Alford, Ogilvie.

Relativity & Gravitation. Galactic dynamics; dark matter; cosmology. Cowsik, Ferrer.

Theoretical Physics. Alford, Carlsson, Cowsik, Dev, Dickhoff, Ferrer, Katz, Krawczynski, Nussinov, Ogilvie, Seidel, Yang.

Experimental

Astrophysics. Solid state, ion microprobe, noble gas mass spectrometric, and electron microscope investigations of ancient stardust in meteorites and interplanetary dust; nucleosynthesis, stellar evolution, origin, and evolution of the solar system, including planetary atmospheres and organic molecules; early chronology from studies of (now) extinct isotopes. Binns, Buckley, Cowsik, Israel, Krawczynski, Liu, Meshik, Ogliore, Pradivtseva, Rauch.

Atmosphere, Space Physics, Cosmic Rays. Laboratory and astronomical searches for dark matter. Binns, Rauch.

Biophysics. Biophysics of neural computation; physics of single neurons; single-molecule imaging; systems cell biology. Mukherji, Wessel.

Condensed Matter Physics. Hydrogen in metals and ionic and complex solids; nucleation and phase transitions in liquid and solids; synchrotron x-ray diffraction and thermophysical property measurements of equilibrium and non-equilibrium liquids; x-ray and electron microscopy; superconductivity and magnetism under extreme pressures; high-Tc superconductivity; pressure-induced insulator-to-metal transitions; elastic and viscoelastic properties of composites; nanocrystalline materials; thin film growth and characterization; wide and narrow-gap semiconductors; extraordinary magnetoresistance; physisorbed (2D) matter; nuclear magnetic resonance; photoluminescence and photoconductivity in conducting polymers; electron microscopy and inelastic electron scattering in solids; tensile stress-dependent transport properties of narrow-gap semiconductors; 2D physics and magnetic frustration in layered double hydroxides. Henriksen, Kelton, Murch.

High Energy Physics. Cosmic-ray elemental and isotopic composition and energy spectra; gamma-ray and x-ray astrophysics of galactic and extragalactic sources; observations from spacecraft and high-altitude balloons; astrophysics of the highest-energy galactic and extragalactic gamma-ray sources; observations with ground-based atmospheric Cherenkov detectors; correlated optical observations of high-energy as-tronomical transients; observations of very-high-energy neutrinos from high-altitude balloons over Antarctica. Binns, Buckley, Israel, Krawczynski, Rauch.

Neuroscience/Neuro Physics. Neural circuits dynamic and computation. Wessel.

Planetary Science. Cosmochemistry. Liu, Ogliore.

Relativity & Gravitation. Tests of the equivalence principle; study of forces in the submillimeter domain, including Casimir forces, axion exchange, and violations of the inverse square law of gravitation. Cowsik.

View additional information about this department at www.gradschoolshopper.com. Check out the "Why Choose Us?" section, find out more about the department's culture and get links to social media networks.

MONTANA STATE UNIVERSITY

DEPARTMENT OF PHYSICS

Bozeman, Montana 59717-3840
http://www.physics.montana.edu

General University Information
President: Waded Cruzado
Dean of Graduate School: Karlene A. Hoo
University website: http://www.montana.edu
School Type: Public
Setting: Rural
Total Faculty: 1,050
Total Graduate Faculty: N/A
Total number of Students: 16,703
Total number of Graduate Students: 1,978

Department Information
Department Chairman: Prof. Yves U. Idzerda, Head
Department Contact: Margaret Jarrett, Graduate Program
  Coordinator
  Total full-time faculty: 20
  Total number of full-time equivalent positions: 46
  Full-Time Graduate Students: 70
  Female Full-Time Graduate Students: 12
  First-Year Graduate Students: 18
  Female First-Year Students: 3
  Total Post Doctorates: 4

Department Address
264 Barnard Hall
Bozeman, MT 59717-3840
Phone: (406) 994-3614 (C)
Fax: (406) 994-4452
E-mail: jarrett@montana.edu
Website: http://www.physics.montana.edu

ADMISSIONS

Admission Contact Information
Address admission inquiries to: Prof. Nicolas Yunes, Dept. of
  Physics, Montana State University, Bozeman, MT 59717
Phone: (406) 994-6182
E-mail: nicolas.yunes@montana.edu
Admissions website: http://www.physics.montana.edu

Application deadlines
Fall admission:
U.S. students: December 15   *Int'l. students*: December 15

Application fee
U.S. students: $60   *Int'l. students*: $60
New graduates are only accepted for Fall term enrollment.

Admissions information
For Fall of 2017:
  Number of applicants: 61
  Number admitted: 39
  Number enrolled: 18

Admission requirements
Bachelor's degree requirements: Four-year Bachelor's degree in
  Physics or a related field is required.
Minimum undergraduate GPA: 3.0

GRE requirements
The GRE is required.
  Quantitative score: 157
  Verbal score: 155
  Analytical score: 3.5
No minimum percentile, only raw score. See "Other admission
  information".

Subjective GRE requirements
The Subjective GRE is required.
  Minimum accepted Advanced GRE score: 570
No minimum percentile, only raw score. See "Other admissions
  information".

TOEFL requirements
The TOEFL exam is required for students from non-English-
  speaking countries.
  PBT score: 600
  iBT score: 80
Overall score of 80 on iBT-TOEFL is required of all international
  students who wish to attend MSU. A score of 26 on the speaking portion is required for teaching assistantships.

Other admissions information
Additional requirements: Successful students in our program usually have GRE scores that exceed: verbal–70%, quantitative–80%, analytical–4.0, and physics–40%.
Undergraduate preparation assumed: Marion or Symon, Classical Mechanics; Griffiths, Electricity and Magnetism; Libof
  or Gasiorowicz, Quantum Mechanics; Reif, Statistical and
  Thermal Physics.

TUITION

Tuition year 2018–19:
Tuition for in-state residents
  Full-time students: $7,150 annual
Tuition for out-of-state residents
  Full-time students: $21,000 annual
Credit hours per semester to be considered full-time: 6
Deferred tuition plan: Yes
Health insurance: Available at the cost of $3,450 per year.
Other academic fees: $460 - $900 in mandatory & incidental fees
  per academic term. Cost depends on credits being taken. Stu-
  dents must also provide their own health insurance.
Academic term: Semester
Number of first-year students who received full tuition waivers: 18

Teaching Assistants, Research Assistants, and Fellowships
Number of first-year
  Teaching Assistants: 18
Average stipend per academic year
  Teaching Assistant: $17,200
  Research Assistant: $18,000
  Fellowship student: $20,000

FINANCIAL AID

Application deadlines
Fall admission:
U.S. students: October 1
Spring admission:
U.S. students: March 1

Loans
Loans are available for U.S. students.
Loans are not available for international students.
GAPSFAS application required: No
FAFSA application required: No

For further information
Address financial aid inquiries to: Dr. Nicolas Yunes, Dept. of Physics, Montana State University, Bozeman, MT 59717.
Phone: (406) 994-6182
E-mail: nicolas.yunes@montana.edu
Financial aid website: http://www.montana.edu/wwwfa/

HOUSING

Availability of on-campus housing
Single students: Yes
Married students: Yes
Childcare Assistance: No

For further information
Address housing inquiries to: Family & Graduate Housing, 1502 W Garfield, Bozeman, MT 59717.
Phone: (406) 994-3730
E-mail: housing@montana.edu
Housing aid website: http://www.montana.edu/fgh

Table A—Faculty, Enrollments, and Degrees Granted

Research Specialty	2017–18 Faculty	Enrollment Fall 2017 Master's	Enrollment Fall 2017 Doctorate	Number of Degrees Granted 2017–18 (2013–18) Master's	Number of Degrees Granted 2017–18 (2013–18) Terminal Master's	Number of Degrees Granted 2017–18 (2013–18) Doctorate
Astronomy	1	–	–	–	–	–
Astrophysics	4	1	6	3(1)	–	–(1)
Atmosphere, Space Physics, Cosmic Rays	3	–	4	1(1)	–	–
Condensed Matter Physics	8	–	5	1(4)	1(2)	1(3)
Optics	3	5	11	1(5)	5(3)	1(4)
Physics and other Science Education	3	–	2	–(2)	–(2)	–(1)
Relativity & Gravitation	3	–	24	5(6)	1(1)	2(5)
Solar Physics	5	–	12	1(3)	–(4)	1(8)
Total	30	6	64	12(34)	7(19)	5(27)
Full-time Grad. Stud.	–	6	64	–	–	–
First-year Grad. Stud.	–	–	18	–	–	–

GRADUATE DEGREE REQUIREMENTS

Master's: Twenty credits plus a thesis or 30 credits without a thesis in an approved program with satisfactory performance are required. An M.S. examination and two semesters of residency are required. There are no language requirements.

Doctorate: A minimum of 40 credits of acceptable course work; dissertation; satisfactory performance on comprehensive and dissertation examinations, and four semesters of residency are required. There are no language requirements.

Thesis: Thesis may be written in absentia.

SPECIAL EQUIPMENT, FACILITIES, OR PROGRAMS

Optical physics and laser spectroscopy laboratories, including lasers ranging from the ultrastable (few Hz linewidths) to the ultrafast (femtosecond pulses), for research in spectral hole burning phenomena, LIDAR and LADAR, ultrafast holography, smart pixel sensors, optical frequency standards, and ultrastable optical lasers and cavities; Spectral Information Technology Laboratory (Spectrum Lab) and Optical Technology Center (OpTeC), fostering collaborations with local optics industries, and with several national and international laboratories and companies; millimeter-wave magneto-spectroscopy facility; Magnetic Nanostructure Growth and Characterization Facility for synthesis using MBE, PLD, and MoCVD and characterization of magnetic films, particles, and interfaces using X-ray synchrotron techniques; Image and Chemical Analysis Laboratory; Montana Space Grant Consortium, a statewide program for research, education, and outreach in space science; Space Science and Engineering Laboratory with facilities for the design, development, and testing of small satellite hardware and solar and space physics spaceflight instrumentation; public outreach programs in astrophysics, solar physics, and Mars exploration.

Table B—Separately Budgeted Research Expenditures by Source of Support

Source of Support	Departmental Research	Physics-related Research Outside Department
Federal government	$5,755,383	
State/local government	$325,017	
Non-profit organizations		
Business and industry	$27,500	
Other		
Total	$6,107,900	

FACULTY

Professor
Babbitt, William R., Ph.D., Harvard University, 1987. *Optics.* Applied optics.

Cone, Rufus, Ph.D., Yale University, 1971. *Condensed Matter Physics, Optics.* Quantum optics, optical materials, lasers.

Cornish, Neil, Ph.D., University of Toronto, 1996. *Cosmology & String Theory, Relativity & Gravitation, Theoretical Physics.* Modeling gravitational waves, exotic astrophysical objects.

Francis, Gregory E., Ph.D., Massachusetts Institute of Technology, 1987. *Physics and other Science Education.* Inquiry-based learning.

Idzerda, Yves, Ph.D., University of Maryland, 1986. Department Head. *Condensed Matter Physics, Nano Science and Technology, Solid State Physics, Surface Physics.* Magnetism, reduced dimensionality, x-ray synchrotron techniques with magnetic contrast.

Kankelborg, Charles, Ph.D., Stanford University, 1996. *Solar Physics.* Rocket-based EUV Snapshot Imaging Spectrograph (ESIS).

Link, Bennett, Ph.D., University of Illinois, 1991. *Astrophysics, Theoretical Physics.* Neutron stars and compact stellar objects.

Longcope, Dana, Ph.D., Cornell University, 1993. *Plasma and Fusion, Solar Physics, Theoretical Physics.* Magnetic reconnection.

Neumeier, John J., Ph.D., University of California, San Diego, 1990. *Condensed Matter Physics, Low Temperature Physics.* Thermal expansion, phase transitions.

Rebane, Aleksander, Ph.D., University of Estonia, 1985. *Optics.* Non-linear optics, two-photon processes.

Associate Professor

Qiu, Jiong, Ph.D., Nanjing University, 1998. *Solar Physics, Theoretical Physics.* Solar surface dynamics.

Vorontsov, Anton, Ph.D., Northwestern University, 2004. *Condensed Matter Physics, Low Temperature Physics, Theoretical Physics.* Superconductivity, superfluidity, magnetism.

Yunes, Nico, Ph.D., Pennsylvania State University, 2008. *Cosmology & String Theory, Relativity & Gravitation, Theoretical Physics.* Gravitational waves and quantum gravity.

Assistant Professor

Borys, Nicholas, Ph.D., University of Utah, 2011. *Condensed Matter Physics, Nano Science and Technology, Optics, Quantum Foundations.* Quantum information, 2D materials, Nanooptics.

D'Urso, Brian, Ph.D., Harvard University, 2003. *Condensed Matter Physics, Quantum Foundations, Relativity & Gravitation.* Quantum Systems, quantum coherence and gravity.

Lohfink, Anne, Ph.D., University of Maryland, 2014. *Astronomy, Astrophysics, Relativity & Gravitation.* Super-massive black holes, gravity, neutron stars.

Reines, Amy, Ph.D., University of Virginia, 2011. *Astronomy, Astrophysics, Relativity & Gravitation.* Dwarf galaxies, super-massive black holes, neutron stars.

Sample, John, Ph.D., University of California - Berkeley, 2013. *Atmosphere, Space Physics, Cosmic Rays.* Experimental atmospheric and magnetospheric physics.

Willoughby, Shannon, Ph.D., Tulane University, 2003. *Astronomy, Condensed Matter Physics, Physics and other Science Education, Theoretical Physics.* Inquiry-based learning, physics and astronomy education.

Emeritus

Hermanson, John C., Ph.D., University of Chicago, 1966. *Condensed Matter Physics, Surface Physics, Theoretical Physics.* Surface physics theory.

Kirkpatrick, Larry, Ph.D., Massachusetts Institute of Technology, 1968. *High Energy Physics, Physics and other Science Education.* Science education.

Schmidt, V. Hugo, Ph.D., University of Washington, 1961. *Condensed Matter Physics, Energy Sources & Environment.* Alternative energy.

Smith, Richard J., Ph.D., Iowa State University, 1975. *Condensed Matter Physics, Materials Science, Metallurgy, Surface Physics.* Ion beams and surface physics.

Tsuruta, Sachiko, Ph.D., Columbia University, 1964. *Astrophysics, Theoretical Physics.* Neutron stars and compact objects.

Wheeler, Gerald, Ph.D., Stony Brook University, 1972. *Nuclear Physics, Physics and other Science Education.* Experimental nuclear physics, science education.

Professor Emeritus

Carlsten, John, Ph.D., Harvard University, 1974. *Optics.* Nonlinear optics, laser spectroscopy, atomic physics.

Research Professor

Acton, Loren W., Ph.D., University of Colorado, 1965. *Solar Physics.* Satellite observations of the sun.

Avci, Recep, Ph.D., University of Illinois, 1978. Director of ICAL. *Biophysics, Condensed Matter Physics, Surface Physics.* Advanced surface and material characterization.

Canfield, Richard C., Ph.D., University of Colorado, 1968. *Solar Physics.* Satellite observations of the sun.

Klumpar, David M., Ph.D., University of New Hampshire, 1972. *Atmosphere, Space Physics, Cosmic Rays.* Experimental space physics; space instrumentation.

Research Assistant Professor

DesJardins, Angela, Ph.D., Montana State University, 2007. Director, Montana Space Grant Consortium. *Solar Physics.* space instrumentation, high altitude ballooning.

Nidever, David, Ph.D., University of Virginia, 2009. *Astronomy, Relativity & Gravitation.* Galaxy formation, star evolution.

Teaching Professor

Riedel, Carla M., Ph.D., University of Minnesota, 1996. *Nuclear Physics.* Nuclear physics.

Teaching Assistant Professor

Childs, Nicholas B., Ph.D., Montana State University, 2012. *Condensed Matter Physics, Physics and other Science Education, Surface Physics.* Physics education research, fuel cell materials.

Rugheimer, Paul P., Ph.D., University of Wisconsin - Madison, 2004. *Condensed Matter Physics, Physics and other Science Education, Surface Physics.* Thin film physics.

DEPARTMENTAL RESEARCH SPECIALTIES AND STAFF

Theoretical

Astronomy. Galaxy Formation. Nidever.

Astrophysics. Neutron stars; active galactic nuclei; super massive black holes; gamma-ray bursters. Link, Lohfink, Reines, Riedel, Tsuruta.

Condensed Matter Physics. Correlated many-body (collective) effects such as superconductivity and superfluidity; influence of magnetic fields, impurities, and fluctuations on superconducting properties. Vorontsov.

Physics and other Science Education. Developing and implementing innovative programs for primary and secondary teacher education; developing techniques in education of non-science majors. Francis, Willoughby.

Relativity & Gravitation. Gravitational waves; black holes; quantum theory of gravity; early universe; experimental relativity. Cornish, Wheeler, Yunes.

Experimental

Atmosphere, Space Physics, Cosmic Rays. Space instrumentation, including ultraviolet optics, to investigate the high-speed dynamics of magnetic reconnection in solar flares; solar magnetic activity; auroral physics; magnetospheric physics; development of space technologies and small satellites; heliophysics. Acton, Canfield, DesJardins, Kankelborg, Klumpar, Longcope, Qiu, Sample.

Atomic, Molecular, & Optical Physics. Linear and nonlinear optical laser spectroscopy; coherent optical transients; optical hole burning; Raman scattering; solid-state laser material. Babbitt, Cone, Rebane.

Condensed Matter Physics. Measurements of physical properties to temperatures as low as 0.3 K; measurements of thermal expansion using a novel dilatometer capable of detecting subangstrom length changes of specimens to study phase transitions and critical phenomena; characterization of magnetic thin films, nanoparticles, and buried interfaces for spin-transport devices; X-ray absorption spectroscopy, magnetic circular dichroism, X-ray resonant magnetic scattering; ceramics for fuel cells fabricated and tested for their electrical properties; characterization of defects in advanced materials at the atomic level using EPR, ENDOR, and optical spectroscopy. Avci, Borys, Childs, Cone, D'Urso, Idzerda, Neumeier, Rugheimer, Schmidt.

Solar Physics. Acton, Canfield, DesJardins, Kankelborg, Longcope, Qiu, Sample.

MONTANA TECHNOLOGICAL UNIVERSITY

GEOSCIENCES AND ENGINEERING

Butte, Montana 59701

http://www.mtech.edu/academics/gradschool/

General University Information
Chancellor: Donald M. Blackketter
Dean of Graduate School: Beverly K. Hartline
University website: http://www.mtech.edu/
School Type: Public
Setting: Urban
Total Faculty: 217
Total Graduate Faculty: 102
Total number of Students: 2,978
Total number of Graduate Students: 242

Department Information
Department Chairman: Dr. Beverly K. Hartline, Dean
Department Contact: Beverly Hartline, Dean
  Total full-time faculty: 58
  Total number of full-time equivalent positions: 62
  Full-Time Graduate Students: 98
  Female Full-Time Graduate Students: 0
  First-Year Graduate Students: 42
  Female First-Year Students: 19
  Total Post Doctorates: 2

ADMISSIONS

Admission Contact Information
Address admission inquiries to: 1300 West Park Street Box 20, MG207, Butte, MT 59701-8997
Phone: (406) 496-4304
E-mail: gradschool@mtech.edu
Admissions website: http://www.mtech.edu/academics/gradschool/apply/

Application deadlines
Fall admission:
U.S. students: April 1   *Int'l. students*: March 1
Spring admission:
U.S. students: October 1   *Int'l. students*: September 1

Application fee
U.S. students: $50   *Int'l. students*: $50
These are priority admissions deadlines. Applications will be accepted after these dates and considered for admission, on a space-available basis.

Admissions information
For Fall of 2018:
  Number of applicants: 115
  Number admitted: 69
  Number enrolled: 62

Admission requirements
Bachelor's degree requirements: Bachelor's or International equivalent required with a GPA of at least 3.0. For some programs students with an undergraduate GPA between 2.75 and 3.0 can be admitted provisionally, and students with an undergraduate GPA between 2.5 and 2.75 can be admitted provisionally on probation.
Minimum undergraduate GPA: 3.0

GRE requirements
The GRE is required.
  General Test Scores are required for the following programs:
- Electrical Engineering

- Materials Science Ph.D. and Master's degree programs in:
- Environmental Engineering
- Metallurgical/Mineral Processing
- Geoscience
- Geochemistry
- Geology
- Geological Engineering
- Geophysical Engineering
- Hydrogeology
- Hydrogeological Engineering
- General Engineering GRE scores are considered in combination with other application materials. There is no minimum score. Most admitted students have scores above 140 V and 150 Q.

Subjective GRE requirements
The Subjective GRE is not required.

TOEFL requirements
The TOEFL exam is required for students from non-English-speaking countries.
  PBT score: 547
  iBT score: 78
A minimum IELTS Academic score of 6.5 is also acceptable. International students who have done undergraduate or graduate coursework at a US, Canadian, or UK university do not need to provide TOEFL or IELTS scores.

Other admissions information
Additional requirements: Petroleum Engineering requires two writing samples in English on a technical topic. International applicants must provide a course-by-course transcript evaluation by WES or ECE.
Undergraduate preparation assumed: Bachelor's degree applicable to the specific graduate degree specialty of interest.

TUITION

Tuition year 2017–18:
Tuition for in-state residents
  Full-time students: $3,017.08 per semester
  Part-time students: $395.6 per credit
Tuition for out-of-state residents
  Full-time students: $9,710.83 per semester
  Part-time students: $1,139.35 per credit
Semester tuition is capped at the amount for 12 credits. Mandatory fees are an additional ~$80 per credit hour. Montana Tech is part of the Western Regional Graduate Programs agreement, where students from other WRGP states qualify for in-state tuition if pursuing MS degrees in Metallurgy, Geosciences, or Technical Communication.
Credit hours per semester to be considered full-time: 9
Deferred tuition plan: Yes
Health insurance: Available at the cost of $3,400 per year.
Other academic fees: Books, supplies, building fees, insurance, laboratory fees. Health insurance is required of students enrolled in 7 credits or more. If students do not have other coverage and opt out, the cost through the university is $1,474 per semester.
Academic term: Semester
Number of first-year students who received full tuition waivers: 25
Number of first-year students who received partial tuition waivers: 12

Teaching Assistants, Research Assistants, and Fellowships

Number of first-year
   Teaching Assistants: 23
   Research Assistants: 9
   Fellowship students: 1
Average stipend per academic year
   Teaching Assistant: $10,000
   Research Assistant: $10,800
   Fellowship student: $10,000
GTA and GRA are competitively available. Montana Tech is a member of the Sloan Indigenous Graduate Partnership, which provides fellowship and other support for qualified students.

FINANCIAL AID

Application deadlines
Fall admission:
U.S. students: March 1   *Int'l. students*: March 1
Spring admission:
U.S. students: October 15   *Int'l. students*: October 15

Loans
Loans are available for U.S. students.
Loans are not available for international students.
GAPSFAS application required: No
FAFSA application required: Yes

For further information
Address financial aid inquiries to: Shauna Savage, Financial Aid Supervisor, 1300 West Park St, Butte, MT 59701.
Phone: (406) 496-4223
E-mail: financialaid@mtech.edu
Financial aid website: https://www.mtech.edu/financial-aid/

HOUSING

Availability of on-campus housing
Single students: Yes
Married students: Yes
Childcare Assistance: No

For further information
Address housing inquiries to: Annie Telling, Housing Office, 1300 West Park Street, Butte, MT 59701.
Phone: (406) 496-4425
E-mail: atelling@mtech.edu
Housing aid website: https://www.mtech.edu/student-life/housing/

Table A—Faculty, Enrollments, and Degrees Granted

Research Specialty	2017–18 Faculty	Enrollment Fall 2017 Master's	Enrollment Fall 2017 Doctorate	Number of Degrees Granted 2017–18 Master's	Number of Degrees Granted 2017–18 Terminal Master's	Number of Degrees Granted 2017–18 Doctorate
Electrical Engineering	5	6	–	4	–	–
Engineering, Biomaterials, Nanotechnology	12	–	17	–	–	–
Geology/Geochemistry	7	27	–	16	–	–
Geophysics	5	7	–	4	–	–
Mechanical/ Environmental/Civil/ Mining/Petroleum	29	43	–	24	–	–
Metallurgy	12	8	–	6	–	3
Total	**58**	**91**	**17**	**54**	**–**	**–**
Full-time Grad. Stud.	–	85	17	–	–	–
First-year Grad. Stud.	–	41	6	–	–	–

GRADUATE DEGREE REQUIREMENTS

Master's: Thirty to 37 semester credits, including a 1-credit technical seminar and a 1-credit writing seminar. Thesis (30-31 credit) and non-thesis (36-37 credit) options.

Doctorate: Collaborative Materials Science program with University of Montana and Montana State University. Sixty semester credits at least 18 for dissertation and at least 32 for course work. Twenty credit core first-year curriculum. Qualifying exam, candidacy exam dissertation, and dissertation defense.

Other Degrees: Master's programs have thesis and non-thesis options. A thesis can be accomplished by preparing paper for publication in a peer-reviewed journal.

Thesis: Thesis must conform to a standard format. All theses are submitted electronically and archived by ProQuest.

SPECIAL EQUIPMENT, FACILITIES, OR PROGRAMS

Montana Tech has a 22-node high performance computing (HPC) cluster for faculty and student research and teaching use. The system includes 352 CPU cores or 704 threads. Two of the nodes include three NVIDIA Tesla K20 graphical processing units (GPU), which adds 7488 CUDA cores on each node for additional processing power. A total of 91 TB storage space is available for storing large data sets and simulation results. A full-time HPC Application Scientist is available to help new users get setup on the system and assist them in their computational research. The HPC system is remotely accessible and available to all MUS faculty and students. The system is being used for a variety of projects from computational material science modeling at the atomic level, DNA sequence comparison and analysis of bacterias to grizzly bear population modeling in the greater Glacier National Park area. Software packages that are available for research and student use include COMSOL, Matlab, LAMMPS, BLAST+, R and Tensorflow.

Montana Tech also has two 3D data visualization systems with a variety of visualization software packages. Both 3D visualization systems use stereo projection, shutter glasses, and a tracking system to enable a researcher to directly interact with the 3D imagery. Some of the available software includes Arc Scene for GIS data, LidarViewer, Google Earth, VisIt, and VMD for molecular dynamics data.

Montana Tech also has two 3D data visualization systems with a variety of visualization software packages. Both 3D visualization systems use stereo projection, shutter glasses, and a tracking system to enable a researcher to directly interact with the 3D imagery. Some of the available software includes Arc Scene for GIS data, LidarViewer, Google Earth, VisIt, and VMD for molecular dynamics data.

MBMG includes the Ground Water Information Center (GWIC), the Ground Water Assessment Program GWAP), and the Ground Water Investigation Program (GWIP), the Montana Earthquake Office, geological mapping, and performs other studies that produce and make available extensive information on mineral, water, and geological resources throughout Montana. The MBMG sponsors several M.S. thesis projects in these areas. The Geographic Information Systems (GIS) laboratory is fully equipped to produce and analyze digital maps and other spatial data, particularly geologic, and hydrogeologic maps. MBMG's Analytical Laboratory is licensed by the state of Montana to analyze public water supplies and it has a QA/QC program meeting the criteria established by the U.S. Environmental Protection Agency (EPA) and the U.S. Geological Survey (USGS). Available instrumentation includes the following major instruments.

- Thermo ICAP inductively coupled argon plasma emission spectrophotometer (ICAPES)

- Thermo X-series® Inductively Coupled Plasma/Mass Spectrometer (ICP/MS) for trace-metal determination

- Dionex ion chromatographs for anion determination

- Agilent gas chromatograph with mass spectrometer detector (GS/MS) for organic compounds,

- Agilent gas chromatograph with electron capture detector (ECD) to measure low level pesticide and chlorinated compounds in water and soil

- ELISA testing in magnetic particle and 96 well plate formats for determining endocrine disrupting compounds in surface and ground waters

- Beckman scintillation counter for determination of radon in water

- Picarro water isotope analyzer

- Picarro carbon isotope analyzer

The Center for Advanced Mineral, Metallurgical, and Materials Processing (CAMP) is the campus center of research excellence in materials science and engineering. Co-located with the Metallurgical and Materials Engineering (M&ME) department and the Materials Ph.D. program with extensive laboratory facilities and equipment related to mineral, materials, and metallurgical processing, characterization, and testing are available, along with a faculty/student machine shop.

The facilities include a Thermal Processing Area, housing a pilot plant roaster; a Roasting/Calcining Lab with induction, box, and kiln furnaces; the Materials Manufacturing Laboratory with a freeform fabricator, two types of porosimeters, and an autoclave, as well as sample-preparation and wet-chemistry equipment. A nearby lab houses a ThermoFisher ICAP6000 inductive coupled plasma (ICP) spectrometer, an ion chromatograph and an Agilent 300A Micro Gas Chromatograph. The Separations/Recycling Laboratory includes various chemical, density, electrostatic, hydrophobic, magnetic, and particle-size separators. The Comminution Labor contains equipment, such as crushers, grinding mills, pulverizers, splitters, and sieves. The Physical Metallurgy Laboratory houses a cold pressure roll and vacuum furnace. Metallographic Laboratory 1 houses samples, microscopes, and sample-preparation equipment, as well as a macro-hardness tester. Metallographic Laboratory 2 includes manual polishing wheels, submerged cut-off and diamond-blade saws. Metallographic Laboratory 3 contains automatic polishing equipment, as well as sample preparation benches. The Microhardness Laboratory houses three microhardness testers and a Neophot21. The Imaging Laboratory houses a computer-aided optical microscope and a tabletop imaging SEM. The X-ray Laboratory has an X-ray diffraction (XRD) instrument and a Bruker A20A4 X-ray fluorescence (XRF) spectrometer. The Scanning Electron Microscopy (SEM) Laboratory houses two instruments: a Leo 1430VP SEM with two energy-dispersive X-ray analyzers (SEM/EDX) for mineral liberation analysis (MLA), and a Hitachi high voltage SEM. A TESCAN MIRA3 GMU variable pressure Schottky field emission scanning electron microscope (FE-SEM) will be online Fall 2017. In a nearby darkroom is a Renishaw Raman microscope/spectrometer equipped with four laser wavelengths for chemistry, materials, metallurgical, geological, and other applications.

Additional capability includes Materials Thermochemistry, Environmental Hydrometallurgy, and the Corrosion research capability, collectively housing a Carbon/Sulfur analyzer, a TA Instruments Q5000 ThermoGravimetric Analyzer (TGA), a Netsch DIL 402C dilatometer, a TA Instruments Q800 dynamic mechanical analyzer (DMA), a scanning calorimeter, several furnac-

es—for characterizing various types of materials, water purification systems, drying ovens, weighing scales, potentiostats, galvanostats, plating equipment, and electrochemical cells.

Geological Engineering – has a Geomechanics Laboratory equipped with a $1-million 330,000-lb load frame with the capacity to test specimens under confinement pressure up to 20,000 psi and at temperatures up to 100 degrees C. The Laboratory also has a recently upgraded servo-controlled direct-shear apparatus and superfine surface grinding and polishing equipment for rapidly preparing specimens polished thin sections and slabs of geological and other materials for examination by transmitted and reflected light microscopy and/or scanning electron microscopy. A 1-ton capacity shake table is being acquired and installed during 2014–15. The new Underground Mine Education Center (UMEC) on located campus and is available for underground studies, for example, for research in drilling, blasting, equipment, rock mechanics, ventilation, instrumentation, communication, real-time underground monitoring, and automation.

Environmental Engineering – Houses a Metal-Contamination Research Laboratory with instruments for analyzing and detecting trace amounts of mercury and other toxic heavy metals. The suite of equipment includes a Thermo inductively coupled argon plasma emission spectrometer (iCAPES), four different types of mercury analyzers, and a Leica microscope with imaging software to take pictures of mercury-contaminated specimens. The fully equipped sample preparation laboratory includes a microwave digester to prepare samples for the iCAPES. The laboratory benefits from co-ownership of the patent on a metal nanoparticle filter capable of removing trace metals from air and water.

General Engineering – Has several labs with devices to test and characterize asphalt, concrete, soil, timber, metals, composites, and ceramics. Research on nanomaterials, fluids, and energy conversion is also done. The Nanonics Near-Field Scanning Optical Microscope (NSOM) with Atomic Resolution Microscope, along with nanofiber-pulling equipment allows research on functionalizing nanomaterials. Equipment for materials testing includes standard machines for tensile/compression, impact/toughness, three-point bending, hardness, and fatigue testing. The testing devices include a full range of systems for analysis of materials of many different descriptions. Characterization equipment for nondestructive evaluation includes dye-penetrant, magnetic-particle, eddy-current, ultrasonic, and radiographic testing, as well as optical microscopes, a probe station, and soil analysis equipment. There is also a range of manufacturing equipment in both subtractive (milling, lathe, and cutting equipment) and additive (welding, arc, laser, friction, stir, and 3D printing) forms. The standard range of specialized software is available, including Auto-CAD, Solidworks, Civil3D, MATLAB, MathCAD, Octave, and COMSOL.

Geophysical Engineering facilities include a tank for developing small-scale models of soil structures, three field vehicles (including trucks and an ATV), and a full complement of seismic, magnetic, electric, and gravitational geophysics equipment to make field measurements. Equipment includes EM-31 and EM-34 devices (two of each) to actively image variations in subterranean electrical conductivity, as well as a GDP-32 multipurpose meter. Two IRIS resistivity meters and proton precession total field magnetometers with 1 nT and 10 nT sensitivity, round out the complement of electrical and magnetic measurement equipment.

The department also owns one Worden and two Lacost-Romberg gravimeters with 0.1 mGal sensitivity, for measuring density variations. Two vehicle-mounted accelerated weight drop machines (500 pound and 100 pound) and a 120-channel 24-bit digital recording system are used with a 96-geophone array to measure seismic activity. Also available is a Mala ground-penetrating radar system. All of the above equipment is fully complemented with modern software to interpret, process, and image the measurements. These software packages include:

- Seismic
  o Landmark Graphics Corporation ProMax seismic processing/interpretation software
  o Kingdom Suite seismic interpretation software
  o OpendeTect seismic interpretation software
  o Vista seismic processing software
  o SPW seismic processing software
  o Rayfract refraction tomography software
  o IXRefraX layered/GRM refraction software
  o IXSEG2SEGY seismic utility software
  o Hampson-Russel AVO and modeling software
  o jTIPS well log modeling software
  o MESA Expert seismic survey design software
  o Surfseis surface wave analysis software
  o Petrel reservoir and seismic modeling software

Table B—Separately Budgeted Research Expenditures by Source of Support

Source of Support	Departmental Research	Physics-related Research Outside Department
Federal government	$5,019	
State/local government	$6,045	
Non-profit organizations		
Business and industry	$346	
Other	$1,649	
Total	**$13,059**	

Table C—Separately Budgeted Research Expenditures by Research Specialty

Research Specialty	No. of Grants	Expenditures ($)
Electrical Engineering	6	$717,000
Geology/Geochemistry	11	$249,000
Environmental	3	$38,000
Mechanical/NanoEngineering	4	$1,310,000
Total	**24**	**$2,314,000**

FACULTY

Professor

Cameron, Douglas, Ph.D., University of California at Los Angeles, 1979. *Geology/Geochemistry*. Geochemistry.

Downey, Jerome P., Ph.D., Colorado School of Mines, 1991. Program Director of Materials Science Ph.D. at Montana Tech. *Materials Science, Metallurgy*. Materials science and metallurgical engineering. High temperature process research; energy and environmental considerations; recycling; hydrometallurgy; pyrometallurgy; corrosion; wastewater treatment.

Gammons, Christopher, Ph.D., Penn State University, 1988. *Geology/Geochemistry*. Aqueous geochemistry at high and low temperatures, economic geology, acid mine drainage, stable isotopes.

Ganesan, Kumar, Ph.D., Washington State University Pullman. *Other*. Inventory of mercury from historic mining and its impact on soil and watersheds in Montana. Director of EPA-EPSCoR funded research activities in Montana. Evaluating

Montana coal for removing toxic metals from acid rock drains. Funded by DOE/EPSCoR. Southridge, SC. Field Evaluation of Montana coal for removing cadmium, zinc and iron from active acid mine drainage. Funded by DOE/EPSCoR.

Girard, Jim, Ph.D., University of Montana. *Geophysics*. Geophysical engineering.

Huang, Hsin-Hsiung, Ph.D., Stanford University. *Materials Science, Metallurgy*. Theory and thermo geosciences.

MacLaughlin, Mary, Ph.D., UC Berkeley, 1997. *Geology/Geochemistry*. Geological engineering.

Madigan, Bruce, Ph.D., Colorado School Of Mines, 1994. Welding process and procedure. Welding Metallurgy, Nondestructive process and procedure.

Morrison, John, Ph.D., University of Idaho. *Electrical Engineering*. Electrical engineering.

Speece, Marvin, Ph.D., The University of Wyoming, 1992. Department Chair of Geophysical Engineering. *Geophysics*. Geophysical engineering. Hydrogeophysics: groundwater & pollutant tracking. Antarctic tectonics and climate.

Trudnowski, Daniel J., Ph.D., Montana State University, 1991. Department Head. *Electrical Engineering, Energy Sources & Environment*. Electrical engineering: control systems; power system modeling, analysis, and stability; signal processing.

White, Ronald, Ph.D., University of Wisonsin, Madison, 1968. Director, Center for Advanced Mineral and Metallurgical Processing (CAMP). *Materials Science, Metallurgy*. Research focused on the development of CAMP into an internationally recognized Center of Excellence in materials science and engineering involving faculty and students from a wide variety of scientific and engineering disciplines.

Wolfgram, Diane, Ph.D., UC Berkeley, 1977. *Geology/Geochemistry*. Geological engineering/geology.

Young, Courtney, Ph.D., University of Utah, 1995. Department chair. *Materials Science, Metallurgy*. Materials science, metallurgical engineering. Extractive metallurgy. Surface Chemistry, Electrochemistry & Spectroscopy; Mineral Processing/Extractive Metallurgical Engineering; Mineral Characterization; Flotation; Physical Separations; Leaching; Cyanide; Uranium; Gold Processing; Absorption & Applications thereof to Recycling and Waste-Water Remediation.

Associate Professor

Camm, Thomas, Ph.D., University of Idaho. Mine management and leadership, mine safety and health, integrating benefit/cost analysis with engineering design, mineral economics and mine evaluation.

Donnelly, Matthew, Ph.D., Montana State University. *Electrical Engineering*. electrical engineering, power grid stability and control, integration of renewable energy sources, energy policy.

Gleason, William, Ph.D., University of Montana/Montana Tech, 2006. *Materials Science, Metallurgy*. Materials science and metallurgical engineering.

Hailer, Katie, Ph.D., University of Montana, 2006. *Geology/Geochemistry*. Geochemistry.

Hoffman, Todd, Ph.D., Stanford University. His research involves improved recovery for conventional and unconventional oil reservoirs, fracture reservoir modeling and ensuring data consistency while history matching.

Kukay, Brian, Ph.D., Utah State University, 2008. *Energy Sources & Environment*. Our team's research interests focus on the inspection, testing, and monitoring of buildings and bridges. More specifically, novel applications and inspection techniques are explored through a combination of experiments, models, and engineering calculations. When successful, an inspector or engineer can more readily answer the following question, "Should a damaged component be repaired, replaced, or can it remain as is?".

Moon, Thomas, Ph.D., University of Washington. *Electrical Engineering*. Electrical engineering and geophysical engineering.

Shaw, Glenn, Ph.D., UC Merced School of Engineering, 2000. *Geology/Geochemistry*. Hydrogeology; groundwater-surface water interactions; contaminant transport; geochemical tracers in groundwater and surface water.

Skinner, Jack, Ph.D., University of California Davis, 2007. *Materials Science, Metallurgy, Other*. Energy systems; microscale and nanoscale theory and design; microfabrication and nanofabrication; advanced materials; plasmonics; device characterization; integration of microscale and nanoscale technologies.

Smith, Larry, Ph.D., University of New Mexico, 1988. *Geology/Geochemistry*. Stratigraphy, sedimentology, Quaternary geology, subsurface and surface geologic mapping, and petroleum geology.

Sudhakar, K V., Ph.D., Indian Institute of Science, 1997. *Materials Science, Metallurgy*. Materials science; metallurgical engineering.

Zhou, Xiaobing, Ph.D., Universtiy of Alaska Fairbanks. *Geophysics*. Geophysical engineering.

Assistant Professor

Cox, Alysia, Ph.D., Massachusetts Institute of Technology. *Geology/Geochemistry*. Proteins, Genome products of microbes and their interaction.

Das, Avimanyu, Ph.D., University of Utah, 1994. Mineral Processing and Extractive Metallurgy. Flowsheet development, Process modelling, Statistical Analysis and Optimization, Slag remediation. Fluid-particle interaction, Metallurgical and mineral waste treatment, Coal preparation, Physical separation, Hydrometallurgical treatment, Comminution and Gravity concentration, Particulate system characterization, processing and design. Transport phenomena in metallurgy; High temperature processing; Recycling, remediation and waste utilization.

Hill, Bryce, Ph.D., University of Utah, 2011. *Electrical Engineering*. Electrical engineering.

Jiang, Daqian, Ph.D., University of Connecticut, 2010. Position: 2017-present, Assistant professor, Environmental Engineering Dept., Montana Tech. Interest: Bio-electrochemical water treatment processes Life cycle analysis Macroscopic material flow analysis.

Khalil, Mohamed, Ph.D., Justus Liebig University, 2002. Six years post-doctoral scholarship at the center of geophysics, Faculty of Science, Lisbon University, Portugal. Application of Resistivity and Electromagnetic methods for environmental, engineering, and groundwater investigations.

Miah, Khalid, Ph.D., University of Texas, Austin, 2009. *Geophysics*. Active research interests include seismic signal processing, numerical modeling, and tomography. Developing distributed acoustic sensing tools and related methodologies using fiber optic technology is an area of recent interest. I am actively seeking collaboration and/or partnership with industries and research organizations (university, government, and non-profit) for oil and gas exploration; minerals exploration and mine safety; geothermal energy; CO2 capture and sequestration (CCS); and impact assessment of various human activities from natural resource exploration projects.

Nagisetty, Raja, Ph.D., University of Louisville, 2009. Surface water quality, surface and ground water interactions and stream restoration Short statement of research interests: My primary research interests are to assess the water quality impairments and design various best management practices to effectively process pollutants for various streams and watersheds. Specifically, I am interested in assessing fate and transport of nutrients pre- and post-stream restoration.

Pramanilk, Brahmananda, Ph.D., University of Mississippi, 2013. Developing test methodologies and evaluating new technologies. Creating new physical models and measurement techniques. Designing experiments, acquiring data, analyzing results, and communicating findings. Experimental and computational solid mechanics and impact dynamics. Dynamic Mechanical Analysis and fractured surface microscopy. High-speed digital stereo imaging and projection Moiré..

Prieto, Dario, Ph.D., Northwestern University, 2013. Materials science, Surface science. Synthesis-structure-function relations, composite materials, surface chemistry, adsorption and catalysis, mine waste valorization, and engineering education.

Richards, Lee, Ph.D., Montana State University, 2006. Drilling. Drilling fluids. Well control. Mobile drilling rigs. Environmental Interactions within the oil field. Microbial interactions and growth in drilling fluids.

Roos, Chris, M.S., Montana Tech. Mining safety advancement. International mining improvements.

Rosenthal, Scott, Other, Colorado School of Mines. Department Chair, Mining Engineering. Rock fragmentation, underground mine access design; mine operations costing; equipment selection, operation, and cost modeling.

Schrader, Susan, Ph.D., New Mexico Institute of Mining and Technology. Proppant conductivity modeling Improvements in the in-situ combustion processes Navier Stokes equations Knowledge engineering Applications of soft computing to petroleum engineering Numerical analysis as applied to simulation Climate change modeling.

Todd, Burt, Ph.D., University of Kansas, 1990. Department Head. *Energy Sources & Environment*. - Reservoir simulation of unconventional reservoirs. - Production engineering, especially related to gas wells and liquid loading. Short statement of research interests: I am interested in any research opportunities that will aid Montana Oil and gas producers. The primary focus, therefore, is Enhanced Oil Recovery in the Bakken shale of the Williston Basin. However, I am also interested in multiphase flow in pipes, and liquid removal from producing gas wells.

Yang, Xufei, Ph.D., Tsinghua University. Air Diffusion Modeling, Risk Analysis and Toxicology, and Environmental Process Engineering. He also manages the Air Quality Research Lab and is actively exploring research opportunities in relation to aerosols, air quality and climate change.

Zodrow, Katherine, Ph.D., Yale, 2014. Water treatment. Her research focuses on developing new water treatment membrane materials and coatings, characterizing interactions between bacteria and water treatment systems, and developing processes for industrial water and wastewater treatment.

Instructor

Getty, John, M.S., Montana State University, 2008. *Geophysics*. Fracture stimulation is one of two technologies that have enabled oil and gas production from formations that previously were thought to be not economically producible. Proppants play a critical role in holding open the induced fractures. But their job is a tough one. High closures stresses, high temperature, and high fluid flow rates all conspire to create an erosive and destructive environment. Our laboratory, and the students employed there, study the performance of existing and novel materials with the goal of improving their long-term performance.

Wold, Josh, M.S., Montana Tech. *Electrical Engineering*. Battery Test Systems.

DEPARTMENTAL RESEARCH SPECIALTIES AND STAFF

Theoretical

Materials Science, Metallurgy. Extractive metallurgy, mineral processing, materials for energy storage conservation and conversion, materials synthesis processing and fabrication, bio-inspired materials, biomimetic materials, nano-materials, plasmonics, materials failure analysis, numerical modelling, hydro- and pyro-metallurgy, flotation, lunar materials synthesates. Cameron, Downey, Gleason, Hailer, Huang, Kukay, MacLaughlin, Prieto, Skinner, Sudhakar, Young.

Experimental

Electrical Engineering. Signals and systems, controls, and electrical power systems; development of a battery diagnostic instrumentation system for NASA for next-generation hybrid an electric vehicles; development of blade pitching control algorithms to improve the efficiency of wind turbines; researching new control schemes for improving and performance and preventing blackouts in large power grids; designing and implementing an instrumentation and control system for mine waste remediation. Donnelly, Hill, Miah, Moon, Morrison, Trudnowski, Wold.

Environmental Engineering. Air, water quality, and pollution control; hazardous waste minimization, treatment, and control; waste cleanup; water chemistry of heavy metals, and hazardous organics; ground and surface water modeling; air emission inventories; biosorption of heavy metals; wetland research, land reclamation, atmospheric diffusion processes; cleanup of "RCRA" and "super-fund" sites. Ganesan, Nagisetty.

General Engineering. Civil Engineering (structural engineering, geotechnical, and water hydraulics and hydrology fields); Mechanical Engineering (mechanical power and machines, energy studies, and concurrent engineering); Welding Engineering (advanced studies of welding processes, automated manufacturing, welded design, welding metallurgy and nondestructive evaluation). Kukay, Madigan, Pramanilk, Skinner.

Geochemistry. Determination of the thermodynamic properties or minerals; determination of the migration of pollutant species within a soil or hydrologic environment; geobotanical/ biogeochemical search for ore deposits. Cameron, Cox, Gammons, Hailer, Zodrow.

Geological Engineering. Environmental impacts for construction; resource development; industrial projects. Gammons, MacLaughlin, Shaw, Wolfgram, Zodrow.

Geology. Origin of hydrothermal talc mineralization in SW Montana; water-rock interaction and acid mine drainage in Butte; bio-geochemistry of natural wetlands near abandoned mines. Cox, Gammons, Shaw, Zodrow.

Geophysical Engineering. Oil reservoir characterization; seismic processing/interpretation; electrical resistivity studies; neural network analysis/application; remote sensing analysis; ground penetrating radar studies; shallow seismic investigations; application of artificial neural networks; Antarctic history; gravity and magnetic studies. Unexploded ordinance discrimination and characterization; geothermal characterization; finite element/finite difference modeling; carbon sequestration; groundwater investigations. Girard, Miah, Moon, Speece, Zhou.

Hydrogeological Engineering. Environmental problems; resource supply problems; issues associated with mining or agricultural activities; research participation with the Montana Bureau of Mines and Geology. Gammons, Shaw, Wolfgram, Zodrow.

Materials Science & Engineering. Energy materials, metallurgy biomaterials, materials synthesis, processing, characterization, and fabrication. Includes nanoscience and nanotechnology. Das, Downey, Ganesan, Gleason, MacLaughlin, Prieto, Skinner, Sudhakar, Young.

Metallurgical / Mineral Processing. Dual ecosystem enhancement by slag remediation of acid-rick drainage; impregnation activated carbon for extracting gold from thiosulfate solutions; electroless plating of platinum for fuel-cell development; arsenic removal by modified ferrihydrite precipitation; simultaneous ferrous oxidation/copper reduction in membrane systems); alkaline sulfide leaching of gold; selenium and thallium removal by zero valence iron; characterization of powder prints for fuel cells and nanopolysilicon power formation. Das, Downey, Gleason, Huang, Madigan, Pramanilk, Prieto, Sudhakar, Young.

Mining Engineering. Mechanics of geologic materials; blasting; materials handling; mine valuation; ventilation; geostatistics; mine design; mine safety; environmental management and design of of mines. Camm, Roos, Rosenthal.

Petroleum Engineering. Advanced levels of reservoir engineering (all aspects of modeling the reservoir, studying fluid movement, and maximizing oil and gas recovery); drilling engineering (all aspects of wellbore drilling, casing design and cementing, and well completion); production engineering (removing crude oil, gas, and water form the reservoir to the surface and separating and treating each fluid). Hoffman, Prieto, Schrader, Todd, Yang, Zodrow.

View additional information about this department at www.gradschoolshopper.com. Check out the "Why Choose Us?" section, find out more about the department's culture and get links to social media networks.

MONTANA UNIVERSITY SYSTEM

MATERIALS SCIENCE PHD PROGRAM

Butte, Montana 59701
http://www.mtmatsci.org

General University Information
President: Montana University System
Dean of Graduate School: Beverly Hartline, Karlene Hoo, and Scott Whittenberg
University website: http://www.mtmatsci.org
School Type: Public
Setting: Suburban
Total Faculty: 3,000
Total Graduate Faculty: 1,500
Total number of Students: 30,000
Total number of Graduate Students: 4,000

Department Information
Department Chairman: Dr. Robert Walker, Chair
Department Contact: Dr. Jerome Downey, Program Director & Admissions Chair
Total full-time faculty: 47
Total number of full-time equivalent positions: 15
Full-Time Graduate Students: 46
Female Full-Time Graduate Students: 15
First-Year Graduate Students: 10
Female First-Year Students: 3
Total Post Doctorates: 2

Department Address
1300 West Park Street
Butte, MT 59701
Phone: (406) 496-4578
Fax: (406) 496-4664
E-mail: jdowney@mtech.edu
Website: http://www.mtmatsci.org

ADMISSIONS

Admission Contact Information
Address admission inquiries to: Dr. Jerry Downey, 1300 West Park Street, Butte, MT 59701
Phone: (406) 496-4578
E-mail: jdowney@mtech.edu
Admissions website: http://www.mtmatsci.org/

Application deadlines
Fall admission:
U.S. students: September 3   *Int'l. students*: September 1

Application fee
U.S. students: $50   *Int'l. students*: $50
Please check each campus web site for campus-specific information, requirements, process, and amenities: www.mtech.edu/academics/gradschool/, www.montana.edu/gradschool/ and www.umt.edu/grad/

Admissions information
For Fall of 2018:
Number of applicants: 39
Number admitted: 10
Number enrolled: 9

Admission requirements
Bachelor's degree requirements: Completion of an undergraduate program equivalent to that required to obtain a B.S. degree in materials science, materials engineering, physics, chemistry, metallurgy, or a related science or engineering field.
Minimum undergraduate GPA: 3.0

GRE requirements
The GRE is required.
GRE scores considered in combination with other application materials.

Subjective GRE requirements
The Subjective GRE is not required.

TOEFL requirements
The TOEFL exam is required for students from non-English-speaking countries.
PBT score: 580
iBT score: 92
Provisional admission is possible with lower scores. IELTS: 7.0

TUITION

Tuition year 2017–18:
Tuition for in-state residents
Full-time students: $3,000 per semester
Part-time students: $250 per credit
Tuition for out-of-state residents
Full-time students: $11,000 per semester
Part-time students: $950 per credit
Full-time tuition quoted is for 12 credit hours per semester. Additional credits do not increase tuition.
Credit hours per semester to be considered full-time: 9
Deferred tuition plan: Yes
Health insurance: Available at the cost of $3,500 per year.
Other academic fees: Each campus has its own fees to cover IT, athletic fees, technology, campus health service. They might total about $150 per credit for all students.
Academic term: Semester
Number of first-year students who received full tuition waivers: 10

Teaching Assistants, Research Assistants, and Fellowships
Number of first-year
Teaching Assistants: 8
Research Assistants: 8
Average stipend per academic year
Teaching Assistant: $14,400
Research Assistant: $14,400
Full year (12 month) stipend for TA, RA, or combination is $24,000.

FINANCIAL AID

Application deadlines
Fall admission:
U.S. students: April 1   *Int'l. students*: April 1

Loans

Loans are available for U.S. students.

Loans are not available for international students.

GAPSFAS application required: No

FAFSA application required: Yes

For further information

Address financial aid inquiries to: Campus program director.

HOUSING

Availability of on-campus housing

Single students: Yes

Married students: Yes

For further information

Address housing inquiries to: Campus Housing Office on each campus. Please check with the graduate school for the campus of interest.

Table A—Faculty, Enrollments, and Degrees Granted

Research Specialty	2016–17 Faculty	Enrollment Fall 2016		Number of Degrees Granted 3		
		Master's	Doc-torate	Master's	Terminal Master's	Doc-torate
Biomaterials	17	–	5	–	–	–
Electronic, photonic, magnetic materials	12	–	6	–	–	1
Energy Materials	15	–	8	–	–	1
Materials Science, Metallurgy	14	–	4	–	–	–
Nano Science and Technology	11	–	3	–	–	1
Total	45	–	26	–	–	–
Full-time Grad. Stud.	–	–	15	–	–	–
First-year Grad. Stud.	–	–	6	–	–	–

GRADUATE DEGREE REQUIREMENTS

Doctorate: Qualifying Exam: Written and comprehensive is taken at the end of the first year of full-time study. Candidacy Exam is typically taken before the start of the third year. It consists of two parts: a written proposal describing the proposed dissertation research; and an oral defense of the proposal to the student's doctoral committee. A written dissertation describing original research must be prepared, submitted, presented orally, and defended. Every student is expected to attend an annual program summer symposium, and to present a talk or poster after advancing to candidacy.

Other Degrees: The participating campuses, Montana Tech, University of Montana, and Montana State University have several other graduate programs at the master's and doctoral levels in various engineering fields, chemistry, physics, and life sciences. Courses offered in these programs may be useful electives for Materials Science Ph.D. students in this program.

SPECIAL EQUIPMENT, FACILITIES, OR PROGRAMS

Research facilities and equipment at the three participating campuses are available to this program. These include

* University of Montana's (UM) Core Computational Facility and the Montana High Performance Computer at Montana Tech

* UM's Center for Computational Biology

* UM's Mass Spectrometry Facility

* UM's EMtrix electron microscopy facility

* UM's Spectroscopy Core Laboratory

* Machine shops and electronic shops

* Montana State University's (MSU) Center for Biofilm Engineering and its Microscopy Facility

* MSU's Chemistry and Proteomics & Mass Spectrometry Facility

* MSU's Image and Chemical Analysis Laboratory (ICAL)

* MSU's Ion Beam Group

* MSU's Montana Microfabrication Facility (MMF)

* MSU's Nuclear Magnetic Resonance Laboratory

* MSU's Energy Research Institute (ERI)

* MSU's extensive research facilities for bulk and thin-film processing; thermal analysis (up to 1600 C), image/chemical/structure/performance characterization capabilities; microfabrication and specimen preparation facilities

* MTech's Center for Advanced Mineral, Metallurgical and Materials Processing (CAMP)

* MTech's Metal Contamination Reserach Laboratory

* MTech's Geomechanics Laboratory

* MTech's Nanomaterials and Plasmonics facility

* Montana Bureau of Mines and Geology facilities at MTech

FACULTY

Professor

Cairns, Doug, Montana State University - M&IE. Materials for energy storage, conversion and conservation: materials, polymer/ceramic matrix composites, manufacturing and structural performance link for new engineering systems. Materials synthesis, processing & fabrication: Materials, polymer/ceramic matrix composites, manufacturing & structural performance link for new engineering systems.

Cameron, Doug, Montana Tech - Chemistry. Biomaterials: Biofuel characterization and environmental factors affecting algal biofuel production. Electronic, photonic & magnetic materials: Biofuel characterization and environmental factors affecting algal biofuel production.

Carlson, Ross, Montana State University - Chemical and Biological Engineering. Biomaterials: Metabolomic systems analysis and biofuel production.

Codd, Sarah, Montana State University - Mechanical and Industrial Engineering. Materials synthesis, processing & fabrication: Magnetic resonance imaging and microscopy studies of new transport phenomena in complex systems.

Cone, Rufus, Montana State University - Physics. Electronic, phototonic and magnetic materials: Resonant optical materials for quantum information signal processing, and solid state lasers.

Dickensheets, David, Montana State University - Electrical Engineering. Biomaterials: Microfabrication of optical instrumentation for biological imaging; optical microscopy of tissues.

Downey, Jerry, Montana Tech - M&ME. Materials science, Metallurgy: Vapor phase transport. Determination of fundamental properties of ionic melts. Materials synthesis, processing & fabrication: Vapor phase transport. Determination of fundamental properties of ionic melts.

Ganesan, Kumar, Montana Tech - Environmental Engineering. Electronic, phototonic and magnetic materials: Development of nano-metallic filters to remove contaminants from water and air. Materials synthesis, processing and fabrication: Development of Nano-metallic filters to remove contaminants from water and air.

Holian, Andrij, University of Montana - BMED. Biomaterials: Biocompatibility and mechanisms of interactions studies using multiple in vitro and in vivo approaches.

Hoo, Karlene, Ph.D., Montana State University–Chemical and Biological Engineering. Energy efficient processes: sustainable designs, dynamic operability; Multivariate/robust statistics: chemometrics, process analytical technologies; Modeling and management of hydraulic fracturing processes; Design, development and analysis of complex chemical processes (batch and continuous); Control methods: autonomous, plant–wide, model–based, adaptive and robust; System identification: reduced–order models, parameter estimation, artificial neural networks; Dynamic and stochastic optimization, uncertainty propagation.

Idzerda, Yves, Montana State University - Physics. physics department chair. Electronic, phototonic and magnetic materials: Interfacial and nanostructured behavior in oxide materials. Materials for energy storage, conversion and conservation: Interfacial and nanostructured behavior in oxide materials.

MacLaughlin, Mary, Montana Tech - Geological Engineering. Materials synthesis, processing and fabrication: Mechanical behavior and engineering properties of geomaterials; Numerical modeling (FE/FD, discrete element) of shear failure and fracture.

Madigan, Bruce, Montana Tech - General Engineering. Materials synthesis, processing and fabrication: Application and automation of welding processes for additive manufacturing.

Pedulla, Marisa, Montana Tech - Biological Sciences. Biomaterials: Interaction of bio-compatible nanoparticles with biological systems, including bacterial and eukaryotic viruses and their host cells.

Ross, Sandy, University of Montana - Chemistry. Biomaterials: Time-resolved spectroscopy, model bio-membranes (nanodiscs and limsomes); single-molecule spectroscopy. Materials for energy storage, conversion, and conservation: Time-resolved spectroscopy; model bio-membranes (nonodiscs and limpsomes); single-molecule spectroscopy.

Seymour, Joseph, Montana State University - Chemical and Biological Engineering. Materials synthesis, processing, and fabrication: Magnetic resonance microscopy to study transport phenomena in porous media including bioreactive systems and hydrogels.

Shaw, Steven, Montana State University - Elec. & Comp. Engineering & Energy Research Institute. Electronic, phototonic, and magnetic materials: System identification and controls, energy and fuel-cell systems, instrumentation.

Walker, Robert, Montana State University - Chemistry & Biochemistry. Biomaterials: Nonlinear optical studies of absorption, film formation and bioaccumulation at solid-liquid and model membrane interfaces. Materials for energy storage, conversion & conservation: High temperature surface spectroscopy for probing oxidation and degradation in solid oxide electrochemical cells.

White, Ronald J., Ph.D., Montana Tech, 1968. Director, Center for Advanced Mineral and Metallurgical Processing (CAMP). Research specialties: Mathematical modeling, computer simulation, space physiology, materials science. Research interests: Research focused on the development of CAMP into an internationally recognized Center of Excellence in materials science and engineering involving faculty and students from a wide variety of scientific and engineering disciplines.

Young, Courtney, Montana Tech - M&ME. Materials Science and Metallurgy: Metal recovery, hydrometallurgy, mineral processing, separations, recycling, waste treatment, photoconversion and coal gasification.

Associate Professor

Chu, Xi, University of Montana - Chemistry. Materials for energy storage, conversion and conservation: Electronic structure, geometry, and dynamics of molecules of technological or fundamental interest.

Gannon, Paul, Montana State University - Chemical and Biological Engineering. Materials for energy storage, conversion and conservation: High temperature material corrosion in silicon processing and energy conversion devices. Materials synthesis, processing & fabrication: High-temperature corrosion and corrosion protection in metals and ceramics, thin-film coatings.

Gleason, William, Montana Tech - M&ME. Electronic, phototonic and magnetic materials: Metallic membrane hydrogen purification.

Kukay, Brian, Montana Tech - General Engineering. Materials synthesis, processing & fabrication: Destructive, semi-destructive, and non-destructive evaluation of structural materials.

Malovichko, Galina, Montana State University - Physics. Electronic, phototonic, and magnetic materials: Magnetic resonance study of intrinsic, extrinsic and radiation defects in photonic materials and materials for telecommunications and computing.

Miller, David, Montana State University - Physics. Materials for energy storage, conversion, and conservation: Mechanical behavior and active materials; composites piezoelectrics, and shape memory alloys. Materials synthesis, processing, and fabrication: Mechanical behavior and active materials; composites piezoelectrics, and shape memory alloys.

Skinner, Jack, Montana Tech - General Engineering. Electronic, phototonic, and magnetic materials: Plasmonics; metamaterials; Nano science and technology micro/nano-scale structures. Materials for energy storage, conversion, and conservation: Plasmonics; metamaterials; micro/nano-scale structures.

Sofie, Stephen, Montana State University - Mechanical & Industrial Engineering. Materials for energy storage, conversion, and conservation: Materials synthesis (nano-micro/scale), electro-ceramics, materials for thermo-electrics and high-temperature electrochemistry, innovative processing. Materials synthesis, processing, and fabrication: Materials synthesis (nano-micro/scale), electro-ceramics, materials for thermo-electrics and high-temperature electrochemistry, innovative processing.

Sudhakar, KV, Montana Tech - M&ME. Biomaterials: Mechanical behavior & surface characteristics of non-toxic, low modulus beta titanium alloys for medicine and healthcare.

Thomas, Aaron, University of Montana - Chemistry. Electronic, phototonic and magnetic materials: Transport phenomena and separations; mechanical gas separations and biological separations in MEMS devices.

Assistant Professor

Amendola, Roberta, Montana State University - Mechanical and Industrial Engineering. Materials synthesis, processing & fabrication: Degradation of materials, tribological behavior, thermo-mechanical performance, oxidation, surface engineering and rapid development of novel compositions and customized microstructures.

Anderson, Ryan, Montana State University - Chemical and Biological Engineering. Materials for energy storage, conversion & conservation: Heat transfer and fluid flow in clean energy applications including aqueous and solid oxide fuel cells.

Avci, Recep, Montana State University - Physics. *Materials Science, Metallurgy*. Biomaterials: Biocorrosion, bacterial immobilization, bacteria manipulation at nonoscale, bacteria trapping and concentration, bio-sensors.

Chang, Connie, Montana State University. *Chemical Physics.* Chemical and Biological Engineering. Biomaterials: Understanding the growth and mechanics of "organoids", three-dimensional mini-organs that are derived from stem cells. Using microfluidic techniques to culture and screen these organoids. Work involves drop-based microfluidics, a unique method that creates picoliter-sized, monodisperse emulsions in which we can encapsulate and assay single cells.

Cox, Alysia, Ph.D., Massachusetts Institute of Technology. Geology/Geochemistry. Proteins, Genome products of microbes and their interaction.

Grumstrup, Erik, Montana State University - Chemistry and Biochemistry. Electronic, phototonic and magnetic materials: Ultrafast hotochemistry and charge transport in semiconducting nano-materials.

June, Ron, Montana State University - Mechanical and Industrial Engineering. Biomaterials: Cartilage during drug delivery and mechanical transduction. Materials synthesis, processing & fabrication: Cartilage drug delivery and mechanotransduction.

Macaluso, David, University of Montana - General Engineering. Biomaterials: Experimental atomic physics. Electronic, photonic and magnetic materials: Experimental atomic physics.

Pramanik, Brahmananda, Ph.D., University of Mississippi, 2013. *Engineering Physics/Science, Systems Science/Engineering.* Bio-inspired materials, Composites, Nano-reinforcement, Materials for energy absorption, High strain rate material characterization, Impact dynamics.

Prieto, Dario, Ph.D., Northwestern University, 2013. Materials science, Surface science. Synthesis-structure-function relations, composite materials, surface chemistry, adsorption and catalysis, mine waste valorization, and engineering education.

Ryan, Cecily, Ph.D., Stanford University, 2016. biodegradable and bioderived polymers and composites; material properties of composites including interfacial compatibility; sustainable materials and energy product lifecycles.

Serban, Monica, Montana State University. *Medical, Health Physics.* The broad theme of the Serban Group's research is the design and development of novel biomaterials for biomedical applications. The current building blocks used are hyaluronic acid, silk fibroin, gelatin and glucaric acid. The emphasis of our work is on maximizing the intrinsic properties of each of these materials through processing and chemical modifications, and create novel systems that address unmet medical needs.

Stadie, Nick, Montana State University. *Biophysics, Chemical Physics.* Energy storage and conversion: Design and synthesis of novel porous carbon materials based on ordered, nanostructured surfaces with the ultimate goal of fine control of both topology and chemical composition. Understanding the unique physical interplay between these surfaces and energy-rich guests such as ions and small molecular fuels is of particular interest toward developing new directions in applications such as batteries, supercapacitors, and mobile gas storage.

Wettstein, Stephanie, Montana State University - Chemical and Biological Engineering. Materials synthesis, processing & fabrication: Synthesis of platform chemicals including bio-fuels from lignocellulosic biomass using novel catalytic and separation processes.

Wilking, James, Montana State University - Chemical and Biological Engineering. Biomaterials: Soft materials and complex fluids; material properties of microbial biofilms and nanomaterials synthesis.

Zodrow, Katherine, Ph.D., Yale, 2014. Water treatment, developing new water treatment membrane materials and coatings, characterizing interactions between bacteria and water treatment systems, and developing processes for industrial water and wastewater treatment.

DEPARTMENTAL RESEARCH SPECIALTIES AND STAFF

Theoretical

Materials Science, Metallurgy. Molecular modeling and theoretical research associated with the experimental programs in energy materials, bio-materials, electronic/photonic/magnetic materials, and materials processing and fabrication including extractive metallurgy. White.

Experimental

Biomaterials. Includes bio-inspired materials, bio-mimetic materials, and interactions between materials and biological systems. This research bridges the gap between benchtop investigations and clinical applications with the goal of improving health. Other important applications are in environmental sensors and micro-scale structural materials. Activities include inorganic-organic hybrids for tissue engineering scaffolds, biomimetic chemistry methods to synthesize multifunctional nanostructured materials, biofilms, replacement bones, and using nanodiscs and liposomes to understand the dynamics of protein binding to membranes. Avci, Cameron, Carlson, Dickensheets, Holian, June, Macaluso, Pedulla, Ross, Seymour, Sofie, Sudhakar, Wilking.

Electronic, Photonic, and Magnetic Materials. EPM materials have applications in quantum information and cryptography, information storage, signal processing, communications, electronics, imaging and sensing techniques, and laser components. These materials and phenomena are studied in nanoparticles, thin-film, bulk, and single-crystal form and also in optical waveguides and other device configurations. Theoretical directions are diverse, including determination of structure/function relationships, electronic structure calculations, optical energy levels plus coherence and spin dynamics for ions, properties of alloy phases, and unique phases of matter. Chu, Cone, Grumstrup, Macaluso, Malovichko, Miller, Ross, Shaw, Sofie.

Materials for Energy Storage, Conversion, and Conservation. Fundamental and applied highly interdisciplinary research in the area of materials for energy storage, conversion, and conservation. Broadly this research focuses on transforming resources, such as sunlight, wind, and biomass, into fuels that can be used at later times to provide reliable electric power. Research addresses critical materials issues for developing sustainable means of producing and storing chemical fuels, improving energy efficiency, and for converting natural and renewable resources into clean, economical, and sustainable sources of energy. Amendola, Cairns, Cameron, Carlson, Downey, Ganesan, Gannon, Idzerda, Macaluso, Shaw, Skinner, Sofie, Thomas, Walker, Wettstein, Young.

Materials synthesis, processing, amd fabrication. This specialty encompasses an exceptionally broad range of research that extends from extraction and refining of bulk materials to the synthesis of high-value-added advanced materials, which have application-specific properties. The program pools expertise in solid-state physics, metallurgy, polymer chemistry, ceramics, composites, and process engineering to conduct research that responds to and anticipates current and emerging industrial needs and interests. Codd, Downey, Ganesan, Gleason, Kukay, Macaluso, MacLaughlin, Madigan, Seymour, Shaw, Sofie, Sudhakar, Wettstein, Young.

CREIGHTON UNIVERSITY

DEPARTMENT OF PHYSICS

Omaha, Nebraska 68178
http://physicsweb.creighton.edu

General University Information
President: Daniel S. Hendrickson, S.J., Ph.D.
Dean of Graduate School: Gail M. Jensen
University website: http://www.creighton.edu
School Type: Private
Setting: Urban
Total Faculty: 887
Total Graduate Faculty: 324
Total number of Students: 8,393
Total number of Graduate Students: 1,735

Department Information
Department Chairman: Prof. Gintaras K. Duda, Chair
Department Contact: Michael G. Nichols, Graduate Program
  Director
  Total full-time faculty: 10
  Total number of full-time equivalent positions: 10
  Full-Time Graduate Students: 10
  Female Full-Time Graduate Students: 1
  First-Year Graduate Students: 6
  Total Post Doctorates: 2

Department Address
2500 California Plaza
Omaha, NE 68178
Phone: (402) 280-2159
Fax: (402) 280-2140
E-mail: mnichols@creighton.edu
Website: http://physicsweb.creighton.edu

ADMISSIONS

Admission Contact Information
Address admission inquiries to: Director, Physics Graduate Program, Department of Physics, Creighton University, 2500 California Plaza, Omaha, NE 68178
Phone: (402) 280-2870
E-mail: gradschool@creighton.edu
Admissions website: https://gradschool.creighton.edu/future-students

Application deadlines
Fall admission:
U.S. students: September 1   *Int'l. students*: September 1
Spring admission:
U.S. students: December 1   *Int'l. students*: September 1

Application fee
U.S. students: $50   *Int'l. students*: $50

Admissions information
For Fall of 2017:
  Number of applicants: 19
  Number admitted: 12
  Number enrolled: 8

Admission requirements
Bachelor's degree requirements: A Bachelors degree in Physics or Engineering-related field is required.

GRE requirements
The GRE is required.
No minimum score

Subjective GRE requirements
The Subjective GRE is not required.

TOEFL requirements
The TOEFL exam is required for students from non-English-speaking countries.
  PBT score: 550
  iBT score: 90
Alternate English Proficiency Requirements: IELTS - Overall 6.5 (no section below 6.0) Duolingo - 61 or above

Other admissions information
Undergraduate preparation assumed: A typical student will have completed undergraduate courses in Classical Mechanics (Taylor, Marion, etc.), Quantum Mechanics (Griffiths, Townsend, etc.), Electricity and Magnetism (Griffiths, Corson and Lorrain, etc.), and Statistical Mechanics/Thermodynamics (Kittel, Reif, etc.).

TUITION

Tuition year 2018–19:
  Full-time students: $850 per credit
  Part-time students: $850 per credit
Teaching and Research Assistants do not pay tuition.
Credit hours per semester to be considered full-time: 8
Deferred tuition plan: No
Health insurance: Available at the cost of $2,430 per year.
Other academic fees: University Fee: $583/semester (full-time); $61 (part-time) University Technology Fee: $249/semester (full-time); $102/semester (part-time).
Academic term: Semester
Number of first-year students who received full tuition waivers: 5

Teaching Assistants, Research Assistants, and Fellowships
Number of first-year
  Teaching Assistants: 4
  Research Assistants: 1
Average stipend per academic year
  Teaching Assistant: $11,576
  Research Assistant: $11,576

FINANCIAL AID

Application deadlines
Fall admission:
U.S. students: July 23   *Int'l. students*: July 23
Spring admission:
U.S. students: December 12   *Int'l. students*: December 12

Loans
Loans are available for U.S. students.
Loans are not available for international students.
GAPSFAS application required: No
FAFSA application required: Yes

For further information

Address financial aid inquiries to: Office of Financial Aid, Creighton University, 2500 California Plaza, Omaha, NE 68178.

Phone: (402) 280-2731

E-mail: finaid@creighton.edu

Financial aid website: http://www.creighton.edu/financialaid

HOUSING

Availability of on-campus housing

Single students: No

Married students: No

For further information

Address housing inquiries to: Department of Residence Life, 136 Swanson Hall, Creighton University, 2500 California Plaza, Omaha, NE 68178.

Phone: (402) 280-3900

E-mail: ResidenceLife@creighton.edu

Housing aid website: http://www.creighton.edu/studentlife/departmentofresidencelife/housinginformation/

Table A—Faculty, Enrollments, and Degrees Granted

Research Specialty	2017–18 Faculty	Enrollment Fall 2017 Master's	Enrollment Fall 2017 Doctorate	Number of Degrees Granted 2017–18 (2013–18) Master's	Number of Degrees Granted 2017–18 (2013–18) Terminal Master's	Number of Degrees Granted 2017–18 (2013–18) Doctorate
Astrophysics	2	3	–	–	1(2)	–
Atomic, Molecular, & Optical Physics	1	3	–	–	–(1)	–
Biophysics	3	3	–	–	1(4)	–
Condensed Matter Physics	1	2	–	–	–(2)	–
Medical, Health Physics	1	5	–	–	2(2)	–
Nano Science and Technology	1	2	–	–	–(1)	–
Nuclear Physics	1	2	–	–	1(4)	–
Quantum Computing	1	–	–	–	–	–
Non-specialized	–	–	–	–	1(2)	–
Total	11	20	–	–	6(18)	–
Full-time Grad. Stud.	–	14	–	–	–	–
First-year Grad. Stud.	–	8	–	–	–	–

GRADUATE DEGREE REQUIREMENTS

Master's: Plan A (thesis option) requires 30 credit hours of graduate-level courses, including six credit hours of Thesis Research. Plan B (non-thesis option) requires 33 credit hours of graduate-level courses, including three credit hours of Directed Independent Research for which a report is required. A minimum of 15 credit hours must be in physics in either Plan. In both Plans, all students are required to take the core graduate courses in classical mechanics, electromagnetics, quantum mechanics, and statistical mechanics. Full-time students must enroll in Graduate Seminar each semester. M.S., Major in Medical Physics: Requires 43 credits of graduate-level courses including core physics and medical and health physics courses, research, and clinical experience. A minimum grade average of 3.0 (B) is required, with no more than two grades of C. A three-part comprehensive exam offered three times each year on (1) Mechanics and Heat, (2) Electricity, Magnetism and optics, (3) Modern Physics is required to be passed. Each part can be taken separately. At least one part must be passed in the first year of study. Ordinarily a student must devote two semesters and a summer session to resident graduate study.

Thesis: Theses may be written in absentia.

SPECIAL EQUIPMENT, FACILITIES, OR PROGRAMS

Atomic, Molecular, and Optical Physics: 767 nm frequency-stabilized diode laser, 1.6 W tapered-amplifier diode laser, frequency-stabilized HeNe laser, acousto-optic modulators, spectrum analyzer, rf sources, ultrahigh vacuum equipment, X-ray fluorescence analyzers, high-resolution Si(li) detectors and a silicon PIN detector.

Condensed Matter Physics: Turbomolecular pump, 1500 C furnace, IR detector, glove box, laminar flow bench, muffle furnaces, vacuum oven, capacitance bridge, lock-i n amplifier, photon correlation spectrometer, fluorescence correlation spectrometer. 5W CW 532-nm laser, 25W CW 1064-nm laser, C02 laser.

Biophysics: Femtosecond Ti:S laser, confocal laser scanning microscope, holographic microscope, Frequency Domain fluorimeter, fiber-optic UV-VIS-NIR absorption and fluorescence spectrometers, Cary 60 UV VIS spectrometer, 10W Nd: YAG laser, Optical stretcher, sterile cell culture facilities, inverted tissue culture microscopes, Zeiss 510 NLO LSM with FLIM electronics.

Computational molecular biophysics: AMD opteron and Intel Xeon multi-core workstations with 64-bit Linux operating system.

Astrophysics/ Astro-particle Physics: Multi-node networked Intel-based workstations for simulations. Robotic Telescope facility.

Energy Sources & Environment: Epilog 120W laser cutter, 3D scanner, MakerBot 3D printer, two StrataSys Dimensions series 3D printers, ADMET Universal Testing Machine.

Nuclear Physics: Compton-scattering spectrometer, gamma-gamma and beta-gamma angular correlation spectrometers, HPGe gamma-ray detector, NIM electronics, Computing cluster.

Nanoscience and technology: Agilent Atomic Force Microscope, Kurt J. Lesker high vacuum, three-source thermal evaporator, Advanced Research Systems (ARS) 7 K closed-cycle cryostat with optical access, GMW 1.2 T electromagnet, Keithley SourceMeter Unit (3A, 40V), Perkin-Elmer Fourier Transform Infrared Spectroscopy, ElVax X-ray Fluorescence Spectroscopy, Perkin-Elmer Differential Scanning Calorimeter, Newport Apex Monochromator light source, Ocean Optics UV-Vis Spectrom-eter, Admet 10 kN Universal Testing Machine, Bareiss Shore A and D Durometers, Filmetrics Spectral Reflectance, Headway Photoresist Spinner, Plasma Etch Reactive Ion Etcher. Solvent induced ordering of block copolymers facility. Thin film deposition and testing facility.

Quantum computing: Linux workstations with software for scientific programming and simulations, including Mathematica, Python with SciPy, and Octave/Matlab.

Table B—Separately Budgeted Research Expenditures by Source of Support

Source of Support	Departmental Research	Physics-related Research Outside Department
Federal government	$284,801	
State/local government		
Non-profit organizations	$1,967	
Business and industry	$74,304	
Other	$266,331	
Total	$627,403	

Table C—Separately Budgeted Research Expenditures by Research Specialty

Research Specialty	No. of Grants	Expenditures ($)
Astrophysics	4	$25,600
Atomic, Molecular, & Optical Physics	2	$15,000
Biophysics	2	$69,960
Energy Sources & Environment	2	$74,304
Medical, Health Physics	1	$188,000
Nano Science and Technology	1	$6,000
Nuclear Physics	1	$222,000
Quantum Computing	1	$11,000
Total	**14**	**$611,864**

FACULTY

Professor

Duda, Gintaras, Ph.D., University of California, Los Angeles, 2003. *Astrophysics, Cosmology & String Theory, Particles and Fields, Physics and other Science Education.* Astroparticle physics; theoretical elementary particle physics; physics education research.

Nichols, Michael G., Ph.D., University of Rochester, 1996. *Biophysics, Medical, Health Physics, Optics.* Experimental biological physics; tissue spectroscopy and microscopy; photodynamic therapy of cancer; cellular mechanics.

Seger, Janet E., Ph.D., University of Wisconsin-Madison, 1991. *High Energy Physics, Nuclear Physics.* Theoretical and experimental high-energy nuclear physics.

Sidebottom, David L., Ph.D., Kansas State University, 1989. *Condensed Matter Physics.* Glass science; dynamic light scattering; optical spectroscopy; dielectric spectroscopy.

Associate Professor

Baruth, Andrew G., Ph.D., University of Nebraska-Lincoln, 2009. *Condensed Matter Physics, Energy Sources & Environment, Nano Science and Technology.* Magnetic and electronic behavior of 3D nanostructures, block copolymer self assembly, magnetic heterostructures, solar cells, superconductivity.

Gabel, Jack R., Ph.D., Catholic University of America, 2000. *Astrophysics.* Observational astrophysics; UV, optical, IR spectroscopy; accretion hydrodynamics; photoionization modeling of astrophysical plasmas.

Soto, Patricia, Ph.D., University of Groningen, 2004. *Biophysics.* Computational molecular biophysics, biomolecular modeling, structural bioinformatics, protein conformational dynamics, pathological protein folding.

Wrubel, Jonathan P., Ph.D., Cornell University, 2006. *Atomic, Molecular, & Optical Physics.* Atomic, molecular, and optical physics; optics; laser-cooling and trapping; ultracold atoms; Feshbach resonances; Bose-Einstein condensates; spinors.

Assistant Professor

Ekpenyong, Andrew E., Ph.D., University of Cambridge, 2012. *Biophysics, Condensed Matter Physics, Medical, Health Physics, Optics.* Microfluidics and photonics in medicine. Cell and Tissue Mechanics. Physics of Cancer. Physics of Living Matter.

Wong, Tom, Ph.D., University of California, San Diego, 2014. Quantum Computing: Quantum algorithms; quantum walks; adiabatic quantum computing; quantum search; quantum networks; scientific computing.

Emeritus

Cherney, Michael G., Ph.D., University of Wisconsin-Madison, 1987. *High Energy Physics, Nuclear Physics.* Experimental high-energy nuclear physics (relativistic heavy ion physics); control systems; nuclear science education; energy sources and environment.

Cipolla, Sam J., Ph.D., Purdue University, 1969. *Atomic, Molecular, & Optical Physics.* Experimental atomic physics; inner-shell ionization; response modeling of radiation detectors.

Zepf, Thomas H., Ph.D., Saint Louis University, 1963. *Atomic, Molecular, & Optical Physics, Condensed Matter Physics.* Optical physics.

Adjunct Faculty

Hill, Brian, M.S., Creighton University, 2004. *Medical, Health Physics.* Therapeutic radiological physics.

Instructor

Stuva, David R., M.S., Creighton University, 1983. General physics.

Posdoctoral Research Associate

Adam, Jarsolov, Ph.D., Czech Technical University, 2016. *Nuclear Physics.* Relativistic heavy ion collisions.

Anson, Christopher, Ph.D., The Ohio State University, 2014. *High Energy Physics, Nuclear Physics.* Relativistic heavy ion collisions.

DEPARTMENTAL RESEARCH SPECIALTIES AND STAFF

Theoretical

Astrophysics. Characterization and detection of dark matter; prompt atmospheric lepton flux in high energy cosmic rays; high-energy cosmic rays beyond the GZK cutoff. Duda.

Biophysics. Protein structure, dynamics, and self-assembly; protein folding and misfolding; protein-membrane interactions. Soto.

Quantum computing. Quantum algorithms for searching databases and networks; continuous-time and discrete-time quantum walks; quantum walks with weighted edges, self-loops, and variable walk-query ratios; adiabatic quantum computing. Wong.

Experimental

Astrophysics. Observations and analysis of active galactic nuclei using UV, optical, IR spectra from space-based and large ground-based observations; photoionization modeling of astrophysical plasmas; studies of energetic mass outflows from quasars; accretion processes. Gabel.

Atomic, Molecular, & Optical Physics. Laser-cooling of potassium atoms to produce Bose-Einstein condensates; study of the spin dynamics (spinor physics) of ultracold atoms; nonlinear matter-wave physics in BECs. Wrubel.

Atomic, Molecular, & Optical Physics. Atomic inner-shell ionization; X-ray fluorescence. Cipolla.

Biophysics. Development and application of novel optical techniques to biology and medicine; Metabolic imaging; Multiphoton and confocal laser scanning fluorescence microscopy; Molecular photophysics. Vis/Near-IR tissue spectroscopy; Photodynamic therapy (PDT) of cancer. Studies of cellular mechanics use an optical stretcher apparatus and holographic microscope. Nichols.

Biophysics. Microfluidics and photonics in medicine. Cell and Tissue Mechanics. Physics of Cancer. Physics of Living Matter. Ekpenyong.

Condensed Matter Physics. Ionic motion in glasses; dynamic light scattering of the glass transition. Evaluation of cryopreserving agents. Sidebottom.

Nano Science and Technology. Nanoscale systems involving novel magnetic and electronic phenomena at heterostructure interfaces; solar cells; self-assembly of block copolymers. Baruth.

Nuclear Physics. High-energy nuclear physics (relativistic heavy ion physics) in STAR collaboration at RHIC (Brookhaven National Laboratory) and ALICE collaboration at the LHC (CERN). Adam, Anson, Cherney, Seger.

UNIVERSITY OF NEBRASKA-LINCOLN

DEPARTMENT OF PHYSICS AND ASTRONOMY

Lincoln, Nebraska 68588-0299
http://www.unl.edu/physics

General University Information
Chancellor: Ronnie Green
Dean of Graduate School: Dr. Tim Carr
University website: http://www.unl.edu/
School Type: Public
Setting: Urban
Total Faculty: 1,705
Total Graduate Faculty: 1,960
Total number of Students: 26,079
Total number of Graduate Students: 4,606

Department Information
Department Chairman: Prof. Daniel R. Claes, Chair
Department Contact: Jennifer Becic, Graduate Program
   Associate
   Total full-time faculty: 29
   Total number of full-time equivalent positions: 29
   Full-Time Graduate Students: 82
   Female Full-Time Graduate Students: 9
   First-Year Graduate Students: 17
   Female First-Year Students: 5
   Total Post Doctorates: 14

Department Address
208 Jorgensen Hall
855 N 16th Street
Lincoln, NE 68588-0299
Phone: (402) 472-2770
Fax: (402) 472-6148
E-mail: PAGrad@unl.edu
Website: http://www.unl.edu/physics

ADMISSIONS

Admission Contact Information
Address admission inquiries to: Office of Graduate Studies, 1100
   Seaton Hall, Lincoln, NE 68588-0619
Phone: (402) 472-2875
E-mail: graduate@unl.edu
Admissions website: http://www.unl.edu/gradstudies/prospective

Application deadlines
Fall admission:
U.S. students: January 31   *Int'l. students*: January 31
Spring admission:
U.S. students: September 30   *Int'l. students*: September 30

Application fee
U.S. students: $50   *Int'l. students*: $50
Steps for Admission website: http://www.unl.edu/gradstudies/
   prospective/steps

Admissions information
For Fall of 2018:
   Number of applicants: 111
   Number admitted: 41
   Number enrolled: 13

Admission requirements
Bachelor's degree requirements: Bachelor's degree is required.
Minimum undergraduate GPA: 3.0

GRE requirements
The GRE is required.
There is no minimum requirement for the GRE, though the pre-
   ferred Quantitative score is greater than 150. The average new
   Revised GRE scores for 2017–2018 admissions were ver-
   bal–152; quantitative–163; and analytical-3.4.

Subjective GRE requirements
The Subjective GRE is recommended.
The Physics GRE is recommended but not required. There is no
   minimum physics GRE requirement.

TOEFL requirements
The TOEFL exam is required for students from non-English-
   speaking countries.
   PBT score: 550
   iBT score: 80
The minimum score for computer-based TOEFL is 213. The minimum score for the IELTS is 6.5

Other admissions information
Undergraduate preparation assumed: Analytical Mechanics, G.
   Fowles and G. Cassiday; Quantum Mechanics, D. Griffiths;
   Introduction to Electrodynamics, D. Griffiths; Thermodynam-
   ics and Statistical Mechanics, R.J. Hardy and Ch. Binek.

TUITION

Tuition year 2018–19:
Tuition for in-state residents
   Full-time students: $323.25 per credit
   Part-time students: $323.25 per credit
Tuition for out-of-state residents
   Full-time students: $925.25 per credit
   Part-time students: $925.25 per credit
Teaching and Research Assistants do not pay tuition. All students
   admitted into the program receive a Teaching Assistantship,
   Research Assistantship, or some combination of the two.
Credit hours per semester to be considered full-time: 9
Deferred tuition plan: No
Health insurance: Yes, $986.05 (Fall); $1,365.71 (Spring/Sum-
   mer).
Other academic fees: Graduate Students pay only 21% of the
   total health insurance for each year. Program and facilities
   fees: $611/semester if enrolled 7+ hours; library and technol-
   ogy fees: $17.25 per credit hour; registration fee $20. One-
   time new international student fee of $150, & $70/semester
   thereafter.
Academic term: Semester
Number of first-year students who received full tuition waivers: 14

Teaching Assistants, Research Assistants, and Fellowships
   Number of first-year
      Teaching Assistants: 13
      Research Assistants: 1
      Fellowship students: 3

Average stipend per academic year
Teaching Assistant: $24,048
Research Assistant: $24,048
Fellowship student: $2,500
TA/RA Stipends are for 10 months. Students are typically supported for the two summer months as well. Full tuition waiver and 79% health insurance premium being covered is in addition to the stipend.

FINANCIAL AID

Loans

Loans are available for U.S. students.
Loans are not available for international students.
GAPSFAS application required: No
FAFSA application required: Yes

For further information

Address financial aid inquiries to: Scholarships and Financial Aid, University of Nebraska-Lincoln, 17 Canfield Admin Building, Lincoln, NE 68588-0411.
Phone: (800) 742-8800 (ext 2030)
E-mail: financialaid@unl.edu
Financial aid website: http://www.unl.edu/scholfa/

HOUSING

Availability of on-campus housing

Single students: Yes
Married students: Yes
Childcare Assistance: Yes

For further information

Address housing inquiries to: University Housing, 1115 N. 16th St., Lincoln, NE 68588-0622.
Phone: (800) 742-8800 (ext 3561)
E-mail: housing@unl.edu
Housing aid website: http://housing.unl.edu/

Table A—Faculty, Enrollments, and Degrees Granted

Research Specialty	2018–19 Faculty	Enrollment Fall 2018		Number of Degrees Granted 2017–18 (2010–18)		
		Master's	Doctorate	Master's	Terminal Master's	Doctorate
Atomic, Molecular, & Optical Physics	9	–	36	4(19)	2(3)	4(17)
Condensed Matter Physics	12	–	47	6(33)	–	9(43)
High Energy Physics	6	–	7	1(4)	–(2)	1(3)
Non-specialized	–	–	–	–	–	–
Total	28	–	90	11(56)	2(5)	14(63)
Full-time Grad. Stud.	–	–	90	–	–	–
First-year Grad. Stud.	–	–	14	–	–	–

GRADUATE DEGREE REQUIREMENTS

Master's: Option I (for both terminal degree students and those continuing in the Ph.D. program): 30 credit hours of coursework with a minimum of 15 credits in physics plus a thesis. Option II (for students wishing an interdisciplinary degree program): 36 credit hours of coursework including a minimum of 18 hours in physics and a minimum of nine hours in each of one or more minor subject areas and no thesis required. Option III (for students continuing in the PhD program only): 36 credit hours of coursework with a minimum of 18 hours in physics and no thesis required. There is no foreign language required for any option. Required examinations include: (1) Preliminary Examination on elementary physics, minimum grade of "B" required, and (b) a comprehensive examination (written and/or oral) covering the student's program of study.

Doctorate: Ninety credit hours including research credits. A maximum of 45 credit hours can be transferred. A grade of "B" or better grade point average is required. There is no foreign language requirement. Twenty-seven credit hours and 18 consecutive months must be completed in residence. Required examinations include: (1) Preliminary Examination on elementary physics, minimum grade of 'B' required (2) comprehensive examination based on one week of intensive research on a topic approved by the supervisory committee, and (3) oral examination in defense of thesis.

Thesis: Thesis may be written in absentia.

SPECIAL EQUIPMENT, FACILITIES, OR PROGRAMS

Astronomy: a 16-inch rooftop observatory equipped with a CCD camera is operational for student use. The 6-inch Minnich Solar Telescope equipped with an $H\alpha$ filter provides safe views of the sun, allowing student studies of sunspots and solar prominences.

Condensed Matter and Materials Physics: The CMMP group operates laboratories for investigations of a broad range of phenomena and materials. The experimental systems include: two SQUID, alternating-gradient, and vibrating-sample magnetometers; several magneto-optic Kerr-effect (MOKE) systems; pump-probe and high-frequency (8 GHz) systems for fast magnetization dynamics; high-field superconducting and pulsed-field solenoids; high-sensitivity microcantilever torque magnetometer; electron-transport measurements including resistivity, magnetoresistance, and Hall effect; scanning-probe microscopes for magnetic and ferroelectric nanostructure studies; angle-resolved, angle-integrated, and inverse photoemission; X-ray photoemission; low-energy electron diffraction; several thin-film growth systems including molecular-beam epitaxy (MBE), sputtering, e-beam evaporation, chemical-vapor deposition, electrodeposition, and others; neutron accelerator source; optical and high-frequency dielectric measurements; collaborative studies at large-scale facilities including synchrotron light and neutron sources. Computational facilities include several workstations. Many other materials growth and structural characterization measurements are available in the Central Facilities operated by the Nebraska Center for Materials and Nanoscience (for more information, see http://www.unl.edu/ncmn/facilities.shtml).

Atomic, Molecular, Optical, and Plasma Physics: Behlen Laboratory houses the Extreme Light Laboratory featuring its ultrahigh-intensity petawatt laser, DIOCLES, built to study the interactions of light with matter at the highest attainable field strengths. With the recent installation of new ten-times-higher-energy pump lasers, DIOCLES has a peak power of 1-petawatt, and operates at the highest duty cycle of any laser in its class. At its focus, it is capable of directly increasing an electron's relativistic mass by a factor of 20. Jorgensen Hall houses two amplified femtosecond laser systems, with repetition rates of 1 and 10 kHz and average powers of 2 and 10 W, respectively. These lasers are used to study ultrafast molecular dynamics and ionization using an ion mass spectrometer and a femtosecond electron diffractometer. Jorgensen Hall also houses an electron matter optics laboratory. In this laboratory, a 50-W Nd:YAG laser, 0-10 keV electron beam, nano-fabricated gratings at 100 nanometer periodicity, 2-D particle imaging systems, a state-of-the-art femtosecond electron pulse source, and an electron interferometer that is unique in the world today are available. A source of polarized electrons to study chiral molecules and fluorescence is also available.

High Energy Physics: The HEP group performs its research at the Large Hadron Collider at CERN in Geneva, Switzerland; at the Pierre Auger Observatory in Mendoza Province, Argentina; and at the Askaryan Radio Array experiment at the South Pole. The group manages a clean room facility for research and development on pixel detectors and operates a Tier-2 computing center on campus for CMS with an international user base for data analysis.

All: Excellent instrument (five full-time machinists) and electronics (two full-time technicians) shops are on site.

Library: Love Library houses an extensive collection of physics and astronomy periodicals, books, and monographs. Most research journals are available online, as are powerful journal databases. In addition, faculty participation in the Digital Commons, the University Libraries' open access repository, demonstrates a commitment to open science and scholarly preservation.

Table B—Separately Budgeted Research Expenditures by Source of Support

Source of Support	Departmental Research	Physics-related Research Outside Department
Federal government	$11,219,603	$12,846,001
State/local government	$94,126	$2,655,793
Non-profit organizations	$145,740	$1,798,903
Business and industry	$1,789,000	$684,594
Other		
Total	$13,248,469	$17,985,291

Table C—Separately Budgeted Research Expenditures by Research Specialty

Research Specialty	No. of Grants	Expenditures ($)
Atomic, Molecular, & Optical Physics	16	$2,212,744
Condensed Matter Physics	28	$7,692,580
High Energy Physics	7	$3,343,145
Total	51	$13,248,469

FACULTY

Professor

Adenwalla, Shireen, Ph.D., Northwestern University, 1989. *Condensed Matter Physics, Materials Science, Metallurgy.* Experimental condensed-matter physics; magnetization dynamics in coupled systems; magneto-electric interactions in heterostructures; neutron detectors.

Batelaan, Herman, Ph.D., University of Utrecht, 1991. *Atomic, Molecular, & Optical Physics.* Experimental atomic physics; laser cooling and trapping; matter optics and interferometry; ultrafast electron/photon physics.

Binek, Christian, Ph.D., University of Duisburg, 1995. Coordinator of interdisciplinary research group of the Materials Research Science and Engineering Center (MRSEC) at the University of Nebraska; Leader of theme 1 in the Center for Nanoferroic Devices (CNFD), and PI in theme 1 of The Center for Spintronic Materials, Interfaces, and Novel Architectures (C-spin). *Applied Physics, Condensed Matter Physics, Nano Science and Technology, Statistical & Thermal Physics.* Experimental condensed-matter physics; magnetic heterostructures and model systems; voltage-controlled magnetism; spintronics.

Bloom, Kenneth, Ph.D., Cornell University, 1997. *High Energy Physics, Particles and Fields.* Experimental high-energy physics focusing on top-quark physics, Higgs boson char-

acterization and searches for new phenomena at the Large Hadron Collider; developments in high-throughput computing that support particle physics research.

Claes, Daniel R., Ph.D., Northwestern University, 1991. Department Chair. *High Energy Physics, Particles and Fields.* Experimental high-energy physics; D0 at Fermilab; CMS experiment at CERN's large hadron collider; the cosmic ray observatory project (CROP) in Nebraska.

Dowben, Peter A., Ph.D., University of Cambridge, 1981. Charles Bessey Professor of Physics. *Chemical Physics, Condensed Matter Physics, Statistical & Thermal Physics.* Electronic structure of solids and surfaces; nonmetal to metal transitions; surface magnetism; surface ferroelectricity; organic molecular interfaces.

Ducharme, Stephen, Ph.D., University of Southern California, 1986. *Condensed Matter Physics.* Experimental condensed matter and optical physics; physics and applications of molecular and polymer ferroelectric materials;nanoscale ferroelectricity.

Fabrikant, Ilya I., Ph.D., Riga Institute of Physics, 1971. *Atomic, Molecular, & Optical Physics.* Theoretical atomic and molecular physics; atomic processes involving negative ions; electron-molecule and electron-cluster collisions; strong-field ionization of atoms and molecules.

Gay, Timothy J., Ph.D., University of Chicago, 1980. *Atomic, Molecular, & Optical Physics, Nuclear Physics.* Experimental atomic, molecular, and nuclear physics; polarized electrons.

Gruverman, Alexei, Ph.D., Ural State University, 1990. *Condensed Matter Physics, Nano Science and Technology.* Fundamental studies of nanoscale physical phenomena in multiferroic and polar materials by means of scanning probe microscopy techniques; static and dynamic properties of ferroic domains; scaling behavior of ferroelectric-based devices, electronic properties of polar surfaces; SPM-assisted methods for fabrication of nanostructures; SPM studies of electromechanical and mechanical properties of biocompatible materials and biological systems.

Liou, Sy-Hwang, Ph.D., Johns Hopkins University, 1985. *Condensed Matter Physics.* Experimental condensed-matter physics; magnetic properties of thin films; magnetic domain imaging; magnetic sensors.

Sellmyer, David J., Ph.D., Michigan State University, 1965. University Professor and George Holmes Distinguished Professor; Director of the Nebraska Center for Materials and Nanoscience. *Condensed Matter Physics, Materials Science, Metallurgy, Nano Science and Technology.* Experimental studies of nanoscale self- and cluster-assembled magnetic structures; exchange-coupled and high-energy magnetic materials; extremely high-density magnetic recording media; new spintronic materials.

Snow, Gregory R., Ph.D., Rockefeller University, 1983. *High Energy Physics, Particles and Fields, Physics and other Science Education.* Experimental high-energy physics; D0 experiment at Fermilab; CMS experiment at CERN's Large Hadron Collider; the Cosmic Ray Observatory Project (CROP) and the Action at a Distance project in Nebraska; the Pierre Auger Cosmic Ray Observatory in Argentina.

Starace, Anthony F., Ph.D., University of Chicago, 1971. George Holmes University Professor; Director, Atomic, Molecular, Optical, and Plasma Physics Program of Excellence. *Atomic, Molecular, & Optical Physics, Computational Physics, Theoretical Physics.* Theory of intense laser-atom interactions and processes that elucidate few-body dynamics, including attosecond and other ultrafast atomic and molecular processes; strong-field atomic processes such as above-threshold ionization/detachment, high-order harmonic generation, laser-assisted electron-atom scattering, and intense laser acceleration of electrons; photoionization and photo-detachment processes; atoms in strong external static fields; coherent control of atomic processes; and ultrafast electron diffraction for imaging electronic motion in atoms and molecules.

Tsymbal, Evgeny Y., Ph.D., Russian Academy of Sciences, Moscow, 1988. George Holmes University Distinguished Professor; Director, Materials Research Science and Engineering Center. *Condensed Matter Physics*. Theory of electronic, magnetic, ferroelectric, and transport properties of of materials and structures.

Umstadter, Donald P., Ph.D., University of California, Los Angeles, 1987. Leland J. and Dorothy H. Olson Chair. *Atomic, Molecular, & Optical Physics, Optics, Plasma and Fusion*. Extreme nonlinear optics of high-intensity laser interactions; relativistic plasmas; compact laser-driven particle accelerators and ultra-short-duration X-ray sources; high-energy density physics and extreme states of matter.

Associate Professor

Belashchenko, Kirill, Ph.D., Kurchatov Institute, 1999. *Computational Physics, Condensed Matter Physics, Materials Science, Metallurgy*. Electronic theory of magnetism and magnetic materials, spin-dependent transport, alloy theory.

Centurion, Martin, Ph.D., California Institute of Technology, 2005. Susan J. Rosowski Associate Professor of Physics. *Atomic, Molecular, & Optical Physics, Optics, Physics of Beams*. Experimental ultrafast atomic, molecular, optical, and plasma physics. We use diffractive imaging of molecules with femtosecond electron pulses to investigate dynamical processes such as photochemical reactions and the interaction of matter with intense laser fields. Our group also focuses on developing and using novel femtosecond electron sources and 3D imaging of molecules with atomic resolution.

Kravchenko, Ilya, Ph.D., University of Kansas, 1999. *Atmosphere, Space Physics, Cosmic Rays, High Energy Physics, Particles and Fields*. Experimental high-energy physics.

Shadwick, Bradley A., Ph.D., University of Texas at Austin, 1995. Vice-Chair of Physics and Astronomy. *Computational Physics, Computer Science, Mechanics, Physics of Beams, Plasma and Fusion*. Intense laser-plasma interactions; advanced accelerator concepts; plasma theory; Hamiltonian systems and methods; advanced numerical methods; cluster computing.

Uiterwaal, Kees, Ph.D., Utrecht University, 1994. Graduate Committee Chair. *Atomic, Molecular, & Optical Physics, Chemical Physics, Optics*. Photoexcitation and photoionization in ultrashort and intense laser pulses; molecular photochemistry; spatially-resolved time-of-flight ion mass spectrometry; nonlinear optical effects; holographic spatial pulse shaping; optical vortices; optical orbital angular momentum.

Assistant Professor

Fuchs, Matthias, Ph.D., Ludwig-Maximilians University, Munich, 2010. *Atomic, Molecular, & Optical Physics, Plasma and Fusion*. Experimental ultrafast and high-field X-ray science. We develop a compact ultrafast next-generation X-ray source based on laser-plasma acceleration. We use the femtosecond X-ray pulses to investigate ultrafast processes in chemical reactions and solids. Our group also studies high-field nonlinear QED effects at both optical wavelengths using PetaWatt lasers and at X-ray wavelengths using X-ray free-electron lasers (XFELs).

Golf, Frank, Ph.D., University of California at San Diego, 2011. *High Energy Physics*. Compact muon solenoid (CMS) experiment at CERN.

Hong, Xia, Ph.D., Yale University, 2006. *Applied Physics, Condensed Matter Physics, Low Temperature Physics, Nano Science and Technology*. Materials science; epitaxial growth and nanofabrication of complex oxide heterostructures; transport studies of nanoscale and low-dimensional electron systems.

Huang, Peisi, Ph.D., University of Wisconsin-Madison, 2013. *Particles and Fields*. Theoretical particle physics, including new physics beyond the Standard Model, Higgs physics, collider physics and particle cosmology.

Kovalev, Alexey, Ph.D., Technical University of Delft, 2006. *Condensed Matter Physics, Theoretical Physics*. Theoretical condensed-matter physics; spintronics; spin-dependent transport; quantum information processing.

Xu, Xiaoshan, Ph.D., Georgia Institute of Technology, 2007. *Condensed Matter Physics*. Experimental condensed matter physics.

Emeritus

Burrow, Paul D., Ph.D., University of California, Berkeley, 1966. *Atomic, Molecular, & Optical Physics*. Temporary negative ions, dissociative electron attachment.

Jaecks, Duane H., Ph.D., University of Washington, 1964. *Atomic, Molecular, & Optical Physics, History & Philosophy of Physics/Science*. Experimental study of unusual states of atoms and molecules formed in various dynamical processes, including photoionization and molecular dissociation using polarized photon-scattered particle correlation measurements and three-particle coincidence measurements; history of scientific instruments with an emphasis on optical instrumentation.

Jaswal, S. S., Ph.D., Michigan State University, 1964. *Condensed Matter Physics, Electromagnetism, Nano Science and Technology*. Theoretical condensed matter physics; electron and magnetic properties of solids, surfaces, interfaces, and nanostructures.

Jones, C. Edward, Ph.D., University of California, Berkeley. *Particles and Fields*. Particle theory.

Kirby, Roger D., Ph.D., Cornell University, 1969. *Condensed Matter Physics, Nano Science and Technology, Optics*. Experimental condensed matter physics; thin film magnetism; fabrication of nanostructural materials; magneto-optic properties; magneto-optic recording; spin dynamics measured using femtosecond laser pump-probe experiments.

Schmidt, Edward G., Ph.D., Australian National University, 1970. *Astronomy, Astrophysics*. Astronomy and astrophysics; variable stars; spectroscopy and photometry; stellar interiors and evolution.

Research Associate Professor

Banerjee, Sudeep, Ph.D., University of Mumbai, 2000. *Atomic, Molecular, & Optical Physics, Nuclear Physics, Physics of Beams, Other*. Atomic, molecular, and optical physics; lasers and optics; physics of beams; plasma physics; nuclear physics; laser-driven electron acceleration, MeV X-ray sources; nuclear interrogation.

Bettis, Clifford L., Ph.D., University of Oklahoma, 1976. *Nonspecialized*. Educational physics.

Lee, Kevin M., Ph.D., University of Nebraska-Lincoln, 1997. *Physics and other Science Education*. Astronomy education; instructional technology; photometric observations of variable stars.

Liu, Yi, Ph.D., Tohoku University, 1988. *Applied Physics, Electromagnetism, Materials Science, Metallurgy, Nano Science and Technology, Physics and other Science Education*. High-resolution and analytical electron microscopy.

Research Assistant Professor

Chen, Shouyuan, Ph.D., University of Michigan. *Atomic, Molecular, & Optical Physics, Optics, Physics of Beams*. Experimental atomic, molecular, and optical physics; high-intensity laser plasma interaction; laser wakefield acceleration; non-linear Thomson scattering; quantum electrodynamics.

Komesu, Takashi, Ph.D., University of Nebraska-Lincoln, 2002. *Condensed Matter Physics, Electromagnetism, Low Temperature Physics*. Materials Science, Condensed Matter Physics, Solid State Physics.

Ngoko Djiokap, Jean Marcel, Ph.D., Université catholique de Louvain, 2010. Theoretical atomic, molecular, optical and plasma physics; ultrafast and strong field physics.

Paudel, Tula, Ph.D., Case Western Reserve University, 2009. *Condensed Matter Physics*. Condensed Matter Physics, Computational Physics, Materials Physics.

Adjunct Professor

Boag, Neil, Ph.D., University of Bristol, 1980. Experimental condensed matter physics.

Dominguez, Aaron, Ph.D., University of California at San Diego, 1998. *High Energy Physics*. Compact muon solenoid (CMS) experiment at CERN.

Enders, Axel, Ph.D., Max-Planck-Institute for Microstructure Physics and Physics Department of the Martin Luther University, 1999. *Condensed Matter Physics*. Multi-functional surface-supported hybrid nanostructures; innovative nano-materials synthesis strategies; low- and variable temperature scanning tunneling microscopy; electron spectroscopy; magneto-optics; magnetic dichroism.

Fridkin, Vladimir, Ph.D., Russian Academy of Sciences, 1958. Experimental condensed matter physics; ferroelectricity.

Hadjipanayis, George C., Ph.D., University of Manitoba, 1979. Experimental condensed matter physics; magnetic materials and applications.

Losovyj, Yaroslav, Ph.D., University of L'viv, 1984. *Condensed Matter Physics*. Condensed matter physics.

Manakov, Nikolai L., Ph.D., Voronezh State University, 1971. *Atomic, Molecular, & Optical Physics*. Theoretical atomic physics; mathematical physics; theory of intense laser-atom interactions.

Mei, Wai-Ning, Ph.D., State University of New York at Buffalo, 1979. *Condensed Matter Physics*. Theoretical condensed matter physics; surface physics and molecular dynamics simulations of molecular crystals.

Adjunct Associate Professor

Frolov, Mikhail V., Ph.D., Voronezh State University, 2000. *Atomic, Molecular, & Optical Physics*. Theoretical atomic physics; multiphoton processes in intense laser fields; strong field phenomena.

Krajewska, Katarzyna, Ph.D., University of Warsaw, 2004. *Atomic, Molecular, & Optical Physics, Particles and Fields*. Theoretical high-field physics; quantum electrodynamics in high-intensity laser fields; ultrafast and strong-field atomic physics.

Courtesy Professor

Eckhardt, Craig J., Ph.D., Yale University, 1967. *Chemical Physics, Condensed Matter Physics*. Experimental chemical physics; electronic and vibrational spectra of molecules and molecular crystals; dielectric properties of molecular crystals; detonation mechanism of energetic materials; optical properties of solids; lattice dynamics of molecular crystals; organized molecular monolayers; nanotribology.

Woollam, John A., Ph.D., Michigan State University, 1967. Professor, Electrical Engineering. *Condensed Matter Physics*. Experimental condensed matter physics; optical and electrical properties of solids.

Zeng, Xiao Cheng, Ph.D., Ohio State University, 1989. Professor, Chemistry. *Computational Physics*. Computational

and theoretical studies of equilibrium and kinetic properties of liquids, solids, and nanomaterials.

Other

Harbison, Rebecca A., Ph.D., Cornell University, 2013. Assistant Professor of Practice. *Astronomy*. Planetary rings.

DEPARTMENTAL RESEARCH SPECIALTIES AND STAFF

Theoretical

Atomic, Molecular, & Optical Physics. Theory of intense laser-atom interactions and of processes that elucidate few-body dynamics, including attosecond and other ultrafast atomic and molecular processes; strong-field atomic processes such as above-threshold ionization/detachment, high-order harmonic generation, laser-assisted electron-atom scattering, and intense laser acceleration of electrons; photoionization and photo-detachment processes; atoms in strong external static fields; coherent control of atomic processes; and ultrafast electron diffraction for imaging electronic motion in atoms and molecules. Starace.

Atomic, Molecular, & Optical Physics. Theory of electron-atom and electron-molecule collisions; electron attachment to molecules and clusters, including systems of biological interest; strong-field ionization of atoms and molecules. Fabrikant.

Atomic, Molecular, & Optical Physics. Intense laser-matter interactions; high-energy-density physics; plasma-based light sources. Shadwick.

Condensed Matter Physics. Theory of electronic, magnetic, ferro-electric, and transport properties of nanostructures. Tsymbal.

Condensed Matter Physics. Electronic theory of magnetism and magnetic materials, spin-dependent transport, alloy theory. Belashchenko.

Condensed Matter Physics. Theoretical condensed-matter physics; spintronics; spin-dependent transport; quantum information processing. Kovalev.

High Energy Physics. Theoretical particle physics, including new physics beyond the Standard Model, Higgs physics, collider physics and particle cosmology. Huang.

Plasma. Intense short-pulse laser-plasma interactions with applications to advanced accelerators and light sources; kinetic theory of plasmas; Hamiltonian structure and methods; advanced numerical methods; large-scale simulations; computational methods. Shadwick.

Experimental

Atomic, Molecular, & Optical Physics. Vacuum field interaction of atoms and electrons; decoherence in matter interferometry. Batelaan.

Atomic, Molecular, & Optical Physics. Nonlinear optics of high-intensity laser light in relativistic plasmas, with applications to compact particle accelerators and ultra-short duration X-ray sources; high-energy-density physics and extreme states of matter. Umstadter.

Atomic, Molecular, & Optical Physics. Photoexcitation and photoionization in intense, ultrashort laser pulses; molecular photochemistry; spatially resolved time-of-flight ion mass spectrometry; nonlinear optical effects; holographic spatial pulse shaping; optical vortices; optical orbital angular momentum. Uiterwaal.

Atomic, Molecular, & Optical Physics. Atomic, molecular, and optical physics. Experimental ultrafast molecular dynamics; diffractive imaging; femtosecond electron sources; 3D imaging of molecules. Centurion.

Atomic, Molecular, & Optical Physics. Polarized electron collisions with atoms and molecules; development of polarized electron sources and electron polarimeters; neutrino mass measurements. Gay.

Atomic, Molecular, & Optical Physics. Experimental ultrafast and high-field X-ray science; development of a laser-driven compact ultrafast X-ray lightsource; laser-wakefield acceleration; ultrafast X-ray interactions; high-field interactions; nonlinear X-ray optics. Fuchs.

Condensed Matter Physics. Physics and applications of molecular and polymer ferroelectric materials; nanoscale ferroelectricity. Ducharme.

Condensed Matter Physics. Electronic and magnetic properties of nanostructural materials; magnetic domain imaging applications of SPM; magnetic sensors. Liou.

Condensed Matter Physics. Magnetism in cluster-assembled nanostructure; magneto-electronic devices; fundamental limits on magnetic recording density; exchange-coupled and hybrid permanent-magnetic materials. Sellmyer.

Condensed Matter Physics. Multiferroic and polar materials using SPM techniques; SPM-assisted methods for fabrication of nano-structures; studies of electromechanical properties of biocompatible materials. Gruverman.

Condensed Matter Physics. Magnetic/ferromagnetic/ferroelectric thin film interactions piezoelectric strain effects, exchange bias, solid-state neutron detector development. Adenwalla.

Condensed Matter Physics. Molecular beam epitaxial growth of magnetic heterolayer structures; extrinsic control of exchange bias; model systems in statistical physics. Binek.

Condensed Matter Physics. Self-assembled magnetic and molecular nanostructures, low- and variable temperature STM; spin-polarized STM.

Condensed Matter Physics. Electronic structure of solids and surfaces; nonmetal to metal transitions; surface magnetism; surface ferroelectricity; organic molecular interfaces. Dowben.

Condensed Matter Physics. Epitaxial growth and nanofabrication of complex oxide heterostructures; transport studies of nanoscale and low-dimensional electron systems. Hong.

Condensed Matter Physics. Low dimensional complex oxides and their interface with organic semiconductors. Xu.

High Energy Physics. The Cosmic Ray Observatory Project (CROP)and the Action at a Distance Project are education and outreach projects to study extensive cosmic-ray air showers with particle detectors located at high schools throughout Nebraska. Claes, Snow.

High Energy Physics. The Askaryan Radio Array experiment at the South Pole. Kravchenko.

High Energy Physics. The Compact Muon Solenoid (CMS) Experiment at CERN, Geneva, Switzerland studies the newly-observed Higgs boson, searches for new particles that are expected from physics beyond the standard model, and makes precision measurements of Standard Model phenomena. The group has hardware, software and physics analysis responsibilities for the experiment, including the hosting of a Tier-2 computing facility on campus. The group has significant responsibilities in the construction of a future silicon pixel detector for CMS. Bloom, Claes, Kravchenko, Snow.

High Energy Physics. The Pierre Auger Observatory, the world's largest cosmic ray experiment in Argentina. Snow.

View additional information about this department at www.gradschoolshopper.com. Check out the "Why Choose Us?" section, find out more about the department's culture and get links to social media networks.

UNIVERSITY OF NEBRASKA-LINCOLN

NEBRASKA CENTER FOR MATERIALS AND NANOSCIENCE

Lincoln, Nebraska 68588-0298
http://www.unl.edu/ncmn/

General University Information
Chancellor: Ronnie Green
Dean of Graduate School: Tim Carr
University website: http://www.unl.edu/
School Type: Public
Setting: Urban
Total Faculty: 1,705
Total Graduate Faculty: 1,960
Total number of Students: 26,079
Total number of Graduate Students: 4,606

Department Information
Department Chairman: Prof. David J. Sellmyer, Director
Department Contact: Shelli Krupicka, Administrative
 Coordinator
 Total full-time faculty: 101
 Total number of full-time equivalent positions: 7
 Full-Time Graduate Students: 251
 Female Full-Time Graduate Students: 84
 Total Post Doctorates: 66

Department Address
N201 Voelte-Keegan Nanoscience Research Center
855 N. 16th Street
Lincoln, NE 68588-0298
Phone: (402) 472-7886
Fax: (402) 472-6148
E-mail: ncmn@unl.edu
Website: http://www.unl.edu/ncmn/

ADMISSIONS

Admission Contact Information
Address admission inquiries to: Admissions, Office of Graduate
 Studies, 1100 Seaton Hall, University of Nebraska-Lincoln,
 Lincoln, NE 68588-0619
Phone: (402) 472-2875
E-mail: graduate@unl.edu
Admissions website: http://www.unl.edu/gradstudies/

Application deadlines
Fall admission:
U.S. students: January 31   *Int'l. students*: January 31

Application fee
U.S. students: $50   *Int'l. students*: $50
Application deadlines and fees vary by program. Please check
 directly with program of interest for most accurate application
 information.

Admissions information
For Fall of 2018:

Admission requirements
Bachelor's degree requirements: A Bachelor's degree in Physics,
 Chemistry, Materials Science, Engineering, or Mathematics
 is required.
Minimum undergraduate GPA: 3.0

GRE requirements
The GRE is recommended but not required.
No minimum requirement.

Subjective GRE requirements
The Subjective GRE is recommended.
Varies by program.

TOEFL requirements
The TOEFL exam is required for students from non-English-
 speaking countries.
 PBT score: 550
 iBT score: 79

Other admissions information
Additional requirements: Application deadlines and admission
 requirements vary by program. Please check directly with program of interest for additional and most accurate information.

TUITION

Tuition year 2018–2019:
Tuition for in-state residents
 Full-time students: $323.25 per credit
Tuition for out-of-state residents
 Full-time students: $925.25 per credit
Teaching and Research Assistants do not pay tuition.
Credit hours per semester to be considered full-time: 9
Deferred tuition plan: No
Health insurance: Yes, Student Cost: $986.05 (Fall); $1,365.71
 (Spring/Summer).
Other academic fees: Financial aid and other deadlines vary by
 program. Please check with program of interest for accurate
 information.
Academic term: Semester

Teaching Assistants, Research Assistants, and Fellowships
 Number of first-year
 Teaching and Research Assistants do not pay tuition. Average
 stipend information is not available. First-year numbers not
 available because assistantships and fellowships are offered
 by individual departments.

FINANCIAL AID

Application deadlines
Fall admission:
U.S. students: April 1   *Int'l. students*: April 1

Loans
Loans are available for U.S. students.
Loans are not available for international students.
GAPSFAS application required: No
FAFSA application required: Yes

For further information
Address financial aid inquiries to: Scholarships & Financial Aid,
 17 Canfield Administration Building, P.O. Box 880411, Lin-
 coln, NE 68588-0411.
Phone: (402) 472-2030
E-mail: finaid2@unl.edu
Financial aid website: http://www.unl.edu/scholfa/

HOUSING

Availability of on-campus housing
Single students: Yes
Married students: Yes

For further information
Address housing inquiries to: Office of University Housing, 1115 N. 16th Street, Lincoln, NE 68588-0622.
Phone: (402) 472-3561
E-mail: housing@unl.edu
Housing aid website: http://housing.unl.edu/

Table A—Faculty, Enrollments, and Degrees Granted

Research Specialty	2017–18 Faculty	Enrollment Fall 2017 Master's	Enrollment Fall 2017 Doctorate	Number of Degrees Granted 2017–18 Master's	Number of Degrees Granted 2017–18 Terminal Master's	Number of Degrees Granted 2017–18 Doctorate
Chemical Physics	21	25	51	–	–	–
Condensed Matter Physics	24	16	31	–	–	–
Materials Science, Metallurgy	52	43	85	–	–	–
Other	10	–	–	–	–	–
Total	107	84	167	–	–	–
Full-time Grad. Stud.	–	84	167	–	–	–
First-year Grad. Stud.	–	–	–	–	–	–

GRADUATE DEGREE REQUIREMENTS

Master's: Several options exist, including thesis and non-thesis. Generally, 30 or 36 hours of coursework are required, depending on the option chosen. See Graduate Studies Bulletin for details.

Doctorate: Ninety credit hours are required, with research credits included. A grade of B or better is required. No foreign language is required. Twenty-seven hours and 18 consecutive months must be completed in residence.

Thesis: Thesis may be written in absentia.

SPECIAL EQUIPMENT, FACILITIES, OR PROGRAMS

The Nebraska Center for Materials and Nanoscience operates and coordinates the following Central Service Facilities: X-ray Structural Characterization, Electron Nanoscopy Instrumentation, Surface and Materials Characterization, Nanomaterials and Thin Films, Nanofabrication Cleanroom, and Cryogenics Instrumentation. A brief description of each facility is as follows.

The X-ray Structural Characterization Facility hosts (1) Rigaku SmartLab high-resolution X-ray Diffractometer with in-plane diffraction option, (2) Bruker-AXS D8 Discover X-ray Diffractometer for medium resolution and General Area Detector Diffraction System (GADDS) for 2D diffraction applications, (3) Rigaku D/Max-B, (4) PANalytical Empyrean, (5) Rigaku Multiflex Diffractometers for powder diffraction applications, and (6) Bruker Single Crystal Diffractometer with Photon 100 CMOS detector for X-ray Crystallography. The facility provides a Meiji optical microscope with a polarizer attachment for single crystal screening. Crystallographic databases from International Center for Diffraction Data (ICDD) and Cambridge Structural Database (CSD) are subscribed by the facility to assist users for phase identification, quantification, and molecular visualization needs. It also provides several analysis software suites to assist users for in-depth analysis of their powder, thin films, nanoparticles, and single crystal diffraction data.

The Electron Nanoscopy Instrumentation Facility offers researchers the best tools for atomic-scale and submicron materials analysis. The facility houses three electron microscopes, including the latest 200 kV analytical (scanning) transmission electron microscope (FEI Tecnai Osiris), a high-resolution scanning electron microscope (FEI Nova NanoSEM450) and a JEOL JEM2010 transmission electron microscope, with a Gatan Erlangsen CCD camera. The instruments for sample preparation are well equipped.

The Cryogenics Instrumentation Facility maintains a continuous supply of the liquid nitrogen necessary for on-campus use. The facility hosts a MPMS (Superconducting Quantum Interference Device (SQUID)) magnetometer for characterization of the magnetic properties of samples. The facility also hosts a high magnetic field annealing system which combines high temperature annealing with a high magnetic field to potentially modify the magnetic properties of thin film and alloys.

The Nanomaterials and Thin Films Facility provides state-of-the-art instruments for fabricating material samples and devices. Instruments available include a sputtering system, a Pulsed Laser Deposition (PLD) system and a multipurpose Hex deposition system to fabricate a variety of thin films, especially nanostructured films, including multilayers, granular solids, clusters, etc. The sputtering system has two RF, three DC sputtering guns, load lock chamber, and the substrate holder will allow simultaneous rotation, heating, RF bias and deposition at up to 850 °C in suitable sputtering environment. The PLD system has six programmable target sockets; in situ heating up to 950 °C and an in situ Reflection High Energy Electron Diffraction (RHEED) is available for monitoring the layer-by-layer growth of the PLD films. The Hex system is a unique system, which combines a sputtering source and an E-beam source for metals and oxides with a thermal evaporator for polymers and an organic evaporator for organic materials. The facility also maintains several systems available for the synthesis of novel materials in bulk quantities, an Arc-melter (for producing alloys), a Melt spinner for quenching (rapid solidification), a ball mill system to synthesize nanosized materials and tube furnaces for annealing, doping, and sintering. Furthermore, the facility hosts a Surface Area and Porosity Analyzer for sample characterization.

The Surface and Materials Characterization Facility (SMCF) provides state-of-the-art instruments for nanometer-scale surface, thermal, and mechanical characterization of materials. The facility contains three scanning probe microscopies (SPM): (1) Bruker Dimension Icon® Atomic Force Microscopy, (2) Digital Instruments Dimension 3100 Scanning Probe Microscopy, and (3) DI EnviroScope Atomic Force Microscopy (ESCOPE). The facility provides a large variety of SPM applications, such as Atomic Force Microscopy (AFM), Magnetic Force Microscopy (MFM), Electrostatic Force Microscopy (EFM), Scanning Tunneling Microscopy (STM), Piezoresponse Microscopy (PFM), Surface Potential (PeakForce KPFM), PeakForce Tunneling (PF-TUNA) and Conductive AFM, and Quantitative Nanomechanical Property Mapping (PF-QNM). The SPM system is capable of many imaging modes (Contact mode, Tapping mode, ScanAsyst peakforce tapping mode, Lift mode, Phase imaging mode) in air, fluid, vacuum, or a purged gas, as well as a heating/cooling environment. A new X-ray Photoelectron Spectroscopy (XPS) system has now been added to SMCF. The technique, also known as Electron Spectroscopy for Chemical Analysis (ESCA), is useful for analyzing the surface chemistry of materials. This instrument also has an option for Ultraviolet Photoelectron Spectroscopy (UPS), which can be used to investigate the valence-band electronic structure of a material. The facility also contains a variety of equipment to characterize the mechanical and thermal properties of a wide range of materials. Primary equipment includes a DSC204 F1 Phoenix Differential Scanning Calorimeter, a TGA

209 F1 Libra Thermogravimetric Analyzer, an Olympus BX51 Microscope equipped with Mettler Toledo FP900 Thermal stage, and a Tukon 2500 Knoop/Vickers Hardness Tester. Sample preparation equipment includes Sartorius Cubis MSU2.7S-000-DM Microbalance, BUEHLER ISOMet 1000 Precision Saw, and BUEHLER MiniMet 1000 grinder-polisher.

The Nanofabrication Cleanroom Facility operates a 4000 sq. ft. clean room with a full suite of leading-edge tools for fabricating and characterizing nanoscale devices and structures. Equipment includes electron beam lithography system (Carl Zeiss Supra40 SEM + Raith pattern generator), mask aligner (SUSS MJB-4), maskless laser lithography system (Heidelberg DWL66), focused ion-beam workstation (FEI Strata200), reactive ion etching system (Trion minilock), deep RIE system (Oxford PlasmaPro Estrelas100), Ion beam etching and sputtering system (intlvac Nanoquest I), e-beam evaporation system (AJA ORION8000), stylus profilometer (Dektak-XT), reflective thin-film thickness measurement system (Filmetrics F40), wet etching benches and fume hoods, optic microscope, Four-probe resistivity measurement stand, ovens, wire bonder, and others.

The Specialized Research facilities include many state-of-the-art research facilities, including 14 Tesla NMR spectrometer equipped for solid-state NMR, NIMA Langmuir-Blodgett Trough for mono-layer and multi-layer films, atomic force microscopes, high-field superconductive solenoids, SQUID magnetometers, Raman and Brillouin laser light-scattering facilities, a comprehensive laboratory for the study of magnetic materials, a number of photoemission and inverse photoemission spectrometers (including spin-polarized inverse photoemission), and dedicated minicomputers for theoretical calculations. In addition, pulsed laser facilities, atomic force microscope, and a comprehensive ellipsometer laboratory are available.

Table B—Separately Budgeted Research Expenditures by Source of Support

Source of Support	Departmental Research	Physics-related Research Outside Department
Federal government	$12,846,001	$11,219,603
State/local government	$2,655,793	$94,126
Non-profit organizations	$1,798,903	$145,740
Business and industry	$684,594	$1,789,000
Other		
Total	$17,985,291	$13,248,469

Table C—Separately Budgeted Research Expenditures by Research Specialty

Research Specialty	No. of Grants	Expenditures ($)
Chemical Physics	20	$2,641,032
Condensed Matter Physics	39	$6,463,689
Materials Science, Metallurgy	109	$8,880,570
Total	168	$17,985,291

FACULTY

Distinguished University Professor

Lu, Yongfeng, Ph.D., Osaka University, 1991. Laser material processing and characterization at micrometer and nanometer scales.

Sellmyer, David J., Ph.D., Michigan State University, 1965. Nanomagnetics and magnetoelectronics, including self- and cluster-assembled structures, dilute magnetic semiconductors

and oxides, exchange-coupled nanocomposites, and fundamental limits on magnetic storage density.

Takacs, James M., Ph.D., California Institute of Technology, 1981. Synthesis of novel polymers.

Tsymbal, Evgeny Y., Ph.D., Russian Academy of Sciences, Moscow, 1988. Theory of electronic structure and spin-dependent transport in nanoscale magnetic systems.

Woollam, John A., Ph.D., Michigan State University, 1967. Ellipsometric studies of oxide surfaces; magneto-optic films; optical coatings and electrochromics.

Zeng, Xiao Cheng, Ph.D., Ohio State University, 1989. Statistical mechanics of liquids and solids; phase transition; computer simulations.

Chair Professor

Alexander, Dennis R., Ph.D., Kansas State University, 1976. Ultra-fast lasers; nanoparticle production; surface modifications using full spectrum lasers.

Berkowitz, David B., Ph.D., Harvard University, 1990. Organic catalyst development and new methods for catalyst screening.

Dowben, Peter A., Ph.D., University of Cambridge, 1981. Surface science; magnetic and ferroelectric films.

Dussault, Patrick H., Ph.D., California Institute of Technology, 1986. Synthesis and properties of organic materials.

Dzenis, Yuris A., Ph.D., University of Texas, Arlington, 1994. Composite materials and mechanics.

Gay, Timothy J., Ph.D., University of Chicago, 1980. Experimental atomic physics; state-selected ion-atom collisions; spin-polarized sources.

Gruverman, Alexei, Ph.D., Ural State University, 1990. Ferroelectrics; piezoelectrics; scanning probe microscopy.

Ianno, Natale (Ned) J., Ph.D., University of Illinois, 1981. Electronic properties of semiconductors and superconductors.

Langell, Marjorie, Ph.D., Princeton University, 1979. Surface chemistry; Auger and photoemission studies of transition metal oxides.

Nastasi, Michael, Ph.D., Cornell University, 1986. Materials for extreme nuclear environments; irradiation induced phase transformations; ion irradiation modification of materials.

Rajca, Andrzej T., Ph.D., University of Kentucky, 1985. High-spin organic polyradicals; synthesis of two-dimensional magnets from polyradicals.

Rajurkar, K. P., Ph.D., Michigan Technological University, 1982. Non-conventional machining at macro, micro, and nano scales; stochastic modeling of manufacturing processes and systems.

Saraf, Ravi, Ph.D., University of Massachusetts, Amherst, 1987. Nanoscale material fabrication and devices; biophysics.

Schubert, Mathias, Ph.D., Universität Leipzig, 1997. Condensed matter spectroscopy; ferroic semiconductor thin films and nanostructures.

Shield, Jeffrey E., Ph.D., Iowa State University, 1992. Microstructural evolution of materials; rapid solidification.

Turner, Joseph A., Ph.D., University of Illinois at Urbana-Champaign, 1994. Wave propagation and vibrations, including ultrasonics, NDE, materials characterization, AFM dynamics, and nanoindentation.

Viljoen, Hendrik J., Ph.D., University of Pretoria, 1985. Synthesis and processing of materials with CVD.

Yang, Yiqi, Ph.D., Purdue University, 1991. Biopolymeric materials; biotextiles; industrial applications of agricultural by-products.

Professor

Adenwalla, Shireen, Ph.D., Northwestern University, 1989. Experimental condensed matter physics.

Barnes, Caren M., M.S., University of Missouri, Kansas City, 1974. The effects of polishing on dental materials and dental tissues.

Bartelt-Hunt, Shannon, Ph.D., University of Virginia, 2004. Protein attachment to environmental surfaces; physical-chemical transport of environmental contaminants.

Batelaan, Herman, Ph.D., University of Utrecht, 1991. Experimental atomic physics; laser cooling and trapping; matter optics and interferometry; ultra-fast electron/photon physics.

Belashchenko, Kirill, Ph.D., Kurchatov Institute, 1999. Electronic structure theory; magnetic, transport, and structural properties of materials and nanostructures.

Binek, Christian, Ph.D., University of Duisburg, 1995. Magnetic heterostructures in basic research and spintronic applications.

Bobaru, Florin, Ph.D., Cornell University, 2001. Computational mechanics; numerical optimization of advanced materials and systems.

Cornelius, Christopher J., Ph.D., Chemical Engineering Virginia Tech, 2000. Dissertation: Physical and gas permeation properties of a series of novel hybrid inorganic-organic composites based on a synthesized fluorinated polyimide. Advisor: Dr. Eva Marand.

Ducharme, Stephen, Ph.D., University of Southern California, 1986. Organic ferroelectric materials; ferroelectricity, piezoelectricity, and piezoelectricity at the nanoscale.

Feng, Ruqiang, Ph.D., Johns Hopkins University, 1992. Experimental mechanics of materials, including high strain rate, shock wave, impact experiments, and the study of inelastic deformation and failure mechanisms of ceramics.

Harbison, Gerard S., Ph.D., Harvard University, 1984. Solid-state NMR spectroscopy; quantum chemical calculations on endohedral fullerenes and ionic crystalline solids.

Kim, Yong-Rak, Ph.D., Texas A&M University, 2003. Sustainable infrastructure; transportation materials; multi-scale-multi-physics modeling.

Larsen, Gustavo, Ph.D., Yale University, 1992. Surface chemistry and catalysis.

Liou, Sy-Hwang, Ph.D., Johns Hopkins University, 1985. Ultrafine particle magnetic films; high-temperature superconducting films.

Negahban, Mehrdad, Ph.D., University of Michigan, 1988. Mechanical effects of phase transition in polymers under large strains.

Pannier, Angela K., Ph.D., Northwestern University, 2007. Biomaterials for non-viral gene delivery and tissue engineering applications.

Parkhurst, Lawrence J., Ph.D., Yale University, 1965. Optical properties of DNA; solid state protein thermodynamics.

Redepenning, Jody G., Ph.D., Colorado State University, 1985. Electrochemistry; biocompatible materials.

Sutter, Eli, Ph.D., Sofia Univ., 1994. Novel materials and materials for energy applications.

Sutter, Peter, Ph.D., ETH Zurich, 1996. Surfaces, interfaces, two-dimensional materials; in-situ microscopy and spectroscopy.

Wang, Jian, Ph.D., Rensselaer Polytechnic Inst., Troy, NY, 2006. Quantitative exploration of the structure-properties relationships of structural and nanostructured materials using multiscale methods and techniques.

Watkins, David K., Ph.D., Florida State University, 1984. Electron microscopy studies of minerals.

Yang, Jiashi, Ph.D., Princeton University, 1994. Electromechanical materials and devices.

Associate Professor

Baesu, Eveline, Ph.D., University of California, Berkeley, 1998. Continuum mechanics; plasticity; electrodynamics of continuum media.

Centurion, Martin, Ph.D., California Institute of Technology, 2005. Ultrafast molecular dynamics; diffractive imaging of molecules.

Cheung, Chin Li (Barry), Ph.D., Harvard University, 2002. Synthesis and characterization of materials at the nanoscale.

Gu, Linxia, Ph.D., University of Florida, 2004. Soft-tissue mechanics; multi-scale and multi-physics modeling.

Hong, Xia, Ph.D., Yale University, 2006. Epitaxial complex oxide thin films and nanostructures; two-dimensional electron systems.

Hu, Jiong, Ph.D., Iowa State University, 2005. Eco-efficient infrastructure materials; innovative infrastructure materials development; advanced materials characterization.

Kidambi, Srivatsan, Ph.D., Michigan State University, 2007. Tissue engineering and biomaterials; drug delivery; stem cells.

Lai, Rebecca Y., Ph.D., University of Texas, Austin, 2003. Ligand-induced folding in biopolymers; electrochemical biosensors; surface plasmon resonance biosensors.

Li, Hui, Ph.D., The University of Iowa, 2004. Quantum chemistry; intermolecular interaction; combined quantum mechanics and molecular mechanics (QM/MM) methods; catalysis.

Li, Yusong, Ph.D., Vanderbilt University, 2005. Fate and transport of contaminants; numerical modeling.

Ndao, Sidy, Ph.D., Rensselaer Polytechnic Institute, 2010. Micro/nano systems energy conversion, storage and power generation; two-phase heat transfer in microdomains and nanodomains; microfluidics and functional nanofluids; microscale combustion.

Ryu, Sangjin, Ph.D., MIT, 2009. Microfluidics; cell mechanics; biophysics; atomic force microscopy.

Schubert, Eva Franke, Ph.D., University of Leipzig, 1998. Ion beam processing; nanostructured thin-film fabrication for optical, electromechanical, and magnetic device applications.

Sinitskii, Alexander, Ph.D., Moscow State University, 2008. Carbon nanomaterials; graphene; nanoelectronics.

Tan, Li, Ph.D., University of Michigan, 2002. Unconventional nanolithography; nanoimprint lithography; polymer thin films and devices/sensors.

Zhang, Jian, Ph.D., University of Pittsburgh, 2008. Synthetic chemistry, physical chemistry, and theoretical modeling to provide a fundamental understanding of nanoscale interactions so that noble metal nanoparticles, metal-organic frameworks, and carbon-based nanomaterials can be rationally designed and synthesized to have desired electrocatalytic, gas sorption, and photocatalytic properties for clean energy-related applications.

Zhang, Zhaoyan, Ph.D., Pennsylvania State University, 2000. Experimental and theoretical study of laser material interactions.

Assistant Professor

Alexandrov, Vitaly, Ph.D., Max Planck Institute for Solid State Research/University of Stuttgart, 2009. Computational materials science and chemistry.

Argyropoulos, Christos, Ph.D., Queen Mary, University of London, 2011. Nanophotonics; plasmonics; metamaterials; metasurfaces; computational electromagnetics.

Ciftci, Ozan, Ph.D., Gaziantep University, 2009. Food lipids; food nanotechnology; particle formation; supercritical fluid technology.

Cui, Bai, Ph.D., Imperial College London, 2011. Corrosion; materials for nuclear energy; high-temperature alloys and ceramics; electron microscopy.

Dishari, Shudipto Konika, Ph.D., National University of Singapore, 2010. Nanomaterials and polymers for energy and biomedical applications.

Eun, Jongwan, Ph.D., University of Wisconsin-Madison, 2014. Waste Containment System; Multiphase transport phenomenon through porous and nonporous medium; Soil mechanics.

Iverson, Nicole M., Ph.D., Rutgers University and University of Medicine and Dentistry of New Jersey, 2010. Single wall carbon nanotube sensors, nitric oxide, in vivo delivery of nanomaterials.

Kim, Seunghee, Ph.D., Georgia Institute of Technology, 2012. Hydro-thermo-chemo-geomechanical coupling; fluid flow in porous media; carbon geologic storage; energy geo-storage.

Kovalev, Alexey, Ph.D., Delft University of Technology, 2006. Spintronics; condensed matter physics; quantum information.

Morin, Stephen A., Ph.D., University of Wisconsin – Madison, 2011. Postdoctoral Fellow, Harvard University, 2011–2013. Hybrid (composite) nanomaterial design, synthesis, characterization; soft/hard mater interactions; mechanical control of nanomaterials/chemistry.

Nejati, Siamak, Ph.D., Drexel University, 2013. Interfacial Phenomena; Polymers; Chemical Vapor Deposition.

Rao, Prahalada, Ph.D., Oklahoma State University, 2013. Advanced Manufacturing; Sensing; Process Monitoring; Machine Learning; and Big Data Analytics.

Sealy, Michael P., Ph.D., University of Alabama, 2014. Laser-based manufacturing; additive manufacturing, medical devices; corrosion; fatigue; finite element modeling.

Xu, Xiaoshan, Ph.D., Georgia Institute of Technology, 2007. Condensed matter and material physics; thin film and nanostructure growth; multi-ferroics.

Yang, Ruiguo, Ph.D., Michigan State University, 2014. Nanomedicine; nanofibers; smart material actuators.

Zhou, Qin, Ph.D., UC Berkeley, 2011. Nanomaterial devices, mechanics, and physics. Nanoelectromechanical systems.

Emeritus

Brand, Jennifer I., Ph.D., University of California, San Diego, 1992. Ceramic thin films from cluster beams; supercritical fluid technology.

Burrow, Paul D., Ph.D., University of California, Berkeley, 1966. Experimental molecular physics; scattering of electrons from atoms and molecules; temporary negative ions.

Diestler, Dennis J., Ph.D., California Institute of Technology, 1967. Theoretical studies of the fluid solid interface.

Eckhardt, Craig J., Ph.D., Yale University, 1967. Statics and dynamics of molecular crystals; solid state optical spectroscopy; Langmuir-Blodgett films; crystal engineering of organic solids.

Jaswal, Sitaram S., Ph.D., Michigan State University, 1964. Theory of electronic structure of magnetic compounds and multilayers.

Kirby, Roger D., Ph.D., Cornell University, 1969. Magneto-optic properties of thin films; light scattering.

Pearlstein, Edgar A., Other, Carnegie Institute of Technology, 1950. Doctor of Science. Defects in solids; electrical noise.

Robertson, Brian W., Ph.D., University of Glasgow, Scotland, 1979. Electron microscopy and techniques; nanofabrication; sensor materials and devices.

Soukup, Rodney J., Ph.D., University of Minnesota, 1969. Semiconductors; solar energy studies.

Research Professor

Skomski, Ralph, Ph.D., Dresden University of Technology, 1991. Theoretical solid state magnetism; micromagnetics; permanent magnetism.

Research Assistant Professor

Fernandez-Ballester, Lucia, Ph.D., California Institute of Technology, 2007. Polymer physics; polymer processing and crystallization.

Hassan, Ashraf Aly, Ph.D., University of Cincinnati, 2010. Fate & transport of engineered nanoparticles in the environment (water, soil, and air); emission control technologies; biological treatment of recalcitrant air toxics; use of innovative technology in atmospheric and indoor air pollution control, treatment, fate, transport of emerging contaminants; advanced water/wastewater treatment processes development.

Distinguished Adjunct Professor

Mei, Wai Ning, Ph.D., State University of New York at Buffalo, 1979. Surface structure determination using multiple-scattering theory, molecular dynamics simulations of alkali halides, and molecular solids.

Adjunct Professor

Darr, Joshua P., Ph.D., Washington University, St. Louis, MO, 2006. Aerosol particles; fluoresence spectroscopy; Fourier transform infrared spectroscopy; and scanning electron microscopy.

Darveau, Scott A., Ph.D., University of Chicago, 1998. Thin-film photovoltaic materials; Raman microscopy/laser spectroscopy.

Dutta, Diganta, Ph.D., Old Dominion University, 2015. Nanoscale characterization of biological cells and tissues; microfluidics.

Exstrom, Christopher, Ph.D., University of Minnesota, 1995. Characterization and development of novel solar cell film materials; preparation and characterization of novel solvatochromic transition-metal-based materials.

Fridkin, Vladimir, Ph.D., Institute of Crystallography, Academy of Sciences of the USSR, 1965. Ferroelectricity; ferroelectric polymers; phase transitions.

Hadjipanayis, George C., Ph.D., Manitoba, 1979. Experimental condensed matter physics; magnetic materials and applications.

Kharel, Parashu, Ph.D., Wayne State University, 2008. Experimental investigation of novel magnetic materials, spintronics, permanent magnets.

Liu, J. Ping, Ph.D., University of Amsterdam, 1994. Magnetic materials.

Namavar, Fereydoon, Ph.D., Katholieke Universiteit Leuven, 1978. Nanotechnology; alternative surfaces for medical implants; smart surfaces; smart drugs and sensors for medical application.

Palencia, Hector, Ph.D., UNL/UNAM, 2005. Catalysis/nanocatalysts; biofuels; organic synthesis.

Reece, Timothy J., Ph.D., University of Nebraska-Lincoln, 2007. Brewster angle microscopy; Langmuir films; semiconductor devices.

Sabirianov, Renat, Ph.D., UTU, 1993. Defects and impurities in magnetic materials.

Smith, Robert W., Ph.D., Oregon State University, 1989. Synthesis, crystal growth, and structural characterization of new materials through X-ray diffraction techniques.

Adjunct Associate Professor

Liu, Yi, Ph.D., Tohoku University, 1988. High-resolution and analytical electron microscopy.

Visiting Professor

Boag, Neil, Ph.D., University of Bristol, 1981. Materials science and synthesis.

DEPARTMENTAL RESEARCH SPECIALTIES AND STAFF

Theoretical

Chemical Physics. Density-functional calculations of clusters, carbon nanotubes, layered nanostructures, magnetic systems. Alexandrov, Eckhardt, Hui Li, Viljoen, Zeng.

Condensed Matter Physics. Structural and vibrational properties of crystalline and amorphous solids using the methods of statistical mechanics; giant magnetoresistance in magnetic metallic multi-layers, spin-dependent tunneling in magnetic tunnel junctions, spin injection into semiconductors; permanent-magnet materials, magnetic nanostructures, time-dependent magnetization processes, spin structure of half-metallic ferromagnets, and quantum entanglement in nanodots. Argyropoulos, Belashchenko, Jaswal, Kovalev, Skomski, Tsymbal.

Mechanics. Large deformation thermomechanical and mechanical response characterization; continuum thermodynamic modeling; fluid-solid interfacial phenomena. Baesu, Bobaru, Feng, Negahban, Rajurkar, Tan.

Experimental

Chemical Physics. Synthesis and study of unnatural analogs of biological molecules, catalyst development; design and synthesis of inorganic/bio-organic nanoscaled components; development of new robust macrocyclic ligands; synthesis of peroxide-containing natural products, new methods for organic oxidations based on ozone, singlet oxygen, and hydrogen peroxide; nanotribology, mechanochemistry, energetic materials supramolecules, and organic ferroelectrics; influence of oxidation state on chemical and physical properties of metal-containing materials; structure and properties of solids, NMR; surface properties of transition-metal oxides and other metal compounds; interactions between DNA, RNA, and proteins; design and synthesis of stable high-spin polyradicals; electrochemistry, electrochemical deposition; structure function studies in supramolecular systems; organic synthesis and chemistry, piezoelectric devices. Berkowitz, Centurion, Cheung, Ciftci, Dishari, Dussault, Eckhardt, Harbison, Iverson, Lai, Langell, Larsen, Morin, Nejati, Pannier, Parkhurst, Rajca, Redepenning, Takacs, Viljoen, Jian Zhang.

Condensed Matter Physics. Structural characterization of materials, magnetic systems, polymers, development of solid-state neutron detectors; exchange bias in magnetic metal/insulator heterosystems, matrix insulated magnetic nanoparticles; interplay between magnetic and electric properties of heterogeneous metallic magnetic systems; electronic band structure and the influence of electronics structure on various phase transitions; ferroelectric nanostructures and polymers; polarized electron physics; magnetism dynamics in thin films, superlattices; magnetic interactions in patterned nanostructures, quantum conductance and magnetoresistance in nanocontacts, nanofabrications; high-anisotropy magnetic nanocluster-assembled films, nanotube magnetism, spin-logic nanostructures, exchange-coupled nanocomposites. Adenwalla, Batelaan, Binek, Burrow, Dowben, Ducharme, Dutta, Gay, Gruverman, Hong, Kirby, Liou, Yi Liu, Pearlstein, Sellmyer, Peter Sutter, Xu.

Materials Science, Metallurgy. Developing new materials and more efficient materials production processes for deposition of thin films, microfibers, and microparticles; novel devices; thin-film deposition, high-density plasma processing, nanoscale processing; catalysis, adsorption, and materials design; microscale and nanoscale laser material processing and characterization; magnetic and electronic thin films, nanoscale wires and devices, and electron probe-based characterization; deposition and characterization of thin films of wear-resistant materials, piezoelectric oxide ceramics; optical properties of semiconductors and nanoscale materials, ellipsometry; deposition and study of semiconductor films; synthesis and development of novel biofunctional materials; microstructural evolution of materials during processing; composite materials comprising a polymeric matrix; piezoelectric materials; electrical breakdown of gases and semiconductors, plasma processing of semiconductors; laser-materials interactions. Alexander, Bobaru, Brand, Cornelius, Cui, Dzenis, Eun, Feng, Fernandez-Ballester, Gu, Hu, Ianno, Seunghee Kim, Yong-Rak Kim, Yusong Li, Lu, Nastasi, Ndao, Negahban, Rajurkar, Rao, Ryu, Saraf, Eva Schubert, Mathias Schubert, Sealy, Shield, Soukup, Eli Sutter, Tan, Turner, Wang, Woollam, Jiashi Yang, Zhaoyan Zhang, Zhou.

Mechanics. Electromechanical effects, fiber networks, and biomechanics; mesh-free methods, structural and multidisciplinary optimization of solids; functional nanomaterials and nanomanufacturing; experimental and computational mechanics of materials; active materials, composites, micromechanics, and microstructure mechanics; stochastic wave propagation, experimental ultrasonics, structural acoustics; frequency stability of piezoelectric crystal resonators. Baesu, Bartelt-Hunt, Bobaru, Brand, Dzenis, Feng, Fernandez-Ballester, Gu, Hassan, Kidambi, Yusong Li, Ndao, Negahban, Pannier, Rajurkar, Tan, Turner, Wang, Jiashi Yang, Zhaoyan Zhang.

View additional information about this department at www.gradschoolshopper.com. Check out the "Why Choose Us?" section, find out more about the department's culture and get links to social media networks.

UNIVERSITY OF NEVADA, LAS VEGAS

DEPARTMENT OF PHYSICS AND ASTRONOMY

Las Vegas, Nevada 89154-4002
http://www.physics.unlv.edu

General University Information
President: Marta Meana, Acting President
Dean of Graduate School: Kate Hausbeck Korgan
University website: http://www.unlv.edu
School Type: Public
Setting: Urban
Total Faculty: 1,033
Total Graduate Faculty: 900
Total number of Students: 29,702
Total number of Graduate Students: 4,288

Department Information
Department Chairman: Prof. Stephen Lepp, Chair
Department Contact: Gail Michel-Parsons, Administrative
  Assistant IV
  Total full-time faculty: 18
  Total number of full-time equivalent positions: 18
  Full-Time Graduate Students: 32
  Female Full-Time Graduate Students: 0
  First-Year Graduate Students: 4
  Total Post Doctorates: 10

ADMISSIONS

Admission Contact Information
Address admission inquiries to: Graduate Program Admissions,
  Department of Physics and Astronomy, 4505 S Maryland
  Pkwy, MS 4002, Las Vegas, NV 89154-4002
Phone: (702) 895-3320
E-mail: gradcollege@unlv.edu
Admissions website: http://graduatecollege.unlv.edu/admissions/

Application deadlines
Fall admission:
U.S. students: May 1   *Int'l. students*: May 1
Spring admission:
U.S. students: October 1   *Int'l. students*: October 1

Application fee
U.S. students: $60   *Int'l. students*: $95

Admissions information
For Fall of 2018:
  Number of applicants: 25
  Number admitted: 5
  Number enrolled: 5

Admission requirements
Bachelor's degree requirements: Bachelor's degree is required.
Minimum undergraduate GPA: 2.75

GRE requirements
The GRE is required.
  Mean GRE score range (25th–75th percentile): 65th

Subjective GRE requirements
The Subjective GRE is required.
  Mean Advanced GRE score range (25th–75th percentile): 65th
Physics Graduate Program: The Advanced GRE is not required
  for M.S. applicants in Physics. However, the Physics GRE
  is required for Ph.D. applicants without an M.S. degree in

Physics. Astronomy and Astrophysics Graduate Program: The
  Advanced GRE is not required for either the M.S. or the Ph.D.
  applicants.

TOEFL requirements
The TOEFL exam is required for students from non-English-
  speaking countries.
  PBT score: 550
  iBT score: 80

Other admissions information
Additional requirements: The applicant must have completed 18
  semester credits of upper division physics.
Undergraduate preparation assumed: Mechanics level—Marion,
  Classical Dynamics; Electricity and Magnetism level—
  Wangsness, Electromagnetic Fields; Quantum Mechanics lev-
  el—Griffiths, Quantum Mechanics; Mathematics level—
  through Advanced Calculus.

TUITION
Tuition year 2018–19:
Tuition for in-state residents
  Full-time students: $274.75 per credit
  Part-time students: $274.75 per credit
Tuition for out-of-state residents
  Full-time students: $274.75 per credit
  Part-time students: $274.75 per credit
Credit hours per semester to be considered full-time: 6
Deferred tuition plan: Yes
Health insurance: Available
Other academic fees: There will be additional fees.
Academic term: Semester
Number of first-year students who received full tuition waivers: 4

Teaching Assistants, Research Assistants, and Fellowships
  Number of first-year
    Teaching Assistants: 3
    Research Assistants: 1
  Minimum stipends: Master's - $11,250.00 Physics Ph.D. -
  $18,250.00 Astronomy Ph.D. - $19,250.00

FINANCIAL AID

Application deadlines
Fall admission:
U.S. students: May 1   *Int'l. students*: May 1
Spring admission:
U.S. students: October 1   *Int'l. students*: October 1

Loans
Loans are available for U.S. students.
Loans are not available for international students.
GAPSFAS application required: No
FAFSA application required: No

For further information
Address financial aid inquiries to: Graduate Program Admissions, Department of Physics and Astronomy, 4505 S Maryland Pkwy, Las Vegas, NV 89154.

Phone: (702) 895-3424
Financial aid website: http://www.unlv.edu/finaid

HOUSING

Availability of on-campus housing
Single students: Yes
Married students: No

For further information
Address housing inquiries to: Housing and Residential Life, 4505
S Maryland Pkwy, Las Vegas, NV 89154.
Phone: (702) 895-3489
E-mail: housing@unlv.edu
Housing aid website: http://housing.unlv.edu/

Table A—Faculty, Enrollments, and Degrees Granted

Research Specialty	2017–18 Faculty	Enrollment Fall 2018		Number of Degrees Granted 2017–18 (2013–18)		
		Master's	Doctorate	Master's	Terminal Master's	Doctorate
Astronomy	1	–	–	–(1)	–	–
Astrophysics	6	2	8	2(3)	–	3(6)
Atomic, Molecular, & Optical Physics	2	3	2	1(2)	–	1(1)
Chemical Physics	–	–	–	–	–	–
Condensed Matter Physics	7	7	7	2(6)	1(1)	1(3)
Plasma and Fusion	–	–	–	–	–	–
Polymer Physics/Science	1	–	–	–	–	–
Total	17	12	17	5(12)	1(1)	5(10)
Full-time Grad. Stud.	–	11	15	–	–	–
First-year Grad. Stud.	–	2	2	–	–	–

GRADUATE DEGREE REQUIREMENTS

Master's: A minimum of 30 graduate credits is required for the Master of Science degree in Physics or Astronomy, including a minimum of 15 credits (excluding thesis) in 700-level courses and six semester hours of research for thesis credit. A final oral exam is required on course work and thesis except for the satisfactory performance on an Astronomy Qualifying Exam for the Astronomy Non-Thesis Option. A grade point average of at least 3.0 is required in all course work that is part of the degree program.

Doctorate: A minimum of 60 semester credits past the Bachelor's degree, including at least 36 graduate-level semester credits in classroom courses in physics, astronomy, or related fields and specified core courses. Course work used to satisfy the requirement for a Master's degree may be included. A minimum grade of B (3.00) is required in each course that is used in the degree program. A minimum of 18 semester credits of dissertation. Qualifying exam and oral defense of the dissertation.

Thesis: Thesis may be written in absentia with special approval only.

SPECIAL EQUIPMENT, FACILITIES, OR PROGRAMS

Department Facilities and Funding Sources

The Department resides in the Robert L. Bigelow Physics Building completed in 1994. Inside this 70,000 square-foot building, there are seven laboratories, other teaching and research laboratories, and supporting facilities, including two modern machine shops, a glass shop, and an electronics shop. The Computational Physics Laboratory, partially funded by the W. M. Keck Foundation, has a parallel/distributed computing system with a peak performance of about 8 GFlops. Research in the department is supported by NSF, DOD, DOE, NASA, EPA, the W. M. Keck Foundation, the Bigelow Foundation, and the UNLV Foundation.

Atomic, Molecular, and Optical Physics

The AMO group consists of six faculty members: four experimentalists and two theorists. The research projects include non-linear optics, studies of macromolecules, photon correlation spectroscopy, spectroscopy of molecular ions, studies of laser-produced low-energy plasmas and trapped ions, atomic and molecular collisions, and modeling of molecular clouds in the interstellar medium. All four research laboratories are equipped with lasers, ultra-high vacuums, and spectroscopy facilities. Modeling and calculations are conducted in the Computational Physics Laboratory, which is partially funded by the W. M. Keck Foundation.

Astronomy/Astrophysics

Faculty research interests include star formation in galaxies, active galactic nuclei, clusters of galaxies, gamma-ray bursts, quasars, large-scale structure of the universe, and variable stars. Faculty members have guaranteed access to SWIFT and successfully compete for time on other national facilities. Department facilities include an automated telescope in southern Arizona and access to the Lowell Observatory's 31-inch telescope in Flagstaff, Arizona, through UNLV's participation in the National Undergraduate Research Observatory.

Condensed Matter and High Pressure Physics

The UNLV High Pressure Science and Engineering Center (HiPSEC), recently established with support from the U.S. Department of Energy, brings together physicists, chemists, geoscientists, and mechanical engineers to consider fundamental experimental, computational, and engineering problems of materials under high pressures. Faculty and research staff study the equilibrium thermochemical properties, mechanical properties, reaction kinetics, and reaction products at static pressures using in situ X-ray diffraction, absorption, emission, and light-scattering spectroscopy from infrared to X-ray wavelengths, and other chemical and physical methods. Experiments are conducted at three in-house laboratories and in national laboratories, including an X-ray beam line in the Advanced Photon Source at the Argonne National Laboratory. In addition, along with experimental studies of complex fluids, state-of-the-art computational techniques are used to study highly correlated electron systems, including d- and f-band metals, clusters, thin films, quantum dots, and novel materials.

HiPSEC - High Pressure Science and Engineering Center

The High Pressure Science and Engineering Center (HIPSEC) was established in 1998 as a university-based teaching and research center. HiIPSEC has the broad goals of advancing materials science research at high pressure, training scientists and involving UNLV science faculty in multidisciplinary research.

Table B—Separately Budgeted Research Expenditures by Source of Support

Source of Support	Departmental Research	Physics-related Research Outside Department
Federal government	$2,717,595.15	
State/local government	$59,000	
Non-profit organizations	$14,347.47	
Business and industry		
Other		
Total	$2,790,942.62	

Table C—Separately Budgeted Research Expenditures by Research Specialty

Research Specialty	No. of Grants	Expenditures ($)
Astronomy	14	$362,014.05
Condensed Matter Physics	7	$2,414,581.1
Physics and other Science Education	3	$14,347.47
Total	24	$2,790,942.62

FACULTY

Chair Professor

Lepp, Stephen H., Ph.D., University of Colorado Boulder, 1984. Department Chair. *Astrophysics, Atomic, Molecular, & Optical Physics.* Atomic and molecular theory.

Professor

Chen, Changfeng, Ph.D., Peking University, 1987. *Condensed Matter Physics.* Condensed matter theory.

Cornelius, Andrew L., Ph.D., Washington University, St. Louis, 1996. *Condensed Matter Physics.* Condensed matter experimental.

Kwong, Victor H. S., Ph.D., University of Toronto, 1979. *Atomic, Molecular, & Optical Physics.* Laser induced plasmas; ion charge transfer processes.

Pang, Tao, Ph.D., University of Minnesota, 1989. *Condensed Matter Physics.* Condensed matter theory.

Porter, Timothy, Ph.D., Arizona State University, 1988. *Condensed Matter Physics.* Primary research areas include condensed matter physics, surface physics, materials science and applied and experimental physics.

Pravica, Michael G., Ph.D., Harvard University, 1998. *Condensed Matter Physics.*

Proga, Daniel, Ph.D., Nicolaus Copernicus Astronomical Center, Warsaw, Poland, 1996. *Astrophysics.* High-energy astrophysics.

Shelton, David P., Ph.D., University of Manitoba, 1979. *Atomic, Molecular, & Optical Physics.* Nonlinear optical properties of atoms and molecules.

Zhang, Bing, Ph.D., Peking University, 1997. *Astronomy, Astrophysics.* Gamma Ray Bursts.

Zygelman, Bernard, Ph.D., City University of New York, 1983. *Atomic, Molecular, & Optical Physics.* Atomic and molecular theory.

Associate Professor

Rhee, George, Ph.D., Leiden University, 1989. *Astronomy.* Extragalactic astronomy.

Assistant Professor

Martin, Rebecca, Ph.D., University of Cambridge, 2010. *Astrophysics.*

Salamat, Ashkan, Ph.D., University College London, 2009. *Condensed Matter Physics.*

Steffen, Jason, Ph.D., University of Washington, 2006. *Astrophysics.* Exoplanets.

Zhu, Qiang, Ph.D., State University of New York at Stony Brook, 2013. *Condensed Matter Physics.*

Zhu, Zhaohuan, Ph.D., University of Michigan-Ann Arbor, 2011. *Astrophysics.* Astrophysical Fluid Dynamics, Protoplanetary Disks, Star and Planet Formation, Disk Instabilities, Planet Detection, Planet Statitics.

Emeritus

Cloud, Stanley D., Ph.D., University of Oregon, 1968. Nuclear physics; teaching instrumentation.

Farley, John W., Ph.D., Columbia University, 1977. *Atomic, Molecular, & Optical Physics.* Laser spectroscopy of molecular ions.

Smith, Diane Pyper, Ph.D., University of California, Santa Cruz, 1968. *Astronomy.* Stellar photometry and spectroscopy.

Weistrop, Donna E., Ph.D., California Institute of Technology, 1971. Extragalactic astronomy.

Zane, Leonard I., Ph.D., Duke University, 1970. Special relativity.

Adjunct Faculty

Nagamine, Kentaro, Ph.D., Princeton University, 2001. *Astrophysics.*

Adjunct Professor

Livio, Mario, Ph.D., Tel Aviv University, 1978. *Astrophysics.*

Perry, Dale L., Ph.D., University of Houston, 1974.

Shaffer, David, Ph.D., California Institute of Technology, 1974.

DEPARTMENTAL RESEARCH SPECIALTIES AND STAFF

Theoretical

Astronomy. Astronomical phenomena of atomic and molecular systems; atomic and molecular collisions. Lepp, Proga, Rhee, Zhang.

Astrophysics. Interacting galaxies; digital image processing, gamma ray bursts. Lepp, Martin, Proga, Rhee, Steffen, Zhang, Zhaohuan Zhu.

Atomic, Molecular, & Optical Physics. Fundamental research, charge transfer and astro-physical data. Zygelman.

Condensed Matter Physics. High-temperature superconductivity; quantum liquids; disordered systems; correlated electron systems; spin systems. Chen, Pang, Qiang Zhu.

Experimental

Astronomy. Galactic clustering and evolution. Photoelectric photometry, spectrophotometry, and spectroscopy of peculiar, upper main-sequence stars; observation and photometry of interacting galaxies.

Atomic, Molecular, & Optical Physics. Dynamic behavior of macromolecular systems; non-linear optics of atoms and molecules. Farley, Kwong, Shelton.

Condensed Matter Physics. Material characterization in high pressure. Cornelius, Kwong, Porter, Pravica, Salamat.

View additional information about this department at www.gradschoolshopper.com. Check out the "Why Choose Us?" section, find out more about the department's culture and get links to social media networks.

UNIVERSITY OF NEVADA, RENO

DEPARTMENT OF PHYSICS

Reno, Nevada 89557-0220
http://www.unr.edu/physics

General University Information
President: Marc Johnson
Dean of Graduate School: David Zeh
University website: http://www.unr.edu/
School Type: Public
Setting: Urban
Total Faculty: 2,069
Total Graduate Faculty: 1,086
Total number of Students: 20,060
Total number of Graduate Students: 2,886

Department Information
Department Chairman: Prof. Paul Neill, Chair
Department Contact: Jonathan Weinstein, Director of Graduate Studies
  Total full-time faculty: 24
  Total number of full-time equivalent positions: 17
  Full-Time Graduate Students: 40
  Female Full-Time Graduate Students: 10
  First-Year Graduate Students: 10
  Female First-Year Students: 3
  Total Post Doctorates: 4

Department Address
University of Nevada
MS 0220
Reno, NV 89557-0220
Phone: (775) 784-6792
Fax: (775) 784-1398
E-mail: physdept@unr.edu
Website: http://www.unr.edu/physics

ADMISSIONS

Admission Contact Information
Address admission inquiries to: Director of Graduate Studies, Department of Physics, University of Nevada, Reno, NV 89557-0220
Phone: (775) 784-6821
E-mail: jdweinstein@unr.edu
Admissions website: http://www.unr.edu/grad/

Application deadlines
Fall admission:
U.S. students: February 1   *Int'l. students*: February 1
Spring admission:
U.S. students: November 1   *Int'l. students*: October 1

Application fee
U.S. students: $60   *Int'l. students*: $95
Spring application is discouraged, and students are only admitted in exceptional cases. Please contact the graduate program director before applying for admission in the Spring semester.

Admissions information
For Fall of 2018:
  Number of applicants: 30
  Number admitted: 14
  Number enrolled: 8

Admission requirements
Bachelor's degree requirements: A Bachelor's degree or Master's degree in physics is required.
Minimum undergraduate GPA: 3.0

GRE requirements
The GRE is required.
No minimum score set.

Subjective GRE requirements
The Subjective GRE is recommended.
  No minimum score set.

TOEFL requirements
The TOEFL exam is required for students from non-English-speaking countries.
  PBT score: 550
  iBT score: 79
A minimum score of 24 on the speak portion of the iBT is required to guarantee financial support as a teaching assistant.

Other admissions information
Additional requirements: Applicants with degrees in related majors are considered, but may be required to take undergraduate physics courses based on coursework completed and interview.
Undergraduate preparation assumed: Boas, Mathematical Methods in the Physical Sciences; Marion and Thornton, Classical Dynamics; Griffiths, Introduction to Electrodynamics; Griffiths, Introduction to Quantum Mechanics; Hecht, Optics; Kittel, Thermal Physics.

TUITION

Tuition year 2018–19:
Tuition for in-state residents
  Full-time students: $274.75 per credit
Tuition for out-of-state residents
  Full-time students: $274.75 per credit
Graduate assistantships include a tuition fee waiver.
Credit hours per semester to be considered full-time: 6
Deferred tuition plan: No
Health insurance: Yes, $0 (all fees paid by department).
Academic term: Semester

Teaching Assistants, Research Assistants, and Fellowships
Number of first-year
  Teaching Assistants: 8
Average stipend per academic year
  Teaching Assistant: $19,000
  Research Assistant: $22,800
Assistantships are provided for all first-year students. The current Teaching Assistant stipend is $1,900 per month ($1,650 per month for master's students) for 10 months. No separate application for financial aid is required.

FINANCIAL AID

Loans
Loans are available for U.S. students.
Loans are not available for international students.
GAPSFAS application required: No

FAFSA application required: No

For further information

Address financial aid inquiries to: Director of Graduate Studies, Department of Physics, University of Nevada, Reno, NV 89557-0220.
Phone: (775) 784-6821
E-mail: jdweinstein@unr.edu

HOUSING

Availability of on-campus housing
Single students: Yes
Married students: Yes

For further information
Address housing inquiries to: Residential Life, Housing and Food Services, University of Nevada, MS 0060, Reno, NV 89557-0060.
Phone: (775) 784-1113
E-mail: housing@unr.edu
Housing aid website: http://www.unr.edu/housing

Table A—Faculty, Enrollments, and Degrees Granted

Research Specialty	2018–19 Faculty	Enrollment Master's	Enrollment Doctorate	Degrees Granted Master's	Degrees Granted Terminal Master's	Degrees Granted Doctorate
Astrophysics	1	–	–	–	–	–
Atomic, Molecular, & Optical Physics	5	–	–	–	–	–
Climate/Atmospheric Science	3	–	–	–	–	–
Plasma and Fusion	10	–	–	–	–	–
Total	**19**	–	–	–	–	–
Full-time Grad. Stud.	–	–	–	–	–	–
First-year Grad. Stud.	–	–	–	–	–	–

GRADUATE DEGREE REQUIREMENTS

Master's: Plan A requires 30 graduate credits including six thesis credits. Plan B requires 32 graduate course credits. Minimum "B" average is required. There is no language requirement. A final oral examination on thesis work is required under Plan A; a final written and oral examination on coursework is required under Plan B. Twenty-four credits under Plan A and 26 credits under Plan B must be earned in residence.

Doctorate: Forty-eight course credits and 24 dissertation credits are required. Minimum "B" average is required. Written and oral comprehensive examinations and a final oral defense of dissertation are required. A minimum of six semesters beyond the bachelor's degree in residence are required, including at least two in succession.

Other Degrees: Master's and Ph.D. programs in atmospheric sciences are offered in association with the Desert Research Institute with courses and research topics in atmospheric physics. A Ph.D. program in chemical physics is offered in association with the Chemistry Department.

Thesis: Thesis may be written in absentia.

SPECIAL EQUIPMENT, FACILITIES, OR PROGRAMS

2-TW Z-pinch pulsed-power device for plasma/X-ray physics and two 100 TW class lasers at the Nevada Terawatt Facility.

Cryogenic atomic physics laboratory, and ion atomic physics laboratory.

Well-equipped atmospheric physics laboratories on campus and at the Desert Research Institute.

Multiple computing clusters optimized for atomic physics and plasma physics/HED calculations.

Table B—Separately Budgeted Research Expenditures by Source of Support

Source of Support	Departmental Research	Physics-related Research Outside Department
Federal government	$3,816,034	
State/local government		
Non-profit organizations		
Business and industry		
Other		
Total	**$3,816,034**	

FACULTY

Professor
Arnott, Patrick, Ph.D., Washington State University, 1988. *Climate/Atmospheric Science*. Acoustic and optical sensing of the earth's atmosphere.

Bauer, Bruno, Ph.D., University of California, Los Angeles, 1992. *Plasma and Fusion*. Experimental research involving high-power lasers, Z-pinches linear and nonlinear plasma waves, and instabilities.

Derevianko, Andrei, Ph.D., Auburn University, 1996. *Atomic, Molecular, & Optical Physics, Theoretical Physics*. Theoretical atomic and molecular physics; many-body methods; tests of fundamental symmetries; cold atoms; atomic clocks; dark matter searches.

Mancini, Roberto C., Ph.D., University of Buenos Aires, 1983. *Plasma and Fusion, Theoretical Physics*. Atomic and radiation physics of high-energy-density plasmas; stark-broadened line shapes; radiation transport; X-ray spectroscopy of plasmas; multi-objective spectroscopic data analysis.

Neill, Paul A., Ph.D., Queen's University, Belfast, 1984. Alignment and orientation studies in electron atom collisions; ionization and charge transfer in ion-atom collisions.

Associate Professor
Weinstein, Jonathan, Ph.D., Harvard University, 2002. *Atomic, Molecular, & Optical Physics*. Experimental research involving cryogenically cooled atoms and molecules.

Assistant Professor
Holmes, Heather, Ph.D., University of Utah, 2010. *Atmosphere, Space Physics, Cosmic Rays*. Atmospheric physics, numerical weather prediction, and chemical transport modeling.

Sawada, Hiroshi, Ph.D., University of Rochester, 2008. *Plasma and Fusion*. High Energy Density Plasma (HEDP) physics, and short pulse laser-solid interaction and fast electron transport relevant to laser fusion schemes such as Inertial Confinement Fusion (ICF) and Fast Ignition (FI).

Tscherbul, Timur, Ph.D., Moscow State University, 2005. *Atomic, Molecular, & Optical Physics*. Theoretical atomic physics. Cold molecule collisions, quantum coherence.

White, Thomas, Ph.D., Oxford, 2015. *Plasma and Fusion*. High-energy-density physics and laboratory astrophysics.

Williams, Joshua, Ph.D., Auburn, 2012. *Atomic, Molecular, & Optical Physics*. Experimental atomic physics. Photoionization and ultrafast dynamics.

Research Professor

Kantsyrev, Victor L., Ph.D., Institute of Analytical Instrumentation, Moscow, 1992. *Plasma and Fusion*. X-ray spectroscopy of laser-produced plasmas and Z-pinch plasmas.

Safronova, Alla, Ph.D., Lebedev Physical Institute, Moscow, 1986. *Atomic, Molecular, & Optical Physics, Plasma and Fusion, Theoretical Physics*. Spectroscopy and modeling of hot, dense plasmas.

Research Associate Professor

Ivanov, Vladimir, Ph.D., Lebedev Physical Institute, 1987. *Plasma and Fusion*. Experimental studies of Z-pinch and laser produced plasmas.

Research Assistant Professor

Covington, Aaron, Ph.D., University of Nevada, Reno, 1997. *Atomic, Molecular, & Optical Physics, Plasma and Fusion*. Experimental studies of photon interactions with atoms, molecules, and solids; Nevada Terawatt Facility.

Wiewior, Piotr, Ph.D., Warsaw University, 1999. *Plasma and Fusion*. Plasma physics and laser physics.

Lecturer

Bach, Bernhard, Ph.D., College of William and Mary, 1995. Design and fabrication of optical systems and physics education research.

Bennum, David, Ph.D., University of Nevada, Reno, 1973. *Physics and other Science Education*. Observational investigation of superplanets and applications of astronomy research to education.

Lewis, Krisitin A., Ph.D., University of Nevada - Reno, 2007. Physics and astronomy education research.

Rodrígue, Melodi, Ph.D., University of Nevada, Reno, 1998. *Physics and other Science Education*. Physics and astronomy education research.

DEPARTMENTAL RESEARCH SPECIALTIES AND STAFF

Theoretical

Atomic, Molecular, & Optical Physics. Precision calculations of atomic structure for tests of the Standard Model; research to improve the accuracy of atomic clocks; calculations and models of atomic interactions and spectroscopy in dense plasma environments; quantum computing; physics of ultracold degenerate gases. Molecular collisions, quantum coherence. Derevianko, Safronova, Tscherbul.

Plasma and Fusion. The fields of Plasma Physics and High Energy Density Science are some of the department's core strengths, with active research in experiment, theory, and modeling. Research groups are carrying out theoretical, computational, experimental and applied investigations into many physical systems under extremes of pressure, temperature, and density. Research areas include studies of the formation and time evolution of plasmas, and investigations of conditions ranging from the physics of the upper atmosphere to extreme pressures and temperatures found in astrophysical events. Mancini, Safronova.

Experimental

Atmospheric Physics. Gas particle conversion; laboratory studies of nucleation and growth of particulates; cloud condensation nuclei; aerosol removal by scavenging; trace elements in snow; atmospheric remote sensing. Arnott, Holmes.

Atomic, Molecular, & Optical Physics. Cold atomic and molecular collisions; laser cooling and trapping of atoms; quantum information science; photoionization and electron-impact ionization and fragmentation of atomic and molecular ions; collisional and photodetachment of negative ions; optomechanics and quantum precision sensors; hybrid quantum systems and quantum computing. Covington, Neill, Weinstein, Williams.

Plasma and Fusion. The Physics Department has a number of distinctive research facilities that enhance the research activities in plasma physics and high-energy density science, including a 2 TW Z-pinch accelerator, a 100 TW, 350 femtosecond laser, and a ninety-six node cluster computer. In addition to these rich on-campus resources, additional research is done through collaborations at national research facilities such as the Rochester's Laboratory for Laser Energetics, Sandia National Laboratory, and Livermore National Laboratory. Bauer, Covington, Ivanov, Kantsyrev, Mancini, Sawada, White, Wiewior.

Relativity & Gravitation.

UNIVERSITY OF NEW HAMPSHIRE

DEPARTMENT OF PHYSICS & ASTRONOMY

Durham, New Hampshire 03824
http://www.physics.unh.edu

General University Information

President: James W. Dean Jr.
Dean of Graduate School: Cari Moorhead
University website: http://www.unh.edu
School Type: Public
Setting: Rural
Total Faculty: 968
Total Graduate Faculty: 585
Total number of Students: 14,800
Total number of Graduate Students: 2,179

Department Information

Department Chairman: Prof. Karsten Pohl, Chair
Department Contact: Katie Makem-Boucher, Administrative Manager
  Total full-time faculty: 34
  Total number of full-time equivalent positions: 21
  Full-Time Graduate Students: 64
  Female Full-Time Graduate Students: 16
  First-Year Graduate Students: 13
  Female First-Year Students: 3
  Total Post Doctorates: 19

Department Address

9 Library Way
Durham, NH 03824
Phone: (603) 862-2669
E-mail: katie.makem@unh.edu
Website: http://www.physics.unh.edu

ADMISSIONS

Admission Contact Information

Address admission inquiries to: Graduate Admission Coordinator, Physics Department, Demeritt Hall, Durham, NH 03824
Phone: (603) 862-2669
E-mail: physics.grad.info@unh.edu
Admissions website: http://www.gradschool.unh.edu/apply.php

Application deadlines

Fall admission:
U.S. students: January 15   Int'l. students: January 15

Application fee

U.S. students: $65   Int'l. students: $65
Application deadline for funding is January 15; after that on a rolling basis until April 15. Please ensure that your letters of recommendation arrive in time, ideally by mid-January. Spring admission is by approval only.

Admissions information

For Fall of 2018:
  Number of applicants: 80
  Number admitted: 25
  Number enrolled: 12

Admission requirements

Bachelor's degree requirements: A Bachelor's degree in Physics or astronomy is usually required, but exceptions have been made.

GRE requirements

The GRE is required.
GRE is required. There is no set minimum score required for admission. Request official test scores to be sent directly to the Graduate School by the testing service. Test scores more than five years old may not be acceptable. Student copies and photocopies of scores are not considered official. Our CEEB code is 3918.

Subjective GRE requirements

The Subjective GRE is required.

TOEFL requirements

The TOEFL exam is required for students from non-English-speaking countries.
  PBT score: 550
  iBT score: 80
Non-native English-speaking International applicants are required to submit TOEFL examination scores. Demonstration of a sufficient level of English Language proficiency is a prerequisite for admission. Submitted scores that fall below our minimum requirement will be considered unacceptable and grounds for denying admission.

Other admissions information

Undergraduate preparation assumed: The level of preparation should be comparable with that provided at University of New Hampshire for the Bachelor's of Science degree in Physics. This includes two semesters of advanced quantum mechanics (Griffiths, Introduction to Quantum Mechanics), two semesters of advanced E&M (Pollack & Stump, Electromagnetism), and advanced classical mechanics (Thornton & Marion, Classical Dynamics of Particles and Systems).

TUITION

Tuition year 2018–19:
Tuition for in-state residents
  Full-time students: $13,840 annual
  Part-time students: $770 per credit
Tuition for out-of-state residents
  Full-time students: $27,130 annual
  Part-time students: $1,270 per credit
The university reserves the right to adjust tuition and/or related expenses. Any changes will be announced as far in advance as possible.
Credit hours per semester to be considered full-time: 9
Deferred tuition plan: No
Health insurance: Available at the cost of $2,280 per year.
Other academic fees: All full-time degree students are required to have adequate health insurance as condition of enrollment. Students with F1 or J1 visas are required to use the UNH plan. Total mandatory fees are $2,095 per year for full-time students and $1,047.50 per year for part-time students.
Academic term: Semester
Number of first-year students who received full tuition waivers: 13

Teaching Assistants, Research Assistants, and Fellowships

Number of first-year
Teaching Assistants: 10
Fellowship students: 1
Average stipend per academic year
Teaching Assistant: $18,640
Research Assistant: $18,640
Fellowship student: $18,640
Most first-year students serve as a TA and then move to an RA, beginning with the summer after their first year. Students serving as either a TA or RA are provided with both a stipend and a full tuition waiver.

FINANCIAL AID

Application deadlines
Fall admission:
U.S. students: January 15   *Int'l. students*: January 15

Loans
Loans are available for U.S. students.
Loans are not available for international students.
GAPSFAS application required: No
FAFSA application required: Yes

For further information
Address financial aid inquiries to: Financial Aid Office, 11 Garrison Avenue, Stoke Hall, Durham, NH 03824.
Phone: (603) 862-3600
Financial aid website: http://financialaid.unh.edu/

HOUSING

Availability of on-campus housing
Single students: Yes
Married students: Yes
Childcare Assistance: No

For further information
Address housing inquiries to: Department of Housing, 10 Academic Way, Durham, NH 03824.
Phone: (603) 862-2120
E-mail: housing.office@unh.edu
Housing aid website: http://www.unh.edu/housing/graduate-family

Table A—Faculty, Enrollments, and Degrees Granted

Research Specialty	2018–19 Faculty	Enrollment Fall, 2018		Number of Degrees Granted 2017–18 (2012–18)		
		Master's	Doctorate	Master's	Terminal Master's	Doctorate
Applied Optics	1	–	–	–	–	–
Condensed Matter Physics	6	2	3	–	–(2)	3(7)
High Energy Astrophysics	8	–	8	–	–	–(3)
High Energy Theory	3	–	2	–	–	–(1)
Medical Imaging	2	–	1	–	–	1(1)
Nuclear Physics	6	–	6	–	–	2(3)
Physics Education	1	1	–	–	–(1)	–(1)
Space Science	21	–	20	–(1)	2(7)	2(23)
Non-specialized	–	–	20	–	–(2)	–
Total	48	2	60	–	2(10)	8(31)
Full-time Grad. Stud.	–	2	58	–	–	–
First-year Grad. Stud.	–	–	10	–	–	–

GRADUATE DEGREE REQUIREMENTS

Master's: Students are required to satisfactorily complete an approved course program of five required courses plus: (1) nine additional credits of graduate coursework plus a master's thesis and an oral thesis defense; or (2) 12 additional credits of graduate coursework plus a research project and an oral examination in the form of a seminar. There are no residency or foreign language requirements.

Doctorate: Students are required to complete satisfactorily an approved course program of seven required courses plus four additional courses at the graduate level, pass a written comprehensive examination on their undergraduate physics topics by the middle of their second year in the program, pass an oral qualifying examination in which a thesis proposal is presented and discussed, demonstrate proficiency in teaching (typically by service as a teaching assistant), complete a dissertation, and pass an oral dissertation examination. Students must satisfy a one-year residence requirement. Students can earn a master's degree after completing 30 graduate credits and passing the written comprehensive examination and the oral qualifying examination. There is no foreign language requirement.

SPECIAL EQUIPMENT, FACILITIES, OR PROGRAMS

Many faculty hold joint appointments in the Space Science Center (SSC), part of the Institute for the Study of Earth, Oceans, and Space (EOS). The SSC fosters research and graduate education in all of the space sciences, with studies ranging from the ionosphere to the Earth's magnetosphere, the local solar system, and out to the farthest reaches of the universe. Researchers and students have access to a CRAY XE6m-200 supercomputer with 4100 compute cores and 180 TB of storage. The SSC also maintains facilities that are used to design and fabricate space flight hardware, including clean rooms, thermal/vacuum chambers, and EMC/EMI test facilities. The SSC maintains a close relationship with Southwest Research Institute (SwRI), which has a department (SwRI-EOS) on the University of New Hampshire campus, co-located with the Space Science Center.

Faculty in the Condensed Matter Group are also part of the Materials Science Program, a Ph.D. program that offers research opportunities in the areas of science and engineering that cross traditional departmental boundaries, with an emphasis on the synthesis and characterization of nanoscale materials.

Several faculty members participate in the Applied Mathematics Program, a Ph.D. program designed to facilitate interdisciplinary research among graduate students and participating faculty. This interdisciplinary program gives students the opportunity to explore the frontier where the sciences meet cutting-edge mathematical analysis and high-performance computing.

Table B—Separately Budgeted Research Expenditures by Source of Support

Source of Support	Departmental Research	Physics-related Research Outside Department
Federal government	$17,518,522.48	
State/local government		
Non-profit organizations		
Business and industry		
Other		
Total	$17,518,522.48	

Table C—Separately Budgeted Research Expenditures by Research Specialty

Research Specialty	No. of Grants	Expenditures ($)
High Energy Astrophysics and Gravitational Wave Astrophysics	25	$1,812,652.49
Space Science	99	$14,917,824.57
Condensed Matter Physics	3	$139,746.01
Nuclear Physics	3	$597,761.7
Optics	1	$45,238.79
Physics Education	1	$5,298.92
Total	132	$17,518,522.48

FACULTY

Chair Professor

Dwyer, Joseph R., Ph.D., University of Chicago, 1994. Peter T. Paul Chair of Space Science; member of Space Science Center. *Astrophysics, Atmosphere, Space Physics, Cosmic Rays, Solar Physics*. Atmospheric electricity; thunderstorm and lightning physics; high energy atmospheric physics; X-ray emissions from lightning; terrestrial gamma-ray flashes and terrestrial electron beams; gas discharge phenomena.

Professor

Berglund, Per, Ph.D., University of Texas, Austin, 1993. *Cosmology & String Theory, High Energy Physics, Particles and Fields, Theoretical Physics*. String theory, string compactifications, Calabi-Yau manifolds, mirror symmetry.

Chandran, Benjamin D. G., Ph.D., Princeton University, 1997. Member of Space Science Center; member of Integrated Applied Mathematics Program. *Astrophysics, Atmosphere, Space Physics, Cosmic Rays, Plasma and Fusion, Solar Physics, Theoretical Physics*. Studies of plasma turbulence; the role of turbulence in the solar wind and galaxy-cluster plasmas; cosmic-ray propagation; particle acceleration in solar flares; the origin of astrophysical magnetic fields; space mission involvement includes the Parker Solar Probe.

Clemmons, James H., Ph.D., University of California, Berkeley, 1992. Member of Space Science Center. *Atmosphere, Space Physics, Cosmic Rays*. Instrumentation- and analysis-based investigation of the physics of geospace, including ionosphere-thermosphere coupling, phenomena associated with the aurora, magnetospheric particles and fields; space mission involvement includes numerous sounding rocket missions, Freja, Polar, TWINS, Streak, Van Allen Probes, Magnetospheric Multiscale, LAICE, and LLITED.

Hersman, F. William, Ph.D., Massachusetts Institute of Technology, 1982. *Medical, Health Physics, Nuclear Physics, Optics*. Development of high-power wavelength-locked lasers for optical pumping with applications in defense technology; investigation of the properties and utility of hyperpolarized xenon, particularly as a contrast agent in magnetic resonance imaging.

Holtrop, Maurik, Ph.D., Massachusetts Institute of Technology, 1995. *Accelerator, Nuclear Physics*. Experimental nuclear and particle physics using electron and photon scattering experiments at the Thomas Jefferson National Accelerator Facility.

Kistler, Lynn M., Ph.D., University of Maryland, 1987. Director of the Space Science Center; member of Space Science Center. *Atmosphere, Space Physics, Cosmic Rays, Solar Physics*. Magnetospheric physics, with specific emphasis on the sources, transport, and acceleration of magnetospheric particle populations, including the design, fabrication, and testing of state-of-the-art instrumentation for spacecraft and the analysis of the data collected by these instruments; space mission involvement includes FAST, Equator-S, CLUSTER, ACE, STEREO, Van Allen Probes, MMS, ARASE, and Solar Orbiter.

McConnell, Mark L., Ph.D., University of New Hampshire, 1987. Director of the Earth, Oceans, and Space Department of the Southwest Research Institute (SwRI-EOS); member of Space Science Center. *Astrophysics, Atmosphere, Space Physics, Cosmic Rays, Solar Physics*. Experimental X-ray and gamma-ray astronomy using balloon and satellite platforms; X-ray and gamma-ray polarimetry of gamma-ray bursts and solar flares; suborbital balloon projects currently include GRAPE and ASCOT; space mission involvement includes CGRO, RHESSI, INTEGRAL, and FERMI.

Meredith, Dawn C., Ph.D., California Institute of Technology, 1987. *Physics and other Science Education*. Physics education.

Pohl, Karsten, Ph.D., University of Pennsylvania, 1997. Member of Materials Science Program. *Condensed Matter Physics, Nano Science and Technology, Surface Physics*. Experimental condensed matter physics and materials science focused on the study of the interplay of electronic, vibrational, and structural surface properties at the atomic scale.

Raeder, Joachim, Ph.D., University of Köln, 1989. Member of Space Science Center; member of Integrated Applied Mathematics Program. *Applied Mathematics, Atmosphere, Space Physics, Cosmic Rays, Computational Physics, Theoretical Physics*. Space physics; space weather solar-terrestrial relationships; plasmas and magnetic fields in space; solar wind-magnetosphere-ionosphere-thermosphere coupling; geomagnetic activity; geomagnetic storms and substorms; large-scale modeling of magnetospheres; data assimilation; cometary physics; computational fluid dynamics; numerical methods; high-performance computing; space mission involvement includes GIOTTO and THEMIS.

Ryan, James M., Ph.D., University of California, Riverside, 1978. Member of Space Science Center. *Astrophysics, Atmosphere, Space Physics, Cosmic Rays, Solar Physics*. Terrestrial, solar, and astrophysical cosmic rays, neutrons, and gamma-rays; space mission involvement includes SMM, CGRO, RHESSI, and various balloon experiments; radioactive materials detection for homeland security applications.

Schwadron, Nathan, Ph.D., University of Michigan, 1996. Member Space Science Center. Presidential Chair. Norman S. And Anna Marie Waite Professor. *Astrophysics, Atmosphere, Space Physics, Cosmic Rays, Nuclear Physics, Planetary Science, Solar Physics*. Heliospheric phenomena related to the solar wind, the heliospheric magnetic field, pickup ions, cometary X-rays, energetic particles, and cosmic rays; space mission involvement includes Ulysses, New Horizons, IBEX, and LRO. Roles in IMAP, IBEX, LRO, and Parker Solar Probe programs in addition to theory and modeling programs for energetic particles. PI of the Cosmic Ray Telescope for the Effects of Radiation, PI of the IMAP-Lo instrument and Deputy PI of the IMAP mission.

Spence, Harlan, Ph.D., University of California, Los Angeles, 1989. Director, Institute for the Study of Earth, Oceans and Space (EOS); member of Space Science Center. *Astrophysics, Atmosphere, Space Physics, Cosmic Rays, Planetary Science, Solar Physics*. Theoretical and experimental space plasma physics; cosmic rays and radiation belt processes; heliospheric, planetary magnetospheric, lunar, and auroral physics; space mission involvement includes POLAR, LRO, IBEX, TWINS, Van Allen Probes, FIREBIRD, and MMS.

Torbert, Roy B., Ph.D., University of California, Berkeley, 1979. Member of Space Science Center. *Atmosphere, Space Physics, Cosmic Rays*. Space plasma physics; physics of magnetospheres, aurora, and early solar system formation; space mission involvement includes WIND, POLAR, CLUSTER, Equator-S, MMS, and the Van Allen Probes.

Associate Professor

Connell, James, Ph.D., Washington University, 1988. Member of Space Science Center. *Astrophysics, Atmosphere, Space Physics, Cosmic Rays, Solar Physics.* The measurement of energetic particle radiation in space, including galactic cosmic rays, solar energetic particles, and the anomalous cosmic rays; space mission involvement includes GOES-17 and GOES-18.

Germaschewski, Kai, Ph.D., Heinrich-Heine University Düsseldorf, 2001. Member of Space Science Center; member of Integrated Applied Mathematics Program. *Applied Mathematics, Atmosphere, Space Physics, Cosmic Rays, Computational Physics, Plasma and Fusion.* Space physics; plasma physics; numerical simulations.

Keesee, Amy M., Ph.D., West Virginia University, 2006. Member of Space Science Center. *Atmosphere, Space Physics, Cosmic Rays, Plasma and Fusion.* Magnetospheric physics related to storms and substorms, with particular focus on the magnetotail and plasma sheet; space mission involvement with TWINS.

Lessard, Marc, Ph.D., Dartmouth College, 1997. Member of Space Science Center. *Atmosphere, Space Physics, Cosmic Rays.* Dynamics of the magnetosphere, ionosphere and upper atmosphere, emphasizing ultra-low frequency (ULF) waves, auroral processes, ionospheric feedback to magnetospheric drivers and similar topics. Experimental methods involve rocket- and satellite-borne instrumentation, as well as ground-based sensors. Research focus is on high-latitude (e.g., polar regions) space sciences.

Liu, Ningyu, Ph.D., Pennsylvania State University, 2006. Member of Space Science Center. *Astrophysics, Atmosphere, Space Physics, Cosmic Rays, Electromagnetism.* Atmospheric electricity; space physics; plasma physics; gas discharge phenomena; computational electrodynamics; high-performance computing.

Slifer, Karl, Ph.D., Temple University, 2004. *Accelerator, High Energy Physics, Low Temperature Physics, Nuclear Physics.* Medium Energy Nuclear and Particle Physics, Spin Structure of the Proton, Tensor Spin Observables, and Dynamic Nuclear Polarization. Experimental nuclear and particle physics using electron and proton scattering from polarized targets at Jefferson Lab and Fermilab.

Assistant Professor

Foucart, Francois V. O., Ph.D., Cornell University, 2011. *Astrophysics, Computational Physics, Relativity & Gravitation.* Studies merging black holes and neutron stars as sources of gravitational waves and electromagnetic transients. Develops numerical methods for general relativistic simulations of astrophysical systems, magnetohydrodynamics, and radiation transport. Studies accretion onto the supermassive black holes present at the center of most galaxies.

Hollen, Shawna M., Ph.D., Brown University, 2013. Member of Materials Science Program. *Condensed Matter Physics, Low Temperature Physics, Nano Science and Technology, Solid State Physics, Surface Physics.* Experimental research includes studying sensitivity of 2D material surfaces to environment and chemical modification; coupling to 2D superconductors; atomic-scale electronic structure; implications for device applications in flexible electronics, spintronics, and optoelectronics.

Kislat, Fabian, Ph.D., Humboldt University Berlin, 2011. Member of Space Science Center. *Astrophysics, Low Temperature Physics.* Experimental X-ray and gamma-ray astronomy and development of cryogenic gamma-ray detectors; X-ray polarimetry of black holes and neutron stars with X-Calibur

(balloon-borne) and the future satellite mission IXPE; tests of spacetime symmetry with astrophysical observations.

Long, Elena, Ph.D., Kent State University, 2012. *Accelerator, Low Temperature Physics, Nuclear Physics, Physics and other Science Education.* Experimental nuclear and particle physics using electron scattering off of polarized targets experiments at the Thomas Jefferson National Accelerator Facility.

Mattingly, David, Ph.D., University of Maryland, 2003. *Relativity & Gravitation, Theoretical Physics.* Development of new methods to test fundamental symmetries in general relativity and hypotheses about quantum gravity. Interface between black hole physics and quantum gravity.

Prescod-Weinstein, Chanda, Ph.D., University of Waterloo, 2011. *Astrophysics, Cosmology & String Theory, Particles and Fields, Physics and other Science Education, Theoretical Physics.* Development of models that describe particle physics phenomena in the early universe. Late time cosmological interests include dark matter phenomenology. Astrophysical interests include using X-ray studies of neutron stars as quantum chromodynamics laboratories. Secondary expertise in the intersection of gender studies and science, technology, and society studies.

Zang, Jiadong, Ph.D., Fudan University, 2012. Member of Materials Science Program. *Condensed Matter Physics, Theoretical Physics.* Exploring topological aspects of both electronic and magnetic systems. Focused on low-dimensional transports, magnetization dynamics, and strong correlations.

Professor Emeritus

Balling, Ludwig C., Ph.D., Harvard University, 1965. *Atomic, Molecular, & Optical Physics.*

Calarco, John R., Ph.D., University of Illinois at Urbana-Champaign, 1969. *Accelerator, Nuclear Physics.* Investigating the structure of nucleons and light nuclei using the scattering of electrons or the absorption of gamma-rays as the primary probe.

Dawson, John, Ph.D., Stanford University, 1962. *Nuclear Physics, Theoretical Physics.* Theoretical nuclear models; electron scattering; heavy ion collisions.

Echt, Olof, Ph.D., University of Konstanz, 1979. Member of Materials Science Program. *Chemical Physics, Condensed Matter Physics, Materials Science, Metallurgy.* Pulsed-laser deposition of thin films; photophysics of fullerenes; implantation of ions into fullerenes; ion-molecule reactions in atomic clusters and doped helium nanodroplets.

Forbes, Terry, Ph.D., University of Colorado Boulder, 1978. Member of Space Science Center. *Astrophysics, Atmosphere, Space Physics, Cosmic Rays, Solar Physics, Theoretical Physics.* Theories of solar flares, including magnetic reconnection; space mission involvement includes YOHKOH, SOHO, TRACE, and HINODE.

Heisenberg, Jochen, Ph.D., University of Hamburg, 1966. *Nuclear Physics, Theoretical Physics.* Theoretical nuclear physics.

Hollweg, Joseph, Ph.D., Massachusetts Institute of Technology, 1968. *Atmosphere, Space Physics, Cosmic Rays, Solar Physics.* Dynamics of the solar atmosphere and solar wind; waves in plasmas.

Kaufmann, Richard, Ph.D., Yale University, 1960. *Atmosphere, Space Physics, Cosmic Rays, Theoretical Physics.* Theoretical studies of the Earth's magnetosphere.

Lee, Martin A., Ph.D., University of Chicago, 1971. Member of Space Science Center; member of Integrated Applied Mathematics Program. *Applied Mathematics, Astrophysics, Atmosphere, Space Physics, Cosmic Rays, Computational Physics, Solar Physics, Theoretical Physics.* Theoretical space physics, astrophysics, and plasma physics, including heliospheric plasmas, solar cosmic rays, and shock acceleration processes; space mission involvement includes SOHO.

Möbius, Eberhard, Ph.D., Ruhr University Bochum, 1977. Member of Space Science Center. *Astrophysics, Atmosphere, Space Physics, Cosmic Rays, Solar Physics.* Acceleration of ions in the earth's magnetosphere, in interplanetary space and in solar flares; interaction of interstellar gas with the solar wind and the study of the local interstellar medium; space mission involvement includes AMPTE, FAST, ACE, CLUSTER, Equator-S, STEREO, and IBEX.

Research Professor

Farrugia, Charles, Ph.D., University of Bern, 1984. Member of Space Science Center. *Atmosphere, Space Physics, Cosmic Rays, Solar Physics.* Magnetohydrodynamic flow of the solar wind around the magnetosphere; processes at the magnetopause and its boundary layers; magnetosphere-ionosphere coupling; interplanetary coronal mass ejections, magnetic cloud, small solar wind transients; the interaction of the solar wind with the magnetosphere; prediction of strong geomagnetic disturbances from the inner heliosphere; magnetic reconnection; space mission involvement includes Wind, STEREO, Cluster, and MMS.

Galvin, Antoinette, Ph.D., University of Maryland, 1982. Member of Space Science Center; Director of the NASA EPSCoR program in New Hampshire. *Atmosphere, Space Physics, Cosmic Rays, Solar Physics.* Studies of heliophysics particle populations (solar wind, magnetosphere, pickup ions, and accelerated suprathermals), including their origins, evolution, and interactions in the inner heliosphere, and solar wind interactions with planetary bodies (space weather); the design, fabrication, and operation of state-of-the-art particle composition experiments for space missions; space mission involvement includes ISEE-1, ISEE-3, Ulysses, Geotail, SOHO, Wind, ACE, STEREO, Solar Orbiter, and SCOPE.

Isenberg, Philip A., Ph.D., University of Chicago, 1977. Member of Space Science Center. *Atmosphere, Space Physics, Cosmic Rays, Solar Physics, Theoretical Physics.* Theoretical space plasma physics; solar wind acceleration; solar wind interactions with neutral particles from comets and the interstellar medium; solar flares.

Kucharek, Harald, Ph.D., Technical University of Munich, 1989. Member of Space Science Center. *Atmosphere, Space Physics, Cosmic Rays, Solar Physics.* Kinetic numerical simulation (MHD, hybrid, and full-particle simulations) of physical processes in collisionless plasmas, in the earth's magnetosphere, and the heliosphere; solar wind composition and particle acceleration at the earth's bow shock and at interplanetary structures such as coronal mass ejections (CMEs) and corotating interaction regions (CIRs); space mission involvement includes SOHO, ACE, CLUSTER, IBEX, Solar Probe Plus, and SCOPE.

Smith, Charles, Ph.D., College of William and Mary, 1981. Member of Space Science Center. *Atmosphere, Space Physics, Cosmic Rays, Solar Physics.* A wide range of plasma physics investigations centered on the solar wind, its origin and evolution, particle acceleration, and the propagation of cosmic rays through the heliosphere; space mission involvement includes ISEE, Pioneer-Venus, Voyager, WIND, Ulysses, ACE, and the Van Allen Probes.

Vasquez, Bernard, Ph.D., University of Maryland, 1992. Member of Space Science Center. *Atmosphere, Space Physics, Cosmic Rays.* Studies of the solar wind; waves; discontinuities; ion kinetics; and numerical simulations.

Research Associate Professor

Bloser, Peter F., Ph.D., Harvard University, 2000. Member of Space Science Center. *Astrophysics, Atmosphere, Space Phys-* ics, Cosmic Rays, Solar Physics. Experimental gamma-ray astronomy and solar physics; space mission involvement includes various balloon experiments.

Lopate, Clifford, Ph.D., University of Chicago, 1989. Member of Space Science Center. *Astrophysics, Atmosphere, Space Physics, Cosmic Rays, Solar Physics.* Studies of heliospheric energetic particles in the 1-10,000 MeV energy range (the sources of these particles are cosmic rays, anomalous components, solar particle events, and planetary magnetospheres); space missions involvement includes GOES-16 and GOES-17; research involvement also includes space instrumentation development.

Lugaz, Noe, Ph.D., University of Michigan, 2007. Member of Space Science Center. *Atmosphere, Space Physics, Cosmic Rays, Solar Physics.* Solar-terrestrial physics with focus on solar eruptions and coronal mass ejections from the sun to the earth: initiation, propagation, interaction, and effect on Earth's magnetosphere; combining large, parallel numerical simulations; the analysis of remote-sensing observations from coronagraphs and heliospheric imagers and space plasma measurements.

Research Assistant Professor

Huang, Chia-Lin, Ph.D., Boston University, 2008. Member of Space Science Center. *Atmosphere, Space Physics, Cosmic Rays.* Combining numerical simulations and satellite data to study solar-terrestrial physics with focus on solar wind effect on Earth's magnetospheric dynamics and radiation belt; space mission involvement includes Van Allen Probes.

Lin, Dacheng, Ph.D., Massachusetts Institute of Technology, 2009. *Astrophysics.* Observational X-ray astronomy; the accretion process in neutron star low-mass X-ray binaries and around black holes across mass scale: black-hole X-ray binaries, ultra-luminous X-ray sources, off-nuclear intermediate-mass black hole, active galactic nuclei, and tidal disruption events; space mission involvement includes Chandra, XMM-Newton, Swift, RXTE, ROSAT, and HST.

Affiliate Professor

Brooks, William K., Ph.D., Duke University, 1988. *Accelerator, Nuclear Physics.* Topics in high energy nuclear physics having to do with the propagation of QCD color charge through strongly interacting systems. ATLAS heavy ion physics at the LHC and in deep inelastic scattering off atomic nuclei with CLAS at Jefferson Lab.

Krzanowski, James E., Ph.D., Massachusetts Institute of Technology, 1983. Director of the Materials Science Program; member of Materials Science Program. *Condensed Matter Physics.* Thin film deposition and hard coatings, pulsed laser deposition, electron microscopy and materials characterization, mechanical and tribological properties of coatings.

Lashmore, David S., Ph.D., University of Virginia, 1977. Member of Materials Science Program. *Condensed Matter Physics.* Research and development of high-energy density batteries, high strength non-carbon based yarns of complex chemistries fabricated from bottom-up assembly of nanostructured elements, new technologies for additive manufacturing, and composite materials and manufacturing technologies.

McKibben, R. Bruce, Ph.D., University of Chicago, 1972. Member of Space Science Center. *Astrophysics, Atmosphere, Space Physics, Cosmic Rays, Solar Physics.* Observational studies of galactic cosmic rays, solar energetic particles, and particles accelerated in interplanetary space or in planetary magnetospheres, using measurements from heliospheric and near-Earth spacecraft; space mission involvement includes Pioneer 10, Pioneer 11, and Ulysses.

Affiliate Associate Professor

Ruset, Iulian, Ph.D., University of New Hampshire, 2005. *Medical, Health Physics.* Development of instrumentation and techniques for medical imaging with polarized gases.

DEPARTMENTAL RESEARCH SPECIALTIES AND STAFF

Theoretical

Atmospheric Electricity. Research on various aspects of thunderstorms, lightning, and their effects in the near-earth space environment, including electrical properties of thunderstorms, lightning physics, X-ray, gamma-ray and radio emissions from thunderstorms and lightning, transient luminous events (jets, sprites, etc.), ionospheric impact of thunderstorms and lightning; work also includes studies to understand electrical discharges due to conventional discharge or relativistic runaway processes. Observations include balloon and ground-based x-ray observations of thunderstorms and lightning, high-speed imaging of lightning and transient luminous events, and radio interferometer observations of lighting discharges. Dwyer, Liu.

Condensed Matter Physics. Exploring topological aspects of both electronic and magnetic systems. Focused on low-dimensional transports, magnetization dynamics, and strong correlations. Zang.

High Energy Astrophysics and Gravitational Wave Astrophysics. Mergers of compact binaries containing black holes or neutron stars, gravitational-wave and electromagnetic signatures of binary mergers, r-process nucleosynthesis, accretion disks around supermassive black holes, numerical simulations in general relativity, and the heating and acceleration of jets. Chandran, Foucart, Prescod-Weinstein.

High Energy Physics. High energy and gravitational physics. String compactifications, astrophysical and cosmological consequences of string theory and other quantum gravity models, inflationary cosmology, dark matter, black hole physics and holography in modified gravitational theories. Berglund, Dawson, Mattingly, Prescod-Weinstein.

Nuclear Physics. Studies of theoretical nuclear models, electron scattering, heavy ion collisions, and condensed ultra-cold atomic systems. Dawson, Heisenberg.

Space Plasma Theory. The research activities of Space Plasma Theory Group encompass a broad range of subfields, including theoretical plasma physics, solar and heliospheric physics, magnetospheric physics, and plasma astrophysics. Chandran, Forbes, Germaschewski, Hollweg, Isenberg, Kaufmann, Lee, Lugaz, Raeder, Vasquez.

Experimental

Applied Optics. Development of high-power laser systems for ballistic missile defense. Hersman, Ruset.

Atmospheric Electricity. Research on various aspects of thunderstorms, lightning, and their effects in the near-earth space environment, including electrical properties of thunderstorms, lightning physics, X-ray and gamma-ray emissions from thunderstorms and lightning, transient luminous events (jets, sprites, etc.), ionospheric impact of thunderstorms and lightning; work has also included studies to understand electrical discharges due to conventional discharge or relativistic runaway processes. Dwyer, Liu.

Condensed Matter Physics. Research involving scanning tunneling microscopy and electron spectroscopies, thin-film deposition, and high-resolution mass spectrometry to investigate electronic and structural properties of nanoscale materials. Echt, Hollen, Krzanowski, Lashmore, Pohl.

Experimental Space Plasma. Investigations of the Earth's environment in the solar system looking at space as a laboratory for plasma physics; satellite and sounding rocket investigations of the solar-terrestrial radiation environment. Active satellite programs for which UNH has contributed hardware include Cluster, ACE, STEREO, IBEX, the Van Allen Probes, the FIREBIRD cubesat, the Magnetospheric Multiscale (MMS) mission, and GOES-16 and -17; upcoming missions for which UNH is building instruments include Solar Orbiter (launch 2020) and IMAP (launch 2024). Clemmons, Farrugia, Galvin, Huang, Kistler, Kucharek, Lessard, Möbius, Schwadron, Smith, Spence, Torbert.

High Energy Astrophysics. Research involving high-energy radiations addressing a wide variety of astrophysical problems, including high-energy emissions from solar flares, gamma-ray bursts, x-ray binaries, and pulsars; studies are conducted using x-ray and gamma-ray detectors placed on suborbital balloon platforms and on orbital satellites (such as CGRO); work has also included the application of radiation detector technology to homeland security issues and studies of terrestrial gamma-ray flashes. Bloser, Dwyer, Kislat, Lin, Liu, McConnell, Ryan.

Medical Imaging. Investigation of spin exchange optical pumping (SEOP) to identify new technologies for producing nuclear polarized gases and new applications of these gases as inhaled diagnostic tracers with magnetic resonance imaging. Hersman, Ruset.

Nuclear Physics. Using electron- and photon-scattering experiments (conducted at various accelerator facilities, including the Jefferson Laboratory) to improve our understanding of the atomic nucleus. Brooks, Calarco, Holtrop, Long, Slifer.

Physics Education Research and Physics and Society. Research to determine how students learn and developing teaching methodologies to improve student learning. Research that uses gender; ethnic; and science, technology and society studies to understand physics culture and broaden participation in physics. Meredith, Prescod-Weinstein.

Space Radiation. Research in high-energy space particle radiation, including ions and electrons; space weather studies; measurements of cosmic ray and solar energetic particles, including detailed elemental and isotopic composition; work has included the High Energy Telescope (HET) for the Ulysses mission; currently have two Energetic Heavy Ion Sensors (EHIS) in orbit on GOES-16 and -17, with two more EHIS's delivered for GOES-T and -U, and a spare flight instrument in-build; research also includes instrument development work in preparation for future space-flight opportunities. Connell, Lopate, McKibben.

View additional information about this department at www.gradschoolshopper.com. Check out the "Why Choose Us?" section, find out more about the department's culture and get links to social media networks.

NEW JERSEY INSTITUTE OF TECHNOLOGY

DEPARTMENT OF PHYSICS

Newark, New Jersey 07102
http://physics.njit.edu/

General University Information
President: Joel Bloom
Dean of Graduate School: Sotirios Ziavras
University website: http://www.njit.edu/graduatestudies/
School Type: Public
Setting: Urban
Total Faculty: 489
Total Graduate Faculty: 170
Total number of Students: 10,044
Total number of Graduate Students: 2,833

Department Information
Department Chairman: Prof. Andrei Sirenko, Chair
Department Contact: Andrei Sirenko, Professor & Chair
  Total full-time faculty: 22
  Total number of full-time equivalent positions: 30
  Full-Time Graduate Students: 25
  Female Full-Time Graduate Students: 5
  First-Year Graduate Students: 7
  Female First-Year Students: 2
  Total Post Doctorates: 4

Department Address
Tiernan Building # 463
161 Warren Street
Newark, NJ 07102
Phone: (973) 596-3562
Fax: (973) 596-5794
E-mail: andrei.sirenko@njit.edu
Website: http://physics.njit.edu/

ADMISSIONS

Admission Contact Information
Address admission inquiries to: Admissions, New Jersey Institute
  of Technology, Newark, NJ 07102-1982
Phone: 1-800-925-NJIT or 973-596-3300
E-mail: admissions@njit.edu
Admissions website: http://www.njit.edu/admissions/
  contactadmissions.php

Application deadlines
Fall admission:
U.S. students: December 15   *Int'l. students*: December 15
Spring admission:
U.S. students: September 1   *Int'l. students*: September 1

Application fee
U.S. students: $120   *Int'l. students*: $120
The Department of Physics also participates in the Interdisciplinary Program in Materials Science and Engineering at NJIT. If financial aid is needed, the deadline is December 15, 2018. The deadlines are for Ph.D. admission. MS program has rolling admission, financial aid is not available.

Admissions information
For Fall of 2018:
  Number of applicants: 30
  Number admitted: 11

Number enrolled: 4

Admission requirements
Bachelor's degree requirements: Bachelor's degree in Physics
  is required.
Minimum undergraduate GPA: 3.0

GRE requirements
The GRE is required.
  Quantitative score: 160
  Verbal score: 150

Subjective GRE requirements
The Subjective GRE is recommended.
Good GRE Physics score is a plus, but not necessary for application consideration.

TOEFL requirements
The TOEFL exam is required for students from non-English-speaking countries.
  PBT score: 550
  iBT score: 80

Other admissions information
Additional requirements: Scientific publications and research experience help in the admissions process.
Undergraduate preparation assumed: Classical Mechanics; Electromagnetism; Quantum Mechanics; Thermodynamics; Solid State Physics; Optics.

TUITION

Tuition year 2017–18:
Tuition for in-state residents
  Full-time students: $18,500 annual
  Part-time students: $1,006 per credit
Tuition for out-of-state residents
  Full-time students: $27,340 annual
  Part-time students: $1,444 per credit
Additional fees apply; tuition based on nine credits per semester; see http://www.njit.edu/bursar/tuition/grad-tuition.php.
Credit hours per semester to be considered full-time: 9
Deferred tuition plan: Yes
Health insurance: Yes, $1247.00.
Other academic fees: Per credit; see http://www.njit.edu/healthservices/health-insurance.php.
Academic term: Semester

Teaching Assistants, Research Assistants, and Fellowships
Number of first-year
  Teaching Assistants: 4
Average stipend per academic year
  Teaching Assistant: $22,000
  Research Assistant: $22,000
  Fellowship student: $25,000
Department has 13 TA lines. Students are supported with TA for two years. After that they are expected to switch to RA support.

FINANCIAL AID

Application deadlines
Fall admission:
U.S. students: December 15   *Int'l. students*: December 15

Loans
Loans are available for U.S. students.
Loans are not available for international students.
GAPSFAS application required: No
FAFSA application required: Yes

For further information
Address financial aid inquiries to: Admissions, New Jersey Institute of Technology, Newark, NJ 07102-1982.
Phone: (973) 596-3300
Financial aid website: http://www.njit.edu/financialaid/

HOUSING

Availability of on-campus housing
Single students: Yes
Married students: No

For further information
Address housing inquiries to: Admissions Office, New Jersey Institute of Technology, Newark, NJ 07102-1982.
Phone: (973) 596-3039
E-mail: reslife@njit.edu
Housing aid website: http://www.njit.edu/reslife/

Table A—Faculty, Enrollments, and Degrees Granted

Research Specialty	2015–16 Faculty	Enrollment Fall 2015		Number of Degrees Granted 2015–16 (2011–16)		
		Master's	Doctorate	Master's	Terminal Master's	Doctorate
Applied Physics	4	13	19	6(30)	–	3(25)
Astrophysics	5	–	–	–	–	–(6)
Atomic, Molecular, & Optical Physics	2	–	–	–	–	2(7)
Biophysics	3	–	–	–	–	–(2)
Condensed Matter Physics	2	–	–	–	–	–(3)
Materials Science, Metallurgy	3	–	–	–	–	1(7)
Total	19	13	19	6(30)	–	3(25)
Full-time Grad. Stud.	–	13	19	–	–	–
First-year Grad. Stud.	–	7	–	–	–	–

GRADUATE DEGREE REQUIREMENTS

Master's: The interdisciplinary NJIT-Rutgers (Newark) joint M.S. degree in Applied Physics requires 30 credits; 24 credits are coursework, of which 18 credits are physics courses (including mathematical physics or applied mathematics) and 6 credits are electives. Four graduate physics courses, Classical Mechanics, Classical Electrodynamics I, Quantum Mechanics I, and Statistical Mechanics are mandatory. Six credits are thesis research; with the approval of the academic adviser, the student can choose a three-credit project plus an additional three-credit course to replace the six-credit thesis.

Doctorate: For entering students with B.S. or B.A. degrees, the interdisciplinary NJIT-Rutgers (Newark) joint Ph.D. degree in Applied Physics requires 75 credits (above the 600 level), of which 39 credits are coursework and 36 credits are dissertation research. Of the coursework, 24 credits are physics courses (including mathematical physics or applied mathe-

matics) and 15 credits are electives. Of the 24 credits of physics courses, Classical Mechanics, 621 Classical Electrodynamics I and II, 631 Quantum Mechanics I and II, and Statistical Mechanics are mandatory. For entering students with M.S. or M.A. degrees, the Joint NJIT-Rutgers (Newark) Ph.D. degree in Applied Physics requires 54 credits (above the 600 level), of which 18 credits are coursework and 36 credits are dissertation research. Of the coursework, nine credits are physics courses (including mathematical physics or applied mathematics) and nine credits are electives.

Thesis: Ph.D. thesis is a requirement for all doctoral students.

SPECIAL EQUIPMENT, FACILITIES, OR PROGRAMS

Center for Solar-Terrestrial Research; Big Bear Solar Observatory (BBSO); Apollo CdTe Solar Cell Research Center; Space Weather Research Laboratory; Microelectronics Research Center with class 10 clean room silicon IC process facility and device research laboratories; Owens Valley Solar Array (OVSA); THz spectroscopy laboratory; laser spectroscopy laboratory; surface science laboratory; bio-sensor laboratory. Interdisciplinary applied physics research is carried out in collaboration with Electrical Engineering, Chemistry, Biomedical Engineering, and Biological Sciences faculty and with the University of Medicine and Dentistry of New Jersey (UMDNJ). There is also extensive cooperative research with the National Solar Observatory, Brookhaven National Laboratory, National Renewable Energy Laboratory, US Army Research Lab, and other industrial and federal research laboratories. The Department of Physics at NJIT also operates the Interdisciplinary Program in Materials Science and Engineering. For information on this program, contact Prof. Sirenko at sirenko@njit.edu

Table B—Separately Budgeted Research Expenditures by Source of Support

Source of Support	Departmental Research	Physics-related Research Outside Department
Federal government	$8,400,000	
State/local government		
Non-profit organizations		
Business and industry	$600,000	
Other		
Total	$9,000,000	

Table C—Separately Budgeted Research Expenditures by Research Specialty

Research Specialty	No. of Grants	Expenditures ($)
Applied Physics	3	$1,100,000
Biophysics	1	$300,000
Condensed Matter Physics	3	$200,000
Optics	3	$300,000
Solar Physics	40	$7,100,000
Total	50	$9,000,000

FACULTY

Professor
Cao, Wenda, Ph.D., Purple Mountain Observatory, Chinese Academy of Sciences, China, 2001. Director of BBSO. *Optics, Solar Physics*. Solar physics.

Chin, Ken K., Ph.D., Stanford University, 1986. Director, Apollo Center for CdTe Solar Cell Research. *Applied Physics, Condensed Matter Physics, Energy Sources & Environment, Ma-*

terials Science, Metallurgy, Solid State Physics. Semiconductors; solar cells; solid-state physics; power transmission.

Federici, John, Ph.D., Princeton University, 1989. Distinguished Professor/Professor Rank II. *Applied Physics, Biophysics, Materials Science, Metallurgy, Optics.* Terahertz spectroscopy; sensors; biophotonics.

Gary, Dale E., Ph.D., University of Colorado, 1982. Distinguished Professor/Professor Rank II. *Applied Physics, Astronomy, Astrophysics, Planetary Science, Solar Physics.* Radio solar physics.

Gatley, Ian, Ph.D., California Institute of Technology, 1978. *Applied Physics, Astronomy, Astrophysics, Atmosphere, Space Physics, Cosmic Rays, Optics.* Infrared astronomy.

Gerrard, Andrew, Ph.D., Pennsylvania State University, 2002. *Astronomy, Atmosphere, Space Physics, Cosmic Rays, Heliophysics and Space Weather, Solar Physics.* Upper atmospheric research.

Kosovichev, Alexander, Ph.D., Moscow University, 1980. Director of the Center for Computational Heliophysics at NJIT. *Heliophysics and Space Weather, Plasma and Fusion, Solar Physics, Theoretical Physics.*

Levy, Roland, Ph.D., Columbia University, 1973. Distinguished Professor/Professor Rank II. *Applied Physics, Materials Science, Metallurgy, Solid State Physics.* CVD; PVD; materials synthesis.

Murnick, E. Daniel, Ph.D., Massachusetts Institute of Technology, 1966. Chair of Physics Department at Rutgers U. Distinguished Professor/Professor Rank II. *Atomic, Molecular, & Optical Physics, Biophysics, Medical, Health Physics.* Laser spectroscopy and applied physics.

Ravindra, N. M., Ph.D., Indian Institute of Technology, Roorkee, 1982. *Applied Physics, Condensed Matter Physics, Materials Science, Metallurgy, Nano Science and Technology, Physics and other Science Education, Solid State Physics.*

Sirenko, Andrei, Ph.D., A. F. Ioffe Physical Technical Institute, Russia, 1993. Chair of the Physics Department and Program Director-Interdisciplinary Program in Materials Science and Engineering. *Materials Science, Metallurgy, Optics, Solid State Physics.* Optics; materials and device physics.

Thomas, Gordon, Ph.D., University of Rochester, 1972. *Biophysics, Optics.* Optics; biophysics.

Tyson, Trevor, Ph.D., Stanford University, 1993. Distinguished Professor/Professor Rank II. *Condensed Matter Physics, Solid State Physics.* Condensed matter physics.

Wang, Haimin, Ph.D., California Institute of Technology, 1988. Distinguished Professor/Professor Rank II. Director of the Applied Physics Graduate Program. *Astronomy, Astrophysics, Atmosphere, Space Physics, Cosmic Rays, Solar Physics.* Solar physics; space weather.

Wu, Zhen, Ph.D., Columbia University, 1984. At Rutgers U. *Atomic, Molecular, & Optical Physics.* Atomic and molecular physics; laser spectroscopy and surface science.

Associate Professor

Ahn, Keun, Ph.D., Johns Hopkins University, 2000. *Computational Physics, Condensed Matter Physics, Solid State Physics.* Condensed matter physics.

Dias, Cristiano, Ph.D., McGill University. *Biophysics.* Computational biophysics.

Prodan, Camelia, Ph.D., University of Houston, 2005. *Biophysics.* Biophysics.

Russo, L. O., Ph.D., New Jersey Institute of Technology, 1975. *Solid State Physics.* Solid-state physics.

Zhou, Tao, Ph.D., Max Planck Institute for Solid State Research, 2004. *Applied Physics, Optics.* Optical spectroscopy.

Assistant Professor

Chen, Bin, Ph.D., University of Virginia, 2013. *Solar Physics.* Solar physics; space weather; radio intrumentation.

Nowadnick, Elizabeth A., Ph.D., Stanford University, 2013. *Computational Physics, Theoretical Physics.* Theoretical condensed matter physics.

Thomas, Benjamin, Ph.D., Lyon 1 University, 2013. *Applied Physics, Optics.* Experimental physics, optics, light interaction based insturments.

Research Professor

Farrow, Reginald, Ph.D., Stevens Institute of Technology, 1984. *Applied Physics, Nano Science and Technology, Solid State Physics.* Solid-state semiconductors and biophysics.

Fleishman, Gregory, Ph.D., Ioffe Institute for Physics and Technology, St. Petersburg, Russia, 1998. *Astrophysics, Solar Physics.* Non-thermal electromagnetic emission in structural astrophysical medium.

Goode, Philip R., Ph.D., Rutgers University, 1969. *Astronomy, Astrophysics, Solar Physics.*

Jing, Ju, Ph.D., New Jersey Institute of Technology, 2005. *Solar Physics.* Solar magnetic fields; solar activity.

Kim, Hyomin, Ph.D., University of New Hampshire, Durham, NH, 2010. *Atmosphere, Space Physics, Cosmic Rays.* Space instrumentation.

Lanzerotti, Louis J., Ph.D., Harvard University, 1965. *Astronomy, Astrophysics, Atmosphere, Space Physics, Cosmic Rays, Heliophysics and Space Weather.* Geophysics and space plasma physics.

Liu, Chang, Ph.D., New Jersey Institute of Technology, 2007. *Solar Physics.* Solar flares and coronal mass ejections; solar magnetic fields.

Nita, Gelu, Ph.D., New Jersey Institute of Technology, 2004. *Solar Physics.* Solar microwave radiation.

Soto-Chavez, Rualdo, Ph.D., University of Texas at Austin. *Astrophysics.* Relativistic Wave Phenomena in Astrophysical Plasmas.

Xu, Yan, Ph.D., New Jersey Institute of Technology, 2005. *Astrophysics.* Solar Physics.

Yurchyshyn, Vasyl, Ph.D., Astronomical Observatory, Kiev, Ukraine, 1998. *Solar Physics.* Solar flares; solar coronal mass ejecta.

Research Assistant Professor

Frissell, Nataniel, Ph.D., Virginia Polytechnic Institute and State University, 2016. *Electrical Engineering.* Terrestrial Physics.

Lecturer

Georgiou, George E., Ph.D., Columbia University, 1980. Semiconductors.

Gokce, Oktay, Ph.D., Montana State University, 1981. Chemical engineering.

Janow, Richard, Ph.D., City University of New York, 1977. *Condensed Matter Physics.*

Jerez, Andrez, Ph.D., Rutgers University, 1996. *Condensed Matter Physics.*

Maljian, Libarid A., M.S., Rutgers University, 2000. *Astronomy, Astrophysics.*

Opyrchal, Halina, Ph.D., Institute of Low Temperature and Structure Research, Polish Academy of Sciences, 1975. *Solid State Physics.*

Piatek, Slawomir, Ph.D., Rutgers University, 1994. *Astronomy, Astrophysics.* Solar physics.

Shneidman, Vitaly, Ph.D., Academy of Sciences, Ukraine. *Condensed Matter Physics, Solid State Physics, Statistical & Thermal Physics.* Computational physics.

Laboratory Director

Maeng, Sung, Ph.D., New Jersey Institute of Technology. Materials Science and Engineering., 2005. UG Laboratory Director.

Laboratory Coordinator

Zhou, Xuechong, Ph.D., City University of New York, 2005. Laboratory personnel. *Optics*. Semiconductors and optics.

DEPARTMENTAL RESEARCH SPECIALTIES AND STAFF

Experimental

Atomic, Molecular, & Optical Physics. Atomic, molecular, and applied laser physics. Two postdoctoral fellows. Federici, Murnick, Sirenko, Benjamin Thomas, Wu, Tao Zhou.

Biophysics. Biophysics-diagnostics and sensors. Four postdoctoral fellows. Dias, Farrow, Federici, Prodan, Gordon Thomas.

Materials Science, Metallurgy. Solid-state physics; materials science. Six postdoctoral fellows. Chin, Federici, Levy, Ravindra, Russo, Tyson, Wu.

Solar Physics. Solar-terrestrial physics. Cao, Chen, Fleishman, Gary, Gerrard, Goode, Jing, Kosovichev, Lanzerotti, Liu, Nita, Wang, Xu, Yurchyshyn.

Solid State Physics. Magnetic oxides, ferroelectrics, synchrotron radiation. Two postdoctoral fellows. Ahn, Chin, Levy, Nowadnick, Ravindra, Sirenko, Tyson.

View additional information about this department at www.gradschoolshopper.com. Check out the "Why Choose Us?" section, find out more about the department's culture and get links to social media networks.

PRINCETON UNIVERSITY

DEPARTMENT OF PHYSICS

Princeton, New Jersey 08544
http://princeton.edu/physics

General University Information
President: Christopher Eisgruber
Dean of Graduate School: Dean Sarah-Jane Leslie
University website: http://www.princeton.edu
School Type: Private
Total Faculty: 1,175
Total number of Students: 7,910
Total number of Graduate Students: 3,570

Department Information
Department Chairman: Prof. Herman Verlinde, Chair
Department Contact: James Olsen, Director of Graduate Studies
  Total full-time faculty: 39
  Full-Time Graduate Students: 135
  Female Full-Time Graduate Students: 29
  First-Year Graduate Students: 25
  Female First-Year Students: 7
  Total Post Doctorates: 31

ADMISSIONS

Admission Contact Information
Address admission inquiries to: Graduate Admissions Office, Clio Hall, Princeton University, Princeton, NJ 08544
Phone: (609) 258-3030
E-mail: gs@princeton.edu
Admissions website: http://www.princeton.edu/gradschool/

Application deadlines
Fall admission:
U.S. students: December 15   *Int'l. students*: December 15

Application fee
U.S. students: $90   *Int'l. students*: $90

Admissions information
For Fall of 2017:
  Number of applicants: 623
  Number admitted: 66
  Number enrolled: 29

Admission requirements
Bachelor's degree requirements: A bachelor's degree is required.

GRE requirements
The GRE is required.

Subjective GRE requirements
The Subjective GRE is required.
We do not have a minimum GRE score for admission.

TOEFL requirements
The TOEFL exam is required for students from non-English-speaking countries.

The Graduate School does not have a minimum TOEFL or IELTS score requirement. If you are offered admission and accept our offer and have scored below a 27 on the Speaking sub-section of the TOEFL iBT or below an 8.0 on the Speaking sub-section of the IELTS you will be required to take an English placement test at the start of the fall term. Students who do not pass the test will be required to enroll in English Language Program classes.

TUITION
Tuition year 2018–2019:
  Full-time students: $49,450 annual
Deferred tuition plan: No
Health insurance: Available at the cost of $1800 per year.

Teaching Assistants, Research Assistants, and Fellowships
Number of first-year
  Fellowship students: 29
Average stipend per academic year
  Teaching Assistant: $32,050
  Research Assistant: $29,000
  Fellowship student: $29,000

FINANCIAL AID

Loans
Loans are not available for U.S. students.
Loans are not available for international students.
GAPSFAS application required: No
FAFSA application required: No

For further information
Address financial aid inquiries to: Asst. Dean of Financial Affairs, Graduate School, 204 Nassau Hall, Princeton, NJ 08544.
Phone: (609) 258-3030
E-mail: gs@princeton.edu
Financial aid website: http://gradschool.princeton.edu/costs-funding

HOUSING

Availability of on-campus housing
  Single students: Yes
  Married students: Yes

For further information
Address housing inquiries to: Graduate Housing Department MacMillan Building, Princeton University, Princeton, NJ 08544.
Phone: (609) 258-4360
E-mail: gradhsg@princeton.edu
Housing aid website: http://gradschool.princeton.edu/admission/admitted-degree-students/additional-requirements/graduate-housing

Table A—Faculty, Enrollments, and Degrees Granted

Research Specialty	2018–2019 Faculty	Enrollment Fall 2018 Master's	Enrollment Fall 2018 Doctorate	Number of Degrees Granted 2017–2018 Master's	Number of Degrees Granted 2017–2018 Terminal Master's	Number of Degrees Granted 2017–2018 Doctorate
Atomic, Molecular, & Optical Physics	3	–	10	–	–	–
Biophysics	6	–	18	–	–	3
Computational Physics	2	–	5	–	–	–
Condensed Matter Physics	8	–	44	–	–	4
Cosmology & String Theory	5	–	12	–	–	5
High Energy Physics	12	–	36	–	–	5
Particles and Fields	2	–	10	–	–	2
Other	–	–	–	–	–	–
Total	39	–	–	–	–	19
Full-time Grad. Stud.	–	–	135	–	–	–
First-year Grad. Stud.	–	–	25	–	–	–

GRADUATE DEGREE REQUIREMENTS

Master's: The master's degree is conferred only after passing a general examination. (Students who want to work toward a master's degree only will not be admitted.).

Doctorate: The formal course requirements include three core courses to be taken between the beginning of the first year of study and the end of the second year. (This requirement is part of the general examination.) Students taking these courses must achieve a grade of B or higher. In addition, one year of residency is required; prelim exam, experimental project, prethesis project and the dissertation are required.

Thesis: Thesis may be written in absentia.

SPECIAL EQUIPMENT, FACILITIES, OR PROGRAMS

Theoretical research spans most of the central topics of modern physics. The department has decades-old traditions of excellence and leadership in these core areas of fundamental physics, and it is also rapidly building strength in newer areas, such as theoretical biology. In the newer areas, interaction between physics and other departments is critical, and major university-supported interdisciplinary initiatives provide a strong framework for this cooperation. There is also productive interaction between theorists in the department and those at the nearby Institute for Advanced Studies, although there is no formal connection between these institutions.

The high-energy theory group works on quantum field theory, particle phenomenology and cosmology, string theory and quantum gravity models in various dimensions, and dualities between gauge theories and strings. Some members of the group are also interested in applications of quantum field theory and string theory to problems in statistical mechanics, the theory of turbulence, heavy-ion collisions, and condensed matter physics.

The cosmology theory group uses astrophysical, particle physics, and superstring theory combined with observations to study gravitation and the origin, composition, and evolution of the universe.

The theoretical condensed matter group works on quantum many-body theory of systems involving strong correlations and/or disorder, statistical mechanics, biological systems, and systems far from equilibrium.

The mathematical physics group is concerned with problems in statistical mechanics, atomic and molecular physics, quantum field theory, and, in general, with the mathematical foundations of theoretical physics.

The theoretical biophysicists work on problems in statistical mechanics and information theory that arise in studying nervous systems, gene expression networks, the organization of genomes, and the mechanisms of evolution.

Experiments in high-energy particle physics are directed toward understanding the fundamental interactions and particle structures at extremely small distances. The apparatus is designed and constructed in the physics shops in Jadwin Hall or at the nearby Elementary Particles Laboratory, which contains special facilities for the fabrication of detectors. The experiments are performed at large national and international laboratories, which currently include CERN (Switzerland), Fermilab (Illinois), and SLAC (California). The data are then analyzed at Princeton University.

The nuclear and particle astrophysics group is active in experimental studies of solar neutrinos and dark matter. The goal of the solar neutrino program is to explore neutrino oscillations and solar processes through a measurement of the low-energy 7Be neutrino. Neutrinos will be detected with the Borexino liquid scintillation detector located in the Gran Sasso underground laboratory in Italy.

The dark matter group is designed to detect WIMPs in the galaxy by their collisions with either xenon or argon nuclei in a scintillation-ionization detector made of the rare gas atoms. Experiments are under development to provide a definitive search for rare WIMP collisions by combining the unique scintillation properties of the rare gas atoms with the low background methods developed for the Borexino solar neutrino experiment.

Research in the condensed-matter physics group seeks to understand electronic behavior in novel low-dimensional solids in which interaction and correlation effects are dominant. Problems investigated have included the fractional and integer quantum Hall effects, high-temperature superconductivity, Kondo effect in quantum dots, spin-density-wave states in organic conductors, highly frustrated quantum-spin systems, and novel excitations in low-dimensional magnetic systems.

The research involves close collaborations between experimentalists and theorists, as well as with faculty in the Chemistry and Electrical Engineering Departments.

Experimental groups are also engaged in researching novel patterning techniques using diblock copolymers (with faculty in Chemical Engineering) and techniques for single-molecule detection and separation of biological molecules (with Molecular Biology and the Genomics Center).

In the experimental cosmology group, students often design and build specialized instrumentation to make unique and precise measurements, or analyze cosmological data. In recent years, experimental work has emphasized measurements of the anisotropy and polarization of the cosmic microwave background. Among other projects, Princeton is actively involved in all aspects of the WMAP satellite, is the lead institution for the ACT project, and is a collaborator on the QUIET experiment.

Research in atomic physics is primarily focused on spin-polarized gases, liquids, and solids, on their properties, interactions, and a wide range of applications. Among applications currently being developed are searches for violation of CP symmetry beyond the Standard Model, tests of Lorentz invariance, development of miniature atomic clocks, ultrasensitive atomic magnetometers, and new biomedical techniques, such as lung imaging and mapping of the magnetic fields generated by the brain.

Biological physics spans a huge range of subjects, from neurobiology to genomics to fundamentals of protein action. Princeton has strengths in nearly all areas of modern biological physics. Many faculty with a strong physics background who are involved in biological physics are not solely in the Physics Department but have joint appointments with other departments or are completely in other departments. There is a strong community spirit to biological physics among these departments despite the vast range of subjects being studied.

For more information, please visit www.princeton.edu/physics.

Table B—Separately Budgeted Research Expenditures by Source of Support

Source of Support	Departmental Research	Physics-related Research Outside Department
Federal government	$18,770,070	$3,324,295
State/local government		
Non-profit organizations	$1,812,005	$310,514
Business and industry	$57,405	$208
Other		
Total	$20,639,480	$3,635,017

Table C—Separately Budgeted Research Expenditures by Research Specialty

Research Specialty	No. of Grants	Expenditures ($)
Astrophysics	30	$2,925,249
Atomic, Molecular, & Optical Physics	13	$829,855
Biophysics	16	$1,112,680
Condensed Matter Physics	49	$5,401,953
Nuclear Physics	8	$1,191,763
Particles and Fields	52	$12,751,706
Other	2	$61,290
Total	170	$24,274,496

FACULTY

Professor

Aizenman, Michael, Ph.D., Belfer Graduate School of Science, Yeshiva Univ., 1975. Mathematical physics.

Austin, Robert, Ph.D., University of Illinois, 1975. *Biophysics*. Biophysics.

Bernevig, Bogdan an Andrei, Ph.D., Stanford University. Condensed matter.

Bialek, William, Ph.D., University of California, Berkeley, 1983. *Biophysics*. Biophysics.

Calaprice, Frank, Ph.D., University of California, Berkeley, 1967. Nuclear physics.

Callan, Curtis G., Ph.D., Princeton University, 1964. Theoretical physics.

Dunkley, Jo, Ph.D., University of Oxford, 2005. Professor, Departments of Physics and Astrophysical Sciences, Princeton University Senior Beecroft Fellow, visitor at University of Oxford. *Astrophysics*. Astrophysics.

Galbiati, Cristiano, Ph.D., University of Milan, 1999. Nuclear physics.

Gubser, Steven, Ph.D., Princeton University, 1998. Particle theory.

Haldane, F. Duncan M., Ph.D., University of Cambridge, 1978. Condensed matter.

Hasan, M. Zahid, Ph.D., Stanford University, 2001. *Condensed Matter Physics*. Condensed matter physics.

Huse, David A., Ph.D., Cornell University, 1983. Condensed matter physics.

Klebanov, Igor, Ph.D., Princeton University, 1986. Theoretical physics.

Marlow, Daniel R., Ph.D., Carnegie Mellon University, 1981. High energy physics.

McDonald, Kirk, Ph.D., California Institute of Technology, 1972. High energy physics.

Meyers, Peter, Ph.D., University of California, Berkeley, 1983. High energy physics.

Olsen, James, Ph.D., University of Wisconsin-Madison, 1998. Associate Chair for Graduate Studies and Teaching. High energy physics.

Ong, Nai-Phuan, Ph.D., University of California, Berkeley, 1976. Condensed matter physics.

Page, Lyman, Ph.D., Massachusetts Institute of Technology, 1989. Cosmology; gravitation; relativity.

Petta, Jason, Ph.D., Cornell University, 2003. Condensed matter.

Polyakov, Alexander, Ph.D., Landau Institute, USSR, 1969. Theoretical physics.

Pretorius, Frans, Ph.D., University of British Columbia, 2002. Theoretical cosmology.

Romalis, Michael, Ph.D., Princeton University, 1997. Atomic physics.

Shaevitz, Joshua, Ph.D., Stanford University, 2004. Molecular biology.

Sondhi, Shivaji Lal, Ph.D., University of California, Los Angeles, 1992. Condensed matter physics.

Staggs, Suzanne, Ph.D., Princeton University, 1993. Cosmology; gravitation; relativity.

Steinhardt, Paul, Ph.D., Harvard University, 1978. Cosmology.

Tully, Christopher, Ph.D., Princeton University, 1998. High energy physics.

Verlinde, Herman, Ph.D., Utrecht University, 1988. Particle theory.

Yazdani, Ali, Ph.D., Stanford University, 1995. Condensed matter.

Associate Professor

Gregor, Thomas, Princeton University, 2005. *Biophysics*. Biophysics.

Jones, William C., Ph.D., California Institute of Technology, 2005. Cosmology.

Assistant Professor

Bakr, Waseem, Ph.D., Harvard University, 2011. Atomic Physics.

Giombi, Simone, Ph.D., State University of New York at Stony Brook, 2007. *Nuclear Physics*. High Energy Theory.

Leifer, Andrew, Ph.D., Harvard University, 2012. Assistant Professor, Department of Physics and Princeton Neuroscience Institute. *Neuroscience/Neuro Physics*. Neuroscience/Neuro Physics.

Lisanti, Mariangela, Ph.D., Stanford University. *Particles and Fields*. Particle Phenomenology.

Pufu, Silviu, Ph.D., Princeton University, 2011. *High Energy Physics*. High Energy Theory.

Emeritus

Anderson, Philip, Ph.D., Harvard University, 1949. *Condensed Matter Physics*. Condensed Matter Physics.

Chikin, Paul, Ph.D., University of Pennsylvania, 1971. *Condensed Matter Physics*.

Gross, David, Ph.D., University of California, Berkeley, 1966. *Theoretical Physics*. Theoretical Physics.

Groth, Edward, Ph.D., Princeton University, 1971. Cosmology; gravitation and relativity.

Happer, William, Ph.D., Princeton University, 1964. Atomic physics.

Nappi, Chiara, Ph.D., University of Naples, 1976. *Particles and Fields, Theoretical Physics*. High Energy Theory.

Peebles, P. James, Ph.D., Princeton University, 1962. *Cosmology & String Theory, Theoretical Physics*. Theoretical cosmology Physics.

Piroue, Pierre, Ph.D., University of Geneva, 1958. *High Energy Physics*. High Energy Physics.

Smith, A. J. Stewart, Ph.D., Princeton University, 1966. High energy physics.

Taylor Jr., Joseph, Ph.D., Harvard, 1968. *Astrophysics*. Astrophysics.

Professor Emeritus

Lieb, Elliott, Ph.D., Massachusetts Institute of Technology, 1956. Mathematical physics.

Affiliate Professor

Bhatt, Ravindra, Ph.D., U. Illinois, Urbana, 1976. Professor of Electrical Engineering. *Electrical Engineering*. Electrical Engineering.

Car, Roberto, Ph.D., Laurea, Milan, 1971. Chemistry.

Dafermos, Mihalis, Ph.D., Princeton University, 2001. Professor of Mathematics. *Other*. Mathematical Physics Partial Differential Equations.

Houck, Andrew, Ph.D., Harvard University, 2005. Professor of Electrical Engineering. *Electrical Engineering*. Electrical Engineering.

Leibler, Stanislas, Ph.D., University of Paris, 1981. Professor, The Rockefeller University Professor, Institute for Advanced Study. *Biophysics*. theoretical and experimental biologist and physicist.

Shayegan, Mansour, Ph.D., Massachusetts Institute of Technology, 1983. *Electrical Engineering*. Electrical engineering.

Sinai, Yakov, Ph.D., Moscow State University, 1960. Professor Mathmatics. *Other*. Ergodic Theory & Dynamical Systems.

Spergel, David N., Ph.D., Harvard University, 1985. Astrophysical sciences.

Tank, David, Ph.D., Cornell University, 1983. *Biophysics*. Biophysics.

Torquato, Salvatore, Ph.D., Stony Brook University, 1980. Chemistry.

Visiting Professor

Adler, Stephen L., Ph.D., Princeton University, 1964. Visiting Lecturer with rank of Professor. Theoretical physics.

Arkani-Hamed, Nima, Ph.D., University of California, Berkeley, 1997. Visiting professor with rank of professor. *Particles and Fields*. particle physics phenomenology.

Leibler, Stanislas, Ph.D., University of Paris, 1984. Visiting professor with rank of professor. *Biophysics*. theoretical and experimental biologist and physicist.

Maldacena, Juan, Ph.D., Princeton University, 1996. quantum gravity, string theory, and quantum field theory.

Seiberg, Nathan, Ph.D., Tel Aviv University, 1982. Visiting Lecturer with rank of Professor. Particle theory.

Witten, Edward, Ph.D., Princeton University, 1976. Visiting Lecturer with rank of Professor. Theoretical physics.

Associate Faculty

Tsui, Dan, Ph.D., University of Chicago, 1967. Electrical engineering and computer science.

Wingreen, Ned, Ph.D., Cornell University, 1989. Molecular biology.

DEPARTMENTAL RESEARCH SPECIALTIES AND STAFF

Theoretical

Condensed Matter Physics. The theoretical condensed matter group works on quantum many-body theory of systems involving strong correlations and/or disorder, statistical mechanics, biological systems, and systems far from equilibrium. For more information, visit www.princeton.edu/physics. Bernevig, Haldane, Sondhi.

Cosmology & String Theory. Working closely with the experimental group, we use astrophysical, particle physics and *string* theory combined with observations to study gravitation and the origin and evolution of our universe. In cosmology and astrophysics, Einstein's General Theory of Relativity (GR) is the foundation for everything from models of the universe to the collision of black holes. Our group is a pioneer in the use of numerical GR to understand such things as the gravitational wave signature of merging black hole and neutron star systems, the properties of spacetime and matter fields approaching the big bang, and elements of string theory. The study of the nature of large-scale structure was pioneered in this group *three* decades ago, and we continue to make leading contributions to theories of the origin of this structure. Crucial elements in the work include the measurements by the experimental group of the *2.725* K thermal background radiation, deep observations of galaxies, and the Sloan Digital Sky Survey that operates out of the *neighboring* Department of Astrophysical Sciences. The origin of the physical universe and the cosmological model that describes its evolution must ultimately be explained by fundamental physics. Our group also studies the relationship between particle or string* physics and theories of the very early universe, dark matter, the cosmological constant and quintessence. These studies have profound implications for both fundamental physics and cosmology. Dunkley, Giombi, Klebanov, Pretorius, Pufu, Steinhardt, Verlinde.

High Energy Physics. High Energy Experiment - The goal of high energy physics is the understanding of the elementary particles that are the fundamental constituents of matter. The fabulous success of the Standard Model has given us a framework for interpretation of most particle interactions, but it has also created a foundation from which we can begin to explore a deeper level of issues such as the origin of mass, the preponderance of matter over antimatter in the Universe, the identity of "dark matter," the physics of the Big Bang, and the microscopic structure of space-time. High Energy Theory - The research effort of the high energy theory group covers a wide range of fields, including quantum field theory, string theory, quantum gravity models in various dimensions, the theory of turbulence, particle cosmology, phenomenology of the Standard Model and beyond, and also computer simulations of problems that arise in these areas. Giombi, Gubser, Klebanov, Nappi, Pufu, Steinhardt, Verlinde, Witten.

Mathematical Physics. The mathematical physics group is concerned with problems in statistical mechanics, atomic and molecular physics, quantum field theory, and, in general, with the mathematical foundations of theoretical physics. This includes such subjects as quantum mechanics (both nonrelativistic and relativistic), atomic and molecular physics, disorder effects in condensed matter, the existence and properties of the phases of model ferromagnets, the stability of matter, the theory of symmetry and symmetry breaking in quantum field theory (both in general and in concrete models), and mathematical developments in functional analysis, algebra and modern probability theory, to which such subjects lead. In addition to the physics faculty, students in mathematical physics have contact with the faculty of the mathematics department. Aizenman, Lieb.

Particles and Fields. The particle and nuclear astrophysics program addresses questions of fundamental physics in astrophysical systems. Current research topics include Solar Neutrinos, WIMP Dark Matter searches, Neutrino-less Double Beta Decay, and detection of Ultra-High Energy Neutrinos. Calaprice, Galbiati.

Experimental

Atomic, Molecular, & Optical Physics. Research in atomic physics is primarily focused on spin-polarized gases, liquids, and solids, on their properties, interactions, and a wide range of applications. Among applications currently being developed are searches for violation of CP symmetry beyond the standard model, tests of Lorentz invariance, development of miniature atomic clocks, ultra-sensitive atomic magnetometers, and new biomedical techniques, such as lung imaging and mapping of the magnetic fields generated by the brain. For more information, please visit www.princeton.edu/physics. Bakr, Romalis.

Biophysics. Biological physics spans a huge range of subjects, from neurobiology to genomics to fundamentals of protein action. Princeton has strengths in nearly all areas of modern biological physics. Many faculty with a strong physics background who are involved in biological physics are not solely in the Physics Department but have joint appointments with other departments or are completely in other departments. There is a strong community spirit to biological physics among these departments despite the vast range of subjects being studied. For more information, please visit www.princeton.edu/physics. Gregor, Leifer.

Condensed Matter Physics. Research in the condensed matter physics group seeks to understand electronic behavior in novel low-dimensional solids in which interaction and correlation effects are dominant. Problems investigated have included the fractional and integer quantum Hall effects, high-temperature superconductivity, Kondo effect in quantum dots, spin-density-wave states in organic conductors, highly frustrated quantum-spin systems, and novel excitations in low-dimensional magnetic systems. The research involves close collaborations between experimentalists and theorists, as well as with faculty in the Chemistry and Electrical Engineering Departments. Experimental groups are also engaged in researching novel patterning techniques using diblock copolymers (with faculty in Chemical Engineering) and techniques for single-molecule detection and separation of biological molecules (with Molecular Biology and the Genomics Center). For more information, please visit www.princeton.edu/physics. Hasan, Ong, Petta, Yazdani.

Cosmology & String Theory. Research on cosmology takes place in a number of places in the Princeton community. The experimental and observational cosmology group in the Physics Department is involved in measurements of the cosmic microwave background (CMB), surveys of large scale cosmic structure, and observations of galactic clusters. The CMB is the after glow of the hot early stages of the expansion of our universe. In the angular distribution of its temperature and polarization is encoded the history of the evolution of the universe and the values of the cosmological parameters. Measurements have reached the stage where we now have a "standard model of cosmology" and we are exploring the details of the model. These are exciting times. Efforts are underway to find gravitational radiation from the Big Bang, to determine the sum of the neutrino masses, to map out the earliest cosmic structures, and to find the parameters of the fields that produced the Big Bang. Through comparisons with optical surveys we measure how the universe evolved and test theories of gravity. With a new ballon-born optical telescope, we will measure the masses of dozens of galaxy clusters through their gravitational lensing effect. Groth, Jones, Page, Staggs.

Nuclear Physics. The nuclear and particle astrophysics group is active in experimental studies of solar neutrinos and dark matter. The goal of the solar neutrino program is to explore neutrino oscillations and solar processes through a measurement of the low-energy 7Be neutrino. Neutrinos will be detected with the Borexino liquid scintillation detector located in the Gran Sasso underground laboratory in Italy. For more information, please visit www.princeton.edu/physics. Lisanti.

Particles and Fields. Experiments in high-energy particle physics are directed toward understanding the fundamental interactions and particle structures at extremely small distances. The apparatus is designed and constructed in the physics shops in Jadwin Hall or at the Elementary Particles Laboratory a block away, which contains special facilities for the fabrication of detectors. The experiments are performed at large national and international laboratories, which currently include CERN (Switzerland), Fermilab (Illinois), KEK (Japan), and SLAC (California). The data are then analyzed at Princeton. For more information, please visit www.princeton.edu/physics. Olsen, Piroue, Tully.

View additional information about this department at www.gradschoolshopper.com. Check out the "Why Choose Us?" section, find out more about the department's culture and get links to social media networks.

RUTGERS — THE STATE UNIVERSITY OF NEW JERSEY

DEPARTMENT OF PHYSICS AND ASTRONOMY

Piscataway, New Jersey 08854
http://www.physics.rutgers.edu

General University Information
President: Robert L. Barchi
Dean of Graduate School: Jerome J. Kukor
University website: http://www.rutgers.edu/
School Type: Public
Setting: Suburban
Total Faculty: 3,000
Total Graduate Faculty: 6,500
Total number of Students: 58,000
Total number of Graduate Students: 8,200

Department Information
Department Chairman: Prof. Robert Bartynski, Chair
Department Contact: Ronald Gilman, Graduate Director
  Total full-time faculty: 56
  Total number of full-time equivalent positions: 56
  Full-Time Graduate Students: 115
  Female Full-Time Graduate Students: 21
  First-Year Graduate Students: 23
  Female First-Year Students: 7
  Total Post Doctorates: 51

Department Address
136 Frelinghuysen Road
Piscataway, NJ 08854
Phone: (848) 445-8775
Fax: (732) 445-4343
E-mail: graduate@physics.rutgers.edu
Website: http://www.physics.rutgers.edu

ADMISSIONS

Admission Contact Information
Address admission inquiries to: Dr. Ronald Gilman, Graduate
  Program Director, Department of Physics and Astronomy,
  136 Frelinghuysen Road, Piscataway, NJ 08854-8019
Phone: (848) 445-8765
E-mail: graduate@physics.rutgers.edu
Admissions website: http://gradstudy.rutgers.edu

Application deadlines
Fall admission:
U.S. students: January 1   *Int'l. students*: January 1
Spring admission:
U.S. students: November 1   *Int'l. students*: November 1

Application fee
U.S. students: $70   *Int'l. students*: $70
Later applications will be considered until July 15, depending
  on availability of positions.

Admissions information
For Fall of 2017:
  Number of applicants: 336
  Number admitted: 39
  Number enrolled: 10

Admission requirements
Bachelor's degree requirements: Bachelor's degree in Physics
  or related field is required.
Minimum undergraduate GPA: 3.0

GRE requirements
The GRE is required.
We do not enforce a minimum GRE score. Students admitted
  generally have GRE scores above 50th percentile.

Subjective GRE requirements
The Subjective GRE is required.
We do not enforce a minimum GRE physics score. Students ad-
  mitted generally have a score above 40th percentile.

TOEFL requirements
The TOEFL exam is required for students from non-English-
  speaking countries.
PBT score: 560
iBT score: 83

Other admissions information
Additional requirements: No minimum scores specified. The Advanced Physics average was 70% for students admitted. Students from non-English speaking countries are required to
  demonstrate proficiency in English via the TOEFL or IELTS
  exam.

TUITION

Tuition year 2018–19:
Tuition for in-state residents
  Full-time students: $17,232 annual
  Part-time students: $718 per credit
Tuition for out-of-state residents
  Full-time students: $29,304 annual
  Part-time students: $1,216 per credit
Credit hours per semester to be considered full-time: 9
Deferred tuition plan: Yes
Health insurance: Yes, $912.00.
Other academic fees: $1,865 - $2,184 annual computer fees,
  School fees and Campus fees for full time students.
Academic term: Semester
Number of first-year students who received full tuition waivers: 10

Teaching Assistants, Research Assistants, and Fellowships
Number of first-year
  Teaching Assistants: 8
  Fellowship students: 2
Average stipend per academic year
  Teaching Assistant: $25,969
  Research Assistant: $25,969
  Fellowship student: $29,000
Teaching and research assistants receive full remission of fees
  and health insurance. Fellowships provide modest health in-
  surance but no fee remission.

FINANCIAL AID

Application deadlines
Fall admission:
U.S. students: September 1   *Int'l. students*: September 1
Spring admission:
U.S. students: November 1   *Int'l. students*: November 1

Loans
Loans are available for U.S. students.
Loans are not available for international students.
GAPSFAS application required: No
FAFSA application required: Yes

For further information
Address financial aid inquiries to: Prof. R. Gilman, Graduate Program Director, Rutgers University, Department of Physics and Astronomy, 136 Frelinghuysen Rd., Piscataway, NJ 08854-8019.
Phone: (848) 445-8775
E-mail: graduate@physics.rutgers.edu
Financial aid website: http://studentaid.rutgers.edu/

HOUSING

Availability of on-campus housing
Single students: Yes
Married students: Yes

For further information
Address housing inquiries to: Graduate Student Housing, 581 Taylor Rd., Piscataway, NJ 08854.
Phone: (848) 932-4371
E-mail: oncampus@rci.rutgers.edu
Housing aid website: http://housing.rutgers.edu/

Table A—Faculty, Enrollments, and Degrees Granted

Research Specialty	2015–16 Faculty	Enrollment Fall 2015 Master's	Enrollment Fall 2015 Doctorate	Number of Degrees Granted 2017–2018 Master's	Number of Degrees Granted 2017–2018 Terminal Master's	Number of Degrees Granted 2017–2018 Doctorate
Astronomy	9	2	22	–	1	3
Biophysics	7	–	10	–	–	2
Condensed Matter Physics	26	–	46	1	3	3
Nuclear Physics	7	–	14	1	–	1
Particles and Fields	14	–	19	–	–	5
Statistical & Thermal Physics	1	–	–	–	–	–
Other	7	2	1	–	–	–
Total	71	4	112	2	4	14
Full-time Grad. Stud.	–	4	112	–	–	–
First-year Grad. Stud.	–	–	10	–	–	–

GRADUATE DEGREE REQUIREMENTS

Master's: The M.S. degree program is designed for part-time as well as full-time students. A comprehensive oral examination is required of all M.S. candidates. The M.S. degree requires 30 credits of which up to 12 may be in upper class undergraduate courses (300–400 series). The candidate may choose to write a thesis (in which case, 6 of the 30 required credits may be devoted to this thesis research) or to submit an essay (which is to be based on material from a course he or she has taken). The thesis must be defended in the oral

examination. There is no formal GPA requirement, but no more than three courses with grades of "C" can be counted toward the degree. There is no foreign language requirement.

Doctorate: The candidacy exam consists of an oral exam on a current topic in research. Candidates must present a written report on a current area of research, followed by an oral presentation and exam. The exam tests the candidate's ability to grasp the relevance, goals, techniques, and underlying physics of a current area of research. The exam is normally taken at the start of the second year. In addition, candidates are required to complete a set of core courses with grades of B or better, or pass an exam if exemption is requested based on previous course work. A dissertation of original research is required. There is a residence requirement of one year, but no foreign language requirement.

Other Degrees: Master of Science for Teachers (MST) degree: The MST degree is primarily a subject matter-oriented degree for practicing teachers, although others may be accepted. The requirements for the MST degree in physics consist of 30 credits, a comprehensive examination, and an essay or thesis. The courses are chosen in consultation with the departmental advisor to fit the needs of each individual student. The first aim is to give each candidate the opportunity to further his or her knowledge of physics. Both undergraduate and graduate courses may be used, depending on each person's previous experience.

Thesis: Thesis may be written in absentia.

SPECIAL EQUIPMENT, FACILITIES, OR PROGRAMS

The department has 60 faculty members. An additional 15 faculty members from other departments, including chemistry, mathematics, and medical / biophysics programs, are members of the graduate program.

The department is housed in a modern, fully equipped research laboratory with networks of workstations and PCs that provide easy computer access for all students and faculty members.

The astrophysics group is focused on galactic dynamics and cosmology and has developed Fabry-Perot interferometers for observatories in Chile and South Africa. Rutgers astronomers have a 10% share of observing time at the 11 meter Southern African Large Telescope.

Condensed matter theory faculty members study strongly correlated electron systems and electronic properties of materials. The multidisciplinary Laboratory for Surface Modification includes seven physics faculty members and members of the chemistry, materials science, and engineering departments. Research in condensed matter experiment spans low temperature physics, mesoscopic electronics organic conductors, optical scattering spectroscopies, magnetic and multiferroic materials, and two-dimensional systems (e.g., graphene). New research initiatives focus on the synthesis of novel materials and their characterization using optical, scanning-probe, X-ray/neutron diffraction, and transport techniques.

High-energy theory research includes, phenomenological studies and abstract approaches such as string theory and conformal field theories. High-energy experimentalists do research at CERN hadron collider. They search for supersymmetry, the Higgs particle and dark matter with leptons, photons, and jets and also study the top quark and gauge bosons. They are also developing detectors and detection technologies for high radiation environments.

Nuclear physics research in both theory and experiment span a broad range of questions, including the structure of the nucleon, the interaction of neutrinos with nuclei, the limits of angular momentum, and stability in nuclei, and nucleosynthesis. Experiments are carried out at Jefferson Lab in Virginia, Fermilab Texas A&M, Argonne National Lab and Michigan State University.

Table B—Separately Budgeted Research Expenditures by Source of Support

Source of Support	Departmental Research	Physics-related Research Outside Department
Federal government	$11,000,000	
State/local government		
Non-profit organizations		
Business and industry		
Other		
Total	$11,000,000	

FACULTY

Chair Professor

Chakalian, Jak, Ph.D., University of British Columbia. *Condensed Matter Physics*. Experimental condensed matter physics.

Professor

Andrei, Eva Y., Ph.D., Rutgers University, 1980. Member, National Academy of Science. *Condensed Matter Physics, Low Temperature Physics*. Experimental condensed matter physics.

Andrei, Natan, Ph.D., Princeton University, 1979. *Condensed Matter Physics, High Energy Physics*. Theoretical elementary particle/condensed matter physics.

Baker, Andrew, Ph.D., California Institute of Technology, 2000. *Astronomy*. Observational physics.

Banks, Thomas, Ph.D., Massachusetts Institute of Technology, 1973. *Cosmology & String Theory, Particles and Fields*. Theoretical elementary particle physics.

Bartynski, Robert, Ph.D., University of Pennsylvania, 1986. Chair of the Department. *Condensed Matter Physics, Surface Physics*. Experimental condensed matter physics.

Bhanot, Gyan, Ph.D., Cornell University, 1979. *Biophysics*. Systems biology, cancer and population genetics.

Blumberg, Girsh, Ph.D., Estonian Academy of Sciences, 1987. *Condensed Matter Physics, Solid State Physics*. Experimental condensed matter physics.

Case, David, Ph.D., Harvard University, 1977. *Biophysics, Chemical Physics*. Theoretical chemistry of biomolecules.

Chandra, Premala, Ph.D., University of California, Santa Barbara, 1988. *Condensed Matter Physics*. Condensed matter theory.

Cheong, Sang-Wook, Ph.D., University of California, Los Angeles, 1989. *Condensed Matter Physics, Materials Science, Metallurgy, Solid State Physics*. Experimental condensed matter physics; material science.

Cizewski, Jolie A., Ph.D., Stony Brook University, 1978. *Nuclear Physics*. Experimental nuclear physics.

Coleman, Piers, Ph.D., Princeton University, 1984. *Condensed Matter Physics*. Theoretical condensed matter physics.

Croft, Mark, Ph.D., University of Rochester, 1977. *Condensed Matter Physics, Solid State Physics*. Experimental condensed matter physics.

Diaconescu, Duiliu-Emanuel, Ph.D., Rutgers University, 1998. *Cosmology & String Theory, Particles and Fields*. Theoretical high-energy physics.

Etkina, Eugenia, Ph.D., Moscow State Pedagogical University, 1997. Professor of Education. *Physics and other Science Education*. Physics education.

Friedan, Daniel, Ph.D., University of California, Berkeley, 1980. *Cosmology & String Theory, Particles and Fields, Theoretical Physics*. Theoretical elementary particle physics.

Garfunkel, Eric, Ph.D., University of California, Berkeley, 1983. *Chemical Physics, Solid State Physics, Surface Physics*. Experimental surface science.

Gawiser, Eric, Ph.D., University of California, Berkeley, 1999. *Astronomy, Astrophysics*. Observational astrophysics, cosmology.

Gershenson, Michael E., Ph.D., Institute of Radio Engineering and Electronics (Moscow), 1982. *Condensed Matter Physics, Solid State Physics*. Experimental condensed matter physics.

Gershtein, Yuri, Ph.D., Moscow Inst. For Physics and Tech., 1996. *High Energy Physics, Particles and Fields*. Experimental high energy physics.

Gilman, Ronald, Ph.D., University of Pennsylvania, 1985. Associate Chair and Graduate Program Director. *Nuclear Physics*. Experimental nuclear physics.

Goldin, Gerald A., Ph.D., Princeton University, 1969. *Quantum Foundations, Theoretical Physics*. Mathematical physics.

Goldstein, Sheldon, Ph.D., Yeshiva University, 1974. *Quantum Foundations, Statistical & Thermal Physics, Theoretical Physics*. Statistical mechanics; foundations of quantum mechanics.

Gustafsson, Torgny, Ph.D., Chalmers University of Technology, Sweden, 1973. *Condensed Matter Physics, Solid State Physics, Surface Physics*. Experimental condensed matter physics; experimental surface physics.

Halkiadakis, Eva, Ph.D., Rutgers University, 2001. *High Energy Physics, Particles and Fields*. Experimental particle physics.

Haule, Kristjan, Ph.D., University of Ljubljana, 2002. *Condensed Matter Physics, Solid State Physics*. Theoretical condensed matter physics.

Hughes, John, Ph.D., Columbia University, 1984. *Astronomy, Astrophysics*. Observational astronomy.

Jha, Saurabh, Ph.D., Harvard University, 2002. *Astronomy, Astrophysics*. Observational cosmology.

Keeton, Charles, Ph.D., Harvard University, 1998. *Astronomy, Astrophysics*. Astronomy.

Kiryukhin, Valery, Ph.D., Princeton University, 1997. *Condensed Matter Physics, Solid State Physics*. Experimental condensed matter physics.

Kloet, Willem M., Ph.D., Utrecht, Netherlands, 1973. *Nuclear Physics*. Theoretical nuclear physics.

Kotliar, B. Gabriel, Ph.D., Princeton University, 1983. *Condensed Matter Physics*. Theoretical condensed matter physics.

Lath, Amitabh, Ph.D., Massachusetts Institute of Technology, 1994. *High Energy Physics, Particles and Fields*. Experimental elementary particle physics.

Lebowitz, Joel, Ph.D., Syracuse University, 1956. Member National Academy of Science. *Statistical & Thermal Physics*. Theoretical statistical mechanics; math physics.

Lukyanov, Sergei, Ph.D., Landau Institute, 1989. *Particles and Fields, Theoretical Physics*. Theoretical high-energy physics.

Moore, Gregory, Ph.D., Harvard University, 1986. *Cosmology & String Theory, Particles and Fields, Theoretical Physics*. Theoretical particle physics.

Morozov, Alexandre, Ph.D., University of Washington, 2003. *Biophysics*. Biophysics.

Murnick, Daniel E., Ph.D., Massachusetts Institute of Technology, 1966. *Applied Physics, Atomic, Molecular, & Optical Physics, Nuclear Physics*. Experimental nuclear and atomic physics.

Neuberger, Herbert, Ph.D., Tel Aviv University, 1979. *Particles and Fields*. Theoretical elementary particle physics.

Olson, Wilma, Ph.D., Stanford University, 1971. *Biophysics*. Biological physics theory and simulation.

Podzorov, Vitaly, Ph.D., Rutgers University, 2002. *Condensed Matter Physics, Solid State Physics*. Experimental condensed matter physics.

Pryor, Carlton, Ph.D., Harvard University, 1982. Associate Chair for Undergraduate Education. *Astronomy*. Experimental astrophysics.

Rabe, Karin, Ph.D., Massachusetts Institute of Technology, 1987. Member National Academy of Science. *Condensed Matter Physics, Solid State Physics*. Theoretical condensed matter physics; theoretical surface physics.

Ransome, Ronald, Ph.D., University of Texas, Austin, 1981. *Nuclear Physics*. Experimental nuclear physics.

Schnetzer, Stephen R., Ph.D., University of California, Berkeley, 1981. *High Energy Physics, Particles and Fields*. Experimental elementary particle physics.

Sengupta, Anirvan, Ph.D., Bombay University, 1994. *Biophysics*. Biological physics.

Shinbrot, Troy, Ph.D., University of Maryland, 1992. *Biophysics, Fluids, Rheology, Statistical & Thermal Physics*. Computational bioengineering; self-assembly; mixing; chaos theory.

Soffer, Avraham, Ph.D., Tel-Aviv University, 1984. *Statistical & Thermal Physics, Theoretical Physics*. Theory of partial differential evolution equations; Schrödinger operators and scattering theory; general mathematical physics.

Somalwar, Sunil, Ph.D., University of Chicago, 1988. *High Energy Physics, Particles and Fields*. Experimental elementary particle physics.

Somerville, Rachel, Ph.D., University of California, Santa Cruz, 1997. *Astronomy, Astrophysics*. Astrophysics.

Thomas, Scott, Ph.D., University of Texas, Austin, 1993. *High Energy Physics, Particles and Fields*. Theoretical elementary particle physics.

Vanderbilt, David, Ph.D., Massachusetts Institute of Technology, 1981. Member National Academy of Science. *Condensed Matter Physics, Solid State Physics*. Theoretical condensed matter physics; theoretical surface physics.

Yuzbashyan, Emil, Ph.D., Princeton University, 2004. *Condensed Matter Physics*. Theoretical condensed matter physics.

Zamick, Larry, Ph.D., Massachusetts Institute of Technology, 1961. *Nuclear Physics*. Theoretical nuclear physics.

Associate Professor

Chou, John Paul, Ph.D., Harvard University, 2008. *High Energy Physics, Particles and Fields*. Experimental particle physics.

Hinch, B. Jane, Ph.D., University of Cambridge, 1987. *Chemical Physics, Solid State Physics, Surface Physics*. Surface studies using atomic and molecular scattering.

Oh, Seaongshik, Ph.D., University of Illinois, 2003. *Condensed Matter Physics, Materials Science, Metallurgy, Solid State Physics*. Experimental condensed matter physics.

Salur, Sevil, Ph.D., Yale University, 2006. *High Energy Physics, Nuclear Physics*. Experimental nuclear physics.

Shih, David, Ph.D., Princeton University, 2006. *High Energy Physics, Particles and Fields*. Theoretical high energy physics.

Wu, Weida, Ph.D., Princeton University, 2004. *Condensed Matter Physics, Materials Science, Metallurgy, Solid State Physics*. Experimental condensed matter physics.

Zimmermann, Frank M., Ph.D., Cornell University, 1995. *Condensed Matter Physics, Solid State Physics, Surface Physics*. Experimental surface science physics.

Assistant Professor

Brooks, Alyson, Ph.D., University of Washington, 2008. *Astronomy, Astrophysics*. Theoretical astrophysics.

Buckley, Matthew, Ph.D., Univerity of California, Berkeley, 2008. *Astrophysics, Particles and Fields*. Theoretical particle physics, dark matter.

Khiabanian, Hossein, Ph.D., Brown University. *Biophysics*. Computational biology and cancer genomics.

Lee, Sang-Hyuk, Ph.D., New York University, 2007. *Biophysics*. Single-molecule biophysics.

Noronha-Hostler, Jacquelyn, Ph.D., Goethe-Universita ̈t, 2010. *Nuclear Physics*. Relativistic heavy-ion collisions, quark-gluon plasma, jets.

Pixley, Jedediah, Ph.D., Rice University. *Condensed Matter Physics*. Theoretical condensed matter physics.

Research Professor

Batson, Philip E., Ph.D., Cornell University, 1976. *Condensed Matter Physics, Materials Science, Metallurgy, Solid State Physics*. Experimental condensed matter physics.

DEPARTMENTAL RESEARCH SPECIALTIES AND STAFF

Theoretical

Astrophysics. Evolution, structure, and dynamics of galaxies, dark matter, gravitational lensing, gravitational N-body simulations. Brooks, Buckley, Keeton, Somerville.

Biophysics. Bhanot, Case, Khiabanian, Morozov, Olson, Sengupta, Shinbrot.

Condensed Matter Physics. Strongly correlated electron systems, novel superconductors, quantum phase transitions, quantum computing, electronic and structural properties of solids, dielectric and ferroelectric materials, magnetism and multiferroics, equilibrium and non-equilibrium statistical mechanics. Natan Andrei, Chandra, Coleman, Haule, Kotliar, Lebowitz, Pixley, Rabe, Vanderbilt, Yuzbashyan, Zimmermann.

Mathematical and statistical physics. Statistical mechanics, foundations of quantum mechanics, mathematical physics. Goldin, Goldstein, Lebowitz, Soffer.

Nuclear Physics. Nuclear structure; quark dynamics; few-nucleon problem; relativistic heavy-ion reactions; dibaryon resonances; electron scattering; intermediate-energy, hadron scattering. Kloet, Noronha-Hostler, Zamick.

Particles and Fields. String theory, cosmology, high energy phenomenology, lattice gauge theory, conformal field theory. Banks, Buckley, Diaconescu, Friedan, Lukyanov, Moore, Neuberger, Shih, Thomas.

Experimental

Astrophysics. Galaxies and clusters of galaxies, cosmology and dark energy, supernovae, galaxies at high redshift, X-ray sources, imaging spectrophotometry, star clusters and dwarf galaxies. Baker, Gawiser, Hughes, Jha, Pryor.

Biophysics. Lee.

Condensed Matter Physics. Surface physics: geometric structure, electronic structure, molecular adsorption, thin fills; superconductivity; electrical and thermal transport; superfluidity in helium; 2D electron gas; spin resonance; synchrotron radiation. Eva Andrei, Bartynski, Batson, Blumberg, Chakalian, Cheong, Croft, Garfunkel, Gershenson, Gustafsson, Hinch, Kiryukhin, Murnick, Oh, Podzorov, Wu, Zimmermann.

High Energy Physics. LHC physics. Chou, Gershtein, Halkiadakis, Lath, Salur, Schnetzer, Somalwar.

Nuclear Physics. Nuclear structure; magnetic moments, nuclei far from stability, nuclear astrophysics; intermediate energy electron and proton scattering; neutrino scattering; relativistic heavy ion scattering. Cizewski, Gilman, Ransome, Salur.

STEVENS INSTITUTE OF TECHNOLOGY

DEPARTMENT OF PHYSICS AND ENGINEERING PHYSICS

Hoboken, New Jersey 07030
http://www.stevens.edu/ses/physics/

General University Information
President: Nariman Farvadin
Dean of Graduate School: Costas Chassapis, Dean of Grad. Academics
University website: http://www.stevens.edu
School Type: Private
Setting: Urban
Total Faculty: 516
Total Graduate Faculty: Not separated
Total number of Graduate Students: 3,793

Department Information
Department Chairman: Prof. Ting Yu, Director
Department Contact: Diane E. Gioia, Administrative Assistant
  Total full-time faculty: 8
  Total number of full-time equivalent positions: 8
  Full-Time Graduate Students: 26
  Female Full-Time Graduate Students: 4
  Total Post Doctorates: 3

Department Address
524 Burchard Bldg.
6th & River Streets
Hoboken, NJ 07030
Phone: (201) 216-5665
Fax: (201) 216-5638
E-mail: dgioia@stevens.edu
Website: http://www.stevens.edu/ses/physics/

ADMISSIONS

Admission Contact Information
Address admission inquiries to: Costas Chassapis, Dean of Graduate Academics
Phone: (216) 216-5564
E-mail: Costas Chassapis@stevens.edu
Admissions website: http://stevens.edu/admissions

Application deadlines
Fall admission:
U.S. students: February 1   *Int'l. students*: February 1
Spring admission:
U.S. students: October 1   *Int'l. students*: October 1

Application fee
U.S. students: $60

Admissions information
For Fall of 2018:
  Number of applicants: 40
  Number admitted: 25
  Number enrolled: 15

Admission requirements
Bachelor's degree requirements: Bachelor's degree in Science or Engineering is required.
Minimum undergraduate GPA: 3.0

GRE requirements
The GRE is required.

Mean GRE score range (25th–75th percentile): Not calculated

Subjective GRE requirements
The Subjective GRE is required.

TOEFL requirements
The TOEFL exam is required for students from non-English-speaking countries.
PBT score: 530

Other admissions information
Additional requirements: No minimum acceptable score for admission is specified. The average GRE scores for admissions were not calculated. The average GRE Advanced score for admissions is not available.
Undergraduate preparation assumed: "Physics for Scientists and Engineers: A Strategic Approach with Modern Physics w/ Mastering Physics" 5 volume boxed set. Author Randall D. Knight, Publisher Pearson Addison Wesley.

TUITION

Tuition year 2017–2018:
Tuition for in-state residents
  Full-time students: per credit
  Part-time students: per credit
Tuition for out-of-state residents
  Full-time students: per credit
  Part-time students: per credit
  Full-time students: $1,626 per credit
  Part-time students: $1,626 per credit
Credit hours per semester to be considered full-time: 9
Deferred tuition plan: No
Health insurance: Yes, $1835.00.
Academic term: Semester
Number of first-year students who received full tuition waivers: 1

Teaching Assistants, Research Assistants, and Fellowships
  Number of first-year
    Fellowship students: 1
  Average stipend per academic year
    Teaching Assistant: $23,924
    Research Assistant: $23,924
    Fellowship student: $23,924

FINANCIAL AID

Application deadlines
Fall admission:
U.S. students: September 1   *Int'l. students*: September 1
Spring admission:
U.S. students: September 1   *Int'l. students*: September 1

Loans
Loans are available for U.S. students.
Loans are available for international students.
GAPSFAS application required: Yes
FAFSA application required: Yes

For further information

Address financial aid inquiries to: Costas Chassapis.
Phone: (201) 216-5524
E-mail: costas.chassapis@stevens.edu
Financial aid website: http://www.stevens.edu/sit/graduate/tuition/index.cfm

HOUSING

Availability of on-campus housing

Single students: Yes
Married students: No

For further information

Address housing inquiries to: Student Housing, Trina Ballantyne, Dean of Residence Life, Dining Services & Center Operation.
Phone: (201) 216-5128
E-mail: tballant@stevens.edu
Housing aid website: http://www.stevens.edu/housing

Table A—Faculty, Enrollments, and Degrees Granted

Research Specialty	2016–17 Faculty	Enrollment Fall 2016		Number of Degrees Granted 2012–13 (2009–14)		
		Master's	Doctorate	Master's	Terminal Master's	Doctorate
Applied Physics	1	–	3	1(2)	–	1(12)
Atmosphere, Space Physics, Cosmic Rays	1	–	3	1	–	1(12)
Atomic, Molecular, & Optical Physics	3	–	8	–(1)	–	1(15)
Condensed Matter Physics	3	–	4	1(1)	–	1(9)
Electromagnetism	–	–	–	–	–	–(1)
Optics	3	–	5	1	–(1)	1(9)
Quantum Foundations	1	–	–	–(1)	–	–(4)
Statistical & Thermal Physics	–	–	–	–	–	–(1)
Non-specialized	–	–	–	6(15)	–(18)	–
Total	**12**	**–**	**23**	**10(20)**	**–(19)**	**3(63)**
Full-time Grad. Stud.	–	–	23	–	–	–
First-year Grad. Stud.	–	–	2	–	–	–

GRADUATE DEGREE REQUIREMENTS

Master's: Thirty semester hour credits; 3.0 GPA in physics courses and overall; no residence requirement; no language or other comprehensive exams; thesis optional.

Doctorate: Ninety semester hour credits (including Master's credits) of which 50 minimum to be in courses, and 30 minimum to be dissertation research; 3.0 GPA in physics courses and overall; one-year residence; no language requirement; comprehensive/qualifying exam (one combined exam); dissertation.

SPECIAL EQUIPMENT, FACILITIES, OR PROGRAMS

The Department has particular strength in areas of applied physics, such as optics, atomic and plasma physics, nanotechnology, and condensed matter physics, quantum physics.

Table B—Separately Budgeted Research Expenditures by Source of Support

Source of Support	Departmental Research	Physics-related Research Outside Department
Federal government	$6,845.28	
State/local government		
Non-profit organizations		
Business and industry		
Other		
Total	**$6,845.28**	

Table C—Separately Budgeted Research Expenditures by Research Specialty

Research Specialty	No. of Grants	Expenditures ($)
Atmosphere, Space Physics, Cosmic Rays	1	$207,125
Nano Science and Technology	1	$312,000
Optics	1	$551,000
Quantum Foundations	5	$5,775,158
Other	1	
Total	**9**	**$6,845,283**

FACULTY

Chair Professor

Yu, Ting, Ph.D., Imperial College, University of London, UK, 1998. Physics Department Chair. *Atomic, Molecular, & Optical Physics*. Atomic, molecular, and optical physics (AMO); quantum information and quantum optics.

Professor

Stamnes, Knut, Ph.D., University of Colorado, 1978. *Atmosphere, Space Physics, Cosmic Rays*. Electron transport and thermalization; kinetic theory; radiation transport; satellite remote sensing; biophotonics for noninvasive diagnostic of biological tissue.

Whittaker, Edward A., Ph.D., Columbia University, 1982. *Optics*. Laser techniques; optical diagnosis of gas phase materials; processing reactors; Brillouin scattering; quantum optics.

Associate Professor

Malinovskaya, Svetlana, Ph.D., Novosibirsk State University, 1993. *Other*. Laser-matter interaction; coherent control; quantum optics.

Martini, Rainer, Ph.D., Rheinisch-Westfaelische Technischen Hochschule Aachen, Germany, 1999. Serves on numerous Institute Committees. *Optics, Other*. High-sensitivity laser spectroscopy.

Search, Christopher, Ph.D., University of Michigan, 2002. *Atomic, Molecular, & Optical Physics*. Bose-Einstein condensation; quantum optics; nonlinear optics.

Strauf, Stefan, Ph.D., Universität Bremen, Germany, 2001. *Nano Science and Technology, Optics, Other*. Nanophotonics; quantum optics.

Assistant Professor

Huang, Yuping, Ph.D., Michigan State University, 2009. Quantum Optics.

Teaching Associate Professor

Lukic, Vladimir, Ph.D., University of Illinois, 2005. *Astrophysics, Condensed Matter Physics*. Mesoscopics, Superconductors, Small Bodies of the Solar System.

Adjunct Associate Professor

Hutt, Marvin, Ph.D., New York University, 1987. *Optics*. Optical engineering.

Lenzing, Harry, M.S., Stevens Institute of Technology, 1962. *Optics*. Satellite-tracking systems; passive intermodulation (PIM).

Visiting Professor

Supplee, James, Ph.D., University of Texas, Dallas, 1979. *Optics*. Spectroscopy and semiclassical optics.

Senior Lecturer

Pastore, Robert A., Ph.D., Stevens Institute of Technology, 2000. Electronics.

Ion Surface Interactions.
Laser Matter Interactions. Malinovskaya.
Quantum Information and Quantum Optics. Yu.
Quantum Optics. Malinovskaya, Search.
Semiconductor Solid State Theory.

Experimental

Atmosphere, Space Physics, Cosmic Rays. Radiation transport in planetary media including the coupled atmosphere-snow/ice-ocean system. Stamnes.

High Sensitivity Laser Spectroscopy. Martini, Strauf, Supplee, Whittaker.

Nanophotonics. Strauf.

Optical Control of Quantum Systems. Martini, Strauf.

Optical Diagnosis of Gas Phase Materials. Whittaker.

Other.

DEPARTMENTAL RESEARCH SPECIALTIES AND STAFF

Theoretical

Electron Transport.

View additional information about this department at www.gradschoolshopper.com. Check out the "Why Choose Us?" section, find out more about the department's culture and get links to social media networks.

NEW MEXICO STATE UNIVERSITY

DEPARTMENT OF ASTRONOMY

Las Cruces, New Mexico 88003
http://astronomy.nmsu.edu/

General University Information
President: John D. Floros
Dean of Graduate School: Loui Reyes
University website: http://nmsu.edu
School Type: Public
Setting: Suburban
Total Faculty: 1,048
Total Graduate Faculty: 988
Total number of Students: 14,432
Total number of Graduate Students: 2,719

Department Information
Department Chairman: Prof. Jon Holtzman, Head
Department Contact: Ofelia Acosta, Administrative Assistant, Int.
  Total full-time faculty: 10
  Total number of full-time equivalent positions: 10
  Full-Time Graduate Students: 23
  Female Full-Time Graduate Students: 11
  First-Year Graduate Students: 7
  Female First-Year Students: 3
  Total Post Doctorates: 2

ADMISSIONS

Admission Contact Information
Address admission inquiries to: Chair, Graduate Committee, Dept. of Astronomy, Box 30001/MSC 4500, Las Cruces, NM 88003-0001
Phone: (575) 646-4438
E-mail: gradapps@astronomy.nmsu.edu
Admissions website: http://astronomy.nmsu.edu/graduate/admissions

Application deadlines
Fall admission:
U.S. students: January 15   *Int'l. students*: January 15

Application fee
U.S. students: $40   *Int'l. students*: $50
NMSU uses an online application system, the Hobsons ApplyYourself system. Please e-mail gradapps@astronomy.nmsu.edu if you experience any problems with this system.

Admissions information
For Fall of 2018:
  Number of applicants: 89
  Number admitted: 19
  Number enrolled: 6

Admission requirements
Bachelor's degree requirements: Bachelors degree in Astronomy, Physics, other Science, or Engineering is required.
Minimum undergraduate GPA: 3.0

GRE requirements
The GRE is required.

Subjective GRE requirements
The Subjective GRE is not required.

TOEFL requirements
The TOEFL exam is required for students from non-English-speaking countries.
PBT score: 530

Other admissions information
Additional requirements: No minimum score for admission is specified. Typical average scores for GRE verbal–570; quantitative–700.
Undergraduate preparation assumed: Math: differential equations; Physics: mechanics, modern physics, some of optics, electricity and magnetism, statistical mechanics, thermodynamics, etc.

TUITION

Tuition year 2018–19:
Tuition for in-state residents
  Full-time students: $301.5 per credit
  Part-time students: $301.5 per credit
Tuition for out-of-state residents
  Full-time students: $929.9 per credit
  Part-time students: $364.68 per credit
Credit hours per semester to be considered full-time: 9
Deferred tuition plan: Yes
Health insurance: Yes, $15.62/pay period.
Academic term: Semester
Number of first-year students who received full tuition waivers: 6

Teaching Assistants, Research Assistants, and Fellowships
Number of first-year
  Teaching Assistants: 3
  Research Assistants: 4
  Fellowship students: 6
Average stipend per academic year
  Teaching Assistant: $16,964
  Research Assistant: $16,964
  Fellowship student: $16,964
Most students usually get RA support in the summer, which would bring the total year stipend to around $22,619.

FINANCIAL AID

Application deadlines
Fall admission:
U.S. students: January 31

Loans
Loans are available for U.S. students.
Loans are not available for international students.
GAPSFAS application required: No
FAFSA application required: Yes

For further information
Address financial aid inquiries to: Department of Astronomy, Box 30001/MSC 4500, Las Cruces, NM 88003-8001.
Phone: (575) 646-4438
E-mail: gradapps@astronomy.nmsu.edu

HOUSING

Availability of on-campus housing
Single students: Yes
Married students: Yes
Childcare Assistance: No

For further information
Address housing inquiries to: Housing Department, Box 30001/
MSC 3BB, Las Cruces, NM 88003-0001.
Phone: (575) 646-3202
E-mail: hsgandcl@nmsu.edu
Housing aid website: http://housing.nmsu.edu

Table A—Faculty, Enrollments, and Degrees Granted

| Research Specialty | 2018–19 Faculty | Enrollment Fall 2018 | | Number of Degrees Granted 2017–18 (2017–18) | | |
		Master's	Doctorate	Master's	Terminal Master's	Doctorate
Astronomy	10	21	23	2	–	6
Total	10	23	23	–(2)	–	6(5)
Full-time Grad. Stud.	–	23	23	–	–	–
First-year Grad. Stud.	–	6	6	–	–	–

GRADUATE DEGREE REQUIREMENTS

Master's: The M.S. program is closely geared to the Ph.D. program, and is normally achieved en route to the Ph.D. Students who might only be interested in a Masters should contact the Department.

Doctorate: A minimum of 64 credits of graduate work in astronomy and related fields of which 33 are in formal courses. Qualification is ascertained during the student's third semester and a comprehensive oral given after formal course work is completed. Written exam evaluations are based on monthly cumulative examinations. A dissertation and a final oral examination on the dissertation is also required. The residence requirement is two consecutive semesters of full-time graduate work after the first 30 credits.

Thesis: Thesis may be written in absentia.

SPECIAL EQUIPMENT, FACILITIES, OR PROGRAMS

The Department is a member of the Astrophysical Research Consortium (ARC), which operates a state-of-the-art 3.5-m telescope at Apache Point, NM, and the Sloan Digital Sky Survey with a dedicated 2.5-m telescope. The Department also operates a 1-m telescope at Apache Point. The department is home to NASA's Planetary Data System's Atmospheres Node archive of planetary atmosphere-related mission data.

Table B—Separately Budgeted Research Expenditures by Source of Support

Source of Support	Departmental Research	Physics-related Research Outside Department
Federal government	$1,917,823.75	
State/local government	$1,424,285.57	
Non-profit organizations		
Business and industry		
Other	$3,345,155.48	
Total	$6,687,264.8	

Table C—Separately Budgeted Research Expenditures by Research Specialty

Research Specialty	No. of Grants	Expenditures ($)
Astronomy	55	$6,687,264.8
Total	55	$6,687,264.8

FACULTY

Professor

Chanover, Nancy, Ph.D., New Mexico State University, 1997. *Astronomy, Planetary Science*. Planetary atmospheres; astrobiology; instrument development.

Churchill, Chris, Ph.D., University of California, Santa Cruz, 1997. *Astronomy*. Quasar absorption lines galaxies and intergalactic medium.

Holtzman, Jon, Ph.D., University of California, Santa Cruz, 1989. *Astronomy*. Stellar populations and chemical abundances. Spiral galaxies. Instrument development.

Klypin, Anatoly, Ph.D., University of Moscow, 1980. *Astronomy, Cosmology & String Theory*. Extragalactic astronomy; cosmology.

Murphy, James, Ph.D., University of Washington, 1991. *Astronomy, Planetary Science*. Atmospheric sciences; planetary atmospheres; Mars exploration missions.

Walterbos, Reinirus, Ph.D., Leiden University, 1986. *Astronomy*. Interstellar medium; stellar populations; extragalactic.

Associate Professor

Jackiewicz, Jason, Ph.D., Boston University, 2002. *Astronomy, Solar Physics*. Helioseismology.

McAteer, James, Ph.D., Queens University, Belfast, 2003. Solar physics. *Astronomy, Solar Physics*.

Assistant Professor

Finlator, Kristian, Ph.D., University of Arizona, 2009. *Astronomy*. Numerical simulations of galaxy formation and evolution.

Prescott, Moire, Ph.D., University of Arizona, 2009. *Astronomy*. Studies of galaxy formation through observations of Lyman alpha clouds.

Emeritus

Beebe, Herbert, Ph.D., Indiana University, 1969. *Astronomy, Atmosphere, Space Physics, Cosmic Rays*. Atmospheres; spectral line formation.

Research Professor

Beebe, Reta F., Ph.D., Indiana University, 1969. *Astronomy, Planetary Science*. Planetary atmospheres; planetary physics; radiative transfer; cool star atmospheres; equation of state.

Webber, William R., Ph.D., University of Iowa, 1957. *Astronomy, Atmosphere, Space Physics, Cosmic Rays, Planetary Science*. Interplanetary physics; cosmic rays; delta-ray astronomy.

Research Faculty

Harrison, Tom, Ph.D., University of Minnesota, 1989. *Astronomy*. Infrared astronomy.

Research Scientist

Neakrase, Lynn, Ph.D., Arizona State Universita. *Planetary Science*. Planetary atmospheres. Mars. Dust devils.

Research Fellow

Johnson, Joni, Ph.D., University of Minnesota, 1990. *Astronomy*. Cataclysmic variables.

DEPARTMENTAL RESEARCH SPECIALTIES AND STAFF

Theoretical

Astrophysics. Finlator, Jackiewicz, Klypin.

Cosmology & String Theory. Numerical simulations of large scale structure and galaxy formation. Finlator, Klypin.

Solar Physics. Jackiewicz, McAteer.

Experimental

Astronomy. Herbert Beebe, Reta Beebe, Chanover, Churchill, Finlator, Harrison, Holtzman, Jackiewicz, Johnson, Klypin, McAteer, Murphy, Prescott, Walterbos, Webber.

Planetary Science. Reta Beebe, Chanover, Murphy, Neakrase.

Solar Physics. Jackiewicz, McAteer.

View additional information about this department at www.gradschoolshopper.com. Check out the "Why Choose Us?" section, find out more about the department's culture and get links to social media networks.

NEW MEXICO STATE UNIVERSITY

DEPARTMENT OF PHYSICS

Las Cruces, New Mexico 88003-8001
http://physics.nmsu.edu

General University Information
Chancellor: Dan Arvizu
Dean of Graduate School: Loui Reyes
University website: http://www.nmsu.edu
School Type: Public
Setting: Urban
Total Faculty: 1,048
Total Graduate Faculty: 988
Total number of Students: 14,432
Total number of Graduate Students: 2,719

Department Information
Department Chairman: Prof. Heinz Nakotte, Head
Department Contact: Vassilios Papavassiliou, Graduate
 Program Head
 Total full-time faculty: 16
 Total number of full-time equivalent positions: 16
 Full-Time Graduate Students: 37
 Female Full-Time Graduate Students: 9
 First-Year Graduate Students: 11
 Female First-Year Students: 2
 Total Post Doctorates: 3

Department Address
1255 N. Horseshoe Drive
MSC 3D, Box 30001
Las Cruces, NM 88003-8001
Phone: (575) 646-3831 (C)
Fax: (575) 646-1934
E-mail: roschris@nmsu.edu
Website: http://physics.nmsu.edu

ADMISSIONS

Admission Contact Information
Address admission inquiries to: Graduate Student Services, MSC
 3G, New Mexico State University, P.O. Box 30001, Las Cru-
 ces, NM 88003-8001
Phone: (575) 646-2736
E-mail: gradinfo@nmsu.edu
Admissions website: http://gradschool.nmsu.edu/

Application deadlines
Fall admission:
U.S. students: February 15   *Int'l. students*: February 15
Spring admission:
U.S. students: September 1   *Int'l. students*: November 1

Application fee
U.S. students: $40   *Int'l. students*: $50

Admissions information
For Fall of 2018:
 Number of applicants: 45
 Number admitted: 11
 Number enrolled: 5

Admission requirements
Bachelor's degree requirements: Bachelor's degree in Physics
 or a related field is required.
Minimum undergraduate GPA: 3.0

GRE requirements
The GRE is required.
 Mean GRE score range (25th–75th percentile): 298-314
No minimum GRE scores have been established.

Subjective GRE requirements
The Subjective GRE is required.
 Mean Advanced GRE score range (25th–75th percentile): 610-760
Physics GRE is required for financial assistance by the depart-
 ment. No minimum score has been established.

TOEFL requirements
The TOEFL exam is required for students from non-English-
 speaking countries.
 PBT score: 550
 iBT score: 79
IELTS scores are also accepted as an alternative to TOEFL. Minimum IELTS score is 6.5 for regular admission. Applicants
 may be admitted to NMSU with scores lower than those
 above, but admission in such cases will be 'conditional;' see
 http://isss.nmsu.edu/index-8/ for details.

Other admissions information
Additional requirements: A minimum GPA of 3.0 or equivalent
 is required for admission as a Ph.D. student or for regular
 (not provisional) admission as a Master's student.
Undergraduate preparation assumed: Physics: Marion, Classical
 Dynamics; Griffiths, Electromagnetism; Kittel and Kroemer,
 Thermal Physics; Townsend, Quantum Mechanics. Mathematics: Thomas, Calculus and Analytical Geometry; Boyce
 and di Prima, Boundary Value Problems.

TUITION

Tuition year 2018–19:
Tuition for in-state residents
 Full-time students: $2,713.5 per semester
 Part-time students: $301.5 per credit
Tuition for out-of-state residents
 Full-time students: $8,369.1 per semester
 Part-time students: $364.68 per credit
Part-time, out-of-state tuition figure is for up to six credit hours
 per semester. More details are at https://hr.nmsu.edu/uar/
 wp-content/uploads/sites/24/2018/05/Tuition-Fee-Rates-
 Fall_2018_Final_Rev.pdf Out-of-state students awarded with
 a graduate assistantship are also offered a waiver of out-of-
 state tuition; such students pay the in-state tuition rates.
Credit hours per semester to be considered full-time: 9
Deferred tuition plan: Yes
Health insurance: Not available.
Other academic fees: Tuition and fees are described in detail at
 http://uar.nmsu.edu/tuition-rates/
Academic term: Semester
Number of first-year students who received partial tuition waivers: 10

Teaching Assistants, Research Assistants, and Fellowships
Number of first-year
 Teaching Assistants: 9
 Research Assistants: 1
Average stipend per academic year

Teaching Assistant: $19,650
Research Assistant: $19,650

Most incoming, full-time, graduate students are offered a Teaching or Research Assistantship. Exceptions are usually for students who have an outside fellowship or grant.

FINANCIAL AID

Application deadlines
Fall admission:
U.S. students: February 15   Int'l. students: February 15
Spring admission:
U.S. students: November 1   Int'l. students: September 1

Loans
Loans are available for U.S. students.
Loans are not available for international students.
GAPSFAS application required: No
FAFSA application required: Yes

For further information
Address financial aid inquiries to: NMSU Financial Aid and Scholarship Services, MSC 5100, P.O. Box 30001, Las Cruces, NM 88003-8001.
Phone: (575) 646-4105
E-mail: financialaid@nmsu.edu
Financial aid website: http://fa.nmsu.edu

HOUSING

Availability of on-campus housing
Single students: Yes
Married students: Yes
Childcare Assistance: No

For further information
Address housing inquiries to: NMSU Housing & Campus Life, MSC 3BB / P.O. Box 30001, Las Cruces, NM 88003-8001.
Phone: (575) 646-3202
E-mail: hsgandcl@nmsu.edu
Housing aid website: http://housing.nmsu.edu

Table A—Faculty, Enrollments, and Degrees Granted

Research Specialty	2017–18 Faculty	Enrollment Fall 2017 Master's	Enrollment Fall 2017 Doctorate	Number of Degrees Granted 2017–18 (2013–18) Master's	Number of Degrees Granted 2017–18 (2013–18) Terminal Master's	Number of Degrees Granted 2017–18 (2013–18) Doctorate
Applied Physics	–	–	–	–	–	–(1)
Atomic, Molecular, & Optical Physics	–	–	–	–	–(1)	1(2)
Chemical Physics	–	–	1	–	–	–
Condensed Matter Physics	6	1	12	–	2(3)	3(10)
Geophysics	2	–	2	–	–(2)	1(2)
High Energy Nuclear Physics	5	–	10	–	–	1(7)
High Energy Physics	1	–	1	–	–	–
Non-committed	–	–	7	–	–	–
Physics Education	–	–	–	–	–	–(1)
Relativity & Gravitation	–	–	–	–	–	–(1)
Space Physics	–	1	–	–	1(2)	–
Non-specialized	–	2	–	5(12)	1(4)	–
Total	14	4	33	5(12)	4(12)	6(24)
Full-time Grad. Stud.	–	4	33	–	–	–
First-year Grad. Stud.	–	1	9	–	–	–

GRADUATE DEGREE REQUIREMENTS

Master's: Satisfactory completion of a minimum of 30 semester credits, of which at least 21 credits are in formal courses, including one laboratory course; a minimum residence requirement of two consecutive semesters of full-time graduate work; no foreign language required; overall GPA of at least 3.0 at the time of application for admission to candidacy. Several program options available: (1) thesis, qualifying examination, and final oral exam; (2) successful completion of doctoral comprehensive exam; and (3) course work option (at least 27 credits in formal courses) and successful completion of qualifying exam and final oral exam.

Doctorate: At least 36 credits in formal courses and a minimum of 72 total credits of graduate work are required. These include 24 credits of graduate core courses and one laboratory course; foreign language not required; qualifying examination, comprehensive exam, dissertation, and final oral on dissertation required; a minimum residence requirement of two consecutive semesters of full-time graduate work.

Other Degrees: Space physics concentration for M.S. physics degree.

Thesis: Thesis may be written in absentia.

SPECIAL EQUIPMENT, FACILITIES, OR PROGRAMS

Cooperative research programs are conducted that involve using the particle accelerators at Fermilab and Brookhaven National Laboratory; with Los Alamos National Laboratory; with Sandia National Laboratories; with the Physical Science Laboratory at NMSU; and with local industries. Specialized research equipment on campus includes a spectroscopic ellipsometer; a high-resolution, X-ray diffractometer; a 10-meter, small-angle, X-ray diffractometer; liquids, energy-dispersive diffractometer; 2 two-crystal, vacuum, X-ray spectrometers; a high-resolution, electron spectrometer; an energy-dispersive, X-ray spectrometer, one electron microscope; specimen-preparation equipment; ultra-high-vacuum chambers; mass spectrometers; an X-ray, photo-emission spectrometer; low-energy, electron-diffraction, spherical and planar, Fabry-Perot interferometers; a near-field, optical microscope; an atomic-force microscope; a femtosecond laser; a nanosecond, optical, parametric oscillator; a tunable-diode laser; standalone Nd: YAG lasers; 1- and 2-D detector arrays; a streak camera, a gravity meter; a magnetometer; a broadband seismometer; and a PuBe neutron source. Departmental computing facilities include Linux clusters and numerous Windows, MAC, and Linux workstations.

Table B—Separately Budgeted Research Expenditures by Source of Support

Source of Support	Departmental Research	Physics-related Research Outside Department
Federal government	$1,850,000	
State/local government		
Non-profit organizations		
Business and industry		
Other		
Total	$1,850,000	

FACULTY

Professor
Burkardt, Matthias, Ph.D., Friedrich-Alexander University of Erlangen-Nürnberg, 1989. Undergraduate advisor. *High Energy Physics, Nuclear Physics, Particles and Fields, Theoretical Physics*. Quantum chromodynamics; nucleon structure.

Engelhardt, Michael, Ph.D., Friedrich-Alexander University of Erlangen-Nürnberg, 1994. Undergraduate advisor. *Computational Physics, High Energy Physics, Nuclear Physics, Particles and Fields, Theoretical Physics*. Nucleon structure; quantum chromodynamics.

Kiefer, Boris, Ph.D., University of Michigan, 2002. Undergraduate advisor, SPS advisor. *Applied Physics, Computational Physics, Condensed Matter Physics, Energy Sources & Environment, Nano Science and Technology, Solid State Physics*. Computational material science; energy conversion technologies; earth and planetary materials.

Nakotte, Heinrich, Ph.D., University of Amsterdam, 1994. Undergraduate advisor for engineering physics students. *Condensed Matter Physics, Solid State Physics*. Magnetic properties of materials; neutron scattering.

Pate, Stephen F., Ph.D., University of Pennsylvania, 1987. Undergraduate physics program head. *High Energy Physics, Nuclear Physics, Particles and Fields*. Nucleon structure; spin physics; relativistic heavy-ion physics; electron and neutrino scattering.

Vasiliev, Igor V., Ph.D., University of Minnesota, 2000. *Computational Physics, Condensed Matter Physics, Nano Science and Technology, Solid State Physics*. Theoretical condensed matter physics.

Zollner, Stefan, Ph.D., Universitat Stuttgart, 1991. Department Head. *Applied Physics, Materials Science, Metallurgy, Nano Science and Technology, Optics, Solid State Physics*. Optical properties of materials; spectroscopic ellipsometry; semiconductor process integration.

Associate Professor

Hearn, Thomas M., Ph.D., California Institute of Technology, 1985. Undergraduate advisor. *Geophysics*. Seismic tomography; seismology.

Papavassiliou, Vassilios, Ph.D., Yale University, 1988. Graduate Program Head. *High Energy Physics, Nuclear Physics, Particles and Fields*. Nucleon structure; spin physics; relativistic heavy-ion physics; electron and neutrino scattering.

Urquidi, Jacob, Ph.D., Texas Tech University, 2001. *Atomic, Molecular, & Optical Physics, Condensed Matter Physics, Fluids, Rheology*. Studies of materials using X-ray and neutron scattering.

Assistant Professor

Cooper, Robert L., Ph.D., University of Michigan, 2008. *High Energy Physics, Nuclear Physics, Particles and Fields*. Neutrino oscillations and cross sections, neutron physics, neutron imaging, dark matter.

Fohtung, Edwin, Ph.D., Albert-Ludwigs University of Freiburg, 2010. *Applied Physics, Condensed Matter Physics, Energy Sources & Environment, Nano Science and Technology, Optics, Solid State Physics*. Solid-state physics; neutron scattering; energy research; remote sensing; X-ray and electron optics.

Schlegel, Marc, Ph.D., Ruhr-University Bochum, 2006. *High Energy Physics, Nuclear Physics, Particles and Fields, Theoretical Physics*. Theoretical nuclear and particle physics, Quantum Chromodynamics, nucleon structure.

Waszek, Lauren, Ph.D., University of Cambridge, 2012. *Geophysics*. Seismic tomography; global seismology.

Professor Emeritus

Burleson, George R., Ph.D., Stanford University, 1960. Nuclear and elementary particle physics.

Burr, Alex F., Ph.D., Johns Hopkins University, 1966. Physics education.

Gibbs, William R., Ph.D., Rice University, 1961. *Nuclear Physics, Particles and Fields, Theoretical Physics*. Hadronic interactions; quantum chromodynamics.

Goedecke, George H., Ph.D., Rensselaer Polytechnic Institute, 1961. *Quantum Foundations, Relativity & Gravitation, Theoretical Physics*. Foundations of quantum mechanics; general relativity; scattering theory; acoustics; optics; stochastic electrodynamics; sound propagation in turbulence and turbulence modelling.

Kanim, Stephen, Ph.D., University of Washington, 1999. *Other*. Physics education.

Kyle, Gary S., Ph.D., University of Minnesota, 1979. Nuclear and particle physics.

Liefeld, Robert J., Ph.D., Ohio State University, 1959. X-ray physics; electron, atomic, and solid-state physics; physics education.

Ni, James F., Ph.D., Cornell University, 1984. *Geophysics*. Observational seismology; mantle dynamics; continental rifting.

Zund, Joseph, Ph.D., University of Texas, Austin, 1964. General relativity.

Teaching Professor

Burkardt, Michaela, Ph.D., Friedrich-Alexander University of Erlangen-Nürnberg, 1992. *Physics and other Science Education*. Physics education.

DeAntonio, Michael, Ph.D., New Mexico State University, 1993. *Applied Physics, Climate/Atmospheric Science, Optics, Physics and other Science Education*. Polarimetry; ion mobility spectroscopy; remote sensing; atmospheric physics; nonlinear optics; physics education.

Affiliate Professor

Bruce, Charles, Ph.D., New Mexico State University, 1970. *Atmosphere, Space Physics, Cosmic Rays, Atomic, Molecular, & Optical Physics, Climate/Atmospheric Science, Condensed Matter Physics, Optics*. Aerosol physics; optical properties of nanoparticles.

Chylek, Petr, Ph.D., Charles University. Light scattering; atmospheric physics.

Goldman, Terrance, Ph.D., Harvard University, 1973. Theoretical nuclear physics.

Higbie, Paul, Ph.D., Massachusetts Institute of Technology, 1968. *Atmosphere, Space Physics, Cosmic Rays*. Space physics.

Louis, William C., Ph.D., University of Michigan, 1978. *High Energy Physics, Nuclear Physics*. Neutrino physics.

Ostashev, Vladimir E., Ph.D., University of Moscow, 1979. Acoustical and optical wave propagation in random media.

Rielage, Keith R., Ph.D., Washington University, 2002. *High Energy Physics*. Neutrino physics, dark matter.

Strottman, Daniel, Ph.D., State University of New York, 1969. Theoretical nuclear physics.

Tompkins, Harland G., Ph.D., University of Wisconsin-Milwaukee, 1971. *Applied Physics, Optics, Surface Physics*. Spectroscopic ellipsometry; vacuum science; surface physics.

Laboratory Coordinator

Carreto-Parra, Francisco, M.S., University of Texas El Paso, 2007. *Non-specialized*.

Posdoctoral Research Associate

Karpov, Dmitry, M.S., Tomsk State Polytechnical University, 2018. *Applied Physics, Condensed Matter Physics, Energy Sources & Environment, Nano Science and Technology, Optics, Solid State Physics*. Solid-state physics; neutron scattering; energy research; remote sensing; X-ray and electron optics.

Ren, Lu, Ph.D., University of Pittsburgh, 2016. *High Energy Physics, Nuclear Physics*. Neutrino physics, nucleon structure, nuclear models.

Yu, Haiwang, Ph.D., Peking University, 2016. *High Energy Physics, Nuclear Physics*. Quantum Chromodynamics, nucleon structure, heavy flavor.

DEPARTMENTAL RESEARCH SPECIALTIES AND STAFF

Theoretical

Computational Physics. Engelhardt, Kiefer, Vasiliev.

Condensed Matter Physics. Fohtung, Karpov, Kiefer, Nakotte, Vasiliev.

Geophysics. Seismology, continental rifting. Hearn, Ni, Waszek.

Hadronic Physics. Hadron-hadron interactions; lepton scattering; nucleon structure; quantum chromodynamics; lattice QCD. Matthias Burkardt, Engelhardt, Gibbs.

Materials Science. Thermochemical, kinetic, electronic, and magnetic properties of advanced functional materials. Kiefer, Vasiliev.

Nano Science and Technology. Kiefer, Vasiliev.

Optics. Scattering by particles of arbitrary shape and structure; single and multiple scattering; aerosol effects; inverse scattering theory; non-linear effects; quantum optics. Bruce, Goedecke.

Experimental

Applied Physics. Energy research; remote sensing. Bruce, DeAntonio, Fohtung, Karpov, Kiefer, Nakotte, Urquidi, Zollner.

Atomic, Molecular, & Optical Physics. Raman scattering; Rayleigh-Brillouin scattering; Doppler limited IR absorption; soft X-ray emission and absorption spectroscopy; X-ray line and continuum isochromats; photo and Auger electron spectroscopy; plasma and laser spectroscopy; spectroscopic ellipsometry. Bruce, DeAntonio, Urquidi, Zollner.

Condensed Matter Physics. Fohtung, Karpov, Nakotte, Zollner.

Geophysics. Regional seismic tomography; seismic anisotropy; crustal and upper mantle seismic structure; attenuation of regional seismic waves; continental collision; continental rifting; subduction and plate boundary processes; crustal and mantle attenuation in Asia and North America; nuclear monitoring. Hearn, Ni, Waszek.

High-Energy Nuclear Physics. Quark-gluon structure of matter; spin physics; hadronic interactions; electron and neutrino scattering. Cooper, Papavassiliou, Pate, Ren, Yu.

Materials Science. Fabrication and properties of opto-electronic materials; optical and magneto-optical properties of nano-structured materials; electron, optical, and scanning probe microscopy. Fohtung, Nakotte, Urquidi, Zollner.

Nano Science and Technology. Fohtung, Karpov, Nakotte, Zollner.

Neutrino physics. Neutrino interactions with nucleons and nuclei. Cooper, Papavassiliou, Pate, Ren.

Optics. Laser Raman spectroscopy; laser absorption and emission spectroscopy; quantum optics, near-field optics; spectroscopic ellipsometry. Bruce, DeAntonio, Fohtung, Karpov, Urquidi, Zollner.

Solid State Physics. Fohtung, Karpov, Nakotte, Urquidi, Zollner.

View additional information about this department at www.gradschoolshopper.com. Check out the "Why Choose Us?" section, find out more about the department's culture and get links to social media networks.

BINGHAMTON UNIVERSITY (STATE UNIVERSITY OF NEW YORK)

DEPARTMENT OF PHYSICS, APPLIED PHYSICS, AND ASTRONOMY

Binghamton, New York 13902-6000
http://www2.binghamton.edu/physics

General University Information
President: Harvey Stenger
Dean of Graduate School: Aondover Tarhule
University website: http://www2.binghamton.edu
School Type: Public
Setting: Suburban
Total Faculty: 866
Total Graduate Faculty: 496
Total number of Students: 16,695
Total number of Graduate Students: 3,283

Department Information
Department Chairman: Dr. Bruce White, Chair
Department Contact: Judy Coderre, Administrator
  Total full-time faculty: 18
  Total number of full-time equivalent positions: 18
  Full-Time Graduate Students: 43
  Female Full-Time Graduate Students: 0
  First-Year Graduate Students: 7
  Female First-Year Students: 3
  Total Post Doctorates: 3

Department Address
4400 Vestal Parkway East
Science II, Room 256
Binghamton, NY 13902-6000
Phone: (607) 777-4609
Fax: (607) 777-2546
E-mail: physics@binghamton.edu
Website: http://www2.binghamton.edu/physics

ADMISSIONS

Admission Contact Information
Address admission inquiries to: C. Nelson, Graduate Director,
  Department of Physics, Applied Physics, and Astronomy,
  Binghamton University, PO Box 6000, Binghamton NY
  13902-6000
Phone: (607) 777-4317
E-mail: cnelson@binghamton.edu
Admissions website: http://www2.binghamton.edu/grad-school/

Application deadlines
Fall admission:
U.S. students: February 15   *Int'l. students*: February 15
Spring admission:
U.S. students: February 15   *Int'l. students*: February 15

Application fee
U.S. students: $75   *Int'l. students*: $75
Applications must be submitted online in addition to submitting
  documents as a single PDF to the Department.

Admissions information
For Fall of 2018:
  Number of applicants: 42
  Number admitted: 11
  Number enrolled: 7

Admission requirements
Bachelor's degree requirements: Bachelor's degree is required.
Minimum undergraduate GPA: 3.0

GRE requirements
The GRE is required.
  Quantitative score: 156
  Verbal score: 153
  Analytical score: 3.0
Physics Subject GRE is recommended.

Subjective GRE requirements
The Subjective GRE is recommended.

TOEFL requirements
The TOEFL exam is required for students from non-English-
  speaking countries.
  PBT score: 550
  iBT score: 100

Other admissions information
Additional requirements: Specialization in physics at the undergraduate level is desirable but not essential for admission.
  Three letters of reference are required.
  No minimum acceptable score for admission is specified.
Undergraduate preparation assumed: One year of general physics; one year of Electromagnetic Theory (Griffiths; Introduction to Electrodynamics); one semester of Classical Mechanics (Taylor; Classical Mechanics); at least a semester of
  quantum mechanics (Townsend, Griffiths, Shankar, or Cohen-
  Tannoudji; Quantum Mechanics); and mathematics through
  partial differential equations. Appropriate laboratory experience at the upper undergraduate levels is desirable..

TUITION

Tuition year 2018–19:
Tuition for in-state residents
  Full-time students: $5,545 per semester
  Part-time students: $462 per credit
Tuition for out-of-state residents
  Full-time students: $11,325 per semester
  Part-time students: $944 per credit
Credit hours per semester to be considered full-time: 12
Deferred tuition plan: No
Health insurance: Yes, $15.79 bi-weekly.
Other academic fees: $2,051 (maximum except international stu-
  dents). International students should add an average of $1,300 per
  calendar year for international student health insurance and service
  fees.
Academic term: Semester
Number of first-year students who received full tuition waivers: 10

Teaching Assistants, Research Assistants, and Fellowships
Number of first-year
  Teaching Assistants: 12
  Fellowship students: 2
Average stipend per academic year
  Teaching Assistant: $23,000
  Research Assistant: $23,000
  Fellowship student: $23,000

FINANCIAL AID

Loans

Loans are available for U.S. students.
Loans are available for international students.
GAPSFAS application required: No
FAFSA application required: No

For further information

Address financial aid inquiries to:
Phone: 607-777-2428
E-mail: finaid@binghamton.edu
Financial aid website: https://www.binghamton.edu/financial-aid/funding-needs/graduate-students.html

HOUSING

Availability of on-campus housing

Single students: Yes
Married students: Yes

For further information

Address housing inquiries to: Director of Graduate Housing.
Phone: 607-777-2321
E-mail: reslife@binghamton.edu
Housing aid website: https://www.binghamton.edu/grad-school/student-life/housing-transportation.html

Table A—Faculty, Enrollments, and Degrees Granted

Research Specialty	2014–15 Faculty	Enrollment Fall 2014 Master's	Enrollment Fall 2014 Doctorate	Number of Degrees Granted 2011–12 (2004–10) Master's	Number of Degrees Granted 2011–12 (2004–10) Terminal Master's	Number of Degrees Granted 2011–12 (2004–10) Doctorate
Applied Physics	2	–	6	–(8)	–	–
Atomic, Molecular, & Optical Physics	–	–	3	–	–	–
Biophysics	1	–	2	–	–	–
Chemical Physics	–	–	–	–	–	–
Condensed Matter Physics	3	–	12	–(3)	–	–
Energy Sources & Environment	4	–	10	–	–	–
Engineering Physics/Science						
Low Temperature Physics	–	–	–	–	–	–
Materials Science, Metallurgy	1	–	4	–(2)	–	–
Optics	2	–	6	–(1)	–	–
Statistical & Thermal Physics	1	–	–	–(2)	–	–
Non-specialized	1	–	–	–	–	–
Total	15	–	43	–(16)	–	–
Full-time Grad. Stud.	–	–	43	–	–	–
First-year Grad. Stud.	–	–	7	–	–	–

GRADUATE DEGREE REQUIREMENTS

Master's: Thirty graduate credit hours with at least a "B" average. There is a two-semester residence requirement. Students have a choice of thesis or comprehensive examination.

Doctorate: At least 24 credit hours of course study (in residence) and 24 additional credit hours of dissertation work. Passing a written qualifying examination, in three parts, covering the core areas of physics and successful defense of dissertation are required.

Other Degrees: Master of Science in physics with a specialization in applied physics is designed for students seeking careers in applied physics. Emphasis is to provide a comprehensive education in fundamental physical principles and their applications to enhance the ability to evolve with changing technology and to avoid technical obsolescence. Student may study part-time and complete a degree in three years or complete a full-time graduate assistantship and complete the degree in two years or less. Thesis topics may be drawn from employment with the consent of the department and employer. M.A.T. and M.S.T. programs are designed for students who wish to teach physics at the secondary level. The M.A.T. program is designed for students with a physics background who need education courses; the M.S.T. program is designed for teachers who want to improve their physics background. The credits in professional education courses required for certification are offered, as well as additional work in physics and allied fields. Certified teachers may enroll in the M.S.T. program, in which almost all of the training involves substantive physics coursework.

Thesis: Thesis may be written in absentia.

SPECIAL EQUIPMENT, FACILITIES, OR PROGRAMS

AC and DC magnetic susceptibility bridges; X-ray diffractometers; 100,000 kilogauss superconducting magnet; 15″ iron core magnet; differential scanning calorimeters; sputtering equipment; vacuum deposition stations; dilution refrigerator; Raman spectrometer; clean room; splat quencher; resistivity bridges; hydrator; cryo-cooler; dielectric analyzer; thermogravimetric analyzer; dynamic mechanical analyzer; thermomechanical analyzer; scanning electron microscope; high-pressure intensifier; squid magnetometer; femtosecond lasers; Low temperature STM; Linux cluster for computatoinal physics.

Table B—Separately Budgeted Research Expenditures by Source of Support

Source of Support	Departmental Research	Physics-related Research Outside Department
Federal government	$4,500,000	$12,000,000
State/local government	$300,000	$500,000
Non-profit organizations		
Business and industry	$500,000	$1,000,000
Other		
Total	$5,300,000	$13,500,000

FACULTY

Professor

Cotts, Eric J., Ph.D., University of Illinois, 1983. *Applied Physics, Materials Science, Metallurgy, Physics and other Science Education, Solid State Physics*. Experimental solid-state physics.

Nelson, Charles A., Ph.D., University of Maryland, 1968. Graduate Director. *Astrophysics, High Energy Physics, Particles and Fields*. Theoretical high-energy physics.

Suzuki, Masatsugu, Ph.D., University of Tokyo, 1977. Undergraduate Director. *Materials Science, Metallurgy, Solid State Physics*. Experimental solid-state physics.

White, Bruce E., Ph.D., Cornell University, 1995. Department Chair. *Applied Physics, Condensed Matter Physics, Electrical Engineering, Energy Sources & Environment, Low Temperature Physics, Materials Science, Metallurgy, Nano Science and Technology, Solid State Physics*.

Associate Professor

Kolmogorov, Aleksey, Ph.D., Penn State University, 2004. *Computational Physics, Energy Sources & Environment, Statistical & Thermal Physics*. Development and modeling of new materials with ab initio methods.

Lawler, Michael, Ph.D., University of Illinois at Urbana-Champaign, 2006. *Condensed Matter Physics, Solid State Physics*.

Levy, Stephen, Ph.D., University of California Santa Barbara, 2003. *Biophysics, Nano Science and Technology, Polymer Physics/Science*.

Mativetsky, Jeffrey, Ph.D., McGill University, 2006. *Applied Physics, Condensed Matter Physics, Energy Sources & Environment, Nano Science and Technology, Solid State Physics*. Relationships between nanoscale structure and electrical function in organic materials for solar cells and electronics.

Piper, Louis, Ph.D., University of Warwick, 2003. *Applied Physics, Condensed Matter Physics, Energy Sources & Environment, Nano Science and Technology, Solid State Physics, Surface Physics*.

Shim, Bonggu, Ph.D., University of Texas @ Austin, 2006. *Applied Physics, Atomic, Molecular, & Optical Physics, Nonlinear Dynamics and Complex Systems, Optics*. Nonlinear interactions with matter using high-power, ultrashort laser pulses.

Assistant Professor

Aynajian, Pegor, Ph.D., Max Planck Institute (University of Stuttgart), 2009. *Condensed Matter Physics, Low Temperature Physics, Solid State Physics*.

Lee, Wei-Cheng, Ph.D., U. Texas (Austin), 2008. *Computational Physics, Condensed Matter Physics, Solid State Physics*.

Margine, Roxana, Ph.D., Penn State University, 2007. *Computational Physics, Condensed Matter Physics, Solid State Physics*. Develop and apply ab initio computational methods for modeling of emerging materials with applications in energy transport and electronics.

Smeu, Manuel, Ph.D., McGill University, 2012. *Computational Physics*.

Adjunct Professor

Poliks, Barbara, Ph.D., Jagiellonian University, 1982. *Applied Physics, Condensed Matter Physics, Polymer Physics/Science, Solid State Physics*. Computer simulations of polymeric systems, including proteins and materials.

DEPARTMENTAL RESEARCH SPECIALTIES AND STAFF

Theoretical

Computational Physics. Kolmogorov, Lawler, Lee, Margine, Poliks, Smeu, White.

Condensed Matter Physics. Lawler, Lee.

Experimental

Applied Physics.

Biophysics. Levy, Poliks.

Condensed Matter Physics. Low-temperature condensed-matter physics; localized magnetic moments in metallic crystals; induced valence changes in impurity doped metals; Raman spectroscopy; properties of disordered materials, amorphous metals, and layered materials.

View additional information about this department at www.gradschoolshopper.com. Check out the "Why Choose Us?" section, find out more about the department's culture and get links to social media networks.

COLUMBIA UNIVERSITY

DEPARTMENT OF PHYSICS

New York, New York 10027
http://physics.columbia.edu/

General University Information
President: Lee Bollinger
Dean of Graduate School: Carlos J. Alonso
University website: http://columbia.edu
School Type: Private
Setting: Urban
Total Faculty: 3,566
Total Graduate Faculty: 700
Total number of Students: 25,459
Total number of Graduate Students: 15,067

Department Information
Department Chairman: Prof. Robert Mawhinney, Chair
Department Contact: Randy Torres, Director of Academic
   Administration
   Total full-time faculty: 36
   Full-Time Graduate Students: 106
   Female Full-Time Graduate Students: 0
   First-Year Graduate Students: 12
   Female First-Year Students: 5
   Total Post Doctorates: 16

Department Address
538 West 120th Street
704 Pupin Hall MC 5255
New York, NY 10027
Phone: (212) 854-3366
Fax: (212) 854-3379
E-mail: rt2255@columbia.edu
Website: http://physics.columbia.edu/

ADMISSIONS

Admission Contact Information
Address admission inquiries to: Office of Graduate Admissions,
   108 Low Library
Phone: (212) 854-8903
E-mail: gsas-admit@columbia.edu
Admissions website: http://gsas.columbia.edu/admissions

Application deadlines
Fall admission:
U.S. students: January 5   *Int'l. students*: January 5

Application fee
U.S. students: $110

Admissions information
For Fall of 2018:
   Number of applicants: 472
   Number admitted: 40
   Number enrolled: 12

Admission requirements
Bachelor's degree requirements: Bachelor's degree is preferred.

GRE requirements
The GRE is required.

Subjective GRE requirements
The Subjective GRE is required.

TOEFL requirements
The TOEFL exam is required for students from non-English-
   speaking countries.
   PBT score: 600
   iBT score: 100

Other admissions information
Additional requirements: No minimum acceptable score is specified.

TUITION

Tuition year 2018–19:
   Full-time students: $46,216 annual
All regular graduate students in physics are given full financial
   aid, which includes exemption from all tuition and medical
   fees.
Deferred tuition plan: No
Other academic fees: $5,984/yr. paid by GSAS.
Academic term: Semester

Teaching Assistants, Research Assistants, and Fellowships
Number of first-year
   Teaching Assistants: 12
   Fellowship students: 12
Average stipend per academic year
   Teaching Assistant: $39,133
   Research Assistant: $39,133

FINANCIAL AID

Loans
Loans are not available for U.S. students.
Loans are not available for international students.
GAPSFAS application required: No
FAFSA application required: No

For further information
Address financial aid inquiries to: Thomas Tarduogno, Director
   of Financial Aid.
Phone: (212) 854-3809
E-mail: tt22@columbia.edu
Financial aid website: http://gsas.columbia.edu/financial-aid

HOUSING

Availability of on-campus housing
   Single students: Yes
   Married students: Yes

For further information
Address housing inquiries to: Office of Institutional Real Estate,
   University Apartment Housing, 400 W 119th Street, New
   York, NY 10027.
Phone: (212) 854-9423
E-mail: housing@columbia.edu
Housing aid website: http://housingservices.columbia.edu/

Table A—Faculty, Enrollments, and Degrees Granted

Research Specialty	2017–2018 Faculty	Enrollment Fall 2017 Master's	Enrollment Fall 2017 Doctorate	Number of Degrees Granted 2017–2018 (2009–18) Master's	Number of Degrees Granted 2017–2018 (2009–18) Terminal Master's	Number of Degrees Granted 2017–2018 (2009–18) Doctorate
Applied Physics	–	–	1	–	–	–(9)
Astronomy	–	–	–	–	–	–
Astrophysics	6	–	18	–	–	2(42)
Atomic, Molecular, & Optical Physics	1	–	2	–	–	1(4)
Biophysics	1	–	2	–	–	1(2)
Chemical Physics	–	–	3	–	–	–
Condensed Matter Physics	4	–	26	–	–	2(22)
Engineering Physics/Science	–	–	–	–	1(1)	–
High Energy Physics	5	–	11	–	–	3(37)
Nuclear Physics	2	–	7	–	–	1(15)
Theoretical Physics	16	–	10	–	–	3(33)
Non-specialized	1	–	26	30(202)	1(10)	–
Total	36	–	106	30(177)	1(10)	11(135)
Full-time Grad. Stud.	–	–	106	–	–	–
First-year Grad. Stud.	–	–	26	–	–	–

GRADUATE DEGREE REQUIREMENTS

Master's: M.A. 30 points of courses including at least 24 within the department at an appropriate level. Two semesters of residence. No requirements for grade average, foreign languages, comprehensive or qualifying examination, or thesis.

Doctorate: Master's degree plus four semesters of residence, qualifying examination, and thesis. No requirement for foreign language. No course requirement beyond the Master's degree, except that courses must show competence in electromagnetic theory, quantum mechanics, and statistical mechanics. Grades must be satisfactory.

Other Degrees: M.Phil. All requirements for the Ph.D. except thesis and final departmental examination.

Thesis: Thesis may be written in absentia.

SPECIAL EQUIPMENT, FACILITIES, OR PROGRAMS

In addition to experimental facilities for astrophysics, atomic, condensed matter, and molecular in Pupin Laboratory on campus, extensive facilities for high-energy, nuclear physics, and astrophysics are located at the Nevis Laboratories on an estate at Irvington-on-Hudson, New York.

Table B—Separately Budgeted Research Expenditures by Source of Support

Source of Support	Departmental Research	Physics-related Research Outside Department
Federal government	$14,469,246	
State/local government		
Non-profit organizations		
Business and industry	$1,025,103	
Other	$1,573,531	
Total	$17,067,880	

Table C—Separately Budgeted Research Expenditures by Research Specialty

Research Specialty	No. of Grants	Expenditures ($)
Astrophysics	110	$7,819,832
Condensed Matter Physics	37	$3,813,994
Nuclear Physics	3	$707,765
Particles and Fields	11	$3,792,876
Theoretical Physics	7	$933,413
Total	168	$17,067,880

FACULTY

Professor

Aleiner, Igor, Ph.D., University of Minnesota, 1996. Theoretical condensed matter physics.

Altshuler, Boris, Ph.D., Leningrad Institute for Nuclear Physics, 1979. Theoretical condensed matter physics.

Aprile, Elena, Ph.D., University of Geneva, 1982. Experimental high-energy astrophysics; gamma-ray astronomy.

Bassov, Dmitri N., Ph.D., Lebedev Physics Institute, 1991. *Condensed Matter Physics, Nano Science and Technology.* Novel electronic and magnetic materials, correlated electron systems, unconventional superconductors, development of advanced techniques for infrared/optical spectroscopy and nano-imaging.

Beloborodov, Andrei, Ph.D., Lebedev Physical Institute, Moscow, 1995. Theoretical astrophysics.

Brooijmans, Gustaaf, Ph.D., Université Catholique de Louvian, 1998. Experimental high-energy particle physics.

Christ, Norman, Ph.D., Columbia University, 1966. Theoretical particle physics; lattice field theory.

Cole, Brian, Ph.D., Massachusetts Institute of Technology, 1992. Experimental relativistic heavy-ion nuclear physics.

Denef, Frederik, Ph.D., Leuven University, 1999. Theoretical physics.

Greene, Brian, Ph.D., University of Oxford, 1987. Theoretical high-energy physics; string theory.

Hailey, Charles, Ph.D., Columbia University, 1983. Experimental high-energy astrophysics.

Halpin-Healy, Timothy, Ph.D., Harvard University, 1987. Barnard College faculty. Theoretical statistical physics.

Hughes, Emlyn, Ph.D., Columbia University, 1987. Experimental particle physics.

Hui, Lam, Ph.D., Massachusetts Institute of Technology, 1996. Theoretical astrophysics.

Marka, Szabolcs, Ph.D., Vanderbilt University, 1999. Experimental astrophysics and BioOptics.

Mawhinney, Robert D., Ph.D., Harvard University, 1987. Theoretical particle physics; lattice field theory.

Miller, Amber, Ph.D., Princeton University, 2000. Experimental astrophysics.

Millis, Andrew, Ph.D., Massachusetts Institute of Technology, 1986. Theoretical condensed matter physics.

Mueller, Alfred H., Ph.D., Massachusetts Institute of Technology, 1965. Theoretical particle physics.

Mukherjee, Reshmi, Ph.D., Columbia University, 1993. Barnard College faculty. Experimental astrophysics.

Parsons, John, Ph.D., University of Toronto, 1990. Experimental particle physics.

Pinczuk, Aron, Ph.D., University of Pennsylvania, 1969. Condensed matter physics.

Ruderman, Malvin A., Ph.D., California Institute of Technology, 1951. Theoretical astrophysics.

Shaevitz, Michael, Ph.D., Ohio State University, 1975. Experimental particle physics.

Tuts, Michael, Ph.D., Stony Brook University, 1979. Experimental particle physics.

Uemura, Yasutomo J., University of Tokyo, 1982. Experimental condensed matter physics.

Weinberg, Erick J., Ph.D., Harvard University, 1973. Theoretical high-energy physics.

Zajc, William, Ph.D., University of California, Berkeley, 1982. Experimental relativistic heavy-ion nuclear physics.

Associate Professor

Dean, Cory, Ph.D., McGill University, 2009. Condensed matter physics.

Humensky, Thomas B., Ph.D., Princeton University, 2003. Gamma-ray astrophysics.

Levin, Janna, Massachusetts Institute of Technology, 1993. Barnard College faculty. Theoretical astrophysics.

Metzger, Brian D., Ph.D., University of California, Berkeley, 2009. Astrophysics, Theoretical physics, Theoretical high-energy astrophysics.

Nicolis, Alberto, Ph.D., Scuola Normale Superiore, Pisa, 2003. Theoretical cosmology.

Pasupathy, Abhay, Ph.D., Cornell University, 2004. Experimental condensed matter physics.

Sahin, Ozgur, Ph.D., Stanford University, 2005. Biological physics.

Zelevinsky, Tanya, Ph.D., Harvard University, 2004. Atomic, molecular, and optical physics.

Assistant Professor

Asenjo-Garcia, Ana, Ph.D., Universidad Complutense de Madrid, 2014. *Condensed Matter Physics, Theoretical Physics.* Quantum optics, atomic physics, nanophotonics, many body physics, open quantum systems.

Johnson, Bradley R., Ph.D., University of Minnesota, 2004. Cosmic microwave background studies: SKIP (new project), EBEX, PIPER, and APEX-SZ.

Karagiorgi, Georgia S., Ph.D., Massachusetts Institute of Technology, 2010. *High Energy Physics.* Experimental Particle Physics.

Rosen, Rachel A., Ph.D., New York University, 2009. Theoretical particle physics and cosmology.

Will, Sebastian A., Ph.D., Johannes Gutenberg University Mainz, 2011. *Atomic, Molecular, & Optical Physics.* Atomic, molecular, and optical physics.

Adjunct Professor

Budick, Burton, Ph.D., University of California, Berkeley, 1962. Experimental particle physics.

May, Morgan, Ph.D., Columbia University, 1975. Experimental particle physics and nuclear physics.

Senior Lecturer

Dodd, Jeremy, Ph.D., University College London, 1990. Experimental particle physics.

DEPARTMENTAL RESEARCH SPECIALTIES AND STAFF

Theoretical

Astrophysics. Beloborodov, Greene, Hui, Levin, Metzger, Nicolis, Rosen, Ruderman.

Condensed Matter Physics. Aleiner, Altshuler, Asenjo-Garcia, Millis.

High Energy Physics. Christ, Denef, Greene, Levin, Mawhinney, Mueller, Nicolis, Weinberg.

Nuclear Physics. Nuclear physics and relativistic heavy-ion physics.

Statistical & Thermal Physics. Statistical mechanics and low-temperature physics. Aleiner, Altshuler, Halpin-Healy, Millis.

Experimental

Astrophysics. UV, X-ray, gamma-ray, gravitational-wave and high-energy neutrino astronomy/astrophysics; dark matter searches, experiments using ground-based detectors, rockets, balloons, and satellites. Aprile, Hailey, Humensky, Johnson, Marka, Miller, Mukherjee.

Atomic, Molecular, & Optical Physics. Hughes, Will, Zelevinsky.

Biophysics. Marka, Sahin.

Condensed Matter Physics. Bassov, Dean, Pasupathy, Pinczuk, Uemura.

High Energy Physics. Brooijmans, Hughes, Humensky, Karagiorgi, Mukherjee, Parsons, Shaevitz, Tuts.

Nuclear Physics. Relativistic heavy-ion nuclear physics. Cole, Zajc.

View additional information about this department at www.gradschoolshopper.com. Check out the "Why Choose Us?" section, find out more about the department's culture and get links to social media networks.

CORNELL UNIVERSITY

DEPARTMENT OF PHYSICS

Ithaca, New York 14853
http://www.physics.cornell.edu

General University Information
President: Martha Pollack
Dean of Graduate School: Barbara Knuth
University website: http://www.cornell.edu
School Type: Private
Setting: Rural
Total Faculty: 1,650
Total Graduate Faculty: 1,425
Total number of Students: 23,016
Total number of Graduate Students: 5,776

Department Information
Department Chairman: Prof. Eanna Flanagan, Chair
Department Contact: Kacey Acquilano, Graduate Field
  Assistant
  Total full-time faculty: 49
  Total number of full-time equivalent positions: 41
  Full-Time Graduate Students: 183
  Female Full-Time Graduate Students: 34
  First-Year Graduate Students: 31
  Female First-Year Students: 6
  Total Post Doctorates: 45

Department Address
117 Clark Hall
Ithaca, NY 14853
Phone: (607) 255-7561
E-mail: physics@cornell.edu
Website: http://www.physics.cornell.edu

ADMISSIONS

Admission Contact Information
Address admission inquiries to: Kacey Acquilano, Physics De-
  partment, Cornell University, 117 Clark Hall, Ithaca, NY
  14853
Phone: (607) 255-7561
E-mail: physics@cornell.edu
Admissions website: http://physics.cornell.edu/prospective-
  graduate-students

Application deadlines
Fall admission:
U.S. students: December 15   *Int'l. students*: December 15

Application fee
U.S. students: $105   *Int'l. students*: $105
The Graduate Field of Physics is committed to creating opportunities for economically disadvantaged students. In addition to offering generous funding to all admitted PhD students, we encourage applicants who are experiencing financial
  hardships to seek an application fee waiver if the cost of the
  application fee or GRE exam will be a barrier.

Admissions information
For Fall of 2018:
  Number of applicants: 588
  Number admitted: 118
  Number enrolled: 29

Admission requirements
Bachelor's degree requirements: Bachelor's degree from an accredited institution is required; major in physics is recommended, but not required.
Minimum undergraduate GPA: 3.4

GRE requirements
The GRE is required.
  Quantitative score: 150
  Verbal score: 145
  Analytical score: 3.5
We do not employ strict cut offs for GRE scores or GPAs. We
  instead consider the entire application package. Applicants
  ranked in the admissible range typically have scores above
  these numbers. Applicants who have been granted a fee
  waiver by the Graduate School may request to have their application reviewed without GRE scores. All successful applications are held to the same high academic standards.

Subjective GRE requirements
The Subjective GRE is required.
  Minimum accepted Advanced GRE score: 600
  Mean Advanced GRE score range (25th–75th percentile): 860-
  990
We do not employ strict cut offs for Physics GRE scores.

TOEFL requirements
The TOEFL exam is required for students from non-English-
  speaking countries.
  PBT score: 620
  iBT score: 105
Internet-based TOEFL minimums: writing score of 20, listening
  score of 15, reading score of 20, and speaking score of 22. The
  IELTS is also accepted with an overall band score minimum
  of 7.0 and a speaking subscore minimum of 7.0.

TUITION

Tuition year 2018–19:
  Full-time students: $29,500 annual
All regular graduate students in physics are normally appointed
  to positions that provide a stipend, health insurance, and full
  support for tuition.
Deferred tuition plan: No
Health insurance: Available
Other academic fees: $84 student activity per year.
Academic term: Semester

Teaching Assistants, Research Assistants, and Fellowships
Number of first-year
  Teaching Assistants: 17
  Fellowship students: 12
Average stipend per academic year
  Teaching Assistant: $28,817
  Research Assistant: $26,953
  Fellowship student: $30,466
Information for Fall 2018. Fellowships are those offered with
  admission. Many opt to defer their fellowship in the first year
  and TA instead.

FINANCIAL AID

Application deadlines
Fall admission:
U.S. students: December 15   *Int'l. students*: December 15

Loans
Loans are available for U.S. students.
Loans are available for international students.
GAPSFAS application required: No
FAFSA application required: No

For further information
Address financial aid inquiries to: Kacey Acquilano, Physics Department, Cornell University, 117 Clark Hall, Ithaca, NY 14853.
Phone: (607) 255-7561
E-mail: physics@cornell.edu
Financial aid website: http://physics.cornell.edu/prospective-graduate-students#financial-aid

HOUSING

Availability of on-campus housing
Single students: Yes
Married students: Yes
Childcare Assistance: Yes

For further information
Address housing inquiries to: Housing & Dining Office, Cornell University, 206 Robert Purcell Community Center, Ithaca, NY 14853.
Phone: (607) 255-5368
E-mail: dining@cornell.edu
Housing aid website: http://living.cornell.edu/live/

Table A—Faculty, Enrollments, and Degrees Granted

Research Specialty	2018–19 Faculty	Enrollment Fall 2017 Master's	Enrollment Fall 2017 Doctorate	Number of Degrees Granted 2017–18 (2013–18) Master's	Number of Degrees Granted 2017–18 (2013–18) Terminal Master's	Number of Degrees Granted 2017–18 (2013–18) Doctorate
Accelerator	5	–	14	3(10)	–(1)	2(11)
Atomic, Molecular, & Optical Physics	1	–	3	1(5)	–(1)	1(6)
Biophysics/Soft Matter	7	–	19	3(16)	1(1)	2(16)
Condensed Matter Experiment	10	–	40	6(35)	–(2)	7(26)
Condensed Matter Theory	7	–	26	2(23)	–(3)	6(22)
Cosmology & String Theory	6	–	28	6(20)	–	3(16)
High Energy Physics	6	–	18	1(14)	–	3(8)
Particles and Fields	6	–	9	3(12)	–	1(9)
Physics and other Science Education	1	–	1	–	–	–
Non-specialized	–	–	25	–	–(2)	–
Total	49	–	183	25(135)	1(10)	25(114)
Full-time Grad. Stud.	–	–	183	–	–	–
First-year Grad. Stud.	–	–	31	–	–	–

GRADUATE DEGREE REQUIREMENTS

Master's: Four semesters of residence are required. Qualifying examination after one year is required. Thesis and/or master's examination is required. Maximum time allowed for degree is four years (minimum two years). There is no foreign language requirement. Master's degree is earned as part of admission to candidacy examination for PhD. A professional Master's degree is not offered.

Doctorate: Six semesters of residence are required, at least four of which must be full-time at Cornell. Qualifying examination after one year is required. Admission to candidacy examination is required in the third year. There are no fixed course requirements except one semester of Advanced Physics Laboratory. There is no foreign language requirement. Maximum time allowed for degree is seven years. Thesis and oral thesis examination are required. Three-person special committees direct the course program and supervise research individually for each student. Research in adjacent fields is permissible.

Thesis: Physics allows both submission of dissertation or thesis as well as the option to collate previously published research papers.

SPECIAL EQUIPMENT, FACILITIES, OR PROGRAMS

A $1.9 + 1.9$ GeV e+e− CESR test accelerator; Center for Bright Beams; Cornell-BNL ERL Test Accelerator; CESR facility also provides high-intensity, high-energy X-rays for NSF-funded synchrotron radiation facility Cornell High-Energy Synchrotron Source (CHESS) and NIH Research Resource MacCHESS (protein crystallographic studies); Center for Advanced Computing; Cornell Center for Materials Research (CCMR), and National Submicron Facility with specialized workshops and equipment; Electron and Optical Microscopy Facility; Nanobiotechnology Center; National Nanofabrication Facility; Kavli Institute at Cornell for Nanoscale Science; Atkinson Center for a Sustainable Future; Energy Materials Center at Cornell.

Table C—Separately Budgeted Research Expenditures by Research Specialty

Research Specialty	No. of Grants	Expenditures ($)
Laboratory of Atomic and Solid State Physics	–	$8,010,919
Cornell Laboratory for Accelerator-Based Sciences and Education	–	$48,610,291
Total	–	$56,621,210

FACULTY

Professor

Alexander, James P., Ph.D., University of Chicago, 1985. *High Energy Physics*.

Arias, Tomas A., Ph.D., Massachusetts Institute of Technology, 1992. *Computational Physics, Condensed Matter Physics, Theoretical Physics*.

Cohen, Itai, Ph.D., University of Chicago, 2001. *Biophysics, Condensed Matter Physics, Engineering Physics/Science, Fluids, Rheology, Polymer Physics/Science*.

Csaki, Csaba, Ph.D., Massachusetts Institute of Technology, 1997. *High Energy Physics, Particles and Fields, Theoretical Physics*.

Davis, J.C. Seamus, Ph.D., University of California, Berkeley, 1989. *Condensed Matter Physics*.

Elser, Veit, Ph.D., University of California, Berkeley, 1984. *Computational Physics, Condensed Matter Physics, Theoretical Physics*.

Flanagan, Eanna, Ph.D., California Institute of Technology, 1993. Department Chair. *Astrophysics, Cosmology & String Theory*.

Gibbons, Lawrence K., Ph.D., University of Chicago, 1993. *High Energy Physics*.

Ginsparg, Paul, Ph.D., Cornell University, 1981. *Computational Physics, Computer Science, Particles and Fields, Statistical & Thermal Physics, Theoretical Physics.* Digital knowledge networks.

Grossman, Yuval, Ph.D., Weizmann Institute of Science, 1996. *Particles and Fields, Theoretical Physics.*

Gruner, Sol M., Ph.D., Princeton University, 1977. *Biophysics, Condensed Matter Physics, Nano Science and Technology.*

Hoffstaetter, Georg, Ph.D., Michigan State University, 1994. *Accelerator.*

LeClair, Andre, Ph.D., Harvard University, 1987. *Particles and Fields, Theoretical Physics.*

Lepage, G. Peter, Ph.D., Stanford University, 1978. *Computational Physics, Particles and Fields, Theoretical Physics.*

Liepe, Matthias, Ph.D., University of Hamburg, 2001. *Accelerator, Particles and Fields.*

McAllister, Liam, Ph.D., Stanford University, 2005. *Cosmology & String Theory, Theoretical Physics.*

McEuen, Paul, Ph.D., Yale University, 1991. *Biophysics, Condensed Matter Physics, Nano Science and Technology, Optics.*

Mueller, Erich, Ph.D., University of Illinois at Urbana-Champaign, 2001. *Atomic, Molecular, & Optical Physics, Condensed Matter Physics, Theoretical Physics.*

Parpia, Jeevak M., Ph.D., Cornell University, 1979. Department Chair. *Condensed Matter Physics, Low Temperature Physics, Nano Science and Technology, Optics.*

Patterson, J. Ritchie, Ph.D., University of Chicago, 1990. *High Energy Physics.*

Perelstein, Maxim, Ph.D., Stanford University, 2000. Director of Graduate Studies. *High Energy Physics, Particles and Fields, Theoretical Physics.*

Ralph, Daniel C., Ph.D., Cornell University, 1993. *Condensed Matter Physics, Low Temperature Physics, Nano Science and Technology.*

Rubin, David L., Ph.D., University of Michigan, 1983. *Accelerator.*

Ryd, Anders, Ph.D., University of California, Santa Barbara, 1996. *High Energy Physics.*

Sethna, James P., Ph.D., Princeton University, 1981. *Biophysics, Condensed Matter Physics, Statistical & Thermal Physics, Theoretical Physics.*

Shan, Jie, Ph.D., Columbia University, 2001. *Condensed Matter Physics, Nano Science and Technology.*

Shen, Kyle, Ph.D., Stanford University, 2005. Director of Undergraduate Studies. *Condensed Matter Physics, Surface Physics.*

Teukolsky, Saul, Ph.D., California Institute of Technology, 1973. *Astrophysics, Computational Physics, Relativity & Gravitation, Theoretical Physics.*

Thom-Levy, Julia, Ph.D., University of Hamburg, 2001. *High Energy Physics.*

Thorne, Robert E., Ph.D., University of Illinois, 1987. *Biophysics, Condensed Matter Physics, Fluids, Rheology, Statistical & Thermal Physics.*

Wang, Jane, Ph.D., University of Chicago, 1996. *Biophysics, Computational Physics, Statistical & Thermal Physics.*

Wang, Michelle D., Ph.D., University of Michigan, 1993. *Biophysics, Optics, Polymer Physics/Science.*

Wasserman, Ira M., Ph.D., Harvard University, 1978. *Astrophysics, Relativity & Gravitation.*

Wittich, Peter, Ph.D., University of Pennsylvania, 2000. *High Energy Physics.*

Associate Professor

Bazarov, Ivan, Ph.D., Far Eastern State University, 2000. *Accelerator.*

Franck, Carl P., Ph.D., Princeton University, 1978. *Biophysics, Fluids, Rheology, Statistical & Thermal Physics.*

Kim, Eun-Ah, Ph.D., University of Illinois Urbana-Champaign, 2005. *Condensed Matter Physics, Theoretical Physics.*

Niemack, Michael, Ph.D., Princeton, 2008. Experimental cosmology and astrophysics.

Assistant Professor

Hartman, Thomas, Ph.D., Harvard University, 2010. *Cosmology & String Theory, Relativity & Gravitation.*

Holmes, Natasha, Ph.D., University of British Columbia, 2014. *Physics and other Science Education.*

Mak, Kin Fai, Ph.D., Columbia University, 2010. *Condensed Matter Physics, Nano Science and Technology.*

Maxson, Jared, Ph.D., Cornell University, 2015. *Accelerator.*

Nowack, Katja, Ph.D., Delft University of Technology, 2009. *Condensed Matter Physics.*

Ramshaw, Brad, Ph.D., University of British Columbia, 2012. *Condensed Matter Physics.*

Adjunct Professor

Bodenschatz, Eberhard, Ph.D., University of Bayreuth, 1989. *Biophysics.*

Lawler, Michael, Ph.D., University of Illinois-Urbana Champaign, 2006. *Condensed Matter Physics, Theoretical Physics.*

Levy, Stephen, Ph.D., University of California, Santa Barbara, 2003. *Condensed Matter Physics.*

Myers, Chris, Ph.D., Cornell University, 1991. *Biophysics, Condensed Matter Physics, Theoretical Physics.*

Umrigar, Cyrus, Ph.D., Northwestern University, 1980. *Condensed Matter Physics, Theoretical Physics.*

DEPARTMENTAL RESEARCH SPECIALTIES AND STAFF

Theoretical

Astrophysics. Relativistic astrophysics; numerical relativity; cosmology; neutron stars; black holes; exoplanets; dark energy; gravitational waves; accretion disks and jets. Flanagan, Teukolsky, Wasserman.

Atomic, Molecular, & Optical Physics. Bose-Einstein condensation; degenerate Fermi gases; quantum simulation and emulation. Mueller.

Biophysics. Insect flight; symmetry breaking; viral capsids; mechanics of root growth; protein folding; biological networks; plant pathogens; mechanical properties of DNA; statistical mechanics of DNA; bioinformatics; and variability. Elser, Myers, Sethna, Jane Wang.

Computational Physics. Ab initio quantum mechanical description of materials; multi-scale modeling; numerical relativity; numerical quantum field theories; lattice QCD; joint density functional theories; solvation and solid-liquid interfaces; quantum Monte Carlo methods; optimization; fluid mechanics; image reconstructions; phase retrieval algorithms. Arias, Elser, Lepage, Teukolsky, Jane Wang.

Condensed Matter Physics. Electronic structure of solids and liquids; graphene; high-Tc superconductors; quasi-crystals; ultra-cold atoms. Arias, Elser, Kim, Lawler, Mueller, Myers, Sethna, Umrigar.

Cosmology & String Theory. String theory; inflation; AdS/CFT; signatures of inflation in CMB spectrum; string compactifications; particle cosmology. Grossman, Hartman, McAllister, Perelstein.

High Energy Physics. Phenomonology; electroweak symmetry breaking; supersymmetry; astroparticle physics; flavor physics; neutrinos; leptogenesis. Csaki, Grossman, Perelstein.

Particles and Fields. Quantum electrodynamics; gauge theories of strong interactions; spectroscopy of new heavy mesons;

hadronic structure of the photon; numerical QCD; effective field theories; supersymmetric models. Csaki, Ginsparg, Grossman, LeClair, Lepage, Perelstein.

Statistical & Thermal Physics. Turbulence; statistical mechanics of non-linear fits; avalanches; shock waves; computational linguistics; quasi-crystals; phase transitions. Ginsparg, Sethna, Jane Wang.

Experimental

Accelerator. Design, construction, and operation of particle accelerators; Cornell Electron Storage Ring (CESR): CESR Test-Accelerator; Energy Recovery Linear accelerator (ERL); muon g-2; International Linear Collider (ILC); linear and non-linear beam dynamics; microwave superconductivity; superconducting RF cavities; damping rings; photoinjectors; photocathode research and development; lasers; X-ray production; beam instrumentation. Bazarov, Hoffstaetter, Liepe, Maxson, Rubin.

Biophysics. Single-molecule biophysics; mechanical manipulation; precision instrumentation; physics of cryopreservation. Bodenschatz, Franck, Gruner, McEuen, Thorne, Michelle Wang.

Condensed Matter Physics. Ultraviolet, visible, infrared, and Raman studies of solids; nuclear and electron spin resonance; electronic and thermal transport properties; phase transitions in one and two dimensions. Cohen, Davis, Gruner, Levy, Mak, McEuen, Nowack, Parpia, Ralph, Ramshaw, Shan, Shen, Thorne.

Cosmology and Astrophysics. Measuring the cosmic microwave background and the high-redshift universe. Developing experimental techniques for millimeter and sub-millimeter cosmology and astrophysics observations. Niemack.

Fluids, Rheology. Fluid dynamics in insect flight; wetting and contact line pinning of fluids on surfaces; rheology of colloidal suspensions; drop breakup and dynamics. Cohen, Franck, Thorne.

High Energy Physics. Accelerator-based: collaboration in and detector development for experiments at proton-proton colliders (CMS experiment at CERN's Large Hadron Collider [LHC]), electron-positron colliders (b factories, International Linear Collider [ILC]) and in precision muon physics (muon g-2 at Fermilab). The work focuses on understanding nature's most fundamental particle content and particle interactions with an emphasis on the origin of mass and electroweak symmetry breaking and on the dark matter content of the universe, including probes of supersymmetry, extra dimensions, and composite states. Non-accelerator-based: studies of the Cosmic Microwave Background (CMB) radiation, currently utilizing the Atacama Cosmology Telescope (ACT) to explore the nature of the early universe. Alexander, Gibbons, Patterson, Ryd, Thom-Levy, Wittich.

Low Temperature Physics. Superfluidity in 3He and 4He; phase transitions in liquid 3He, 4He, and mixtures and in solid 3He. Hoffstaetter, Parpia, Ralph.

Nano Science and Technology. Dynamics of charge, spin, thermal, and mechanical degrees of freedom in nanoscale and single-molecule devices; new nanofabrication techniques; advanced microscopy/spectroscopy; single-molecule biophysics; graphene and other atomic-membrane materials; self-assembling materials. Gruner, Mak, McEuen, Parpia, Ralph.

Optics. Optical trapping; single-molecule fluorescence; nanophotonics. Hoffstaetter, McEuen, Parpia, Michelle Wang.

Physics and other Science Education. Design, validation, and employment of assessments of student learning; development and evaluation of pedagogical techniques; studies of lecture, lab, and recitation instruction; social and contextual elements of student learning, attitudes, and beliefs; foundational understanding of learning and instruction; applications of cognitive science and psychology. Holmes.

Statistical & Thermal Physics. Phase transitions in water/ice, aqueous mixtures and colloids: phase behavior at high pressures; self-assembly of nanocomposites. Cohen, Franck, Gruner, Thorne.

View additional information about this department at www.gradschoolshopper.com. Check out the "Why Choose Us?" section, find out more about the department's culture and get links to social media networks.

THE GRADUATE CENTER -
THE CITY UNIVERSITY OF NEW YORK

PH.D. PROGRAM IN PHYSICS

New York, New York 10016-4309

https://www.gc.cuny.edu/Page-Elements/Academics-Research-Centers-Initiatives/Doctoral-Programs/Physics

General University Information
President: Chase F. Robinson
Dean of Graduate School: Joshua C. Brumberg
University website: http://www.gc.cuny.edu/home
School Type: Public
Setting: Urban
Total Faculty: 1,700
Total Graduate Faculty: 1,700
Total number of Students: 4,100
Total number of Graduate Students: 4,100

Department Information
Department Chairman: Prof. Igor L. Kuskovsky, Chair
Department Contact: Daniel Moy, Assistant Program Officer
Total full-time faculty: 85
Total number of full-time equivalent positions: 2
Full-Time Graduate Students: 106
Female Full-Time Graduate Students: 0
First-Year Graduate Students: 21
Female First-Year Students: 9
Total Post Doctorates: 2

Department Address
365 Fifth Avenue
Room # 4317
New York, NY 10016-4309
Phone: 212 817-8650
E-mail: dmoy@gc.cuny.edu
Website: https://www.gc.cuny.edu/Page-Elements/Academics-Research-Centers-Initiatives/Doctoral-Programs/Physics

ADMISSIONS

Admission Contact Information
Address admission inquiries to: Office of Admissions, The Graduate Center CUNY, 365 Fifth Avenue, New York, NY 10016-4309
Phone: 212 817-7470
E-mail: Admissions@gc.cuny.edu
Admissions website: http://www.gc.cuny.edu/Prospective-Current-Students/Prospective-Students/Admissions

Application deadlines
Fall admission:
U.S. students: January 10   *Int'l. students*: January 10

Application fee
U.S. students: $125   *Int'l. students*: $125
Application fee is waived to: Graduates of the City University of New York. Admissions Questions may be directed to one of the following offices: - General Questions: Admissions office, Admissions@gc.cuny.edu Physics Requirements: Ph.D. Program in Physics, physics@gc.cuny.edu

Admissions information
For Fall of 2018:
   Number admitted: 21

Admission requirements
Bachelor's degree requirements: Required.

GRE requirements
The GRE is required.
GRE General Examination: we do not require minimum scores as applicants are evaluated by the totality of their academic accomplishments.

Subjective GRE requirements
The Subjective GRE is not required.
   Minimum accepted Advanced GRE score: 0
   Mean Advanced GRE score range (25th–75th percentile): N/A
GRE Physics is not required, but recommended.

TOEFL requirements
The TOEFL exam is required for students from non-English-speaking countries.
Will also accept scores from IELTS in lieu of TOEFL scores. Applicants from non-English speaking countries are not required to submit English language tests if they are graduates of a college or university teaching coursework in English.

Other admissions information
Additional requirements: A minimum of 2 letters of recommendation.
   Transcripts from all colleges and universities attended.
Undergraduate preparation assumed: Standard syllabus of physics undergraduate courses.

TUITION

Tuition year 2018–2019:
Tuition for in-state residents
   Full-time students: annual
All students (United States and international) are awarded a 5-year Science Scholarship; including $30,000 financial aid per annum (for Fall 2018 new students), full tuition waiver for 10 semesters and low-cost health insurance.
Credit hours per semester to be considered full-time: 7
Deferred tuition plan:
Health insurance: Yes, estimate: $425 individual and $2500 for full family coverage.
Other academic fees: Less than $200 per semester for various fees: including registration, student activities and technology.
Academic term: Semester

Teaching Assistants, Research Assistants, and Fellowships
   Number of first-year
      Fellowship students: 25
   Average stipend per academic year
      Teaching Assistant: $14,000
      Research Assistant: $16,000
      Fellowship student: $16,000

First Year students are fully supported by The Graduate Center and are not required to teach. Total financial support for each student in Years 1 to 5 via combination a of TA, RA. Fellowships CANNOT BE LESS than $30,000 per year.

FINANCIAL AID

Loans

Loans are available for U.S. students.
Loans are available for international students.
GAPSFAS application required: No
FAFSA application required: Yes

For further information

Address financial aid inquiries to: Phyllis Schulz, Executive Director of Fellowships and Financial Aid, Office of Financial Aid, The Graduate Center CUNY, 365 Fifth Avenue, New York, NY 10016-4309.
Phone: 212-817-7460
E-mail: financialaid@gc.cuny.edu
Financial aid website: http://www.gc.cuny.edu/Prospective-Current-Students/Current-Students/Financial-Assistance

HOUSING

Availability of on-campus housing

Single students: Yes
Married students: Yes

For further information

Address housing inquiries to: The Graduate Center, City University of New York, Attn: Jane Tartaro, Housing Office, 365 Fifth Ave., New York, NY 10016-4309.
Phone: 212 817-7605
E-mail: gchousing@gc.cuny.edu
Housing aid website: http://www.gc.cuny.edu/Prospective-Current-Students/Student-Life/Housing

Table A—Faculty, Enrollments, and Degrees Granted

Research Specialty	Faculty	Enrollment Fall 2017		Number of Degrees Granted 14 (87)		
		Master's	Doctorate	Master's	Terminal Master's	Doctorate
Total	–	–	–	–	–	–
Full-time Grad. Stud.	–	–	107	–	–	–
First-year Grad. Stud.	–	–	21	–	–	–

GRADUATE DEGREE REQUIREMENTS

Doctorate: Pass Qualifying (1st) Examination. Pass Proposed Research (2nd) Examination. 60 or more credits of coursework, including research credits. Accepted dissertation.
Other Degrees: Master of Philosophy.

SPECIAL EQUIPMENT, FACILITIES, OR PROGRAMS

The Initiative for the Theoretical Sciences (ITS) is based at The Graduate Center and its faculty are focused on research in many areas.

To learn more about the ITS: https://www.gc.cuny.edu/Page-Elements/Academics-Research-Centers-Initiatives/Initiatives-and-Committees/Initiative-for-the-Theoretical-Sciences-(ITS)

Advanced Science Research Center at The Graduate Center is a billion-dollar new state-of-the art research facility open for students and faculty in the City University of New York. Other universities and industry may apply for access to use the labs.

Click onto this link for more details: http://www.asrc.cuny.edu/

Access to the CUNY High Performance Computing Center, located at the College of Staten Island CUNY is available to CUNY students, faculty and their collaborators.

Click onto this link for more details: https://cunyhpc.csi.cuny.edu/

View additional information about this department at www.gradschoolshopper.com. Check out the "Why Choose Us?" section, find out more about the department's culture and get links to social media networks.

RENSSELAER POLYTECHNIC INSTITUTE

DEPARTMENT OF PHYSICS, APPLIED PHYSICS, AND ASTRONOMY

Troy, New York 12180-3590
https://science.rpi.edu/physics

General University Information
President: Shirley A. Jackson
Dean of Graduate School: Stanley M. Dunn
University website: http://www.rpi.edu/index.html
School Type: Private
Setting: Suburban
Total Faculty: 462
Total number of Students: 7,633
Total number of Graduate Students: 1,213

Department Information
Department Chairman: Prof. Vincent Meunier, Head
Department Contact: Joan Perras, Assistant to the Department
  Head
  Total full-time faculty: 17
  Total number of full-time equivalent positions: 17
  Full-Time Graduate Students: 32
  Female Full-Time Graduate Students: 1
  First-Year Graduate Students: 8
  Total Post Doctorates: 4

Department Address
110 8th Street
Troy, NY 12180-3590
Phone: (518) 276-6310
Fax: (518) 276-6680
E-mail: perraj@rpi.edu
Website: https://science.rpi.edu/physics

ADMISSIONS

Admission Contact Information
Address admission inquiries to: Graduate Admissions, Rensse-
  laer Polytechnic Institute, 110 8th Street, Troy, New York
  12180-3590
Phone: (518) 276-6216
E-mail: gradadmissions@rpi.edu
Admissions website: http://admissions.rpi.edu/graduate/contact/
  index.html

Application deadlines
Fall admission:
U.S. students: January 1   *Int'l. students*: January 1
Spring admission:
U.S. students: August 15   *Int'l. students*: August 15

Application fee
U.S. students: $75   *Int'l. students*: $75

Admissions information
For Fall of 2018:
  Number of applicants: 128
  Number admitted: 32

Admission requirements
Bachelor's degree requirements: Bachelor's degree is required
  with courses and grades demonstrating ability and preparation
  adequate for graduate study in Physics. Remedial courses
  available as needed.
Minimum undergraduate GPA: 3.2

GRE requirements
The GRE is required.
  Quantitative score: 146
  Verbal score: 156
  Analytical score: 4.0
The above are the suggested minimum.

Subjective GRE requirements
The Subjective GRE is required.
  Minimum accepted Advanced GRE score: 600
The above is the suggested minimum.

TOEFL requirements
The TOEFL exam is required for students from non-English-
  speaking countries.
  PBT score: 600
  iBT score: 100
The above are the suggested minimum.

Other admissions information
Undergraduate preparation assumed: Students are normally expected to have taken intermediate-level courses in mechanics,
  electricity and magnetism, quantum physics, statistical mechanics, and experimental physics. Typical texts are Marion
  and Thornton, Griffiths, Brehm and Mullin, Stowe, and Liboff.
  However, students may take a limited number of remedial
  courses after enrollment where inadequate preparation has
  been available, but where other courses and grade records indicate adequate ability.

TUITION

Tuition year 2018–2019:
Tuition for in-state residents
  Full-time students: annual
  Part-time students: per credit
  Full-time students: $52,550 annual
  Part-time students: $2,190 per credit
Credit hours per semester to be considered full-time: 12
Deferred tuition plan: No
Health insurance: Yes, $1,200.00.
Other academic fees: Fees & Insurance: $2,890. Estimated Liv-
  ing Expenses: $14,249. Books and Supplies: $2,950.
Academic term: Semester
Number of first-year students who received full tuition waivers: 8

Teaching Assistants, Research Assistants, and Fellowships
Number of first-year
  Teaching Assistants: 11
Average stipend per academic year
  Teaching Assistant: $23,000
  Research Assistant: $23,000
  Fellowship student: $28,750
  The average fellowship amount is based on the institute's
  Presidential Fellowship for the past academic year.

FINANCIAL AID

Application deadlines
Fall admission:

U.S. students: February 1　　　　*Int'l. students*: February 1
Spring admission:
U.S. students: November 1　　　　*Int'l. students*: November 1

Loans

Loans are available for U.S. students.
Loans are not available for international students.
GAPSFAS application required: No
FAFSA application required: Yes

For further information

Address financial aid inquiries to: Office of Financial Aid.
Phone: (518) 276-6813
E-mail: finaid@rpi.edu
Financial aid website: http://admissions.rpi.edu/aid/index.html

HOUSING

Availability of on-campus housing

Single students: Yes
Married students: Yes

For further information

Address housing inquiries to: Office of Residence Life, Rens-
　　selaer Polytechnic Institute, 110 8th Street, Troy, New York
　　12180-3590.
Phone: (518) 276-6284
E-mail: res_life@rpi.edu
Housing aid website: http://reslife.rpi.edu/setup.do

Table A—Faculty, Enrollments, and Degrees Granted

Research Specialty	2017–2018 Faculty	Enrollment Spring 2018		Number of Degrees Granted 2016–2017 (2012–2017)		
		Master's	Doctorate	Master's	Terminal Master's	Doctorate
Astronomy and Astrophysics	4	1	6	–	3(18)	1(2)
Condensed Matter Physics	9	–	21	–(4)	5(15)	3(19)
Optics	6	1	6	–(2)	3(7)	2(9)
Particles and Fields	4	–	1	–(2)	–(2)	2(6)
Total	23	2	34	–(8)	11(42)	8(36)
Full-time Grad. Stud.	–	2	34	–	–	–
First-year Grad. Stud.	–	2	6	–	–	–

GRADUATE DEGREE REQUIREMENTS

Master's: Thirty credit hours with a minimum GPA of 3.0; one
academic year (2 semesters) residency minimum. No foreign
language and no comprehensive exams are required. Thesis
or research projects are required (six to nine credit hours for
a thesis or three credit hours for a research project), but may
be waived for students who pass Ph.D. candidacy exam. A
maximum of six credit hours can be transferred from other
institutions.

Doctorate: Seventy-two credit hours (typically including 30-45
credit hours of research) with a minimum GPA of 3.0 are
required. There is a three academic year (six semesters) residency minimum. No foreign language is required. Qualifying
examination (10 hours, written), covering advanced
undergraduate-level material, must be passed by end of first
year. Qualifying exams may be waived for high physics
GRES score or high performance in classes at Rensselaer.
Candidacy exam (oral, on physics related to proposed thesis
research area), written dissertation, and thesis defense required.

SPECIAL EQUIPMENT, FACILITIES, OR PROGRAMS

Astronomy and Astrophysics

Students' thesis research in astronomy and astrophysics enjoys
access to world-class ground-based telescopes located at observing sites in the southern hemisphere and China. Our faculty
cooperates with the international Large Sky Area Multi-Object
Fiber Spectroscopic Telescope (LAMOST), the Sloan Digital
Sky Survey, and the very popular MilkyWay@Home project.

For students' education in observational astronomy and for public
outreach, the department maintains the Hirsch Observatory. It
houses a fully automated Boller and Chivens 16″ Cassegrain
Telescope, a Quantum Scientific Imaging (QSI) imaging camera
with filter wheel, and a Santa Barbara Instrument Group (SBIG)
spectrograph. Many smaller telescopes are also available to students.

Biological Physics, Condensed Matter and Optics

State-of-the art equipment for graduate students' experimental
research in optics and condensed matter physics is provided in
the physics department. The equipment includes optical, electronic, and cryogenic instruments, surface science techniques and
materials growth equipment. Examples are Atomic Force Microscopy, Auger Electron Spectroscopy, Ellipsometry, High-
Resolution Low Energy Electron Diffraction, Reflection High-
Energy Electron Diffraction, X-Ray Crystallography, and Super-
Resolution Microscopy. Also available for research are terahertz
radiation sources and ultrafast laser systems. Students engage in
absorption, light scattering, and photoluminescence spectroscopy
using systems operating from the terahertz frequency band to the
ultraviolet part of the electromagnetic spectrum.

Students interested in nanofabrication will find excellent facilities
in Rensselaer's Micro and Nano-Fabrication Clean Room
(MNCR). This is a state-of-the-art, 5,700-square-foot, Class 100
multi-user facility which supports research and education in nanotechnology, biotechnology, microelectronics, solid state lighting, energy, and other fields. The MNCR offers infrastructure for
end-to-end device fabrication, characterization, metrology and
testing by the graduate student user on substrates ranging from
a few millimeters in size to full wafers 200 mm in diameter for
high-speed electronics, power devices, integrated circuits, microsystems, and other applications. Fabrication of structures as small
as 20 nm is possible in the MNCR, and structures as small as
1.5 nm can be achieved. In addition, the facility has several dedicated staff members to provide process solutions, training, and
teaching.

The Center for Biotechnology and Interdisciplinary Research on
our campus offers extensive and high-quality facilities for students' experimental research in biological physics at the molecular, cellular, and tissue level.

Students conducting research in theoretical biological and condensed matter physics use Rensselaer's own supercomputer. The
Blue Gene/Q is one of the world's most powerful university-
based supercomputers. Theoretical methods implemented by our
students on this machine and other computers are density functional theory calculations, Monte-Carlo Simulations as well as
classical and quantum mechanical molecular dynamics simulation.

In addition, the Department's research activities are affiliated
with numerous research centers on campus: The Center for Computational Innovations, the Center for Future Energy Systems,
the Center for Materials, Devices and Integrated Systems, the
Network Science and Technology Center, the Institute for Data
Exploration and Applications, the Rensselaer Nanotechnology

Center, the Scientific Computation Research Center, the Smart Lighting Engineering Research Center, and the Data Science Research Center.

Particle and Fields

Rensselaer research in particle astrophysics is involved in one of the leading experiments that could detect WIMP dark matter, the XENON experiment in the Gran Sasso Mountain in central Italy.

Students pursuing thesis research in theoretical particle physics apply lattice field theories and implement the calculations on the Blue Gene/Q supercomputer.

Table B—Separately Budgeted Research Expenditures by Source of Support

Source of Support	Departmental Research	Physics-related Research Outside Department
Federal government	$2,191,350	
State/local government	$916,053	
Non-profit organizations		
Business and industry	$100,354	
Other		
Total	$3,207,757	

Table C—Separately Budgeted Research Expenditures by Research Specialty

Research Specialty	No. of Grants	Expenditures ($)
Astronomy and Astrophysics	2	$143,005
Condensed Matter Physics	19	$2,382,172
Optics	2	$625,855
Particles and Fields	1	$56,726
Total	24	$3,207,758

FACULTY

Professor

Jackson, Shirley A., Ph.D., Massachusetts Institute of Technology, 1973. President, Rensselaer Polytechnic Institute. *Particles and Fields.* Theoretical elementary particle physics.

Korniss, Gyorgy, Ph.D., Virginia Tech, 1997. *Computational Physics, Computer Science, Condensed Matter Physics, Nonlinear Dynamics and Complex Systems, Statistical & Thermal Physics.* Statistical mechanics; dynamics in complex networks.

Lin, Shawn-Yu, Ph.D., Princeton University, 1992. *Optics.* Design, nanofabrication, and experimental testing of active 3D photonic crystals.

Lu, Toh-Ming, Ph.D., University of Wisconsin, Madison, 1976. Associate Director, Center for Integrated Electronics; Ray Palmer Baker Distinguished Professor. *Materials Science, Metallurgy, Nano Science and Technology, Solid State Physics, Surface Physics.* Thin films and interfaces.

Meunier, Vincent, Ph.D., University of Namur, 1999. Department Head; Gail and Jeffrey L. Kodosky '70 Constellation Professor of Physics, Information Technology, and Entrepreneurship. *Computational Physics, Condensed Matter Physics, Materials Science, Metallurgy, Nano Science and Technology, Solid State Physics, Surface Physics.* Computational solid state physics, electronic transport, energy storage, and low-dimensional structures; nano science.

Newberg, Heidi, Ph.D., University of California, Berkeley, 1992. Director, Hirsch Observatory. *Astronomy, Astrophysics, Computational Physics.* Astrophysics, computational astronomy, and Galactic structure.

Persans, Peter D., Ph.D., University of Chicago, 1982. *Applied Physics, Condensed Matter Physics, Materials Science, Metallurgy, Optics, Physics and other Science Education, Solid State Physics.* Spectroscopy of semiconductors, thin films, optical materials.

Schroeder, John, Ph.D., Catholic University of America, 1974. *Biophysics, Condensed Matter Physics, Solid State Physics.* Physics and biological physics high pressure.

Shur, Michael, Ph.D., A. F. Ioffe Institute, 1967. Patricia W. and C. Sheldon Roberts '48 Chaired Professor in Solid State Electronics; Professor of Electrical, Computer, and Systems Engineering; Professor of Physics, Applied Physics and Astronomy; Director, Center for Broadband Data Transport Science and Technology (Primary appointment with ECSE). *Applied Mathematics, Applied Physics, Condensed Matter Physics, Nano Science and Technology, Solid State Physics.* Semiconductor physics, ballistic transport, terahertz radiation, smart lighting, LED's.

Terrones, Humberto, Ph.D., University of London, 1992. Rayleigh Endowed Chair of Theoretical Physics. *Condensed Matter Physics, Nano Science and Technology, Solid State Physics, Other.* Theory, experiment, and characterization of 2D materials and complex atomic structures.

Wang, Gwo-Ching, Ph.D., University of Wisconsin, Madison, 1978. Travelstead Institute Chair. *Applied Physics, Condensed Matter Physics, Surface Physics.* Growth and characterization of nanostructures and thin films.

Wetzel, Christian M., Ph.D., Technical University, Munich, 1993. *Applied Physics, Condensed Matter Physics, Electrical Engineering, Energy Sources & Environment, Engineering Physics/Science, Low Temperature Physics, Materials Science, Metallurgy, Nano Science and Technology, Optics, Solid State Physics.* III-V nitride semiconductor physics, materials and devices in particular for lighting, photovoltaics, and electronics.

Zhang, Shengbai, Ph.D., University of California, Berkeley, 1989. Gail and Jeffrey L. Kodosky '70 Senior Constellation Professor of Physics, Information Technology, and Entrepreneurship. *Condensed Matter Physics.* Computational condensed matter theory, lower-dimension materials, topological insulators, defects in optoelectronic and photovoltaic materials, and physics and chemistry of energy storage materials.

Associate Professor

Giedt, Joel, Ph.D., University of California, Berkeley, 2002. *Computational Physics, Cosmology & String Theory, High Energy Physics, Particles and Fields, Theoretical Physics.* Particle phenomenology; lattice field theory; string compactifications; high-energy mathematical and computational physics.

Wilke, Ingrid, Ph.D., ETH Zuerich, 1993. *Applied Physics, Optics, Solid State Physics.* Ultrafast optics, photonics, optoelectronics and terahertz science and technology.

Yamaguchi, Masashi, Ph.D., Hokkaido University, 1991. *Acoustics, Applied Physics, Chemical Physics, Condensed Matter Physics, Electrical Engineering, Electromagnetism, Low Temperature Physics, Materials Science, Metallurgy, Mechanics, Nano Science and Technology, Optics, Polymer Physics/Science, Solid State Physics, Statistical & Thermal Physics.* THz wave generation, pulse shaping, THz spectroscopy; acoustic/thermal transport in nanoscale materials; phonon and electron dynamics in condensed matter.

Assistant Professor

Brown, Ethan, Ph.D., University of California, Los Angeles, 2010. *Nuclear Physics, Particles and Fields.* Experimental astroparticle physics, dark matter direct detection, neutrinoless double beta decay, liquid xenon detectors, novel gas purification and diagnostics.

N'Gom, Moussa, Ph.D., University of Michigan, Ann Arbor, 2009. *Applied Physics, Atomic, Molecular, & Optical Physics, Optics, Quantum Foundations.* Quantum optics, ultrafast optics, light modulation, quantum entanglement, plasmonics, nanostructures.

Wertz, Esther A., Ph.D., Université Paris-Sud 11, 2010. *Atomic, Molecular, & Optical Physics, Condensed Matter Physics, Electromagnetism, Nano Science and Technology, Optics.* Light-matter interactions of single molecules with plasmonic nanostructures; super-resolution microscopy.

Professor of the Practice

Washington, Morris, Ph.D., New York University, 1976. Associate Director, Center for Integrated Electronics. *Condensed Matter Physics.* Photonic and electronic devices.

Affiliate Professor

Szymanski, Boleslaw, Ph.D., The Institute of Computer Science, the Polish Academy of Sciences, 1976. Claire and Roland Schmitt Distinguished Professor of Computer Science; Founding Director, Institute Center for Network Science and Technology. *Computational Physics, Computer Science, Condensed Matter Physics, Nonlinear Dynamics and Complex Systems, Statistical & Thermal Physics.* network science, computer and sensor networks; distributed and parallel computing.

Affiliate Assistant Professor

Chakrapani, Vidhya, Ph.D., Case Western Reserve University, 2007. Assistant professor, Dept of Chemical & Biological Eng. *Applied Mathematics, Energy Sources & Environment, Engineering Physics/Science, Materials Science, Metallurgy, Nano Science and Technology, Optics, Solid State Physics, Surface Physics.* Semiconductor photochemistry, solar energy conversion, advanced materials.

Sundararaman, Ravishankar, Ph.D., Cornell University, 2013. Assistant Professor, Materials Science and Engineering. *Chemical Physics, Computational Physics, Condensed Matter Physics, Nano Science and Technology, Optics, Solid State Physics.* Computational materials science, nanomaterials, energy conversion and storage, electrochemistry, plasmonics and nanophotonics.

Lecturer

Ciolek, Glenn E., Ph.D., University of Illinois at Urbana-Champaign, 1993. *Astrophysics, Computational Physics, Plasma and Fusion, Theoretical Physics.* star formation, interstellar medium, plasma astrophysics, magnetohydrodynamics, interstellar dust, shock waves and nonlinear flows, computational astrophysics.

Kim, Yong Sung, Ph.D., Iowa State University, 2006. *Computational Physics, Condensed Matter Physics, Electromagnetism, Nano Science and Technology, Optics, Solid State Physics.* Computational photonics, photonic crystal, nano optical devices.

Martin, Charles H., Ph.D., Rensselaer, 2016. *Astronomy, Astrophysics.* Astronomy and Astrophysics; Milky Way Halo Substructure and Tidal Stream.

Michael, Joseph D., Ph.D., Rensselaer Polytechnic Institute, 1988. *Accelerator, Applied Physics, Atomic, Molecular, & Optical Physics, Electrical Engineering, Electromagnetism, Engineering Physics/Science, Optics, Physics of Beams, Plasma and Fusion.*

DEPARTMENTAL RESEARCH SPECIALTIES AND STAFF

Theoretical

Astrophysics. Current research focuses on determining the location of dark matter in the Milky Way. We perform n-body simulations of the tidal disruption of dwarf galaxies in the Milky Way halo, using MilkyWay@home, a 0.5 PetaFLOPS volunteer computing platform built in-house. We compare the simulations to actual Milky Way data to determine the best parameters for the simulations, thus constraining the amount and distribution of dark matter in the halo. We are testing predictions of dark matter distribution for particular dark matter particles against the measured positions and motions of stars in the Milky Way. Newberg.

Condensed Matter Physics. Theoretical and computational studies performed include the electronic structure of nanostructured material, models for the structure and electronic properties of surfaces and interfaces and the binding and mobility of adsorbed atoms on metal surfaces, molecular electronics and spintronics, as well as developing understanding of far-from-equilibrium physics. Active research activities also include a number of other aspects of condensed matter physics research such as studies devoted to light-material interactions for solar-energy harvesting, photo catalysis, energy conversion, sensing, and structural transformation in inorganic and organic semiconductors. Many-body interactions encountered in electron-phonon coupling for excited-state energy relaxation, and superconductivity are also parts of the research portfolio. The researchers pay particular attention to emerging materials such as low-cost solar cell materials, topological insulators, porous nanostructures, two-dimensional layered structures, and van der Waals solids with exotic electronic structures and defect properties for applications in electronics, optoelectronics, spintronics, and beyond. Finally, significant activities are realized on the physics of surfaces and the physics, chemistry, and dynamics of interfaces between solids and between solid and liquid. The various condensed matter theory efforts rely significantly on large-scale supercomputing approaches, using resources from Rensselaer's Center for Computational Innovations. Meunier, Terrones, Zhang.

Particle Physics. Activities in this area primarily focus on investigations on beyond the standard model applications of lattice field theory. This includes strongly coupled supersymmetric systems such as arise in hidden sector models of spontaneous supersymmetry breaking. We have also studied models of compositeness in the Higgs sector of the Standard Model, with electroweak symmetry broken by strong dynamics of a new gauge force. This has led us into developing software for the study of resonance properties from first principles, which is also useful for lattice quantum chromodynamics. A key focus of ongoing research is dualities in gauge theories, such as S-duality (electric/magnetic) in $N=4$ super-Yang-Mills, and gauge/gravity dualities (AdS/CFT). This allows us to study quantum gravity in numerical simulations. Much of our work has an eye toward string-inspired particle phenomenology, which we have worked on in the past. Giedt.

Stochastic Dynamics on Complex Networks. One of the major developments of the last two decades has been the ever-increasing interconnectivity of a broad class of information networks, including physical and data network types arising in telecommunication, social networks, and transportation and energy infrastructures. This interconnectivity has led to immense temporal and spatial complexity in modern networks and a critical need for basic mathematical theory and statistical modeling of complex interacting networks. Our current research in this direction includes structure and dynamics of social, information, and biological networks and applications to social dynamics, network vulnerability, epidemic models, and synchronization problems. On-campus collaborations and facilities are at the Social Cognitive Network Academic Research Center (SCNARC) and at the Network Science and Technology Center (NeST). Korniss.

Experimental

Astrophysics. Experimental research in the astrophysics group focuses on near-field cosmology, in which local galaxies are studied as examples to understand the properties of the Universe, including dark matter and dark energy. We particularly focus on the dynamics and structure of the Milky Way as revealed by large, international photometric and spectroscopic surveys such as the Sloan Digital Sky Survey (SDSS) and the Large Area Multi-Object Spectroscopic Telescope (LAMOST), and by astrometric surveys such as Gaia. Dwarf galaxies are ripped apart by tidal forces in the Milky Way into tidal streams. These streams are used to constrain the processes by which the Milky Way galaxy formed, and the distribution of the dark matter within it. The dwarf galaxies also excite wavelike structures in the Milky Way disk that could explain how spiral galaxy structure is formed and sustained. Newberg.

Condensed Matter Physics. The experimental condensed matter research distinguishes between the bulk of matter, its surface and interface, and proceeds in close partnership with theory and computational studies. Of interest are new concepts, materials, and techniques for nanotechnology and green technology such as renewable energy, energy conservation and conversion, storage, and delivery. Some projects are interdisciplinary and take part in dedicated Centers across the Institute. One fundamental research is molecular electronics, which studies the quantum transport of molecules that exhibit conductance switching and rectification behavior. These measurements use scanning probe microscopy and nano junctions measured at liquid He temperature. Another project aims at improving our understanding of materials, their structure, and devices. The metals, semiconductors, and insulators are prepared in thin film deposition (including oblique angle deposition) and epitaxial growth (including van der Waals epitaxy). Their structural, electronic transport, spin, and optical properties are characterized and compared to theoretical and computational investigations. Other studies include wide band gap semiconductors, photonic crystals, polymers, semiconductor nanoparticle composites, dielectrics, magnetic, metallic thin films, two-dimensional layered materials, plasmonics and nanostructures. The department makes use of state-of-the-art characterization techniques such as electron, x-ray, ultraviolet, visible, infrared, Raman, terahertz, and scanning probe spectroscopies and microscopies. Local facilities include the Mirco and Nano Fabrication Clean Room and the Electron Microscope Laboratory. Lu, Shur, Terrones, Wang, Washington, Wetzel.

Optical Physics. Research in optical physics covers a wide range of activities related to photons and their interaction with various materials. Experimental and theoretical research is ongoing to provide innovative solutions to today's problems in both fundamental and application. The goals are the development of novel nanoelectronic and nanophotonic devices, creative solutions for homeland security, renewable energies, biological and biomedical investigations, solar harvesting, and smart lighting. Research includes photonic crystals, plasmonics, photonic nanostructures, light emitting diodes, terahertz photonics, spectroscopy, imaging, chemical and biological sensing and identification, ultrafast and nonlinear phenomena, the development of novel ultrafast spectroscopic techniques, development of novel optical materials including wideband gap and narrow band gap semiconductors, nanowires and their arrays, semiconducting quantum dots and quantum wells. One such research effort aims to understand the fundamental interactions between single quantum emitters and plasmonic nano-antennas. By studying the changes in the single molecule emission properties through super-resolution imaging, we can learn about the interactions of the fluorophore with its environment at the nanometer scale. Major facilities include ultrafast lasers and ultrafast and terahertz spectroscopy systems, a micro and nanofabrication clean room for semiconductor processing, linear and nonlinear optical absorption, luminescence, and super-resolution microscopy. Lin, Persans, Schroeder, Wertz, Wetzel, Wilke, Yamaguchi.

Particle Astrophysics. Rensselaer research in particle astrophysics is involved in one of the leading experiments that could detect WIMP dark matter, the XENON experiment in the Gran Sasso Mountain in central Italy. Students also perform R&D for neutrino and dark matter experiments the high purity xenon laboratory at Rensselaer. The nature and structure of matter and energy remains one of mankind's leading research frontiers. The faculty members involved in this area are engaged in experimental and theoretical studies of the fundamental interactions of matter at sub-femtometer distances. Another research focus is on the direct detection of dark matter with the XENON1T experiment operated in the LNGS laboratory in Italy, and the search for neutrinoless double beta decay with the nEXO experiment. Research & development efforts for these and future experiments address xenon purification techniques to operate the most radiopure detectors in the world. Brown.

View additional information about this department at www.gradschoolshopper.com. Check out the "Why Choose Us?" section, find out more about the department's culture and get links to social media networks.

STATE UNIVERSITY OF NEW YORK AT ALBANY

DEPARTMENT OF PHYSICS

Albany, New York 12222
http://www.albany.edu/physics

General University Information
President: Havidan Rodriguez
Dean of Graduate School: Kevin Williams
University website: http://www.albany.edu
School Type: Public
Setting: Suburban
Total Faculty: 1,000
Total number of Students: 17,040
Total number of Graduate Students: 4,936

Department Information
Department Chairman: Prof. Keith Earle, Chair
Department Contact: Keith Earle, Chair
  Total full-time faculty: 16
  Total number of full-time equivalent positions: 3
  Full-Time Graduate Students: 46
  Female Full-Time Graduate Students: 5
  First-Year Graduate Students: 7
  Female First-Year Students: 2
  Total Post Doctorates: 1

Department Address
Physics 216
1400 Washington Avenue
Albany, NY 12222
Phone: (518) 442-4501
Fax: (518) 442-5260
E-mail: Physics@albany.edu
Website: http://www.albany.edu/physics

ADMISSIONS

Admission Contact Information
Address admission inquiries to: Paul LaBate, Physics 216, Albany, NY 12222
Phone: (518) 442-4501
E-mail: physics@albany.edu
Admissions website: http://www.albany.edu/graduate/graduate-admissions.php

Application deadlines
Fall admission:
U.S. students: February 15   *Int'l. students*: February 15
Spring admission:
U.S. students: November 15   *Int'l. students*: November 15

Application fee
U.S. students: $75   *Int'l. students*: $75

Admissions information
For Fall of 2018:
  Number of applicants: 120
  Number admitted: 17
  Number enrolled: 15

Admission requirements
Bachelor's degree requirements: A bachelor's degree in Physics or a related field is required.

GRE requirements
The GRE is not required.

Subjective GRE requirements
The Subjective GRE is not required.

TOEFL requirements
The TOEFL exam is required for students from non-English-speaking countries.
  PBT score: 600
  iBT score: 100
The minimum accepted computer-based exam (CBT) score is 250.

Other admissions information
Additional requirements: GPA, GRE, letters of recommendation, and research alignment with faculty specializations are all considered for admission.
Undergraduate preparation assumed: Symon, Mechanics; Griffiths, Introduction to Electrodynamics; Griffiths, Quantum Mechanics.

TUITION

Tuition year 2018–19:
Tuition for in-state residents
  Full-time students: $11,090 annual
  Part-time students: $462 per credit
Tuition for out-of-state residents
  Full-time students: $22,650 annual
  Part-time students: $944 per credit
Credit hours per semester to be considered full-time: 12
Deferred tuition plan: No
Health insurance: Available at the cost of $1,174 per year.
Other academic fees: $75 application fee. $250 enrollment deposit. Various university fees.
Number of first-year students who received full tuition waivers: 9

Teaching Assistants, Research Assistants, and Fellowships
Number of first-year
  Teaching Assistants: 9
Average stipend per academic year
  Teaching Assistant: $18,500

FINANCIAL AID

Application deadlines
Fall admission:
U.S. students: February 15   *Int'l. students*: February 15
Spring admission:
U.S. students: November 15   *Int'l. students*: November 15

Loans
Loans are available for U.S. students.
Loans are not available for international students.
GAPSFAS application required: No
FAFSA application required: Yes

For further information

Address financial aid inquiries to: Student Financial Center, Campus Center G-26, 1400 Washington Avenue, Albany, NY 12222.

Phone: (518) 442-3202

E-mail: sfc@albany.edu

Financial aid website: http://www.albany.edu/studentservices

HOUSING

Availability of on-campus housing

Single students: No

Married students: No

Childcare Assistance: No

For further information

Address housing inquiries to: Residential Life, State University of New York at Albany, State Quad U-Lounge, 1400 Washington Avenue, Albany, NY 12222.

Phone: (518) 442-5875

E-mail: reslife@albany.edu

Housing aid website: http://www.albany.edu/housing/index.shtml

Table A—Faculty, Enrollments, and Degrees Granted

Research Specialty	2018–19 Faculty	Enrollment Fall 2018		Number of Degrees Granted 2017–18 (2018–19)		
		Master's	Doctorate	Master's	Terminal Master's	Doctorate
Biophysics	2	1	3	–	–	1
Computational Physics	1	–	6	–	–	1
Condensed Matter Physics	–	–	–	–(4)	–	–(6)
Optics	3	2	5	–	–	1(6)
Particles and Fields	3	4	12	–	–	1(6)
Solid State Physics	1	3	6	1(4)	–(5)	–(5)
Theoretical Physics	2	4	6	3(5)	1(3)	–(5)
Total	12	14	38	4(13)	1(8)	5(39)
Full-time Grad. Stud.	–	2	38	–	–	–
First-year Grad. Stud.	–	5	9	–	–	–

GRADUATE DEGREE REQUIREMENTS

Master's: Thirty graduate course credits, at least 24 on campus, including core, elective, and research courses, are required. Master's thesis or passage of comprehensive examination is required.

Doctorate: Sixty credit hours beyond the bachelor's degree, including core, elective, and research courses with at least two full-time semesters, are required. Transfer credit of up to 30 hours is allowed. Students are required to pass a written comprehensive examination, followed by an oral qualifying examination. Dissertation and dissertation defense examinations are required. Dissertation research may be conducted off-campus in approved programs.

Thesis: Thesis may be written in absentia.

SPECIAL EQUIPMENT, FACILITIES, OR PROGRAMS

Transmission electron microscope and ion beam laboratories study defects and other materials properties. EPR and Raman facilities are used to study biological physics. X-ray research includes applications to materials and medicine. Particle experimentalists are members of either the ATLAS collaboration at CERN or the LUX/LZ dark matter experiments. Robotics laboratory studies intelligent behaviors. Cooperative programs have been established with nearby General Electric Research and Development Center (Watervliet Arsenal, NY), State Public Health, and IBM Watson Research Laboratories.

FACULTY

Professor

Caticha, Ariel, Ph.D., California Institute of Technology, 1985. Foundations of physics, information physics. Fundamental problems in quantum, statistical, and gravitational physics.

Kuan, Tung-sheng, Ph.D., Cornell University, 1977. Materials science, electron microscopy.

Lanford, William A., Ph.D., University of Rochester, 1972. Materials science, thin films, ion beam analysis.

MacDonald, Carolyn A., Ph.D., Harvard University, 1986. Medical physics, optics (X-ray and visible).

Associate Professor

Earle, Keith, Ph.D., Cornell University, 1994. Biophysics, EPR spectroscopy, magnetic resonance.

Ernst, Jesse, Ph.D., University of Rochester, 1995. Experimental particle physics, machine learning.

Goyal, Philip, Ph.D., University of Cambridge, 2005. Information physics, foundations of quantum mechanics.

Jain, Vivek, Ph.D., University of Hawaii, 1988. Experimental particle physics, colliders.

Knuth, Kevin, Ph.D., University of Minnesota, 1995. Computational physics, foundations of physics, space physics (study of exoplanets), robotics.

Lunin, Oleg, Ph.D., Ohio State University, 2000. Theoretical particle physics, string theory.

Assistant Professor

Fotso, Herbert F., Ph.D., Louisiana State University, 2011. Theoretical condensed matter physics, quantum optics, computational physics.

Khmaladze, Alexander T., Ph.D., University of South Florida, 2008. Optics, biophysics, Raman spectroscopy.

Levy, Cecilia, Ph.D., University of Muenster, 2014. Experimental particle physics, dark matter searches.

Petruccelli, Jonathan, Ph.D., University of Rochester, 2010. Experimental and theoretical optics, computational imaging.

Robbins, Daniel G., Ph.D., University of Chicago, 2006. Theoretical particle physics, string theory.

Szydagis, Matthew M., Ph.D., University of Chicago, 2010. Experimental particle physics, dark matter searches.

Professor Emeritus

Alam, M. Sajjad, Ph.D., Indiana University, 1975.

Benenson, Raymond E., Ph.D., University of Wisconsin-Madison, 1955.

Inomata, Akira, Ph.D., Rensselaer Polytechnic Institute, 1964.

Kimball, John C., Ph.D., University of Chicago, 1969.

Marsh, Bruce B., Ph.D., University of Rochester, 1962.

Roth, Laura M., Ph.D., Radcliffe Institute for Advanced Study, 1957.

Scholes, Charles P., Ph.D., Yale University, 1969.

Scholz, Wilfried W., Ph.D., University of Freiburg, 1964.

DEPARTMENTAL RESEARCH SPECIALTIES AND STAFF

Theoretical

Computational Physics. Applications of computational methods and data analysis to condensed matter physics, optics, particle physics, and planetary science. Ernst, Fotso, Knuth, Petruccelli, Szydagis.

Condensed Matter Physics. Strongly correlated electron systems, high temperature superconductors. Fotso.

Cosmology & String Theory. String theory, conformal field theory, quantum gravity. Lunin, Robbins.

Information Physics. Foundations of quantum mechanics and statistical physics; extraction of information from complex data. Caticha, Earle, Goyal, Knuth.

Optics. Computational optical modeling and imaging, quantum optics. Fotso, MacDonald, Petruccelli.

Experimental

Biophysics. Applications of ESR, EPR, and Raman spectroscopy to study of bioinorganic molecules; medical applications of x-ray optics. Earle, Khmaladze, MacDonald.

Materials Science, Metallurgy. Thin films, ion beam analysis, electron microscopy. Kuan, Lanford.

Optics. Optics in visible and x-ray domains, laser physics, Raman spectroscopy. Khmaladze, MacDonald, Petruccelli.

Particles and Fields. Physics (beyond) Standard Model on ATLAS, dark matter searches on LUX/LZ, machine learning. Ernst, Jain, Levy, Szydagis.

View additional information about this department at www.gradschoolshopper.com. Check out the "Why Choose Us?" section, find out more about the department's culture and get links to social media networks.

STONY BROOK UNIVERSITY, STATE UNIVERSITY OF NEW YORK

DEPARTMENT OF PHYSICS AND ASTRONOMY

Stony Brook, New York 11794-3800
http://www.physics.sunysb.edu

General University Information
President: Samuel Stanley
Dean of Graduate School: Richard Gerrig
University website: http://www.stonybrook.edu
School Type: Public
Setting: Suburban
Total Faculty: 1,900
Total Graduate Faculty: 1,500
Total number of Students: 26,000
Total number of Graduate Students: 8,600

Department Information
Department Chairman: Prof. Axel Drees, Chair
Department Contact: Jacobus Verbaarschot, Graduate Program
  Director
  Total full-time faculty: 64
  Total number of full-time equivalent positions: 66
  Full-Time Graduate Students: 161
  Female Full-Time Graduate Students: 25
  First-Year Graduate Students: 28
  Female First-Year Students: 6
  Total Post Doctorates: 44

Department Address
100 Nicolls Road
Stony Brook, NY 11794-3800
Phone: (631) 632-8100
Fax: (631) 632-8176
E-mail: jacobus.verbaarschot@stonybrook.edu
Website: http://www.physics.sunysb.edu

ADMISSIONS

Admission Contact Information
Address admission inquiries to: Prof. Jacobus Verbaarschot, Director of Graduate Program, Department of Physics and Astronomy, Stony Brook University, NY 11794-3800
Phone: (631) 632-8123
E-mail: jacobus.verbaarschot@stonybrook.edu
Admissions website: http://graduate.physics.sunysb.edu

Application deadlines
Fall admission:
U.S. students: January 15   *Int'l. students*: January 15
Spring admission:
U.S. students: October 15   *Int'l. students*: October 15

Application fee
U.S. students: $100   *Int'l. students*: $100
Spring admission, contact the Director of Graduate Program first.

Admissions information
For Fall of 2018:
  Number of applicants: 575
  Number admitted: 89
  Number enrolled: 28

Admission requirements
Bachelor's degree requirements: Bachelor's degree in Physics
  or related area is required.
Minimum undergraduate GPA: 3.0

GRE requirements
The GRE is required.
  Quantitative score: 160
  Verbal score: 155
  Analytical score: 3.0
  Mean GRE score range (25th–75th percentile): 320-350
Used new GRE for Mean. It is the sum of verbal and quantitative.

Subjective GRE requirements
The Subjective GRE is required.
  Minimum accepted Advanced GRE score: 600
  Mean Advanced GRE score range (25th–75th percentile): 650-900
The Physics GRE is required but is not very important in most
  cases

TOEFL requirements
The TOEFL exam is required for students from non-English-
  speaking countries.
  PBT score: 600
  iBT score: 90
The Speaking score should be at least 19.

Other admissions information
Additional requirements: Numbers of students that were admitted, and enrolled include PhD students only, and Master students are not included.
Undergraduate preparation assumed: Typical undergraduate preparation includes courses in classical mechanics, electrodynamics, quantum mechanics, and statistical mechanics/thermal physics.

TUITION

Tuition year 2017–18:
Tuition for in-state residents
  Full-time students: $11,090 annual
  Part-time students: $462 per credit
Tuition for out-of-state residents
  Full-time students: $22,650 annual
  Part-time students: $944 per credit
Credit hours per semester to be considered full-time: 12
Deferred tuition plan: Yes
Health insurance: Available at the cost of $ 2822 per year.
Other academic fees: $ 848 per semester. Health insurance international students is $ 1470, and for TAs it is $ 424, both for the academic year.
Academic term: Semester
Number of first-year students who received full tuition waivers: 32

Teaching Assistants, Research Assistants, and Fellowships
Number of first-year
  Teaching Assistants: 26
  Research Assistants: 2
  Fellowship students: 1

Average stipend per academic year
Teaching Assistant: $23,000
Research Assistant: $28,000
Fellowship student: $33,000

FINANCIAL AID

Loans
Loans are available for U.S. students.
Loans are not available for international students.
GAPSFAS application required: No
FAFSA application required: Yes

For further information
Address financial aid inquiries to:
Financial aid website: http://www.stonybrook.edu/commcms/finaid/

HOUSING

Availability of on-campus housing
Single students: Yes
Married students: Yes
Childcare Assistance: Yes

For further information
Address housing inquiries to: Regina Lagrasta, Assistant Director, Residence Life, Room 138, Administration Building.
Housing aid website: http://studentaffairs.stonybrook.edu/res/index.html

Table A—Faculty, Enrollments, and Degrees Granted

Research Specialty	2018–19 Faculty	Enrollment Fall 2018		Number of Degrees Granted 2017–18 (2013–18)		
		Master's	Doctorate	Master's	Terminal Master's	Doctorate
Accelerator Physics	2	2	5	–	2(6)	–(3)
Astronomy	12	2	7	1	2(9)	1(5)
Atomic, Molecular, & Optical Physics	6	2	16	1	1(7)	3(9)
Computational Physics	4	2	5	–	2(4)	2(4)
Condensed Matter Physics	8	2	9	1	1(5)	2(20)
Cosmology	7	–	10	–	2(6)	2(15)
High Energy Physics	8	2	6	1	–(3)	2(9)
Nuclear Physics	13	2	24	–	2(8)	5(20)
Particles and Fields	6	2	6	1	–(1)	4(11)
Physical Biology	2	1	5	–	1(1)	–(6)
Statistical Mechanics	3	1	3	–	–(3)	1(5)
Non-specialized	–	54	57	6	–(7)	–
Total	71	73	150	11	11(60)	20(103)
Full-time Grad. Stud.	–	73	150	–	–	–
First-year Grad. Stud.	–	40	29	–	–	–

GRADUATE DEGREE REQUIREMENTS

Master's: Master of Science in Instrumentation (M.S.I.) requires a minimum of 2 years of study; one semester of teaching; minor project and Master's thesis. Master of Arts (M.A.) requires 30 graduate credits with average grade of B (GPA of 3.0) in approved program with satisfactory performance; either passing approved courses and exams or thesis is required; no residence or language requirements. Master of Arts in Teaching (M.A.T.) requires 41 graduate credits with 15 in physics, 20 in education and 6 in supervised teaching, as well as an approved teaching project. E-mail SPD@stonybrook.edu for more information.

Doctorate: Satisfactory performance in approved course program; successful completion of written comprehensive examination, dissertation, and dissertation examination. One year of teaching required. One year of residence required. No language requirements.

Other Degrees: In addition to the PhD degree in Physics, we offer a PhD degree in Physics with concentration in Astronomy and a PhD degree in Physics with concentration in Physical Biology.

SPECIAL EQUIPMENT, FACILITIES, OR PROGRAMS

The Department of Physics and Astronomy participates with other departments in programs in physical biology, chemical physics and medical physics. A physics student in one of these programs may do thesis research under the supervision of a faculty member in the Physics Graduate Program or in one of the cooperating departments.

The C. N. Yang Institute for Theoretical Physics carries out research in particle physics, nuclear physics, statistical mechanics, string and supergravity theory, and the Simons Center for Geometry and Physics focuses on mathematical physics and string theory.

The Laufer for Physical and Quantitative Biology is an interdisciplinary center that advances biology and medicine through discoveries in physics, mathematics and computational science. PhD students working with faculty in this center follow the Physics PhD program with Concentration in Physical Biology.

Cooperative programs are conducted at the nearby Brookhaven National Lab, including research at the National Synchrotron Light Source, and in the Center for Functional Nanomaterials.

The Center for Accelerator Science and Education (CASE) coordinates efforts in accelerator physics. Experiments in particle physics are carried out at the Relativistic Heavy Ion Collider (BNL), at Super-Kamiokande (Japan), and at the Large Hadron Collider (CERN).

The astronomy group makes regular use of various large optical telescopes, large millimeter wave telescopes and arrays, and space observatories. It has a partnership with the Caltech Palomar Observatory, and it is a member of the SMARTs consortium operating several telescopes at Cerro Tololo, Chile. tk;4Several faculty are affiliated with the New York Center for Computational Science NYCCS and use its 100 T flops supercomputer and other supercomputers for computational science.

Table B—Separately Budgeted Research Expenditures by Source of Support

Source of Support	Departmental Research	Physics-related Research Outside Department
Federal government	$22,570,979	
State/local government		
Non-profit organizations	$1,700,000	
Business and industry		
Other		
Total	$24,270,979	

Table C—Separately Budgeted Research Expenditures by Research Specialty

Research Specialty	No. of Grants	Expenditures ($)
Astronomy / Astrophysics (Experimental)	4	$496,976
Astronomy / Astrophysics (Theoretical)	5	$547,582
Atomic, Molecular, & Optical Physics	6	$1,565,696
Physical Biology (Theoretical)	1	$829,000
Condensed Matter Physics (Experimental)	4	$400,419
Condensed Matter Physics (Theoretical)	7	$859,745
Cosmology & String Theory (Theoretical)	3	$388,007
High Energy Physics (Experimental)	7	$12,288,405
Nuclear Physics (Experimental)	4	$1,814,369
Nuclear Physics (Theoretical)	5	$913,792
Particles and Fields (Theoretical)	2	$1,856,280
Accelerator Physics	8	$581,400
Statistical & Thermal Physics (Theoretical)	1	$29,308
Total	57	$22,570,979

FACULTY

Chair Professor

Zamolochikov, Alexander, Institute of Theoretical and Mathematical Physics. Moscow, 1978. *Particles and Fields, Statistical & Thermal Physics, Theoretical Physics*. Theoretical Physics.

Professor

Allen, Philip B., Ph.D., University of California, Berkeley, 1969. *Condensed Matter Physics*. Theoretical solid-state physics.

Alvarez-Gaume, Luis, Ph.D., Stony Brook University, 1981. Director of the Simons Center. *Cosmology & String Theory, Particles and Fields*. Field Theory, Cosmology.

Armitage, Philip J., Ph.D., Cambridge, 1996. *Astrophysics*. Theoretical Astrophysics.

Averin, Dmitrii V., Ph.D., Moscow State University, 1987. *Solid State Physics*. Solid-state theory.

Deshpande, Abhay, Ph.D., Yale University, 1995. Director of the Undergraduate Program. *Nuclear Physics*. Polarized photons, RHIC.

Dill, Ken, Ph.D., University of California, San Diego, 1978. Director of the Laufer Center. *Biophysics*. Protein structure; computational biophysics.

Drees, Axel, Ph.D., Heidelberg University, 1989. Chair. *Nuclear Physics*. Relativistic heavy ions.

Goldhaber, Alfred S., Ph.D., Princeton University, 1964. *Particles and Fields*. Theoretical physics; nuclear theory; particle physics.

Gonzalez-Garcia, Concha, Ph.D., University of Valencia, 1991. *Particles and Fields*. Theoretical physics.

Hemmick, Thomas, Ph.D., University of Rochester, 1989. Director of CASE. *Nuclear Physics*. Experimental relativistic heavy ion physics.

Hobbs, John, Ph.D., University of Chicago, 1991. *High Energy Physics*. Experimental high-energy physics.

Jung, Chang Kee, Ph.D., Indiana University, 1986. *High Energy Physics*. Experimental high-energy physics; neutrino physics.

Kharzeev, Dmitri, Ph.D., Moscow State University, 1990. *Particles and Fields*. Heavy ion physics and particle theory.

Koch, Peter M., Ph.D., Yale University, 1974. *Atomic, Molecular, & Optical Physics*. Atomic physics; chaos.

Komargodski, Zohar, Ph.D., Weizmann Institute of Science, 2008. *Particles and Fields*. Theoretical Physics.

Korepin, Vladimir, Ph.D., University of Leningrad, 1977. *Statistical & Thermal Physics*. Theoretical physics; quantum computing.

Kumar, Krishna S., Ph.D., Syracuse University, 1990. *Nuclear Physics*. Experimental nuclear and particle physics.

Lattimer, James M., Ph.D., University of Texas, 1976. *Astrophysics*. Nuclear astrophysics.

Likharev, Konstantin K., Ph.D., Moscow State University, 1969. *Condensed Matter Physics, Neuroscience/Neuro Physics*. Mesoscopic physics; neuroscience.

Litvinenko, Vladimir, Ph.D., Novosibirsk, 1989. *Physics of Beams*. Accelerator physics.

McCarthy, Robert L., Ph.D., University of California, Berkeley, 1971. *High Energy Physics*. Experimental high-energy physics.

McCoy, Barry M., Ph.D., Harvard University, 1967. *Statistical & Thermal Physics, Theoretical Physics*. Theoretical statistical mechanics.

Mendez, Emilio, Ph.D., Massachusetts Institute of Technology, 1979. Director of the Center for Functional Nanomaterials. *Condensed Matter Physics*. Experimental solid-state physics.

Metcalf, Harold J., Ph.D., Brown University, 1967. *Atomic, Molecular, & Optical Physics*. Experimental atomic physics; laser cooling.

Mihaly, Laszlo, Ph.D., Eotvos University, Budapest, 1977. *Condensed Matter Physics*. Experimental solid-state physics.

Misewich, James, Ph.D., Cornell University, 1984. Optics, nanomaterials, ultrafast studies, and surface science.

Nekrasov, Nikita, Ph.D., Princeton University, 1996. Mathematical Physics.

Perna, Rosalba, Ph.D., Harvard University, 1968. *Astrophysics*. High-energy astrophysics.

Rastelli, Leonardo, Ph.D., Massachusetts Institute of Technology, 2000. *Cosmology & String Theory*. Theoretical physics.

Rijssenbeek, Michael, Ph.D., University of Amsterdam, 1974. *High Energy Physics*. Experimental high-energy physics.

Roček, Martin, Ph.D., Harvard University, 1979. *Cosmology & String Theory, Particles and Fields*. Theoretical physics.

Shrock, Robert, Ph.D., Princeton University, 1975. *Particles and Fields*. Theoretical physics; string theory.

Shuryak, Edward, Ph.D., Novosibirsk, USSR, 1974. *Nuclear Physics, Particles and Fields*. Nuclear theory, Quark gluon plasma, instantons.

Siegel, Warren, Ph.D., University of California, Berkeley, 1977. *Cosmology & String Theory, Particles and Fields*. Theoretical physics.

Stephens, Peter W., Ph.D., Massachusetts Institute of Technology, 1978. *Condensed Matter Physics*. Experimental solid-state physics; powder X-ray scattering.

Sterman, George, Ph.D., University of Maryland, 1974. Director of the Yang Institute for Theoretical Physics. *Particles and Fields, Theoretical Physics*. Theoretical Physics.

van Nieuwenhuizen, Peter, Ph.D., Utrecht, 1971. *Cosmology & String Theory, Particles and Fields*. Theoretical physics; supergravity.

Verbaarschot, Jacobus J., Ph.D., University of Utrecht, 1982. Graduate Program Director. *Nuclear Physics, Particles and Fields, Theoretical Physics*. Theoretical physics, strong interactions, random matrix theory.

Walter, Frederick M., Ph.D., University of California, Berkeley, 1981. *Astronomy*. Star Formation; Chromospheres and Coronae.

Weinacht, Thomas, Ph.D., University of Michigan, 2000. *Atomic, Molecular, & Optical Physics*. Experimental atomic physics.

Zahed, Ismail, Ph.D., Massachusetts Institute of Technology, 1983. *Nuclear Physics, Particles and Fields, Theoretical Physics*. Theoretical nuclear physics.

Associate Professor

Abanov, Alexandre, Ph.D., University of Chicago, 1997. Deputy Director of the Simons Center. *Condensed Matter Physics, Statistical & Thermal Physics, Theoretical Physics*. Theoretical condensed matter.

Calder, Alan, Ph.D., Vanderbilt University, 1997. *Astrophysics.* Computational astrophysics.

Dawber, Matthew, Ph.D., University of Cambridge, 2003. *Condensed Matter Physics.* Experimental solid-state physics.

Du, Xu, Ph.D., University of Florida, 2004. *Condensed Matter Physics.* Experimental condensed matter, graphene.

Essig, Rouven, Ph.D., Rutgers University, 2008. *Cosmology & String Theory, Particles and Fields.* Theoretical particle physics, cosmology, dark matter.

Fernandez-Serra, Maria Victoria, Ph.D., University of Cambridge, 2005. *Condensed Matter Physics.* Computational condensed matter.

Koda, Jin, Ph.D., University of Tokyo, 2002. *Astronomy.* Astronomy.

McGrew, Clark, Ph.D., University of California, Irvine, 1994. *High Energy Physics.* Experimental high-energy; neutrino physics.

Meade, Patrick, Ph.D., Cornell University, 2006. *Particles and Fields.* Theoretical Physics, Particle Phenomenology.

Schneble, Dominik, Ph.D., University of Konstanz, 2002. *Atomic, Molecular, & Optical Physics.* Experimental atomic physics.

Teaney, Derek, Ph.D., Stony Brook University, 2001. *Nuclear Physics, Particles and Fields.* Theoretical nuclear physics., relativistic heavy ion physics.

Tsybychev, Dmitri, Ph.D., University of Florida, 2004. *High Energy Physics.* Experimental high-energy physics.

Wei, Tzu-Chieh, Ph.D., University of Illinois at Urbana-Champaign, 2004. *Particles and Fields.* Quantum computing.

Zingale, Michael, Ph.D., University of Chicago, 2000. *Astrophysics.* Computational astrophysics.

Assistant Professor

Allison, Thomas, Ph.D., University of California at Berkeley, 2010. Atomic, molecular, and optical experiment.

Farr, Will M., Ph.D., Massachusetts Institute of Technology, 2002. *Astrophysics.* Computational Astrophysics.

Figueroa, Eden, Ph.D., University of Calgary/University of Konstanz, 2008. Atomic, molecular and optical experiment.

Giacinto, Piacquadio, Ph.D., Universit, 2010. *High Energy Physics.* Experimental High Energy Physics.

Kiryluk, Joanna, Ph.D., University of Warsaw, 2000. *Nuclear Physics, Particles and Fields.* Neutrino and Heavy Ion Physics.

Liu, Mengkun, Ph.D., Boston University, 2012. *Condensed Matter Physics.* Experimental Condensed Matter Physics.

Loverde, Marilena, Ph.D., Columbia University, 2009. *Astronomy, Astrophysics, Cosmology & String Theory.* Cosmology.

Sehgal, Neelima, Ph.D., Rutgers University, 2008. *Astronomy, Cosmology & String Theory.* Dark matter and cosmology.

Syritsyn, Sergey, Ph.D., MIT, 2010. *Nuclear Physics, Particles and Fields.* Lattice QCD.

Vafaei-Najafabadi, Navid, Ph.D., UCLA, 2016. *Physics of Beams.* Experimental Accelerator Physics.

von der Linden, Anja, Ph.D., Ludwig Maximilian University, Munich, 2007. *Cosmology & String Theory.* Cosmology.

Wilking, Michael, Ph.D., University of Colorado, Boulder, 2009. *High Energy Physics.* Neutrino Physics.

Emeritus

Yang, Chen Ning, Ph.D., University of Chicago, 1984. *Particles and Fields.* Theoretical physics.

Research Professor

da Via, Cinazia, Ph.D., University of Glasgow, 1997. *High Energy Physics.* Experimental high Energy Phytsics.

Grannis, Paul D., Ph.D., University of California, Berkeley, 1965. *High Energy Physics.* Experimental high-energy physics.

Nomerotski, Andre, Ph.D., University of Padua, 1996. *Astrophysics.* Space Telescopes.

Semenov, Vasili, Ph.D., Moscow State University, 1975. *Condensed Matter Physics, Nano Science and Technology.*

Research Associate Professor

Swesty, Douglas, Ph.D., Stony Brook Univer, 1993. *Astrophysics.* Computational Astrophysics.

Distinguished Adjunct Professor

Ben-Zvi, Ilan, Ph.D., Weizmann Institute of Science, 1970. *Physics of Beams.* Accelerator Physics.

Adjunct Professor

Bergeman, Thomas, Ph.D., Harvard University, 1971. *Atomic, Molecular, & Optical Physics.* Theoretical Atomic Physics.

Eisaman, Matthew, Ph.D., Harvard University, 2006. *Condensed Matter Physics.*

Gu, Genda, Ph.D., Harbin Institute of Technology, 1989. *Accelerator.* Accelerator Physics.

Hao, Yue, Ph.D., Indiana University, 2008. *Physics of Beams.*

Johnson, Christopher J., Ph.D., University of California San Diego, 2011. *Atomic, Molecular, & Optical Physics.*

Karsch, Frithjof, Ph.D., Bielefeld University, 1982. Professor at the University of Bielefeld. *Particles and Fields.* Lattice gauge theory.

Kayran, Dmitry, Ph.D., Novosibirsk State University, 2001. *Physics of Beams.* Accelerator Physics.

Ku, Wei, Ph.D., University of Tennessee, 2000. *Condensed Matter Physics.* Theoretical condensed matter.

Petrovic, Cedomir, Ph.D., Florida State University, 2000. *Condensed Matter Physics.*

Takai, Helio, Ph.D., University of Rio de Janeiro, 1986. *High Energy Physics.* Experimental particle physics.

Venugopalan, Raju, Ph.D., Stony Brook University, 1992. *Nuclear Physics, Particles and Fields.* Theoretical Nuclear Physics.

Zhu, Yimei, Ph.D., Nagoya University, 1987. *Optics.* Microscopy.

Affiliate Professor

Jia, Jangyong, Ph.D., Stony Brook University, 2003. *Nuclear Physics.* Experimental Relativistic Nuclear Physics.

Lacey, Roy, Ph.D., Stony Brook University, 1987. *Nuclear Physics.* Relativistic heavy ion physics.

Mujica-Parodi, Lilia, Ph.D., Columbia U, 1998. *Biophysics.* Biomedical Engineering.

Wang, Jin, Ph.D., University of Illinois, 1991. Biological Physics.

DEPARTMENTAL RESEARCH SPECIALTIES AND STAFF

Theoretical

Accelerator Physics. Litvinenko.

Astrophysics. Cosmology, galaxy formation, and evolution. Nuclear astrophysics, neutrino astrophysics. Neutron stars; equation of state of dense matter; stellar collapse. Dark matter, dark energy. Armitage, Calder, Essig, Lattimer, Sehgal, Zingale.

Atomic and Molecular Physics. Theory of ultracold quantum gases, non-linear optics. Bose-Einstein condensation, Ultrafast processes. Bergeman, Weinacht.

Condensed Matter Physics. Superconductivity; electron-phonon interactions; magnetic properties; optical properties; quantum computing, Coulomb blockade, quantum Hall effect, density-functional theory; properties of water; low-dimensional systems. Abanov, Allen, Averin, Fernandez-Serra, Likharev, Semenov.

Nuclear Physics. Quantum Chomo Dynamics; Relativistic Heavy Ion Collisions; Lattice QCD; Nucleon-nucleon interaction; meson exchange currents and other mesonic effects in nuclei; effective interactions in nuclei and nuclear matter; heavy ion reactions; Fermi liquid theory; variational and extended semi-classical models of large systems; studies of dense nuclear matter; random matrix theory. Goldhaber, Karsch, Kharzeev, Shuryak, Syritsyn, Teaney, Verbaarschot, Zahed.

Physical Biology. Protein structure; computational biophysics; biomolecular networks; neuroscience. Dill, Likharev, Mujica-Parodi, Wang.

Statistical Mechanics. Mathematical studies of solvable models; relation between statistical mechanics and field theory; Ising models; lattice gauge fields; random matrix theory. Abanov, Dill, Komargodski, Korepin, McCoy, Nekrasov, Verbaarschot, Wang, Wei, Zamolochikov.

String Theory and Cosmology. Quantum theory of gravitation; supergravity; supersymmetry; superstrings; cosmology, dark matter. Alvarez-Gaume, Essig, Komargodski, Loverde, Sehgal, von der Linden.

Theoretical Particle Physics. Quantum field theory; unified gauge theory of weak, electromagnetic, and strong interactions; general gauge theory; nonperturbative effects in gauge theories; perturbative QCD; QCD at finite temperature and density. Alvarez-Gaume, Essig, Goldhaber, Gonzalez-Garcia, Karsch, Kharzeev, Meade, Nekrasov, Roček, Shrock, Shuryak, Siegel, Sterman, van Nieuwenhuizen, Venugopalan, Verbaarschot, Zahed.

Theoretical Physics. The largest theoretical physics group at Stony Brook is the Yang Institute for Theoretical Physics. About the same number of theoretical physicists work in the physics department on condensed matter physics, astro-physics, nuclear physics, particle physics and statistical mechanics. Abanov, Allen, Alvarez-Gaume, Averin, Bergeman, Calder, Dill, Essig, Fernandez-Serra, Goldhaber, Gonzalez-Garcia, Karsch, Kharzeev, Komargodski, Korepin, Ku, Lattimer, Likharev, Litvinenko, Loverde, McCoy, Meade, Nekrasov, Perna, Rastelli, Roček, Sehgal, Shrock, Shuryak, Siegel, Sterman, Syritsyn, Teaney, van Nieuwenhuizen, Verbaarschot, von der Linden, Wang, Wei, Yang, Zahed, Zamolochikov, Zingale.

Experimental

Accelerator Physics. Ben-Zvi, Hao, Litvinenko, Vafaei-Najafabadi.

Astronomy. Cosmology; galactic structure and evolution; interstellar molecular clouds; quasar absorption lines; stellar astronomy; chromospheres; coronae; compact objects; star formation. Pre-main sequence objects; high mass star formation; Exoplanets. Koda, Nomerotski, Sehgal, von der Linden, Walter.

Atomic, Molecular, & Optical Physics. Coherent control of molecules and atoms with tailored, ultrafast laser pulses. Cooling, trapping, and laser spectroscopy of atoms. Ultracold quantum gases. Quantum chaos studies with microwave systems and driven atoms. Allison, Figueroa, Johnson, Metcalf, Schneble, Weinacht.

Condensed Matter Physics. Superconductivity; Josephson effect; X-ray scattering; single electronics; magnetic flux quantum devices; quantum wells, fractional quantum Hall effect; optical spectroscopy, ferroelectrics; graphene; powder X-ray scattering. Dawber, Du, Eisaman, Likharev, Liu, Mendez, Mihaly, Misewich, Petrovic, Semenov, Stephens, Zhu.

High Energy Physics. Particle interactions in high energy collisions; properties of the top and bottom quarks and electroweak bosons; studies of the strong interaction; search for new particles. Rare kaon decays. Neutrino oscillations; Study of the Higgs boson. da Via, Giacinto, Grannis, Hobbs, Jung, Kiryluk, McCarthy, McGrew, Rijssenbeek, Takai, Tsybychev, Wilking.

Nuclear Physics. Relativistic heavy ion collisions; properties of quark-gluon plasma; polarized protons. Deshpande, Drees, Hemmick, Kiryluk, Kumar.

SYRACUSE UNIVERSITY

DEPARTMENT OF PHYSICS

Syracuse, New York 13244-1130
http://physics.syr.edu/

General University Information
Chancellor: Kent Syverud
Dean of Graduate School: Peter Vanable
University website: http://www.syracuse.edu
School Type: Private
Setting: Urban
Total Faculty: 1,757
Total Graduate Faculty: 1,757
Total number of Students: 21,970
Total number of Graduate Students: 6,752

Department Information
Department Chairman: Prof. Eric A. Schiff, Chair
Department Contact: Physics Main Office Staff, Physics Main
   Office Staff
   Total full-time faculty: 29
   Total number of full-time equivalent positions: 28
   Full-Time Graduate Students: 78
   Female Full-Time Graduate Students: 15
   First-Year Graduate Students: 18
   Female First-Year Students: 3
   Total Post Doctorates: 20

Department Address
201 Physics Building
Syracuse, NY 13244-1130
Phone: (315) 443-3901
Fax: (315) 443-9103
E-mail: phyadmin@syr.edu
Website: http://physics.syr.edu/

ADMISSIONS

Admission Contact Information
Address admission inquiries to: Department of Physics at Syr-
   acuse University, C/O:Graduate Coordinator, 201 Physics
   Building, Syracuse, NY 13244
Phone: (315) 443-3901
E-mail: graduate@phy.syr.edu
Admissions website: http://physics.syr.edu/graduate/apply.html

Application deadlines
Fall admission:
U.S. students: January 15   *Int'l. students*: January 15

Application fee
U.S. students: $75   *Int'l. students*: $75
Late applications are accepted until all available slots are filled.

Admissions information
For Fall of 2017:
   Number of applicants: 134
   Number admitted: 51
   Number enrolled: 15

Admission requirements
Bachelor's degree requirements: Bachelor's degree in physics
   is recommended but not required.
Minimum undergraduate GPA: 3.0

GRE requirements
The GRE is required.
   Quantitative score: 147
   Verbal score: 140
   Analytical score: 2.5

Subjective GRE requirements
The Subjective GRE is required.
   Minimum accepted Advanced GRE score: 560

TOEFL requirements
The TOEFL exam is required for students from non-English-
   speaking countries.
   PBT score: 600
   iBT score: 90

Other admissions information
Additional requirements: Three Letters of recommendation and
   personal statement.
Undergraduate preparation assumed: At least one semester of
   each: Classical Mechanics, Quantum Mechanics and Electromagnetic Theory (see e.g. textbooks by Griffiths).

TUITION

Tuition year 2017–18:
   Full-time students: $1,500 per credit
   Part-time students: $1,500 per credit
Almost all department graduate students have their tuition cov-
   ered by a graduate assistantship, except in rare cases.
Credit hours per semester to be considered full-time: 9
Deferred tuition plan: Yes
Health insurance: Yes, $1,672.00.
Other academic fees: $836 student fees.
Academic term: Semester
Number of first-year students who received full tuition waivers: 17

Teaching Assistants, Research Assistants, and Fellowships
Number of first-year
   Teaching Assistants: 12
   Fellowship students: 2
Average stipend per academic year
   Teaching Assistant: $24,250
   Research Assistant: $24,250
   Fellowship student: $25,290

FINANCIAL AID

Application deadlines
Fall admission:
U.S. students: January 15   *Int'l. students*: January 15

Loans
Loans are available for U.S. students.
Loans are available for international students.
GAPSFAS application required: Yes
FAFSA application required: Yes

For further information

Address financial aid inquiries to: Financial Aid Office, 200 Bowne Hall, Syracuse, NY 13244-1140.
Phone: (315) 443-1513
E-mail: finmail@syr.edu
Financial aid website: http://financialaid.syr.edu

HOUSING

Availability of on-campus housing

Single students: No
Married students: No

For further information

Address housing inquiries to: Off-Campus and Commuter Services, 754 Ostrom Avenue, Syracuse, NY 13244.
Phone: (315) 443-5489
E-mail: offcampus@syr.edu
Housing aid website: http://occs.syr.edu/

Table A—Faculty, Enrollments, and Degrees Granted

Research Specialty	2016–2017 Faculty	Enrollment Fall 2016		Number of Degrees Granted 2015–2016 (2008–16)		
		Master's	Doctorate	Master's	Terminal Master's	Doctorate
Astrophysics	1	–	2	1(5)	–(1)	–(3)
Biophysics	4	–	2	–(3)	–(1)	1(12)
Experimental Condensed Matter Physics	4	–	10	–(5)	–(3)	1(10)
Experimental High Energy Physics	7	–	11	1(1)	–	3(13)
First Year/Undecided	–	1	17	1(12)	1(12)	–
Medium Energy Physics	1	–	2	–(2)	–	–(2)
Relativity & Gravitation	3	–	10	1(4)	–(1)	2(9)
Theoretical Condensed Matter Physics	5	–	14	–(5)	–(2)	3(17)
Theoretical Particle Physics & Cosmology	5	–	9	1(1)	–	–(16)
Total	30	1	77	3(38)	1(20)	10(82)
Full-time Grad. Stud.	–	–	77	–	–	–
First-year Grad. Stud.	–	1	16	–	–	–

GRADUATE DEGREE REQUIREMENTS

Master's: Minimum of one year in residence is required. A student admitted to graduate work in the department must take the comprehensive examination. The Master's degree can be achieved in one of three ways: (1) 24 hours of coursework including a thesis, (2) 30 hours of coursework including a minor problem and passing the qualifying examination, or (3) 36 hours of coursework and passing the qualifying examination. A "B" average in coursework must be maintained to be eligible for a degree. There is no foreign language requirement.

Doctorate: Satisfactory performance in a course program approved by the student's research committee, which may include courses taken for the M.S. degree. Students must pass a written qualifying examination and a preliminary oral research examination. Students must write and defend a thesis on significant original research. There is no foreign language requirement. A total of 48 credits are required for the degree, maintaining at least a "B" average.

Thesis: Thesis may be written in absentia.

SPECIAL EQUIPMENT, FACILITIES, OR PROGRAMS

The department is a strong participant in the Syracuse Biomaterials Institute of Syracuse University and has a world leading Soft Matter Program. The high energy physics group is the major US group involved in the LHCb project at CERN in Geneva. The gravitational wave group is extremely strong and includes the past spokesperson for the collaboration and leading experimentalists and data analysts in the LIGO Scientific Collaboration. The physics research laboratories include a number of clean and shielded rooms, several advanced cryostats served by a helium liquefier, advanced quantum optical equipment, laboratory equipment designed to simulate interstellar chemical reactions, high energy particle detector construction facilities, neutrino detector technology testbeds, excellent microscopes for biophysics work, and high speed cameras and related equipment for soft matter physics. The Department of Physics also hosts the University's Surface Imaging Laboratory, with atomic force and electron microscopes. Students also travel to a number of national facilities, including the Laser Interferometer Gravitational Wave Observatory (LIGO), Jefferson National Laboratory, and to the Cornell NanoScale Science Facility.

Table B—Separately Budgeted Research Expenditures by Source of Support

Source of Support	Departmental Research	Physics-related Research Outside Department
Federal government	$7,004,649	
State/local government		
Non-profit organizations	$216,507	
Business and industry		
Other		
Total	$7,221,156	

Table C—Separately Budgeted Research Expenditures by Research Specialty

Research Specialty	No. of Grants	Expenditures ($)
Astrophysics	1	$244,729
Biophysics	2	$348,975
Experimental Condensed Matter Physics	9	$1,555,711
Theoretical Condensed Matter Physics	11	$1,171,978
Experimental High Energy Physics	10	$1,544,003
Theoretical Particle Physics & Cosmology	4	$516,471
Medium Energy Physics	1	$426,868
Relativity & Gravitation	9	$1,357,858
Total	47	$7,166,593

FACULTY

Distinguished University Professor

Marchetti, M. Cristina, Ph.D., University of Florida, 1982. Associate Director of Syracuse Biomaterials Institute; William R. Kenan, Jr. Professor. *Biophysics, Condensed Matter Physics, Fluids, Rheology, Statistical & Thermal Physics*. Theoretical condensed-matter physics.

Stone, Sheldon, Ph.D., University of Rochester, 1972. *High Energy Physics, Particles and Fields*. Experimental particle physics.

Chair Professor

Bowick, Mark, Ph.D., California Institute of Technology, 1983. *Condensed Matter Physics*. Theoretical condensed-matter physics.

Brown, Duncan, Ph.D., University of Wisconsin-Milwaukee, 2004. Graduate program director. *Astrophysics, Computational Physics, Relativity & Gravitation*. Theoretical astrophysics; relativity.

Saulson, Peter, Ph.D., Princeton University, 1981. Martin A. Pomerantz '37 Professor of Physics. *Relativity & Gravitation*. Experimental relativity and astrophysics.

Professor

Artuso, Marina, Ph.D., Northwestern University, 1986. *High Energy Physics, Particles and Fields*. Experimental elementary particles and fields.

Blusk, Steven, Ph.D., University of Pittsburgh, 1995. *High Energy Physics, Particles and Fields*. Experimental elementary particles physics.

Catterall, Simon, Ph.D., University of Oxford, 1989. Associate Chair. *Computational Physics, Particles and Fields, Theoretical Physics*. Theoretical elementary particles physics; computational physics.

Middleton, Alan, Ph.D., Princeton University, 1990. Department Chair. *Applied Mathematics, Computational Physics, Condensed Matter Physics, Statistical & Thermal Physics*. Theoretical condensed-matter physics; computational physics.

Movileanu, Liviu, Ph.D., University of Bucharest, 1997. Member of Syracuse Biomaterials Institute. *Biophysics, Condensed Matter Physics*. Experimental biophysics.

Plourde, Britton, Ph.D., University of Illinois at Urbana-Champaign, 2000. *Condensed Matter Physics, Low Temperature Physics, Nano Science and Technology, Quantum Foundations*. Experimental condensed-matter physics.

Rosenzweig, Carl, Ph.D., Harvard University, 1972. *Particles and Fields*. Theoretical elementary particles and fields physics.

Schiff, Eric, Ph.D., Cornell University, 1979. *Condensed Matter Physics, Solar Physics, Solid State Physics*. Experimental condensed-matter physics; solar energy.

Skwarnicki, Tomasz, Ph.D., Inst. of Nuclear Physics, Krakow, 1986. Chair of Graduate Admissions. *High Energy Physics, Particles and Fields*. Experimental elementary particles physics.

Souder, Paul A., Ph.D., Princeton University, 1971. *Nuclear Physics, Particles and Fields*. Experimental elementary particles and fields physics; medium energy.

Vidali, Gianfranco, Ph.D., Pennsylvania State University, 1982. *Astrophysics, Condensed Matter Physics, Surface Physics*. Laboratory astrophysics and surface science.

Associate Professor

Ballmer, Stefan, Ph.D., Massachusetts Institute of Technology, 2006. *Relativity & Gravitation*. Theoretical physics; gravitational waves.

Hubisz, Jay, Ph.D., Cornell University, 2006. Undergraduate program director. *Cosmology & String Theory, High Energy Physics, Particles and Fields*. Theoretical particle physics and cosmology.

LaHaye, Matthew, Ph.D., University of Maryland, College Park, 2005. *Condensed Matter Physics, Nano Science and Technology*. Experimental condensed-matter physics; nanomechanics.

Laiho, John, Ph.D., Princeton University, 2004. *Computational Physics, Particles and Fields, Theoretical Physics*. Theoretical elementary particle physics; Lattice QCD.

Manning, M. Lisa, Ph.D., University of California, Santa Barbara, 2008. *Biophysics, Condensed Matter Physics, Fluids, Rheology, Statistical & Thermal Physics*. Soft condensed matter; biophysics; granular materials; glasses.

Schwarz, Jennifer, Ph.D., Harvard University, 2002. *Biophysics, Condensed Matter Physics, Statistical & Thermal Physics*. Theoretical condensed-matter physics.

Soderberg, Mitchell, Ph.D., University of Michigan, 2000. *High Energy Physics, Particles and Fields*. Experimental elementary particles physics: neutrinos.

Watson, Scott, Ph.D., Brown University, 2005. *Cosmology & String Theory, Particles and Fields*. Particle physics; cosmology.

Assistant Professor

Patteson, Alison E., Ph.D., University of Pennsylvania, Philadelphia, 2016. *Biophysics, Condensed Matter Physics*. Nonequilibrium dynamics of bacterial suspensions, Cytoskeletal polymers in animal cell migration, Engineering microfluidic technologies for cell culture assays, Rheology of active cellular materials.

Paulsen, Joseph, Ph.D., University of Chicago, 2013. *Condensed Matter Physics*. Surface-tension driven flows, memories in disordered materials, and elasticity and geometry of this sheets.

Rudolph, Matthew, Ph.D., Massachusetts Institute of Technology, 2011. *High Energy Physics*. Experimental particle physics, searches for new physics with precision measurements at the Large Hadron Collider, and hardware and software development for high energy physics.

Whittington, Denver, Ph.D., Indiana University, 2012. *High Energy Physics, Particles and Fields*. Experimental elementary particles physics: neutrinos.

Research Professor

Wang, Jianchun, Ph.D., Massachusetts Institute of Technology, 1997. *High Energy Physics, Particles and Fields*. Experimental elementary particles physics.

Research Assistant Professor

Holmes, Richard, Ph.D., University of Maryland, 1985. *Nuclear Physics, Particles and Fields*. Experimental elementary particles physics.

Mountain, Raymond, Ph.D., University of Notre Dame, 1992. *High Energy Physics, Particles and Fields*. Experimental elementary particles physics.

Teaching Assistant Professor

Freeman, Walter, Ph.D., University of Arizona, 2011. *Particles and Fields, Physics and other Science Education*. Lattice particle physics, educational research.

DEPARTMENTAL RESEARCH SPECIALTIES AND STAFF

Theoretical

Biophysics. Collective behavior of biological molecules, especially actins and motor proteins; interaction of living cells to form structure; pattern formation of active material; rheology of biological tissue. Bowick, Manning, Marchetti, Schwarz.

Computational Physics. Gravitational-wave data analysis and source modeling; grid computing; connections between algorithms and physical principles; study of condensed-matter order and optimal distributions on curved interfaces; analysis of phase transitions and phase structure in disordered systems; simulations of lattice quantum field theories; numerical simulations on parallel computers; technicolor and supersymmetric theories; models beyond Standard Model Physics. Bowick, Brown, Catterall, Laiho, Middleton.

Condensed Matter Physics. Soft condensed-matter physics; statistical mechanics; nonequilibrium dynamics including two-dimensional matter, collective behavior of biological molecules, interaction of living cells, jamming in granular materials, superconductors, hysteresis in magnets, colloidal particles, topological defects, glassy materials, networks, and relationship between algorithms and physics. Bowick, Manning, Marchetti, Middleton, Schwarz.

Cosmology & String Theory. Theoretical models of dark and cosmic acceleration; inflation and alternatives; origin and evolution of cosmological structures. Catterall, Hubisz, Watson.

Particles and Fields. Quantum gravity; supersymmetry; renormalization theory; chiral symmetries; monopoles and dyons in curved space-time; noncommutative geometry; random surfaces, electroweak theory; quantum chromodynamics; general quantum field theory; constrained field theories; geometric quantization; phenomenological particle dynamics; simulations of lattice QCD; supersymmetric field theories on space-time lattices; quark gluon plasma. Particle cosmology. Theories with extra dimensions. Simulations of lattice quantum field theories; technicolor and supersymmetric theories; holographic models of strings; models beyond Standard Model physics. Catterall, Hubisz, Laiho, Rosenzweig, Watson.

Experimental

Astrophysics. Laboratory studies of physical and chemical processes occurring in the interstellar medium and in planetary atmospheres, including formation of molecular hydrogen and hydrogenation and oxidation reaction on interstellar and/or planetary dust grain analogs. Vidali.

Biophysics. Single-molecule biophysics; membrane biophysics; bionanotechnology and biosensors; protein design; development of new optical technologies; photosensory transduction in microorganisms; bioinformatics; self-organized beating of cilia; phylogenetics and molecular clocks. Movileanu, Patteson.

Condensed Matter Physics. Much of the activity in this area is described under low-temperature physics and under solar physics. Additionally, soft condensed matter physics: tabletop experiments studying nonlinear and emergent behaviors in soft systems; examples include the wrinkling, crumpling, and folding of thin elastic sheets, and the arrangements of solid particles in a sludge. These scenarios feature soft, easily deformed materials that are common in nature and industry. The overarching goal is to uncover the fundamental principles that govern their behavior when they are pushed far away from the low-energy or spatially-uniform states that they prefer. LaHaye, Paulsen, Plourde, Schiff.

High Energy Physics. Experimental studies of the fundamental electroweak and strong interactions as manifested by the decays of beauty and charm quarks and the search for exotic particles; b & c quark decays are studied at the LHCb experiment at the CERN LHC hadron collider Geneva, Switzerland, concentrating on rare and CP violating decays; searches for exotic particle production, including unusual decays of the Higgs boson, are also done using LHCb; study of nucleon structure, including spin and quark components carried out at JLab; R&D into advanced silicon micro-pattern detectors, such as pixel sensors, and their related readout electronics. Members of the group have discovered several new particles, including the B, Ds, and Y(1D); made the first measurements of several very important decay modes of these objects; and is also starting an effort in neutrino physics. Artuso, Blusk, Holmes, Mountain, Skwarnicki, Soderberg, Souder, Stone, Wang, Whittington.

Low Temperature Physics. Quantum coherent superconducting circuits; measurement and coupling of circuits for quantum computing; vortex dynamics in nanofabricated thin-film devices; superconducting microwave resonant circuits; nanoelectromechanical systems (NEMS); quantum dynamics of mechanical systems; sensitive environmental gas and biosensors; measurements at millikelvin temperatures. LaHaye, Plourde.

Nano Science and Technology. Much of the activity in this area is described under low-temperature physics (for example nanoscopic mechanical systems) and under biophysics (nanopore technology). LaHaye, Movileanu, Plourde.

Nuclear Physics. Medium-energy physics: use of spin degrees of freedom to study quantum chromodynamics and the Standard Model at low energies. Experiments are under way at the Thomas Jefferson National Accelerator Facility (JLab). Holmes, Souder.

Relativity & Gravitation. Gravitational-wave detection and astrophysics: searches for gravitational waves using the Laser Interferometer Gravitational Wave Observatory (LIGO); commissioning and technology development for advanced gravitational wave detectors; gravitational wave source modeling and phenomenology; developing tests of general relativity using gravitational waves. Ballmer, Brown, Saulson.

Solar Physics. Electronic and optical properties of unconventional semiconductors (e.g., amorphous silicon, porous titania, and silicon); solar cell device physics; thin-film growth (plasma, hot-wire); hybrid organic-inorganic semiconductor devices; v surface physics (i.e., structure, kinetics, dynamics, and reactions). Schiff.

View additional information about this department at www.gradschoolshopper.com. Check out the "Why Choose Us?" section, find out more about the department's culture and get links to social media networks.

UNIVERSITY AT BUFFALO, THE STATE UNIVERSITY OF NEW YORK

DEPARTMENT OF PHYSICS

Buffalo, New York 14260-1500
http://www.physics.buffalo.edu

General University Information
President: Satish K. Tripathi
Dean of Graduate School: Graham Hammill
University website: http://www.buffalo.edu
School Type: Public
Setting: Suburban
Total Faculty: 2,533
Total Graduate Faculty: 1,550
Total number of Students: 30,648
Total number of Graduate Students: 9,445

Department Information
Department Chairman: Prof. Hong Luo, Chair
Department Contact: Nicole D. Pannullo, Assistant to the Chair
  Total full-time faculty: 26
  Total number of full-time equivalent positions: 26
  Full-Time Graduate Students: 92
  Female Full-Time Graduate Students: 16
  First-Year Graduate Students: 19
  Female First-Year Students: 2
  Total Post-Doctorates: 8

Department Address
Fronczak Hall 239
North Campus
Buffalo, NY 14260-1500
Phone: (716) 645-2007
Fax: (716) 645-2507
E-mail: physicsoffice@buffalo.edu
Website: http://www.physics.buffalo.edu

ADMISSIONS

Admission Contact Information
Address admission inquiries to: Director of Graduate Studies, Physics Department, Fronczak Hall 239, Buffalo, NY 14260-1500
Phone: (716) 645-2007
E-mail: ubphysics@buffalo.edu
Admissions website: http://www.physics.buffalo.edu/graduate.html

Application deadlines
Fall admission:
U.S. students: February 1   *Int'l. students*: February 1

Application fee
U.S. students: $75   *Int'l. students*: $75
For consideration of fellowship awards and assistantships, an application and supporting materials must be completed and officially submitted by January 1, 2016. For Frequently Asked Questions (FAQs), refer to http://www.physics.buffalo.edu/graduate/faq.html.

Admissions information
For Fall 2017:
  Number of applicants: 147
  Number admitted: 58
  Number enrolled: 19

Admission requirements
Bachelor's degree requirements: A bachelor's degree in Physics with an average of B or above is required, although exceptions can be made in some circumstances. An applicant must satisfy the department of his/her ability to perform graduate work in physics.
Minimum undergraduate GPA: 3.0

GRE requirements
The GRE is required.
  Quantitative score: 162
  Verbal score: 152
  Analytical score: 3.5
  Mean GRE score range (25th–75th percentile): 65
Our institution code is 2925 and the Physics Department code is 0808.

Subjective GRE requirements
The Subjective GRE is required.
  Minimum accepted Advanced GRE score: 685
  Mean Advanced GRE score range (25th–75th percentile): 65
GRE advanced subject exam in physics is required for financial support and is otherwise highly recommended for all applicants. Our institution code is 2925 and the Physics Department code is 0808.

TOEFL requirements
The TOEFL exam is required for students from non-English-speaking countries.
  PBT score: 550
  iBT score: 79
If applying for an assistantship, the minimum acceptable total score is 600 (paper-based) or 90 (internet-based). In lieu of TOEFL, IELTS is acceptable with a total score minimum of 6.5 (no individual score less than 6.0). Our institution code is 2925 and the Physics Department code is 76.

Other admissions information
Additional requirements: Foreign students applying for Teaching Assistantships must pass the Speaking Proficiency English Assessment Kit (SPEAK) test before being assigned teaching duties. The test is offered on campus at the beginning of each semester.
Undergraduate preparation assumed: Fowles and Cassiday, Analytical Mechanics; Griffiths, Introduction to Electrodynamics; Reif, Statistical and Thermal Physics; Bransden and Joachain, Quantum Mechanics.

TUITION

Tuition year 2017–18:
Tuition for in-state residents
  Full-time students: $5,435 per semester
  Part-time students: $453 per credit

Tuition for out-of-state residents
Full-time students: $11,105 per semester
Part-time students: $925 per credit

Additional fee rates, at full-time status, consist of comprehensive fee ($2069.00), activity fee ($134.00), and academic excellence fee ($393.00). Tuition & fees are subject to change. Enrollment in a monthly payment plan is available. Additional information about financial aid, billing, registration and academic record services is available at UB's Student Response Center website: http://sarfs.buffalo.edu/src.php. International cost of attendance is available at The Graduate School's "Cost of Attendance" page at http://grad.buffalo.edu/Admissions/International_Student_Admissions/costs-of-attendance.html.

Credit hours per semester to be considered full-time: 12
Deferred tuition plan: Yes
Health insurance: Available at the cost of $2,084 per year.
Other academic fees: UB has a deferred tuition plan. It provides assistance to veterans & dependents eligible under Chapter 35 (Veterans Deferred Tuition Payment Plan). For information, call 716-645-2271.
Academic term: Semester
Number of first-year students who received full tuition waivers: 9

Teaching Assistants, Research Assistants, and Fellowships

Number of first-year
Teaching Assistants: 9
Fellowship students: 1
Average stipend per academic year
Teaching Assistant: $16,500
Research Assistant: $19,000
Fellowship student: $23,500
Assistantships are considered full-time status at 9 credit hours per semester.

FINANCIAL AID

Application deadlines
Fall admission:
U.S. students: February 1   *Int'l. students*: February 1

Loans
Loans are available for U.S. students.
Loans are not available for international students.
GAPSFAS application required: No
FAFSA application required: Yes

For further information
Address financial aid inquiries to: Student Response Center, Office of Financial Aid, 232 Capen Hall, Buffalo, NY 14260-1631., If you are a U.S. citizen or Permanent Resident, you may apply for need-based aid in the form of loans, grants, and/or work study grants by completing a Free Application for Federal Student Aid (FAFSA), which is available at the Office of Financial Aid.
Phone: (716) 645-8232
E-mail: UBFA@buffalo.edu
Financial aid website: http://financialaid.buffalo.edu/

HOUSING

Availability of on-campus housing
Single students: Yes
Married students: Yes
Childcare Assistance: Yes

For further information
Address housing inquiries to: University Residence Halls and Apartments, 106 Spaulding Quad, University at Buffalo, Buffalo, NY 14261-0054.

Phone: (716) 645-2171 / Toll Free: 866-285-8806
Housing aid website: http://www.ub-housing.buffalo.edu/

Table A—Faculty, Enrollments, and Degrees Granted

Research Specialty	2017–18 Faculty	Enrollment Fall 2017		Number of Degrees Granted 2017–18 (2013–18)		
		Master's	Doctorate	Master's	Terminal Master's	Doctorate
Acoustics	1	–	–	–	–	–
Applied Physics	6	1	8	–	–	–
Astrophysics	2	–	4	–	–	–
Atmosphere, Space Physics, Cosmic Rays	1	–	–	–	–	–
Atomic, Molecular, & Optical Physics	1	–	–	–	–	–
Biophysics	4	2	6	–(1)	–	1(6)
Computational Physics	5	–	6	–	–	–
Condensed Matter Physics	14	7	22	–(6)	–	4(28)
Cosmology & String Theory	2	1	4	–(1)	–	–(2)
Engineering Physics/Science	1	–	2	–	–	–
Geophysics	1	–	–	–	–	–
High Energy Physics	6	3	8	–(2)	1	1(5)
Low Temperature Physics	2	1	11	–	–	–(2)
Materials Science, Metallurgy	8	1	9	–	–	–
Mechanics	1	–	–	–	–	–
Medical, Health Physics	–	–	–	–	–	–
Nonlinear Dynamics and Complex Systems	–	–	–	–	–	–(1)
Nuclear Physics	–	–	–	–	–	–
Optics	2	–	–	–	–	–
Particles and Fields	7	–	3	–	–	–
Physics and other Science Education	4	–	2	–	–	–
Statistical & Thermal Physics	3	–	–	–	–	–
Theoretical Physics	1	2	–	–	–	1(6)
Total	24	18	83	–(15)	–	9(53)
Full-time Grad. Stud.	–	18	83	–	–	–
First-year Grad. Stud.	–	8	13	–	–	–

GRADUATE DEGREE REQUIREMENTS

Master's: Three options are available: (1) a thesis program, (2) a qualifying exam program, and (3) a project program. In the thesis program, a minimum of 30 credit hours is required. At least 15 credit hours are to be devoted to formal graduate course work, with the remaining hours culminating in a thesis. The qualifying exam program requires 30 credit hours of graduate courses plus passing the departmental qualifying exam at the M.S. level. The project program requires 30 credit hours: 15 credit hours of specified courses, 9 credit hours of other graduate courses and 6 credit hours of research (PHY 600).

Doctorate: A minimum of 72 semester hours of credit must be earned, with at least 36 in graduate physics lecture courses. To ensure breadth in the student's Ph.D. program, the department will evaluate his/her graduate work and may require the student to take specific courses in related fields. Within 18 months of enrollment, the qualifying exam must be passed. After an additional 18 months, a short defense of the proposed Ph.D. project must be presented to the candidate's Ph.D. committee. A doctoral dissertation is required, as well as an oral exam that consists of a defense of the dissertation and other topics determined by the candidate's committee.

Thesis: Thesis may be written in absentia.

SPECIAL EQUIPMENT, FACILITIES, OR PROGRAMS

The department has active experimental and theoretical research programs in condensed matter physics, biophysics, high energy and elementary particles physics, and programs in computational physics, photonics/biophotonics, statistical physics, and astrophysics and cosmology.

The department is located on UB's North Campus and has a variety of research facilities, including a helium liquefier, SQUID magnetometer, MBE systems, atomic and magnetic force microscopes, pulsed terahertz spectrometer, Raman spectrometer, and a 15 Tesla superconducting magnet.

Department members are users of several major national facilities, including the National Synchrotron Light Source at Brookhaven National Laboratories, the Tevatron at the Fermi National Accelerator Laboratory, the LHC at CERN, the National High Magnetic Field Laboratory (Tallahassee, Florida), the Center for Free Electron Laser Studies at the University of California, Santa Barbara, the W. M. Keck Foundation Free Electron Laser Center at Vanderbilt University (Nashville, Tennessee), and the Cornell Nanofabrication Facility.

The Physics Department has a joint B.S./M.S. in Computational Physics in cooperation with the Computer Science Department (CSE). A graduate student in physics can also pursue an Advanced Certificate in Computational Science or in Professional Science Management in Biophysics as additional credential.

Table B—Separately Budgeted Research Expenditures by Source of Support

Source of Support	Departmental Research	Physics-related Research Outside Department
Federal government	$2,737,339.03	
State/local government		
Non-profit organizations		
Business and industry		
Other	$760,096.71	
Total	**$3,497,435.74**	

Table C—Separately Budgeted Research Expenditures by Research Specialty

Research Specialty	No. of Grants	Expenditures ($)
Biophysics	20	$816,607.64
Condensed Matter Physics	32	$1,684,876.06
Cosmology & String Theory	6	$218,869.91
Low Temperature Physics	5	$77,850.07
Particles and Fields	12	$699,232.06
Total	**75**	**$3,497,435.74**

FACULTY

Professor

Cerne, John, Ph.D., University of California, Santa Barbara, 1996. *Condensed Matter Physics, Materials Science, Metallurgy.* Experimental condensed matter physics; strongly correlated electronic materials; magnetic semiconductors; magnetic oxides; graphene; high-temperature superconductors; magneto-polarimetry; experimental biophysics; "two-dimensional semiconductors" between "magnetic oxides"; "graphene"

Hu, Xuedong, Ph.D., University of Michigan, 1996. Director of Graduate Studies. *Condensed Matter Physics.* Theoretical condensed matter physics; theoretical study of nanostructure physics; solid state quantum information processing.

Iashvili, Ia, Ph.D., Humboldt University, Berlin, 2000. *High Energy Physics, Particles and Fields, Physics and other Science Education.* Experimental elementary particle physics; research, development, and construction of particle detectors; searches for Higgs and supersymmetric particles; precision measurements of particle properties at current and future accelerators.

Kharchilava, Avto, Ph.D., Tbilisi State University, 1990. *High Energy Physics, Particles and Fields, Physics and other Science Education.* Particle detectors R&D, experimental setup optimization, data taking and processing. Simulation/visualization of physics processes and detector response. Precision measurements of the Standard Model physics processes, study of the top quark, B-physics, Higgs boson properties. Searches for New Physics Phenomena at hadron colliders.

Kinney, William H., Ph.D., University of Colorado, 1996. *Astrophysics, Cosmology & String Theory, Particles and Fields.* Theoretical cosmology; high-energy physics; astrophysics.

Krotscheck, Eckhard, Ph.D., Universität zu Köln, 1974. SUNY Distinguished Professor. Quantum many-body theory; theoretical condensed matter physics.

Luo, Hong, Ph.D., Purdue University, 1988. Department Chair. *Applied Physics, Condensed Matter Physics, Materials Science, Metallurgy.* Experimental condensed matter physics; molecular beam epitaxy; microscopy; spintronics; semiconductor nanostructures.

Markelz, Andrea, Ph.D., University of California, Santa Barbara, 1995. *Applied Physics, Atomic, Molecular, & Optical Physics, Biophysics, Condensed Matter Physics, Materials Science, Metallurgy, Optics.* Experimental protein dynamics using terahertz time domain spectroscopy and UV/Vis/IR ultrafast spectroscopy; experimental condensed matter physics: nanosystems spectroscopy and device development.

Petrou, Athos, Ph.D., Purdue University, 1983. *Condensed Matter Physics.* Experimental solid-state physics.

Prasad, Paras, Ph.D., University of Pennsylvania, 1971. SUNY Distinguished Professor; Department of Chemistry (joint appointment). *Atomic, Molecular, & Optical Physics, Condensed Matter Physics.* Theoretical photonics; ultrafast optical processes; nonlinear optics.

Sen, Surajit, Ph.D., University of Georgia, 1990. *Acoustics, Biophysics, Computational Physics, Condensed Matter Physics, Engineering Physics/Science, Materials Science, Metallurgy, Mechanics, Physics and other Science Education, Statistical & Thermal Physics.* Theoretical non-equilibrium many-particle physics; nonlinear dynamics; granular materials; meta-materials; dust flow studies; battle problems; disease modeling; mathematical physics; science and math education at the middle school level; non-equilibrium problems in statistical physics; dynamics of strongly nonlinear systems; solitary wave - local excitation interactions in non-interchangeable systems; quasi-equilibrium; impact mitigation; nano-scale fluids; nano-scale crystals.

Stojkovic, Dejan, Ph.D., Case Western Reserve University, 2001. *Astrophysics, Cosmology & String Theory, High Energy Physics.* Theoretical cosmology; high-energy physics; gravity; astrophysics.

Wackeroth, Doreen, Ph.D., University of Karlsruhe, 1995. Associate Chair. *High Energy Physics, Particles and Fields.* Theoretical particle physics; phenomenology of particle physics at present and future colliders; electroweak physics; perturbative quantum chromodynamics; supersymmetry.

Zeng, Hao, Ph.D., University of Nebraska-Lincoln, 2001. *Applied Physics, Condensed Matter Physics, Materials Science,*

Metallurgy. Experimental condensed matter physics; nano-scale magnetism; spintronics; nanomaterial synthesis and self-assembly.

Zutic, Igor, Ph.D., University of Minnesota, 1998. *Condensed Matter Physics*. Theoretical condensed matter physics; spin-polarized transport and spintronics; high-temperature and un-conventional superconductivity; ferromagnetic semiconductors; quantum dots; theoretical nanoscience; computational physics.

Associate Professor

Ganapathy, Sambandamurthy, Ph.D., Indian Institute of Science, 2000. *Applied Physics, Condensed Matter Physics, Low Temperature Physics, Materials Science, Metallurgy*. Experimental condensed matter physics; quantum transport in nano-structures; nanoelectronics; quantum phase transitions.

Han, Jong, Ph.D., Ohio State University, 1997. *Computational Physics, Condensed Matter Physics*. Theoretical condensed matter physics; quantum transport theory; strongly correlated systems; quantum simulations; nanoscale magnetism.

Pralle, Arnd, Ph.D., Ludwig-Maximilians-University, Munich and European Molecular Biology Lab (EMBL), Heidelberg, 1999. *Applied Physics, Biophysics, Statistical & Thermal Physics*. Experimental biophysics; soft condensed matter physics; molecular and cellular mechanics and forces; spatio-temporal patterning; single-molecule spectroscopy.

Rappoccio, Salvatore, Ph.D., Harvard University, 2005. *High Energy Physics*. Experimental high-energy physics.

Zhang, Peihong, Ph.D., Pennsylvania State University, 2001. *Computational Physics, Condensed Matter Physics, Materials Science, Metallurgy*. Theoretical condensed matter physics; electronic structure theory; nanostructured materials; dilute magnetic semiconductors; wide gap semiconductors; electron-phonon renormalization in metals; quasi-particle properties in strongly correlated materials; high-performance computing.

Zheng, Wenjun, Ph.D., Stanford University, 2003. *Biophysics, Computational Physics*. Theoretical computational modeling of protein structures and dynamics.

Assistant Professor

Banerjee, Priya, Ph.D., SUNY Albany, 2011. *Biophysics*.

Gozpinar, Serdar, Ph.D., Brandeis University, 2012. *Biophysics, High Energy Physics*. Experimental High Energy Physics.

Williams, Ciaran, Ph.D., University of Durham, 2010. *High Energy Physics, Particles and Fields, Theoretical Physics*. The calculation of higher order corrections in QCD; analytic methods involving unitarity techniques; improving predictions for Higgs boson cross sections; matrix element methods.

Teaching Assistant Professor

Lehman, Landon, Ph.D., University of Notre Dame, 2017. *High Energy Physics, Theoretical Physics*. Professor Lehman received his Bachelor's degree in Physics (along with a minor in Mathematics) from Purdue University in 2012. He went on to obtain his PhD in Theoretical High Energy Physics from the University of Notre Dame in 2017. His PhD work was primarily on the mathematical problem of counting operators in effective field theories. Professor Lehman joined the Department of Physics as teaching faculty in 2017.

Adjunct Professor

Bird, Jonathan P., Ph.D., University of Sussex, 1990. Experimental condensed matter physics; nanoelectronics; nanomaterials characterization.

Cartwright, Alexander N., Ph.D., University of Iowa, 1995. Experimental condensed matter physics; time-resolved optical spectroscopy; ultrafast optical measurements.

Dimock, Jonathan, Ph.D., Harvard University, 1971. Mathematical physics.

Mitin, Vladimir, Ph.D., Ukrainian Academy of Science, 1987. Condensed matter theory, modeling, and simulations; nano-electronic, microelectric, and optoelectronic devices and materials; transport and noise in heterostructures; thin films; quantum wells and quantum wires; material characterization; heat dissipation in low-dimensional structures and devices; particle, molecular dynamics, and Monte Carlo methods of simulation of thyristors; three-terminal lasers; photodetectors; terahertz generators and devices based on quantum wells, quantum wires, and wide-bandgap semiconductors.

DEPARTMENTAL RESEARCH SPECIALTIES AND STAFF

Theoretical

Acoustics. Sen.
Astrophysics. Kinney, Stojkovic.
Biophysics. Sen, Zheng.
Computational Physics. Han, Sen, Zhang, Zheng.
Condensed Matter Physics. Han, Hu, Krotscheck, Sen, Zhang, Zutic.
Cosmology & String Theory. Kinney, Stojkovic.
Engineering Physics/Science. Sen.
High Energy Physics. Stojkovic, Wackeroth.
Materials Science, Metallurgy. Sen, Zhang.
Mechanics. Sen.
Particles and Fields. Kinney, Wackeroth, Williams.
Physics and other Science Education. Sen.
Statistical & Thermal Physics. Sen.

Experimental

Applied Physics. Ganapathy, Luo, Markelz, Pralle, Zeng.
Atomic, Molecular, & Optical Physics. Markelz, Prasad.
Biophysics. Banerjee, Markelz, Pralle.
Condensed Matter Physics. Cerne, Ganapathy, Luo, Markelz, Petrou, Zeng.
High Energy Physics. Iashvili, Kharchilava, Lehman, Rappoccio.
Low Temperature Physics. Ganapathy.
Materials Science, Metallurgy. Cerne, Ganapathy, Luo, Markelz, Zeng.
Optics. Markelz.
Particles and Fields. Iashvili, Kharchilava, Rappoccio.
Physics and other Science Education. Iashvili, Kharchilava.
Statistical & Thermal Physics. Pralle.

UNIVERSITY OF ROCHESTER

DEPARTMENT OF PHYSICS AND ASTRONOMY

Rochester, New York 14627
http://www.pas.rochester.edu

General University Information
President: Richard Feldman
Dean of Graduate School: Margaret Kearney
University website: http://www.rochester.edu
School Type: Private
Setting: Urban
Total Faculty: 1,294
Total number of Students: 5,937
Total number of Graduate Students: 2,459

Department Information
Department Chairman: Prof. Dan Watson, Chair
Department Contact: Laura Blumkin, Graduate Program
  Coordinator
  Total full-time faculty: 27
  Full-Time Graduate Students: 110
  Female Full-Time Graduate Students: 20
  First-Year Graduate Students: 17
  Female First-Year Students: 4
  Total Post Doctorates: 5

Department Address
Bausch & Lomb Hall, Box 270171
Wilson Blvd.
Rochester, NY 14627
Phone: (585) 275-4356
Fax: (585) 273-3237
E-mail: grad@pas.rochester.edu
Website: http://www.pas.rochester.edu

ADMISSIONS

Admission Contact Information
Address admission inquiries to: Laura Blumkin, Physics and Astronomy Graduate Office, Box 270171, Rochester, NY 14627
Phone: (585) 275-4356
E-mail: laura.blumkin@rochester.edu
Admissions website: http://www.pas.rochester.edu/graduate/applying.html

Application deadlines
Fall admission:
U.S. students: January 15   *Int'l. students*: January 15

Application fee
There is no application fee required.

Admissions information
For Fall of 2018:
  Number of applicants: 313
  Number admitted: 82
  Number enrolled: 17

Admission requirements
Bachelor's degree requirements: A Bachelor's degree is required.

GRE requirements
The GRE is required.
No minimum required for application.

Subjective GRE requirements
The Subjective GRE is required.
No minimum required for application.

TOEFL requirements
The TOEFL exam is required for students from non-English-speaking countries.
No minimum required for application.

Other admissions information
Additional requirements: Our admission application can be found at: https://apply.grad.rochester.edu. We do ask for a personal statement, CV, and 3 letters of recommendation submitted through the online application, GRE, GRE Physics and TOEFL for non-native English speakers.
Undergraduate preparation assumed: Classical Mechanics in J.B. Marion, Classical Dynamics of Particles and Systems; Electricity and Magnetism, for example, in D. J. Griffiths, Introduction to Electrodynamics; Thermodynamics, Kinetic Theory, and Statistical Mechanics, for example, by C. Kittel and H. Kroemer, Thermal Physics; Quantum Mechanics for example in R. L. Liboff, Introductory Quantum Mechanics. Mathematics, good knowledge of advanced calculus, ordinary differential equations; functions of complex variable, boundary value problems, modern algebra.

TUITION

Tuition year 2018–19:
  Full-time students: $19,488 per semester
Full tuition scholarships are available. Applicants are considered automatically for scholarships; no additional scholarship application is required at this time.
Credit hours per semester to be considered full-time: 12
Deferred tuition plan: Yes
Health insurance: Available at the cost of $2448 per year.
Other academic fees: All active students pay a $10 per semester Graduate Organizing Group Fee. International Students pay an additional fee of $25.
Academic term: Semester
Number of first-year students who received full tuition waivers: 17

Teaching Assistants, Research Assistants, and Fellowships
Number of first-year
  Teaching Assistants: 16
  Research Assistants: 1
  Fellowship students: 2
Average stipend per academic year
  Teaching Assistant: $27,744
  Research Assistant: $27,744
  Fellowship student: $30,000
Most first-year graduate students will hold teaching assistant positions.

FINANCIAL AID

Loans
Loans are available for U.S. students.
Loans are not available for international students.
GAPSFAS application required: No

FAFSA application required: Yes

For further information
Address financial aid inquiries to: Laura Blumkin, Physics and Astronomy Graduate Office, Box 270171, Rochester, NY 14627.
Phone: (585) 275-4356
E-mail: laura.blumkin@rochester.edu
Financial aid website: http://enrollment.rochester.edu/financial/grads

HOUSING

Availability of on-campus housing
Single students: Yes
Married students: Yes
Childcare Assistance: No

For further information
Address housing inquiries to: Laura Blumkin, Physics and Astronomy Graduate Office, Box 270171, Rochester, NY 14627.
Phone: (585) 275-4356
E-mail: laura.blumkin@rochester.edu
Housing aid website: http://www.rochester.edu/reslife

Table A—Faculty, Enrollments, and Degrees Granted

Research Specialty	2016–17 Faculty	Enrollment Fall 2018 Master's	Enrollment Fall 2018 Doctorate	Number of Degrees Granted 2017–18 (2006–18) Master's	Number of Degrees Granted 2017–18 (2006–18) Terminal Master's	Number of Degrees Granted 2017–18 (2006–18) Doctorate
Astronomy	–	–	–	–	–	–
Astrophysics	12	–	8	1(9)	–	2(22)
Atomic, Molecular, & Optical Physics	13	–	21	3(50)	–	8(46)
Biophysics	2	–	6	1(5)	–	1(3)
Chemical Physics	–	–	–	–(3)	–(1)	–(4)
Condensed Matter Physics	14	–	11	3(12)	–	3(16)
Engineering Physics/Science	–	–	–	–(6)	–	–(3)
Medical, Health Physics	2	–	–	–(1)	–	–(7)
Nuclear Physics	2	–	–	–(4)	–	–(1)
Particles and Fields	15	–	23	3(35)	–(1)	2(29)
Plasma and Fusion	8	–	25	10(29)	–	2(13)
Non-specialized	–	–	19	4(21)	–	–
Other	1	–	–	–(14)	–(1)	–(1)
Total	69	–	113	25(172)	–(5)	18(149)
Full-time Grad. Stud.	–	–	113	–	–	–
First-year Grad. Stud.	–	–	17	–	–	–

GRADUATE DEGREE REQUIREMENTS

Master's: Master's Degree Enroute to Ph.D. Only 30 graduate credits; no minimum grade average required; no language or residency requirements; Master's exam and thesis required. Degrees awarded in physics only.

Doctorate: Ninety credit hours beyond Bachelor's degree in approved program required; no minimum GPA; minimum one-year residency and full-time enrollment required; no language or computer language required; written preliminary-oral qualifying exams required; thesis and oral thesis exam required. Degrees available in physics or physics and astronomy.

Thesis: Thesis may be written in absentia with approval from Advisor and Dean of Graduate Studies.

SPECIAL EQUIPMENT, FACILITIES, OR PROGRAMS
Laboratory for Laser Energetics: http://www.lle.rochester.edu/

Table B—Separately Budgeted Research Expenditures by Source of Support

Source of Support	Departmental Research	Physics-related Research Outside Department
Federal government	$7,635,046	
State/local government		
Non-profit organizations		
Business and industry		
Other	$26,198	
Total	$7,661,244	

Table C—Separately Budgeted Research Expenditures by Research Specialty

Research Specialty	No. of Grants	Expenditures ($)
Astrophysics	21	$1,210,274
Experimental Condensed Matter	1	$123,585
Theoretical Condensed Matter	2	$87,366
Nuclear Physics	1	$196,034
Experimental Quantum Optics	7	$867,258
Theoretical Quantum Optics	9	$814,033
Experimental High Energy Physics	22	$3,787,388
Theoretical High Energy Physics	1	$212,191
Physics and other Science Education	4	$363,115
Total	68	$7,661,244

FACULTY

Professor
Agrawal, G. P., Ph.D., Indian Institute of Technology, New Delhi, 1974. *Applied Physics, Optics*. Nonlinear photonics; lasers; optical communications.

Betti, R., Ph.D., Massachusetts Institute of Technology, 1992. *Engineering Physics/Science, Plasma and Fusion*. Theoretical plasma physics; nuclear and mechanical engineering; computational and plasma physics.

Bigelow, N. P., Ph.D., Cornell University, 1989. *Atomic, Molecular, & Optical Physics*. Experimental and theoretical quantum optics and quantum physics; studies of BEC; laser-cooled and trapped atoms.

Blackman, E. G., Ph.D., Harvard University, 1995. *Astronomy, Astrophysics, Plasma and Fusion*. Theoretical astrophysics; astrophysical plasmas and magnetic fields; accretion and ejection phenomena; relativistic and high-energy astrophysics.

Bocko, M. F., Ph.D., University of Rochester, 1984. *Condensed Matter Physics, Electrical Engineering*. Superconducting electronics; quantum computing; musical acoustics; digital audio technology; sensors; condensed matter.

Bodek, A., Ph.D., Massachusetts Institute of Technology, 1972. *Nuclear Physics, Particles and Fields*. Experimental elementary particle physics; proton-antiproton collisions; QCD and structure functions; neutrino physics; electron scattering, and tile-fiber calorimetric detectors; Physics with W, Z and Higgs Bosons at the Large Hadron Collider (LHC).

Boyd, R. W., Ph.D., University of California, Berkeley, 1977. *Atomic, Molecular, & Optical Physics, Optics*. Nonlinear optics.

Cline, D., Ph.D., University of Manchester, 1963. *Nuclear Physics*. Extreme states of nuclei pairing and shape correlations in nuclei.

Collins, Gilbert (Rip), Ph.D., University. *Plasma and Fusion.* High Energy Density Physics.

Das, A., Ph.D., Stony Brook University, 1977. *Particles and Fields.* Theoretical particle physics; finite temperature field theory; integrable systems; phenomenology, noncommutative field theory, and string/M theory.

Demina, R., Ph.D., Northeastern University, 1994. *High Energy Physics, Particles and Fields.* Experimental particle physics; proton-antiproton collisions; top and electroweak physics.

Douglass, D. H., Ph.D., Massachusetts Institute of Technology, 1959. *Applied Physics, Astrophysics, Atmosphere, Space Physics, Cosmic Rays, Condensed Matter Physics, Energy Sources & Environment, Geophysics, Low Temperature Physics, Materials Science, Metallurgy, Relativity & Gravitation.* Experimental condensed matter physics; climate change and pollution.

Eberly, J. H., Ph.D., Stanford University, 1962. *Atomic, Molecular, & Optical Physics.* Theoretical quantum optics; quantum entanglement; cavity QED; atoms in strong laser fields; nonlinear optical pulse propagation.

Ferbel, T., Ph.D., Yale University, 1963. *Particles and Fields.* Experimental elementary particle physics; studies of the top quark in hadronic collisions.

Forrest, W. J., Ph.D., University of California, San Diego, 1974. *Astronomy, Astrophysics, Electrical Engineering, Low Temperature Physics.* Observational astrophysics; infrared astronomy; stellar and planetary formation; low-mass stars and brown dwarfs; development of infrared detector arrays and instrumentation.

Foster, T. H., Ph.D., University of Rochester, 1990. Biological and medical physics.

Frank, A., Ph.D., University of Washington, Seattle, 1992. *Astronomy, Astrophysics, Computational Physics, Plasma and Fusion.* Theoretical astrophysics; astrophysical plasmas; numerical hydrodynamics and magnetohydrodynamics.

Gao, Y., Ph.D., Purdue University, 1986. *Condensed Matter Physics.* Experimental condensed matter physics; surface physics.

Guo, Chunlei, Ph.D., University of Connecticut, 1999. *Atomic, Molecular, & Optical Physics, Condensed Matter Physics.* High-intensity femtosecond laser interactions with matter.

Hagen, C. R., Ph.D., Massachusetts Institute of Technology, 1962. *Particles and Fields.* Theoretical elementary particle physics; quantum field theory, particularly 2+1 dimensional theories.

Helfer, H. L., Ph.D., University of Chicago, 1953. Emeritus. Theoretical astrophysics and plasma physics; high-energy astrophysics; dark matter in galactic halos.

Jordan, Andrew N., Ph.D., University of California, Santa Barbara, 2002. *Atomic, Molecular, & Optical Physics, Condensed Matter Physics, Statistical & Thermal Physics.* Theoretical quantum optics and condensed matter; quantum physics.

Knight, Peter, Ph.D., University of Sussex, 1971. *Atomic, Molecular, & Optical Physics.* Entanglement, quantum information.

Knox, R. S., Ph.D., University of Rochester, 1958. Emeritus. *Atomic, Molecular, & Optical Physics, Biophysics, Chemical Physics, Condensed Matter Physics, Energy Sources & Environment, Statistical & Thermal Physics.* Theoretical biological physics and condensed matter physics; energy-balance models of climate.

Knox, W. H., Ph.D., University of Rochester, 1984. *Condensed Matter Physics, Medical, Health Physics, Optics.* Ultrafast sciences and technology, telecommunications; ultrafast biomedical optics, and optics education.

Manly, S. L., Ph.D., Columbia University, 1989. *Nuclear Physics, Particles and Fields.* Experimental relativistic heavy ion physics; experimental elementary particle physics.

McCrory, Robert L., Ph.D., Massachusetts Institute of Technology, 1973. *Accelerator, Particles and Fields, Plasma and Fusion.* Nuclear and mechanical engineering; computational hydrodynamics; physics of inertial fusion; National Nuclear Security policy.

McFarland, K. S., Ph.D., University of Chicago, 1994. *Nuclear Physics, Particles and Fields.* Experimental elementary particle physics; neutrino physics; electroweak unification; top quark properties.

Melissinos, A. C., Ph.D., Massachusetts Institute of Technology, 1958. Emeritus. *Particles and Fields.* Experimental particle physics; high intensity laser particle interactions; searches for relic gravitational radiation (retired).

Milonni, Peter W., Ph.D., University of Rochester, 1974. *Atomic, Molecular, & Optical Physics, Electromagnetism, Optics.* Effects of the quantum vacuum; the Casimir force; laser-atom interactions; nonlinear optics; and QED of dielectric materials.

Orr, L., Ph.D., University of Chicago, 1991. *Particles and Fields.* Theoretical elementary particle physics; phenomenology, quantum chromodynamics and electroweak physics.

Pipher, J. L., Ph.D., Cornell University, 1971. Emeritus. *Astronomy, Astrophysics.* Observational astrophysics; infrared astronomy; galactic and extragalactic star formation; low-mass stars and brown dwarfs; development of infrared detector arrays and instrumentation; detector physics.

Quillen, Alice, Ph.D., California Institute of Technology, 1993. *Astronomy, Astrophysics.* Observational astrophysics; galactic structure and dynamics; active galactic nuclei; dynamics of planetary and protoplanetary systems; celestial mechanics.

Rajeev, S. G., Ph.D., Syracuse University, 1984. *Math Physics. Particles and Fields, Relativity & Gravitation, Statistical & Thermal Physics.* Theoretical particle physics; nonperturbative quantum field theory applied to strong interactions; mathematical physics.

Rothberg, L., Ph.D., Harvard University, 1983. *Astrophysics, Chemical Physics.* Experimental chemical physics; organic electronics and biomolecular sensing.

Savedoff, M. P., Ph.D., Princeton University, 1957. Emeritus. Theoretical astrophysics; stellar interiors; interstellar matter; high-energy astrophysics.

Schröder, Wolf-Udo, Ph.D., Technical University of Darmstadt, 1971. *Nuclear Physics.* Experimental nuclear physics; dynamics of complex nuclear reactions; fundamental properties of nuclear matter; nuclear transmutation; nuclear technology applications; nuclear plasma physics.

Seyler, Charles E., Ph.D., University of Iowa, 1975. *Plasma and Fusion.* Theoretical Plasma Physics.

Shapir, Y., Ph.D., Tel Aviv University, 1981. *Applied Physics, Condensed Matter Physics, Nano Science and Technology, Polymer Physics/Science, Statistical & Thermal Physics.* Theoretical condensed matter physics; statistical mechanics; critical phenomena in ordered and disordered systems; fractal growth.

Slattery, P. F., Ph.D., Yale University, 1967. *Particles and Fields.* Experimental elementary particle physics; investigation of QCD via direct photon production; top quark studies and searches for new phenomena using high energy colliders.

Sobolewski, R., Ph.D., Polish Academy of Science, Warsaw, 1983. *Applied Physics, Condensed Matter Physics, Electrical Engineering, Electromagnetism, Engineering Physics/Science, Low Temperature Physics, Materials Science, Metallurgy, Nano Science and Technology, Optics.* Applied superconductivity, ultrafast electronics and optoelectronics.

Stroud, Carlos R., Washington University, 1969. *Applied Physics, Atomic, Molecular, & Optical Physics, Optics.* Quantum optics; short-pulse excitation of atoms and molecules; quantum information; optical physics.

Tarduno, J. A., Ph.D., Stanford University, 1987. *Astrophysics.* Geophysics, geomagnetism, and geodynamics; plate tectonics and polar wander; geomagnetic reversals; fine particle magnetism; planetary astrophysics.

Teitel, S. L., Ph.D., Cornell University, 1981. *Condensed Matter Physics, Statistical & Thermal Physics.* Statistical and condensed matter physics.

Thomas, J. H., Ph.D., Purdue University, 1966. Emeritus. *Astrophysics, Fluids, Rheology.* Emeritus. Theoretical astrophysics; astrophysical plasmas; astrophysical fluid dynamics and magnetohydrodynamics; solar physics.

Thorndike, E. H., Ph.D., Harvard University, 1960. Emeritus. *Particles and Fields.* Emeritus. Experimental elementary particle physics; weak decays of bottom and charm quarks.

Van Horn, H. M., Ph.D., Cornell University, 1965. Emeritus. *Astrophysics.* Theoretical astrophysics; degenerate stars.

Watson, D. M., Ph.D., University of California, Berkeley, 1983. *Astronomy, Astrophysics.* Observational astrophysics; infrared astronomy; stellar and planetary formation; development of infrared detector arrays and instrumentation.

Wolfs, F. L. H., Ph.D., University of Chicago, 1987. *Astrophysics, Electrical Engineering, Nuclear Physics, Particles and Fields.* Experimental high-energy/nuclear physics; dark-matter searches.

Zhong, Jianhui, Ph.D., Brown University, 1988. *Biophysics, Medical, Health Physics.* Biological and medical physics; advanced medical imaging; novel MRI techniques; physiological properties; biological tissues.

Associate Professor

Dery, H., Ph.D., University of Technion, Haifa, 2004. *Applied Physics, Computer Science, Condensed Matter Physics, Electrical Engineering, Engineering Physics/Science, Nano Science and Technology.* Materials Science; theory of semiconductor spin electronics.

Garcia-Bellido, Aran, Ph.D., Royal Holloway, University of London, 2002. *Particles and Fields.* Experimental particle physics, with interests in supersymmetry and physics of the top quark, and in particular electroweak production of single top quarks.

Ren, Chuang, Ph.D., University of Wisconsin-Madison, 1998. Associate Professor of Mechanical Engineering. *Plasma and Fusion.* Theoretical and computational plasma physics; controlled fusion.

Vamivakas, Nick, Ph.D., Boston University, 2007. *Optics.* Quantum optoelectronics; optical metrology.

Assistant Professor

BenZvi, Segev, Ph.D., Columbia University, 2007. *Astrophysics, High Energy Physics.* Experimental elementary particle physics; gamma-ray and neutrino astrophysics.

Dan, Bergstralh, Ph.D., University of North Carolina. Biology.

Franco, Ignacio, Ph.D., University of Toronto, 2007. *Chemical Physics.* theory and computation as applies to dynamical processes occurring at the nanoscale.

Froula, Dustin, Ph.D., University of California at Davis, 2002. Senior Scientist at the Laboratory for Laser Energetics. *Plasma and Fusion.* Experimental plasma physics.

Ghoshal, Gourab, Ph.D., University of Michigan, Ann Arbor, 2009. *Computational Physics, Condensed Matter Physics.* Complex network theory in data science, applied to condensed-matter, biological systems and computational physics.

Gourdain, Pierre, Ph.D., Ecole Centrale de Lyon, 2001. *Plasma and Fusion.* Experimental plasma physics; high-energy density plasmas generated with pulsed power or laser irradiation; Hall magnetohydrodynamics; laboratory astrophysics.

Haefner, Ralf, D.Phil., Oxford. brain and cognitive sciences.

Nakajima, Miki, California Institute of Technology. *Geophysics.* Earth and Environmental Sciences.

Nichol, John M., Ph.D., University of Illinois at Urbana-Champaign, 2013. *Condensed Matter Physics.* Experimental condensed matter physics, quantum information processing, spin physics, low temperature physics.

Oakes, Patrick W., Ph.D., Brown University, 2009. *Biophysics.* High-resolution quantitative microscopy; cell mechanics; mechanobiology; active materials, optogenetics, cytoskeletal dynamics; liquid crystal behavior; and micro-patterning.

Wu, Stephen, Ph.D., University of California, Berkeley. *Condensed Matter Physics.*

Research Professor

Duke, Charles B., Ph.D., Princeton University, 1963. *Condensed Matter Physics.* Theoretical condensed matter physics; geophysics and climate.

Howell, John, Ph.D., Pennsylvania State University, 2000. *Applied Physics, Atomic, Molecular, & Optical Physics, Optics.* Experimental quantum optics and quantum physics; quantum cryptography and quantum computation.

Rygg, Ryan, Ph.D., MIT. *Plasma and Fusion.* Mechanical Engineering.

Visiting Professor

Visser, Taco D., Ph.D., University of Amsterdam, 1992. *Optics.* Theoretical optics; coherence theory; scattering and diffraction; surface plasmons.

DEPARTMENTAL RESEARCH SPECIALTIES AND STAFF

Theoretical

Astrophysics. Astrophysics. Astrophysical fluid dynamics and magnetohydrodynamics, astrophysical plasmas, computational astrophysics. Accretion disks and hypersonic outflows associated with young stars and degenerate objects. Evolution of protonplanetary disks. Celestial mechanics. Galactic dynamics. Stellar formation and death; planetary nebulae. High-energy astrophysics. Dark matter in galaxy haloes. Dynamo theory of magnetic-field generation in stars, galaxy disks, and planets. Origin and long-term behavior of Earth's magnetic field; field reversals and geodynamics. Physics of sunspots and solar magnetic flux tubes. Laboratory simulation of high-energy-density astrophysical plasmas. Blackman, Frank, Helfer, Quillen, Thomas. Collaborating faculty at the Laboratory of Laser Energetics. Blackman, Frank, Helfer, Quillen, Thomas.

Atomic, Molecular, & Optical Physics. Coherence phenomena in the interaction of light with matter. Subjects include coherent control, quantum entanglement, Bose-Einstein condensates, quantum dots, nanophotonics, atoms in intense laser fields, wave packet states of atoms and molecules, quantum imaging, single-cycle and half-cycle EM pulses, amplitude-coherent chemistry, correlation-induced spectral changes, solitons and inverse scattering theory, diffraction tomography. Two postdoctoral research associates. Agrawal, Bigelow, Boyd, Eberly, Howell, Jordan, Knight, Milonni, Stroud, Visser.

Condensed Matter Physics. Theory of thermodynamic and transport properties of disordered systems also near phase transitions. Statistical mechanics, complex networks, and data science. Theory of flux phases in type II superconductors and Josephson junctions. Scaling properties in clusters and polymers. Complex fluids, colloids, and biosystems. Theory of mesoscopic physics: electronic transport and noise properties.

Quantum physics in the solid state – entanglement, measurement and information. Dery, Duke, Ghoshal, Jordan, R. Knox, Rajeev, Shapir, Teitel.

High Energy Physics. Nuclear Physics. String theory; matrix model, integrable models; Lagrangian field theory; thermofield theory; phenomenology, nonperturbative methods in field theory; structure functions of hadrons; supersymmetry and renormalization in quantum mechanics. One postdoctoral research associate. Das, Ghoshal, Hagen, Orr.

Plasma and Fusion. Plasma Physics. Astrophysical plasmas in extreme environments. Fundamental processes common to laboratory and astrophysical plasmas. Space plasmas interaction of intense lasers with matter. High-energy-density physics with intense lasers. Hydrodynamic, magnetohydrodynamic, and plasma instabilities; particle acceleration. Interaction of intense lasers with matter. Inertial confinement fusion and high-energy-density physics. Compression and heating of pellets to ignition relevant conditions. Betti, Blackman, Frank, Gourdain, McCrory, Seyler.

Experimental

Astrophysics. Astrophysics. Observations with space-based and ground-based telescopes, and extensive archival work based upon our group's observations with the NASA Spitzer Space Telescope and ESA Herschel Space Observatory. Evolution of protostellar envelopes and protoplanetary disks, and the formation of stars and planets. Early stellar and planetary evolution. Brown dwarfs. Mineralogy of dust and chemistry of gases in protoplanetary and debris disks. Structure, dynamics, star formation histories, and chemical evolution of the Milky Way, other galaxies, and nearby young stellar associations. High-resolution imaging of young stellar systems using adaptive optics. Evolution of stellar rotation, magnetic activity, solar wind, and interaction between the Sun and the magnetic field of early Earth. Origin and long-term behavior of Earth's magnetic field; field reversals and geodynamics. Development of infrared detector arrays and instruments for infrared astronomy. BenZvi, Forrest, Pipher, Quillen, Tarduno, Watson.

Atomic, Molecular, & Optical Physics. Quantum interference effects and nonclassical states of light, search for locality violation with photons, Bose-Einstein condensation, laser cooling and trapping of atoms and molecules; atom optics; generation of nonclassical states of the atom; ultra-cold collisions; cold molecules; novel light sources. Nonlinear optics, quantum coherence; optical solitons. High-intensity laser-plasma and laser-atom interactions. Collaborating faculty at the Institute of Optics. One postdoctoral research associate. Bigelow, Boyd, Guo, Howell, W. Knox, Stroud.

Biological and Medical Physics. Biological and Medical Physics. Experimental and theoretical research in single molecule spectroscopy and manipulation, photodynamic therapy, diffusion tensor and functional MRI mechanisms and techniques, tissue optics, light scattering, biomolecular sensing, interactions of nanoparticles with biomolecules, and microscopy. Foster, Oakes, Zhong.

Condensed Matter Physics. Semiconductor heterojunctions; surface phenomena; synchrotron radiation photoemission; femtosecond time resolved photoemission; ultrafast dynamics in solids; interfaces in organic semiconductors; scanning tunneling microscopy; superconductivity and superconducting films; electron tunneling spectroscopy; metallic, magnetic, and superconducting nanowires; electron-beam lithography and mesoscopic structures. Bocko, Dery, Douglass, Duke, Gao, Guo, W. Knox, Rothberg, Sobolewski, Wu.

High Energy Physics. Proton-antiproton colliding beam experiment at the Fermi National Accelerator Laboratory—FNAL (CDF and DZERO); proton-proton colliding beam experiments at the CERN LHC Large Hadron Collider (LHC/CMS) $e+e-$; Neutrino experiments (Fermilab/MINERvA) and (Jparc/T2K). Electron scattering on nuclear targets (JLAB/JUPITER). R+D for future Linear Colliders. Dark matter search at SUSEL (LUX). Thirteen senior scientists and research associates. BenZvi, Bodek, Demina, Ferbel, Garcia-Bellido, Manly, McFarland, Melissinos, Slattery, Thorndike, Wolfs.

Nuclear Physics. Structure of exotic nuclei far from stability, relativistic heavy-ion physics, electron scattering. Two postdoctoral research associates. Bodek, Cline, Schröder.

Plasma and Fusion. Inertial confinement fusion and high-energy-density physics with high-energy and high-intensity lasers at the Laboratory for Laser Energetics, University of Rochester. Laser-plasma interactions and instabilities. Hydrodynamic instabilities. Equation of state at extreme conditions. Compression and heating of capsules to ignition relevant conditions. Plasma diagnostics. Collins, Froula, Gourdain, Ren, Rygg, Seyler.

View additional information about this department at www.gradschoolshopper.com. Check out the "Why Choose Us?" section, find out more about the department's culture and get links to social media networks.

UNIVERSITY OF ROCHESTER

THE INSTITUTE OF OPTICS

Rochester, New York 14627
http://www.hajim.rochester.edu/optics/

General University Information

President: Richard Feldman
Dean of Graduate School: Margaret Kearney
University website: http://www.rochester.edu
School Type: Private
Setting: Suburban
Total Faculty: 1,329
Total Graduate Faculty: Not separated.
Total number of Students: 6,046
Total number of Graduate Students: 3,424

Department Information

Department Chairman: Prof. P. Scott Carney, Chair
Department Contact: Kai Davies, Admin Asst
  Total full-time faculty: 33
  Total number of full-time equivalent positions: 25
  Full-Time Graduate Students: 158
  Female Full-Time Graduate Students: 41
  First-Year Graduate Students: 50
  Female First-Year Students: 13
  Total Post Doctorates: 25

Department Address

The Institute of Optics, University of Rochester
275 Hutchison Road
Rochester, NY 14627
Phone: (585) 275-7720
Fax: (585) 276-1451
E-mail: gradadmissions@optics.rochester.edu
Website: http://www.hajim.rochester.edu/optics/

ADMISSIONS

Admission Contact Information

Address admission inquiries to: Kai Davies, Admin Asst, Optics
  Graduate Admissions Committee, University of Rochester,
  PO Box 270186, Rochester, NY 14627-0186
Phone: (585) 275-7720
E-mail: gradadmissions@optics.rochester.edu
Admissions website: http://www.hajim.rochester.edu/optics/
  index.html

Application deadlines

Fall admission:
U.S. students: January 15   *Int'l. students*: January 15

Application fee

U.S. students: $60   *Int'l. students*: $60

Admissions information

For Fall of 2018:
  Number of applicants: 228
  Number admitted: 64
  Number enrolled: 52

Admission requirements

Bachelor's degree requirements: Bachelor's degree in Physics
  or engineering is required.
Minimum undergraduate GPA: 3.0

GRE requirements

The GRE is required.
  Mean GRE score range (25th–75th percentile): 1260-1420
The GRE is required for Ph.D. applicants and recommended for
  M.S. applicants.

Subjective GRE requirements

The Subjective GRE is not required.

TOEFL requirements

The TOEFL exam is required for students from non-English-
  speaking countries.
  PBT score: 620
  iBT score: 105

Other admissions information

Additional requirements: The average GPA for admitted M.S.
  students is 3.4/4.0. The average GPA for admitted Ph.D. students is 3.7/4.0. The average GRE scores for admitted students are 80th percentile in all categories.
  The minimum accepted computer-based TOEFL score is 260.
  IELTS is also accepted with a minimum score of 7.2.

TUITION

Tuition year 2018–2019:
  Full-time students: $51,072 annual
Tuition is waived for Ph.D. students.
Credit hours per semester to be considered full-time: 12
Deferred tuition plan: Yes
Health insurance: Available at the cost of $2,460 per year.
Academic term: Semester
Number of first-year students who received full tuition waivers: 15
Number of first-year students who received partial tuition waivers: 30

Teaching Assistants, Research Assistants, and Fellowships

Number of first-year
  Teaching Assistants: 15
  Fellowship students: 16
Average stipend per academic year
  Teaching Assistant: $2,500
  Research Assistant: $30,000
  Fellowship student: $32,000
Ph.D. students perform TA duties during their second year
  in the program.

FINANCIAL AID

Loans

Loans are available for U.S. students.
Loans are not available for international students.
GAPSFAS application required: No
FAFSA application required: Yes

For further information

Address financial aid inquiries to: Financial Aid Office.
Phone: (585) 275-3226
E-mail: elisabeth.carosa@rochester.edu
Financial aid website: https://enrollment.rochester.edu/financial-
  aid/

HOUSING

Availability of on-campus housing
Single students: Yes
Married students: Yes
Childcare Assistance: No

For further information
Address housing inquiries to: University Apartments Office, 1351 Mt. Hope Avenue, Rochester, NY 14620.
Phone: (585) 275-5824
E-mail: uapts@reslife.rocheter.edu
Housing aid website: http://www.rochester.edu/reslife

Table A—Faculty, Enrollments, and Degrees Granted

Research Specialty	2016 - 2017 Faculty	Enrollment Fall 2016		Number of Degrees Granted 2016–2017		
		Master's	Doctorate	Master's	Terminal Master's	Doctorate
Optics	30	51	89	21	–	12
Total	29	51	89	18	–	10
Full-time Grad. Stud.	–	46	91	–	–	–
First-year Grad. Stud.	–	31	16	–	–	–

GRADUATE DEGREE REQUIREMENTS

Master's: M.S. degrees require 30 hours of coursework, including 16 hours of required core courses. The M.S. degrees are normally completed in 9 -12 months. A thesis-based M.S. degree is normally completed in 18-24 months. There are no residence or foreign language requirements. In a co-op program, students take the first semester of courses, work full-time for 12 months, and then return to campus for the final semester of classes.

Doctorate: General requirements: one year of full-time residence, 90 hours of graduate work (60 hours beyond the M.S.), two semesters of teaching assistantship, successful completion of a written preliminary examination and an oral qualifying examination, and completion and defense of a doctoral dissertation. There is no language requirement.

Thesis: Thesis may not be written in absentia.

SPECIAL EQUIPMENT, FACILITIES, OR PROGRAMS

Instruction is offered in optical instrumentation and design, quantum optics and electronics, laser engineering, optics of thin films, electro-optics, holography, interferometry, and most other areas of optical physics and engineering. Well-equipped laboratories allow student thesis research in such areas as ultrahigh-resolution dye laser spectroscopy, semiconductor lasers, optical physics, nano-optics, optical communications, fiber optics, imaging, nonlinear optics, diffractive optics, gradient index optics, interferometry, image processing, optical materials, and high-power laser physics. In addition to extensive facilities within the Institute, thesis research may be carried out at the Laboratory for Laser Energetics, the School of Medicine and Dentistry, and the Center for Visual Science. Joint projects applying optical techniques in all of these areas are currently under way.

Table B—Separately Budgeted Research Expenditures by Source of Support

Source of Support	Departmental Research	Physics-related Research Outside Department
Federal government	$3,982,395	
State/local government	$243,153	
Non-profit organizations	$728,569	
Business and industry	$3,124,260	
Other	$71,925	
Total	$8,150,302	

FACULTY

Chair Professor

Agrawal, Govind, Ph.D., Indian Institute of Technology, 1974. James C. Wyant Professor of Optics, Professor of Physics, Senior Scientist at the Laboratory for Laser Energetics; Chair, Undergraduate Program Committee. *Applied Physics, Optics*. Semiconductor lasers and amplifiers; nonlinear optical phenomena; optical fiber communications.

Bigelow, Nicholas, Ph.D., Cornell University, 1989. Lee A. DuBridge Professor of Physics; Chair of Faculty Senate. *Atomic, Molecular, & Optical Physics, Optics*. Quantum optics and quantum physics.

Eberly, Joseph H., Ph.D., Stanford University, 1962. Andrew Carnegie Professor of Physics. *Atomic, Molecular, & Optical Physics, Optics*. Multiphoton processes; quantum electrodynamics; resonant interaction of light with atoms and molecules.

Fienup, James R., Ph.D., Stanford University, 1975. Robert E. Hopkins Professor of Optics; Professor of Electrical and Compute Engineering; Professor in the Center for Visual Science; Senior Scientist at the Laboratory for Laser Energetics. *Optics*. Phase retrieval; unconventional imaging; image processing; wave-front sensing.

Moore, Duncan T., Ph.D., University of Rochester, 1974. Rudolf and Hilda Kingslake Professor in Optical Engineering Science; Vice Provost for Entrepreneurship; Professor of Biomedical Engineering; Professor of Business Administration in the Simon Graduate School. *Optics*. Geometrical optics; optical instrumentation; gradient index glass; interferometry; medical optics.

Rolland, Jannick, Ph.D., University of Arizona, 1990. Brian J. Thompson Professor of Optical Engineering; Director, Robert E. Hopkins Center for Optical Design and Engineering; Director NSF/IUCRC: Center for Freeform Optics; Professor of Biomedical Engineering; Professor in the Center for Visual Science. *Optics*. Optical system design; instrumentation and system engineering; optical coherence tomography; head-worn displays.

Williams, David, Ph.D., University of California, San Diego, 1979. William G. Allyn Professor of Medical Optics; Dean for Research in Arts, Sciences and Engineering; Professor of Brain and Cognitive Sciences; Professor of Ophthalmology; Professor of Biomedical Engineering; Director of the Center for Visual Science. *Medical, Health Physics, Optics*. Sensitivity and resolution of the human visual system to patterns that are modulated in wavelength, space, and time.

Zhang, Xi-Cheng, Ph.D., Brown University, 1986. Director and M. Parker Givens Professor of The Institute of Optics. *Atomic, Molecular, & Optical Physics, Nonlinear Dynamics and Complex Systems, Optics, Quantum Foundations, Other*. Photonic quantum information systems, nonlinear optics, laser physics, and terahertz waves.

Professor

Alonso, Miguel, Ph.D., University of Rochester, 1996. Chair, Graduate Admissions Committee. *Applied Mathematics, Optics.* Mathematical models for wave propagation; theory of partial coherence; connection between the ray and wave models.

Boyd, Robert W., Ph.D., University of California, Berkeley, 1977. *Atomic, Molecular, & Optical Physics, Optics.* Nonlinear optics; infrared detection and generation.

Brown, Thomas, Ph.D., University of Rochester, 1987. Director, Robert E. Hopkins Center for Optical Design and Engineering. *Nano Science and Technology, Optics.* Integrated optics; fiber optics: optical properties of solids; quantum electronics.

Foster, Thomas, Ph.D., University of Rochester. *Medical, Health Physics, Optics.* Medical optics; photodynamic therapy.

Guo, Chunlei, Ph.D., University of Connecticut, 1999. *Atomic, Molecular, & Optical Physics, Optics.* High-intensity laser interactions with matter.

Knox, Wayne, Ph.D., University of Rochester, 1983. Professor of Physics; Senior Scientist at the Laboratory for Laser Energetics. Ultrafast science and technology; telecommunications; optoelectronics.

Krauss, Todd, Ph.D., Cornell University, 1998. Chair and Professor, Department of Chemistry. *Chemical Physics, Nano Science and Technology, Optics.* Nanoscale materials and devices.

Kruschwitz, Jennifer, Ph.D., Rochester Institute of Technology, 2015. *Optics.* Optical Interference Coatings and Color.

Stroud, Carlos R., Ph.D., Washington University, St. Louis, 1969. Professor of Physics. *Atomic, Molecular, & Optical Physics, Optics.* Quantum optics; short-pulse excitation of atoms and molecules.

Wicks, Gary, Ph.D., Cornell University, 1981. *Nano Science and Technology, Optics.* III–V semiconductors-epitaxial growth; optical properties; optical devices.

Associate Professor

Bentley, Julie, Ph.D., University of Rochester, 1995. *Optics.* Lens design.

Berger, Andrew, Ph.D., Massachusetts Institute of Technology. Associate Professor of Biomedical Engineering. *Medical, Health Physics, Optics.* Biomedical optics; Raman spectroscopy; optical analysis of blood and tissue.

Marciante, John R., Ph.D., University of Rochester, 1997. *Optics.* Lasers, waveguide, and fiber optics.

Yoon, Geunyoung, Ph.D., Osaka University. *Medical, Health Physics, Optics.* Biomedical and visual optics; adaptive optics.

Zavislan, James, Ph.D., University of Rochester, 1988. Associate Dean for Education and New Initiatives; Associate Professor of Biomedical Engineering; Associate Professor of Dermatology; Associate Professor of Ophthalmology. *Medical, Health Physics, Optics.* Optical engineering; medical optical instrumentation.

Assistant Professor

Cardenas, Jaime, Ph.D., University of Alabama Huntsville. *Optics.* Nanoscale and Integrated Photonics.

Lin, Qiang, Ph.D., University of Rochester, 2006. Assistant Professor of Electrical and Computer Engineering. *Electrical Engineering, Nano Science and Technology, Optics.* Nonlinear optics; quantum optics; nanoscopic photonic structures.

Vamivakas, Nick, Ph.D., Boston University, 2007. Assistant Professor of Quantum Physics. *Atomic, Molecular, & Optical Physics, Nano Science and Technology, Optics.* Solid-state quantum optics and information science; nanoscale optics-based sensing.

Research Associate Professor

Dai, Jianming, Ph.D., Tianjin University, 1994. *Optics.* Ultrafast lasers and phenomena, terahertz optoelectronics.

DEPARTMENTAL RESEARCH SPECIALTIES AND STAFF

Theoretical

Optics. Alonso, Eberly, Fienup, Rolland, Stroud.

Experimental

Atomic, Molecular, & Optical Physics. Agrawal, Bentley, Berger, Bigelow, Boyd, Brown, Fienup, Foster, Guo, Knox, Krauss, Lin, Marciante, Moore, Rolland, Stroud, Vamivakas, Wicks, Williams, Yoon, Zavislan, Zhang.

View additional information about this department at www.gradschoolshopper.com. Check out the "Why Choose Us?" section, find out more about the department's culture and get links to social media networks.

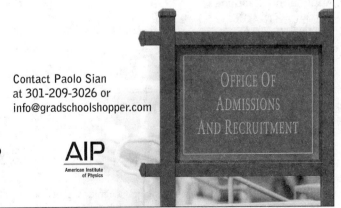

APPALACHIAN STATE UNIVERSITY

DEPARTMENT OF PHYSICS AND ASTRONOMY

Boone, North Carolina 28608
http://physics.appstate.edu

General University Information
Chancellor: Sheri Noren Everts
Dean of Graduate School: Michael McKenzie
University website: http://www.appstate.edu
School Type: Public
Setting: Rural
Total Faculty: 952
Total Graduate Faculty: 645
Total number of Students: 18,811
Total number of Graduate Students: 1,794

Department Information
Department Chairman: Dr. Jennifer L. Burris, Chair
Department Contact: Brad Johnson, Graduate Program
 Director
 Total full-time faculty: 24
 Total number of full-time equivalent positions: 24
 Full-Time Graduate Students: 46
 Female Full-Time Graduate Students: 6
 First-Year Graduate Students: 20
 Female First-Year Students: 3

Department Address
525 Rivers Street
ASU Box 32106
Boone, NC 28608
Phone: (828) 262-7318
Fax: (828) 262-2049
E-mail: johnsonbj2@appstate.edu
Website: http://physics.appstate.edu

ADMISSIONS

Admission Contact Information
Address admission inquiries to: Dontrell Parson, Office of Gradu-
 ate Admissions, ASU Box 32068, Boone, NC 28608
Phone: (828) 262-2130
E-mail: gradadmissions@appstate.edu
Admissions website: http://graduate.appstate.edu

Application deadlines
Fall admission:
U.S. students: July 1   *Int'l. students*: February 1
Spring admission:
U.S. students: November 1   *Int'l. students*: July 1

Application fee
U.S. students: $65   *Int'l. students*: $65

Admissions information
For Fall of 2018:
 Number of applicants: 25
 Number admitted: 20
 Number enrolled: 18

Admission requirements
Bachelor's degree requirements: Bachelor's degree in Physics
 or a related discipline is required, with an undergraduate GPA
 of 3.0 or better preferred.
Minimum undergraduate GPA: 2.5

GRE requirements
The GRE is required.
To be considered for regular admission to a degree program in
 the Graduate School at Appalachian, an applicant must meet
 or exceed one of the criteria below, using the test required
 for admission to the program (GRE) ●3.0 GPA in the last
 earned degree and official scores from the GRE, OR ●2.5 GPA
 in the last earned degree and official scores at the 25th percentile level from the GRE. These are the minimum requirements
 and do NOT guarantee admission to the program

Subjective GRE requirements
The Subjective GRE is not required.
The Physics GRE is NOT required.

TOEFL requirements
The TOEFL exam is required for students from non-English-
 speaking countries.
 PBT score: 550
 iBT score: 79
Minimum Scores: For the internet based TOEFL, 79 with no sub-
 section under 11. The IELTS minimum score is 6.5 (7.0 to
 be considered for financial assistance).

TUITION

Tuition year 2018–2019:
Tuition for in-state residents
 Full-time students: $7,961 annual
 Part-time students: $5,495.6 annual
Tuition for out-of-state residents
 Full-time students: $21,393 annual
 Part-time students: $15,569.6 annual
In-state rate for 0-2 hours per semester, including fees: $1070.95.
 Out-of-state rate for 0-2 hours per semester: $2749.95.
Credit hours per semester to be considered full-time: 9
Deferred tuition plan: No
Health insurance: Not available.
Other academic fees: $ (included in above).
Academic term: Semester
Number of first-year students who received partial tuition waivers: 1

Teaching Assistants, Research Assistants, and Fellowships
Number of first-year
 Teaching Assistants: 13
 Research Assistants: 1
Average stipend per academic year
 Teaching Assistant: $12,000
 Research Assistant: $15,000
 Fellowship student: $15,000

FINANCIAL AID

Application deadlines
Fall admission:
U.S. students: July 1   *Int'l. students*: April 1
Spring admission:
U.S. students: November 1   *Int'l. students*: August 1

Loans

Loans are available for U.S. students.

Loans are not available for international students.

GAPSFAS application required: No

FAFSA application required: Yes

For further information

Address financial aid inquiries to: Financial Aid Office, ASU
   P.O. Box 32059, Boone, NC 28608.
Phone: (828) 262-2190
E-mail: financialaid@appstate.edu
Financial aid website: http://financialaid.appstate.edu

HOUSING

Availability of on-campus housing

Single students: Yes
Married students: No
Childcare Assistance: No

For further information

Address housing inquiries to: University Housing Office, P.O.
   Box 32111, 287 Rivers St., Boone, NC 28608.
Phone: (828) 262-2160
E-mail: housing@appstate.edu
Housing aid website: http://housing.appstate.edu

Table A—Faculty, Enrollments, and Degrees Granted

Research Specialty	2017–2018 Faculty	Enrollment Fall 2017 Master's	Enrollment Fall 2017 Doctorate	Number of Degrees Granted 2017–2018 (2016–2017) Master's	Number of Degrees Granted 2017–2018 (2016–2017) Terminal Master's	Number of Degrees Granted 2017–2018 (2016–2017) Doctorate
Astronomy	5	–	–	3(3)	–	–
Astrophysics	3	–	–	–(1)	–	–
Atomic, Molecular, & Optical Physics	4	–	–	2(1)	–	–
Biophysics	2	–	–	2(1)	–	–
Climate/Atmospheric Science	2	–	–	1(2)	–	–
Electrical Engineering	2	–	–	1(1)	–	–
Energy Sources & Environment	3	–	–	1(1)	–	–
Engineering Physics/Science	5	–	–	30(35)	–	–
Fluids, Rheology	1	–	–	1(1)	–	–
Materials Science, Metallurgy	1	–	–	1	–	–
Nano Science and Technology	4	–	–	3(2)	–	–
Optics	3	–	–	3(2)	–	–
Physics and other Science Education	3	–	–	–	–	–
Total	–	–	–	40(35)	–	–
Full-time Grad. Stud.	–	46	–	–	–	–
First-year Grad. Stud.	–	20	–	–	–	–

GRADUATE DEGREE REQUIREMENTS

Master's: Three different concentrations in the Master's in Engineering Physics Degree: Systems and Laboratory Automation Concentration, comprehensive exam required, with thesis - 30 credit hours minimum; without thesis - 36 credit hours minimum; Professional Science Master's – Instrumentation & Automation Concentration, 37 credit hours minimum, internship and comprehensive exam required; and Professional Science Master's – Nanoscience for Advanced Materials Concentration, 41 credit hours minimum, internship and com-

prehensive exam required. Dual-degree also available: Professional Science Master's and Master's of Business Administration - Up to 18 hours of the 36-hour Professional Science Master's coursework is applied directly toward the 36-hour MBA program.

SPECIAL EQUIPMENT, FACILITIES, OR PROGRAMS

Modern laboratory facilities provide invaluable hands-on experience in cutting-edge research projects. Currently, these include: observational astronomy and astrophysics at Dark Sky Observatory; ultrahigh vacuum technology and microscopy, including time-of-flight secondary ion mass spectrometry, and an ion-storage facility; state-of-the-art optics laboratories including AppalAir atmospheric optical studies, the BiyOSeF Research Labs with Raman spectroscopy, fluorescence anisotropy, optical tweezers, and Raman - Tweezers; an applied electrostatics laboratory; surface analysis for nanoscale systems and materials science; a cryopumped thin film vacuum deposition system; and microscopy including (SEM), (FIB), (AFM), (STM), and X-ray microanalysis.

The Engineering Physics Program offers three different concentrations. The standard concentration in Systems and Laboratory Automation has both a thesis and non-thesis option. The other two concentrations are Professional Science Master's (PSM) concentrations in Instrumentation and Automation or in Nanoscience for Advanced Materials. These concentrations include advanced training in engineering physics, along with technical writing coursework and MBA-level coursework. All three concentrations can be completed in two years. In addition, PSM students have the option to stay a third year taking coursework in the Business School and graduating with both an MS in Engineering Physics and an MBA.

Table B—Separately Budgeted Research Expenditures by Source of Support

Source of Support	Departmental Research	Physics-related Research Outside Department
Federal government	$1,241,764	
State/local government	$99,385	
Non-profit organizations		
Business and industry	$16,045	
Other	$28,000	
Total	$1,385,194	

Table C—Separately Budgeted Research Expenditures by Research Specialty

Research Specialty	No. of Grants	Expenditures ($)
Astrophysics	1	$64,000
Biophysics	1	$128,382
Nano Science and Technology	1	$30,000
Optics	1	$28,000
Curriculum Development & Student Experiences	3	$1,102,173
Electrostatics	1	$20,000
Outreach	2	$12,639
Total	10	$1,385,194

FACULTY

Professor

Allen, Patricia E., Ph.D., Iowa State University, 1990. *Physics and other Science Education, Surface Physics*. Physics education pedagogy.

Briley, Michael M., Ph.D., University of Maryland, 1990. *Astronomy, Astrophysics*. Stellar spectroscopy/photometry; abundances and populations.

Burris, Jennifer L., Ph.D., Colorado State University, 2003. Departmental Chair. *Atomic, Molecular, & Optical Physics, Biophysics, Optics, Physics and other Science Education*. Raman spectroscopy, biophysics, Raman-tweezers, and optics.

Calamai, Anthony G., Ph.D., North Carolina State University, 1990. Distinguished Professor of Science Education, College of Arts & Sciences. *Astrophysics, Atomic, Molecular, & Optical Physics, Optics*. Experimental atomic, molecular, and optical physics; laboratory astrophysics.

Caton, Daniel B., Ph.D., University of Florida, 1981. Director, Dark Sky Observatory. *Astronomy, Astrophysics*. Computer applications to astronomical instrumentation; photoelectric photometry of eclipsing binary stars.

Clements, J. Sid, Ph.D., Florida State University, 1980. Fellow, IEEE. *Electrical Engineering, Electromagnetism, Engineering Physics/Science*. Experimental applied electrostatics (aerospace and industrial); electrical discharges; electronic instrumentation.

Coffey, Tonya S., Ph.D., North Carolina State University, 2004. *Materials Science, Metallurgy, Nano Science and Technology, Physics and other Science Education, Surface Physics*. Nanotribology; tribology; ultrahigh vacuum technology; microscopy; microanalysis.

Gray, Richard O., Ph.D., University of Toronto, 1986. Fellow, Royal Astronomical Society. *Astronomy, Astrophysics, Computational Physics, Energy Sources & Environment, Optics*. Stellar spectroscopy/photometry.

Sherman, James P., Ph.D., Colorado State University, 2002. *Atmosphere, Space Physics, Cosmic Rays, Energy Sources & Environment, Optics*. Optics, laser physics, and applications to environmental physics.

Thaxton, Christopher S., Ph.D., North Carolina State University, 2004. *Atmosphere, Space Physics, Cosmic Rays, Climate/Atmospheric Science, Computational Physics, Geophysics, Nonlinear Dynamics and Complex Systems*. Geophysics, computational physics, sediment transport and erosion studies, electronics, computer interfacing.

Associate Professor

Hester, Brooke C., Ph.D., University of Maryland, 2010. Undergraduate Program Director. *Biophysics, Medical, Health Physics, Optics*. Optical trapping, Raman-tweezers, biophysics, and fluorescence anisotropy.

Smith, Rachel L., Ph.D., University of California, Los Angeles, 2011. Director, Astronomy & Space Observation Research Laboratory. Nature Research Center, North Carolina Museum of Natural Sciences. *Astronomy, Astrophysics*. Geochemistry, protostellar objects, cosmochemistry.

Assistant Professor

Amet, François, Ph.D., Stanford University, 2014. *Applied Physics, Atomic, Molecular, & Optical Physics, Condensed Matter Physics, Nano Science and Technology, Surface Physics*. Transport properties of 2D materials, Fractional quantum Hall effect and symmetry-broken quantum Hall phases, Topological insulators, Topological superconductivity, Correlated electron materials, Ballistic transport and mesoscopic effects in Dirac materials, Quantum and nonlinear optics, semiconductor lasers, laser dynamics.

McGahee, Courtney, Ph.D., Clemson University, 2014. *Astronomy, Astrophysics*. Stellar spectroscopy, evolution, Galactic astronomy.

Professor Emeritus

Mamola, Karl C., Ph.D., Dartmouth College, 1973. *Physics and other Science Education*. Physics Education.

Pollock, Joseph T., Ph.D., University of Florida, 1982. *Astronomy, Astrophysics*. Quasars; electronic imaging; asteroids.

Rokoske, Thomas L., Ph.D., Auburn University, 1973. Electronics; microcomputer applications; robotics; electrical conduction mechanisms in thin films.

Russell, Phillip E., Ph.D., University of Florida, 1982. *Materials Science, Metallurgy, Nano Science and Technology, Surface Physics*.

Instructor

Hawkins, R. Lee, M.S., Appalachian State University, 1990. *Astronomy, Astrophysics, Engineering Physics/Science*.

Thomas, Scott A., Ph.D., University of North Carolina - Charlotte, 2004. Demonstrations Manager. *Electrical Engineering, Engineering Physics/Science, Systems Science/Engineering, Other*.

Senior Lecturer

Johnson, Bradley G., M.S., Appalachian State University, 2009. Graduate Program Director.

Ramsdell, Carla S., M.S., University of Florida, 1991. Sustainability Liaison, College of Arts & Sciences. *Other*. Sustainability, Thermodynamics.

Sitar, David J., M.S., Eastern Michigan University. Physics-Secondary Education Program Coordinator; Rankin "Go-To" Laboratory Facility Director. *Astronomy, Physics and other Science Education*. Astronomy Education.

Lecturer

Ingram, Daniel S., M.S., Appalachian State University, 2016. *Engineering Physics/Science*. Robotics.

Madison, Benjamin P., M.S., Appalachian State University, 2014. *Engineering Physics/Science*. Programmable Logic Circuits.

Lecturer / Lab Supervisor

Sherman, Leah B., Ph.D., University of Michigan, 2002. *Physics and other Science Education*. Physics Education.

DEPARTMENTAL RESEARCH SPECIALTIES AND STAFF

Experimental

Astronomy. Appalachian astronomers benefit from unique facilities at the Dark Sky Observatory, in addition to using large ground-based observatories like the Keck telescope or the National Optical Astronomy Observatory. Current research efforts focus on stellar spectroscopy, stellar populations, eclipsing binary stars, exoplanet detection, and the chemistry of forming planetary systems. Briley, Caton, Gray, McGahee, Smith.

Atmospheric and Environmental Physics. Faculty members are involved in interdisciplinary research initiatives in collaboration with the Environmental Science Program. Facilities include the Appalachian Atmospheric Interdisciplinary Research Program (AppalAIR), an air quality and climate research station which provides data for the Appalachian area. Facilities also include the Terrestrial Surface Processes Lab. Projects entail the modeling of granular flow, sediment transport, and river streams, as well as research on air pollution and transport, the impact of aerosols on climate and the forecast of high-impact events (severe weather) in the context of climate variability and change. Additionally, the Ion Trapping Lab conducts work on molecular ions that are abundant in the Ionosphere and active in ozone and IR production in that region. Calamai, James Sherman, Thaxton.

Atomic, Molecular, & Optical Physics. The department includes the Biophysics and Optical Sciences Facility (BiyOSeF) and the Ion Trap Laboratory. Using automated optical tweezers, Raman spectroscopy, fluorescence anisotropy, and a Laser Tweezers Raman Spectroscopy (LTRS) system, faculty at Appalachian explore the properties of microorganisms, proteins, and other biological molecules. Faculty also conduct research on the radiative properties and reaction rates of low-charge-state ions produced and stored in a UHV environment. Burris, Calamai, Hester, James Sherman.

Nanoscience and Condensed Matter Physics. he department includes state of the art microscopy facilities, as well as nano-fabrication capabilities ranging from UHV thin-film deposition to e-beam lithography. Faculty use scanning probe microscopy and scanning electron microscopy techniques to explore the properties of organic semiconductor thin films or the growth of metallic nanoparticles. Research at Appalachian

also entails the fabrication of two-dimensional van-der-Waals heterostructures and quantum transport in mesoscopic superconducting devices. Amet, Coffey.

Robotics and Electronics. Faculty members are collaborating with NASA to develop instrumentation related to the space shuttle program and Mars rover programs. The department is also involved in the development of remote sensing instrumentation (Braille display, stream monitoring, telemetry. . .), and is a part of Team Sunergy, Appalachian's solar vehicle team. Burris, Clements, Hester, Johnson, Rokoske, Thaxton.

View additional information about this department at www.gradschoolshopper.com. Check out the "Why Choose Us?" section, find out more about the department's culture and get links to social media networks.

DUKE UNIVERSITY

DEPARTMENT OF PHYSICS

Durham, North Carolina 27708-0305
http://www.phy.duke.edu

General University Information
President: Vincent Price, Ph.D.
Dean of Graduate School: Paula D. McClain, Ph.D.
University website: http://www.duke.edu
School Type: Private
Setting: Suburban
Total Faculty: 3,637
Total number of Students: 15,192
Total number of Graduate Students: 8,660

Department Information
Department Chairman: Prof. Warren S. Warren, Chair
Department Contact: Patricia Hight Davis, Administrative
  Manager
  Total full-time faculty: 45
  Total number of full-time equivalent positions: 56
  Full-Time Graduate Students: 144
  Female Full-Time Graduate Students: 13
  First-Year Graduate Students: 11
  Female First-Year Students: 1
  Total Post Doctorates: 12

Department Address
120 Physics Building, Box 90305
Science Drive, Duke University
Durham, NC 27708-0305
Phone: (919) 660-2690
Fax: (919) 660-2525
E-mail: patty.hight.davis@duke.edu
Website: http://www.phy.duke.edu

ADMISSIONS

Admission Contact Information
Address admission inquiries to: Stephen Teitsworth, Director of
  Graduate Studies, Department of Physics, Box 90305, Duke
  University, Durham, NC 27708-0305
Phone: (919) 660-2560
E-mail: dgs@phy.duke.edu
Admissions website: http://www.gradschool.duke.edu

Application deadlines
Fall admission:
U.S. students: December 10   *Int'l. students*: December 10

Application fee
U.S. students: $85   *Int'l. students*: $85
All application materials must be received by the deadline. Applications are normally reviewed by the Graduate Admissions Committee. Applications received earlier may be reviewed by other faculty and be recommended to the committee.

Admissions information
For Fall of 2018:
  Number of applicants: 258
  Number admitted: 45
  Number enrolled: 11

Admission requirements
Bachelor's degree requirements: A Bachelor's degree in Physics
  or related subject is required.

GRE requirements
The GRE is required.
While there are no official minimums for the GRE scores, students who obtain a score below 160 in Quantitative, 140 in Verbal, and 3.0 in Writing are admitted rarely and only under exceptional circumstances.

Subjective GRE requirements
The Subjective GRE is required.
While there is no official minimum for the Physics GRE score, students who receive a score of less than 600 are admitted rarely and only under exceptional circumstances.

TOEFL requirements
The TOEFL exam is required for students from non-English-speaking countries.
  iBT score: 90

Other admissions information
Undergraduate preparation assumed: Marion and Thornton,
  Classical Dynamics of Particles and Systems; Griffiths, Introduction to Electrodynamics; Schroeder, Introduction to Thermal Physics; Harris, Modern Physics; Griffiths, Introduction to Quantum Mechanics.

TUITION

Tuition year 2018–19:
  Full-time students: $57,240 annual
All admitted graduate students receive an assistantship (TA, RA,
  or fellowship) that includes tuition and most fees.
Credit hours per semester to be considered full-time: 9
Deferred tuition plan: Yes
Health insurance: Yes, No Charge.
Other academic fees: $40 One time transcript charge. $179.25
  Student recreation, activity, and services fee per term. $409.97
  Health fee per semester, $287.94 Health fee summer.
Academic term: Semester
Number of first-year students who received full tuition waivers: 13

Teaching Assistants, Research Assistants, and Fellowships
  Number of first-year
    Teaching Assistants: 16
    Fellowship students: 2
  Average stipend per academic year
    Teaching Assistant: $31,160.04
    Research Assistant: $31,160.04
    Fellowship student: $31,160.04

FINANCIAL AID

Application deadlines
Fall admission:
U.S. students: February 1   *Int'l. students*: February 1

Loans

Loans are available for U.S. students.
Loans are available for international students.
GAPSFAS application required: No
FAFSA application required: Yes

For further information

Address financial aid inquiries to: Ms. Lisa Wioskowski, Financial Aid Coordinator, Graduate School Office, 2127 Campus Drive, Durham, NC 27708.
Phone: (919) 681-3247
E-mail: lisa.wioskowski@duke.edu
Financial aid website: https://gradschool.duke.edu/financial-support

HOUSING

Availability of on-campus housing

Single students: No
Married students: No
Childcare Assistance: Yes

For further information

Address housing inquiries to: The Chronicle, Advertising Office, 1517 Hull Avenue, Durham, NC 27708.
Phone: 919-684-3811
E-mail: ads@dukechronicle.com
Housing aid website: https://gradschool.duke.edu/admissions/admitted-students/housing

Table A—Faculty, Enrollments, and Degrees Granted

Research Specialty	2017–18 Faculty	Enrollment Fall 2017 Master's	Enrollment Fall 2017 Doctorate	Number of Degrees Granted 2017–18 (2014–18) Master's	Number of Degrees Granted 2017–18 (2014–18) Terminal Master's	Number of Degrees Granted 2017–18 (2014–18) Doctorate
Atomic, Molecular, & Optical Physics	4	–	6	–	–(1)	–(7)
Biophysics	5	–	2	–	–	–(2)
Cosmology & String Theory	4	–	2	–	–	–
High Energy Physics	7	–	9	–	–(1)	3(7)
Medical, Health Physics	4	–	1	–	–	–(1)
Nano Science and Technology	7	–	5	–	–(1)	1(6)
Nanophysics	7	–	3	–	–	–(4)
Nonlinear Dynamics and Complex Systems	10	–	6	–	–	2(9)
Nuclear Physics	5	–	13	–	–	2(12)
Particles and Fields	6	–	8	–	–(1)	1(6)
Photonics and Quantum Information	5	–	5	–	–	–(2)
Physics of Beams	2	–	–	–	1(1)	–(3)
Non-specialized	1	–	16	–	–	–
Total	**67**	**–**	**76**	**–**	**1(5)**	**17(59)**
Full-time Grad. Stud.	–	–	76	–	–	–
First-year Grad. Stud.	–	–	13	–	–	–

GRADUATE DEGREE REQUIREMENTS

Master's: Master of Arts (M.A.): The department admits students only for the Ph.D. degree. However, if the student successfully completes nine graduate physics courses, he/she may be eligible for an M.A if he/she passes a masters level oral exam. There are further graduate school requirements. Master of Science (M.S.): Same as M.A. plus written thesis. Final examination on thesis.

Doctorate: Doctor of Philosophy (Ph.D.): Same as M.A. plus preliminary oral exam before dissertation work. Written dissertation. Final examination on dissertation.

SPECIAL EQUIPMENT, FACILITIES, OR PROGRAMS

Duke University is an institutional member of the Triangle Universities Nuclear Laboratory (TUNL), a Department of Energy (DOE) Center of Excellence in nuclear physics research. The Center operates three DOE-funded particle accelerator facilities on the campus of Duke university: (1) the High-Intensity Gamma-ray Source at the Duke Free Electron Laser Laboratory, (2) the Laboratory for Experimental Nuclear Physics, and (3) the tandem accelerator laboratory. These facilities have substantial inventories of particle detectors and signal-processing electronics that are used in carrying out experimental nuclear-physics research.

Table B—Separately Budgeted Research Expenditures by Source of Support

Source of Support	Departmental Research	Physics-related Research Outside Department
Federal government	$11,054,986	
State/local government		
Non-profit organizations	$11,928	
Business and industry	$90,844	
Other		
Total	**$11,157,758**	

Table C—Separately Budgeted Research Expenditures by Research Specialty

Research Specialty	No. of Grants	Expenditures ($)
Atomic, Molecular, & Optical Physics	8	$464,252
Biophysics	3	$202,073
Condensed Matter Physics	3	$464,325
Cosmology & String Theory	2	$107,477
High Energy Physics	20	$1,662,515
Nano Science and Technology	3	$148,308
Nonlinear Dynamics and Complex Systems	12	$697,915
Nuclear Physics	24	$4,412,127
Photonics and Quantum Information	11	$1,090,257
Particles and Fields	8	$1,198,859
Physics of Beams	8	$709,650
Total	**102**	**$11,157,758**

FACULTY

Professor

Aspinwall, Paul, Ph.D., University of Oxford, 1988. Professor of Mathematics. Gravity and string theory (primary appointment: mathematics).

Baranger, Harold U., Ph.D., Cornell University, 1986. Theoretical condensed matter physics; nanophysics.

Bass, Steffen, Ph.D., J. W. Goethe University, 1997. Associate Chair. *Computational Physics, Nuclear Physics, Particles and Fields, Statistical & Thermal Physics*. Theoretical nuclear and particle physics; relativistic heavy-ion collisions.

Beratan, David N., Ph.D., California Institute of Technology, 1985. *Biophysics, Chemical Physics*. Theoretical chemistry; theoretical molecular biophysics (primary appointment: chemistry).

Bray, Hubert L., Ph.D., Stanford University, 1997. Professor of Mathematics. *Astrophysics, Relativity & Gravitation*. General relativity and astrophysics (primary appointment: mathematics).

Brunel, Nicolas, Ph.D., Pierre and Marie Curie University. Professor of Neurobiology. *Neuroscience/Neuro Physics.* Biophysics, Nonlinear Dynamics and Complex Systems. Theoretical Neuroscience (primary appointment: neurobiology).

Calderbank, Robert, Ph.D., California Institute of Technology, 1980. Director of the Information Initiative at Duke. Error control codes for quantum computing, wireless communication and the internet of things, coding theory for computer architecture, signal processing, machine learning (primary appointment: Computer Science).

Chang, Albert Mien-Fu, Ph.D., Princeton University, 1983. *Condensed Matter Physics, Nano Science and Technology.* Experimental condensed matter physics; nanophysics.

Curtarolo, Stefano, Ph.D., Massachusetts Institute of Technology, 2003. Professor of Mechanical Engineering and Materials Science. *Condensed Matter Physics, Materials Science, Metallurgy, Statistical & Thermal Physics.* Solid-state physics; thermodynamics of materials; computational materials science (primary appointment: mechanical engineering and materials science).

Dobbins, James T., Ph.D., University of Wisconsin at Madison, 1985. Professor of Radiology, Associate Vice Provost. *Medical, Health Physics.* medical imaging; imaging physics; x-ray imaging (primary appointment: radiology).

Driehuys, Bastiaan, Ph.D., Princeton University, 1995. Professor of Radiology. *Medical, Health Physics.* Medical physics; radiology (primary appointment: Department of Radiology and Biomedical Engineering).

Edwards, Glenn S., Ph.D., University of Maryland, 1984. *Biophysics.* Biophysics.

Finkelstein, Gleb, Ph.D., Weizmann Institute of Science, 1998. *Condensed Matter Physics, Nano Science and Technology.* Experimental condensed matter physics; nanophysics.

Gao, Haiyan, Ph.D., California Institute of Technology, 1994. *Nuclear Physics.* Experimental medium energy nuclear physics.

Goshaw, Alfred T., Ph.D., University of Wisconsin-Madison, 1966. *High Energy Physics.* Experimental elementary particle physics; instrumentation.

Greenside, Henry S., Ph.D., Princeton University, 1981. *Biophysics, Nonlinear Dynamics and Complex Systems.* Theoretical neuroscience.

Howell, Calvin, Ph.D., Duke University, 1984. *Nuclear Physics.* few-nucleon systems; applications of nuclear physics in biology, medicine and national security.

Johnson, Allan G., Ph.D., Duke University, 1974. *Medical, Health Physics.* Imaging physics; magnetic resonance imaging (primary appointment: radiology).

Kim, Jungsang, Ph.D., Stanford University, 1999. Professor of Electrical and Computer Engineering. Photonics, quantum information (primary appointment: electrical and computer engineering).

Kotwal, Ashutosh V., Ph.D., Harvard University, 1995. *High Energy Physics.* Experimental elementary particle physics; instrumentation, algorithms and machine learning.

Kruse, Mark, Ph.D., Purdue University, 1996. *High Energy Physics.* Experimental elementary particle physics.

Liu, Jian-Guo, Ph.D., University of California, Los Angeles, 1990. *Computational Physics, Fluids, Rheology, Nonlinear Dynamics and Complex Systems, Other.* Computational physics, non-linear and complex systems, fluid dynamics.

Mehen, Thomas, Ph.D., Johns Hopkins University, 1998. *Nuclear Physics, Particles and Fields.* Theoretical nuclear and particle physics; effective field theory.

Mueller, Berndt, Ph.D., University of Frankfurt, 1973. *Nuclear Physics, Particles and Fields.* Theoretical nuclear and particle physics.

Oh, Seog, Ph.D., Massachusetts Institute of Technology, 1981. *Particles and Fields.* Experimental elementary particle physics.

Petters, Arlie O., Ph.D., Massachusetts Institute of Technology, 1991. *Cosmology & String Theory, Relativity & Gravitation.* General relativity and cosmology; gravitational lensing (primary appointment: mathematics).

Plesser, M. Ronen, Ph.D., Harvard University, 1991. *Cosmology & String Theory, Particles and Fields, Relativity & Gravitation.* String theory; supersymmetry.

Rubinstein, Michael, Ph.D., Harvard University, 1983. *Polymer Physics/Science.* Polymer physics; soft matter physics, biological physics, theoretical, computational, and experimental soft condensed matter physics (primary appointment: mechanical engineering and materials science.).

Samei, Ehsan, Ph.D., University of Michigan, 1997. *Medical, Health Physics.* Medical imaging (primary appointment: radiology).

Schmidt, Christoph, Ph.D., Technical Univeristy Munich, 1988. Experimental Biophysics.

Scholberg, Kate, Ph.D., California Institute of Technology, 1997. Director of Undergraduate Studies. *High Energy Physics.* Experimental elementary particle physics; neutrino physics.

Smith, David R., Ph.D., University of California, San Diego, 1994. *Electrical Engineering, Optics.* Quantum optics; photonic crystals; metamaterials (primary appointment: electrical and computer engineering).

Socolar, Joshua E. S., Ph.D., University of Pennsylvania, 1987. *Condensed Matter Physics, Nonlinear Dynamics and Complex Systems.* Theoretical condensed matter physics; nonlinear systems; regulatory networks.

Springer, Roxanne P., Ph.D., California Institute of Technology, 1990. *Nuclear Physics, Particles and Fields.* Theoretical nuclear and particle physics; effective field theory.

Walter, Christopher, Ph.D., California Institute of Technology, 1997. *Astrophysics, High Energy Physics.* Astrophysics, Cosmology, and High Energy Physics. Observational cosmology; astroparticle physics; experimental elementary particle physics; neutrino physics.

Warren, Warren S., Ph.D., University of California, Berkeley, 1980. *Atomic, Molecular, & Optical Physics, Biophysics, Chemical Physics.* Optical physics, molecular, and biomolecular imaging (primary appointment: chemistry).

Wu, Ying, Ph.D., Duke University, 1995. *Physics of Beams.* Free electron laser physics, beam physics.

Yang, Weitao, Ph.D., University of North Carolina, Chapel Hill, 1986. *Chemical Physics, Computational Physics.* Density functional theory, electronic structures in nano and condensed systems (primary appointment: chemistry).

Associate Professor

Arce, Ayana Tamu Holloway, Ph.D., Harvard University, 2006. *High Energy Physics.* Experimental high-energy physics.

Brown, Kenneth R., Ph.D., University of California Berkeley, 2003. *Atomic, Molecular, & Optical Physics, Quantum Foundations.* Photonics and Quantum Information, Atomic, Molecular & Optical Physics. Ion trap quantum computation; cold molecular ions; quantum controls and quantum error correction (primary appointment: electrical and computer engineering).

Chandrasekharan, Shailesh, Ph.D., Columbia University, 1995. *Computational Physics, Nuclear Physics, Particles and Fields.* Theoretical nuclear and particle physics; lattice field theory.

Charbonneau, Patrick, Ph.D., Harvard University, 2006. *Chemical Physics, Condensed Matter Physics, Statistical & Thermal Physics.* Theoretical condensed matter physics; chemical physics (primary appointment: chemistry).

Delaire, Olivier, Ph.D., California Institute of Technology, 2006. *Condensed Matter Physics.* elementary excitations in condensed-matter systems (phonons, electrons, spins), their couplings (phonon-phonon interaction, electron-phonon coupling, spin-phonon coupling), and their effects on macroscopic material properties.

Lu, Jianfeng, Ph.D., Princeton University, 2009. *Computational Physics.* Electronic structure and many body problems; quantum molecular dynamics; multi-scale modeling and analysis; rare events and sampling techniques.

Mercer, John M., Ph.D., Yale University, 1981. Associate Director of Undergraduate Studies of Physics. *Biophysics.*

Mikkelsen, Maiken H., Ph.D., University of California, Santa Barbara, 2009. *Condensed Matter Physics, Electrical Engineering, Nano Science and Technology.* Experimental condensed matter physics; nanophysics; spintronics; nanophotonics and quantum information science (joint appointment: electrical and computer engineering).

Teitsworth, Stephen W., Ph.D., Harvard University, 1986. *Condensed Matter Physics, Nano Science and Technology, Nonlinear Dynamics and Complex Systems, Statistical & Thermal Physics.* Statistical, nonlinear, and condensed matter physics; experimental and theoretical stochastic non-linear dynamics in electronic transport systems.

Assistant Professor

Barbeau, Philip, Ph.D., University of Chicago, 2009. *Astrophysics, Nuclear Physics.* Experimental particle and astroparticle physics; neutrinos; dark matter.

Barthel, Thomas, Ph.D., RWTH Aachen University, 2009. *Condensed Matter Physics.* Theoretical condensed matter physics.

Buchler, Nicolas Emile, Ph.D., University of Michigan, 2001. *Biophysics, Nonlinear Dynamics and Complex Systems.* Biophysics; non-linear dynamics and complex systems (joint appointment: biology).

Haravifard, Sara, Ph.D., McMaster University, 2010. *Condensed Matter Physics.* Experimental condensed matter physics; neutron and X-ray scattering.

Kapadia, Anuj, Ph.D., Duke University, 2007. *Medical, Health Physics.* (primary appointment: Radiology).

Marvian, Iman, Ph.D., University of Waterloo and Perimeter Institute, 2012. *Condensed Matter Physics, Quantum Foundations.* Quantum information and computation theory.

Scolnic, Daniel, Ph.D., Johns Hopkins University, 2013. *Astronomy, Astrophysics.* Astrophysics and Cosmology.

Troxel, Michael, Ph.D., University of Texas at Dallas, 2014. *Astronomy, Astrophysics.* Astrophysics and Cosmology.

Vossen, Anselm, Ph.D., University of Freiburg, 2008. *Nuclear Physics.* Experimental Nuclear Physics.

Emeritus

Evans, Lawrence E., Ph.D., Johns Hopkins University, 1960. *Particles and Fields.* Theoretical elementary particle physics.

Palmer, Richard G., Ph.D., University of Cambridge, 1973. *Statistical & Thermal Physics.* The application and development of statistical physics methods for many types of complex systems, including glasses and spin glasses, neural networks, genetic algorithms, and economic markets.

Roberson, Russell N., Ph.D., Johns Hopkins University, 1960. *Nuclear Physics.* Experimental nuclear physics.

Robinson, Hugh G., Ph.D., Duke University, 1954. *Atomic, Molecular, & Optical Physics.* Atomic and molecular physics.

Thomas, John E., Ph.D., Massachusetts Institute of Technology, 1979. *Atomic, Molecular, & Optical Physics, Condensed Matter Physics.* Experimental quantum optics; atomic and molecular collision physics.

Tornow, Werner, Ph.D., Universität zu Tübingen, 1974. *Nuclear Physics.* Experimental nuclear physics; neutrino physics.

Weller, Henry R., Ph.D., Duke University, 1967. *Nuclear Physics.* Experimental nuclear physics; nuclear structure; gamma-ray studies.

Research Associate Professor

Fischer, Martin, Ph.D., University of Texas at Austin, 2001. *Atomic, Molecular, & Optical Physics.* exploring novel nonlinear optical contrast mechanisms for molecular imaging.

Adjunct Faculty

Champagne, Art, Ph.D., Yale University, 1982. Director, Triangle Universities Nuclear Laboratory/Professor UNC-Chapel Hill. *Nuclear Physics.* Experimental Nuclear Astrophysics.

Everitt, Henry, Ph.D., Duke University, 1990. *Applied Physics, Condensed Matter Physics, Engineering Physics/Science, Optics.* Experimental condensed matter physics; molecular physics; quantum optoelectronics.

Gauthier, Daniel J., Ph.D., University of Rochester, 1989. *Nonlinear Dynamics and Complex Systems, Optics.* Quantum information science; non-linear and complex systems.

Guenther, Robert D., Ph.D., University of Missouri, 1968. *Applied Physics, Engineering Physics/Science, Optics.* Applied science; tera-hertz optics.

Lawson, Dewey T., Ph.D., Duke University, 1972. *Acoustics.* Acoustics.

Skatrud, David D., Ph.D., Duke University, 1984. *Electrical Engineering, Optics.* Quantum electronics; submillimeter/THz spectroscopy.

Tonchev, Anton, Ph.D., Joint Institute for Nuclear Research, Russia, 1995. *Nuclear Physics.* Experimental nuclear physics.

West, Bruce, Ph.D., University of Rochester, 1970. *Biophysics.* Biophysics.

Lecturer

Brown, Robert G., Ph.D., Duke University, 1982. *Computational Physics, Statistical & Thermal Physics.* Theoretical physics; statistical mechanics and computational physics.

DEPARTMENTAL RESEARCH SPECIALTIES AND STAFF

Theoretical

Biophysics. Theoretical neuroscience; Dynamics of networks of spiking neurons: irregular activity, oscillations; Models of synaptic plasticity, learning and memory: fixed point attractors, temporal sequences. Brunel, Buchler, Greenside, Rubinstein, Socolar.

Computational Physics. Computational physics; numerical techniques for solving non-linear partial differential equations; Monte Carlo algorithms in field theory and statistical mechanics; molecular dynamics; networks; large-scale computations on vector and parallel computers. Computational methods in fluid dynamics, material sciences, plasma physics, and geophysical flow; emergent behavior in flocking and swarming; numerical analysis and scientific computing. Baranger, Barthel, Bass, Robert Brown, Chandrasekharan, Charbonneau, Curtarolo, Greenside, Liu, Yang.

Cosmology & String Theory. String theory; geometry of spacetime, supersymmetry and duality; mirror symmetry, general relativity. Aspinwall, Bray, Petters, Plesser.

Nanophysics. Coherence and correlations in nanoscale systems like quantum dots and carbon nanotubes; coulomb blockade; quantum impurity effects; quantum phase transitions; quantum computing quantum entanglement; quantum information;

thermodynamics of materials; density functional theory. Baranger, Barthel, Beratan, Chandrasekharan, Curtarolo, Marvian, Yang.

Neuroscience/Neuro Physics. Brunel, Greenside.

Particles and Fields. Quantum chromodynamics and weak interactions; heavy quark physics; quark-gluon plasma; heavy-ion collisions; effective field theories of particle and nuclear interactions; lattice field theories and Monte Carlo simulations; strongly coupled field theories; thermalization. Bass, Chandrasekharan, Mehen, Mueller, Springer.

Polymer Physics/Science. Rubinstein.

Quantum Information and Matter. Baranger, Barthel, Kenneth Brown, Chandrasekharan, Marvian.

Statistical and nonlinear physics. Non-linear and complex systems; computational studies of non-linear and biological systems including genetic networks, heart and brain dynamics; collective behavior in matter and dynamical systems; spin glasses and glasses; adaptive algorithms; static and dynamic critical behavior in optics and magnetism; granular materials network dynamics; fractal growth; granular matter; in- and out-of-equilibrium dynamical properties of materials self-assembly; microphase formation; protein aggregation; glass and gel formation; stochastic dynamics of far-from-equilibrium systems. Brunel, Charbonneau, Greenside, Liu, Socolar, Teitsworth.

Experimental

Astrophysics and Cosmology. Walter.

Atomic, Molecular, & Optical Physics. quantum optics; single photon switching; quantum information; new technologies for optical communication; single photon sources; electromagnetic properties of materials; photonic crystals and metamaterials; molecular and biomolecular imaging. Kenneth Brown, Kim, Mikkelsen, Smith, Warren.

Biophysics. Emergent properties and tissue dynamics; fast thermodynamics in laser-tissue interactions; applications of free-electron lasers to biology and medicine; characterization and control of heart dynamics; stochastic processes in biological systems; optical analysis of molecular dynamics in single synapses; optical stimulation of single synapses; development of high-resolution imaging techniques; evolution of bistable and oscillatory dynamics in gene networks. Buchler, Edwards, Schmidt, West.

High Energy Physics. Precision tests of the Standard Model using the top quark, W, Z, and Higgs bosons; searches for new fundamental symmetries and extra dimensions; tests of the QCD hadron production models; studies of neutrino properties; neutrino oscillations; neutrino scattering; neutrino astrophysics; research program based at Fermilab, CERN, ORNL, and in Japan; state-of-the-art wire chamber and silicon detector development and construction; electronics design for high-energy physics experiments. Arce, Barbeau, Goshaw, Kotwal, Kruse, Oh, Scholberg, Walter.

Medical, Health Physics. Biomedical imaging; magnetic resonance imaging; magnetic resonance microscopy, X-ray microscopy, tomography, and microPET; X-ray imaging, breast tomosynthesis, dual-energy imaging, Monte Carlo simulation; radiation dose and image quality; imaging optimization. Dobbins, Driehuys, Johnson, Kapadia, Samei.

Nano Science and Technology. Electronic properties of carbon nanotubes, nanocrystals, semiconductor quantum dots, and self-assembled DNA structures; physics of Luttinger liquids; scanning tunneling; capacitance and atomic force microscopy; optoelectronic processes in semiconductor microstructures; subpicosecond optical characterization of nanostructures; nanometer-scale photonic, plasmonic, and phononic band engineering; solid-state spintronics, quantum information science, nanophotonics; non-linear electronic transport in semiconductor nanostructures. Barthel, Chang, Everitt, Finkelstein, Gauthier, Mikkelsen, Smith, Teitsworth.

Nonlinear Dynamics and Complex Systems. Non-linear and complex systems; granular materials; dynamics of granular flow; chaotic networks; pattern formation and spatio-temporal chaos in far-from-equilibrium fluids and electronic systems; noise-induced dynamics in far-from-equilibrium systems. Gauthier, Teitsworth.

Nuclear Physics. QCD and weak interactions in nuclear physics; nucleon structure, few-nucleon systems, and nucleon-nucleon interactions; electromagnetic nuclear physics; testing QCD using real photon beams; fundamental symmetry studies with ultra-cold neutrons, e.g., search for neutron electric dipole moment; Coherent neutrino scattering, double beta-decay searches; nuclear astrophysics. Barbeau, Gao, Howell, Tonchev, Vossen, Wu.

Photonics and Quantum Information. High-data-rate quantum key distribution; high-brightness hyper-entangled sources; multi-mode quantum communication; multi-element photon counting detector development; solid-state spin qubits. Everitt, Gauthier, Kim, Mikkelsen, Skatrud, Smith.

Physics of Beams. Beam physics; FEL and novel light source development; high-intensity gamma-ray source; FEL applications; plasma accelerators. Wu.

EAST CAROLINA UNIVERSITY

DEPARTMENT OF PHYSICS

Greenville, North Carolina 27858
http://www.ecu.edu/physics

General University Information
Chancellor: Dr. Cecil Staton
Dean of Graduate School: Dr. Paul Gemperline
University website: http://www.ecu.edu
School Type: Public
Setting: Rural
Total Faculty: 2,053
Total Graduate Faculty: 827
Total number of Students: 28,596
Total number of Graduate Students: 5,331

Department Information
Department Chairman: Dr. Jefferson Shinpaugh, Chair
Department Contact: Dr. Michael Dingfelder, Assistant Chair
  for Graduate Studies
Total full-time faculty: 18
Total number of full-time equivalent positions: 18
Full-Time Graduate Students: 40
Female Full-Time Graduate Students: 12
First-Year Graduate Students: 9
Female First-Year Students: 4
Total Post Doctorates: 2

Department Address
Mailstop 563
Howell Science Complex
Greenville, NC 27858
Phone: (252) 328-6739
Fax: (252) 328-6314
E-mail: physicsgrad@ecu.edu
Website: http://www.ecu.edu/physics

ADMISSIONS

Admission Contact Information
Address admission inquiries to: Graduate School, 131 Ragsdale
  Building, East Carolina University, Greenville, NC 27858-
  4353
Phone: (252) 328-6012
E-mail: gradschool@ecu.edu
Admissions website: http://www.ecu.edu/gradschool

Application deadlines
Fall admission:
U.S. students: March 1   *Int'l. students*: March 1

Application fee
U.S. students: $75   *Int'l. students*: $75
The admission process is handled by Graduate School. Please
  see Web site for details.

Admissions information
For Fall of 2018:
Number of applicants: 34
Number admitted: 24
Number enrolled: 9

Admission requirements
Bachelor's degree requirements: A Bachelor's degree in Physics
  or related subject is required.
Minimum undergraduate GPA: 2.7

GRE requirements
The GRE is required.
Quantitative score: 147
Verbal score: 147
Analytical score: 3.5
Mean GRE score range (25th–75th percentile): 301-318
An average 30 percentile score of quantitative + verbal is the
  absolute minimum.

Subjective GRE requirements
The Subjective GRE is not required.

TOEFL requirements
The TOEFL exam is required for students from non-English-
  speaking countries.
iBT score: 78
An iBT TOEFL score of minimum 18 in each section is required,
  with a total minimum score of 78. Also accepted: IELTS: minimum score of 6.5 and Pearson Test of English (PTE): minimum score of 65 with 60 on each section.

Other admissions information
Additional requirements: Three letters of recommendation, a letter of intent, and a CV/Resume are required.
  Minimum GPA for Ph.D. program: 3.0.
Undergraduate preparation assumed: Mathematics: Calculus
  through Differential Equations; Physics: Courses in Mechanics, Electricity and Magnetism, Thermodynamics, Modern
  Physics (Atomic and Nuclear Physics), Intro to Quantum Mechanics, Advanced Laboratory.

TUITION
Tuition year 2018–2019:
Tuition for in-state residents
Full-time students: $4,749 annual
Tuition for out-of-state residents
Full-time students: $17,898 per semester
In-state residents per semester: full time (100%) $2374.50. Out-
  of-state residents per semester: full time (100%) $8949.00.
  Reduced tuition rates for part-time available: one-two hours
  (25%), three-five hours (50%), six-eight hours (75%).
Credit hours per semester to be considered full-time: 9
Deferred tuition plan: Yes
Health insurance: Available at the cost of $2,588 per year.
Other academic fees: Approximately $1,350 per semester for uni-
  versity fees, educational/technology fees, and health services
  fees.
Academic term: Semester
Number of first-year students who received full tuition waivers: 3

Teaching Assistants, Research Assistants, and Fellowships
Number of first-year
  Teaching Assistants: 6
Average stipend per academic year

Teaching Assistant: $21,000
Research Assistant: $23,520

Ph.D. Teaching Assistantship (12 months) $18,360 (entering with BS) - $20,040 (entering with MS) - $21,600 (PhD candidate) plus tuition remission plus health insurance. M.S. Teaching Assistantship (9 months) $11,000.00 plus out-of-state tuition remission.

FINANCIAL AID

Loans

Loans are available for U.S. students.
Loans are not available for international students.
GAPSFAS application required: No
FAFSA application required: No

For further information

Address financial aid inquiries to: Financial Aid Office, Graduate School, 131 Ragsdale, East Carolina University, Greenville, NC 27858-4353.
Phone: (252) 328-6610
E-mail: faques@ecu.edu
Financial aid website: http://www.ecu.edu/financial

HOUSING

Availability of on-campus housing

Single students: Yes
Married students: No
Childcare Assistance: No

For further information

Address housing inquiries to: University Housing Service, Jones Residence Hall, East Carolina University, Greenville, NC 27858-4353.
Phone: (252) 328-4663
E-mail: housing@ecu.edu
Housing aid website: http://www.ecu.edu/studentlife/campusliving

Table A—Faculty, Enrollments, and Degrees Granted

Research Specialty	2017–18 Faculty	Enrollment Spring 2018		Number of Degrees Granted 2017–18 (2013–18)		
		Master's	Doctorate	Master's	Terminal Master's	Doctorate
Acoustics	1	1	–	–	–	–
Atomic, Molecular, & Optical Physics	3	1	9	1(5)	–	2(4)
Biophysics	3	–	4	–(1)	–	–(1)
Computational Physics	3	–	2	–(3)	–	1(2)
Laser	2	–	3	–(1)	–	–(2)
Medical, Health Physics	5	16	8	–	8(26)	–(2)
Physics and other Science Education	1	1	–	–	–	–
Total	18	19	26	1(10)	8(26)	3(11)
Full-time Grad. Stud.	–	19	23	–	–	–
First-year Grad. Stud.	–	9	6	–	–	–

GRADUATE DEGREE REQUIREMENTS

Master's: A minimum of 34 semester hours is required for the Applied Physics (AP) option, a minimum of 39 semester hours is required for the Health Physics (HP) option, and a minimum of 39 semester hours is required for the Medical Physics (MP) option. A major field test is administered upon entrance into the program; for the AP option, candidates must write and defend a thesis based on original research; a thesis is not required for MP and HP students.

Doctorate: A minimum of 48 semester hours beyond the Master's degree is required; a master's degree in physics or related area is preferred; students entering with a BS in physics or a related area will follow the AP master's curriculum; doctoral written and oral exams covering biomedical physics curriculum; thesis required; dissertation required.

Other Degrees: Ph.D. program offers an integrated Ph.D. and MS-MP concentration. MS-MP is CAMPEP accredited.

Thesis: Thesis may be written in absentia; Ph.D. Program: 5 consecutive semester residence requirement.

SPECIAL EQUIPMENT, FACILITIES, OR PROGRAMS

The Department operates in addition to classroom, offices, and well-equipped teaching and research laboratories as well as electronic and machine shops to provide service to faculty and students throughout the University. The Department maintains state-of-the-art computing facilities, including a recently upgraded student computing laboratory with Mac and PCs. Research laboratories include the Accelerator Laboratory, the Biophysics Spectroscopy Laboratory, the Biomedical Laser Laboratory, the Raman Spectroscopy Laboratory, the Radiation Instrumentation Laboratory, and high-performance scientific computing equipment. Equipment in these laboratories includes, but is not limited to, the following: Accelerator Laboratory: a 2-MV tandem light ion accelerator; Biophysics Spectroscopy Laboratory: circular and linear dichroism spectroscopy, photospectrometer, MALDI-TOF mass spectrometer; Biomedical Laser Laboratory: high-power Nd:YAG Q-switched laser system, nanosecond N2 and dye laser system, CW diode-pumped Nd:YAG laser, diode-pumped nd:YVO4 Q-switched laser, harmonic generators with nonlinear crystals, multichannel fluorescence decay time measurement system, UV-VIS-IR spectrophotometer, high-resolution (0.03 nm) spectrometer; Raman Spectroscopy Laboratory: optical tweezers, Raman spectroscopy, confocal Raman imaging; computing: 60 processor parallel cluster with Linux operating system.

Table B—Separately Budgeted Research Expenditures by Source of Support

Source of Support	Departmental Research	Physics-related Research Outside Department
Federal government	$247,000	
State/local government	$89,000	
Non-profit organizations		
Business and industry		
Other		
Total	$336,000	

FACULTY

Professor

Bier, Martin, Ph.D., Clarkson University, 1990. *Biophysics, Neuroscience/Neuro Physics, Nonlinear Dynamics and Complex Systems, Theoretical Physics*. Mathematics, modeling, computational physics.

Dingfelder, Michael, Ph.D., Eberhard-Karls University, Tübingen, 1995. Assistant Chair for Graduate Studies. *Atomic, Molecular, & Optical Physics, Computational Physics, Theoretical Physics, Other*. Theoretical physics, radiation physics and modeling.

Hu, Xin-Hua, Ph.D., University of California, Irvine, 1991. Director, Biomedical Laser Laboratory. *Biophysics, Optics, Other*. Biomedical optics; experimental.

Lapicki, Gregory, Ph.D., New York University, 1975. *Atomic, Molecular, & Optical Physics, Computational Physics, Physics of Beams, Theoretical Physics*. Theoretical atomic physics.

Li, Yong-qing, Ph.D., Academia Sinica, Shanghai, 1989. Director, Biomedical Optics Laboratory. *Biophysics, Optics, Other*. Experimental optical physics and biomedical physics.

Shinpaugh, Jefferson L., Ph.D., Kansas State University, 1990. Director, ECU Accelerator Laboratory. *Accelerator, Atomic, Molecular, & Optical Physics, Physics of Beams*. Experimental atomic and molecular physics.

Associate Professor

DeWitt, Regina, Ph.D., University of Heidelberg, 2002. *Accelerator, Applied Physics, Atomic, Molecular, & Optical Physics, Medical, Health Physics, Other*. Radiation dosimetry, radiation physics, OSL dating.

Jung, Jae Won, Ph.D., Texas A&M University, 2007. *Medical, Health Physics, Other*. Health physics, medical health physics.

Justiniano, Edson L.B., Ph.D., Kansas State University, 1982. *Accelerator, Atomic, Molecular, & Optical Physics, Computational Physics*. Experimental atomic physics.

Kenney, John M., Ph.D., Stony Brook University, 1985. Assistant Chair for Undergraduate Studies. *Biophysics, Chemical Physics, Optics, Other*. Fibril amyloid-like structures; CD-Spectroscopy.

Lin, Zi Wei, Ph.D., Columbia University, 1996. *Atmosphere, Space Physics, Cosmic Rays, Computational Physics, High Energy Physics, Nuclear Physics, Theoretical Physics*. Theoretical physics and radiation transport modeling.

Lu, Jun Qing, Ph.D., University of California, Irvine, 1991. *Computational Physics, Condensed Matter Physics, Theoretical Physics*. Theoretical condensed matter and biomedical physics.

Sprague, Mark W., Ph.D., University of Mississippi, 1994. *Acoustics, Atomic, Molecular, & Optical Physics, Other*. Bioacoustics; sound propagation in condensed media, especially water; sound of fish.

Assistant Professor

Hudson, Nathan, Ph.D., University of North Carolina, 2011. *Biophysics, Other*. Experimental molecular biophysics, structure and dynamics of biomolecules.

Wolf, Steven, Ph.D., Michigan State University, 2012. *Physics and other Science Education*. Physics and STEM education research.

Professor Emeritus

Bissinger, George, Ph.D., University of Notre Dame. *Acoustics, Other*. Acoustics of music instruments.

Day, Orville W., Ph.D., Brigham Young University, 1973. *Computational Physics, Relativity & Gravitation, Theoretical Physics*. Quantum mechanics of atoms and molecules; General Relativity.

Joyce, James M., Ph.D., University of Pennsylvania, 1967. *Biophysics*. Biomedical physics.

Kempf, Ruth, Ph.D., Rensselaer Polytechnic Institute, 1982. *Medical, Health Physics, Other*. Security studies; health physics; radiation biology.

Sayetta, Thomas C., Ph.D., University of South Carolina, 1964. *Non-specialized*.

Sutherland, John C., Ph.D., Georgia Institute of Technology, 1967. *Biophysics, Other*. Biophysics, Spectroscopy.

Toburen, Larry H., Ph.D., Vanderbilt University. *Accelerator, Atomic, Molecular, & Optical Physics, Other*. Experimental radiation physics.

Adjunct Faculty

Feng, Yuanming, Ph.D., Tianjin University, 1997. Medical Physics Residency Director. *Medical, Health Physics*. Clinical medical physics.

Adjunct Professor

Huang, Zhibin, Ph.D., Case Western Reserve University, 2008. *Medical, Health Physics*. Medical physics; clinical radiation therapy.

McLawhorn, Robert A., Ph.D., East Carolina University, 2008. *Medical, Health Physics*. Clinical medical physics.

Rasmussen V, Karl H., Ph.D., University of Wisconsin - Madison, 2009. *Medical, Health Physics*. Clinical medical physics.

DEPARTMENTAL RESEARCH SPECIALTIES AND STAFF

Theoretical

Biophysics. Theoretical study of biological processes on a molecular level; motor proteins; modulated barriers; power line issue; electroporation. Bier.

Computational Physics. Quantum mechanics of atoms and molecules; density functional theory; light scattering from random media; characterization of inhomogeneity in tissue using noncontact laser speckle techniques; Monte Carlo modeling of charged particle track structure; nuclear radiation transport models and codes; biomedical applications of radiation transport models; space radiation physics; mathematical theory of plasma oscillations in black holes; application to general relativity. Day, Dingfelder, Lin, Lu.

Theoretical Radiation Physics. Atomic and molecular collisions; condensed phase collisions; biological targets; penetration of charged particles through matter; inner shell ionization and stopping power. Dingfelder, Lapicki.

Experimental

Bioaccooustics. Atmospheric and underwater acoustics; computational studies on convective effects on sound propagation; acoustic characterization of Sciaenid fish calls. Bissinger, Sprague.

Biomedical Optics. Lasers, photonics, and spectroscopy: experimental and theoretical study of light interaction with biological tissues and cells; optical imaging of turbid medium; flow cytometry; circular and linear dichroism (CD) spectroscopy; spider silk; structure, function, and dynamics of DNA, proteins, and other biological materials; optical tweezers; Raman spectroscopy; confocal Raman imaging. Hu, Kenney, Li, Sutherland.

Experimental Radiation Physics. Experimental atomic physics; ion-atom collisions; charge transfer; recombination and excitation in electron-ion collisions; laser-assisted electron-ion and ion-atom collisions; application of atomic physics to biological physics and trace-element analysis; measurement of cross-sections for collisions involving ions and neutral particles and application of these data in the study of charged particle track structure; accelerator based particle microbeams. DeWitt, Justiniano, McLawhorn, Shinpaugh, Toburen.

Medical, Health Physics. Radiation detection and measurement; dosimetric studies of brachytherapy seeds; dose reconstruction in radiation therapy; dose reconstruction; optically stimulated luminescence; thermoluminescence; MRI physics; accelerator physics; imaging analysis; low-dose-rate brachytherapy; image-guided radiation therapy; robotic brachytherapy; tumor tracking; clinical medical physics. DeWitt, Feng, Huang, Jung, Kempf, McLawhorn, Rasmussen V.

Molecular Biophysics. Molecular biophysics, structure and dynamics of biomolecules. Hudson.

NORTH CAROLINA STATE UNIVERSITY, RALEIGH

DEPARTMENT OF PHYSICS

Raleigh, North Carolina 27695-8202
http://www.physics.ncsu.edu

General University Information
President: Randy Woodson
Dean of Graduate School: Peter Harries (Interim)
University website: http://www.ncsu.edu/
School Type: Public
Setting: Urban
Total Faculty: 2,068
Total Graduate Faculty: 2,400
Total number of Students: 34,767
Total number of Graduate Students: 9,591

Department Information
Department Chairman: Prof. Paul Huffman, Head
Department Contact: Paul Huffman, Professor and Head
  Total full-time faculty: 54
  Total number of full-time equivalent positions: 47
  Full-Time Graduate Students: 138
  Female Full-Time Graduate Students: 26
  First-Year Graduate Students: 27
  Female First-Year Students: 4
  Total Post Doctorates: 20

Department Address
2401 Stinson Drive
Raleigh, NC 27695-8202
Phone: (919) 515-2521
Fax: (919) 515-6538
E-mail: prhuffma@ncsu.edu
Website: http://www.physics.ncsu.edu

ADMISSIONS

Admission Contact Information
Address admission inquiries to: Director of Graduate Programs, Physics Department, Box 8202, NCSU, Raleigh, NC 27695-8202
Phone: (919) 515-8706
E-mail: py-grad-program@ncsu.edu
Admissions website: http://www.physics.ncsu.edu

Application deadlines
Fall admission:
U.S. students: January 3   *Int'l. students*: January 3

Application fee
U.S. students: $75   *Int'l. students*: $85
No application fee for early domestic applicants - see website for details. Late applications will be processed for exceptional applicants if slots are still available.

Admissions information
For Fall of 2018:
  Number of applicants: 145
  Number admitted: 80
  Number enrolled: 27

Admission requirements
Bachelor's degree requirements: Bachelor's degree in Physics (or related field) is required.
Minimum undergraduate GPA: 3.0

GRE requirements
The GRE is recommended but not required.

Subjective GRE requirements
The Subjective GRE is recommended.
  Mean Advanced GRE score range (25th–75th percentile): 700-880
  Typical 1st round admissions decision for students with GRE Physics above 750. Later decisions may include lower scores.

TOEFL requirements
The TOEFL exam is required for students from non-English-speaking countries.
  PBT score: 560
  iBT score: 80
Preferred TOEFL scores for admission are as follows: Listening-20; Reading-20; Writing-20; Speaking-20. For a teaching assistantship, a minimum of 23 on the speaking portion is required. – The paper-based test requires a score of 560 or higher (with scores of 50 on at least two of the three sections and no section score below 45).

Other admissions information
Undergraduate preparation assumed: Griffiths, Electromagnetic Fields and Waves; Hand and Finch, Analytical Mechanics; Gasiorowicz, Quantum Physics. (or equivalent) Thermal physics.

TUITION

Tuition year 2017–2018:
Tuition for in-state residents
  Full-time students: $8,917 annual
Tuition for out-of-state residents
  Full-time students: $25,405 annual
Part-time prorated.
Credit hours per semester to be considered full-time: 9
Deferred tuition plan: Yes
Health insurance: Available at the cost of $2540 per year.
Other academic fees: Required student fees are about $2550 per year.
Academic term: Semester

Teaching Assistants, Research Assistants, and Fellowships
Number of first-year
  Teaching Assistants: 24
  Research Assistants: 1
  Fellowship students: 2
Average stipend per academic year
  Teaching Assistant: $23,532
  Research Assistant: $24,000
  Fellowship student: $24,000

FINANCIAL AID

Application deadlines
Fall admission:
U.S. students: March 1

Loans

Loans are available for U.S. students.
Loans are available for international students.
GAPSFAS application required: No
FAFSA application required: No

For further information

Address financial aid inquiries to: Financial Aid Office, 2016
   Harris Hall, Box 7302.
Phone: (919) 515-2421
Financial aid website: http://www.ncsu.edu/finaid

HOUSING

Availability of on-campus housing

Single students: Yes
Married students: Yes
Childcare Assistance: No

For further information

Address housing inquiries to: Housing Assignments Office, 1112
   Pullen Hall, Box 7315.
Phone: (919) 515-2440
E-mail: housing@ncsu.edu
Housing aid website: http://www.ncsu.edu/housing

Table A—Faculty, Enrollments, and Degrees Granted

Research Specialty	2017–18 Faculty	Enrollment Fall 2017 Master's	Enrollment Fall 2017 Doctorate	Number of Degrees Granted 2017–18 (2013–18) Master's	Number of Degrees Granted 2017–18 (2013–18) Terminal Master's	Number of Degrees Granted 2017–18 (2013–18) Doctorate
Astrophysics	6	–	10	–(6)	–(3)	2(7)
Atomic, Molecular, & Optical Physics	1	–	5	–(1)	–	–
Biophysics	6	–	15	2(4)	–(2)	2(5)
Condensed Matter Physics	13	–	31	5(12)	–(4)	4(36)
Nuclear Physics	10	–	23	1(1)	–(3)	2(14)
Physics and other Science Education	2	–	5	–(1)	–	3(6)
Non-specialized	–	2	11	1(11)	–(6)	–
Other	1	–	–	–	–	1(4)
Total	39	2	116	9(35)	–(18)	9(73)
Full-time Grad. Stud.	–	2	116	–	–	–
First-year Grad. Stud.	–	2	18	–	–	–

GRADUATE DEGREE REQUIREMENTS

Master's: Thirty semester-hours; 3.0/4.0 overall GPA; two semesters residence; no foreign language; no computer language; Option A-comprehensive oral exam and thesis required, or Option B-comprehensive written exam required.
Doctorate: Eight semesters beyond the baccalaureate with a 3.0/4.0 overall GPA; no computer language; comprehensive written and oral exams; thesis required.
Thesis: Thesis may be written in absentia.

SPECIAL EQUIPMENT, FACILITIES, OR PROGRAMS

The majority of the department is located in 55,000 sq. ft. of the recently renovated Riddick Hall. It houses a number of modern laboratories and teaching facilities, including a clean room and shared experimental user facilities. The adjacent NC State Centennial Campus houses several departmental nanoscience/materials laboratories in several buildings. Major facilities for nuclear physics research are provided by the Triangle Universities Nuclear Laboratory. The optical physics and nanoscience/materials laboratories are well-equipped with an atomic force microscope, various laser systems, spectrometers, electron microscopes, materials preparation systems, and extensive data acquisition equipment. Both a student machine shop and a professionally staffed machine shop are available for custom equipment fabrication. In addition, collaboration exists with other departments and with various industrial and governmental laboratories. The computer facilities are state-of-the-art. At the department and research group level, powerful graphics workstations serve as graphics and communications nodes. The University ranks highly in high performance computing (HPC) and has been awarded a very high bandwidth (Internet2) connectivity to National Supercomputing Centers and other nationally prominent Research Universities.

Table B—Separately Budgeted Research Expenditures by Source of Support

Source of Support	Departmental Research	Physics-related Research Outside Department
Federal government	$7,190,875	
State/local government	$529,679	
Non-profit organizations		
Business and industry		
Other	$285,316	
Total	$8,005,870	

FACULTY

Professor

Ade, Harald, Ph.D., Stony Brook University, 1990. *Condensed Matter Physics, Energy Sources & Environment, Nano Science and Technology, Polymer Physics/Science*. Experimental physics.

Aspnes, David E., Ph.D., University of Illinois, 1965. *Condensed Matter Physics, Optics, Solid State Physics*. Experimental physics; optical physics/materials.

Beichner, Robert J., Ph.D., State University of New York at Buffalo, 1989. *Physics and other Science Education*. Physics education research.

Bernholc, Jerzy, Ph.D., Lund University, 1977. *Biophysics, Condensed Matter Physics, Nano Science and Technology, Solid State Physics*. Theoretical physics; nanoscience/materials.

Blondin, John M., Ph.D., University of Chicago, 1987. *Astrophysics, Theoretical Physics*. Theoretical physics; astrophysics.

Brown, J. David, Ph.D., University of Texas, 1985. *Applied Mathematics, Astrophysics, Relativity & Gravitation, Theoretical Physics*. Theoretical physics; astrophysics and relativity.

Clarke, Laura, Ph.D., University of Oregon, 1998. *Condensed Matter Physics, Nano Science and Technology, Optics, Polymer Physics/Science, Statistical & Thermal Physics*. Experimental physics; nanoscience/materials; molecular physics.

Daniels, Karen E., Ph.D., Cornell University, 2002. *Condensed Matter Physics, Fluids, Rheology, Nonlinear Dynamics and Complex Systems, Polymer Physics/Science, Statistical & Thermal Physics*. Experimental physics; nonequilibrium granular and fluid systems.

Ditto, William, Ph.D., Clemson University, 1988. *Nonlinear Dynamics and Complex Systems*. Nonlinear Dynamic Based Synthetic Computing Chaos Computing.

Golub, Robert, Ph.D., Massachusetts Institute of Technology, 1968. *Nuclear Physics*. Experimental physics; ultra-cold neutrons.

Gould, Christopher R., Ph.D., University of Pennsylvania, 1969. *Nuclear Physics*. Experimental physics; nuclear physics.

Hallen, Hans, Ph.D., Cornell University, 1991. *Condensed Matter Physics, Electromagnetism, Optics*. Experimental physics; optics.

Huffman, Paul, Ph.D., Duke University, 1995. *Nuclear Physics*. Experimental physics; low-temperature and nuclear physics.

Ji, Chueng, Ph.D., Korea Advanced Institute of Science & Technology (KAIST), 1982. *High Energy Physics, Particles and Fields, Quantum Foundations, Relativity & Gravitation, Theoretical Physics*. Theoretical physics; nuclear physics.

Krim, Jacqueline, Ph.D., University of Washington, 1984. *Condensed Matter Physics, Nano Science and Technology, Solid State Physics*. Experimental physics; nanoscience/materials.

McLaughlin, Gail, Ph.D., University of California, San Diego, 1996. *Astrophysics, Nuclear Physics, Theoretical Physics*. Theoretical physics; nuclear physics; astrophysics.

Mitas, Lubos, Ph.D., Slovak Academy of Sciences, 1989. *Nano Science and Technology, Solid State Physics, Theoretical Physics*. Theoretical physics; nanoscience/materials.

Reynolds, Stephen P., Ph.D., University of California, Berkeley, 1980. *Astronomy, Astrophysics*. Theoretical physics; astrophysics.

Riehn, Robert, Ph.D., University of Cambridge, 2003. *Biophysics, Condensed Matter Physics, Nano Science and Technology, Polymer Physics/Science*. Experimental physics; biophysics; soft condensed matter.

Roland, Christopher M., Ph.D., McGill University, 1989. *Biophysics, Condensed Matter Physics, Statistical & Thermal Physics, Theoretical Physics*. Theoretical biological physics.

Sagui, Celeste, Ph.D., University of Toronto, 1995. *Biophysics, Statistical & Thermal Physics, Theoretical Physics*. Theoretical physics; biophysics.

Schaefer, Thomas, Ph.D., University of Regensburg, 1992. *Nuclear Physics, Particles and Fields, Quantum Foundations, Theoretical Physics*. Theoretical nuclear/particle physics.

Thomas, John E., Ph.D., Massachusetts Institute of Technology, 1979. *Atomic, Molecular, & Optical Physics*. Atomic physics.

Weninger, Keith, Ph.D., University of California, Los Angeles, 1997. *Biophysics, Plasma and Fusion*. Experimental physics; biophysics.

Young, Albert, Ph.D., Harvard University, 1995. *Nuclear Physics*. Experimental physics; atomic and nuclear physics.

Associate Professor

Dougherty, Daniel, Ph.D., University of Maryland, 2004. *Condensed Matter Physics, Nano Science and Technology, Solid State Physics*. Experimental physics; nanoscale science and technology.

Frohlich, Carla, Ph.D., University of Basel, 2007. *Astrophysics, Nuclear Physics, Theoretical Physics*. Theoretical physics; nuclear physics; astrophysics.

Gundogdu, Kenan, Ph.D., University of Iowa, 2004. *Condensed Matter Physics, Nano Science and Technology, Optics*. Experimental physics; nanoscale science and technology.

Kneller, James, Ph.D., Ohio State University, 2001. *Astrophysics, Nuclear Physics, Theoretical Physics*. Theoretical physics; nuclear physics; astrophysics.

Lim, Shuang Fang, Ph.D., University of Cambridge, 2004. *Biophysics, Nano Science and Technology*. Experimental physics, nanoscale physics, biophysics.

Unsal, Mithat, Ph.D., University of Washington, 2004. *Applied Mathematics, Particles and Fields, Quantum Foundations, Theoretical Physics*.

Wang, Hong, Ph.D., University of North Carolina, Chapel Hill, 2003. *Biophysics*. Experimental Physics, biophysics.

Assistant Professor

Belmonte, Julio, Ph.D., Indiana University Bloomington, 2014. *Biophysics*.

Elting, Mary W., Ph.D., Stanford University, 2012. *Applied Physics*.

Green, Matthew P., Ph.D., Stanford University, 2010. *Nuclear Physics, Particles and Fields*. Experimental physics, Nuclear physics, Neutrino Physics.

Kemper, Alexander F., Ph.D., University of Florida, 2010. *Solid State Physics, Theoretical Physics*. Theoretical Physics, Solid State Physics.

Kumah, Divine P., Ph.D., University of Michigan, 2009. *Solid State Physics, Surface Physics*. Experimental Physics, Solid State Physics, Surface Physics.

Longland, Richard, Ph.D., University of North Carolina Chapel HIll, 2010. *Astrophysics, Nuclear Physics*. Experimental Physics, nuclear physics, astrophysics.

Mack, Katherine, Ph.D., Princeton University, 2009. *Astrophysics, Cosmology & String Theory, Particles and Fields, Theoretical Physics*.

Skokov, Vladimir, Ph.D., Joint Institute for Nuclear Research, 2006. *Nuclear Physics, Particles and Fields, Quantum Foundations, Theoretical Physics*.

Sun, Dali, Ph.D., Institute of Physics, Chinese Academy of Sciences, 2009. *Condensed Matter Physics, Nano Science and Technology*.

Professor Emeritus

Ellison, Donald C., Ph.D., Catholic University of America, 1982. *Astrophysics, Theoretical Physics*. Theoretical physics; astrophysics.

Lucovsky, Gerald, Ph.D., Temple University, 1960. *Nano Science and Technology, Solid State Physics*. Experimental physics; nanoscience/materials.

Paesler, Michael A., Ph.D., University of Chicago, 1975. *Physics and other Science Education*.

Research Professor

Borkowski, Kazimirez, Ph.D., University of Colorado, 1988. *Astronomy, Astrophysics*. Experimental physics; astrophysics.

Research Associate Professor

Bochinski, Jason, Ph.D., University of Oregon, 2000. *Atomic, Molecular, & Optical Physics, Nano Science and Technology, Optics*. Molecular physics; nanoscience/materials.

Kelley, John H., Ph.D., Michigan State University, 1995. *Nuclear Physics*. Experimental physics; nuclear physics.

Lu, Wenchang, Ph.D., Fudan University, 1994. *Condensed Matter Physics, Nano Science and Technology, Solid State Physics*. Theoretical physics; nanoscience/materials.

Teaching Associate Professor

Heyward, Keith, Ph.D., North Carolina State University, 2006. *Physics and other Science Education*.

Senior Lecturer

Egler, Robert E., M.A., 2002. *Astronomy*.

Warren, C. Keith, M.S., Appalachian State University, 1993. *Astronomy, Physics and other Science Education*.

DEPARTMENTAL RESEARCH SPECIALTIES AND STAFF

Theoretical

Computational Biophysics. The computational biological physics groups investigate the connection between the structure and function of biological molecules. In particular, they are interested in exact atomistic descriptions of nucleic acids, proteins, and their interactions. Members of the group are co-authors of widely-used packages for molecular dynamics simulations. Bernholc, Roland, Sagui.

Computational Condensed Matter Physics. Large-scale simulations of real materials, semiconductors, nanotubes, and related nanoscale structures; quantum Monte Carlo simulations; O(N) and multiscale methods; quantum transport; nanostructured materials; phase separation; ferrofluids liquid-state theory; interfaces; diffusion; neural networks; pattern formation; electronic properties of transition-metal oxides and silicates. Bernholc, Kemper, Lu, Mitas.

Theoretical and Computational Astrophysics. Theoretical modeling and numerical simulations of supernovae and remnants, gamma-ray bursts; general relativity, numerical methods for general relativity, gravitational radiation from supernovae and colliding black holes; accretion onto compact objects, and planetary nebulae; shock waves, particle acceleration, and cosmic rays; neutrinos and nucleosynthesis in supernovae and gamma-ray bursts. Blondin, Brown, Frohlich, Kneller, McLaughlin.

Theoretical Particle and Nuclear Physics. Electromagnetic structure studies of hadrons; relativistic quark models; light-cone quantization; B-physics; glueball and hybrid meson spectroscopy; application to astrophysics and cosmology; neutrino phenomenology; nonperturbative vacuum effects and mixing; CP violation; extra dimensions and physics beyond the standard model; QCD-based description of hadronic interactions; BCS methods and chiral symmetry breaking; Hartree-Fock techniques; lattice gauge theory; many body phenomena and computational algorithms, instantons, finite density QCD, superconductivity; nuclear lattice simulations; effective field theory; Gauge theory dynamics and its applications, resurgence theory, applications to QFT and quantum mechanics, interrelations of large-orders in perturbation theory and topological configurations. Ji, Schaefer, Unsal.

Experimental

Astronomy. Radio, infrared, optical, and X-ray observations of supernova remnants, pulsar-wind nebulae, and planetary nebulae. Borkowski, Reynolds.

Atomic, Molecular, & Optical Physics. Ultra-cold Fermi-gases, strongly correlated quantum fluids, laser polarization of atomic vapors,. Thomas.

Biological Physics. Nanoprobe tools at the single-molecule level: single-molecule fluoresence, fluorescence resonance energy transfer, atomic force microscopy, nanofluidic analyis, DNA tightropes, upconversion nanotags, nano-Raman; Specific systems studied include synaptic vesicle fusion, DNA mismatch repair, epigenetics, telomeric chromosome protection, chromosome cohesion, protein conformations, protein-induced DNA conformations, cooperativity, importance of thermally-activated processes. Emergent field are single-cell genetic analysis, development of embryos, and collective properties of active biological particles. Lim, Riehn, Wang, Weninger.

Condensed Matter Physics. Nanotribology, micro/nano electro-mechanical systems, and liquid wetting phenomena; real-time spectroscopy and microscopy of nanostructure growth and dynamics; subwavelength optical probes; atomically precise materials preparation and characterization including ultra-thin films and related device structures; X-ray spectromicroscopy of carbon-based electronics materials; molecular motion on surfaces; organic dielectrics; conduction and polarization of molecular and macromolecular assemblies; sound propagation in granular materials; electronic and magnetic properties of metal-organic interfaces; preparation, characterization, and control of graphene and its interfaces; nonlinear optical characterization of surfaces; ultra-fast laser spectroscopy of dynamical processes in solids. Ade, Aspnes, Bochinski, Clarke, Daniels, Dougherty, Gundogdu, Hallen, Krim, Kumah, Lim.

Experimental Nuclear Physics. Tests of fundamental symmetries; neutron beta decay and electric dipole moments; neutrinos and neutrino oscillations; ultracold neutrons; studies of few nucleon systems; quantum chaos; statistical properties of nuclei; polarized nuclear targets; interactions of neutrinos, majorana demonstrator, Coherent Elastic Neutrino Nucleus Scattering (CEvNS), precision determination of nuclear reaction cross-sections for stellar nucleosynthesis. Golub, Gould, Green, Huffman, Kelley, Longland, Young.

Optics. Near-field optical microscopy and spectroscopy; nano-Raman spectroscopy; optical characterization of electronic materials; ultrafast and nonlinear optical spectroscopy of materials, films, surfaces, and interfaces under static and dynamic conditions; nanoplasmonic materials processing; nanoplasmonic nonlinear materials. Aspnes, Clarke, Gundogdu, Hallen, Lim.

Physics Education Research. Reexamination and redesign of modes of instruction and content for large enrollment courses; assessment of student understanding; role of computers including simulation, visualization, computer-based experiments, and student programming; distance learning. Beichner, Paesler.

View additional information about this department at www.gradschoolshopper.com. Check out the "Why Choose Us?" section, find out more about the department's culture and get links to social media networks.

UNIVERSITY OF NORTH CAROLINA, CHAPEL HILL

DEPARTMENT OF PHYSICS AND ASTRONOMY

Chapel Hill, North Carolina 27599-3255
http://www.physics.unc.edu/

General University Information
President: Margaret Spellings
Dean of Graduate School: Steve Matson
University website: http://www.unc.edu/
School Type: Public
Setting: Urban
Total Faculty: 3,887
Total Graduate Faculty: 1,932
Total number of Students: 29,911
Total number of Graduate Students: 11,049

Department Information
Department Chairman: Prof. Christian Iliadis, Chair
Department Contact: Greg Smith, Human Resources Manager
  Total full-time faculty: 30
  Total number of full-time equivalent positions: 40
  Full-Time Graduate Students: 81
  Female Full-Time Graduate Students: 16
  First-Year Graduate Students: 9
  Female First-Year Students: 1
  Total Post Doctorates: 13

Department Address
CB# 3255, Phillips Hall
Chapel Hill, NC 27599-3255
Phone: (919) 843-4815
Fax: (919) 962-0480
E-mail: physicsgradadmissions@unc.edu
Website: http://www.physics.unc.edu/

ADMISSIONS

Admission Contact Information
Address admission inquiries to: Graduate Admissions, Department of Physics and Astronomy, UNC-Chapel Hill, CB# 3255, Phillips Hall, Chapel Hill, NC 27599-3255
Phone: (919) 962-7173
E-mail: physicsgradadmissions@unc.edu
Admissions website: http://www.physics.unc.edu/

Application deadlines
Fall admission:
U.S. students: December 11   *Int'l. students*: December 11

Application fee
U.S. students: $87.5   *Int'l. students*: $87.5

Admissions information
For Fall of 2018:
  Number of applicants: 144
  Number admitted: 38
  Number enrolled: 9

Admission requirements
Bachelor's degree requirements: Bachelor's degree in physics is required.
Minimum undergraduate GPA: 3.0

GRE requirements
The GRE is required.
  Quantitative score: 158
  Verbal score: 159
  Analytical score: 4.0
  Mean GRE score range (25th–75th percentile): > 50

Subjective GRE requirements
The Subjective GRE is required.
No minimum score required.

TOEFL requirements
The TOEFL exam is required for students from non-English-speaking countries.
  iBT score: 95

Other admissions information
Additional requirements: A score of 95 or better on the internet based TOEFL is required; a score of 100 or better is strongly preferred.
Undergraduate preparation assumed: Symon, Mechanics; Martin, Elements of Thermodynamics; Hecht and Zajac, Optics; Griffiths, Introduction to Electrodynamics; Liboff, Introductory Quantum Mechanics, or comparable.

TUITION
Tuition year 2018–19:
Tuition for in-state residents
  Full-time students: $10,243 annual
Tuition for out-of-state residents
  Full-time students: $27,454 annual
Students in good standing will have their tuition paid by the department.
Credit hours per semester to be considered full-time: 9
Deferred tuition plan: No
Health insurance: Yes, paid by the department.
Other academic fees: In-state: $984.51 per semester. Out-of-state: $984.51 per semester.
Academic term: Semester
Number of first-year students who received full tuition waivers: 9

Teaching Assistants, Research Assistants, and Fellowships
Number of first-year
  Teaching Assistants: 8
  Research Assistants: 1
Average stipend per academic year
  Teaching Assistant: $25,025
  Research Assistant: $25,025
  Fellowship student: $24,000

FINANCIAL AID

Application deadlines
Fall admission:
U.S. students: March 1   *Int'l. students*: March 1

Loans

Loans are available for U.S. students.

Loans are available for international students.

GAPSFAS application required: No

FAFSA application required: Yes

For further information

Address financial aid inquiries to: Graduate Admissions Committee, Department of Physics and Astronomy, CB #3255, Phillips Hall, UNC, Chapel Hill, NC 27599-3255.

Phone: (919) 962-7173

E-mail: physicsgradadmissions@unc.edu

Financial aid website: http://studentaid.unc.edu

HOUSING

Availability of on-campus housing

Single students: Yes

Married students: Yes

Childcare Assistance: Yes

For further information

Address housing inquiries to: UNC Housing Student Academic Services Bldg, 450 Ridge Road, CB5500 Chapel Hill, NC 27599.

Phone: (919) 962-5401

E-mail: housing@unc.edu

Housing aid website: http://housing.unc.edu

Table A—Faculty, Enrollments, and Degrees Granted

Research Specialty	2017–18 Faculty	Enrollment Fall 2017 Master's	Enrollment Fall 2017 Doctorate	Number of Degrees Granted 2017–18 Master's	Number of Degrees Granted 2017–18 Terminal Master's	Number of Degrees Granted 2017–18 Doctorate
Applied Physics	1	–	1	–	–	–
Astronomy	10	–	16	–	–	3
Astrophysics	10	–	5	–	–	–
Biophysics	4	–	7	–	–	2
Condensed Matter Physics	18	–	13	–	–	1
Cosmology & String Theory	1	–	5	–	–	–
Nano Science and Technology	1	–	1	–	–	–
Nuclear Physics	7	–	26	–	–	2
Particles and Fields	3	–	1	–	–	1
Relativity & Gravitation	2	–	4	1	–	–
Other	5	–	3	1	–	1
Total	–	–	82	2	–	10
Full-time Grad. Stud.	–	–	82	–	–	–
First-year Grad. Stud.	–	–	15	–	–	–

GRADUATE DEGREE REQUIREMENTS

Master's: Thirty semester hours required, of which three to six may be for thesis or Master's project (if non-thesis option elected). One comprehensive written examination, which also serves as qualifying examination for Ph.D. Oral examination on thesis, or on a Master's project (if non-thesis option is elected), is required. Residency is required.

Doctorate: No specific graduate course credit requirements, but satisfactory completion of approved sequence of courses; a doctoral written examination covering "core" curriculum; a preliminary oral examination for the dissertation, a dissertation, and oral examination on dissertation. Residency is required.

Thesis: Thesis may be written in absentia. Courses taken as a graduate student before enrolling at Chapel Hill may afford students the opportunity to opt out of one or more first-year core courses and may be eligible for transfer course credit. However, students are required to pass the doctoral written examination, which is offered at the end of the student's first year and covers core material in quantum mechanics, electromagnetic theory, dynamics, and statistical mechanics.

SPECIAL EQUIPMENT, FACILITIES, OR PROGRAMS

The University of North Carolina, together with NC State and Duke Universities, administers the Triangle Universities Nuclear Laboratory's three nuclear accelerators in Durham. Special astronomy facilities of UNC, Chapel Hill, include a 61-cm telescope and a 68-foot planetarium dome with full-dome digital video. Astronomical facilities: observational facilities include the SOAR 4.1-meter telescope in Chile 61 nights time share, 11-meter Southern African Large Telescope (SALT) in South Africa (10 nights), the University's PROMPT robotic telescope array six 0.4-meter telescopes in Chile, one 0.8-meter telescope in Chile under construction, and four 0.4-meter telescopes in Australia under construction. The department is also home to one-of-a-kind microscopes, X-ray technology, and computational facilities. Laboratory facilities include the Goodman Laboratory for Astronomical Instrumentation and the Chapel Hill Analytical and Nanofabrication Laboratory (CHANL).

Table B—Separately Budgeted Research Expenditures by Source of Support

Source of Support	Departmental Research	Physics-related Research Outside Department
Federal government	$6,363,003	$1,113,016
State/local government	$689,819	
Non-profit organizations	$162,000	
Business and industry	$295,962	
Other	$665,541	
Total	$8,176,325	$1,113,016

Table C—Separately Budgeted Research Expenditures by Research Specialty

Research Specialty	No. of Grants	Expenditures ($)
Astronomy	29	$1,065,126
Biophysics	17	$2,783,111
Condensed Matter Physics	19	$1,373,243
Nuclear Physics	19	$3,952,162
Particles and Fields	3	$115,699
Total	87	$9,289,341

FACULTY

Professor

Cecil, Gerald N., Ph.D., University of Hawaii, 1987. Observational astronomy; active galactic nuclei.

Champagne, Arthur E., Ph.D., Yale University, 1982. Experimental nuclear physics.

Clemens, J. Christopher, Ph.D., University of Texas, Austin, 1994. Observational astronomy; astrophysics; astronomical instrumentation.

Dolan, Louise A., Ph.D., Massachusetts Institute of Technology, 1976. Particle theory.

Engel, Jonathan H., Ph.D., Yale University, 1986. Theoretical nuclear physics; violation of fundamental symmetries in nuclei; the role of nuclear effects in solar neutrino and dark matter experiments; r-process nucleosynthesis and quark effects in nuclei.

Evans, Charles R., Ph.D., University of Texas, Austin, 1984. General relativity; numerical hydrodynamics; astrophysics.

Henning, Reyco, Ph.D., Massachusetts Institute of Technology, 2003. Experimental neutrino physics.

Iliadis, Christian, Ph.D., University of Notre Dame, 1993. Department Chair. Experimental nuclear astrophysics.

Khveshchenko, Dmitri, Ph.D., Landau Institute for Theoretical Physics, 1989. Theoretical condensed matter physics; quantum transport in strongly correlated systems.

López, René, Ph.D., Vanderbilt University, 2002. Nanotechnology; nano-optics; ultrashort laser/matter interaction; thin film science.

Lu, Jianping, Ph.D., City University of New York, 1988. High-Tc superconductors; fullerenes and fullerides; strongly correlated electron systems; electronic structure and computational physics; disordered system and quantum transports; complex systems; X-ray imaging.

McNeil, Laurie E., Ph.D., University of Illinois, 1982. Optical studies of materials.

Mersini-Houghton, Laura, Ph.D., University of Wisconsin-Madison, 2000. Theoretical cosmology.

Ng, Yee Jack, Ph.D., Harvard University, 1974. Theoretical particle physics; gravitation.

Qin, Lu-Chang, Massachusetts Institute of Technology, 1994. Electron microscopy; materials science; nanotechnology.

Reichart, Daniel E., Ph.D., University of Chicago, 2000. Gamma-ray bursts; early universe; interstellar extinction; galaxy clusters.

Tsui, Frank, Ph.D., University of Illinois at Urbana-Champaign, 1992. Molecular beam epitaxy of transition metals; scanning tunneling microscopy.

Washburn, Sean, Ph.D., Duke University, 1982. Effects of quantum-mechanical coherence in charge transport in small systems; ballistic transport in semiconductors; nano-scale electro-mechanical systems.

Wilkerson, John, Ph.D., University of North Carolina, Chapel Hill, 1982. Neutrino physics and neutrino astrophysics.

Wu, Yue, Ph.D., Catholic University of Leuven, 1987. Nuclear magnetic resonance; electron spin resonance in solids.

Zhou, Otto, Ph.D., University of Pennsylvania, 1992. Experimental materials science; structure/property relationships in solids.

Associate Professor

Drut, Joaquin E., Ph.D., University of Washington, 2008. Quantum many-body physics; nuclear, atomic and condensed matter physics; nonperturbative computational approaches.

Heitsch, Fabian, Ph.D., University of Heidelberg, 2001. Turbulence and fragmentation in molecular clouds.

Kannapan, Sheila, Ph.D., Harvard University, 2001. Observational astronomy; galaxy formation and evolution.

Oldenburg, Amy, Ph.D., University of Illinois, 2001. Biophysics.

Assistant Professor

Branca, Rosa Tamara, Ph.D., La Sapienza, University of Rome, 2006. Condensed matter physics.

Erickcek, Adrienne L., Ph.D., California Institute of Technology, 2009. Theoretical cosmology, particularly the early Universe; dark matter; cosmological acceleration; modified gravity theories.

Law, Nicholas M., Ph.D., University of Cambridge, 2006. Exoplanets; astronomical instrumentation; adaptive optics; large astronomical surveys; time-domain astronomy; stellar multiplicity.

Mann, Andrew, Ph.D., University of Hawai'i at Manoa, 2013. *Astronomy, Astrophysics.*

Nicholson, Amy N., Ph.D., University of Washington, 2011. Lattice field theory, strongly interacting few-and many-body systems, Monte Carlo sign problems, QCD at non-zero density.

Emeritus

Briscoe, Charles V., Ph.D., Rice University, 1958.

Carney, Bruce W., Ph.D., Harvard University, 1978. Observational astronomy; history of the Milky Way Galaxy.

Choi, Sang-il, Ph.D., Brown University, 1961.

Christiansen, Wayne A., Ph.D., University of California, 1968.

Clegg, Thomas B., Ph.D., Rice University, 1965. Experimental nuclear physics; development of polarized beams.

Dy, Kian S., Ph.D., Cornell University, 1967.

Hernandez, John P., Ph.D., University of Rochester, 1967.

Hooke, William M., Ph.D., Princeton University, 1958.

Hubbard, Paul S., Ph.D., Harvard University, 1958.

Karwowski, Hugon J., Ph.D., Indiana University, 1980. Experimental nuclear physics with polarized nuclei.

Kessemeier, Horst, Ph.D., University of Washington (St. Louis), 1964.

Ludwig, Edward J., Ph.D., Indiana University, 1963.

Macdonald, J. Ross, University of Oxford, 1950.

Rose, James, Ph.D., Yale University, 1977.

Rowan, Lawrence G., Ph.D., University of California, Berkeley, 1963. Solid state experiments using EPR.

Schroeer, Dietrich, Ph.D., Ohio State University, 1965.

Slifkin, Lawrence M., Ph.D., Princeton University, 1950.

Thompson, William J., Ph.D., Florida State University, 1967.

York, James W., Ph.D., North Carolina State University, 1966.

Research Professor

Falvo, Michael, Ph.D., University of North Carolina, Chapel Hill, 1997. Nanoscience.

Kleinhammes, Alfred, Ph.D., Clark University, 1990. Condensed matter physics; nuclear magnetic resonance.

Research Associate Professor

Hill, David B., Ph.D., Wake Forest University, 2003. Mucus structure, rheology, and flow; mucus adhesion; cilia force generation.

O'Brien, E. Timothy, Ph.D., University of California, Santa Barbara, 1974. Cell biology; microscopy.

Teaching Associate Professor

Churukian, Alice, Ph.D., Kansas State University, 2002. Physics education.

Deardorff, Duane L., Ph.D., North Carolina State University, 2001. Undergraduate laboratories; physics education.

Teaching Assistant Professor

Jeglinski, Stefan, Ph.D., University of Utah, 1994. Physics Education.

Wallace, Colin S., Ph.D., University of Colorado Boulder, 2011. Astronomy and Physics Education.

Weinberg-Wolf, Jennifer, Ph.D., University of North Carolina at Chapel Hill, 2006. Physics education.

Young, Daniel, Ph.D., University of New Hampshire, 2014. Astronomy and Physics education.

Adjunct Professor

Chaffee, Fred, Ph.D., 1968. Astronomy.

Christensen, Steven M., Ph.D., University of Texas at Austin, 1975.

Fortner, Brand, Ph.D., University of Illinois at Urbana-Champaign, 1993.

Radford, David C., Ph.D., University of Auckland, 1978.

Rohm, Ryan M., Ph.D., Princeton University, 1985. Quantum field theory; theoretical elementary particle physics.

Rutland, Jonathan, Ph.D., University of North Carolina, 1988. Physics.

Smith, Rachel, Ph.D., University of Los Angeles, 2011. Early solar system chemistry; chemistry of forming planetary systems in the galaxy; solar system evolution and planet formation; life in the universe; origin of life on Earth.

Superfine, Richard, Ph.D., University of California, Berkeley, 1991. Scanning probe microscopy of biological structures.

Tang, Jie, Ph.D., Osaka University, 1993. Materials science; nanotechnology.

DEPARTMENTAL RESEARCH SPECIALTIES AND STAFF

Theoretical

Astrophysics. Astronomy and astrophysics: gravity, astrophysical gas dynamics. Erickcek, Evans, Heitsch.

Condensed Matter Physics. Many-body theory; fullerenes; high-temperature superconductors; correlated electron systems. Drut, Lu.

Nuclear Physics. Nucleosynthesis in stars and supernovae; violation of fundamental symmetries in nuclei; the role of nuclear effects in solar neutrino and dark matter experiments. Drut, Engel, Nicholson.

Particles and Fields. Field theory; particle theory; gravitation and relativity. Quantum theory of fields and particles; superstring theory; cosmology; relativistic dynamics; general relativity; gravitational fields; quantum and supergravity. Dolan, Evans, Mersini-Houghton, Ng.

Experimental

Astrophysics. Astronomy and astrophysics: radio, optical, and X-ray astronomy; stellar spectroscopy and photometry; nucleosynthesis. Cecil, Champagne, Clemens, Iliadis, Kannapan, Law, Mann, Reichart.

Biophysics. Biological and medical physics. Nanoscale properties of biomolecules, DNA, and motors, biophysical properties of fluids, cells and tissues, biomedical imaging technology development in X-ray, optical, and magnetic resonance. Branca, Lu, Oldenburg, Superfine, Washburn, Zhou.

Condensed Matter Physics. Condensed matter physics, materials science, microelectronics. NMR studies of kinetic and thermodynamic properties of metallic supercooled liquids and glasses and interactions and functions of adsorbed molecules in nanomaterials and biological systems; Raman and Brillouin scattering from organic semiconductors; AFM and surface science in virtual reality interfaces to microscopy; low-temperature physics and quantum transport; growth and magnetic susceptibility of magnetic semiconductors; electrical and mechanical interaction of carbon nanotubes with surfaces and other tubes; chaos in biological systems, Optical properties of nanoscale materials, organic and hybrid solar cell materials. Branca, López, McNeil, Qin, Superfine, Tsui, Washburn, Wu, Zhou.

Nuclear Physics. Nuclear astrophysics; radioactive beams; neutrino physics; spin polarization in nuclear reactions; few-body physics. Champagne, Henning, Iliadis, Karwowski, Wilkerson.

View additional information about this department at www.gradschoolshopper.com. Check out the "Why Choose Us?" section, find out more about the department's culture and get links to social media networks.

WAKE FOREST UNIVERSITY

DEPARTMENT OF PHYSICS

Winston-Salem, North Carolina 27109-7507
http://www.physics.wfu.edu/

General University Information
President: Nathan O. Hatch
Dean of Graduate School: Bradley T. Jones, Dean
University website: http://www.wfu.edu/
School Type: Private
Setting: Suburban
Total Faculty: 1,700
Total Graduate Faculty: 550
Total number of Students: 8,116
Total number of Graduate Students: 3,014

Department Information
Department Chairman: Dr. Daniel B. Kim-Shapiro, Chair
Department Contact: Melissa Mitchell, Administrative
  Assistant
  Total full-time faculty: 17
  Total number of full-time equivalent positions: 20
  Full-Time Graduate Students: 30
  Female Full-Time Graduate Students: 9
  First-Year Graduate Students: 10
  Female First-Year Students: 3
  Total Post Doctorates: 5

Department Address
1834 Wake Forest Road
P.O. Box 7507
Winston-Salem, NC 27109-7507
Phone: (336) 758-5337
Fax: (336) 758-6142
E-mail: physics@wfu.edu
Website: http://www.physics.wfu.edu/

ADMISSIONS

Admission Contact Information
Address admission inquiries to: Dean of Graduate School, Wake
  Forest University, 1834 Wake Forest Road Winston-Salem,
  NC 27109
Phone: (336) 758-5301
E-mail: gradschl@wfu.edu
Admissions website: http://graduate.wfu.edu/admissions/
  onlineapp.html

Application deadlines
Fall admission:
U.S. students: January 15   *Int'l. students*: January 15
Spring admission:
U.S. students: November 1   *Int'l. students*: November 1

Application fee
U.S. students: $80   *Int'l. students*: $80
Typically 10-15 students are admitted, of which about 5-8 enroll.

Admissions information
For Fall of 2018:
  Number of applicants: 40
  Number admitted: 15
  Number enrolled: 10

Admission requirements
Bachelor's degree requirements: A Bachelor's degree in Physics
  is required.
Minimum undergraduate GPA: 3.0

GRE requirements
The GRE is required.
  Quantitative score: 160
  Verbal score: 150
  Analytical score: 3.5
  Mean GRE score range (25th–75th percentile): 1200-1370
These minimum values are only guides. Meeting them does not
  assure admission, not meeting them does not prevent ad-
  mission. International students have sometimes lower verbal
  and analytical writing scores.

Subjective GRE requirements
The Subjective GRE is recommended.
  Minimum accepted Advanced GRE score: 640
  Mean Advanced GRE score range (25th–75th percentile): 660-870
These minimum values are just guides. Meeting them does not assure
  admission, not meeting them does not prevent admission.

TOEFL requirements
The TOEFL exam is required for students from non-English-
  speaking countries.
  PBT score: 575
  iBT score: 79
Computer-based TOEFL: 217 International English Language
  Testing System (IELTS): 6.5

Other admissions information
Additional requirements: The verbal and analytical GRE scores quoted
  above are for domestic students. Occasionally, international students
  with lower verbal and analytical GRE scores may be admitted.
  A minimum quantitative GRE score of 700 is required for domestic
  and international students. Quantitative GRE scores are frequently
  well above 700.
Undergraduate preparation assumed: Mechanics—Symon, Mechanics; Electricity and Magnetism—Griffiths, Introduction to Electrodynamics; Quantum Mechanics—Gasiorowicz, Quantum
  Physics; Thermodynamics—Kittel and Kroemer, Thermal Physics.

TUITION

Tuition year 2018–19:
  Full-time students: $38,650 annual
  Part-time students: $19,325 per semester
Usually, all admitted PhD students will receive a full tuition
  waiver and a stipend. Master's students will typically receive
  an 80% tuition waiver.
Credit hours per semester to be considered full-time: 9
Deferred tuition plan: Yes
Health insurance: Yes, variable.
Other academic fees: Health insurance is available for purchase. Stu-
  dents under the age of 26 may be covered by parents' insurance.
  Free satellite parking (plus shuttle) is available. Limited $300 near-
  campus parking and $500 on-campus parking is available.
Academic term: Semester
Number of first-year students who received full tuition waivers: 8
Number of first-year students who received partial tuition waivers: 2

Teaching Assistants, Research Assistants, and Fellowships

Number of first-year
Teaching Assistants: 8
Fellowship students: 1
Average stipend per academic year
Teaching Assistant: $23,193
Research Assistant: $23,193
Fellowship student: $25,193
Research Assistantships and some Teaching Assistantships may receive a summer bonus for a total stipend up to $25,000. Physics Excellence Fellows receive an extra stipend of $2,000 annually for five years.

FINANCIAL AID

Application deadlines
Fall admission:
U.S. students: January 15   *Int'l. students*: January 15
Spring admission:
U.S. students: November 15   *Int'l. students*: November 15

Loans
Loans are available for U.S. students.
Loans are not available for international students.
GAPSFAS application required: No
FAFSA application required: No

For further information
Address financial aid inquiries to: Dean of the Graduate School, Wake Forest University, 1834 Wake Forest Road, Winston Salem, NC 27109.
Phone: (336) 758-5301
E-mail: gradschl@wfu.edu
Financial aid website: https://graduate.wfu.edu/cost-financial-aid-reynolda/

HOUSING

Availability of on-campus housing
Single students: No
Married students: No
Childcare Assistance: No

For further information
Address housing inquiries to: Residence Housing, P.O. Box 7749, Wake Forest Univ., Winston-Salem, NC 27109.
Phone: (336) 758-7777
E-mail: housing@wfu.edu
Housing aid website: http://rlh.wfu.edu/

Table A—Faculty, Enrollments, and Degrees Granted

Research Specialty	2017–18 Faculty	Enrollment Fall 2017 Mas-ter's	Enrollment Fall 2017 Doc-torate	Number of Degrees Granted 2017–18 (2013–18) Mas-ter's	Number of Degrees Granted 2017–18 (2013–18) Terminal Master's	Number of Degrees Granted 2017–18 (2013–18) Doc-torate
Atomic, Molecular, & Optical Physics	2	–	3	–	–(1)	1(3)
Biophysics	6	2	7	–	1(1)	2(9)
Condensed Matter Physics	5	1	8	–(1)	–(2)	3(12)
Medical, Health Physics	3	–	1	–	–	–(4)
Nano Science and Technology	2	1	3	–	1(1)	2(7)
Relativity & Gravitation	3	–	4	–	–	–(1)
Total	14	4	27	–(1)	2(5)	8(36)
Full-time Grad. Stud.	–	2	26	–	–	–
First-year Grad. Stud.	–	–	6	–	–	–

GRADUATE DEGREE REQUIREMENTS

Master's: Thirty semester hours of graduate credit; of those, at least 24 credits must be classes or seminars, and 6 credits can be research. Twelve credits hours must be at the 700 level. Courses must include Phys 711, 712, 741 (Math Methods & Classical Mechanics, Electrodynamics, Quantum Mechanics-I). Participation at the departmental seminar is required. Minimum of 12 months full-time in residence. An oral defense of the thesis and a 3.0 average on courses are required.

Doctorate: Courses must include Physics 711, 712, 741, 742, and 770 (Math Methods & Classical Mechanics, Electrodynamics, Quantum Mechanics-I and -II, Statistical Physics) and three more elective courses at the 600 or 700 level (of which one must be in Physics). A written General Exam at the level of material normally covered in the first year of graduate study serves as the preliminary examination. Within 18 months of completing the preliminary examination, the students submits to her/his advisory committee and defends orally a dissertation research plan. An oral defense of the dissertation, and a 3.0 average on courses are required.

Thesis: Thesis may be written in absentia.

SPECIAL EQUIPMENT, FACILITIES, OR PROGRAMS

Wake Forest is among the top 10% of tier-1 national doctoral universities (US News and World Report), despite its small size. We take pride in being able to provide the personal attention of a liberal arts college and having significant resources that are usually associated with a large research university.

The research in our department is focused on the following areas: experimental and computational biophysics; atomic, molecular and optical physics; experimental and computational condensed matter physics; computational and theoretical relativity and gravitation; medical and health physics; and nanophysics. All research laboratories contain state-of-the-art instrumentation; computational physicists have access to the large deacon cluster.

Table B—Separately Budgeted Research Expenditures by Source of Support

Source of Support	Departmental Research	Physics-related Research Outside Department
Federal government	$1,040,442.05	$310,860.16
State/local government		
Non-profit organizations	$11,902.2	
Business and industry	$20,219.29	
Other	$252,736.96	$294,188.81
Total	$1,325,300.5	$605,048.97

Table C—Separately Budgeted Research Expenditures by Research Specialty

Research Specialty	No. of Grants	Expenditures ($)
Biophysics	6	$534,733.65
Condensed Matter Physics	14	$879,532.92
Nano Science and Technology	3	$466,114.68
Optics	1	$23,115.86
Relativity & Gravitation	1	$25,857.36
Total	25	$1,929,354.47

FACULTY

Chair Professor
Kim-Shapiro, Daniel, Ph.D., University of California, Berkeley, 1993. Director, Translational Science Center. *Biophysics*. Un-

derstanding how blood flow is regulated, particularly by nitric oxide, nitrite and other nitrogen oxides. Various forms of spectroscopy, using light (including polarized light) to learn about biological structure and function.

Professor

Anderson, Paul R., Ph.D., University of California, Santa Barbara, 1983. *Relativity & Gravitation*. General relativity; quantum field theory in curved space.

Bonin, Keith D., Ph.D., University of Maryland, 1984. Department Chair. *Atomic, Molecular, & Optical Physics, Biophysics, Nano Science and Technology, Optics*. Atomic physics; nanophysics; biophysics; optics.

Carroll, David L., Ph.D., Wesleyan University, 1993. Director, Nanotechnology Center. *Nano Science and Technology*. Nanostructures and nanotechnology.

Guthold, Martin, Ph.D., University of Oregon, 1997. Director of Physics graduate program. *Biophysics, Nano Science and Technology*. Biophysics.

Holzwarth, Natalie A. W., Ph.D., University of Chicago, 1975. *Condensed Matter Physics*. Theoretical solid state physics; electronic structure of bulk solids, surfaces, and molecules.

Macosko, Jed, Ph.D., University of California, Berkeley, 1999. *Biophysics*. Biophysics of molecular motors and biopolymers.

Matthews, Eric G., Ph.D., University of North Carolina, 1977. Associate Provost of Information Systems. *Condensed Matter Physics*. Thermally stimulated depolarization of defects in insulators; ab initio calculations of defect properties.

Salsbury, Fred, Ph.D., University of California, Berkeley, 1999. Undergraduate Advisor. Director, Interdisciplinary Program in Structural and Computational Biophysics. *Biophysics, Computational Physics*. Computational biophysics.

Associate Professor

Carlson, Eric, Ph.D., Harvard University, 1988. *Astrophysics, Particles and Fields, Relativity & Gravitation*. Astrophysics and particle physics.

Cho, Samuel, Ph.D., University of California, San Diego, 2007. *Biophysics, Computational Physics, Computer Science*. Computational biophysics, protein and RNA folding, biomolecular assembly, molecular machines, GPU-based programming.

Cook, Gregory B., Ph.D., University of North Carolina, 1990. Undergraduate Advisor. *Astrophysics, Relativity & Gravitation*. General relativity and relativistic astrophysics.

Jurchescu, Oana, Ph.D., University of Groningen, Netherlands, 2006. *Condensed Matter Physics, Nano Science and Technology*. Nanostructures and nanotechnology.

Thonhauser, Timo, Ph.D., Karl-Franzens University, Austria, 2001. *Computational Physics, Condensed Matter Physics*. Density functional theory.

Emeritus

Shields, Howard, Ph.D., Duke University, 1956. *Biophysics*. Biophysics, EPR, (working in the lab of Prof. Kim-Shapiro).

Research Professor

Holzwarth, George M., Ph.D., Harvard University, 1964. *Biophysics*. Physical properties of normal and cancerous cells, dependence of cell growth on substrate properties.

Kerr, William C., Ph.D., Cornell University, 1967. *Statistical & Thermal Physics*. Theoretical solid-state and statistical physics; structural phase transitions.

Williams, Richard T., Ph.D., Princeton University, 1974. *Atomic, Molecular, & Optical Physics, Condensed Matter Physics, Optics*. Femtosecond laser studies of defects and electrons in solids.

Research Associate Professor

Basu, Swati, Ph.D., University of Illinois at Urbana-Champaign, 1994. Understanding how blood flow is regulated, particularly by nitric oxide, nitrite and other nitrogen oxides. Various forms of spectroscopy, using light (including polarized light) to learn about biological structure and function. (Works in the lab of Prof. Kim-Shapiro). *Biophysics*. Prof. Basu is working in Prof. Kim-Shapiro's group.

Ucer, K. Burak, Ph.D., University of Rochester, 1997. *Atomic, Molecular, & Optical Physics, Optics*. Ultrafast lasers and spectroscopy.

Teaching Associate Professor

Dostal, Jack, Ph.D., Montana State University, 2009. Lecturer. *Physics and other Science Education*. Physics education.

Adjunct Professor

Bourland, J. Daniel, Ph.D., University of North Carolina. *Medical, Health Physics*. Radiation oncology.

Santago, Peter, Ph.D., North Carolina State University, 1986. Chair, Computer Science. *Computer Science, Medical, Health Physics*. Image enhancement.

Adjunct Assistant Professor

Hall, Adam, Ph.D., University of North Carolina, Chapel Hill, 2007. *Biophysics, Nano Science and Technology*. Nanopores, Nanobiotechnology.

DEPARTMENTAL RESEARCH SPECIALTIES AND STAFF

Theoretical

Biophysics. Computational and theoretical biophysics, computational systems biology, protein structure/function relationships, biological network modeling, signal transduction network modeling, molecular physics, drug discovery. Cho, Salsbury.

Condensed Matter Physics. Computational materials physics: simulation and prediction of energy storage materials, development of "first principles" simulation methods, condensed matter theory, semi-classical electron dynamics, Berry phase effects, nonlinearity, computational and theoretical materials science, condensed matter physics, solid state physics, density functional theory, first-principles calculations, NMR, van der Waals forces, magnetization. Natalie Holzwarth, Kerr, Matthews, Thonhauser.

Gravitational. Gravitational physics, general relativity, numerical relativity, black holes, neutron stars, compact binaries, initial data, gravitational waves, quantum field theory in curved space, particle physics. Anderson, Carlson, Cook.

Experimental

Atomic, Molecular, & Optical Physics. Electron spin resonance in irradiated organic solids, transport properties, semiconductor trapping centers, laser materials, ultrafast spectroscopy, excitons, scintillators, energy research, optics, optical trapping, mechanical effects of light, optogenetics, optical microscopy. Bonin, Ucer, Williams.

Biophysics. Optics, optical trapping, mechanical effects of light, optogenetics, optical microscopy, motor proteins, kinesin, optical and electron paramagnetic spectroscopy, hemoglobin, nitric oxide, nitrite, sickle cell disease, cardiovascular disease, nanobiotechnology, atomic force and optical microscopy, single molecule experiments, protein-DNA interactions, thrombosis and hemostasis, nanofibers, electrospinning, tissue engineering, drug discovery, Center for Translational Science. Basu, Bonin, Guthold, Hall, George Holzwarth, Kim-Shapiro, Macosko, Shields.

Condensed Matter Physics. Organic and flexible electronics, transport properties, semiconductor trapping centers, laser materials, ultrafast spectroscopy, excitons, scintillators, energy research. Carroll, Jurchescu, Ucer, Williams.

Energy Sources & Environment. The Center is engaged in a broad range of projects from the development of medical technologies, to green energy technologies, to the understanding of the environmental and ethical implications of such nano-based technologies, material design and synthesis, carbon nanotubes, metal nanoparticles, quantum dots, polymers, cage structures, solar cells, biofuels, batteries, high-efficiency organic transistors, new lighting systems, antibiotic resistance, wound healing, tissue regeneration. Carroll, Jurchescu.

Nano Science and Technology. Nanostructures and nanotechnology, nanomotors, solar cells, meta materials and negative index materials, organic electronics, thin-film transistors, field-effect transistors, organic semiconductors, single crystals, microstructure. Bonin, Carroll, Guthold, George Holzwarth, Jurchescu, Macosko.

View additional information about this department at www.gradschoolshopper.com. Check out the "Why Choose Us?" section, find out more about the department's culture and get links to social media networks.

NORTH DAKOTA STATE UNIVERSITY

DEPARTMENT OF PHYSICS

Fargo, North Dakota 58108-6050
http://www.ndsu.edu/physics/

General University Information
President: Dean Bresciani
Dean of Graduate School: Maria-Claudia Tomany
University website: http://www.ndsu.edu/
School Type: Public
Setting: Urban
Total Faculty: 700
Total Graduate Faculty: 534
Total number of Students: 14,432
Total number of Graduate Students: 2,082

Department Information
Department Chairman: Dr. Sylvio May, Chair
Department Contact: Patty Hartsoch, Administrative Assistant
   Total full-time faculty: 10
   Total number of full-time equivalent positions: 10
   Full-Time Graduate Students: 18
   Female Full-Time Graduate Students: 0
   First-Year Graduate Students: 4
   Female First-Year Students: 1
   Total Post Doctorates: 2

Department Address
218 South Engineering, 1211 Albrecht Blvd
NDSU Dept. 2755, P.O. Box 6050
Fargo, ND 58108-6050
Phone: (701) 231-8974
Fax: (701) 231-7088
E-mail: patty.hartsoch@ndsu.edu
Website: http://www.ndsu.edu/physics/

ADMISSIONS

Admission Contact Information
Address admission inquiries to: Dr. Alan Denton, Graduate Coordinator, NDSU Dept. 2755, P.O. Box 6050, Fargo, ND 58108-6050
Phone: (701) 231-7036
E-mail: alan.denton@ndsu.edu
Admissions website: http://www.ndsu.edu/physics/graduate_program/graduate_admission/

Application deadlines
Fall admission:
U.S. students: March 1   *Int'l. students*: March 1
Spring admission:
U.S. students: September 1   *Int'l. students*: September 1

Application fee
U.S. students: $35   *Int'l. students*: $35
We recommend applying as early as possible, since we often make offers to especially qualified students shortly after we receive their applications. Admission deadline (Fall admission) is 30 days before start of term.

Admissions information
For Fall of 2018:
   Number of applicants: 20
   Number admitted: 4

Number enrolled: 4

Admission requirements
Bachelor's degree requirements: Bachelor's degree in Physics or a related field is required.
Minimum undergraduate GPA: 3.0

GRE requirements
The GRE is required.
   Quantitative score: 155
No additional specific scores required.

Subjective GRE requirements
The Subjective GRE is not required.

TOEFL requirements
The TOEFL exam is required for students from non-English-speaking countries.
   PBT score: 553
   iBT score: 81
TA support: TOEFL ibT 81 (Speaking 23, Writing 21), IELTS 7 (Speaking 6, Writing 6)

Other admissions information
Undergraduate preparation assumed: Equivalent of Thornton & Marion, Classical Mechanics; Griffiths, Electrodynamics; Callen, Thermodynamics; Griffiths, Quantum Mechanics; Hecht, Optics; Riley Hobson, Bence, Mathematical Methods.

TUITION

Tuition year 2017–18:
Tuition for in-state residents
   Full-time students: $3,862 per semester
   Part-time students: $321.84 per credit
Tuition for out-of-state residents
   Full-time students: $10,311.5 per semester
   Part-time students: $859.31 per credit
Tuition is waived for all full-time graduate students with financial support.
Credit hours per semester to be considered full-time: 6
Deferred tuition plan: Yes
Health insurance: Yes, $2,200 (approx).
Other academic fees: Student fees: $56.03/credit
Academic term: Semester
Number of first-year students who received full tuition waivers: 3

Teaching Assistants, Research Assistants, and Fellowships
Number of first-year
   Teaching Assistants: 2
   Research Assistants: 1
Average stipend per academic year
   Teaching Assistant: $18,000
   Research Assistant: $20,000
RA stipends include an allotment for health insurance. Under special circumstances, TA stipends may be supplemented to include health benefits.

FINANCIAL AID

Application deadlines
Fall admission:
U.S. students: September 1
Spring admission:
U.S. students: December 1

Loans
Loans are available for U.S. students.
Loans are not available for international students.
GAPSFAS application required: Yes
FAFSA application required: Yes

For further information
Address financial aid inquiries to: Office of Financial Aid and Scholarships, One Stop, NDSU Dept. 2836, P.O. Box 6050, Fargo, ND 58108-6050.
Phone: (701) 231-6200 / 866-924-8969
E-mail: ndsu.onestop@ndsu.edu
Financial aid website: https://www.ndsu.edu/onestop/finaid/

HOUSING

Availability of on-campus housing
Single students: Yes
Married students: Yes

For further information
Address housing inquiries to: Department of Residence Life, NDSU Dept. 5310, P.O. Box 6050, Fargo, ND 58108-6050.
Phone: 1-800-572-8840 / (701) 231-7557
E-mail: NDSU.Residence.Life@ndsu.edu
Housing aid website: http://www.ndsu.edu/reslife/

Table A—Faculty, Enrollments, and Degrees Granted

Research Specialty	2016–17 Faculty	Enrollment Fall 2017 Master's	Enrollment Fall 2017 Doctorate	Number of Degrees Granted 2017–18 (2013–2018) Master's	Number of Degrees Granted 2017–18 (2013–2018) Terminal Master's	Number of Degrees Granted 2017–18 (2013–2018) Doctorate
Biophysics	2	–	4	–(1)	–(1)	1(1)
Nano Science and Technology	1	–	3	–(4)	–(2)	–(2)
Optics	–	–	–	–	–	–
Physics Education Research	3	–	5	3(1)	–	–
Polymer Physics/Science	1	–	3	–(1)	–	1(1)
Soft Matter Physics	3	3	3	1(2)	3	–(2)
Total	10	3	18	4(13)	3(6)	2(8)
Full-time Grad. Stud.	–	3	19	–	–	–
First-year Grad. Stud.	–	1	4	–	–	–

GRADUATE DEGREE REQUIREMENTS

Master's: 30 graduate credits; one-year residency; thesis; oral examination on thesis and general physics through first-year graduate courses.

Doctorate: 90 graduate credits; one-year residency; core sequence in mathematical methods, electromagnetic theory, quantum mechanics, statistical physics, and solid state physics; written and oral comprehensive examination on advanced undergraduate and graduate core sequence courses and research proposal; dissertation; oral defense of dissertation.

Other Degrees: Accelerated Bachelor's to Master's.

Thesis: Thesis may be written in absentia.

SPECIAL EQUIPMENT, FACILITIES, OR PROGRAMS

NDSU's Materials and Nanotechnology Center is located in the Research and Technology Park. The Center is equipped with two state-of-the-art wet labs, a synthesis lab, optical characterization facilities (optical/NIR fluorescence microscopy, laser-scanning confocal microscopy, and light scattering/reflectometry), and surface characterization facilities (nano-indentation and atomic-force microscopy). There are seven fume hoods in the lab space, as well as a number of synthesis tools, including a Beckman Coulter Optima L-80 XP Ultracentrifuge. We also have access to state-of-the-art chemical synthesis facilities in the Departments of Chemistry and Biochemistry and Coatings and Polymeric Materials, including a Photo Emissions Tech Model SS50AAA Solar Simulator equipped with a Keithley 2400 Series Source meter.

NDSU's Center for Computationally Assisted Science and Technology (CCAST) provides large-scale computing resources to NDSU users. Currently, CCAST has two active clusters, Cluster2 and Cluster3, both managed by the TORQUE queuing system, with a Modules package to help users manage their shell environment. Cluster 2 is a 232-node/256-core cluster with 2.66Ghz 5430 Penryn processors, one terabyte of distributed memory, five terabytes of distributed storage, and Gigabit Ethernet. Cluster 3 is a 128-node/1024-core cluster with 2.66Ghz 5550 Nehalem processors, 6.1 terabytes of distributed memory, 20 terabytes of distributed storage, Gigabit Ethernet and 10GB Myrinet interconnect with support for MX low latency messaging. There is also a DEC dedicated Oracle database server.

Table B—Separately Budgeted Research Expenditures by Source of Support

Source of Support	Departmental Research	Physics-related Research Outside Department
Federal government	$1,643,000	
State/local government	$91,000	
Non-profit organizations		
Business and industry		
Other		
Total	$1,734,000	

Table C—Separately Budgeted Research Expenditures by Research Specialty

Research Specialty	No. of Grants	Expenditures ($)
Atomic, Molecular, & Optical Physics	1	$186,000
Nano Science and Technology	3	$640,000
Physics and other Science Education	6	$688,000
Polymer Physics/Science	3	$220,000
Total	13	$1,734,000

FACULTY

Professor

Denton, Alan, Ph.D., Cornell University, 1991. Graduate Program Coordinator. *Biophysics, Chemical Physics, Computational Physics, Condensed Matter Physics, Nano Science and Technology, Solid State Physics, Statistical & Thermal Physics, Theoretical Physics*. Theoretical and computational modeling of soft materials with biological and biomedical applications.

Hobbie, Erik K., Ph.D., University of Minnesota, 1990. Director of Materials and Nanotechnology Graduate Program. *Condensed Matter Physics, Fluids, Rheology, Nano Science and Technology, Optics, Polymer Physics/Science, Solid State*

Physics, Surface Physics. Nanotechnology, polymer science, and biotechnology.

May, Sylvio, Ph.D., Friedrich-Schiller University Jena, 1996. Chair. *Biophysics, Chemical Physics, Computational Physics, Condensed Matter Physics, Polymer Physics/Science, Statistical & Thermal Physics, Theoretical Physics.* Theoretical and computational biophysics.

Associate Professor

Christensen, Warren, Ph.D., Iowa State University, 2007. *Physics and other Science Education.* Physics education research.

Croll, Andrew B., Ph.D., McMaster University, 2009. *Biophysics, Chemical Physics, Condensed Matter Physics, Nano Science and Technology, Polymer Physics/Science, Surface Physics.* Polymer physics, Diblock copolymers, Thin films and confinement, Membrane geometry, Pattern formation and control, Instabilities, Wrinkling and buckling, Stress localization, Polymer mechanics, Adhesion, Physics of nano-composite materials, Capillarity, Polymer fluid dynamics, Friction.

Kryjevskaia, Mila, Ph.D., University of Washington, 2008. *Physics and other Science Education.* Physics education research.

Wagner, Alexander, Ph.D., University of Oxford, 1997. Associate Editor of Phys. Rev. E. *Chemical Physics, Computational Physics, Condensed Matter Physics, Polymer Physics/Science, Statistical & Thermal Physics, Theoretical Physics.* Discrete simulations of complex fluids.

Assistant Professor

Buncher, John B., Ph.D., Purdue University, 2010. *Physics and other Science Education.* Physics education research.

Choi, Yongki, Ph.D., The City University of New York, 2010. *Biophysics, Nano Science and Technology, Optics, Polymer Physics/Science, Surface Physics.* Single-molecule electronics and science.

Kryjevski, Andrei, Ph.D., University of Washington, 2004. *Computational Physics, Nano Science and Technology, Statistical & Thermal Physics, Theoretical Physics.* Computational physics, nano science and technology, statistical & thermal physics, theoretical physics, electronic structure.

Emeritus

Kroll, Daniel M., Ph.D., University of Chicago, 1973. *Biophysics, Chemical Physics, Computational Physics, Condensed Matter Physics, Materials Science, Metallurgy, Polymer Physics/Science, Solid State Physics, Statistical & Thermal Physics, Theoretical Physics.* Theoretical and computational modeling of complex fluids and biomembranes.

Swenson, Orven, Ph.D., Air Force Institute of Technology, 1982. *Atomic, Molecular, & Optical Physics, Optics.* Multiphoton ionization, environmental monitoring.

Adjunct Professor

Croll, Stuart, Ph.D., University of Leeds, 1974. *Chemical Physics, Nano Science and Technology, Polymer Physics/Science.* Coatings and polymeric materials.

Lepper, Kenneth, Ph.D., Oklahoma State University, 2001. *Geology/Geochemistry, Geophysics.* Technique development and advanced applications for Optically Stimulated Luminescence (OSL) dating.

DEPARTMENTAL RESEARCH SPECIALTIES AND STAFF

Theoretical

Dynamics of Fluid Mixtures. Theory and computer simulation of equilibrium and non equilibrium phenomena using Lattice-Boltzmann simulation and other multi-particle collision methods. Wagner.

Electronic Structure of Nanoparticles from First Principles. The ability to control properties of nanomaterials via size, shape, composition, surface structure, and self-assembly has opened new degrees of freedom inaccessible in conventional device design. At the same time, computational studies of nanostructures have become an attractive alternative to actual experiments, since the ability to explore the vast set of all possible configurations experimentally is limited. In recent years, advances in ab initio electronic structure techniques, such as Density Functional Theory, combined with new computational capabilities have enabled accurate calculations for atomistic models of nanoparticles. The results of these studies often serve as a unique source of insight into nanomaterial properties. We study properties of photoexcited semiconductor nanoparticles, such as quantum dots, nanowires, nanofilms, and carbon nanotubes. This requires description of electrons, photons, and atomic vibrations (phonons), all of which are interacting quantum mechanical particles. In our work methods of modern quantum field theory, which have been mostly used in theoretical nuclear and particle physics, are combined with advanced computational electronic structure capabilities. Kryjevski.

Macromolecular Crowding and Depletion. The conformations of flexible polymer coils, such as biopolymers in biological cells, are strongly affected by crowded environments. Correspondingly, depletion-induced interactions between crowders (nanoparticles) in polymer-nanoparticle mixtures depend in range and strength on size, shape, and concentration of depletants. By simulating hard-sphere nanoparticles and random-walk polymers, modeled as fluctuating ellipsoids, we compute polymer shape distributions and depletion-induced potentials. Comparisons with theory, simulations, and experiments show that polymer shape fluctuations play an important role in depletion and crowding phenomena. Denton.

Multiscale Modeling of Soft Nanomaterials. Soft nanomaterials – multicomponent mixtures of macromolecules and nanoparticles – have attracted much attention recently for their rich physical properties and technological applications. For example, colloidal crystals are widely explored for photovoltaic and photonic applications, with practical importance for solar cells, optical switches, and (potentially) quantum computers. In charged colloidal suspensions, microion screening of electrostatic forces between macroions influences the structure and stability of many common materials, from foods to pharmaceuticals. Addition of nanoparticles can modify electrostatic screening, enriching the tunability of interparticle forces and phase stability. In mixtures of polymers and nanoparticles, macromolecular crowding and polymer depletion can induce demixing and modify conformations of soft polymer coils, with biological relevance for protein and RNA folding and phase separation in the cell nucleus. To better understand screening, crowding, and depletion phenomena in these complex systems, we are developing Monte Carlo and molecular dynamics simulations of coarse-grained models. While surmounting computational challenges posed by diverse length and time scales, our multiscale modeling approaches also provide physical insight to guide experiments and help interpret observations. Denton.

Physics Education Research. We conduct discipline-based research in Physics Education. The objective is to examine student understanding, and identify and analyze conceptual and reasoning difficulties that students encounter in studying physics. The next step is to design instructional strategies that target specific student difficulties identified by the research, and to assess the effectiveness of these strategies. Therefore, research, curriculum development, and instruction are all integral parts of our investigation. Buncher, Christensen, Kryjevskaia.

Soft Colloids and Biomembranes. Polyelectrolyte microgels and microcapsules are microscopic gel particles that are swollen in a solvent. Composed of porous, elastic networks of cross-linked polymers, microgels are soft colloids that can encapsulate dye molecules or drugs. Their sensitive response to environmental conditions (e.g., temperature and pH) and influence on flow properties suit microgels to widespread applications in the chemical, pharmaceutical, food, and consumer care industries. We model microgels and microcapsules using molecular simulations and Poisson-Boltzmann theory. Lipid membranes surround all living cells, forming a barrier that ensures integrity and function. We are interested in understanding the physical properties of membranes and relating them to biological functions. Among the interesting questions are how different lipids influence the lateral organization of a lipid bilayer and what the role of membrane-associated proteins is. Some of our work also addresses bending of lipid membranes and electrostatic interactions between the lipid bilayer and adsorbed macroions. Denton, May.

Soft Matter Physics. Colloids, polymers, surfactants, and liquid crystals are widespread in daily life and nature and have practical importance for many technological applications, including paints, cosmetics, emulsions, foods, and pharmaceuticals. These systems contain macromolecules, whose complex intermolecular interactions determine the stability and unusual properties of soft materials. We study soft matter systems collaboratively using a variety of theoretical, computational, and experimental methods. Choi, Andrew Croll, Stuart Croll, Denton, Hobbie, May, Wagner.

Experimental

Flexible Nanotube Networks:. Using single-wall carbon nanotubes (SWCNTs) that have been purified by length and/or electronic type (metallic or semiconducting), we are assembling thin flexible nanotube films on soft polymer substrates and characterizing the coupling between mechanical flexibility and electronic performance. Self-Assembly and Photoluminescent Stability of Silicon Nanocrystals: In this work, we are purifying silicon nanocrystals (quantum dots) in an effort to reduce size polydispersity to the point where superlattice assembly becomes viable over large (macroscopic) length scales. High Performance Polymer Nanocomposites: By mixing silicon nanocrystals (SiNCs) with different polymers, for example, we can make photoluminescent coatings with optical sensitivity to changes in temperature, stress or chemical environment. Transmembrane Nanoparticle Transport: We use fluorescent imaging and microscale time-resolved spectroscopy to measure the specific cellular uptake mechanisms of PEGylated nanoparticles, quantum dots, and cargo carrying copolymer micelles. Denton, Hobbie, May, Wagner.

Polymer Physics/Science. Thin Block Copolymer Films: With modern techniques, creating and characterizing polymer films of nanoscopic thickness has become commonplace. What has quickly become clear is that there are many reasons that thin films differ in behavior from thick films. Here we study these issues by using films with anisotropic internal structure (diblock copolymers) using other forms of confinement (droplets, or cylinders) and by manipulating the stress found within the materials. Supramolecular Assemblies: As anyone who has seen microscopic pictures of tissue can attest, there are many differences between a real tissue and our naive continuum approximation. Inspired by these differences, we examine an idealized system – block copolymer vesicles. Polymersomes (as they are known) form analogously to lipid vesicles, but are much stronger and allow for chemical manipulation, making them ideal for examining questions of adhesion, vitrification, and failure. Stress Localization: When a sheet of paper is bent, it is simple to see that the new shape is accommodated easily by the material. However, if the paper is next bent in an orthogonal direction, it collapses into sharp points and folds. The stress has been focused to a point, rather than spread over the material simply because the sheet is stretched into a geometry of non-zero Gaussian curvature. We examine what the general rules of such a transition might be using an idealized buckling system – wrinkles!. Andrew Croll.

Single-Molecule Electronics and Science. Nanoscale electronic devices like field-effect transistors have long promised to provide sensitive, label-free detection of biomolecules. In particular, single-walled carbon nanotubes have the requisite sensitivity to detect single molecule events, and have sufficient bandwidth to directly monitor single molecule dynamics in real time. With this tool, we investigate the unknown molecular mechanism and complex kinetics of protein activities at a single molecule level. Choi.

View additional information about this department at www.gradschoolshopper.com. Check out the "Why Choose Us?" section, find out more about the department's culture and get links to social media networks.

BOWLING GREEN STATE UNIVERSITY

DEPARTMENT OF PHYSICS AND ASTRONOMY

Bowling Green, Ohio 43403
http://physics.bgsu.edu

General University Information
President: Rodney Rogers
Dean of Graduate School: Margaret Booth
University website: http://bgsu.edu
School Type: Public
Setting: Rural
Total Faculty: 900
Total Graduate Faculty: 500
Total number of Students: 19,000
Total number of Graduate Students: 3,400

Department Information
Department Chairman: Prof. John B. Laird, Chair
Department Contact: John B. Laird, Chair
   Total full-time faculty: 14
   Total number of full-time equivalent positions: 14
   Full-Time Graduate Students: 25
   Female Full-Time Graduate Students: 5
   First-Year Graduate Students: 7
   Female First-Year Students: 1
   Total Post Doctorates: 2

Department Address
104 Overman Hall
Bowling Green State University
Bowling Green, OH 43403
Phone: (419) 372-2421
Fax: (419) 372-9938
E-mail: physics@bgsu.edu
Website: http://physics.bgsu.edu

ADMISSIONS

Admission Contact Information
Address admission inquiries to: Graduate College, 120 McFall
   Center, Bowling Green State University, Bowling Green, OH
   43403
Phone: (419) 372-2791
E-mail: gradcol@bgsu.edu
Admissions website: http://www.bgsu.edu/graduate/admissions.
   html

Application deadlines
Fall admission:
U.S. students: February 28   *Int'l. students*: February 28

Application fee
U.S. students: $45   *Int'l. students*: $75

Admissions information
For Fall of 2018:
   Number of applicants: 70
   Number admitted: 60
   Number enrolled: 5

Admission requirements
Bachelor's degree requirements: A B.S. with major in physics
   or minor in physics with major in cognate field required. One
   year of undergraduate chemistry.

GRE requirements
The GRE is required.

Subjective GRE requirements
The Subjective GRE is not required.

TOEFL requirements
The TOEFL exam is required for students from non-English-
   speaking countries.
   PBT score: 550
   iBT score: 80

Other admissions information
Additional requirements: Transcripts and three letters of recommendation are required.

TUITION

Tuition year 2018–19:
Tuition for in-state residents
   Full-time students: $7,128 annual
   Part-time students: $446 per credit
Tuition for out-of-state residents
   Full-time students: $12,152 annual
   Part-time students: $760 per credit
Credit hours per semester to be considered full-time: 8
Deferred tuition plan: Yes
Health insurance: Available
Other academic fees: $634/semester (full-time)
Academic term: Semester
Number of first-year students who received full tuition waivers: 7

Teaching Assistants, Research Assistants, and Fellowships
   Number of first-year
      Teaching Assistants: 7
   Average stipend per academic year
      Teaching Assistant: $11,750

FINANCIAL AID

Application deadlines
Fall admission:
U.S. students: February 28   *Int'l. students*: February 28

Loans
Loans are not available for U.S. students.
Loans are not available for international students.
GAPSFAS application required: No
FAFSA application required: No

For further information
Address financial aid inquiries to: Dept. of Physics and As-
   tronomy, BGSU, Bowling Green, OH 43403.
Phone: (419) 372-2421
E-mail: physics@bgsu.edu
Financial aid website: http://physics.bgsu.edu/

HOUSING

Availability of on-campus housing
Single students: Yes
Married students: No

For further information
Address housing inquiries to: Off-Campus Student Services, 301 Bowen-Thompson Student Union, BGSU, Bowling Green, OH 43403.
Phone: (419) 372-2843
Housing aid website: http://www.bgsu.edu/off-campus-student-services.html

Table A—Faculty, Enrollments, and Degrees Granted

Research Specialty	2017–18 Faculty	Enrollment Fall 2017 Master's	Enrollment Fall 2017 Doctorate	Number of Degrees Granted 2017–18 (2013–18) Master's	Number of Degrees Granted 2017–18 (2013–18) Terminal Master's	Number of Degrees Granted 2017–18 (2013–18) Doctorate
Acoustics	1	–	–	–	–(1)	–
Astronomy	6	1	–	–	1(5)	–
Computational Physics	1	–	–	–	–(1)	–
Nano Science and Technology	3	6	12	–	1(20)	1(5)
Physics and other Science Education	1	–	–	–	–	–
Solid State Physics	2	3	2	–	3(9)	–
Non-specialized	–	1	–	–	1(5)	–
Total	**14**	**11**	**14**	**–**	**6(41)**	**1(5)**
Full-time Grad. Stud.	–	11	14	–	–	–
First-year Grad. Stud.	–	5	3	–	–	–

GRADUATE DEGREE REQUIREMENTS

Master's: Plan I: 32 semester hours: 3.0 GPA; formal thesis; oral examination on thesis; 24 semester hours in residence; no language requirement. Plan II: 32 semester hours; 3.0 GPA; no thesis, but comprehensive examination and scholarly paper required; 24 semester hours in residence; no language requirement.
Thesis: Thesis may be written in absentia.

SPECIAL EQUIPMENT, FACILITIES, OR PROGRAMS

Ph.D.-preparatory or career-oriented master's degree available. Students can pursue a Ph.D. through the Center for Photochemical Sciences or through a cooperative program with the University of Toledo. Computer access includes many workstations and remote access to the Ohio Supercomputer Center. Laboratory facilities are available for research in nanoscale and solid-state materials, including quantum dots, light-emitting devices, photovoltaics, photonics, spintronics, materials defects, and magnetic resonance. Additional facilities available for graduate student research include electron microscopes and a 0.5-m telescope with a CCD camera.

Table B—Separately Budgeted Research Expenditures by Source of Support

Source of Support	Departmental Research	Physics-related Research Outside Department
Federal government	$668,000	
State/local government	$168,000	
Non-profit organizations		
Business and industry	$4,000	
Other		
Total	**$840,000**	

Table C—Separately Budgeted Research Expenditures by Research Specialty

Research Specialty	No. of Grants	Expenditures ($)
Nano Science and Technology	6	$538,000
Solid State Physics	3	$107,000
Physics and other Science Education	4	$195,000
Total	**13**	**$840,000**

FACULTY

Professor
Fulcher, Lewis P., Ph.D., University of Virginia, 1969. *Acoustics, Fluids, Rheology, Mechanics*. Human phonation; modeling the human larynx.
Laird, John B., Ph.D., Yale University, 1983. *Astronomy, Astrophysics, Physics and other Science Education*. Stellar astronomy; stellar populations; astronomy and physics education.
Layden, Andrew C., Ph.D., Yale University, 1993. *Astronomy, Astrophysics*. Stellar astronomy; variable stars; stellar populations.
Smith, Dale W., Ph.D., University of Washington, 1978. *Astronomy, Physics and other Science Education*. Public education.
Zamkov, Mikhail A., Ph.D., Kansas State University, 2003. *Condensed Matter Physics, Materials Science, Metallurgy, Nano Science and Technology, Solid State Physics, Surface Physics*. Nanosystems; thin films; photovoltaic cells.

Associate Professor
Nardone, Marco, Ph.D., University of Toledo, 2011. *Computational Physics, Condensed Matter Physics, Nano Science and Technology, Solid State Physics*. Semiconductor physics, solid state physics, photovoltaics, device modeling, charge transport in disordered materials.
Sun, Liangfeng, Ph.D., University of Texas, 2006. *Condensed Matter Physics, Materials Science, Metallurgy, Nano Science and Technology, Solid State Physics*. Nanomaterials; surface non-linear optics.
Xi, Haowen, Ph.D., Lehigh University, 1993. *Computational Physics*. Computational physics; convection; econophysics.
Zayak, Alexey T., Ph.D., University of Duisburg-Essen, 2004. *Computational Physics, Condensed Matter Physics, Materials Science, Metallurgy, Nano Science and Technology, Solid State Physics*. Condensed-matter theory; nanoscale systems.

Assistant Professor
Selim, Farida A., Ph.D., Alexandria University, 1999. *Condensed Matter Physics, Materials Science, Metallurgy, Nano Science and Technology, Solid State Physics, Surface Physics*. solid-state materials; structural, optical, electronic, and magnetic properties of oxides.

Emeritus
Boughton, Robert I., Ph.D., Ohio State University, 1968. *Condensed Matter Physics, Low Temperature Physics, Materials Science, Metallurgy, Physics and other Science Education, Solid State Physics*. Low-temperature solid-state physics; physics education.
Crandall, A. Jared, Ph.D., Michigan State University, 1967. *Solar Physics*. Microcomputer interfacing; solar energy research.
Shirkey, Charles T., Ph.D., Ohio State University, 1969.
Stoner, Ronald E., Ph.D., Purdue University, 1966. *Astrophysics, Computational Physics, Physics and other Science Education, Solid State Physics*. Active galaxies; astrophysics; solid-state theory; physics education.

Senior Lecturer

Mandell, Eric S., Ph.D., University of Missouri, 2007. *Astronomy, Astrophysics, Materials Science, Metallurgy, Nano Science and Technology, Physics and other Science Education, Solid State Physics.* Physics education; carbon nanostructures and star dust.

Rogel, Allen B., Ph.D., Indiana University, 2005. *Astronomy, Astrophysics.* Stellar astronomy; cataclysmic variables.

Tiede, Glenn P., Ph.D., Ohio State University, 1997. *Astronomy, Astrophysics.* Stellar populations.

Lecturer

Dellenbusch, Kate E., Ph.D., University of Wisconsin-Madison, 2008. *Astronomy, Astrophysics, Physics and other Science Education.* Extragalactic astronomy; astronomy education.

DEPARTMENTAL RESEARCH SPECIALTIES AND STAFF

Theoretical

Acoustics. Human phonation; modeling the human larynx. Fulcher.

Computational Physics. semiconductor physics; electronic structure; convection; econophysics. Nardone, Xi, Zayak.

Nano Science and Technology. Nanostructures and condensed-matter physics; light-matter interactions. Nardone, Zayak.

Experimental

Acoustics. Measurements of air flow and pressure in the human larynx. Fulcher.

Astronomy. Stellar spectroscopy and abundances; stellar populations; chemical evolution of galaxies; variable stars; cataclysmic variables; interstellar matter; extragalactic astronomy. Dellenbusch, Laird, Layden, Mandell, Rogel, Tiede.

Nano Science and Technology. Nanosystems; non-linear optics and devices; thin-film devices; photovoltaic cells. Mandell, Sun, Zamkov.

Physics and other Science Education. Active learning strategies and materials; teacher preparation; public education. Dellenbusch, Laird, Mandell, Smith, Tiede.

Solid State Physics. Thin films; optical, electronic, magnetic properties oxides; solid-state lighting; photovoltaics. Mandell, Selim, Sun, Zamkov.

CASE WESTERN RESERVE UNIVERSITY

DEPARTMENT OF ASTRONOMY

Cleveland, Ohio 44106-7215
http://astronomy.case.edu

General University Information
President: Barbara R. Snyder
Dean of Graduate School: Charles Rozek
University website: http://case.edu
School Type: Private
Setting: Urban
Total Faculty: 2,972
Total number of Students: 11,340
Total number of Graduate Students: 6,219

Department Information
Department Chairman: Prof. Stacy McGaugh, Chair
Department Contact: Agnes M. Torontali, Department
  Assistant
  Total full-time faculty: 5
  Full-Time Graduate Students: 2
  Female Full-Time Graduate Students: 0

Department Address
10900 Euclid Avenue
Cleveland, OH 44106-7215
Phone: (216) 368-3728
Fax: (216) 368-5406
E-mail: dept@astronomy.case.edu
Website: http://astronomy.case.edu

ADMISSIONS

Admission Contact Information
Address admission inquiries to: Heather L. Morrison
Phone: (216) 368-6698
E-mail: hlm5@case.edu
Admissions website: http://astronomy.case.edu

Application deadlines
Fall admission:
U.S. students: January 15   *Int'l. students*: January 15

Application fee
U.S. students: $50   *Int'l. students*: $50

Admissions information
For Fall of 2018:
  Number of applicants: 45
  Number admitted: 8
  Number enrolled: 3

Admission requirements
Bachelor's degree requirements: Bachelor's degree in physics,
  astronomy, or related field is required.
Minimum undergraduate GPA: 3.0

GRE requirements
The GRE is required.
Applications are considered as a whole. There is no minimum
  required GRE score, nor any meaningful average.

Subjective GRE requirements
The Subjective GRE is not required.
The Physics GRE is optional. Students are encouraged to submit
  these scores when available.

TOEFL requirements
The TOEFL exam is required for students from non-English-
  speaking countries.
PBT score: 550

Other admissions information
Additional requirements: The Department requires a minimum
  undergraduate GPA of 3.00 (out of 4.00 or equivalent) from
  an accredited school. Three letters of recommendation are required.
  The Department reserves the right to modify or waive these
  requirements as it sees fit within the minimum criteria established by the Graduate School.

TUITION

Tuition year 2018–19:
  Full-time students: $22,584 per semester
  Part-time students: $1,882 per credit
Tuition waivers are provided to TAs and RAs.
Credit hours per semester to be considered full-time: 9
Deferred tuition plan: Yes
Health insurance: Yes, $2,174.00.
Other academic fees: Health insurance is covered for TAs and
  RAs.
Academic term: Semester
Number of first-year students who received full tuition waivers: 3

Teaching Assistants, Research Assistants, and Fellowships
Number of first-year
  Teaching Assistants: 3
Average stipend per academic year
  Teaching Assistant: $26,700
  Research Assistant: $26,700
Assistantships are usually available to all Ph.D. students.

FINANCIAL AID

Application deadlines
Fall admission:
U.S. students: January 15   *Int'l. students*: January 15

Loans
Loans are available for U.S. students.
Loans are available for international students.
GAPSFAS application required: No
FAFSA application required: No

For further information
Address financial aid inquiries to: Heather L. Morrison.
Phone: (216) 368-3728
E-mail: hlm5@case.edu

HOUSING

Availability of on-campus housing
  Single students: No
  Married students: No
  Childcare Assistance: No

For further information

Address housing inquiries to: See, https://students.case.edu/campus/graduate/tips/housing.html, https://case.edu/gradstudies/prospective-students/housing-options/.

Housing aid website: http://students.case.edu/housing/housing/graduate/

Table A—Faculty, Enrollments, and Degrees Granted

Research Specialty	2017–18 Faculty	Enrollment Fall 2017		Number of Degrees Granted 2017 (2013–18)		
		Master's	Doctorate	Master's	Terminal Master's	Doctorate
Astronomy	5	–	2	–(5)	–	2(2)
Total	5	–	2	–(5)	–	–(2)
Full-time Grad. Stud.	–	–	2	–	–	–
First-year Grad. Stud.	–	–	1	–	–	–

GRADUATE DEGREE REQUIREMENTS

Doctorate: Approximately two years of courses (with cumulative GPA of 3.0 or above) are required. Students must pass satisfactorily a qualifying examination administered by the department. Dissertation and defense are required. Residency requirement for the Ph.D. is one academic year full-time.

SPECIAL EQUIPMENT, FACILITIES, OR PROGRAMS

The Department owns and operates the Burrell Schmidt telescope, located at Kitt Peak National Observatory in Arizona. This telescope has a 2.6-square-degree field and is optimized for deep surface photometry. The department of Astronomy maintains extensive computational facilities for data processing and theoretical simulations. In addition to departmental computing capabilities, CWRU operates a high performance computational research facility that is available for faculty and student use.

Table B—Separately Budgeted Research Expenditures by Source of Support

Source of Support	Departmental Research	Physics-related Research Outside Department
Federal government	$501,365	
State/local government		
Non-profit organizations		
Business and industry		
Other	$72,381	
Total	**$573,746**	

Table C—Separately Budgeted Research Expenditures by Research Specialty

Research Specialty	No. of Grants	Expenditures ($)
Astronomy	12	$573,746
Total	12	$573,746

FACULTY

Chair Professor

McGaugh, Stacy, Ph.D., University of Michigan, 1992. *Astronomy, Astrophysics, Relativity & Gravitation.* Galaxy formation and evolution; cosmology; dark matter; gravity.

Professor

Luck, R. Earle, Ph.D., University of Texas, Austin, 1977. *Astronomy, Astrophysics.* Studies of stellar and galactic chemical evolution; high-dispersion spectroscopy and stellar abundance analysis.

Mihos, J. Christopher, Ph.D., University of Michigan, 1992. *Astronomy, Astrophysics.* Galaxy evolution; clusters of galaxies; galactic dynamics; observational astronomy; numerical simulation; computational astrophysics.

Morrison, Heather L., Ph.D., Australian National University, 1989. *Astronomy, Astrophysics.* Galactic structure; stellar populations; galaxy evolution; galaxy dynamics.

Associate Professor

Zehavi, Idit, Ph.D., Hebrew University of Jerusalem, 1999. *Astronomy, Astrophysics.* Cosmology; large-scale structure; galaxy and structure formation.

Adjunct Professor

Kriessler, Jeff, Ph.D., Michigan State University, 1997. *Astronomy.* Clusters of galaxies.

Observatory Manager

Harding, Paul, Ph.D., University of Arizona, 2001. *Astronomy, Astrophysics.* Galactic structure; stellar populations; galaxy evolution; observational astronomy; telescope and instrumentation development.

DEPARTMENTAL RESEARCH SPECIALTIES AND STAFF

Theoretical

Astronomy. Galaxy formation and evolution; large-scale structure; galactic dynamics. McGaugh, Mihos, Zehavi.

Astronomy. Cosmology; large-scale structure. McGaugh, Zehavi.

Astronomy. Gravitational physics. McGaugh.

Experimental

Astronomy. Cosmology; large-scale structure. McGaugh, Zehavi.

Astronomy. Stellar chemical composition; stellar spectroscopy. Harding, Luck, Morrison.

Astronomy. Astronomical telescope; instrumentation; detector development. Harding.

Astronomy. Galaxy formation and evolution; galaxy dynamics. Harding, McGaugh, Mihos, Morrison, Zehavi.

CASE WESTERN RESERVE UNIVERSITY

DEPARTMENT OF PHYSICS

Cleveland, Ohio 44106-7079
http://physics.cwru.edu

General University Information
President: Barbara Snyder
Dean of Graduate School: Charles E. Rozek
University website: http://www.cwru.edu
School Type: Private
Setting: Urban
Total Faculty: 3,615
Total Graduate Faculty: 3,615
Total number of Students: 11,824
Total number of Graduate Students: 6,674

Department Information
Department Chair: Prof. Kathleen Kash, Chair
Department Contact: Corbin E. Covault, Director of the
  Graduate Program
  Total full-time faculty: 27
  Total number of full-time equivalent positions: 22
  Full-Time Graduate Students: 46
  Female Full-Time Graduate Students: 7
  First-Year Graduate Students: 12
  Female First-Year Students: 2
  Total Post Doctorates: 13

Department Address
Rockefeller Building
2076 Adelbert Road
Cleveland, OH 44106-7079
Phone: (216) 368-4000
Fax: (216) 368-4671
E-mail: cec8@cwru.edu
Website: http://physics.cwru.edu

ADMISSIONS

Admission Contact Information
Address admission inquiries to: Corbin Covault, Admissions Director, Physics., Case Western Reserve University, 2076 Adelbert Road, Cleveland, OH 44106-7079
Phone: (216) 368-8779
E-mail: cec8@cwru.edu
Admissions website: http://www.phys.case.edu/grad/apply.php

Application deadlines
Fall admission:
U.S. students: January 15   *Int'l. students*: January 15

Application fee
There is no application fee required.
Applications are not generally accepted for Spring semester admission. Advanced graduate transfer students who are seeking to matriculate in January for Spring semester should contact the Director of the Graduate Program (cec8@cwru.edu) prior submitting an application.

Admissions information
For Fall of 2018:
  Number of applicants: 126
  Number admitted: 27
  Number enrolled: 12

Admission requirements
Bachelor's degree requirements: Bachelor's degree in Physics, Mathematics, or related field is required.
Minimum undergraduate GPA: 3.0
All applicants are strongly encouraged to complete the GRE General Test and to arrange to have scores submitted directly to CWRU. The inclusion of GRE scores will considerably strengthen any application. No minimum score is required.

Subjective GRE requirements
The Subjective GRE is recommended.
All applicants are strongly encouraged to complete the GRE Physics Subject Test and to arrange to have scores submitted directly to CWRU. The inclusion of GRE scores will considerably strengthen any application. GRE Physics subject test scores are expected from all domestic applicants who are applying with bachelor's degrees only. Advanced students may submit a record of graduate coursework and graduate level research experience in lieu of GRE Physics subject test results. No minimum score is required.

TOEFL requirements
The TOEFL exam is required for students from non-English-speaking countries.
  PBT score: 557
  iBT score: 90

Other admissions information
Additional requirements: No minimum acceptable GRE score is specified.
Undergraduate preparation assumed: Taylor, Classical Mechanics; Griffiths, Electrodynamics; Kittel, Thermal Physics; Griffiths, Quantum Mechanics; or equivalent textbooks; one or two years of advanced laboratory courses.

TUITION

Tuition year 2018–2019:
  Full-time students: $1,882 per credit
  Part-time students: $1,882 per credit
All admitted PhD students will receive tuition waivers for at least one full year.
Credit hours per semester to be considered full-time: 9
Deferred tuition plan: Yes
Health insurance: Available
Other academic fees: Health insurance will be made fully reimbursable at no net cost to incoming graduate students.
Academic term: Semester
Number of first-year students who received full tuition waivers: 7

Teaching Assistants, Research Assistants, and Fellowships
Number of first-year
  Teaching Assistants: 7
Average stipend per academic year
  Teaching Assistant: $25,276
  Research Assistant: $25,278
  Fellowship student: $25,276
TAs, RAs, and Fellows in the Ph.D. program are generally eligible for full tuition support. M.S. Students are generally not eligible for support at TAs or RAs.

FINANCIAL AID

Application deadlines
Fall admission:
U.S. students: January 15   *Int'l. students*: January 15

Loans
Loans are available for U.S. students.
Loans are available for international students.
GAPSFAS application required: No
FAFSA application required: No

For further information
Address financial aid inquiries to: Director of Admissions, Department of Physics, Case Western Reserve University, 2076 Adelbert Road, Cleveland, OH 44106-7079.
Phone: (216) 368-8779
E-mail: cec8@cwru.edu
Financial aid website: http://physics.cwru.edu

HOUSING

Availability of on-campus housing
Single students: No
Married students: No
Childcare Assistance: No

For further information
Address housing inquiries to: Dean, Graduate Studies, Case Western Reserve University, 10900 Euclid Avenue, Cleveland, OH 44016.
Phone: (216) 368-8779
E-mail: cec8@cwru.edu
Housing aid website: https://case.edu/gradstudies/prospective-students/housing-options

Table A—Faculty, Enrollments, and Degrees Granted

Research Specialty	2017–2018 Faculty	Enrollment Spring 2018 Master's	Enrollment Spring 2018 Doctorate	Number of Degrees Granted 2017–2018 (2013–2018) Master's	Number of Degrees Granted 2017–2018 (2013–2018) Terminal Master's	Number of Degrees Granted 2017–2018 (2013–2018) Doctorate
Biophysics	1	–	4	–	–(2)	–(2)
Condensed Matter Physics	13	–	18	–(2)	1(3)	6(11)
Cosmology and Particle Astrophysics	7	2	15	–(1)	1(2)	5(9)
Medical Imaging and Biophysics	3	–	4	–	–	2(5)
Other	2	1	2	–	1(4)	–(2)
Total	25	3	43	–(3)	3(11)	13(29)
Full-time Grad. Stud.	–	3	43	–	–	–
First-year Grad. Stud.	–	3	4	–	–	–

GRADUATE DEGREE REQUIREMENTS

Master's: 30 graduate credit hours in approved program including six required hours; Master's exam required; thesis option; no residence or language requirement.

Doctorate: Up to 36 hours of coursework is required (may be reduced by graduate coursework done elsewhere) plus 18 hours of thesis coursework; comprehensive and topical exams, dissertation, and dissertation exam required; one-year residency; no language exam required. See http://www.phys.cwru.edu/grad/phd.php.

Thesis: Thesis may be written in absentia.

SPECIAL EQUIPMENT, FACILITIES, OR PROGRAMS

A wide variety of facilities and programs are available within the department, and in addition there are collaborative programs with other departments, including Macromolecular Science, Chemistry, Astronomy, Materials Science, and the Medical School.

In astrophysics research, experiments in collaboration with other universities are being performed to search for high-energy cosmic rays and to explore the Cosmic Microwave Background. High-energy physics experiments are undertaken at various national laboratories. Theoretical work on astrophysics and cosmology, as well as particle, condensed matter physics, and quantum computing, covers a large number of research topics.

Condensed matter studies include measurements of dielectric; optical and nonlinear optical properties; thin-film properties; nanoscopic physics; quantum computing; liquid crystal and complex fluid properties; semiconductor crystal growth; quantum wells, wires, and dots; other nanoscopic structures; spintronics; organic electronics; and photovoltaics.

A wide range of facilities is available in surface physics and in optics. Among the collaborative programs are experimental and theoretical studies of phase transitions in polymers and of liquid crystals, photovoltaic materials, surface physics, the physics of imaging, fluid physics, dark matter detection, and measurements of fundamental parameters in cosmology.

Departmental computing facilities are extensive and are used in both research and courses. Weekly specialized seminars in particle/astrophysics and condensed matter physics take place, in addition to a weekly departmental colloquium.

The Physics Department has been recognized six times by the U.S. Department of Education as meeting vital national needs. Special graduate fellowships may be available.

In addition to a traditional physics program, the Department maintains a Physics Entrepreneurship Masters degree program. The program is designed to empower physicists as entrepreneurs and to enable students and graduates to build on their physics skills to start new high-tech businesses or to launch new product lines in existing companies.

Special Programs Center for Education and Research in Cosmology and Astrophysics: A new center created in collaboration with the Cleveland Museum of Natural History's Shafran Planetarium and CWRU's Astronomy Department to promote research and education in cosmology and astrophysics. http://cerca.case.edu

Institute for Advanced Materials: The Institute for Advanced Materials brings together internationally recognized faculty researchers to engage in multi-disciplinary efforts on a broad range of materials that not only are ubiquitous in everyday life, but are cornerstones to many key technology areas. Specifically, IAM focuses on strategic research that impacts national needs in human health, energy, and the environment. The four focus areas are: Fundamental Materials Research, Materials for Human Health, Materials for Energy, and Materials for Sustainability. http://engineering.case.edu/centers/IAM/

The Institute for the Science of Origins ISO is a collaborative team of faculty members and researchers from diverse scientific disciplines seeking to understand how complex systems emerge and evolve, from the universe to the mind, from microbes to humanity. http://www.case.edu/origins

The Michelson Postdoctoral Lectureship is an annual prize sponsored by Case Western Reserve University. It is awarded to an outstanding recent Physics Ph.D. based on an international competition. The winner spends one week in residence in the Department, and delivers several seminars and a departmental colloquium on his/her research.

Physics Entrepreneurship Masters Degree: To empower physicists as entrepreneurs and enable graduate students to build on their physics skills to start new high-tech businesses or to launch new product lines in existing companies.

Workshops and Conferences: The Department regularly holds national and international meetings on a variety of topics. Recent conferences have included: The Future of Cosmology, Future Physics and Future Facilities, The Cosmic Microwave Background, Great Lakes Cosmology Workshop, the American Vacuum Society Conference, International Workshop on MRI, Einstein's Legacy, and Confronting Gravity.

Outreach: The Department works with high school teachers and students to improve science education locally and nationally. The Department also hosts a Web site of a national program in astronomy education called Ask an Astronomer.

Books by Faculty include Magnetic Resonance Imaging: Physical Properties and Sequence Design by Robert Brown, and A Quantum Approach to Condensed Matter Physics Philip by L. Taylor.

International Programs: The department spearheaded three university-wide student and faculty exchange programs with the University of Calabria, Italy; Nagaoka University of Science and Technology, Japan; the Université Pierre et Marie Curie U. Paris 6, France, and Brazil.

Table B—Separately Budgeted Research Expenditures by Source of Support

Source of Support	Departmental Research	Physics-related Research Outside Department
Federal government	$11,496,898	
State/local government	$3,000,000	
Non-profit organizations	$2,951,133	
Business and industry	$218,176	
Other	$949,542	
Total	$18,615,749	

Table C—Separately Budgeted Research Expenditures by Research Specialty

Research Specialty	No. of Grants	Expenditures ($)
Cosmology and Particle Astrophysics	11	$5,557,949
Condensed Matter Physics	18	$6,151,635
Medical Imaging Physics and Biophysics	9	$3,416,689
Other	11	$3,489,476
Total	49	$18,615,749

FACULTY

Distinguished University Professor

Brown, Robert W., Ph.D., Massachusetts Institute of Technology, 1968. *Medical, Health Physics, Particles and Fields*. Theoretical physics; elementary particles; imaging physics.

Starkman, Glenn, Ph.D., Stanford University, 1988. *Astrophysics, Cosmology & String Theory, Particles and Fields, Theoretical Physics*. Theoretical physics; cosmology; particle physics; astrophysics.

Taylor, Philip L., Ph.D., University of Cambridge, 1962. *Condensed Matter Physics, Theoretical Physics*. Theoretical condensed matter physics; physics of polymers and liquid crystals.

Professor

Alexander, Iwan, Ph.D., Washington State University, 1981. Joint appointment with mechanical engineering. Fluid physics; microgravity.

Chottiner, Gary S., Ph.D., University of Maryland, 1980. *Condensed Matter Physics, Surface Physics*. Experimental condensed matter physics; surface physics.

Covault, Corbin, Ph.D., Harvard University, 1991. *Astrophysics, Atmosphere, Space Physics, Cosmic Rays*. Experimental high-energy astrophysics, particle interactions, cosmic rays.

Kash, Kathleen, Ph.D., Massachusetts Institute of Technology, 1982. *Atomic, Molecular, & Optical Physics*. Experimental condensed matter physics; optics; mesoscopic physics.

Lambrecht, Walter R. L., Ph.D., Ghent University, 1980. *Atomic, Molecular, & Optical Physics, Condensed Matter Physics, Theoretical Physics*. Theoretical condensed matter physics; electronic structure of materials.

Luck, Earle, Ph.D., University of Texas, 1977. Joint appointment with astronomy. *Astronomy*. Stellar and galactic chemical evolution; stellar abundance analysis; spectrum synthesis techniques.

Martens, Michael A., Ph.D., Case Western Reserve University, 1991. *Medical, Health Physics*. Imaging physics.Industrial Physics Magnetic Nanoparticle Imaging High Energy Particle Physics Accelerator Physics.

Mathur, Harsh, Ph.D., Yale University, 1994. *Astrophysics, Condensed Matter Physics, Cosmology & String Theory, Theoretical Physics*. Theoretical condensed matter physics; localization and mesoscopic physics; cosmology and particles.

Mihos, Christopher, Ph.D., University of Michigan, 1992. Joint appointment with astronomy. *Astronomy, Astrophysics, Computational Physics, Cosmology & String Theory*. Observational and computational astrophysics; galactic dynamics; galaxy clusters; galaxy evolution.

Morrison, Heather, Ph.D., Australian National University, 1988. Joint appointment with astronomy. *Astronomy, Astrophysics*. Galaxy structure, formation, and evolution, especially Milky Way and Local Group.

Petschek, Rolfe G., Ph.D., Harvard University, 1981. *Condensed Matter Physics, Statistical & Thermal Physics, Theoretical Physics*. Theoretical physics; statistical physics; condensed matter physics.

Rosenblatt, Charles, Ph.D., Harvard University, 1978. *Condensed Matter Physics, Fluids, Rheology, Optics*. Experimental condensed matter physics; liquid crystals and complex fluids; optics; microgravity; fluid physics.

Ruhl, John, Ph.D., Princeton University, 1993. *Astrophysics, Cosmology & String Theory*. Experimental particle astrophysics, cosmic microwave background.

Singer, Kenneth D., Ph.D., University of Pennsylvania, 1981. *Atomic, Molecular, & Optical Physics, Condensed Matter Physics, Nano Science and Technology, Optics*. Experimental physics; nonlinear optics; organic electronics; photovoltaics; nanophysics.

Strangi, Guiseppe, Ph.D., University of Calabria. *Atomic, Molecular, & Optical Physics, Condensed Matter Physics, Nano Science and Technology, Optics*. Experimental condensed matter physics optics and photonics of soft condensed matter DFB and random lasing opto-plasmonics in nanostructured metamaterials.

Taylor, Cyrus C., Ph.D., Massachusetts Institute of Technology, 1984. *Applied Physics, Particles and Fields, Theoretical Physics*. Theoretical physics, theoretical and experimental elementary particle physics; physics of entrepreneurship.

Associate Professor

Gao, Xuan, Ph.D., Columbia University, 2003. *Condensed Matter Physics, Nano Science and Technology*. Experimental condensed matter physics; applied physics; electronic properties of low dimensional nanostructures; semiconductor nanowires; nanosensors.

Jankowsky, Eckhard, Ph.D., Dresden Institute of Technology, 1996. Joint appointment with biochemistry. Experimental biophysics; single molecule fluorescence; enzyme kinetics.

Monreal, Benjamin, Ph.D., Massachusetts Institute of Technology, 2004. *Astrophysics, Atomic, Molecular, & Optical Physics, High Energy Physics, Particles and Fields.* Neutrino physics, weakly interacting particles, exoplanets.

Zehavi, Idit, Ph.D., Hebrew University of Jerusalem, 1999. *Cosmology & String Theory.* Theoretical astrophysics; cosmology; large-scale structure; galaxy and structure formation.

Assistant Professor

Berezovsky, Jesse, Ph.D., University of California, Santa Barbara, 2007. *Atomic, Molecular, & Optical Physics, Condensed Matter Physics, Quantum Foundations.* Experimental condensed matter; transport, quantum coupling of spins and photons; quantum information.

Fileviez Perez, Pavel, Ph.D., Max Planck Institute for Physics, 2003. *Cosmology & String Theory, Particles and Fields.* Cosmology, standard model theory.

Hinczewski, Micheal, Ph.D., Massachusetts Institute of Technology, 2005. *Biophysics, Statistical & Thermal Physics, Theoretical Physics.* Soft matter: motor proteins, single-molecule force spectroscopy, biopolymers, cell adhesion, signaling networks.

Hinterbichler, Kurt, Ph.D., Columbia University, 2009. *Cosmology & String Theory.* Effective field theory, early universe cosmology, higher spins, extra dimensions/brane worlds, modified gravity and screening mechanisms.

Visiting Assistant Professor

Dimastrogiovanni, Emanuela, Ph.D., University of Padova, 2010. *Cosmology & String Theory.* Massive gravity. Cosmology.

Instructor

Caner, Ed, M.S., Case Western Reserve University, 2003. Director, STEP/PEP: Master's in Entrepreneurship. *Applied Physics.* Science and Technology; physics entrepreneurship.

Copi, Craig J., Ph.D., University of Chicago, 1996. *Astrophysics, Cosmology & String Theory, Theoretical Physics.* Particle-astrophysics, Cosmic microwave background, early Universe.

Driscoll, Diana, Ph.D., Case Western Reserve University, 2001. Director of Introductory Laboratories. *Physics and other Science Education.* Science Education.

Kernan, Peter J., Ph.D., The Ohio State University, 1993. *Astrophysics, Computational Physics, Theoretical Physics.* Particle Astrophysics, scientific computing.

DEPARTMENTAL RESEARCH SPECIALTIES AND STAFF

Theoretical

Biophysics. Soft matter: motor proteins, single-molecule force spectroscopy, biopolymers, cell adhesion, signaling networks. Hinczewski.

Cosmology. Dark Matter, Dark Energy, cosmological pertubations, modified gravity, topology, constraints from cosmic microwave background, early Universe, inflation, extra dimensions, strings, branes. Copi, Dimastrogiovanni, Fileviez Perez, Hinterbichler, Mathur, Starkman.

Electronic Properties of Metals and Semiconductors. Electronic properties of metals and semiconductors; photovoltaics, crystal growth; transport properties in ordered and disordered materials; band structure; deformation potentials; localization, thermo-electricity; interface and surface physics; lattice vibrations. Lambrecht, Mathur, Petschek, Philip Taylor.

Imaging Physics. Algorithm development; bio-data acquisition and analysis; rf coil theory; inverse scattering theory; CT scanning, diagnostic imaging. Brown, Covault, Martens.

Liquid Crystals. Phase transitions, dynamics, symmetry and surface effects, nonlinear behavior. Petschek, Philip Taylor.

Particle Astrophysics. Cosmology and Gravitational Physics. Neutrino astrophysics; early universe cosmology; dark matter; dark energy; large-scale structure; gravitational lensing; black hole evaporation; stellar evolution; cosmic strings; cosmic rays, cosmic microwave background. Copi, Dimastrogiovanni, Fileviez Perez, Mathur, Starkman, Cyrus Taylor.

Particle Physics. Electroweak theory; standard model; cosmology; black hole physics; superstring theory SSC physics; supersymmetry, field theories at finite temperature; quark-gluon plasma; diffractive excitation mechanisms. Fileviez Perez, Mathur, Starkman, Cyrus Taylor.

Polymer Physics/Science. Equations of stat e; phase transitions; dynamical behavior; piezoelectric effects; polymer liquid crystals. Petschek, Philip Taylor.

Relativity & Gravitation. Relativity and Gravitation in Cosmology, early universe, modified gravity. Dimastrogiovanni, Fileviez Perez, Hinterbichler, Starkman.

Statistical & Thermal Physics. Statics and dynamics of phase transitions; pattern formation and dendritic growth; liquid crystals, polymeric liquid crystals, complex fluids; oscillatory chemical reactions; membrane noise. Petschek, Philip Taylor.

Experimental

Electronic Strucure of Matterials. Electronic structure of metals and alloys; surfaces; crystal growth; thin films; amorphous films; dielectric and cohesive properties; dielectric and mechanical relaxation; organic electronics; transport properties of nano-structures, quantum wells, mesoscopic systems, and fuel cells; soft matter. Berezovsky, Gao, Kash, Strangi.

Experimental Cosmology and Particle Astrophysics. Cosmic microwave background; high-energy cosmic rays; gamma ray astrophysics; neutrino detection. Covault, Monreal, Ruhl.

Fluid Physics. Interface instabilities; magnetic levitation. Rosenblatt.

High Energy Particle Physics. Collider physics; hadronic interactions. Covault, Cyrus Taylor.

Liquid Crystals and Complex Fluids. Phase transitions; optical, magnetic, and electrical properties; microgravity; nanostructured LCs, symmetry effects. Chottiner, Rosenblatt.

Nanoscopic Physics. Quantum dots, wires, molecular electronics, nanoscopic surface modification, nanowires, and sensors. Berezovsky, Gao, Kash, Rosenblatt, Singer, Strangi.

Optical Properties of Materials. Linear and nonlinear optical properties of organic, polymeric materials, and mesoscopic systems, photovoltaics, ultrafast spectroscopy. Berezovsky, Kash, Rosenblatt, Singer, Strangi.

Polymer Physics/Science. Phase transformations; dielectric properties; magnetic and electric field effects; optical mechanical properties. Rosenblatt, Singer.

Surface Physics. Surface magnetization; secondary electron emission; surface analysis; physi- and chemisorption. Chottiner.

KENT STATE UNIVERSITY

CHEMICAL PHYSICS INTERDISCIPLINARY PROGRAM

Kent, Ohio 44242
http://www.kent.edu/cpip

General University Information
President: Dr. Beverly Warren
Dean of Graduate School: Dr. Melody Tankersley
University website: http://www.kent.edu
School Type: Public
Total Faculty: 2,689
Total Graduate Faculty: 1,347
Total number of Students: 41,000
Total number of Graduate Students: 6,522

Department Information
Department Chairman: Dr. Antal Jakli, Director
Department Contact: Mary Lyn Bergstrom, Senior Secretary
  Total full-time faculty: 16
  Total number of full-time equivalent positions: 16
  Full-Time Graduate Students: 35
  Female Full-Time Graduate Students: 12
  First-Year Graduate Students: 8
  Female First-Year Students: 2
  Total Post Doctorates: 4

Department Address
1425 Lefton Esplanade
Kent, OH 44242
Phone: (330) 672-2654
Fax: 330-672-2796
E-mail: cpipgrad@kent.edu
Website: http://www.kent.edu/cpip

ADMISSIONS

Admission Contact Information
Address admission inquiries to: Dr. Antal Jakli, Director, Chemical Physics Interdisciplinary Program
Phone: 330-672-2654
E-mail: cpipgrad@kent.edu
Admissions website: http://www.kent.edu/graduatestudies/admissions

Application deadlines
Fall admission:
U.S. students: January 15   *Int'l. students*: January 15

Application fee
U.S. students: $45   *Int'l. students*: $70

Admissions information
For Fall of 2018:
  Number of applicants: 31
  Number admitted: 10
  Number enrolled: 8

Admission requirements
Bachelor's degree requirements: Bachelor's degree in physics, chemistry, chemical physics, materials science, engineering, or a related discipline is required.
Minimum undergraduate GPA: 3.0

GRE requirements
The GRE is recommended but not required.

Subjective GRE requirements
The Subjective GRE is not required.

TOEFL requirements
The TOEFL exam is required for students from non-English-speaking countries.
  PBT score: 525
  iBT score: 71

Other admissions information
Additional requirements: MELAB score of 77.

TUITION

Tuition year 2018–19:
Tuition for in-state residents
  Full-time students: $11,536 other
  Part-time students: $525 per credit
Tuition for out-of-state residents
  Full-time students: $21,524 other
  Part-time students: $978 per credit
Credit hours per semester to be considered full-time: 11
Deferred tuition plan: Yes
Health insurance: Yes, $1,204.00.
Academic term: Semester
Number of first-year students who received full tuition waivers: 7

Teaching Assistants, Research Assistants, and Fellowships
Number of first-year
  Teaching Assistants: 7
  Research Assistants: 1
Average stipend per academic year
  Teaching Assistant: $18,540
  Research Assistant: $18,540
  Fellowship student: $18,540
The University offers fellowships and additional summer support maybe available.

FINANCIAL AID

Loans
Loans are available for U.S. students.
Loans are available for international students.
GAPSFAS application required: No
FAFSA application required: No

For further information
Address financial aid inquiries to: Dr. Antal Jakli, Director, Chemical Physics Interdisciplinary Program.
Phone: 330-672-4886
E-mail: cpipgrad@kent.edu
Financial aid website: http:///www.kent.edu/financialaid

HOUSING

Availability of on-campus housing
  Single students: Yes
  Married students: Yes
  Childcare Assistance: No

For further information

Address housing inquiries to: Department of Residence Services, Kent State University, P.O. Box 5190, Kent, Ohio 44242-0001.
Phone: (330) 672-7000 (or 1-800-706-8941)
E-mail: HOUSING@KENT.EDU
Housing aid website: http://www.kent.edu/housing

Table A—Faculty, Enrollments, and Degrees Granted

Research Specialty	2017–2018 Faculty	Enrollment Fall 2017 Master's	Enrollment Fall 2017 Doctorate	Number of Degrees Granted 2017–2018 (2013–2018) Master's	Number of Degrees Granted 2017–2018 (2013–2018) Terminal Master's	Number of Degrees Granted 2017–2018 (2013–2018) Doctorate
Chemical Physics	15	2	38	2(17)	–	9(39)
Total	–	–	–	–	–	–
Full-time Grad. Stud.	–	2	38	–	–	–
First-year Grad. Stud.	–	–	5	–	–	–

GRADUATE DEGREE REQUIREMENTS

Master's: Liquid Crystal Engineering - Students are required to take 29 credit hours of coursework, 6 credit hours of a master's summer project and 3 credit hours of electives selected in consultation with the student's faculty advisor.

Doctorate: 90 semester-hours of courses, seminar, and research work beyond the Bachelor's degree and the minimum of 60 credit hours after master degree. Passing the candidacy examination and successful defense of dissertation are required.

Other Degrees: MS in Chemical Physics with or without Thesis.

SPECIAL EQUIPMENT, FACILITIES, OR PROGRAMS

The Liquid Crystal Institute (LCI) Prototype Facility offers a wide range of services and capabilities related to fabrication of Micro-optical and display devises using liquid crystals, Microfluidic and biomedical devices, and functional micro- and nano-structures. The facility is centered in a 3,500 square foot Class 100-1,000-10,000 cleanroom facility for manufacturing or prototyping of liquid crystal devise and related research. The facility provides custom LCD devices, which are not available elsewhere.

Our LCI Characterization Facility is equipped with a series of instruments to determine the microscopic structures and properties of bulk and surfaces of liquid crystal, soft and biological materials. The Cryo-Transmission Electron Microscopy (TEM), Scanning Electron Microscopy (SEM) and Atomic Force Micrscopy (AFM) offer atomic/nanoscale material characterization for corss-disciplinary (materials science/biology/nanotechnology) research. Available techniques include, traditional TEM, high resolution TEM (HRTEM), scanning TEM (STEM), cryo-TEM, electron diffraction techniques, energy–filtered TEM, electron energy loss spectroscopy (EELS) and energy dispersive x-ray spectroscopy (EDS). Optical microscopy and spectroscopy equipment (confocal laser scanning microscopy, FTIR microscopy, etc.) is also available.

Our Organic Synthesis Facility provides researchers with liquid crystalline materials that are not readily commercially available for research purposes. Purification service of organic compounds is also available. Formulation of mixtures is also possible when an exact composition is provided. The facility is well known for providing high quality liquid crystalline materials in useable quantities. We have expertise in deuterated materials, esters, cyanobiphenyls, ferroelectrics, diacetylenes, lipid salts, etc.

Through our Industrial Partnership Program, the LCI makes these extensive facilities available to industrial researchers and fosters cooperative research opportunities for both faculty and graduate students.

Table B—Separately Budgeted Research Expenditures by Source of Support

Source of Support	Departmental Research	Physics-related Research Outside Department
Federal government	$1,793,165	
State/local government		
Non-profit organizations		
Business and industry	$755,582	
Other	$889,748	
Total	$3,438,495	

Table C—Separately Budgeted Research Expenditures by Research Specialty

Research Specialty	No. of Grants	Expenditures ($)
Chemical Physics	32	$2,548,747
Other	–	$889,748
Total	32	$3,438,495

FACULTY

Professor

Bos, Philip J., Ph.D., Kent State University, 1978. *Applied Physics, Chemical Physics, Optics*. Dr. Bos's research area is applications of liquid crystals, with focus on optical applications such as displays, lenses and optical wavefront controllers.

Chien, Liang-Chy, Ph.D., University of Southern Mississippi, 1988. *Applied Physics, Chemical Physics, Nano Science and Technology, Optics*. Dr. Chien's research focuses on experiments in multifunctional liquid crystal, nano-structured and polymer materials by design, self-assembled materials and composites, and display, optoelectronic and photonic devices.

Hegmann, Torsten, Ph.D., Martin Luther University, 2001. *Applied Physics, Chemical Physics, Nano Science and Technology*. Dr. Hegmann's research focuses on synthesis, characterization, self-assembly and application of liquid crystal nanocomposites and on the shape -controlled synthesis of metal oxide nanomaterials for brain drug delivery. Recent focus on printing of, nanoparticle alignment layers for liquid crystals and their use in optical devices and sensing. The research team has particular strength in the synthesis and functionalization of nanomaterials for applications including metamaterials, chirality sensors and nanoparticle theranostics.

Jákli, Antal I., Ph.D., Eotvos University (Hungary), 1986. *Applied Physics, Chemical Physics, Optics*. Dr. Jakli's research focuses on bent-core and other unconventional shape liquid crystals. He also works on responsive fiber mats containing ferroelectric particles and liquid crystals dispersed in polymer fibers.

Palffy-Muhoray, Peter, Ph.D., University of British Columbia, 1977. *Applied Mathematics, Applied Physics, Chemical Physics*. Dr. Palffy-Muhoray's research focuses on light-matter interactions in liquid crystals and other complex fluids and soft matter.

Selinger, Jonathan V., Ph.D., Harvard University, 1989. *Applied Physics, Chemical Physics, Theoretical Physics*. Dr. Selinger's research focuses on the theory of liquid crystals, lipid microstructures, nanoparticle suspensions and other soft materials and seeks to make connections between fundamental statistical mechanics and technological applications.

Selinger, Robin L. B., Ph.D., Harvard University, 1989. *Applied Physics, Chemical Physics, Theoretical Physics*. Dr. Selinger's research focuses on fundamental mechanisms of pattern formation and material behavior in soft materials such as liquid crystal elastomers, lipids and liquid crystals. Modeling techniques cover a broad range of length scales, from classical molecular dynamics to coarse-grained and mesoscale models to continuum/finite element methods.

Wei, Qi-Huo, Ph.D., Nanjing University, 1993. *Applied Physics, Chemical Physics, Nano Science and Technology*. Dr. Wei's research is aimed at a fundamental understanding of soft materials and fields confined in low dimensions and new devices for applications in a variety of fields. Current research interests include liquid crystals confined in micro-and nano-environments, diffusion/self-assembly of anisotropic colloids, plasmonic nanoantennas and nanocavities, chemical and biological sensing, defect engineering for liquid crystal materials and devices, micro and nanofabrication.

Yang, Deng-Ke, Ph.D., University of Hawaii, 1989. *Applied Physics, Chemical Physics*. Dr. Yang's research focuses on liquid crystal devices, polymer stabilized liquid crystals and tunable cholesteric liquid crystals.

Yokoyama, Hiroshi, Ph.D., Tokyo Institute of Technology, 1987. *Applied Physics, Chemical Physics, Nano Science and Technology*. Dr. Yokoyama's research areas are, characterization, physics and device applications of surface and thin films of liquid crystals, polymers, and biological materials. Development of novel methods of surface analysis and fabrication utilizing scanned probes and photo-induced molecular processes. Development of new adaptive and responsive composite materials using liquid crystals.

Assistant Professor

Hegmann, Elda, Ph.D., CERSIM/Universite Laval, Quebec, 2003. *Applied Physics, Biophysics, Chemical Physics*. Dr. Hegmann's research focuses on the use of liquid crystals for biological applications. Her main areas of interest are: a)liquid crystals that are able to mimic biological materials and b) biosensors for optical imaging and diagnostics. The materials created in her lab include materials with predictable and controllable/tunable properties for the use of drug delivery systems and therapeutic purposes. Another research area is the imaging of biological cells and their behavior on modified substrates and scaffolds.

Research Professor

Lavrentovich, Oleg D., Ph.D., Ukrainian Academy of Sciences, 1984. *Applied Physics, Chemical Physics*. Dr. Lavrentovich's research focuses on various aspects of liquid crystals and their applications. It ranges from the exploration of fundamental issues such as liquid crystal-enabled electrophoresis and electro-osmosis to fast (nanosecond and microsecond)electro-optic switching and optical response of the liquid crystal. The research embraces both thermotropic and lyotropic liquid crystals, as well as the liquid crystal systems with internal sources of energy (the so-called living liquid crystals).

West, John L., Ph.D., Carnegie Mellon University, 1980. *Applied Physics, Chemical Physics*. Dr. West's research focuses on the development of liquid crystal polymer dispersions and their applications, with a recent focus on electrospun fibers. West is also developing flexible electro-optic devices. His studies include the investigation of the molecular basis of chirality transfer in liquid crystal hosts.

Adjunct Professor

Li, Quan, Ph.D., Chinese Academy of Sciences (Shanghai), 1995. *Applied Physics, Chemical Physics, Nano Science and Technology*. Dr. Li's research area is bio-inspired, light-harvesting materials, fast-switching optoelectronic response materials, light-driven chiral molecular motors, 1D and 3D photonic crystals, functionalized isotropic and anisotropic metal nanoparticles, metal nanocomposites, organogels, liquid crystalline monomers and their networks, functionalized carbon materials, functional supramolecular polymers, and biologically active synthetic and natural compounds for renewable energy, photo display, dynamic photonics, energy saving devices, sensors, drug delivery, etc.

Wall, Bentley, Ph.D., Case University, 1999.

Adjunct Associate Professor

Zheng, Xiaoyu, Ph.D., university of North Carolina at Chapel Hill, 2006. *Applied Mathematics, Applied Physics, Chemical Physics*. Dr. Zheng's research focuses on mathematical modeling and numerical simulations of dynamics of liquid crystals systems.

Senior Research Scientist

Shiyanovskii, Sergij, Kiev State University (Ukraine). *Applied Physics, Chemical Physics*.

DEPARTMENTAL RESEARCH SPECIALTIES AND STAFF

Theoretical

Chemical Physics. Liquid crystal properties, phase behavior, microstructure, defects, and dynamics; surface phenomena; fibers, free-standing films, lipid membranes; bent-core liquid crystals; chirality and chiral symmetry-breaking; electro-optics; negative index materials; liquid crystalline elastomers; nanofluids.

Chemical Physics. Molecular dynamics, Monte Carlo methods, Nonlinear Finite Element analysis, multiscale modeling, fluid dynamics, optics; applications in many areas of soft condensed matter physics.

Chemical Physics. Liquid crystal properties, phase behavior, microstructure, defects, and dynamics; surface phenomena; fibers, free-standing films, lipid membranes; bent-core liquid crystals; chirality and chiral symmetry-breaking; electro-optics; negative index materials; liquid crystalline elastomers; nanofluids.

Chemical Physics. Molecular dynamics, Monte Carlo methods, Nonlinear Finite Element analysis, multiscale modeling, fluid dynamics, optics; applications in many areas of soft condensed matter physics.

KENT STATE UNIVERSITY

DEPARTMENT OF PHYSICS - GRADUATE PROGRAM

Kent, Ohio 44242
http://www.kent.edu/physics

General University Information
President: Beverly Warren
Dean of Graduate School: Melody Tankersley
University website: http://www.kent.edu/
School Type: Public
Setting: Suburban
Total Faculty: 2,726
Total Graduate Faculty: 1,330
Total number of Students: 39,367
Total number of Graduate Students: 5,799

Department Information
Department Chairman: Prof. James Gleeson, Chair
Department Contact: John Portman, Professor & Graduate
  Coordinator
  Total full-time faculty: 28
  Total number of full-time equivalent positions: 28
  Full-Time Graduate Students: 72
  Female Full-Time Graduate Students: 18
  First-Year Graduate Students: 9
  Female First-Year Students: 1
  Total Post Doctorates: 5

Department Address
Smith Hall
Kent State University
Kent, OH 44242
Phone: (330) 672-2246
Fax: (330) 672-2959
E-mail: PhysGPC@kent.edu
Website: http://www.kent.edu/physics

ADMISSIONS

Admission Contact Information
Address admission inquiries to: Cartwright Hall, 650 Hilltop Dr.,
  Kent, OH 44242
Phone: (330) 672-2661
E-mail: gradapps@kent.edu
Admissions website: http://www.kent.edu/graduatestudies/
  admissions

Application deadlines
Fall admission:
U.S. students: January 31   *Int'l. students*: January 31
Spring admission:
U.S. students: August 31   *Int'l. students*: August 31

Application fee
U.S. students: $45   *Int'l. students*: $70
Admissions with TA support are offered almost exclusively to
  Fall applicants. Application materials include: online application form, CV, Goals statement, three letters of recommendation, transcripts, GRE scores, Physics GRE (highly recommended), TOFEL scores (if applicable).

Admissions information
For Fall of 2018:
  Number of applicants: 93
  Number admitted: 16
  Number enrolled: 9

Admission requirements
Bachelor's degree requirements: Bachelor's degree in Physics
  or closely related major.
Minimum undergraduate GPA: 3.0

GRE requirements
The GRE is required.
There is no minimum GRE score.

Subjective GRE requirements
The Subjective GRE is recommended.
The Physics GRE is not required but highly recommended to
  be competitive. The Physics GRE is expected for all domestic
  applicants with undergraduate degree. Advanced students can
  submit graduate course work and research experience instead
  of GRE. There is no minimum score for Physics GRE.

TOEFL requirements
The TOEFL exam is required for students from non-English-
  speaking countries.
  PBT score: 550
  iBT score: 79

Other admissions information
Undergraduate preparation assumed: Mechanics: Marion or
  Taylor; Electricity and Magnetism: Griffiths; Quantum Mechanics: Griffiths; Thermal Physics: Schroder; at least one advanced laboratory course.

TUITION

Tuition year 2018–2019:
Tuition for in-state residents
  Full-time students: $9,090 annual
  Part-time students: $505 per credit
Tuition for out-of-state residents
  Full-time students: $19,362 annual
  Part-time students: $881 per credit
Credit hours per semester to be considered full-time: 8
Health insurance: Available at the cost of $516 per year.
Other academic fees: A $10 Legal Fee and $20 International Stu-
  dent Activity Fee are charged per term.
Academic term: Semester
Number of first-year students who received full tuition waivers: 9

Teaching Assistants, Research Assistants, and Fellowships
Number of first-year
  Teaching Assistants: 9
Average stipend per academic year
  Teaching Assistant: $21,650
  Research Assistant: $24,720 Graduate Assistants can re-
  ceive a $500 Tuition Advance three weeks prior to their first
  pay check.

FINANCIAL AID

Application deadlines
Fall admission:
U.S. students: October 13

Loans
Loans are available for U.S. students.
Loans are not available for international students.
GAPSFAS application required: No
FAFSA application required: Yes

For further information
Address financial aid inquiries to: PO Box 5190, 103 Schwartz
    Center, 800 E. Summit St., Kent, OH 44242.
Phone: (330) 672-2972
E-mail: finaid@kent.edu
Financial aid website: http://www.kent.edu/financialaid

HOUSING

Availability of on-campus housing
Single students: No
Married students: No
Childcare Assistance: No

For further information
Address housing inquiries to: 1425 Petrarca Drive, Kent State
    University, Kent, Ohio 44242.
Phone: 330-672-7000
E-mail: housing@kent.edu
Housing aid website: https://www.kent.edu/housing

Table A—Faculty, Enrollments, and Degrees Granted

Research Specialty	2018–19 Faculty	Enrollment Fall 2018		Number of Degrees Granted 2017–18 (2013–2018)		
		Master's	Doctorate	Master's	Terminal Master's	Doctorate
Biophysics	2	–	5	2(3)	–(2)	1(4)
Nuclear Physics	7	1	17	–(9)	–(2)	3(9)
Quantum Condensed Matter	7	1	14	2(8)	1(1)	3(10)
Soft Condensed Matter	11	–	14	1(7)	–(3)	–(6)
Non-specialized	–	1	19	–	–(18)	–
Total	27	3	69	5(27)	1(26)	7(29)
Full-time Grad. Stud.	–	3	69	–	–	–
First-year Grad. Stud.	–	–	9	–	–	–

GRADUATE DEGREE REQUIREMENTS

Master's: The Master of Arts (M.A.) in Physics is a highly flexible program consisting of 32 hours of graduate coursework
that can be customized according to the academic background
and needs of the individual student. The Master of Science
(M.S.) in Physics consists of 32 hours of graduate coursework
and a research project taking one or two semesters. The research project should result in a written report. Students may
choose to complete a thesis which is to be defended orally.

Doctorate: The Doctor of Philosophy (Ph.D.) in Physics provides
training of professionals to conduct independently conceived
programs of research or teaching in universities or research
laboratories. Original research is required in fundamental or
applied areas of physics, and the Ph.D. dissertation must be
orally defended. Two years of graduate coursework, plus four
years of research are typical. The required physics courses
will prepare the student for the candidacy examination. Students present at least one seminar based on their dissertation
research during their graduate career.

SPECIAL EQUIPMENT, FACILITIES, OR PROGRAMS

Available techniques in experimental condensed matter physics
at Kent State University include nonlinear optics, electro-optics,
tunneling and atomic force microscopy, nuclear magnetic resonance, electron paramagnetic resonance, x-ray scattering, light
scattering, microcalorimetry, millikelvin refrigeration, SQUID
magnetometry, and magnetoresistance and Hall effect measurement. The condensed matter group is also equipped with state
of the art equipment for experimental organic electronics research, starting from gradient sublimation to purify organic compounds, vacuum deposition chambers, and optical/electrical characterization setups. Faculty and students in condensed matter
physics use National Laboratories for neutron scattering and
muon spin spectroscopy experiments in U.S. and abroad, such
as the Spallation Neutron Source (SNS) at the Oak Ridge National Laboratory in Tennessee, the NIST Center for Neutron Research (NIST) in Maryland, the Paul Scherrer Institut (PSI) in
Switzerland and the Rutherford Appleton Laboratory (ISIS) in
U.K.

Many of the condensed matter faculty at Kent State University
are affiliated with the Glenn H. Brown Liquid Crystal Institute
(LCI), the only institute of its kind in the United States. Located
on the Kent Main Campus, the LCI provides materials synthesis
and characterization facilities, and includes a prototype facility
with a 2,500 sq. ft. clean room. In addition, faculty and students
in the soft matter area utilize the facilities, instruments, and beam
lines at the National High Magnetic Field Laboratory (MagLab)
in Florida and the Advanced Light Source (ALS) at Lawrence
Berkeley National Lab.

The nuclear physics faculty participate in experiments at National
and International Laboratories, or perform related theoretical calculations. Current activities are centered at Jefferson Laboratory
(JLab) in Virginia, Brookhaven National Laboratory (BNL) in
New York, and the MAMI facility at Mainz in Germany. After
completing their coursework, students in this area of experiment
typically spend significant portions of their time at these National
Laboratories to work on development and commissioning of new
detectors. The astrophysics faculty performs research which is
directly connected to the measurement of compact star properties
using terrestrial facilities, such as in the Arecibo Observatory,
and space-based facilities, such as the NICER (Neutron star Interior Composition ExploreR) mission payload on the International
Space Station.

Activities in the area of nuclear/particle physics are promoted
by the Physics Department's Center for Nuclear Research (CNR).

The biophysics faculty members perform computational and experimental work on protein folding, allosteric conformational
changes in protein structure, DNA/RNA structure, and DNA-
protein interactions. In addition to in-house protein purification
and characterization instruments and fluorescence microscopes
with single molecule detection capability, researchers also have
access to an on-campus Image and Visualization Center, cell culture facility, DNA microarray, and circular dichroism spectropo-
larimeter with temperature control capability. Computational
work is conducted on clusters maintained by individual research
groups, the College of Arts and Sciences, as well as resources
at the Ohio Supercomputer Center.

The Physics Department is located in Smith Hall in the heart
of Kent State University's Science Complex. A professionally
staffed Machine Shop and an Electronics Shop in Smith Hall pro-

vide a diverse range of support for experimental groups. In addition, a student machine shop is available for educational and research projects. Many additional facilities of relevance to experimental work in soft condensed matter physics are available in the Liquid Crystal Institute. Several faculty members will move to the Integrated Sciences Building to be completed by the Fall 2017 semester, which will have equipment and resources for biophysics and soft matter research, including -80 °C freezers, spectrophotometers, autoclave instrument, and temperature controlled 4 °C and 37 °C rooms.

Table B—Separately Budgeted Research Expenditures by Source of Support

Source of Support	Departmental Research	Physics-related Research Outside Department
Federal government	$2,438,983	
State/local government		
Non-profit organizations		
Business and industry		
Other		
Total	$2,438,983	

Table C—Separately Budgeted Research Expenditures by Research Specialty

Research Specialty	No. of Grants	Expenditures ($)
Biophysics	2	$124,548
Quantum Condensed Matter	5	$228,309
Soft Condensed Matter	18	$1,272,407
Nuclear and Particle Physics	7	$813,718
Total	32	$2,438,982

FACULTY

Professor

Almasan, Carmen, Ph.D., University of S. South Carolina, 1989. Assistant to the Chair. *Condensed Matter Physics, Low Temperature Physics.* Carmen Almasan's recent projects include: experimental condensed matter physics; superconductivity; cuprates; heavy fermions; magnetism; non-fermi liquid behavior; pnictides.

Bos, Philip J., Ph.D., Kent State University, 1978. *Applied Physics, Engineering Physics/Science, Nano Science and Technology, Optics, Other.* Philip Bos' recent projects have involved liquid crystal based displays, optical wavefront controllers, lenses, and Pancharatnam phase devices. Students have found employment at: Motorola, Intel, Apple, Google, Facebook/Oculus, Samsung, Fuji Film, 3M, Eastman Chemical, Compound Photonics, Z-space, KDI, Lincoln Laboratory, and other places.

Gleeson, James T., Ph.D., Kent State University, 1991. Chair of the Physics Department. *Biophysics, Condensed Matter Physics, Polymer Physics/Science, Statistical & Thermal Physics.* James Gleeson's recent projects involve experimental soft condensed matter; complex fluids; liquid crystals; polymers; proteins and DNA.

Jakli, Antal, Ph.D., Loránd Eötvös University, 1986. Director of the Chemical Physics Graduate Program. *Chemical Physics, Condensed Matter Physics, Fluids, Rheology, Optics.* Antal Jakli's research at the Liquid Crystal Institute focuses on the physical properties of soft matter with special emphasis on bent-core liquid crystals, piezoelectricity and ferroelectricity. He has developed two new graduate courses for the Chemical Physics Interdisciplinary Program at KSU and incorpo-

rated them into a textbook, "One and two dimensional fluids," co-authored with A. Saupe (Taylor&Francis, 2006). He co-authored nearly 250 peer-reviewed papers and 10 book chapters, and holds 18 US patents. Since 2009 he is an associate Ed. of Phys. Rev. E handling liquid crystal papers.

Katramatou, A. Mina T., Ph.D., The American University, Washington, DC, 1988. *Nuclear Physics, Physics and other Science Education.* Mina Katramatou's research includes experimental nuclear physics; and the structure of light nuclei.

Keane, Declan, Ph.D., University College Dublin, 1981. *Accelerator, Nuclear Physics.* Declan Keane's research group specializes in the experimental study of high-energy nucleus-nucleus collisions, and searches for new antimatter nuclei. Research members use measurements of anisotropy to learn about fluid-like behavior and phase transitions in the dense and highly excited matter created.

Lavrentovich, Oleg D., Ph.D., Ukrainian Academy of Sciences, 1990. *Other.* Our research focuses on soft matter formed by weakly interacting organic molecules. The emphasis is on systems with orientational order, known as liquid crystals, and their composites, such as dispersions of colloidal particles in liquid crystals, and water dispersions of self-organizing chromonic aggregate. Specialties: lyotropic chromonic liquid crystals, twist-bend nematics, heliconical cholesterics, electrophoresis and electro-osmosis enabled by liquid crystals, nanosecond electro-optics, living liquid crystals, topological defects, chirality and confinement.

Manley, D. Mark, Ph.D., University of Wyoming, 1981. Undergraduate Coordinator. *Nuclear Physics.* Mark Manley is an experimental nuclear physicist whose main research interests involve carrying out multichannel energy-dependent partial-wave analyses with the goal of determining resonance parameters in a consistent and accurate manner.

Mann, Elizabeth, Ph.D., Universite Pierre et Marie Curie (Paris VI), 1992. *Applied Physics, Biophysics, Chemical Physics, Condensed Matter Physics, Fluids, Rheology, Nonlinear Dynamics and Complex Systems, Optics, Polymer Physics/Science, Statistical & Thermal Physics, Surface Physics.* Elizabeth Mann's research interests include lipid, liquid crystalline, and macromolecular films at interfaces: hydrodynamics, transport, phase separation, pattern formation, orientation, optics, line tension, linactants, biosensors.

Margetis, Spyridon, Ph.D., Frankfurt University, 1990. *High Energy Physics, Nuclear Physics, Particles and Fields.* Research interests of Spyridon Margetis include High Energy Nuclear Collisions; High Energy Instrumentation, Vertex Detectors, Phase Transitions and Exotic States of Nuclear Matter, Heavy Flavor Physics, Tracking and Reconstruction Techniques in High Multiplicity Environments, Calibration and Software of Vertex Detectors.

Petratos, Gerassimos, Ph.D., The American University, Washington DC, 1988. *Nuclear Physics.* Gerassimos Petratos' research involves experimental nuclear physics; structure of light nuclei; electromagnetic form factor; deep inelastic scattering.

Portman, John J., Ph.D., University of Illinois, 2000. Graduate Coordinator. *Biophysics, Chemical Physics, Computational Physics, Statistical & Thermal Physics, Theoretical Physics.* John Portman's Research Interests include Theoretical Biological Physics: protein dynamics, protein folding and binding, allostery, intrinsically disordered proteins.

Quader, Khandker F., Ph.D., SUNY at Stony Brook, 1983. *Condensed Matter Physics, Low Temperature Physics, Theoretical Physics.* Kandker Quader's Research involves theoretical condensed matter; correlated quantum matter; ultra cold atoms; many body physics; fermi liquid theroy; superconductivity; critical phenomena; density functional theory.

Selinger, Jonathan, Ph.D., Harvard University, 1989. *Condensed Matter Physics, Statistical & Thermal Physics, Theoretical Physics*. Jonathan Selinger's research focuses on the theory of liquid crystals, nanoparticle suspensions, and related topics in soft materials, and seeks to make connections between fundamental statistical mechanics and technological applications.

Selinger, Robin L. B., Ph.D., Harvard University, 1989. *Computational Physics, Condensed Matter Physics, Polymer Physics/Science, Statistical & Thermal Physics, Theoretical Physics*. Robin Selinger's research interests include modeling and simulation of soft matter: liquid crystals, lipid membranes, liquid crystal elastomers. Defects and microstructural evolution, responsive formation.

Sprunt, Samuel N., Ph.D., Massachusetts Institute of Technology, 1989. *Biophysics, Condensed Matter Physics, Polymer Physics/Science, Statistical & Thermal Physics, Surface Physics*. Samuel Sprunt specializes in experimental soft matter physics; complex fluids; liquid crystals; proteins and DNA; phase transitions; optical properties of complex dielectric media; thin films.

Strickland, Michael, Ph.D., Duke University, 1997. Director of the Center for Nuclear Research. *Computational Physics, High Energy Physics, Nuclear Physics, Plasma and Fusion, Theoretical Physics*. Michael Strickland is a theoretical physicist who specializes in high-energy particle physics, heavy ion collisions, and finite temperature/density quantum field theory. Michael's primary interest is the physics of the quark-gluon plasma (QGP). These plasmas are predicted by quantum chromodynamics (QCD) to have existed until approximately one microsecond after the big bang and are currently being studied terrestrially by experimentalists at the Relativistic Heavy Ion Collider (RHIC) at Brookhaven National Labs and the Large Hadron Collider (LHC) at CERN. These exciting experiments are increasing our knowledge of the behavior of matter under extreme conditions.

Wei, Qi-Huo, Ph.D., Nanjing University. *Applied Physics, Chemical Physics, Condensed Matter Physics, Nano Science and Technology, Optics, Other*. Qi-Huo Wei heads a dynamic group with a multidisciplinary background. Their research is aimed at fundamental understanding of soft materials confined in low dimensions, advanced manufacturing for new soft material engineering, and device applications in a variety of fields. Our current projects include stimuli-responsive and active soft matter, liquid crystal polymers, topological defects, plasmonic photopatterning of molecular orientations, and 3D and 4D printing.

Yang, Deng-Ke, Ph.D., University of Hawaii, 1989. *Applied Physics, Chemical Physics, Optics, Other*. Deng-Ke Yang's specialties include cholesteric liquid crystals, liquid crystal/polymer composites and electro-optic devices. He is co-inventor of bistable cholesteric display (BCD) technology, currently the world's most promising technology for electronic paper.

Yokoyama, Hiroshi, Ph.D., Tokyo Institute of Technology, 1987. Ohio Research Scholar. *Applied Physics, Condensed Matter Physics, Nano Science and Technology, Surface Physics*. Hiroshi Yokoyama has been active in research and education for nearly 40 years in the area of nano-science and technology of soft matter, particularly liquid crystals. His research interest has a wide spectrum from experimental and theoretical study on liquid-crystal surfaces, self-organization and nonequilibrium phenomena in soft condensed matter, to scanning probe microscope instrumentation. He is the former director of the Glenn H. Brown Liquid Crystal Institute from 2011 to 2016. He is currently the President of the International Liquid Crystal Society.

Associate Professor

Balci, Hamza, Ph.D., University of Maryland, 2004. *Applied Physics, Biophysics, Nano Science and Technology, Optics, Other*. Hamza Balci specializes in Experimental Biophysics, DNA-Protein Interactions, DNA Structure, Single Molecule Fluorescence Microscopy.

Dzero, Maxim, Ph.D., Florida State University, 2003. *Condensed Matter Physics, Theoretical Physics*. Maxim Dzero's research interests include theoretical condensed matter physics; strongly correlated quantum systems; many body physics; superconductivity; quantum phase transitions; magnetism; disordered systems; non-equilibrium dynamics of glassy systems.

Ellman, Brett, Ph.D., University of Chicago, 1992. Planetarium Director. *Chemical Physics, Computational Physics, Condensed Matter Physics, Crystallography, Low Temperature Physics, Materials Science, Metallurgy*. Brett Ellman specializes in the Physics of Organic Semiconductors.

Lüssem, Bjorn, Ph.D., University of Bath, 2003. *Applied Physics, Atomic, Molecular, & Optical Physics, Biophysics, Condensed Matter Physics, Electrical Engineering, Engineering Physics/Science, Materials Science, Metallurgy, Optics, Solid State Physics*. The Bjorn Lüssem Lab studies new organic semiconductors and novel organic devices with improved performance. Research spans from clarifying the fundamentals of charge transport in organic semiconductors, to modeling light emission in organic micro cavities, and new protocols for a large scale integration of functional organic circuits.

Schroeder, Almut, Ph.D., University of Karlsruhe, 1991. *Condensed Matter Physics, Low Temperature Physics, Materials Science, Metallurgy, Solid State Physics*. Almut Schroeder studies strongly correlated electron systems, transition metal alloys and heavy fermion compounds, close to quantum phase transitions with experimental tools such as low temperature magnetic susceptibility and transport measurements at KSU and with neutron scattering and muon spin resonance at National Facilities.

Assistant Professor

Dexheimer, Veronica, Ph.D., Johann Wolfgang Goethe University, 2009. Associate Director of the Center for Nuclear Research. *Astrophysics, Computational Physics, Electromagnetism, High Energy Physics, Nuclear Physics, Particles and Fields, Relativity & Gravitation, Statistical & Thermal Physics, Theoretical Physics*. Veronica Dexheimer and her group develop mathematical models to describe the interior of neutron stars, including stages of their evolution and phase transitions that occur in layers of the star. Transitions between the hadronic phase (containing neutrons, protons, electrons and hyperons) and possible quark phase leave signatures on macroscopic observables in the star, such as mass, radius, rotation frequency, surface temperature, magnetic field. These signatures can help us to observe stable deconfined quark matter, the most extreme new kind of matter, for the first time in our universe.

Fregoso, Benjamin, Ph.D., University of Illinois at Urbana-Champange, 2010. *Condensed Matter Physics, Theoretical Physics*. Benjamin Fregoso specializes in Theoretical Condensed Matter Physics: Quantum Liquid Crystal Phases; Quantum Magnetism; Superconductivity; ferroelectricity.

DEPARTMENTAL RESEARCH SPECIALTIES AND STAFF

Theoretical

Astrophysics. Neutron start formation; neutron star equation of state; supernovae dynamics; supernovae equation of state; gravitational waves. Dexheimer.

Biophysics. Theoretical and computational models of protein dynamics, protein folding and binding, allostery, and intrinsically disordered proteins. Portman.

Nuclear and Particle Physics. Quark-gluon plasma; quantum chromodynamics; relativistic heavy ion collisions; finite temperature field theory; relativistic hydrodynamics; relativistic transport; nuclear equation of state. Dexheimer, Strickland.

Quantum Condensed Matter. Strongly correlated electrons; ultracold fermions and bosons; quantum fluids; emergent phenomena; superfluidity; superconductivity; quantum phase transition; quantum critical point; non-equilibrium physics; low temperature transport/magneto-transport; quantum many-body techniques; density functional method; dynamical mean-field theory. Dzero, Fregoso, Quader.

Soft Condensed Matter. Theory and computational modeling of soft matter, liquid crystal/polymer composites, colloids, and polymers; self-assembly and pattern formation; topological defects in complex fluids; active matter and physics of living systems. Jonathan Selinger, Robin Selinger.

Experimental

Biophysics. Protein-DNA Interactions, DNA/RNA Structure, Fluorescence Microscopy, Single Molecule Detection, DNA-based Liquid Crystalline Sensors,Lipid, Liquid Crystalline, and Macromolecular Films at Interfaces, Brewster Angle Microscopy. Balci, Gleeson, Mann, Sprunt.

Nuclear and Particle Physics. Structure of light nuclei; electromagnetic form factor measurements; hadronic physics; heavy ion collisions. Katramatou, Keane, Manley, Margetis, Petratos.

Quantum Condensed Matter. Strongly correlated electrons; superconductivity; quantum phase transition; quantum critical point; low temperature transport/magneto-transport; neutron scattering; muon-spin resonance; charge transport; organic semi-conductors; photovoltaics. Almasan, Ellman, Fregoso, Lüssem, Schroeder.

Soft Condensed Matter. Structure and phase transitions in liquid crystals and related complex fluids; surfaces, interfaces, mono- and mulilayered molecular films and membranes; fluctuations and dynamics of soft matter; active matter and physics of living systems. Balci, Bos, Gleeson, Jakli, Mann, Sprunt, Wei, Yang.

View additional information about this department at www.gradschoolshopper.com. Check out the "Why Choose Us?" section, find out more about the department's culture and get links to social media networks.

MIAMI UNIVERSITY

DEPARTMENT OF PHYSICS

Oxford, Ohio 45056
http://www.MiamiOH.edu/physics

General University Information
President: Gregory Crawford
Dean of Graduate School: James Oris, Dean
University website: http://www.MiamiOH.edu
School Type: Public
Setting: Rural
Total Faculty: 973
Total Graduate Faculty: 598
Total number of Students: 19,452
Total number of Graduate Students: 2,305

Department Information
Department Chairman: Prof. Herbert Jaeger, Chair
Department Contact: Dr. Mahmud Khan, Graduate Director
  Total full-time faculty: 14
  Total number of full-time equivalent positions: 14
  Full-Time Graduate Students: 20
  Female Full-Time Graduate Students: 1
  First-Year Graduate Students: 10

Department Address
500 E. Spring Street
217 Kreger Hall
Oxford, OH 45056
Phone: (513) 529-5625
Fax: (513) 529-5629
E-mail: physics@MiamiOH.edu
Website: http://www.MiamiOH.edu/physics

ADMISSIONS

Admission Contact Information
Address admission inquiries to: Graduate School, 102 Roudebush
  Hall, Oxford, OH 45056
Phone: (513) 529-3734
E-mail: gradschool@MiamiOH.edu
Admissions website: http://www.miamioh.edu/graduate-studies/
  admission/index.html

Application deadlines
Fall admission:
U.S. students: February 15   *Int'l. students*: February 15
Spring admission:
U.S. students: November 1   *Int'l. students*: October 15

Application fee
U.S. students: $50   *Int'l. students*: $50
Late applications may be considered until all positions are filled.

Admissions information
For Fall of 2018:
  Number of applicants: 58
  Number admitted: 10
  Number enrolled: 10

Admission requirements
Bachelor's degree requirements: A bachelor's degree in Physics
  or related areas is required. Consult our Graduate Student Adviser about the appropriateness of related area.
Minimum undergraduate GPA: 2.75

GRE requirements
The GRE is recommended but not required.
Test is recommended - No minimum is set

Subjective GRE requirements
The Subjective GRE is recommended.
Test is recommended - No minimum is set

TOEFL requirements
The TOEFL exam is required for students from non-English-
  speaking countries.
  PBT score: 550
  iBT score: 80
Other equivalent exams may be accepted.

Other admissions information
Additional requirements: A brief statement (one page or less)
  of research interest must be included with the application.
Undergraduate preparation assumed: Classical Mechanics, Symon; Electromagnetism, Griffiths; Quantum Mechanics, Griffiths; Statistical and Thermal Physics, Reif; courses in linear
  algebra and differential equations.

TUITION

Tuition year 2018–19:
Tuition for in-state residents
  Full-time students: $12,068 annual
  Part-time students: $503 per credit
Tuition for out-of-state residents
  Full-time students: $29,456 annual
  Part-time students: $1,228 per credit
Credit hours per semester to be considered full-time: 12
Deferred tuition plan: No
Health insurance: Available at the cost of $1521 per year.
Other academic fees: Transit fee, Student Technology fee, Arm-
  strong Student Center fee, and facilities fee total per academic
  year is $1010. Some individual courses may charge special
  course fees.
Academic term: Semester
Number of first-year students who received full tuition waivers: 10

Teaching Assistants, Research Assistants, and Fellowships
Number of first-year
  Teaching Assistants: 8
  Research Assistants: 2
Average stipend per academic year
  Teaching Assistant: $17,406
  Research Assistant: $17,406

FINANCIAL AID

Application deadlines
Fall admission:
U.S. students: March 15   *Int'l. students*: March 15

Loans
Loans are available for U.S. students.
Loans are available for international students.
GAPSFAS application required: No

FAFSA application required: No

For further information
Address financial aid inquiries to: One Stop for Student Success.
Phone: (513) 529-0001
E-mail: OneStop@MiamiOH.edu
Financial aid website: http://www.miamioh.edu/admission/
finaid/graduate/index.html

HOUSING

For further information
Address housing inquiries to: Graduate School.
Phone: (513) 529-3734
E-mail: gradschool@miamioh.edu
Housing aid website: http://miamioh.edu/graduate-studies/
student-life/housing.html

Table A—Faculty, Enrollments, and Degrees Granted

Research Specialty	2017–18 Faculty	Enrollment Fall 2017 Master's	Enrollment Fall 2017 Doctorate	Number of Degrees Granted 2017–18 (2014–18) Master's	Number of Degrees Granted 2017–18 (2014–18) Terminal Master's	Number of Degrees Granted 2017–18 (2014–18) Doctorate
Applied Physics	3	–	–	–	–(2)	–
Astrophysics	1	1	–	–	1(3)	–
Atomic, Molecular, & Optical Physics	2	6	–	–	1(12)	–
Biophysics	2	5	–	–	4(9)	–
Condensed Matter Physics	3	2	–	–	1(13)	–
Nano Science and Technology	1	1	–	–	1(1)	–
Physics and other Science Education	2	1	–	–	–(1)	–
Quantum Optics & Quantum Information	2	4	–	–	2(10)	–
Other	3	–	–	–	–	–
Total	**14**	**20**	**–**	**–**	**10(51)**	**–**
Full-time Grad. Stud.	–	20	–	–	–	–
First-year Grad. Stud.	–	10	–	–	–	–

GRADUATE DEGREE REQUIREMENTS

Master's: For the thesis option, a minimum of 30 semester hours of graduate course work, research, and thesis credit is required. You must write a thesis proposal and defend it before your thesis committee. Subsequent completion and defense of the thesis are required. For the non-thesis option, a minimum of 36 semester hours of graduate credit is required. A comprehensive examination must also be passed. The thesis option is strongly recommended. For either the thesis or non-thesis option, you are expected to show proficiency in the areas of quantum physics, classical mechanics, electromagnetism, statistical physics, and mathematical methods used in physics. Evidence of proficiency means successful completion of courses at the graduate level. Graduate course work is selected in consultation with the thesis director (thesis option) and graduate program director.

SPECIAL EQUIPMENT, FACILITIES, OR PROGRAMS

Faculty qualified to direct graduate student research maintain or have access to the following: cold atom trap and optical lattice with tunable diode lasers; nanosecond time-resolved fluorescence spectrometer and sectioning microscope; cell culture facility of laminar flow-hood, CO_2 incubators; gamma-ray spectrometer; positron lifetime spectrometer; Quantum Design physical proper-

ties measurement system; grid cluster for computation; and Class 1000 clean room to fabricate nanodevices; Quantum Design helium liquifier;Center for Advanced Microscopy and Imaging (CAMI); Instrumentation Lab. Miami University is a node institution of the Southwest Quantum Information and Technology (SQuInT) network.

Table B—Separately Budgeted Research Expenditures by Source of Support

Source of Support	Departmental Research	Physics-related Research Outside Department
Federal government	$113,885	$65,913
State/local government		$14,484
Non-profit organizations	$123	
Business and industry		
Other		
Total	**$114,008**	**$80,397**

Table C—Separately Budgeted Research Expenditures by Research Specialty

Research Specialty	No. of Grants	Expenditures ($)
Atomic, Molecular, & Optical Physics	2	$113,885
Physics and other Science Education	3	$80,520
Total	**5**	**$194,405**

FACULTY

Chair Professor

Jaeger, Herbert, Ph.D., Oregon State University, 1987. *Applied Physics, Condensed Matter Physics*. Experimental solid state.

Professor

Bali, Samir, Ph.D., University of Rochester, 1994. *Applied Physics, Atomic, Molecular, & Optical Physics*. Experimental quantum optics.

Bayram, S. Burcin, Ph.D., Old Dominion University, 1998. *Atomic, Molecular, & Optical Physics*. Experimental atomic and molecular spectroscopy, quantum optics.

Associate Professor

Alexander, Stephen, Ph.D., Pennsylvania State University, 1990. Chief Departmental Adviser. *Astrophysics, Computational Physics*. Planetary and galactic dynamics.

Blue, Jennifer, Ph.D., University of Minnesota, 1997. *Physics and other Science Education*. Implementation of student-centered teaching, equity issues.

Eid, Khalid, Ph.D., Michigan State University, 2002. Graduate Director. *Applied Physics, Condensed Matter Physics, Nano Science and Technology*. Magnetism, superconductors, and semiconductors.

Urayama, Paul, Ph.D., Princeton University, 2001. *Biophysics*. Metabolic sensing; piezophysiology; high-pressure biotechnology.

Assistant Professor

Khan, Mahmud, Ph.D., Southern Illinois University, 2007. *Condensed Matter Physics, Energy Sources & Environment*. Magnetism; materials for energy applications.

Mirza, Imran, Ph.D., University of Oregon, 2014. *Nano Science and Technology, Quantum Foundations*. Quantum Information Theory. Hybrid atom-cavity optomechanics; propagation of light in non-uniform media; waveguide and cavity quantum electrodynamics; optomechanics; super- and subradiance.

Samson, E. Carlo, Ph.D., University of Arizona, 2012. *Atomic, Molecular, & Optical Physics, Quantum Foundations.* Bose Einstein condensates; superfluidity and quantum vortices; matter wave interferometry; quantum nonequilibrium dynamics.

Vishwanath, Karthik, Ph.D., University of Michigan, 2005. *Biophysics.* Theoretical and experimental approaches in quantitative spectroscopy of turbid materials; tissue optics; coherence-based optical sensing; opto-electronic device development.

Visiting Assistant Professor

Divaratne, Dilupama, Ph.D., Ohio University, 2013. *Condensed Matter Physics, Materials Science, Metallurgy, Nuclear Physics.* experimental low-energy Nuclear Physics.

Leu, Bogdan, Ph.D., Northeastern University, 2006. *Nuclear Physics.* Inelastic X-ray scattering; nuclear resonance scattering.

Senior Lecturer

Beer, Christopher P., Ph.D., Ball State University, 2010. Society of Physics Students Advisor, Astronomy Club Adviser. *Physics and other Science Education.* SCALE-UP.

DEPARTMENTAL RESEARCH SPECIALTIES AND STAFF

Theoretical

Astrophysics. Simulations of the motion of stars in Dwarf Spheroidal Galaxies using an alternative to the dark matter paradigm, i.e. Modified Newtonian Dynamics (MOND). Alexander.

Quantum Optics & Quantum Information. Theoretical and computational modeling of light and matter for generating nonclassical or entangled states of light and atoms. Mirza.

Experimental

Atomic, Molecular, & Optical Physics. Bose-Einstein condensation of dilute alkali gases, dynamics of quantum vorticies in BECs and superfluidity, atom trapping with painted potentials; Laser spectroscopy, time-resolved pump-probe spectroscopy, laser-induced fluorescence in molecules, quantum beat spectroscopy in atomic and molecular systems; dynamics of laser-cooled atoms in magneto-optical traps and optical lattices, electromagnetically induced transparency and absorption in atoms, optical sensing in highly turbid media. Bali, Bayram, Samson.

Biophysics. Monitoring and imaging of pressure effects on biomolecules and cellular physiology; novel label-free optical biosensing of surface ligand-analyte binding, monitoring and imaging of pressure effects on biomolecules and cellular physiology; in vivo optical biosensing, diffuse optics, low-cost instrumentation for use in remote or resource limited settings. Urayama, Vishwanath.

Condensed Matter Physics. Fabrication and characterization of nanoscale materials and devices using a variety of methods such as photo and electron beam lithography, photovoltaic and microfluidic applications, magnetoresistance in nanodevices at cryogenic temperatures, angular correlation spectroscopy of ceramic materials, positron annihilation lifetime spectroscopy, electronic and thermal properties of novel solid-state materials, magnetic and structural transitions, giant magnetoresistance, giant magnetocaloric effect, exchange bias effect, shape memory effects, and permanent magnetic materials. Eid, Jaeger, Khan.

Physics and other Science Education. Strategies for teaching scientific reasoning and problem-solving skills in introductory physics classes; elementary school and K-12 science education. Beer, Blue.

Quantum Optics & Quantum Information. Dynamics of laser-cooled atoms in optical lattices via single-photon correlation measurement; Quantum coherence studies using Bose-Einstein condensates. Bali, Samson.

OHIO UNIVERSITY

DEPARTMENT OF PHYSICS AND ASTRONOMY

Athens, Ohio 45701
http://www.ohio.edu/cas/physastro/

General University Information
President: Duane Nellis
Dean of Graduate School: Joseph Shields
University website: http://www.ohio.edu
School Type: Public
Setting: Rural
Total Faculty: 1,074
Total number of Students: 29,525
Total number of Graduate Students: 6,202

Department Information
Department Chairman: Prof. David Ingram, Chair
Department Contact: Candy Dishong, Assistant Department
 Administrator
 Total full-time faculty: 26
 Total number of full-time equivalent positions: 26
 Full-Time Graduate Students: 76
 Female Full-Time Graduate Students: 18
 First-Year Graduate Students: 15
 Female First-Year Students: 6
 Total Post Doctorates: 2

Department Address
1 Ohio University
Clippinger Laboratories
Athens, OH 45701
Phone: (740) 593-1709
Fax: (740) 593-0433
E-mail: dishong@ohio.edu
Website: http://www.ohio.edu/cas/physastro/

ADMISSIONS

Admission Contact Information
Address admission inquiries to: Chair of Graduate Admissions
 Committee, Department of Physics & Astronomy, 251 Clip-
 pinger Laboratories, Ohio University, Athens, OH 45701
E-mail: physicsgradapps@ohio.edu
Admissions website: http://www.ohio.edu/cas/physastro/

Application deadlines
Fall admission:
U.S. students: January 15   *Int'l. students*: January 15

Application fee
U.S. students: $50   *Int'l. students*: $55

Admissions information
For Fall of 2018:
 Number of applicants: 118
 Number admitted: 43
 Number enrolled: 14

Admission requirements
Bachelor's degree requirements: Bachelors degree in science,
 mathematics, or engineering is required.
Minimum undergraduate GPA: 3.0

GRE requirements
The GRE is recommended but not required.

The Verbal and Quantitative GRE General Tests are recommended.

Subjective GRE requirements
The Subjective GRE is not required.
The Physics GRE Subject Test is optional.

TOEFL requirements
The TOEFL exam is required for students from non-English-
 speaking countries.
 PBT score: 590
 iBT score: 95

Other admissions information
Additional requirements: The degree from an institution outside
 the United States must be equivalent to a four-year program
 in the United States.
 For teaching assistantships, the Test of Spoken English is also
 required for all international students. An examination in English is given upon arrival, and students may be required to
 enroll in English language instruction.
Undergraduate preparation assumed: Students entering with a B.S.
 degree in physics are normally assumed to have completed studies
 in the following basic subjects to the levels indicated. Texts: Mechanics—J. B. Marion and S. T. Thornton, "Classical Dynamics
 of Particles and Systems," fourth edition; Electricity and Magnetism—D. J. Griffiths, "Introduction to Electrodynamics," E. M. Purcell, "Electricity and Magnetism"; Modern Physics—Weidner and
 Sells, "Elementary Modern Physics"; Quantum Mechanics—D. J.
 Griffiths, "Introduction to Quantum Mechanics," second edition;
 Thermophysics—F. Reif, "Fundamentals of Statistical and Thermal
 Physics"; Mathematics—M. L. Boas, "Mathematical Methods in
 the Physical Sciences," calculus, including differential equations,
 Fourier series, complex variables, vector operators, basic algebra,
 including matrices and determinants.

TUITION

Tuition year 2018–19:
Tuition for in-state residents
 Full-time students: $4,094 per semester
Tuition for out-of-state residents
 Full-time students: $8,090 per semester
Tuition waiver for TAs and RAs covers all tuition, including out-
 of-state surcharge.
Credit hours per semester to be considered full-time: 15
Deferred tuition plan:
Health insurance: Available at the cost of $2,180 per year.
Other academic fees: General fee $628/semester. Technology
 fees $130/semester.
Academic term: Semester
Number of first-year students who received full tuition waivers: 15

Teaching Assistants, Research Assistants, and Fellowships
 Number of first-year
 Teaching Assistants: 14
 Research Assistants: 1
 Average stipend per academic year
 Teaching Assistant: $24,504
 Research Assistant: $26,510

FINANCIAL AID

Application deadlines
Fall admission:
U.S. students: January 15   *Int'l. students*: January 15

Loans
Loans are available for U.S. students.
Loans are not available for international students.
GAPSFAS application required: No
FAFSA application required: No

For further information
Address financial aid inquiries to: Graduate Appointments Committee Chair, Department of Physics & Astronomy, 251 Clippinger Laboratories, Ohio University, Athens, OH 45701.
E-mail: physicsgradapps@ohio.edu
Financial aid website: http://www.ohio.edu/cas/physastro/

HOUSING

Availability of on-campus housing
Single students: No
Married students: No
Childcare Assistance: No

For further information
Address housing inquiries to: Housing and Residence Life, Ohio University, Living Learning Center 215, 111 South Green Drive, Athens, OH 45701.
Phone: (740) 593-4090
E-mail: housing@ohio.edu
Housing aid website: http://www.ohio.edu/housing/

Table A—Faculty, Enrollments, and Degrees Granted

Research Specialty	2017–18 Faculty	Enrollment Fall 2017		Number of Degrees Granted 2017–18 (2013–18)		
		Master's	Doctorate	Master's	Terminal Master's	Doctorate
Astrophysics	3	–	8	–(5)	–	–(5)
Biophysics	3	–	4	–(5)	–	–(5)
Condensed Matter Physics	11	1	28	4(25)	2(3)	6(29)
Nuclear Physics	11	1	24	5(24)	2(2)	2(20)
Non-specialized	–	1	9	–	–	–
Total	28	3	73	9(59)	4(5)	8(59)
Full-time Grad. Stud.	–	3	73	–	–	–
First-year Grad. Stud.	–	–	15	–	–	–

GRADUATE DEGREE REQUIREMENTS

Master's: Thirty semester hours minimum; 3.0 ("B") average minimum; thesis optional; residence requirement not specified; no exams except in courses and for thesis; no foreign language required.

Doctorate: There is no specified number of course hours but a series of core courses are required; a minimum 3.0 ("B") average must be maintained. A comprehensive review, two semesters continuous residence minimum, and dissertation are required. No foreign language required.

Other Degrees: Interdepartmental studies (e.g., communications, education) and other special programs available by arrangement.

Thesis: Thesis may be written in absentia.

SPECIAL EQUIPMENT, FACILITIES, OR PROGRAMS

The OHIO Physics & Astronomy Department is housed within Clippinger Laboratories, the Clippinger Research Annex; the Edwards Accelerator Laboratory, and the Surface Science Laboratory. The Department's areas of expertise include condensed matter and nanoscience, nuclear and particle physics, astrophysics, nuclear astrophysics, and biophysics. Research activities are supported by state of the art experimental facilities that include OHIO's 4.5 MV high-intensity accelerator, advanced laser systems, a high capacity helium liquefaction system, specialized microscopy systems, computer clusters and workstations. In addition, the Department has a well-equipped and staffed machine shop which both constructs new equipment as well as maintains existing equipment.

The low-temperature research is supported by our helium recovery and liquefaction facility which re-generates liquid helium from re-cycled helium gas to supply to multiple laboratories doing cryogenic research. Two liquid-helium cooled, low-temperature scanning tunneling microscope (LT-STM) systems are focused on investigating the electronic and mechanical properties of molecules on surfaces which includes also the manipulation of atoms and molecules. Another lab houses a spin-polarized LT-STM system also operating at liquid helium temperature. This system is connected to a molecular beam epitaxy (MBE) growth system for depositing (growing) semiconducting and magnetic thin film layer systems. Other labs contain additional sample preparation facilities including an MBE-STM lab and a pulsed laser deposition (PLD) lab. The samples produced in these labs may be analyzed by a wide variety of additional analytical equipment including x-ray diffractometry high-resolution electron microscopy, atomic force/magnetic force microscopy, and Rutherford backscattering.

The 4.5-MV tandem Pelletron accelerator located in the John E. Edwards Accelerator Laboratory provides ion beams and the associated detection equipment for the study of nuclear reactions of interest for nuclear structure, nuclear astrophysics, materials science, inertial confinement fusion, nuclear energy, homeland security, and other applications. The laboratory is well-equipped for the detection of neutrons, charged particles, and gamma rays and has a well-shielded 30-m tunnel which is ideal for neutron time-of-flight experiments. This research is performed by Ohio University students, faculty, and staff, as well users from other universities and laboratories.

The Department also owns 1/12th of the MDM Observatory, which consists of a 2.4m and 1.3m telescope adjacent to the Kitt Peak National Observatory in Arizona. Both telescopes are equipped for optical and near-infrared imaging and spectroscopy. Department personnel, including graduate students, are able to request time on both telescopes for up to 24 nights per year. A 10" refracting telescope is located on a hill near campus and is used for undergraduate education and training graduate students to conduct scientific public outreach.

Both undergraduate and graduate students within the Department also have access to the state-of-the-art nanoscience facilities located at Argonne National Laboratory through an on-going partnership, and to date many students have spent periods ranging from months to years performing part of their research there.

The in-house computer facilities are excellent and include three 60-node computer clusters, and three NVIDIA TESLA GPU-accelerated workstations (2xK40,8xC1060). In addition, the Ohio Supercomputer Center (OSC) offers statewide computing infrastructure, training, and education.

Table B—Separately Budgeted Research Expenditures by Source of Support

Source of Support	Departmental Research	Physics-related Research Outside Department
Federal government	$1,420,851	
State/local government	$1,440	
Non-profit organizations		
Business and industry		
Other		
Total	**$1,422,291**	

Table C—Separately Budgeted Research Expenditures by Research Specialty

Research Specialty	No. of Grants	Expenditures ($)
Astrophysics	1	$10,409
Biophysics	1	$82,143
Condensed Matter Physics	6	$489,261
Nuclear Physics	7	$839,038
Other	1	$1,440
Total	**16**	**$1,422,291**

FACULTY

Distinguished University Professor

Drabold, David A., Ph.D., Washington University, 1989. Fundamental theory of amorphous materials and glasses, novel methods to model complex materials beyond conventional ab initio techniques. Development of methods to engineer optical gaps in amorphous materials. Studies of Conducting Bridge Random Access Memory materials and transition metal glasses.

Govorov, Alexander O., Ph.D., Institute of Semiconductor Physics (Russia), 1991. Theoretical condensed matter physics; metal and semiconductor nanostructures; plasmonics and bioplasmonics; metamaterials; energy-related research; nanoscience.

Grimes, Steven M., Ph.D., University of Wisconsin-Madison, 1968. Nuclear physics.

Jung, Peter, Ph.D., University of Ulm (Germany), 1985. Non-equilibrium statistical physics; nonlinear stochastic processes; pattern formation; biophysics.

Professor

Brune, Carl R., Ph.D., California Institute of Technology, 1994. *Astrophysics, Nuclear Physics, Plasma and Fusion.* Nuclear astrophysics, radioactive beams, thermonuclear fusion in laboratory plasmas, near-threshold states of nuclei, phenomenological analysis of resonance reactions.

Elster, Charlotte, Ph.D., University of Bonn (Germany), 1986. Nuclear reactions with stable and exotic nuclei. Scattering of nucleons from very light nuclei, modeling light nuclei as few-body systems. Multiple scattering theories with application to nucleon nucleus scattering and nuclear reactions. Computational physics with emphasis on nuclear reactions and few-body systems.

Hicks, Kenneth H., Ph.D., University of Colorado, 1984. Hadronic Particle Physics, Nuclear Physics, Combinatorial Mathematics. Experimental searches for exotic particles, quark-model of the nucleon, partial wave analysis of scattering reactions, mutually orthogonal latin squares, design of experiments.

Hla, Saw-Wai, Ph.D., University of Ljubljana (Slovenia), 1997. Experimental nanoscience.

Ingram, David C., Ph.D., University of Salford (UK), 1980. Departmental Chair. Thin films; atomic collisions in solids; surface physics.

Kordesch, Martin E., Ph.D., Case Western Reserve University, 1984. Surface physics; wide-gap materials.

Neiman, Alexander, Ph.D., Saratov (Russia), 1998. Biophysics and nonlinear stochastic processes.

Phillips, Daniel, Ph.D., Flinders University (Australia), 1995. Theoretical nuclear and particle physics. Descriptions of electromagnetic reactions on light nuclei, proton and neutron polarizabilities, modelling of the structure and reactions of light nuclei. Emergence of "halo" structures near the neutron and proton driplines, and associated ability to describe these systems in terms of a few effective degrees of freedom. Bayesian methods and uncertainty quantification in nuclear physics.

Prakash, Madappa, Ph.D., Bombay University (India), 1979. Theoretical nuclear astrophysics. Structure and evolution of neutrons stars from birth to old age, core-collapse supernovae, binary mergers of compact objects, neutrino interactions in matter, theory of strong interactions, relativistic heavy-ion physics.

Sandler, Nancy, Ph.D., University of Illinois, 1998. Theory of Condensed Matter Systems. Electronic, mechanical and properties of low-dimensional materials in and out-of equilibrium conditions. Interacting systems with emphasis in two-dimensional materials. Topological properties and exotic phases of matter.

Shields, Joseph C., Ph.D., University of California, Berkeley, 1991. Astrophysics; interstellar medium; active galactic nuclei.

Smith, Arthur R., Ph.D., University of Texas, 1995. Experimental surface physics, including surface structure, semiconducting and magnetic materials, molecular beam epitaxy/spin-polarized scanning tunneling microscopy, transition metal nitrides.

Ulloa, Sergio E., Ph.D., State University of New York at Buffalo, 1984. Theoretical Condensed Matter, Electronic transport and optical properties of solids, Many-body correlation effects, Low-dimensional systems and topological response.

Associate Professor

Castillo, Horacio E., Ph.D., University of Illinois, 1998. Theoretical condensed matter.

Chen, Gang, Ph.D., Lehigh University, 2004. Structure of non-crystalline materials, Amorphous semiconductors, Ion transport in amorphous solid electrolytes, Memoristor materials and devices, Neuromorphic computing.

Clowe, Douglas, Ph.D., University of Hawaii, 1998. Observational astrophysics.

Frantz, Justin, Ph.D., Columbia University, 2005. Experimental nuclear physics.

Lucas, Mark, Ph.D., University of Illinois, 1995. Teaching pedagogy, K-12 and general public science outreach, teacher professional development, use of technology in teaching.

Roche, Julie, Ph.D., University B. Pascal (France), 1998. Experimental nuclear and particle physics. Study of the internal structure of hadrons and Search for Physics beyond the Standard Model at the precision frontier.

Stinaff, Eric, Ph.D., Iowa State University, 2002. Experimental nanoscience.

Tees, David F. J., Ph.D., McGill University, 1995. *Biophysics.* Biophysics. Biophysics of cell adhesion, forced unbinding of receptor-ligand bonds, leukocyte adhesion in capillaries, mechanical properties of cancer cells measured using micropipette aspiration, microfluidics and particle tracking microrheology.

Assistant Professor

Chornock, Ryan, Ph.D., University of California, Berkeley, 2009. Observational astrophysics.

Meisel, Zachary, Ph.D., Michigan State University, 2015. Nuclear astrophysics, experimental nuclear physics, neutron star crust and ocean physics, x-ray burst modeling, direct and indirect reaction measurements, nuclear masses.

Seo, Hee-Jong, Ph.D., University of Arizona, 2007. High precision cosmology with large scale structure, Baryon Acoustic Oscillations, redshift-space distortions, cosmic shear.

Research Faculty

King, Paul, Ph.D., College of William and Mary in Virginia, 2000. Experimental nuclear physics.

Massey, Thomas, Ph.D., University of California, 1988. Experimental nuclear physics.

Voinov, Alexander, Ph.D., Joint Institute for Nuclear Research, Dubna, 1994. Experimental nuclear physics.

Adjunct Faculty

Russell, David, Ph.D., University of California, San Diego, 1977. Biophysics.

DEPARTMENTAL RESEARCH SPECIALTIES AND STAFF

Theoretical

Astrophysics. Astronomy and Astrophysics: cosmology; cosmological simulations; neutron stars; supernovae. Prakash, Seo.

Biophysics. Current theoretical and computational research is conducted in the area of neuroscience. Specifically, hair-cell mechanics, mechano-electrical transduction, and electromechanical coupling, neuronal circuitry and arrangement in peripheral sensory systems, signal encoding in peripheral sensors, neurofilament transport and its role for axonal morphology and neuronal function, and actin transport in axons. Castillo, Jung, Neiman.

Condensed Matter Physics. Supercooled liquids and glasses; soft condensed matter physics: colloids, granulars, polymers; theory of topologically disordered materials; computational methodology for electronic structure; electronic structure of molecules, crystalline solids and amorphous solids; quantum dots and rings; nanoparticles; plasmonics; bio-optics; transport and optical properties in low-dimensional systems; physics of interacting low-dimensional systems; spin-orbit interaction in condensed matter systems; correlated electron systems. Castillo, Drabold, Govorov, Sandler, Ulloa.

Nuclear Physics. Computational investigations and analytic models of exotic nuclei, nuclear reactions, nuclear deformation, nucleon structure, nuclear forces, neutron stars, supernovae, and the quark-gluon plasma. Elster, Phillips, Prakash.

Experimental

Astrophysics. Astronomy and astrophysics: optical astronomy; cosmology; time-domain astronomy; dark matter; dark energy; gravitational lensing; baryon acoustic oscillations; supernovae; gamma-ray bursts; black holes; active galactic nuclei; large scale structure; wide-field surveys (LSST, WFIRST, DESI). Chornock, Clowe, Seo, Shields.

Biophysics. The Russell lab is focused on neuro-sensory circuitry. The Tees lab focuses on adhesive and mechanical properties of white blood cells and cancer cells with the aim of better understanding the biophysical basis of cell physiology as well as opening avenues for diagnosis and treatment of disease. The lab has expertise in micropipette aspiration for cell manipulation and assessment of overall cell mechanical properties. Microfluidic devices for micropipette-like experiments are also an active area of investigation. The lab also has a holographic optical trapping system for adhesion experiments. Russell, Tees.

Condensed Matter Physics. X-ray characterization of materials; self assembly of nanostructured materials; glass, disordered materials, and soft condensed matter; single atom/molecule manipulation; low temperature scanning tunneling microscopy/spectroscopy/manipulation; single molecule electronics; molecular machines; nanobiosystems; ion beam analysis of materials; surface and thin film analysis and modification; molecular beam epitaxy; pulsed laser epitaxy; nitride materials; optical spectroscopy; semiconductor nanostructures; atomic-scale magnetism; spin-polarized scanning tunneling microscopy; photonics; quantum optics; quantum dots; quantum information. Chen, Hla, Ingram, Kordesch, Smith, Stinaff.

Nuclear Physics. Experiments are performed at the on-campus Edwards Accelerator Laboratory, or at external facilities including the Thomas Jefferson and Brookhaven National Laboratories. Topics of study include: the quark-gluon plasma, precision tests of the Standard Model, quark substructure of nucleons, spectroscopy of nucleon resonances, exotic nuclei, nuclear reactions—especially as they pertain to astrophysics, statistical nuclear physics, technological applications of nuclear physics. Brune, Frantz, Hicks, Ingram, King, Massey, Meisel, Roche, Voinov.

Physics and other Science Education. The department has a robust outreach presence in the community with opportunities for students to interact with K-12 students and the general public through our biennial open house, strong connections with the Ohio Valley Museum of Discovery, and a variety of special events (local and state science fairs, science olympiad, school visits). Seminars and workshops provide opportunities for students to reflect upon teaching and improve their teaching skills and explore teaching-related job opportunities in the college environment. Special TA assignments provide opportunities to build skills in the use of technology for education as well as various active pedagogies. Lucas.

View additional information about this department at www.gradschoolshopper.com. Check out the "Why Choose Us?" section, find out more about the department's culture and get links to social media networks.

THE OHIO STATE UNIVERSITY

DEPARTMENT OF PHYSICS

Columbus, Ohio 43210
https://physics.osu.edu/

General University Information
President: Michael Drake
Dean of Graduate School: Alicia L. Bertone
University website: http://www.osu.edu
School Type: Public
Setting: Urban
Total Faculty: 7,196
Total Graduate Faculty: 2,894
Total number of Students: 66,444
Total number of Graduate Students: 10,798

Department Information
Department Chairman: Prof. Brian Winer, Chair
Department Contact: Kris Dunlap, Program Coordinator
  Total full-time faculty: 62
  Total number of full-time equivalent positions: 62
  Full-Time Graduate Students: 207
  Female Full-Time Graduate Students: 39
  First-Year Graduate Students: 41
  Female First-Year Students: 6
  Total Post Doctorates: 48

Department Address
191 West Woodruff Avenue
Columbus, OH 43210
Phone: (614) 292-5127
E-mail: gradstudies@physics.osu.edu
Website: https://physics.osu.edu/

ADMISSIONS

Admission Contact Information
Address admission inquiries to: The Ohio State University, Physics Graduate Studies, 191 W. Woodruff Avenue, Columbus, OH 43210
Phone: (614) 292-5127
E-mail: gradstudies@physics.osu.edu
Admissions website: https://physics.osu.edu/graduate-admissions-application

Application deadlines
Fall admission:
U.S. students: December 15   *Int'l. students*: November 30

Application fee
U.S. students: $5   *Int'l. students*: $5
To be considered for a fellowship, please submit all applications materials by December 15. Please note that the online application system for the Autumn 2019 academic year will reference a fee of $70 for domestic and $80 for international students, but the system will only process $5 for either when you go to submit the final payment information.

Admissions information
For Fall of 2018:
  Number of applicants: 365
  Number admitted: 117
  Number enrolled: 41

Admission requirements
Bachelor's degree requirements: Bachelor's degree in Physics or related field is required.
Minimum undergraduate GPA: 3.0

GRE requirements
The GRE is required.
There are no minimum required GRE scores. Applications are reviewed in their entirety.

Subjective GRE requirements
The Subjective GRE is required.
There is no minimum required Physics GRE score.

TOEFL requirements
The TOEFL exam is required for students from non-English-speaking countries.
  PBT score: 650
  iBT score: 79
The average TOEFL scores of those who receive offers of admission range from 100 to 115. International students with TOEFL score below 115 usually require 1 year of English as a Second Language courses to receive teaching certification.

Other admissions information
Additional requirements: There is no minimum GRE score required.
  International Graduate Teaching Associates must demonstrate their fluency in spoken English before they will be allowed to assume classroom teaching duties.
Undergraduate preparation assumed: Symon, Mechanics; Lorrain and Corson, Electromagnetic Fields and Waves; Eisberg and Resnick, Quantum Physics: Reif, Statistical and Thermal Physics.

TUITION

Tuition year 2018–2019:
Tuition for in-state residents
  Full-time students: $16,398 annual
Tuition for out-of-state residents
  Full-time students: $38,902 annual
All incoming 1st year students for Autumn 2018 through Summer 2019 receive full stipend support and full tuition waivers as either GTAs or Fellows. Tuition is based on a 12-month, 3-semester system. Students are still responsible for the additional other fees that are not eligible for coverage.
Credit hours per semester to be considered full-time: 8
Deferred tuition plan: No
Health insurance: Available at the cost of $3252 per year.
Other academic fees: Recreation ($123), activity ($37.50), city bus ($13.50), student union ($74.40), legal fee ($40 paid AU term only).
Academic term: Semester
Number of first-year students who received full tuition waivers: 40
Number of first-year students who received partial tuition waivers: 1

Teaching Assistants, Research Assistants, and Fellowships

Number of first-year
Teaching Assistants: 21
Fellowship students: 19
Average stipend per academic year
Teaching Assistant: $25,728
Research Assistant: $26,724
Fellowship student: $26,000
Note Fellowships range from $26,000 to $33,000 per 12 month year.

FINANCIAL AID

Application deadlines

Fall admission:
U.S. students: December 15   *Int'l. students*: November 30

Loans

Loans are available for U.S. students.
Loans are not available for international students.
GAPSFAS application required: No
FAFSA application required: Yes

For further information

Address financial aid inquiries to: The Ohio State University, Student Financial Aid, PO Box 183029, Columbus, OH 43218-3029.
Phone: 614-292-0300
E-mail: buckeyelink@osu.edu
Financial aid website: http://www.sfa.osu.edu/

HOUSING

Availability of on-campus housing

Single students: Yes
Married students: Yes
Childcare Assistance: No

For further information

Address housing inquiries to: Director, Graduate Student Housing, 350 Morrill Tower, 1910 Cannon Drive, Columbus, OH 43210.
Phone: 614-292-8266
E-mail: housing@osu.edu
Housing aid website: http://housing.osu.edu/

Table A—Faculty, Enrollments, and Degrees Granted

Research Specialty	2018–2019 Faculty	Enrollment Fall 2018 Master's	Enrollment Fall 2018 Doctorate	Number of Degrees Granted 2017–2018 (2013–2018) Master's	Number of Degrees Granted 2017–2018 (2013–2018) Terminal Master's	Number of Degrees Granted 2017–2018 (2013–2018) Doctorate
Astrophysics	8	–	23	5	–	3(19)
Atomic, Molecular, & Optical Physics	7	–	24	3	–	–(27)
Biophysics	5	–	13	2	–	4(15)
Condensed Matter Physics	19	–	70	13	1	16(65)
High Energy Physics	13	–	19	4	1	5(20)
Nuclear Physics	7	–	13	4	–	3(17)
Physics and other Science Education	2	–	6	1	–	–(7)
Non-specialized	1	–	39	–	–	–
Total	62	–	207	32	2	31(170)
Full-time Grad. Stud.	–	–	207	–	–	–
First-year Grad. Stud.	–	–	41	–	–	–

GRADUATE DEGREE REQUIREMENTS

Master's: The master's degree can be earned as a part of the general (candidacy) examination for the Ph.D. The department requires a minimum GPA of 3.3 in the Physics 6 course core curriculum.

Doctorate: Students must complete 80 credit hours of graduate-level coursework including research for the dissertation; of this amount, 30 hours may be transferred from a master's degree at OSU. Students must pass the candidacy examination and have a GPA of 3.3 in the Physics core curriculum, and must satisfactorily complete an oral final examination on the dissertation and submit the dissertation to graduate. There is no language requirement.

Other Degrees: M.S. and Ph.D. in chemical physics are also available.

SPECIAL EQUIPMENT, FACILITIES, OR PROGRAMS

Laboratory facilities and equipment: At the OSU Department of Physics, each research group possesses a unique scientific capability including techniques of scanning tunneling microscopy, spatially resolved ferromagnetic resonance imaging, electron spin resonance characterization, etc. While these capabilities are available through individual research groups, there are also a number of excellent departmental facilities that are shared by all. These facilities include a well-staffed machine shop, an electro-mechanical shop (specializing in electronics design and fabrication, low-temperature system construction, and optics support), and liquid helium and nitrogen facilities. Undergraduate and graduate students also have access to an efficient student machine shop, upon successful completion of mandatory supervised training classes.

In addition, the Physics Department is home to NanoSystems Laboratory (NSL), a campus-wide user facility providing the OSU material science community with cutting-edge characterization equipment. The instruments available at NSL include, but are not limited to: a state-of-the-art Focused Ion Beam/Scanning Electron Microscope (FIB/SEM) with capabilities for electron beam lithography, in situ nanomanipulation and EDS X-ray microanalysis, a high-resolution triple axis X-ray Diffractometer, two Superconducting Quantum Interference Device (SQUID) Magnetometers, two Atomic Force/Magnetic Force Microscopes (AFM/MFM), a new Chemical Vapor Deposition System for diamond growth, two Physical Property Measurement Systems (PPMS) for high-magnetic-field electric and magnetic measurements, one of which has a PPMS-compatible cryogenic AFM/MFM, two Terahertz Spectrometers, an Electron Paramagnetic Resonance Spectrometer, and a rapid turnaround system for low-temperature magneto-transport measurements. NSL also operates a Class 1000 clean room with instruments such as a Langmuir-Blodgett trough for molecular monolayer deposition, a combined magnetron sputtering/electron beam thin film deposition system, and a laser writer for mask-free photo lithography.

Interdisciplinary programs: The Physics Department at The Ohio State University also houses and supports the Center for Cosmology and AstroParticle Physics (CCAPP). CCAPP's mission is to support collaborative research between the OSU Departments of Astronomy and Physics in areas where OSU can make a fundamental impact such as: dark energy, dark matter, and multimessenger particle astrophysics. Through the Center, OSU has joined some of the world's leading research efforts: DES, GLAST, AUGER, Ice-Cube, and SDDSS-III. Of particular importance is the Center's identity as a collection point for the world's best young researchers in the areas of cosmology and particle astrophysics. The Center houses approximately 20 faculty members, seven CCAPP postdocs, and other mission specific postdocs, graduate students, and staff. It typically hosts 100 visitors a year, including 10 mini-workshops and several collaboration meetings. Department of Physics faculty members involved with CCAPP are: Beacom, Beatty, Honscheid, Hughes, Kass, Steigman, Walker, and Winer. Please visit http://www.ccapp.osu.edu for more information.

The Center for Exploration of Novel Complex Materials (ENCOMM) builds on the existing strengths at OSU in electronic, magnetic, and organic materials to address cutting-edge challenges in understanding and developing complex multicomponent materials. These problems are inherently multidisciplinary and require state-of-the-art facilities. ENCOMM builds and nurtures the teams that can address these challenges and compete effectively for multidisciplinary block-funded centers by creating the environment in which these theoretical and experimental teams can form and interact, and to provide the infrastructure needed to perform the research that will define this field. ENCOMM membership extends across the Departments of Physics, Chemistry, Mechanical Engineering, Materials Science and Engineering, Electrical and Computing Engineering, and Biomedical Engineering. ENCOMM formed and nurtured the Interdisciplinary Research Groups that successfully competed for our new NSF-funded Materials Research Science and Engineering Center (MRSEC), listed below. ENCOMM includes 44 faculty members from six departments. Department of Physics faculty members are: Hammel, Johnston-Halperin, Brillson, Epstein, Gramila, Gupta, Jayaprakash, Lemberger, Pelz, Poirier, Putikka, Randeria, Sooryakumar, Stroud, Trevedi, Wilkins, and Yang. Please visit http://www.physics.ohio-state.edu/ENCOMM for more information.

Our Materials Research Science and Engineering Center (MRSEC), also called the Center for Emergent Materials (CEM), is comprised of two interdisciplinary research groups with activities focusing on the general area of magnetoelectronics. The first group, "Towards Spin Preserving, Heterogeneous Spin Networks," is focused on broadening the application of spintronics to new materials through collaborative development of innovative characterization and investigational tools and new materials growth and testing approaches. The second, "Double Perovskite Interfaces and Heterostructures," is creating new functionality in oxide materials by combining novel perovskite compounds into composite structures with controlled interfaces. By tuning magnetic and electronic properties of the constituent materials and exploiting controlled strain at interfaces, new properties emerge. The Center includes 30 graduate research fellows, six postdoctoral researchers, 20 undergraduate students, three staff members, and 25 faculty members. Department of Physics faculty members are: Johnston-Halperin, Gupta, Hammel, Heckler, Epstein, Pelz, Stroud, Brillson, Lemberger, Randeria, Trivedi, and Yang. Please visit http://www.cem.osu.edu for more information.

Table B—Separately Budgeted Research Expenditures by Source of Support

Source of Support	Departmental Research	Physics-related Research Outside Department
Federal government	$8,897,324	
State/local government	$5,050,749	
Non-profit organizations	$173,430	
Business and industry	$757,751	
Other	$1,387,105	
Total	**$16,266,359**	

Table C—Separately Budgeted Research Expenditures by Research Specialty

Research Specialty	No. of Grants	Expenditures ($)
Astrophysics	15	$11,187,943
Atomic, Molecular, & Optical Physics	23	$3,581,454
Biophysics	15	$724,867
Condensed Matter Physics	42	$2,927,571
High Energy Physics	13	$1,688,681
Nuclear Physics	10	$803,501
Physics and other Science Education	3	$352,943
Other	2	
Total	**123**	**$21,266,960**

FACULTY

Professor

Bao, Lei, Ph.D., University of Maryland, 1999. *Physics and other Science Education*. Physics education research: cognitive and computational models of learning process. Biologically plausible neural network models of cognition. Model-based education assessment theory and technology. Experimental and theoretical methods for modeling group learning. Meta-cognitive factors in learning. Education technology and curriculum for in-class polling and Web instruction.

Beacom, John, Ph.D., University of Wisconsin-Madison, 1997. Director of Center for Cosmology and Astro-Particle Physics (CCAPP). *Astrophysics*. Theoretical cosmology and astroparticle physics: neutrinos in astrophysics, cosmology, particle physics, and nuclear physics. Gamma-ray astronomy, cosmic rays, dark matter and other aspects of particle and nuclear astrophysics.

Beatty, James, Ph.D., University of Chicago, 1986. *Astrophysics*. Experimental cosmology and astroparticle physics: the highest energy cosmic rays and neutrinos, Cosmic ray spectrum, composition and anisotropy, radio detection of cosmic rays and neutrinos.

Bockrath, Marc, Ph.D., Univ of California, Berkeley, 1999. *Condensed Matter Physics, Nano Science and Technology*. Electronics and mechanics of systems that have critical dimensions on the nanometer scale. Transport phenomena that arise in nanostructured materials and learning how to control and detect their mechanical motion.

Braaten, Eric, Ph.D., University of Wisconsin-Madison, 1981. *High Energy Physics*. Theoretical high-energy and cold atom physics: quantum field theory, heavy quarks and quarkonium, quark-gluon plasma, perturbative QCD. Strongly interacting quantum gases, Bose-Einstein condensates, few-body physics for atoms with large scattering lengths, Efimov states.

Brillson, Leonard, Ph.D., University of Pennsylvania, 1972. *Condensed Matter Physics, Electrical Engineering*. Experimental condensed matter physics; electrical engineering: semiconductor interface growth, processing, and characterization by ultrahigh vacuum surface science techniques. Schottky barriers and heterojunction band offsets. Optoelectronic, microelectronic and nanoelectronic interface atomic structure. Solar cells, bioelectric sensors, ultraviolet microlasers. Ferroelectric/ferromagnetic complex oxides for spintronics and electromagnetic metamaterials.

Bundschuh, Ralf, Ph.D., University of Potsdam, 1996. *Biophysics*. Theoretical biophysics: RNA structure-statistical mechanics and quantitative prediction. RNA editing. Biological sequence database searches. Biomolecules. Bioinformatics.

Connolly, Amy L., Ph.D., University of California, Berkeley, 2003. *Astrophysics*. Experimental Cosmology and Astroparticle Physics: High energy neutrino astronomy, Connecting neutrino and cosmic ray, measurements with astrophysics.

DiMauro, Louis F., Ph.D., University of Connecticut, 1980. *Atomic, Molecular, & Optical Physics.* Experimental Atomic, Molecular, and Optical Physics: Atomic, chemical and ultrafast optical physics. Strong field interactions. Ultrafast laser physics, Attophysics Nonlinear optics. Short wave length generation Quantum control methods. Many body physics. Application of fourth generation light sources.

Durkin, L. Stanley, Ph.D., Stanford University, 1981. *High Energy Physics.* Experimental High-Energy Physics: Lepton-hadron scattering, Intrinsic properties of neutrinos, Search for massive Higgs particles.

Furnstahl, Richard J., Ph.D., Stanford University, 1986. *Nuclear Physics.* Theoretical Nuclear and Cold Atom Physics: Quantum chromodynamics and nuclear phenomena, Effective field theories at finite density and/or temperature, Bazaar approach to physics education research. Effective field theory for many-body systems, Pairing mechanisms for Fermi gases, Density functional theory.

Gan, K. K., Ph.D., Purdue University, 1985. *High Energy Physics.* Experimental High-Energy Physics: Physics beyond the Standard Model in e+e- and hadron colliders, High-resolution energy and position detectors, Radiation-hard optical data communication.

Gauthier, Daniel, Ph.D., University of Rochester, 1989. *Atomic, Molecular, & Optical Physics, Quantum Foundations.* Network Science Research and Quantum Information Science Research.

Gruzberg, Ilya A., Ph.D., Yale University, 1998. *Condensed Matter Physics.* Theoretical Condensed Matter Physics: Quantum condensed matter physics. Classical condensed matter physics-nonequilibrium growth phenomena. Statistical and mathematical physics.

Hammel, P. Chris, Ph.D., Cornell University, 1984. Director of Center for Emergent Materials. *Condensed Matter Physics.* Experimental Condensed Matter Physics: Magnetic resonance force microscopy, Spin electronics and solid state quantum computing, Nanoscale and multicomponent magnetic systems, Magnetic properties of endohedral fullerenes.

Heinz, Ulrich, Ph.D., Goethe Univ., 1980. *Nuclear Physics.* Theoretical Nuclear Physics: Relativistic heavy-ion collisions — theory and phenomenology, Quantum field systems at high temperature, Thermodynamics and kinetics of quark-gluon plasma.

Hill, Christopher S., Ph.D., University of California, Davis, 2001. *High Energy Physics.* Experimental High-Energy Physics: Searches for evidence beyond the Standard Model. Studies in the properties of the Top Quark.

Hirata, Chris, Ph.D., Princeton University, 2005. *Astrophysics.* Theoretical Cosmology and Astroparticle Physics: Theory and astrophysics of cosmological probes, Cosmic recombination, Weak gravitational lensing.

Ho, Tin-Lun (Jason), Ph.D., Cornell University, 1977. *Condensed Matter Physics.* Theoretical Condensed Matter and Cold Atom Physics: Fundamental issues in dilute quantum gases - scalar and spinor Bose condensates, Fermi gases with large spin, mixtures of Bose and Fermi gases, quantum gases in optical lattices and in rapidly rotating potentials, boson mesoscopics. Processing quantum information with spinor Bose condensates. Quantum Hall effect with internal degrees of freedom. Strongly correlated electron systems, Quantum fluids.

Honscheid, Klaus, Ph.D., University of Bonn, 1988. *Astrophysics, High Energy Physics.* Experimental High-Energy, and Cosmology and Astroparticle physics: Decay properties of heavy quarks, Trigger and data acquisition systems. Dark Matter.

Hughes, Richard E., Ph.D., University of Pennsylvania, 1992. *Astrophysics, High Energy Physics.* Experimental High Energy, and Cosmology and Astroparticle physics: Astroparticle physics using the FGST satellite, Search for the source of dark matter, High-energy physics studies using proton-antiproton collider, Study of the top quark, Development of a trigger track processor. Very high energy gamma-ray astronomy with FGST.

Humanic, Thomas J., Ph.D., University of Pittsburgh, 1979. *Nuclear Physics.* Experimental Nuclear Physics: Relativistic proton and heavy ion collisions, CERN Large Hadron collider-ALICE experiment, Boson interferometry, Extra-dimensional physics, Collision model calculations.

Jayaprakash, Ciriyam, Ph.D., University of Illinois, 1979. *Biophysics, Condensed Matter Physics.* Theoretical condensed-matter physics and Biophysics: Genetic regulatory systems, Modeling of the adaptive immune system in humans, Nonlinear ecological dynamics, Fully developed turbulence.

Jeschonnek, Sabine, Ph.D., University of Bonn, 1996. *Nuclear Physics.* Theoretical Nuclear Physics: Quark-hadron duality, Short-range structures in few-body systems, Coincidence electron scattering reactions at GeV energies.

Kagan, Harris P., Ph.D., University of Minnesota, 1979. *High Energy Physics.* Experimental High-Energy Physics: Electron-positron interactions. High-resolution energy and position detectors.

Kawakami, Roland, Ph.D., University of California, Berkely, 1999. *Condensed Matter Physics.* Experimental Condensed Matter Physics: Spin transport in graphene and other two-dimensional materials. Molecular Beam epitaxy of novel magnetic heterostructures. Ultrafast optical microscopy and spectroscopy.

Kovchegov, Yuri, Ph.D., Columbia University, 1998. *Nuclear Physics.* Theoretical Nuclear Physics: Theoretical nuclear and high energy physics, Theory of strong interactions (QCD) at high energy and high parton density, Heavy ion collisions and deep inelastic scattering, Applications of string theory to QCD.

Lau, ChunNing, Ph.D., Harvard, 2001. *Condensed Matter Physics.* xplore novel physics and phenomena of nanoscale systems such as nanowires, carbon nanotubes and organic molecules. The goal of her research is to understand and exploit such phenomena that arise from quantum confinement of atoms and molecules in order to engineer new classes of electronic and electromechanical devices.

Lisa, Michael A., Ph.D., Michigan State University, 1993. *Nuclear Physics.* Experimental Nuclear Physics: Relativistic heavy ion collisions; nuclear equation of state and study of quark-gluon plasma, Collective effects, Intensity interferometry.

Mathur, Samir, Ph.D., University of Bombay, 1987. *High Energy Physics.* Theoretical High-Energy Physics: String theory, Black holes, General relativity.

Pelz, Jonathan P., Ph.D., University of California, Berkeley, 1988. Vice Chair of Graduate Studies and Research. *Condensed Matter Physics.* Experimental Condensed Matter Physics: Surface and interface science, scanning tunneling, ballistic-electron emission and atomic force microscopies Numerical modeling. Nm-resolution electronic behavior of nanostructures, wide bandgap materials, metal/dielectric interfaces and semiconductor surfaces. Surface science, scanning tunneling microscopy. Step dynamics on semiconductor surfaces. Nanoscale properties of buried wide bandgap semiconductor films and interfaces. Nanoscale properties of magnetic multilayers. Atomic scale surface reactions.

Perry, Robert J., Ph.D., University of Maryland, 1984. Vice Chair for Undergraduate Studies. *Nuclear Physics.* Theoretical Nuclear Physics: Quantum chromodynamics, Light-front field theory, Renormalization group and effective field theory.

Poirier, Michael, Ph.D., University of Chicago, 2001. *Biophysics*. Experimental Biophysics: Chromatin and chromosome structure and function. Chromatin remodeling. Mechanisms of molecular machines. Bacterial population dynamics and diversity.

Putikka, William O., Ph.D., University of Wisconsin-Madison, 1988. *Condensed Matter Physics*. Theoretical Condensed Matter Physics: High-temperature superconductivity-phenomenological and microscopic models, Two-dimensional strongly correlated electrons, Unconventional superconductivity, Spin relaxation in semiconductors, Spintronics, Semiconductor based quantum computers.

Raby, Stuart A., Ph.D., Tel Aviv University, 1976. *High Energy Physics*. Theoretical High-Energy Physics: Physics beyond the Standard Model (grand unified and supersymmetric models), Problems on the interface of particle physics and astrophysics, Understanding electroweak symmetry breaking and fermion masses, Working on the construction of realistic models of particle physics, based on 10 dimensional superstring theory.

Randeria, Mohit, Ph.D., Cornell University, 1987. *Condensed Matter Physics*. Theoretical Condensed Matter and Cold Atom Physics: High Tc superconductivity and strongly correlated electronic systems, Angle-resolved photoelectron spectroscopy, Nanoscale and inhomogeneous superconductors, Quantum gases and BCS-BEC crossover. Strongly interacting quantum gases, BEC-BCS crossover in Fermi gases, Optical lattices.

Schumacher, Douglass, Ph.D., University of Michigan, 1995. *Atomic, Molecular, & Optical Physics*. Experimental Atomic, Molecular, and Optical Physics: Ultrafast nonlinear optics. Intense field laser-matter interactions. High energy density physics. Ultrashort laser-plasma interactions. Nonlinear optics. Partical-in-cell simulation.

Sooryakumar, R., Ph.D., University of Illinois at Urbana-Champaign, 1980. *Condensed Matter Physics*. Experimental Condensed Matter Physics: Application and development of spectroscopy probes (Raman scattering, Brillouin scattering and Kerr microscopy) for probing electronic, vibrational, optical and magnetic behavior of novel materials. Magnetic and spin wave excitations and influence of current injection in hybrid micrometer and sub-micron patterned structures. Elastic excitations and guided acoustic resonances in confined geometries. Development of noninvasive techniques for elastic properties of biological tissues. Photo-induced properties of network glasses.

Trivedi, Nandini, Ph.D., Cornell University, 1987. *Condensed Matter Physics*. Theoretical Condensed Matter and Cold Atom Physics: Strongly correlated superconducting and magnetic materials, Disorder and interaction driven quantum phase transitions, Fermions and bosons in traps, Quantum Monte Carlo simulations. Fermions and bosons in optical lattices, BCS-BEC crossover, Quantum Monte Carlo simulations of cold atoms.

Van Woerkom, Linn D., Ph.D., University of Southern California, 1987. Associate Provost; Director, Honors & Scholars. *Atomic, Molecular, & Optical Physics*. Experimental Atomic, Molecular, and Optical Physics: High-intensity, ultrashort pulse laser-matter interactions. High-energy density physics. Ultrashort pulse and X-ray physics.

Walker, Terrence P., Ph.D., Indiana University, 1987. *Astrophysics*. Theoretical Cosmology and Astroparticle Physics: Neutrino astrophysics, Dark matter candidates and their detection, Big Bang nucleosynthesis.

Winer, Brian L., Ph.D., University of California, Berkeley, 1991. Chair. *Astrophysics, High Energy Physics*. Experimental High-Energy, and Cosmology and Astroparticle Physics: Testing of the Standard Model of particle physics, Detailed studies and measurements of the top quark, Development of DAQ/Trigger Electronics, Exploring the universe with high energy gamma rays, Searching for dark matter. Very-high-energy gamma-ray astronomy with FGST.

Yang, Fengyuan, Ph.D., Johns Hopkins University, 2001. *Condensed Matter Physics*. Experimental Condensed Matter Physics: Fabrication and experimental investigation of structural, electronic and magnetic properties of nanostructured materials. Metallic and oxide epitaxial films. Spintronics in semiconductor nanowires, including spin injection, spin diffusion and spin detection.

Zhong, Dongping, Ph.D., California Institute of Technology, 1999. *Biophysics*. Experimental Biophysics: Femtobiology, Biomolecular interactions, Protein dynamics.

Associate Professor

Carpenter, Linda, Ph.D., Johns Hopkins University, 2006. *High Energy Physics*. Theoretical High-Energy Physics: High-energy physics, Higgs physics and supersymmetry, LHC phenomenology, Model building, Phenomenology of weak scale physics.

Gramila, Thomas, Ph.D., Cornell University, 1990. Vice Chair of Course Coordination. *Condensed Matter Physics*. Experimental Condensed Matter Physics: Properties of electronic materials at low temperatures and high magnetic fields, Two-dimensional electron gases and Quantum Hall effects, Electron interactions and correlation effects. Disordered conductors, magnetic properties.

Gupta, Jay, Ph.D., University of California, Santa Barbara, 2002. *Condensed Matter Physics*. Experimental Condensed Matter Physics: Nanoscale studies of organic magnets and conductors. Evolution of electronic and optical properties in nanoclusters. Microscopic studies of spin-scattering in semiconductors. Atomic-scale chemistry on surfaces.

Heckler, Andrew, Ph.D., University of Washington, 1994. *Physics and other Science Education*. Physics Education Research: Cognitive origins of student difficulties in physics, Learning and transfer of abstract and concrete representations, Hierarchical structure of physics knowledge, Application of PER principles to the classroom.

Johnston-Halperin, Ezekiel, Ph.D., University of California, Santa Barbara, 2003. Director of ENCOMM. *Condensed Matter Physics*. Experimental Condensed Matter Physics: Spin in reduced dimension. Study of spin dynamics, scattering and transport in nanoscale semiconducting materials. Multifunctional magnetic materials. Development and characterization of magnetic materials with multifunctional properties (magnetization coupled to charge, strain, chemical activity, etc.) for spintronic applications. Spin injection/detection in heterostructures. Exploration of spin injection and detection in heterogenous materials such as metal/semiconductor, organic/inorganic, and molecular/bulk heterostructures.

Lafyatis, Gregory P., Ph.D., Harvard University, 1982. *Atomic, Molecular, & Optical Physics*. Experimental Atomic, Molecular, and Optical Physics: Laser physics. Trapping and cooling of atomic particles.

Assistant Professor

Boveia, Antonio, Ph.D., Univ of California, Santa Barbara, 2008. *High Energy Physics*. Study what the universe is made of and how those fundamental pieces interact with each other. Part of the ATLAS Experiment at the Large Hadron Collider (LHC).

Chowdhury, Enam, Ph.D., University of Delaware, 2004. *Atomic, Molecular, & Optical Physics*. Atomic, Molecular, and Optical Physics: Short pulse lasers. Ultra-fast dynamics of solids. Ultra-intense and high energy density laser matter.

Kural, Comert, Ph.D., University of Illinois at Urbana-Champaign, 2007. *Biophysics*. Experimental Biophysics and Computational Biology: Three-dimensional cell and tissue imaging. Dynamics of clathrin-mediated endocytosis in living organisms. Tissue morphogenesis, cell migration and signaling.

Lu, Yuan-Ming, Ph.D., Boston College, 2011. *Condensed Matter Physics*. Theoretical Condensed Matter Physics: Topological phenomena in condensed matter physics. Unconventional superconductivity. Quantum Hall effects. Frustrated magnets and spin liquids. Correlated electron materials.

Peter, Annika, Ph.D., Princeton University, 2008. *Astrophysics*. Theoretical Cosmology and Astroparticle Physics: Dark matter astrophysics, Cosmology Particle Physics, Dynamics of the Milky Way, Dwarf spheroidal galaxies, Solar system.

Valdes Aguilar, Rolando, Ph.D., University of Maryland, 2008. *Condensed Matter Physics*. Experimental Condensed Matter Physics: Terahertz spectroscopy, Strongly correlated systems, Ultrafast spectroscopy.

Emeritus

Agostini, Pierre, Ph.D., University AIX Marseille, 1967. *Atomic, Molecular, & Optical Physics*. Experimental atomic, molecular, and optical physics: muliphoton processes; strong field interaction; high harmonic generation; attosecond pulses; attophysics.

Freeman, Richard R., Ph.D., Harvard University, 1973. *Atomic, Molecular, & Optical Physics*. Experimental Atomic, Molecular, and Optical Physics: Interactions of high-powered lasers with matter. Nonlinear optics laser fusion experiments.

Ling, Ta-Yung, Ph.D., University of Wisconsin-Madison, 1971. *High Energy Physics*. Experimental high-energy physics.

Stroud, David G., Ph.D., Harvard University, 1969. *Condensed Matter Physics*. Theoretical Condensed Matter Physics: Quantum effects in Josephson junction arrays and high-Tc superconductors. Superconducting qubits. Magnetic, superconducting and optical properties of nanostructured materials. Ab initio molecular dynamics simulations of disordered media magnetic, superconducting and optical nanostructures.

Sugarbaker, Evan R., Ph.D., University of Michigan, 1976. *Nuclear Physics*. Experimental Nuclear Physics: Spin, isospin character of nucleons in nuclear matter, Neutrino detection, Relativistic heavy-ion collisions.

Professor Emeritus

Andereck, C. David, Ph.D., Rutgers University, 1980. *Atomic, Molecular, & Optical Physics*. Experimental atomic, molecular, and optical physics: high-energy density physics; high-intensity ultrashort pulse laser interactions with matter; laboratory astrophysics; nonlinear hydrodynamics.

De Lucia, Frank C., Ph.D., Duke University, 1969. *Atomic, Molecular, & Optical Physics*. Experimental atomic, molecular, and optical physics: quantum electronics, millimeter and submillimeter waves, laboratory astrophysics, upper atmospheric physics, molecular spectroscopy and collisions, chemical physics.

Kass, Richard, Ph.D., University of California, Davis, 1978. *High Energy Physics*. Experimental High-Energy Physics: Electron-positron interactions using the BABAR experiment. High energy hadron interactions using the ATLAS experiment. High-resolution energy and position detectors.

Lemberger, Thomas R., Ph.D., University of Illinois, 1978. *Condensed Matter Physics*. Experimental Condensed Matter Physics: Magnetic and electrical properties of films and crystals of conventional and high-temperature superconductors. Tunneling and transport effects in superconductors. Superconductor-to-insulator quantum transition fluctuations. Thin-film fabrication and characterization.

Patton, Bruce R., Ph.D., Cornell University, 1971. *Condensed Matter Physics*. Theoretical Condensed Matter Physics: Structure and properties of electroceramics. Grain growth in anisotropic systems. Pattern recognition and optimization.

Shigemitsu, Junko, Ph.D., Cornell University, 1978. *High Energy Physics*. Theoretical High-Energy Physics: Lattice gauge theory, Nonperturbative approaches to strong interactions, Heavy quark physics, Tests of the consistency of the Standard Model of particle physics.

Wilkins, John W., Ph.D., University of Illinois, 1963. *Condensed Matter Physics*. Theoretical Condensed Matter Physics: Molecular dyanamics, density functional theory, and quantum Monte Carlo for dynamics of microstructural transitions in metals and semiconductors and designing excitations in heterostructures.

Teaching Associate Professor

Kilcup, Gregory P., Ph.D., Harvard University, 1986. *High Energy Physics*. Theoretical High-Energy Physics: Elementary particle theory, Lattice gauge theory, Supercomputing.

DEPARTMENTAL RESEARCH SPECIALTIES AND STAFF

Theoretical

Biophysics. Bundschuh.

Condensed Matter Physics. Gruzberg, Ho, Jayaprakash, Lu, Putikka, Randeria, Stroud, Trivedi, Wilkins.

Cosmology and Astroparticle Physics. Beacom, Hirata, Peter, Walker.

High Energy Physics. Braaten, Carpenter, Kilcup, Mathur, Raby.

Nuclear Physics. Furnstahl, Heinz, Jeschonnek, Kovchegov, Perry.

Experimental

Atomic, Molecular, & Optical Physics. Agostini, Chowdhury, De Lucia, DiMauro, Freeman, Gauthier, Lafyatis, Schumacher, Van Woerkom.

Biophysics. Bockrath, Kural, Lau, Poirier, Sooryakumar, Zhong.

Condensed Matter Physics. Bockrath, Brillson, Gramila, Gupta, Hammel, Johnston-Halperin, Kawakami, Lau, Pelz, Sooryakumar, Valdes Aguilar, Yang.

Cosmology and Astroparticle Physics. Highest-energy cosmic rays and neutrinos; cosmic ray spectrum, composition, and anisotropy; radio detection of cosmic rays and neutrinos; high-energy neutrino astronomy; connecting neutrino and cosmic ray measurements with astrophysics; dark energy; very-high-energy gamma-ray astronomy with FGST. Beatty, Connolly, Honscheid, Hughes, Winer.

High Energy Physics. Boveia, Chowdhury, Durkin, Gan, Hill, Honscheid, Hughes, Kagan, Kass, Winer.

Nuclear Physics. Humanic, Lisa, Sugarbaker.

Physics Education Research. Bao, Heckler, Patton.

UNIVERSITY OF CINCINNATI

DEPARTMENT OF PHYSICS

Cincinnati, Ohio 45221-0011

http://www.artsci.uc.edu/departments/physics.html

General University Information
President: Neville Pinto
Dean of Graduate School: Marshall Montrose
University website: http://www.uc.edu
School Type: Public
Setting: Urban
Total Faculty: 6,656
Total Graduate Faculty: 1,284
Total number of Students: 44,783
Total number of Graduate Students: 10,596

Department Information
Department Chairman: Prof. Leigh Smith, Head
Department Contact: Rostislav Serota, Graduate Director
  Total full-time faculty: 28
  Total number of full-time equivalent positions: 35
  Full-Time Graduate Students: 61
  Female Full-Time Graduate Students: 20
  First-Year Graduate Students: 16
  Female First-Year Students: 6
  Total Post Doctorates: 9

Department Address
UC Physics Dept, 400 Geology/Physics
345 Clifton Court
Cincinnati, OH 45221-0011
Phone: (513) 556-0501
Fax: (513) 556-3425
E-mail: physics.grad@uc.edu
Website: http://www.artsci.uc.edu/departments/physics.html

ADMISSIONS

Admission Contact Information
Address admission inquiries to: Program Manager, Department
  of Physics, P.O. Box 210011, Cincinnati, OH 45221-0011
Phone: (513) 556-0511
E-mail: teaneyd@ucmail.uc.edu
Admissions website: https://grad.catalyst.uc.edu/apply/

Application deadlines
Fall admission:
U.S. students: September 1   *Int'l. students*: September 1

Application fee
U.S. students: $65   *Int'l. students*: $70
Review of applicants begins in February. Admissions decisions
  are rolling.

Admissions information
For Fall of 2017:
  Number of applicants: 67
  Number admitted: 12
  Number enrolled: 5

Admission requirements
Bachelor's degree requirements: Bachelor's degree in Physics
  or a related Science or Engineering discipline is required.

Minimum undergraduate GPA: 3.0 0 0 0.0 930-1380 No minimum score is determined. Results are considered along with
  other admission materials.

Subjective GRE requirements
The Subjective GRE is recommended.
  Mean Advanced GRE score range (25th–75th percentile): 760-
  810
  GRE Physics strongly recommended for international applicants

TOEFL requirements
The TOEFL exam is required for students from non-English-
  speaking countries.
  PBT score: 520
  iBT score: 68
TOEFL can be replaced by other forms of proof of English profi-
  ciency. Go to http://grad.uc.edu/admissions/Admission_
  Criteria.html for details.

Other admissions information
Undergraduate preparation assumed: Symon, Mechanics; Lorrain and Corson, Electromagnetic Fields and Waves; Kittel,
  Thermal Physics: Fermi, Thermodynamics; Anderson, Modern Physics and Quantum Mechanics.

TUITION

Tuition year 2017–18:
Tuition for in-state residents
  Full-time students: $14,468 annual
  Part-time students: $724 per credit
Tuition for out-of-state residents
  Full-time students: $26,210 annual
  Part-time students: $1,311 per credit
Includes General and Campus Life fees.
Credit hours per semester to be considered full-time: 12
Deferred tuition plan: No
Health insurance: Yes, $2,280 with $1,710 covered by grant.
Other academic fees: All graduate students taking more than six
  credits are required to have health insurance. Students who
  wish to purchase the University Health Care Plan may apply
  for grants to cover $855 per semester of the cost. The required
  ITIE fee is $368/year.
Academic term: Semester
Number of first-year students who received full tuition waivers: 14

Teaching Assistants, Research Assistants, and Fellowships
  Number of first-year
    Teaching Assistants: 14
    Fellowship students: 3
  Average stipend per academic year
    Teaching Assistant: $21,000
    Research Assistant: $21,000
    Fellowship student: $23,000

FINANCIAL AID

Application deadlines
Fall admission:
U.S. students: September 1   *Int'l. students*: September 1

Loans

Loans are available for U.S. students.

Loans are not available for international students.

GAPSFAS application required: No

FAFSA application required: No

For further information

Address financial aid inquiries to: Office of Student Financial Aid, PO Box 210125, Cincinnati, Ohio 45221-0125.

Phone: (513) 556-9171

E-mail: financeaid@uc.edu

Financial aid website: http://financialaid.uc.edu/gradstudents .html

HOUSING

Availability of on-campus housing

Single students: Yes

Married students: Yes

Childcare Assistance: No

For further information

Address housing inquiries to: 2921 Scioto Street, PO Box 210045, Cincinnati, OH 45221-0045.

Phone: (513) 556-0682

E-mail: ucgradfa@uc.edu

Housing aid website: http://www.uc.edu/uchousing/graduate_ housing.html

Table A—Faculty, Enrollments, and Degrees Granted

Research Specialty	2017–18 Faculty	Enrollment Fall 2017 Master's	Enrollment Fall 2017 Doctorate	Number of Degrees Granted 2017–18 (2013–18) Master's	Number of Degrees Granted 2017–18 (2013–18) Terminal Master's	Number of Degrees Granted 2017–18 (2013–18) Doctorate
Astrophysics	3	–	2	–(1)	1	1(2)
Chemical Physics	1	–	3	–	–	–(1)
Condensed Matter Physics	8	–	10	–	1(1)	3(26)
Engineering Physics/Science	–	–	1	–	–(2)	–
Medical, Health Physics	–	–	5	–	1(1)	1(6)
Nonlinear Dynamics and Complex Systems	1	6	19	–(27)	–(2)	1(1)
Particles and Fields	11	–	11	–	3(2)	5(21)
Physics and other Science Education	3	–	3	–(1)	1	–(1)
Total	27	6	54	–(28)	7(5)	11(66)
Full-time Grad. Stud.	–	6	54	–	–	–
First-year Grad. Stud.	–	2	14	–	–	–

GRADUATE DEGREE REQUIREMENTS

Master's: There are two options available. Both options require a one-year set of courses and attendance at colloquium and seminar. The thesis option requires graduate research resulting in a thesis. The non-thesis option requires additional coursework and a passing grade on the department's qualifying exam at the master's level.

Doctorate: Satisfactory completion of 90 semester credits of graduate level course work, including seminars and research work on thesis topic. Must pass: written qualifying examinations, oral examination covering chosen field of research, dissertation, public presentation and defense of dissertation. Residency requirement of 30 semester credits. Teaching requirement. No language requirement.

Other Degrees: Numerous interdisciplinary research opportunities exist. Recent interdisciplinary thesis research projects have been in areas such as medical physics, chemistry, or physics applied to various problems in the engineering disciplines. The Department participates in the Interdisciplinary Graduate Degree Program of the Division of Graduate Education and Research. The Program allows custom-tailoring of interdisciplinary studies to the individual student's interests.

Thesis: Thesis may be written in absentia.

SPECIAL EQUIPMENT, FACILITIES, OR PROGRAMS

A wide variety of facilities and programs are available to us, both within the department and elsewhere on campus. We have a modern research laboratory and office building that house our on-campus research activities. We have strong research ties with the Departments of Chemistry, Electrical Engineering, Chemical and Materials Engineering, and Radiology. In particle physics, work is undertaken at the national and international accelerator laboratories (SLAC, Fermilab, and KEK). Our condensed matter laboratories are well-equipped with the normal variety of ultrasensitive measurement, analytical, and sample preparation equipment. Special items include dilution refrigerators for the milli-Kelvin range, argon, and carbon dioxide lasers for Brillouin and Raman studies, and an excellent photolithographic and microelectronics laboratory.

Table B—Separately Budgeted Research Expenditures by Source of Support

Source of Support	Departmental Research	Physics-related Research Outside Department
Federal government	$1,941,468	$903,146
State/local government		
Non-profit organizations		
Business and industry		
Other	$10,000	$10,000
Total	$1,951,468	$913,146

Table C—Separately Budgeted Research Expenditures by Research Specialty

Research Specialty	No. of Grants	Expenditures ($)
Astrophysics	2	$7,670
Condensed Matter Physics	9	$258,902
Particles and Fields	13	$2,549,257
Physics and other Science Education	1	$28,783
Total	25	$2,844,612

FACULTY

Professor

Argyres, Philip C., Ph.D., Princeton University, 1989. *Astrophysics, Cosmology & String Theory, Particles and Fields, Relativity & Gravitation*. Theoretical particle physics.

Beck, Thomas, Ph.D., University of Chicago, 1987. Joint Faculty with Chemistry Department. *Biophysics, Chemical Physics, Computational Physics*. Computational chemical and biophysics.

Esposito, F. Paul, Ph.D., University of Chicago, 1971. *Astrophysics, Particles and Fields, Relativity & Gravitation*. Theoretical physics; general relativity and astrophysics.

Hanson, Margaret M., Ph.D., University of Colorado, 1995. *Astronomy, Astrophysics*. Experimental astronomy and astrophysics.

Jackson, Howard E., Ph.D., Northwestern University, 1971. *Condensed Matter Physics, Nano Science and Technology, Optics*. Experimental condensed matter physics; laser light scattering studies.

Kagan, Alexander L., Ph.D., University of Chicago, 1989. *Particles and Fields*. Theoretical particle physics.

Kinoshita, Kay, Ph.D., University of California, Berkeley, 1981. *High Energy Physics*. Experimental particle physics.

Schwartz, Alan, Ph.D., Harvard University, 1988. *High Energy Physics*. Experimental particle physics.

Sitko, Michael, Ph.D., University of Wisconsin-Madison, 1980. *Astronomy, Astrophysics*. Experimental astronomy; cosmic dust; protostellar disks; comets.

Smith, Leigh M., Ph.D., University of Illinois, 1988. *Condensed Matter Physics, Nano Science and Technology, Optics*. Experimental condensed matter physics.

Sokoloff, Michael D., Ph.D., University of California, Berkeley, 1983. *High Energy Physics*. High-energy experimental physics.

Wijewardhana, L. C. R., Ph.D., Massachusetts Institute of Technology, 1984. *Astrophysics, Cosmology & String Theory, Particles and Fields*. Theoretical particle physics.

Zupan, Jure, Ph.D., University of Ljubljana, 2002. *Astrophysics, Cosmology & String Theory, Particles and Fields*. Theoretical particle physics.

Associate Professor

Bolech, Carlos J., Ph.D., Rutgers University, 2002. *Atomic, Molecular, & Optical Physics, Computational Physics, Condensed Matter Physics*. Theoretical condensed matter physics.

Koenig, Kathleen, Ph.D., University of Cincinnati, 2004. Joint Faculty with Department of Curriculum and Instruction. *Physics and other Science Education*. Acquisition and transfer of scientific reasoning abilities; teaching and learning K-16; retention of STEM majors.

Kogan, Andrei B., Ph.D., Duke University, 2000. *Biophysics, Condensed Matter Physics, Low Temperature Physics, Nano Science and Technology*. Experimental condensed matter physics; biophysics.

Mast, David B., Ph.D., Northwestern University, 1982. *Condensed Matter Physics, Low Temperature Physics, Medical, Health Physics, Nano Science and Technology*. Experimental condensed matter physics.

Serota, Rostislav A., Ph.D., Massachusetts Institute of Technology, 1987. *Condensed Matter Physics, Nonlinear Dynamics and Complex Systems*. Theoretical condensed matter physics.

Wagner, Hans-Peter A., Ph.D., University of Regensburg, 1991. *Condensed Matter Physics, Nano Science and Technology, Optics*. Experimental condensed matter physics.

Assistant Professor

Aurisano, Adam, Ph.D., Texas A&M University, 2012. *High Energy Physics, Particles and Fields*. Experimental High Energy Physics. Neutrino Physics.

Bischoff, Colin, Ph.D., University of Chicago, 2010. *Astronomy, Astrophysics*. Astrophysics, Cosmic Microwave Background, Astronomy.

Brod, Joachim, Ph.D., University of Karlsruhe, Germany, 2009. *High Energy Physics*.

Sousa, Alexandre, Ph.D., Tufts University, 2005. *High Energy Physics*. Experimental high-energy physics; neutrino physics.

Emeritus

Endorf, Robert J., Ph.D., Carnegie Mellon University, 1971. *Physics and other Science Education*. Physics education.

Goodman, Bernard, Ph.D., University of Pennsylvania, 1955.

Johnson, Randy A., Ph.D., University of California, Berkeley, 1975. *High Energy Physics*. Experimental high-energy physics.

Kim, Young H., Ph.D., University of Florida, 1986. *Condensed Matter Physics, Nano Science and Technology*. Experimental condensed matter physics.

Ma, Michael, Ph.D., University of Illinois, 1983. *Condensed Matter Physics*. Theoretical condensed matter physics.

Meadows, Brian T., Ph.D., University of Oxford, 1966. *High Energy Physics*. Experimental high-energy physics.

Pinski, Frank J., Ph.D., Universiy of Minnesota, 1977. *Biophysics, Computational Physics, Condensed Matter Physics*. Computational Biological, Chemical and Solid State Physics.

Suranyi, Peter, Ph.D., Joint Institute for Nuclear Research, Dubna, 1964. Theoretical physics; high-energy theory; statistical mechanics.

Teaching Associate Professor

Plano Clark, Mark, Ph.D., University of North Carolina-Chapel Hill, 1988. *Atomic, Molecular, & Optical Physics*.

Teaching Assistant Professor

Maries, Alexandru, Ph.D., University of Pittsburgh, 2013. *Physics and other Science Education*. Physics Education Research.

DEPARTMENTAL RESEARCH SPECIALTIES AND STAFF

Theoretical

Astrophysics. Dark matter; baryogenesis; brane-world cosmology; black holes. Argyres, Esposito, Suranyi, Wijewardhana, Zupan.

Computational Physics. Computational studies of equilibrium and non-equilibrium properties of quantum and classical condensed matter systems, chemical and biological systems. Beck, Bolech.

Condensed Matter Physics. Strongly correlated systems; quantum disordered systems; nanophysics; mesoscopic physics and open quantum systems; superconductivity; non-equilibrium physics and transport; spintronics; quantum phase transitions; quantum chaos; critical phenomena; competing phases. Topological insulators and superconductors; dynamical response properties of metal electrons; quantum and classical fluids; quasi-one-dimensional conductors: phase transitions and critical phenomena; gas dynamics; high-Tc and unconventional superconductivity; metal-insulator transitions; random magnets; heavy fermions; oxides; quantum impurities and dots; nanoscale superconductors; cold atoms and optical lattices. Bolech, Goodman, Ma, Serota.

Cosmology & String Theory. Dark matter; baryogenesis; brane-world cosmology; supersymmetric gauge theories; supergravity and string/M-theory. Argyres, Esposito, Suranyi, Wijewardhana, Zupan.

Particles and Fields. Flavor physics; electroweak symmetry breaking and fermion mass generation; symmetry and constituent models of hadrons and leptons; grand unified theories; string interaction phenomenology and dynamics; nonperturbative methods in field theory; lattice field theories; phase transitions in quantum field theories; conformal field theories; supersymmetric gauge theories. Argyres, Esposito, Kagan, Suranyi, Wijewardhana, Zupan.

Relativity & Gravitation. Black holes; supergravity; quantum gravity. Argyres, Esposito, Suranyi, Wijewardhana, Zupan.

Experimental

Astronomy. Near-IR spectroscopy of massive young stars; star formation and galactic structure; structure and evolution of young planet-building protostellar disks, inner disk dynamics, and planet-disk interactions; small solar system bodies, solar system formation and evolution. Hanson, Sitko.

Condensed Matter Physics. Semiconductor Physics, Single Electron Transistors, Spins, Semiconductor Nanowires, Two dimensional materials, Ultrafast Physics. Jackson, Kim, Kogan, Mast, Smith, Wagner.

High Energy Physics. At Fermilab: Studying muon neutrino disappearance and muon to electron neutrino oscillations over short distances with the MiniBooNE and MicroBooNE detectors, and over long distances with the NOvA and MINOS+ experiments; developing the Liquid Argon Time Projection Chamber technology for future neutrino experiments. In China: using the Daya Bay Nuclear Reactor complex to measure the final angle in the neutrino mass mixing matrix. At SLAC: heavy quark physics, especially CP violations in B-meson decays using the Babar detector, and charm meson decays. At KEK (Japan): studies of CP violation, mixing, and rare processes in B-meson and D-meson decays, using the Belle detector. At CERN: studies of heavy quark physics including CP violation, mixing, and rare processes in hadrons with b- and c-quarks, using the LHCb detector. Johnson, Kinoshita, Meadows, Schwartz, Sokoloff, Sousa.

Interdisciplinary Research. Econophysics; quantitative finance; cognitive psychology; biological systems. Serota.

Low Temperature Physics. Superconductors; electronic correlation phenomena in semiconductor quantum dots, non-equilibrium Kondo effect, photon-assisted transport, dynamic conductance spectroscopy, coherent manipulation of spin-based quantum systems; Luttinger liquids. Kogan, Mast.

Medical, Health Physics. Development of microminiature microwave and surface acoustic wave devices for biochemical sensors; investigation of membrane structures using near-field scanning microwave microscopy and ultrasonic acoustics. Mast

Nano Science and Technology. Semiconductor Nanowires, Nanoparticle, Two dimensional materials, biosensors, carbon nanotubes. Jackson, Kogan, Mast, Smith, Wagner.

Optics. Laser light scattering including Raman, Brillouin, and photoluminescence; femtosecond and picosecond spectroscopy; electronic and optical properties of low-dimensional semiconductors including quantum dots, nanowires, nanowire heterostructures, and plasmonic nanostructures; electro-optical phenomena in nanostructured materials; study of linear and nonlinear optical properties in organic/semiconductor nanostructures and waveguides: two-photon absorption; nonlinear refractive index; phase coherent photorefractive effect in quantum wells; optical coherence imaging; near-field microwave scanning of HTS materials, composite ceramics, layered semiconductors, and biological samples; phase coherent photorefractive effect in quantum wells; optical coherence imaging; near-field microwave scanning of HTS materials, composite ceramics, layered semiconductors, and biological samples; near field spectroscopy of single wall carbon nanotubes; far-infrared (FIR) studies of metal-insulator transition in highly correlated layered systems, FIR charge dynamics in superconducting cuprates, and FIR absorption by small metal particles. Jackson, Kim, Smith, Wagner.

Physics and other Science Education. Improving introductory physics courses with the implementation of active learning and inquiry; improving the training of graduate teaching assistants; professional development programs for primary, middle school, and high school teachers; collaboration with other science departments, the College of Education, Criminal Justice, and Human Services and local school districts to improve K-16 science teaching. Endorf, Koenig, Maries, Plano Clark.

View additional information about this department at www.gradschoolshopper.com. Check out the "Why Choose Us?" section, find out more about the department's culture and get links to social media networks.

UNIVERSITY OF DAYTON

DEPARTMENT OF ELECTRO-OPTICS AND PHOTONICS

Dayton, Ohio 45469-2951

http://www.udayton.edu/engineering/electrooptics_grad/index.php

General University Information
President: Eric Spina
Dean of Graduate School: Paul Vanderburgh
University website: http://www.udayton.edu/
School Type: Private
Setting: Urban
Total Faculty: 937
Total number of Students: 10,909
Total number of Graduate Students: 3,502

Department Information
Department Chairman: Dr. Partha P. Banerjee, PhD, Chair
Department Contact: Partha P. Banerjee, PhD, Professor and Chair of the Department of Electro-Optics
  Total full-time faculty: 5
  Total number of full-time equivalent positions: 13
  Full-Time Graduate Students: 56
  Female Full-Time Graduate Students: 16
  First-Year Graduate Students: 19
  Female First-Year Students: 7
  Total Post Doctorates: 1

Department Address
300 College Park
Dayton, OH 45469-2951
Phone: (937) 229-2797
Fax: (937) 229-2097
E-mail: pbanerjee1@udayton.edu
Website: http://www.udayton.edu/engineering/electrooptics_grad/index.php

ADMISSIONS

Admission Contact Information
Address admission inquiries to: Graduate Admissions Office, University of Dayton, 300 College Park, Dayton, OH 45469
Phone: (937) 229-2797
E-mail: mbrophy1@udayton.edu
Admissions website: http://www.udayton.edu/gradschool/

Application deadlines
Fall admission:
U.S. students: September 1   *Int'l. students*: September 1

Application fee
Int'l. students: $50
Paper applications are no longer accepted for domestic or international students.

Admissions information
For Fall of 2017:
  Number of applicants: 53
  Number admitted: 43
  Number enrolled: 17

Admission requirements
Bachelor's degree requirements: Bachelor's degree in Physics, Optics, or Engineering is required.
Minimum undergraduate GPA: 3.25

GRE requirements
The GRE is not required.

Subjective GRE requirements
The Subjective GRE is not required.

TOEFL requirements
The TOEFL exam is required for students from non-English-speaking countries.
PBT score: 550
iBT score: 80

Other admissions information
Additional requirements: Students who have degrees in physics or electrical engineering are encouraged to apply. Students from other scientific or engineering fields may be required to take a limited amount of undergraduate work.
Undergraduate preparation assumed: Major in physics or in electrical engineering is assumed.

TUITION

Tuition year 2016–17:
  Full-time students: $890 per credit
  Part-time students: $970 per credit
Tuition year 2016–17 Engineering Master per credit hour $890. Engineering Ph.D. per credit hour $970.
Credit hours per semester to be considered full-time: 6
Deferred tuition plan: No
Health insurance: Available
Academic term: Semester

Teaching Assistants, Research Assistants, and Fellowships
  Number of first-year
    Teaching Assistants: 7
    Research Assistants: 17
  Average stipend per academic year
    Teaching Assistant: $14,000
    Research Assistant: $21,000

FINANCIAL AID

Loans
Loans are available for U.S. students.
Loans are not available for international students.
GAPSFAS application required: Yes
FAFSA application required: Yes

For further information
Address financial aid inquiries to: Office of Scholarships and Financial Aid, University of Dayton, 300 College Park, CPC572, Dayton, OH 45469-2951.
Financial aid website: http://www.udayton.edu/live/financial_aid/

HOUSING

Availability of on-campus housing
  Single students: Yes
  Married students: No

For further information

Address housing inquiries to: Housing Services, Gosiger Hall 212, University of Dayton, Dayton, OH 45469-0950.
Housing aid website: http://housing.udayton.edu/

Table A—Faculty, Enrollments, and Degrees Granted

Research Specialty	2017–18 Faculty	Enrollment Fall 2017		Number of Degrees Granted 2016–17 (2016–17)		
		Master's	Doctorate	Master's	Terminal Master's	Doctorate
Optics	5	26	30	5	–	7
Total	10	26	30	5	–	7
Full-time Grad. Stud.	–	56	56	–	–	–
First-year Grad. Stud.	–	12	5	–	–	–

GRADUATE DEGREE REQUIREMENTS

Master's: M.S. in electro-optics: 24 semester hours of courses (including 18 semester hours of core courses, 3 semester hours of elective, and three 1-semester-hour EO laboratory courses) and six semester hours of thesis in the case of thesis option. A non-thesis option is available in which the thesis is replaced by six semester hours of approved electives.

Doctorate: Ph.D. in electro-optics: A minimum of 90 semester hours beyond the bachelor's degree is required, including 12 semester hours of 600-level EO courses, 30 semester hours of dissertation, and 6 semester hours of mathematics. Comprehensive examination and residency are also required. All entering Ph.D. students are expected to have completed an M.S. in electro-optics or its equivalent.

Other Degrees: A Ph.D. in electrical engineering is available to students who would like to emphasize electro-optics in their dissertation research and meet all other electrical engineering requirements.

Thesis: Thesis may be written in absentia.

SPECIAL EQUIPMENT, FACILITIES, OR PROGRAMS

Electro-optics facilities include a total of 25 research laboratories dedicated to ellipsometry, optical processing, optical metrology, pattern recognition, nonlinear optics, spectroscopy, and nanophotonics fabrication and characterization. A wide range of optical and optical mounting equipment is available, including a variety of pulsed lasers and continuous wave lasers. The LADAR and Optical Communications Institute is a federally funded center that is part of the EO Program. The university is located within minutes of the Wright-Patterson Air Force Base, where opportunities are often available to EO students to work at one of the many government laboratories at this facility, including a graduate co-op program.

Table B—Separately Budgeted Research Expenditures by Source of Support

Source of Support	Departmental Research	Physics-related Research Outside Department
Federal government	$2,000,000	
State/local government		
Non-profit organizations		
Business and industry	$500,000	
Other		
Total	$2,500,000	

FACULTY

Professor

Asari, Vijayan K., Ph.D., Indian Institute of Technology, 1994. Professor of ECE. Image processing, computer vision, pattern recognition, machine learning.

Banerjee, Partha, Ph.D., University of Iowa, 1983. FInstP, Fellow, OSA, SPIE. EO Director; Professor, EO and ECE. Metamaterials, holography, nonlinear optics, photorefractives, acoustooptics.

Chatterjee, Monish, Ph.D., University of Iowa, 1985. Professor of ECE. Holds a joint position in EOP. Nonlinear dynamics and chaos, wave propagation, and acousto-optics.

Evans, Dean, Ph.D., University of Georgia, 2000. Graduate faculty, EO. Research Leader, Hardened Materials and Processing Research Team, AFRL Materials Directorate. Photorefractives, liquid crystals, hybrids, ferroelectric nanoparticles.

Guha, Shekhar, Ph.D., University of Pittsburgh, 1981. Graduate faculty, EO. Project leader, IR optical materials, AFRL. Nonlinear optics, IR materials, lasers.

Hardie, Russell C., Ph.D., University of Delaware, 1992. Professor of ECE. Holds a joint position in EOP. Signal/image processing; pattern recognition; remote sensing.

Haus, Joseph W., Ph.D., Catholic University of America, 1975. Fellow, OSA, SPIE, APS. Professor of EO, LOCI Director. Nonlinear optics, quantum optics, metamaterials.

Peterson, Rita, Ph.D., University of Central Florida, 2000. Graduate faculty, EO. Senior Research Physicist at AFRL Sensors Directorate. Nonlinear optics and lasers.

Rabb, David, Ph.D., Ohio State, 2008. Senior Electronics Engineer, Ladar Technology Branch (RYMM). LIDAR, synthetic aperture systems, holography.

Sarangan, Andrew, Ph.D., University of Waterloo, 1997. Professor and Associate Director of EO. Photodetectors, nanofabrication, thin films, integrated optics, semiconductor lasers.

Vorontsov, Mikhail A., Ph.D., Lomonosov Moscow State University, 1989. Fellow, OSA, SPIE, ARL. LADAR Endowed Chair Professor of EO. Imaging thru' turbulence, Laser beam control, non-linear spatio-temporal dynamics.

Zhan, Qiwen, Ph.D., University of Minnesota, 2002. Professor of EO; Managing Director, UD-Fraunhofer joint research center. Physical optics, nanoscale imaging with applications in metrology, nodestructive evaluation and biophotonics.

Assistant Professor

Agha, Imad, Ph.D., Cornell University, 2009. Assistant Professor of Physics. Holds a joint position in EOP. Quantum optics, quantum communication, nonlinear optics, nanophotonics.

Chong, Andy, Ph.D., Cornell University, 2008. Assistant Professor of Physics. Holds a joint position in EOP. Nonlinear optics, ultrafast fiber lasers and amplifiers, arbitrary optical wave packet generation.

Zhao, Chenglong, Ph.D., Peking University, 2011. Professor in Physics Holds a joint position in EOP. Nanophotonics, plasmonics, metamaterials, graphene, plasmofluidics, optical trapping, imaging and sensing.

Emeritus

Yaney, Perry, Ph.D., University of Cincinnati, 1963. Fellow, APS. Laser spectroscopic optical probe techniques including linear and nonlinear Raman scattering.

Research Faculty

Deng, Cong, Ph.D., University of Dayton, 2005. Research Scientist, EO. LIDAR system, fiber and waveguide, adaptive and active optics, THz and imaging systems.

Dierking, Matt, Ph.D., University of Dayton, 2009. Fellow, AFRL. Graduate faculty, EO. Technical Director, Ladar Technology Branch, AFRL Sensors Dir. Ladar, waveforms & modulation, coherent signal/image processing, synthetic apertures.

Weyrauch, Thomas, Ph.D., Technische Hochschule Darmstadt, 1997. Senior Research Scientist, EO. Light propagation through atmosphere: distortion charac-terization, mitigation; beam control and coherent combining.

Other

McManamon, Paul, Ph.D., Ohio State University, 1977. Fellow IEEE, SPIE, OSA, MSS, AFRL, AIAA. Graduate faculty, EO. Laser radar, electro-optical countermeasure systems, optical phased-array beam steering.

Watson, Edward A., Ph.D., University of Rochester, 1991. Fellow, OSA, SPIE, AFRL. Research scientist, UDRI. Laser radar, optical phased array technology, statistical optics, low light level imaging & pattern recognition, speckle characterization of objects in optical and millimeter wave domains.

DEPARTMENTAL RESEARCH SPECIALTIES AND STAFF

Theoretical

Optics. Image processing; beam propagation; nonlinear optical phenomena. Agha, Banerjee, Chatterjee, Chong, Evans, Guha, Hardie, Haus, McManamon, Peterson, Sarangan, Vorontsov, Watson, Weyrauch, Zhan, Zhao.

Experimental

Optics. Adaptive optics; ellipsometry; guides wave/fiber optics; spectroscopy; nonlinear optics; nanophotonics (materials, fabrication, and characterization); optical design; ultrafast lasers and pulse dynamics; optical metrology; optical processing/digital holography; optical systems and devices; optoelectronic materials. Agha, Banerjee, Chatterjee, Chong, Deng, Dierking, Evans, Guha, Hardie, Haus, McManamon, Peterson, Sarangan, Vorontsov, Weyrauch, Yaney, Zhan, Zhao.

View additional information about this department at www.gradschoolshopper.com. Check out the "Why Choose Us?" section, find out more about the department's culture and get links to social media networks.

OKLAHOMA STATE UNIVERSITY

DEPARTMENT OF PHYSICS

Stillwater, Oklahoma 74078-3072
http://www.physics.okstate.edu

General University Information
President: V. Burns Hargis
Dean of Graduate School: Sheryl Tucker
University website: http://www.okstate.edu
School Type: Public
Setting: Rural
Total Faculty: 1,500
Total Graduate Faculty: 1,100
Total number of Students: 24,274
Total number of Graduate Students: 3,963

Department Information
Department Chairman: Prof. David N. McIlroy, Head
Department Contact: Susan Cantrell, Administrative Associate
   Total full-time faculty: 20
   Total number of full-time equivalent positions: 20
   Full-Time Graduate Students: 39
   Female Full-Time Graduate Students: 5
   First-Year Graduate Students: 10
   Female First-Year Students: 2
   Total Post Doctorates: 3

Department Address
145 Physical Sciences II
Stillwater, OK 74078-3072
Phone: (405) 744-5796
Fax: (405) 744-6811
E-mail: physics@okstate.edu
Website: http://www.physics.okstate.edu

ADMISSIONS

Admission Contact Information
Address admission inquiries to: Oklahoma State University, Department of Physics, ATTN: Graduate Coordinator, Stillwater, OK 74078
Phone: (405) 744-5796
E-mail: physics.grad.coordinator@okstate.edu
Admissions website: http://www.physics.okstate.edu

Application deadlines
Fall admission:
U.S. students: February 1   *Int'l. students*: February 1

Application fee
U.S. students: $50   *Int'l. students*: $75

Admissions information
For Fall of 2018:
   Number of applicants: 94
   Number admitted: 25
   Number enrolled: 14

Admission requirements
Bachelor's degree requirements: Bachelor's degree in Physics (or closely related field) required.
Minimum undergraduate GPA: 3.0

GRE requirements
The GRE is required.
   There is no minimum score requirement.

Subjective GRE requirements
The Subjective GRE is not required.
The Physics Subject Test is strongly recommended, although not required.

TOEFL requirements
The TOEFL exam is required for students from non-English-speaking countries.
   iBT score: 90
IELTS 7.0. Also, iBT Speaking Section score should be at least 19.

Other admissions information
Additional requirements: Three Letters of Reference.
   All college transcripts.
   One to two page Personal Statement.
   Up to date CV.

TUITION

Tuition year 2018–19:
Tuition for in-state residents
   Full-time students: $187 per credit
Tuition for out-of-state residents
   Full-time students: $765 per credit
GTAs and GRAs are eligible for full waiver of all eligible tuition, up to the nominal limits of degree program (e.g. 30 credit-hours for the M.S.; up to 72 credit-hours for the Ph.D.).
Credit hours per semester to be considered full-time: 6
Health insurance: Available at the cost of $180 per year.
Other academic fees: Approx. $170/crdt-hr.
Academic term: Semester
Number of first-year students who received full tuition waivers: 11

Teaching Assistants, Research Assistants, and Fellowships
Number of first-year
   Teaching Assistants: 10
   Research Assistants: 1
   Fellowship students: 2
Average stipend per academic year
   Teaching Assistant: $16,200
   Research Assistant: $18,000
Typically, we recommend admission only if we intend financial support; thus, nearly all students are supported.

FINANCIAL AID

Application deadlines
Fall admission:
U.S. students: February 1   *Int'l. students*: February 1

Loans
Loans are available for U.S. students.
Loans are not available for international students.
GAPSFAS application required: Yes
FAFSA application required: No

For further information

Address financial aid inquiries to: Oklahoma State University, Graduate College, Stillwater, OK 74078.
Phone: (405) 744-6368
E-mail: gradi@okstate.edu
Financial aid website: http://gradcollege.okstate.edu

HOUSING

Availability of on-campus housing
Single students: Yes
Married students: Yes
Childcare Assistance: Yes

For further information
Address housing inquiries to: Oklahoma State University, Residence Life Department, Stillwater, OK 74078.
Phone: (405) 744-5592
E-mail: reslife@okstate.edu
Housing aid website: http://reslife.okstate.edu

Table A—Faculty, Enrollments, and Degrees Granted

Research Specialty	2017–18 Faculty	Enrollment Spring 2018 Master's	Enrollment Spring 2018 Doctorate	Number of Degrees Granted 2017–18 (2013–18) Master's	Number of Degrees Granted 2017–18 (2013–18) Terminal Master's	Number of Degrees Granted 2017–18 (2013–18) Doctorate
Astrophysics	1	–	–	–	–	–
Atomic, Molecular, & Optical Physics	2	1	4	1(2)	–	1(7)
Biophysics	2	–	3	–	–	1(4)
Condensed Matter Physics	3	–	6	–	–	1(1)
High Energy Physics	5	–	7	–(1)	–	–(5)
Optics	2	–	5	–	–	–(2)
Physics Education	1	–	–	–	–	–(1)
Radiation Physics and Dosimetry	3	3	10	4(12)	–	3(11)
Statistical & Thermal Physics	1	–	–	–	–	–
Total	20	4	35	5(17)	–	6(31)
Full-time Grad. Stud.	–	4	35	–	–	–
First-year Grad. Stud.	–	1	6	–	–	–

GRADUATE DEGREE REQUIREMENTS

Master's: Twenty-four semester hours of approved physics courses plus 6 hours thesis. Option in optics and photonics. No language requirement. Last 8 semester hours and 21 total semester hours must be completed in residence. At least a "B" average is required. In addition, a "Professional" M.S. in Physics is offered as a 32 credit hour (Report) plan.

Doctorate: Seventy-two hours of approved courses (including thesis research) beyond Bachelor's degree, or sixty hours beyond M.S. Minimum 30 semester hours and one of last two years in residence. Qualifying exam and dissertation defense. No language requirement. At least a "B" average is required.

SPECIAL EQUIPMENT, FACILITIES, OR PROGRAMS

Materials Growth and Characterization Laboratory; Rubidium and sodium BEC labs; Solid State NMR; femtosecond spectroscopy; optical absorption and fluorescence spectroscopy, Radiation Dosimetry Laboratory, FTIR, Powder XRD Core Facility. Mendenhall Observatory (0.6 m RC robotic telescope); 3D Modeling lab, GPU Cluster and access to high performance computing facilities, high-energy physics electronics lab. The types of experimental techniques in progress include the following: photon correlation, Brillouin scattering, whispering gallery modes, nonlinear optics. The instrumentation includes a variety of solid-state, liquid, and gas lasers, nonlinear optical crystals autocorrelators, streak cameras, FTIR, optical multichannel analyzers, boxcar integrators, and signal averagers, along with the standard monochromators, spectrum analyzers, detectors, and cryogenic equipment required for conventional spectroscopy. U.S. ATLAS member institution in high energy physics. Physics, along with Electrical Engineering, participates in the multidisciplinary Ph.D. Photonics programs.

Table B—Separately Budgeted Research Expenditures by Source of Support

Source of Support	Departmental Research	Physics-related Research Outside Department
Federal government	$464,849	
State/local government	$275,081	
Non-profit organizations		
Business and industry		
Other	$216,422	
Total	$956,352	

Table C—Separately Budgeted Research Expenditures by Research Specialty

Research Specialty	No. of Grants	Expenditures ($)
Biophysics	3	$150,947
Condensed Matter Physics	1	$ 68,242
High Energy Physics	5	$275,326
Medical, Health Physics	2	$ 90,000
Nuclear Physics	5	$224,032
Optics	3	$147,805
Total	19	$956,352

FACULTY

Professor

Babu, K. S., Ph.D., University of Hawaii, 1986. *High Energy Physics*. Theoretical high energy physics; Grand unification model building, fermion masses and mixing; neutrino physics.

Bandy, Donna K., Ph.D., Drexel, 1984. *Theoretical Physics*. Theoretical laser physics; instabilities; nonlinear behavior; optical devices.

McIlroy, David N., Ph.D., University of Rhode Island, 1993. Nanostructures and Condensed Matter. Electronic, optical, and growth properties of one-dimensional nanostructures.

Mintmire, John W., Ph.D., University of Florida, 1980. *Computational Physics*. Computational materials physics, electronic structure theory, nanostructured materials.

Nandi, Satyanarayan, Ph.D., University of Chicago, 1975. *High Energy Physics*. Theoretical high-energy physics, grand unification, supersymmetry, extra dimensions, physics at LHC.

Perk, Jacques H. H., Ph.D., Leiden, 1979. *Theoretical Physics*. Theoretical physics; exactly solvable models in statistical mechanics.

Rizatdinova, Flera, Ph.D., Moscow State University, 1994. *High Energy Physics*. Experimental high energy physics at the LHC. Studies of top quark and Higgs physics, searches for physics beyond the Standard Model. Development of precision tracking detectors for high-luminosity LHC upgrade.

Rosenberger, Albert T., Ph.D., University of Illinois, 1979. *Optics*. Experimental and theoretical optical physics; microresonator optics and plasmonics.

Xie, Aihua, Ph.D., Carnegie Mellon University, 1987. *Biophysics*. Biophysics; structural dynamics of proteins; molecular mechanism of receptor activation in signal transduction; biomedical application of lasers.

Associate Professor

Benton, Eric, Ph.D., Dublin, 2004. *Medical, Health Physics*. Ionizing radiation dosimetry; radiation protection; effects of radiation on living organism.

Khanov, Alexander, Ph.D., University of Rochester, 2004. *High Energy Physics*. Experimental high energy physics at the LHC. Studies of top quark and Higgs physics, searches for physics beyond the Standard Model. Development of heavy flavor tagging algorithms (for b-quark and top-quark jets) and boosted object reconstruction.

Liu, Yingmei, Ph.D., University of Pittsburg, 2004. *Atomic, Molecular, & Optical Physics, Quantum Foundations*. Atom, molecular, and optical physics. Exploring the physics of antiferromagnetic spinor Bose-Einstein condensates with and without optical lattices, and their applications in quantum information science.

Shull, Peter O., Ph.D., Rice University, 1982. *Astronomy, Astrophysics*. Supernova remnants, exoplanets, near-Earth asteroids.

Summy, Gilford, Ph.D., Griffith (Australia), 1995. *Atomic, Molecular, & Optical Physics*. BEC; quantum chaos; atom optics.

Zhou, Donghua, Ph.D., College of William and Mary, 2003. *Biophysics*. Biophysics, protein structures by solution and solid-state NMR, membrane proteins, MD simulation, cancer drug development.

Assistant Professor

Borunda, Mario, Ph.D., Texas A&M, 2008. *Computational Physics*. Developing theoretical and computational techniques to model and analyze the transport properties of atomic, molecular, mesoscopic, and macroscopic systems.

Cho, Jongmin, Ph.D., University of Texas MD Anderson Cancer Center, 2014. *Medical, Health Physics*. Use of positron emission tomography (PET) for treatment verification and the use of gold nanoparticles (GNPs) and hybrid GNPs to enhance the effectiveness of proton radiotherapy.

Haley, Joseph, Ph.D., Princeton University, 2009. *Particles and Fields*. Experimentally particle physics using the ATLAS detector at CERN. Searching for new fundamental particles, such as vector-like quarks, and improving the identification of boosted top quarks and heavy bosons.

Emeritus

Ackerson, Bruce J., Ph.D., University of Colorado, 1976. *Fluids, Rheology, Physics and other Science Education*. Dynamic light scattering, colloids; critical phenomena in fluids. Physics education.

Agarwal, Girish, Ph.D., University of Rochester, 1969. *Quantum Foundations*. Quantum optics; nonlinear optics; quantum information science and foundations of quantum mechanics; surface optics-nanophotonics.

Dixon, G., Ph.D., University of Georgia, 1967. Physics.

Harmon, H. James, Ph.D., Purdue University, 1974. Biophysics; high-resolution high-speed optical spectroscopy; spectroscopy determination of enzyme kinetic intermediates; design of solid-state chemical sensors; photochemical reaction of porphyrins.

Hauenstein, Robert J., Ph.D., California Institute of Technology, 1987. Experimental semiconductor physics, molecular beam epitaxial growth; heterostructures.

Lange, J., Ph.D., Pennsylvania State University, 1964. Solid-state physics; acoustics.

Martin, J., Ph.D., Iowa State University, 1967. Physics.

McKeever, Stephen W. S., Ph.D., University College of N. Wales (Bangor), 1975. *Solid State Physics*. Experimental solid-state physics; thermoluminescence; thermally stimulated polarization currents; radiation dosimetry; semiconductors.

Westhaus, P., Ph.D., Washington University, 1966. Theoretical physics.

Wicksted, James P., Ph.D., City University of New York, 1983. Experimental solid-state physics; Raman and Brillouin scattering, nonlinear-optics, rare-earth doped glasses, nanomaterials.

Wilson, T., Ph.D., University of Florida, 1966. Theoretical physics; electronic structure of point defects.

Research Assistant Professor

Sholom, Sergey, Ph.D., Kiev State University, 1991. *Medical, Health Physics, Solid State Physics*. Dosimetry of external exposure, retrospective dosimetry, accidental dosimetry, EPR-dosimetry, TL-dosimetry, OSL emergency dosimetry.

Adjunct Professor

Ahmad, Salahuddin, Ph.D., University of Victoria, B.C., 1981. Medical Physics.

Akselrod, M., Ph.D., Urals State Technical University, 1983. *Condensed Matter Physics, Medical, Health Physics*. Solid-state physics, radiation dosimetry, fluorescent nuclear track detectors.

Chen, W., Ph.D., University of Oregon, 1988. Physics.

Lucas, A., Ph.D., Oklahoma State University, 2003. *Medical, Health Physics, Nuclear Physics*. Physics.

Perk, H., Ph.D., Stony Brook University, 1973. Theoretical physics.

Yukihara, Eduardo, Ph.D., University of São Paulo, 2001. *Medical, Health Physics, Solid State Physics*. Experimental solid state, radiation dosimetry, medical physics, thermoluminescence, optically stimulated luminescence.

Adjunct Associate Professor

Zheng, Yuanshui, Ph.D., North Carolina State University, 2001. *Medical, Health Physics*. Medical Physics.

Adjunct Assistant Professor

Lee, Taekyu, Ph.D., Purdue University, 2005. *Medical, Health Physics*. Medical Physics.

Peakheart, David, Ph.D., Oklahoma State University, 1991. *Medical, Health Physics*. Medical Physics.

DEPARTMENTAL RESEARCH SPECIALTIES AND STAFF

Theoretical

Atomic, Molecular, & Optical Physics. Density functional theory and electronic structure. Exploring the physics of spin systems in ultracold atoms. Borunda, Mintmire, Rosenberger.

Condensed Matter Physics. Electronic structure of disordered systems; density functional theory, low-dimensional materials, dielectric response theory; optical properties of defects; vibronics; semiconductor molecular beam epitaxy; transport in semiconductors and graphene; quantum Hall effect; application of quantum optimal control theory in solid-sate semiconductor systems; solid-state quantum information. Borunda, Hauenstein, McIlroy, Mintmire.

High Energy Physics. Grand unification; supersymmetry; extra dimension; physics at LHC; fermion masses and mixings; neutrinos. The elementary particle theory group is focused on proposing tests for the theories within and beyond the standard model as they look at unification of forces within the context of supersymmetry, compactification of extra dimensions and string theory. Babu, Nandi.

Optics. Nonlinear behavior of laser systems; modeling of optical instabilities; quantum optics; nonlinear optics. Bandy, Rosenberger.

Quantum Foundations. Decoherence; quantum optics of semiconductor dots; integrated structures and nanomechanical quantum devices; application and development of methods for electronic structure theory such as time-dependent density functional theory, exact diagonalization, and Monte Carlo techniques; semiclassical connections between quantum and classical systems, with an interest in chaotic behavior. Borunda.

Statistical & Thermal Physics. Ising model, stochastic processes, exactly solvable models; low-dimensional systems, quasicrystals. H. Perk, Jacques Perk.

Experimental

Astrophysics. Supernova remnants; exoplanets; near-Earth asteroids. Shull.

Atomic, Molecular, & Optical Physics. Exploring the physics of antiferromagnetic spinor Bose-Einstein condensates with and without optical lattices, and their applications in quantum information science. Liu, Rosenberger, Summy.

Biophysics. Laser effects on biological materials; high-resolution high-speed optical spectroscopy; enzyme kinetics; photochemical reactions of porphyrins; protein dynamics; protein structure; membrane proteins; amyloid proteins; solid-state NMR. Chen, Harmon, Xie, Zhou.

Chemical Physics. Photocatalysis; photoenergy conversion; monolayer surfaces; solid-state catalysts; photoreductive chemistry. Harmon.

Condensed Matter Physics. Optical, electrical, thermal, acoustical, structural, and mechanical properties of solids; laser materials; ESR; energy transfer; epitaxial growth, nanoparticles, and nanotubes. Harmon, Hauenstein, McIlroy, McKeever, Wicksted, Yukihara.

Fluids, Rheology. Light scattering; phase transitions in colloids; dynamics of flow systems. Ackerson.

High Energy Physics. The experimental high-energy physics group performs research with the ATLAS Experiment at CERN's Large Hadron Collider. The group is involved in a wide range of physics analyses, from measurements of the top quark to searches for new physics beyond the Standard Model. Members of the group and involved in improving the identifications of jets that originate from b-quarks (b-tagging) and the identification of highly boosted top quarks and heavy bosons. The group is also involved in the research and development for the ATLAS pixel system. Members of the group developed the optical links and online monitoring software for the recent IBL upgrade of the new ATLAS pixel detector and the group will take a leading role in the development and construction of the electrical services for the ATLAS pixel system upgrades for the HL-LHC. Haley, Khanov, Rizatdinova.

Optics. Coherent effects, nonlinear optics, microresonators and plasmonics. Ackerson, Rosenberger, Wicksted.

Quantum Foundations. Quantum magnetometry and entanglement. Liu.

Radiation Physics, Medical Physics, and Dosimetry. Application and development of detectors and techniques for radiation dosimetry, including optically stimulated luminescence, thermoluminescence, plastic nuclear track detectors, gamma spectroscopy, tissue equivalent proportional counters, and the newly developed fluorescent nuclear track detectors. Applications include medical dosimetry (diagnostic radiology and radiation therapy using photons, electrons, protons, heavy charged particles), accident dosimetry, space dosimetry, etc. Research also includes basic luminescent processes in insulators and the role of cosmic radiation in lightning initiation. Akselrod, Benton, Cho, Lucas, McKeever, Yukihara.

View additional information about this department at www.gradschoolshopper.com. Check out the "Why Choose Us?" section, find out more about the department's culture and get links to social media networks.

UNIVERSITY OF OKLAHOMA

HOMER L. DODGE DEPARTMENT OF PHYSICS AND ASTRONOMY

Norman, Oklahoma 73019
http://www.nhn.ou.edu/

General University Information
President: James L. Gallogly
Dean of Graduate School: Randall Hewes
University website: http://www.ou.edu/
School Type: Public
Setting: Urban
Total Faculty: 1,596
Total Graduate Faculty: 1,463
Total number of Students: 31,250
Total number of Graduate Students: 6,309

Department Information
Department Chairman: Prof. Philip Gutierrez, Chair
Department Contact: Joyce Russell, Student Services
  Total full-time faculty: 25
  Total number of full-time equivalent positions: 25
  Full-Time Graduate Students: 85
  Female Full-Time Graduate Students: 8
  First-Year Graduate Students: 17
  Female First-Year Students: 4
  Total Post Doctorates: 11

Department Address
440 West Brooks St
Norman, OK 73019
Phone: (405) 325-3961
Fax: (405) 325-7557
E-mail: grad@nhn.ou.edu
Website: http://www.nhn.ou.edu/

ADMISSIONS

Admission Contact Information
Address admission inquiries to: Graduate Recruiting and Selection Committee, Homer L. Dodge Department of Physics and Astronomy, University of Oklahoma, 440 West Brooks St., Norman, OK 73019
Phone: (405) 325-3961
E-mail: grad@nhn.ou.edu
Admissions website: http://www.nhn.ou.edu/graduate-students/apply_OU_PhyAst

Application deadlines
Fall admission:
U.S. students: February 1   *Int'l. students*: February 1

Application fee
There is no application fee required.
YOU CAN APPLY IN TWO DIFFERENT WAYS. OPTION 1 (FEE BASED). Use the official online application and pay the application fee ($50 for US applicants and $100 for international applicants). OPTION 2 (NO FEE). Send all of your materials directly to our department. This is the no-fee application option. (See the Department's web page for Prospective Students for instructions.)

Admissions information
For Fall of 2018:
  Number of applicants: 160
  Number admitted: 20
  Number enrolled: 18

Admission requirements
Bachelor's degree requirements: Bachelor's degree in Physics and/or astronomy is required.
Minimum undergraduate GPA: 3.0
  Mean Advanced GRE score range (25th–75th percentile): 310-330
  Although not strictly required, we ask for the GRE because it is an objective and standardized way for us to compare you with other applicants; it forms part of an overall picture of you. If you do not have a GRE score, this will put you at a disadvantage compared with other applicants.

Subjective GRE requirements
The Subjective GRE is recommended.
  Mean Advanced GRE score range (25th–75th percentile): 480-700
  Although not strictly required, we ask for the physics subject GRE because it is an objective and standardized way for us to compare you with other applicants; it forms part of an overall picture of you. If you do not have a physics GRE score, this will put you at a disadvantage compared with other applicants.

TOEFL requirements
The TOEFL exam is required for students from non-English-speaking countries.
  PBT score: 600
  iBT score: 100
Our department has a stated minimum TOEFL of 600/250/100 for paper/computer/IB or IELTS of 7.0. There is some flexibility for candidates who are exceptional in other areas. However, applicants who do not meet the Graduate College's minimum scores of 550/213/79 or 6.5 will not be considered.

Other admissions information
Undergraduate preparation assumed: Marion, Classical Dynamics of Particles and Systems; French, Vibrations and Waves; Griffiths, Introduction to Electrodynamics; Saxon, Elementary Quantum Mechanics; Schroeder, Thermal Physics.

TUITION

Tuition year 2017–2018:
Tuition for in-state residents
  Full-time students: $203.6 per credit
Tuition for out-of-state residents
  Full-time students: $791.2 per credit
Our students are typically supported on teaching and research assistantships that include a tuition waiver for up to 90 hours.
Credit hours per semester to be considered full-time: 9
Deferred tuition plan: No A student health plan is provided as part of TA and RA support.
Other academic fees: $2500/semester.
Academic term: Semester
Number of first-year students who received full tuition waivers: 20

Teaching Assistants, Research Assistants, and Fellowships

Number of first-year
Teaching Assistants: 20
Average stipend per academic year
Teaching Assistant: $21,600
Research Assistant: $21,600
Fellowship student: $26,000

FINANCIAL AID

Loans

Loans are available for U.S. students.
Loans are not available for international students.
GAPSFAS application required: No
FAFSA application required: No

For further information

Phone: (405) 325-4521
Financial aid website: http://www.ou.edu/financialaid.html

HOUSING

Availability of on-campus housing

Single students: Yes
Married students: Yes

For further information

Address housing inquiries to: Housing Office, 1406 Asp Ave., Norman, OK 73019.
Phone: (405) 325-2511
E-mail: housinginfo@ou.edu
Housing aid website: http://www.ou.edu/housingandfood.html

Table A—Faculty, Enrollments, and Degrees Granted

Research Specialty	2018–19 Faculty	Enrollment Fall 2017 Master's	Enrollment Fall 2017 Doctorate	Number of Degrees Granted 2017–18 (2012–18) Master's	Number of Degrees Granted 2017–18 (2012–18) Terminal Master's	Number of Degrees Granted 2017–18 (2012–18) Doctorate
Astrophysics	7	–	15	6(19)	–(7)	–(10)
Atomic, Molecular, & Optical Physics	4	1	15	2(8)	1(1)	2(23)
Condensed Matter Physics	5	3	19	1(15)	–(4)	–(8)
Engineering Physics/Science	10	–	–	2(9)	–(1)	1(1)
High Energy Physics	7	–	22	3(22)	–	–(17)
Physics and other Science Education	2	–	–	–	–	–
Total	25	4	85	14(73)	1(13)	3(59)
Full-time Grad. Stud.	–	4	85	–	–	–
First-year Grad. Stud.	–	–	17	–	–	–

GRADUATE DEGREE REQUIREMENTS

Master's: A student must complete 30 hours of coursework with a thesis or 32 hours of coursework without a thesis taken in accordance with the general rules of the graduate college. The allowable minimum number of credits in physics and astronomy is 18 hours, 6 hours of which must be at the 5000 level or above.

Doctorate: The student must complete a minimum of 36 hours of coursework at the 5000 level or above, excluding the credit hours granted for preparation of the thesis or dissertation describing original research. These hours include 21 hours of specific required courses. Another 54 hours of graduate coursework is required as appropriate for the student's field of research specialization, including research hours. The qualifying examination is offered semiannually and is usually taken at the end of the first year of graduate study. The general examination for the Ph.D. degree consists of a written report and an oral examination, including a presentation of a topic related to the field of specialization and a probing of the student's knowledge of general principles, and is taken before the student begins dissertation research. The Ph.D. in Physics may include an emphasis in astronomy or astrophysics.

Other Degrees: An advanced degree (M.S.) in Engineering Physics is also offered. Specialization areas include astrophysics; atomic, molecular, and optical physics; condensed-matter physics; high-energy physics; and others.

Thesis: Thesis and dissertation may be written in absentia.

SPECIAL EQUIPMENT, FACILITIES, OR PROGRAMS

The Homer L. Dodge Department of Physics and Astronomy has access to many well-equipped facilities for experimental research in atomic, molecular, and optical physics; condensed-matter physics; and materials characterization. These include UHV chambers for laser cooling and trapping, laser spectrometers, molecular beam epitaxy systems, a clean room for nanofabrication and characterization, thin-film deposition and characterization facilities, optical and electron beam lithography, atomic force microscopes, scanning tunneling microscopes, infrared spectrometers, systems for transport and magneto-optic measurements at high magnetic field and low temperature, and an independent facility for scanning and transmission electron microscopy.

Our experimental research programs regularly make use of external facilities such as the National High Magnetic Field Laboratory, Los Alamos National Laboratory, the ATLAS detector for the Large Hadron Collider at CERN, and Oak Ridge National Laboratories. OU is a Tier 2 Data Collection Center for ATLAS.

OU is a permanent member (1/16 share) of the Astrophysical Research Consortium, which includes the 3.5-m and 0.5-m telescopes at Apache Point Observatory. In addition, our astrophysics group routinely has access to Kitt Peak Observatory, the Very Large Array, the MDM Observatory, Subaru, Keck, Gemini, and the Cerro Tololo Inter-American observatories, as well as data from the Hubble Space Telescope, the Spitzer Space Telescope, and the Chandra X-ray telescope.

An instrument and machine shop within the Department with three full-time machinists also supports the experimental research efforts.

Theoretical work is supported by departmental computing resources and the OU Supercomputing Center for Education and Research. For astronomical research, AIPS, IRAF, and IDL software are available.

Table B—Separately Budgeted Research Expenditures by Source of Support

Source of Support	Departmental Research	Physics-related Research Outside Department
Federal government	$3,000,159.5	
State/local government	$379,377	
Non-profit organizations	$174,137	
Business and industry		
Other		
Total	$3,553,673.5	

Table C—Separately Budgeted Research Expenditures by Research Specialty

Research Specialty	No. of Grants	Expenditures ($)
Astrophysics	34	$1,165,870.47
Atomic, Molecular, & Optical Physics	6	$409,324.5
Condensed Matter Physics	12	$755,554.04
High Energy Physics	12	$669,410.49
Total	64	$3,000,159.5

FACULTY

Professor

Abbott, Braden, Ph.D., Purdue University, 1994. *High Energy Physics, Particles and Fields.* Experimental high-energy physics; CERN-ATLAS experiment.

Baer, Howard, Ph.D., University of Wisconsin, 1984. *Cosmology & String Theory, Particles and Fields, Theoretical Physics.* High-energy theory; supersymmetry; dark matter; LHC physics.

Baron, Edward A., Ph.D., Stony Brook University, 1985. *Astrophysics, Computational Physics.* Radiative transfer; stellar evolution; supernovae; numerical astrophysics; parallel algorithms.

Blume, Doerte, Ph.D., Georg-August University, 1998. *Atomic, Molecular, & Optical Physics, Chemical Physics, Computational Physics, Low Temperature Physics, Theoretical Physics.* atomic and molecular physics; few-body physics; ultracold atoms; chemical physics; quantum liquids and quantum gases; Monte Carlo techniques; explicitly correlated Gaussians; development of new algorithms.

Gutierrez, Phillip, Ph.D., University of California, Riverside, 1983. *High Energy Physics, Particles and Fields.* Experimental high-energy physics; CERN-ATLAS experiment.

Kao, Chung, Ph.D., University of Texas, Austin, 1990. *Cosmology & String Theory, Particles and Fields, Theoretical Physics.* Particle theory; electroweak symmetry breaking; supersymmetry and unification; CP violation; dark matter; extra dimensions.

Leighly, Karen, Ph.D., Montana State University, 1991. *Astronomy, Astrophysics.* Active Galactic Nuclei (AGN); spectral synthesis.

Mullen, Kieran, Ph.D., University of Michigan, 1989. *Condensed Matter Physics, Low Temperature Physics, Solid State Physics, Statistical & Thermal Physics, Theoretical Physics.* Theoretical solid-state physics.

Santos, Michael, Ph.D., Princeton University, 1992. *Applied Physics, Condensed Matter Physics, Engineering Physics/Science, Materials Science, Metallurgy, Nano Science and Technology, Solid State Physics.* Experimental semiconductor and surface physics; MBE growth of narrow gap systems.

Strauss, Michael, Ph.D., University of California, Los Angeles, 1988. *High Energy Physics, Particles and Fields.* Experimental high-energy physics; CERN-ATLAS experiment.

Associate Professor

Abraham, Eric, Ph.D., Rice University, 1996. *Atomic, Molecular, & Optical Physics, Chemical Physics, Low Temperature Physics, Optics.* Experimental atomic, molecular, and optical physics: ultracold atoms and molecules; ultracold collisions; atomic clocks; quantum degenerate gases.

Bumm, Lloyd A., Ph.D., Northwestern University, 1991. *Applied Physics, Condensed Matter Physics, Engineering Physics/Science, Materials Science, Metallurgy, Nano Science and Technology, Surface Physics.* Experimental condensed-matter physics; nanophysics; surface physics and chemistry; self-assembly; scanning tunneling microscopy; surface spectroscopy; molecular plasmonics; development of novel instrumentation.

Dai, Xinyu, Ph.D., Pennsylvania State University, 2004. *Astronomy, Astrophysics.* Observational cosmology: gravitational lensing; galaxy clusters; cosmic voids; extragalactic planets; high-energy astrophysics; X-ray astronomy; AGNs; gamma-ray bursts.

Kilic, Mukremin, Ph.D., University of Texas, Austin, 2006. *Astronomy, Astrophysics.* Observational astronomy; supernovae Ia progenitors; white dwarfs; merger systems; gravitational waves; planets; debris disks; galactic cosmochronology.

Marino, Alberto, Ph.D., University of Rochester, 2006. *Atomic, Molecular, & Optical Physics, Optics, Quantum Foundations.* Quantum optics; atomic physics; quantum information; quantum metrology.

Mason, Bruce A., Ph.D., University of Maryland, 1985. *Physics and other Science Education.* Educational digital libraries; technology for physics education; faculty and teacher development.

Sellers, Ian, Ph.D., University of Sheffield, 2004. *Condensed Matter Physics, Energy Sources & Environment, Engineering Physics/Science, Nano Science and Technology, Solid State Physics.* Next-generation photovoltaics; optical and optoelectronic spectroscopy of semiconductor quantum dots; magneto-photoluminescence; solar cell physics.

Uchoa, Bruno, Ph.D., State University of Campinas, 2004. *Condensed Matter Physics.* Quantum critical systems; Dirac materials; Chern insulators; low-dimensional systems; unconventional quasi-particles; strongly correlated systems.

Wisniewski, John P., Ph.D., University of Toledo, 2005. *Astronomy.* Circumstellar disks; extrasolar planets; astronomical polarimetry.

Assistant Professor

Kaib, Nathan, Ph.D., University of Washington, 2010. *Astronomy, Astrophysics, Computational Physics, Mechanics, Planetary Science.* Extrasolar planets; small bodies of the solar system (comets & asteroids); solar system dynamics; dynamics of binary star systems.

Munshi, Ferah, Ph.D., University of Washington, 2013. *Astronomy, Astrophysics.* cosmological simulations, galaxy formation and evolution, dwarf galaxies, dark matter halos.

Schwettmann, Arne, Ph.D., The University of Oklahoma, 2012. *Atomic, Molecular, & Optical Physics, Computational Physics, Low Temperature Physics, Optics.* Experimental atomic, molecular, and optical physics; ultracold atomic gases; Bose-Einstein condensates; cold collisions; matter-wave quantum optics; laser cooling and trapping.

Sinha, Kuver, Ph.D., Rutgers, The State University of New Jersey, 2008. *Cosmology & String Theory, High Energy Physics, Particles and Fields, Theoretical Physics.* Early universe cosmology, string phenomenology, dark matter, physics beyond the Standard Model, collider physics.

Stupak III, John, Ph.D., Stony Brook University, 2012. *High Energy Physics, Particles and Fields.* Experimental high-energy physics; CERN-ATLAS experiment.

White, Daniel R., Ph.D., Ohio State University, 2016. *Physics and other Science Education.*

Professor Emeritus

Branch, David, Ph.D., University of Maryland, 1969. Spectroscopic astrophysics; supernovae.

Cowan, John J., Ph.D., University of Maryland, 1976. Stellar evolution and nucleosynthesis; supernovae; cosmology.

Doezema, Ryan E., Ph.D., University of Maryland, 1971. Experimental solid-state physics; 2D electron systems in semiconductors; superconductivity.

Furneaux, John E., Ph.D., University of California, Berkeley, 1979. *Atomic, Molecular, & Optical Physics, Optics.* Precision molecular spectroscopy.

Henry, Richard C., Ph.D., University of Michigan, 1983. *Astrophysics.* Chemical evolution of galaxies; chemical abundances in nebulae; evolution of intermediate mass stars.

Kantowski, Ronald, Ph.D., University of Texas, Austin, 1966. *Relativity & Gravitation.* Gravitational lens theory.

Milton, Kimball, Ph.D., Harvard University, 1971. *High Energy Physics, Particles and Fields, Theoretical Physics.* High-energy theory, particularly the development of nonperturbative methods to be applied to quantum chromodynamics and other field theories; physics of the quantum vacuum.

Morrison, Michael, Ph.D., Rice University, 1976. Theoretical atomic and molecular physics, particularly electron and positron collisions and near-threshold excitations.

Parker, Gregory, Ph.D., Brigham Young University, 1976. *Atomic, Molecular, & Optical Physics, Chemical Physics, Computational Physics, Theoretical Physics.* Theoretical molecular physics specializing in rearrangement collisions.

Romanishin, William, Ph.D., University of Arizona, 1980. Extragalactic astronomy; clusters of galaxies; active galactic nuclei.

Ryan, Stewart, Ph.D., University of Michigan, 1971. Applied physics; materials characterization.

Skubic, Patrick, Ph.D., University of Michigan, 1977. *High Energy Physics, Particles and Fields.* Experimental high-energy physics; CERN-ATLAS experiment.

Watson, Deborah K., Ph.D., Harvard University, 1977. *Atomic, Molecular, & Optical Physics, Theoretical Physics.* Theoretical atomic and molecular physics; many-body systems; group theory methods; Bose-Einstein condensates; ultracold Fermi systems.

Adjunct Professor

Beasley, William, Ph.D., University of Texas, Dallas, 1974. Meteorology.

Crompton, Robert, Ph.D., University of Adelaide, 1954. Electron and ion diffusion.

MacGorman, Donald, Ph.D., Rice University, 1978. Atmospheric electricity.

Snow, Joel, Ph.D., Yale University, 1983.

DEPARTMENTAL RESEARCH SPECIALTIES AND STAFF

Theoretical

Astronomy. Cosmology; extragalactic astronomy; nucleosynthesis; stellar atmospheres; stellar evolution; supernovae; gravitational lensing; active galactic nuclei. Baron, Kaib, Leighly, Munshi.

Atomic, Molecular, & Optical Physics. Atomic and molecular collisions; ultracold Fermi systems; coherent control of bimolecular collisions; dimensional perturbation theory; electron molecule collision; molecular bosonic gases; optical lattices; computational physics; conical intersections. Blume, Parker, Watson.

Condensed Matter Physics. Low dimensional quantum systems, Dirac materials, graphene, carbon nanotubes, strongly correlated materials, topological matter. Mullen, Uchoa.

High Energy Physics. Quantum field theory; particle physics phenomenology; general relativity; collider physics; supersymmetry; Casimir effect; cosmology; dark matter. Baer, Kantowski, Kao, Milton, Sinha.

Experimental

Astronomy. Binary and variable stars; extragalactic astronomy; extragalactic H regions; supernovae; white dwarfs; gravitational lensing; active galactic nuclei; star formation; circumstellar disks. Dai, Kilic, Leighly, Wisniewski.

Atomic, Molecular, & Optical Physics. atom-based sensing; atomic and molecular scattering; Bose-Einstein condensation; cooling and trapping; hybrid quantum systems; laser spectroscopy; multi-photon ionization; non-linear optics; reactive scattering; quantum optics. Abraham, Marino, Schwettmann.

Condensed Matter Physics. Molecular beam epitaxy; narrow-gap semiconductors; scanning probe microscopy (AFM & STM); electron microscopy (SEM & TEM); nanofabrication; surface physics; molecular plasmonics; photovoltaics; quantum cascade lasers; magneto-optics; topological insulators. Bumm, Santos, Sellers.

High Energy Physics. Experimental investigation of the fundamental particles and interactions, and searches for new particles and interactions, using the ATLAS detector at the CERN LHC. Abbott, Gutierrez, Skubic, Strauss, Stupak III.

UNIVERSITY OF TULSA

PHYS. & ENG. PHYS.

Tulsa, Oklahoma 74104

http://engineering.utulsa.edu/academics/physics-and-engineering-physics/

General University Information
President: Gerard Clancy
Dean of Graduate School: Janet A. Haggerty
University website: http://www.utulsa.edu/
School Type: Private
Setting: Urban
Total Faculty: 340
Total number of Students: 4,597
Total number of Graduate Students: 830

Department Information
Department Chairman: Prof. George P. Miller, Chair
Department Contact: George P. Miller, Kilter Professor & Chair
  Total full-time faculty: 10
  Total number of full-time equivalent positions: 10
  Full-Time Graduate Students: 14
  Female Full-Time Graduate Students: 2
  First-Year Graduate Students: 4
  Female First-Year Students: 2
  Total Post Doctorates: 1

Department Address
800 S. Tucker Dr.
Tulsa, OK 74104
Phone: (918) 631-3029
E-mail: physics@utulsa.edu
Website: http://engineering.utulsa.edu/academics/physics-and-engineering-physics/

ADMISSIONS

Admission Contact Information
Address admission inquiries to: Graduate School, The University of Tulsa, 800 South Tucker Drive, 201 Lofton Hall, Tulsa OK 74104
Phone: (918) 631 2336
E-mail: grad@utulsa.edu
Admissions website: http://graduate.utulsa.edu

Application deadlines
Fall admission:
U.S. students: February 4   *Int'l. students*: February 4

Application fee
U.S. students: $55   *Int'l. students*: $55
Application deadline is the preferred application date and not a hard deadline. If you are a University of Tulsa graduate the application fee is waived.

Admissions information
For Fall of 2017:
  Number of applicants: 62
  Number admitted: 20
  Number enrolled: 4

Admission requirements
Bachelor's degree requirements: BS in physics or engineering physics.
Minimum undergraduate GPA: 3.0

GRE requirements
The GRE is required.
  Mean GRE score range (25th–75th percentile): 50

Subjective GRE requirements
The Subjective GRE is not required.

TOEFL requirements
The TOEFL exam is required for students from non-English-speaking countries.
  PBT score: 550
  iBT score: 80

Other admissions information
Additional requirements: Letters of recommendation, undergraduate transcript, personal statement.
Undergraduate preparation assumed: Introduction to Electrodynamics, Introduction to Quantum Mechanics, Griffiths; Classical Mechanics, Taylor; Essential Mathematical Methods for the Physics Sciences, Riley & Hobson.

TUITION

Tuition year 2018–19:
  Full-time students: $1,235 per credit
  Part-time students: $1,235 per credit
Credit hours per semester to be considered full-time: 9
Health insurance: Available at the cost of $1632 per year.
Other academic fees: One time Graduate student service fee, $100. Student Association Fee, $108, Community Fee $175/semester. International Student Service Fee $180/semester.
Academic term: Semester
Number of first-year students who received full tuition waivers: 4

Teaching Assistants, Research Assistants, and Fellowships
Number of first-year
  Teaching Assistants: 4
Average stipend per academic year
  Teaching Assistant: $13,908
  Research Assistant: $18,000
  Fellowship student: $16,000
In addition to the stipend, all full-time assistantships cover the cost of tuition and health insurance.

FINANCIAL AID

Application deadlines
Fall admission:
U.S. students: January 15   *Int'l. students*: January 15
Spring admission:
U.S. students: January 15   *Int'l. students*: January 15

Loans
Loans are available for U.S. students.
Loans are not available for international students.
GAPSFAS application required: No
FAFSA application required: Yes

For further information

Address financial aid inquiries to: Office of Student Financial Services, Collins Hall, The University of Tulsa, 800 South Tucker Drive, Tulsa, OK 74104.
Phone: (918) 631 2526
E-mail: fined@utulsa.edu
Financial aid website: http://admission.utulsa.edu/financial-aid/

HOUSING

Availability of on-campus housing

Single students: Yes
Married students: Yes

For further information

Address housing inquiries to: Housing & Dining, Fisher Hall, The University of Tulsa, 800 South Tucker Drive, Tulsa, OK 74104.
Phone: (918) 631 2516
E-mail: jane-langston@utulsa.edu
Housing aid website: http://utulsa.edu/campus-life/housing-dining

Table A—Faculty, Enrollments, and Degrees Granted

Research Specialty	2017–18 Faculty	Enrollment Fall 2017		Number of Degrees Granted 2017–18 (2013–17)		
		Master's	Doctorate	Master's	Terminal Master's	Doctorate
Astrophysics	1	–	–	–	–	–
Atomic, Molecular, & Optical Physics	2	1	2	–	–(5)	–
Condensed Matter Physics	1	–	3	–	–(6)	–(2)
Engineering Physics/Science	1	2	–	–	–(2)	–
Materials Science, Metallurgy	–	–	–	–	–	–
Nano Science and Technology	2	–	5	–	1(2)	1(1)
Plasma and Fusion	–	–	–	–(2)	–	1(1)
Relativity & Gravitation	1	–	–	–	–	–
Total	10	–	–	–	1(13)	1(4)
Full-time Grad. Stud.	–	2	10	–	–	–
First-year Grad. Stud.	–	2	2	–	–	–

GRADUATE DEGREE REQUIREMENTS

Master's: Physics: Thirty credit hours required including thesis. Must maintain B grade point average. Engineering Physics: Thirty credit hours required including thesis. Minimum of 4 core physics courses and 2 engineering courses. Must maintain B grade point average.

Doctorate: A total of 72 credit hours including the core physics courses and a minimum of 24 credit hours towards their dissertation. To be admitted to Ph.D candidacy requires a) having a 3.0 GPA, b) passing the qualifying exam, c) forming a research advisory committee, d) successfully defending their dissertation proposal. The final requirement is the completion of a satisfactory written dissertations and its successful presentation and defense.

SPECIAL EQUIPMENT, FACILITIES, OR PROGRAMS

Research facilities include a laser/optics labs with a variety of state-of-the-art equipment such as a diode-seeded alexandrite ring, YAG-pumped dye, and NIR tunable lasers, Nanotechnology labs with a NMR analyzer, a nuclear quadrupole spectrometer, X-ray diffractometer and E-beam and deposition systems. The computational Materials Science, Astrophysics, and Plasma research groups have access to a 1600-core Tandy supercomputer. Total

FACULTY

Professor

Miller, George P., Ph.D., University of Waikato, 1988. *Applied Physics, Atomic, Molecular, & Optical Physics, Engineering Physics/Science, Plasma and Fusion.* Application of Laser Cavity Ringdown Spectroscopy for Atomic and Molecular Spectrometry, Environmental Emission sensors, Fundamental Properties of Low Temperature Plasmas.

Wang, Sanwu, Ph.D., University of Newcastle, 1999. *Computational Physics, Condensed Matter Physics, Nano Science and Technology, Solid State Physics.* Theoretical/Computational Materials Science, Nanoscience and Nanotechnology, Condensed Matter Theory, First –Principles Quantum-Mechanical Computations, Atomic-Scale Dynamics Simulations.

Associate Professor

Grigoriev, Alexei, Ph.D., St. Petersburg University, 2001. *Condensed Matter Physics, Materials Science, Metallurgy, Nano Science and Technology.* Experimental studies of Ferroelectric and Piezoelectric Materials, Multifunctional Materials, Thin films, Superlattices, X-Ray Microdiffraction, Time Resolved X-Ray Scattering, Thin Film Growth.

Hari, Parameswar, Ph.D., University of Utah, 1995. *Condensed Matter Physics, Nano Science and Technology, Solid State Physics.* Experimental studies of Inorganic Solar Cell Materials, Organic and Plastic Photovoltaics, Nuclear Quadruple Resonance, Conductivity and Mobility of Thin Film Semiconductors, Nuclear Magnetic Resonance, Nano Materials, Photodarkening and Photo-Structural Changes in Chalcogenide Glassy Materials, Carbon Nanotube Composites.

Holmstrom, Scott A., Ph.D., Australian National University, 1996. Associate Vice President for Research, Health, and Safety. *Optics.* Experimental Optics, Evanescent Field Spectroscopy, Trace Gas Detection, Collective Excitations in Optical Waveguides.

Assistant Professor

Noble, Scott, Ph.D., University of Texas at Austin, 2003. *Astrophysics, Plasma and Fusion, Relativity & Gravitation.* Computational Astrophysics and Plasma Physics, Accretion Disks, Black Holes and Compact Objects, General Relativity, High-energy Astrophysics.

Zhu, Piefen, Ph.D., Lehigh University, 2014. *Materials Science, Metallurgy, Nano Science and Technology, Optics.* Nanomaterial synthesis and characterization, computational electromagnetic, photonics and electronic materials, optoelectronic devices, semiconductor physics for addressing renewable energy and energy efficiency technologies.

Visiting Assistant Professor

Theiling, Mark, Ph.D., Clemson University, 2009. *Astrophysics.* High energy and nuclear astrophysics.

Zhu, Hongyang, Ph.D., Texas Tech University, 2010. *Condensed Matter Physics, Engineering Physics/Science, Materials Science, Metallurgy.* High-pressure condensed matter, nanofunctional materials.

DEPARTMENTAL RESEARCH SPECIALTIES AND STAFF

Theoretical

Astrophysics. Computational Astrophysics and Plasma Physics, Accretion Disks, Black Holes and Compact Objects, High-energy Astrophysics. Noble.

Condensed Matter Physics. Theoretical/Computational Nanoscience and Nanotechnology, Condensed Matter Theory, First –Principles Quantum-Mechanical Computations, Atomic-Scale Dynamics Simulations. Wang.

Materials Science, Metallurgy. Theoretical/Computational Materials Science. Wang, Piefen Zhu.

Nano Science and Technology. Theoretical/Computational Nanoscience and Nanotechnology. Hari, Wang, Piefen Zhu.

Relativity & Gravitation. General Relativity,cosmological inflation model building. Noble.

Experimental

Applied Physics. Remote Sensing and Modeling of Atmospheric Pollution, Multiphase Flow Instrumentation, Artificial Lift Technology, Environmental Monitors and Sensors. Miller.

Atomic, Molecular, & Optical Physics. Application and of Laser Cavity Ringdown Spectroscopy for Atomic and Molecular Spectrometry. Holmstrom, Miller.

Nano Science and Technology. Nano Materials, Photodarkening Carbon Nanotube Composites. Grigoriev, Hari, Piefen Zhu.

Optics. Holmstrom, Miller, Piefen Zhu.

Plasma and Fusion. Miller.

Solid State Physics. Photo-Structural Changes in Chalcogenide Glassy Materials, Experimental studies of Inorganic Solar Cell Materials, Organic and Plastic Photovoltaics, Conductivity and Mobility of Thin Film Semiconductors. Grigoriev, Hari.

View additional information about this department at www.gradschoolshopper.com. Check out the "Why Choose Us?" section, find out more about the department's culture and get links to social media networks.

OREGON STATE UNIVERSITY

DEPARTMENT OF PHYSICS

Corvallis, Oregon 97331-6507
http://www.physics.oregonstate.edu

General University Information
President: Edward J. Ray
Dean of Graduate School: Stephanie Bernell (Interim)
University website: http://oregonstate.edu/
School Type: Public
Setting: Rural
Total Faculty: 3,691
Total Graduate Faculty: 1,685
Total number of Students: 31,904
Total number of Graduate Students: 5,027

Department Information
Department Chairman: Prof. Heidi Schellman, Head
Department Contact: Kelly Carter, Graduate Coordinator
   Total full-time faculty: 17
   Total number of full-time equivalent positions: 17
   Full-Time Graduate Students: 45
   Female Full-Time Graduate Students: 10
   First-Year Graduate Students: 6
   Female First-Year Students: 1
   Total Post Doctorates: 2

Department Address
301 Weniger Hall
Oregon State University
Corvallis, OR 97331-6507
Phone: (541) 737-1674
E-mail: kelly.carter@oregonstate.edu
Website: http://www.physics.oregonstate.edu

ADMISSIONS

Admission Contact Information
Address admission inquiries to: Department of Physics, Oregon
   State University, 301 Weniger Hall, Corvallis, OR 97331
Phone: (541) 737-1674
E-mail: gradinfo@physics.orst.edu
Admissions website: http://physics.oregonstate.edu/

Application deadlines
Fall admission:
U.S. students: January 1   *Int'l. students*: January 1

Application fee
U.S. students: $75   *Int'l. students*: $85

Admissions information
For Fall of 2018:
   Number of applicants: 123
   Number admitted: 33
   Number enrolled: 11

Admission requirements
Bachelor's degree requirements: A bachelor's degree is required.
Minimum undergraduate GPA: 3.0

GRE requirements
The GRE is recommended but not required.
No minimum score is set.

Subjective GRE requirements
The Subjective GRE is recommended.
Advanced GRE is recommended, but not required.

TOEFL requirements
The TOEFL exam is required for students from non-English-
   speaking countries.
   PBT score: 550
   iBT score: 80
Minimum TOEFL-paper = 600 and TOEFL-iBT = 100 for assistantship eligibility.

Other admissions information
Undergraduate preparation assumed: Halliday and Resnick,
   Fundamentals of Physics; Krane, Modern Physics; Boas,
   Mathematical Methods in the Physical Sciences; Marion,
   Classical Dynamics of Particles and Systems; Brophy, Basic
   Electronics for Scientists; Griffiths, Introduction to Electrody-
   namics; Liboff, Quantum Physics; Hecht, Optics; and Kittel
   and Kroemer, Thermal Physics.

TUITION

Tuition year 2018–19:
Tuition for in-state residents
   Full-time students: $4,185 per quarter
Tuition for out-of-state residents
   Full-time students: $7,929 per quarter
See the Graduate Catalog, https://catalog.oregonstate.edu/
Credit hours per semester to be considered full-time: 9
Deferred tuition plan: Yes
Health insurance: Yes, $1968.00.
Other academic fees: $592/term; $1,968/annual.
Academic term: Quarter
Number of first-year students who received full tuition waivers: 11

Teaching Assistants, Research Assistants, and Fellowships
   Number of first-year
      Teaching Assistants: 11
   Average stipend per academic year
      Teaching Assistant: $19,215
      Research Assistant: $19,215

FINANCIAL AID

Application deadlines
Fall admission:
U.S. students: February 28

Loans
Loans are available for U.S. students.
Loans are not available for international students.
GAPSFAS application required: No
FAFSA application required: No

For further information
Address financial aid inquiries to: Office of Financial Aid and
   Scholarships, 218 Kerr Administration Building, Corvallis,
   OR 97331-2120.
Phone: (541) 737-2241

E-mail: financial.aid@oregonstate.edu
Financial aid website: http://financialaid.oregonstate.edu/

HOUSING

Availability of on-campus housing
Single students: Yes
Married students: Yes
Childcare Assistance: No

For further information
Address housing inquiries to: University Housing and Dining Services, Oregon State University, 102 Buxton Hall, Corvallis, OR 97331-1317.
Phone: (541) 737-4711
Housing aid website: http://oregonstate.edu/uhds

Table A—Faculty, Enrollments, and Degrees Granted

Research Specialty	2016–17 Faculty	Enrollment Fall 2017		Number of Degrees Granted 2017–18 (2012–17)		
		Master's	Doctorate	Master's	Terminal Master's	Doctorate
Astrophysics	1	–	1	–	–	2
Atomic, Molecular, & Optical Physics	4	–	9	–(2)	2	1(3)
Biophysics	2	–	4	–(3)	1	1
Computational Physics	4	1	–	–	–(4)	–(1)
Condensed Matter Physics	3	–	7	1(4)	–	1(11)
High Energy Physics	1	–	3	–	–	–
Materials Science, Metallurgy	1	–	4	1(1)	–	–(1)
Particles and Fields	1	–	–	–	–	–
Physics and other Science Education	2	–	4	2(1)	–	–
Non-specialized	–	–	5	–	–	–(1)
Total	19	1	37	4(11)	3(4)	5(17)
Full-time Grad. Stud.	–	1	37	–	–	–
First-year Grad. Stud.	–	1	5	–	–	–

GRADUATE DEGREE REQUIREMENTS

Master's: Forty-five (45) term hours of credit, with a minimum 3.0 grade point average and no grades below C on the program of study. Each student may choose a minor, approximately 2/3 of the credit in the major and the remaining 1/3 in a minor, which can be in Physics or another department. Thesis is optional. Completion of a project is required if the non-thesis option is chosen. Completion of a minimum of 24 credits (Thesis option) or 30 credits (Project option) from the Physics and specialty courses chosen by the department. Satisfactory performance is also required in a two-hour oral examination on the major and minor subjects.

Doctorate: Broadly viewed, the requirements for the PhD degree are satisfactory completion of minimum course requirements, advancement to candidacy, and completion of a research thesis. The program must contain at least 108 graduate credits with a minimum 3.0 grade point average and no grades below C on the program of study and consist of, at a minimum, 50% graduate stand-alone courses. After admission into the doctoral program, a minimum of one full-time academic year (at least 36 graduate credits) should be devoted to the preparation of the thesis. All PhD candidates are required to take 27 credits from the 9 core courses in the Physics Department and a minimum of 12 credits of advanced courses. A coherent set of courses may be chosen from courses in the Physics

Department or other departments as appropriate. Advancement to PhD candidacy requires satisfactory performance on written and oral comprehensive examinations. Each candidate for the PhD degree must submit a thesis embodying the results of research and have an oral defense of the thesis.
Thesis: Thesis may be written in absentia.

SPECIAL EQUIPMENT, FACILITIES, OR PROGRAMS

OSU has several core facilities for materials research. MASC (Materials Synthesis and Characterization) is a hub that operates a class-100 clean room with multiple thin-film deposition and advanced characterization and lithography capabilities. The OSU Electron Microscopy Facility operates several world class scanning and transmission electron microscopes. The OSU NMR Facility provides state-of-the-art NMR characterization. Within Physics, there are additional thin-film systems including pulsed laser deposition, optical transmission and reflection, and Hall effect measurements. We have three ultra-fast laser and teraherz spectroscopy laboratories and an optical tweezers laboratory. In-house microscopy facilities include AFM, TIRF, confocal, two-photon and near field optical microscopy.

Computational physics research is conducted in several areas, including astrophysics, biophysics and solid state physics. Laboratory courses offer instruction in interfacing computers for laboratory experiments, as well as practical experience in computational physics. The department has access to on-campus machine shops.

Physics education research is conducted in the context of the "Paradigms in Physics" program, a unique curriculum developed for upper-division physics instruction, and in the implementation of interactive teaching techniques in large, lower-division courses. In the "Paradigms in Physics" curriculum, course content has been rearranged to better reflect the way professional physicists think about their field and to incorporate pedagogy that assigns to the students more responsibility for their own learning.

Cooperative arrangements permit students to pursue advanced physics degrees through research in other departments, including chemistry, oceanography and electrical engineering.

Table B—Separately Budgeted Research Expenditures by Source of Support

Source of Support	Departmental Research	Physics-related Research Outside Department
Federal government	$784,458.5	$1,230,403
State/local government		$92,000
Non-profit organizations		$52,144
Business and industry	$63,843.73	$90,205
Other		
Total	$848,302.23	$1,464,752

Table C—Separately Budgeted Research Expenditures by Research Specialty

Research Specialty	No. of Grants	Expenditures ($)
Astrophysics	2	$137,875
Atomic, Molecular, & Optical Physics	1	$56,172
Condensed Matter Physics	6	$744,703
Particles and Fields	2	$192,158
Physics and other Science Education	2	$71,432
Biophysics	4	$262,412
Total	17	$1,464,752

FACULTY

Professor

Jansen, Henri J. F., Ph.D., Groningen, 1981. Theoretical solid state physics.

Lee, Yun-Shik, Ph.D., University of Texas, Austin, 1997. Experimental optical and solid state physics.

Manogue, Corinne A., Ph.D., University of Texas, 1984. *Particles and Fields, Physics and other Science Education.* Theoretical particle physics; physics education research.

McIntyre, David H., Ph.D., Stanford University, 1987. *Atomic, Molecular, & Optical Physics.* Experimental atomic and optical physics.

Schellman, Heidi, Ph.D., University of California, Berkeley, 1984. Department Head. *High Energy Physics, Particles and Fields.* Experimental High Energy Physics.

Tate, Janet, Ph.D., Stanford University, 1988. Experimental solid state physics.

Associate Professor

Giebultowicz, Tomasz M., Ph.D., University of Warsaw, 1975. Experimental solid state physics.

Lazzati, Davide, Ph.D., University of Milan, 2001. Theoretical and numerical astrophysics.

Minot, Ethan D., Ph.D., Cornell University, 2004. Experimental condensed matter physics.

Ostroverkhova, Oksana G., Ph.D., Case Western Reserve University, 2001. Experimental optical and chemical physics.

Roundy, David, Ph.D., University of California, Berkeley, 2001. Theoretical condensed matter physics.

Schneider, Guenter, Ph.D., Oregon State University, 1999. Theoretical condensed matter physics.

Assistant Professor

Gire, Elizabeth, Ph.D., University of California at San Diego, 2007. *Physics and other Science Education.* Physics Education Research.

Graham, Matt, Ph.D., University of California, Berkeley, 2010. Spectroscopy; nano/optoelectronics.

Qiu, Weihong, Ph.D., Ohio State University. Biophysics; single molecule fluorescence.

Sun, Bo, Ph.D., New York University, 2010. *Biophysics.* Collective cell biophysics.

Emeritus

Hetherington, William M., Ph.D., Stanford University, 1977. Experimental optical and chemical physics.

Stetz, Albert W., Ph.D., University of California, Berkeley, 1968. Experimental intermediate energy nuclear physics.

Warren, William W., Ph.D., Washington University, 1965. Experimental solid state physics.

Professor Emeritus

Krane, Kenneth S., Ph.D., Purdue University, 1970. Experimental nuclear and solid state physics.

Landau, Rubin H., Ph.D., University of Illinois, 1970. *Computational Physics, Nuclear Physics, Particles and Fields.* Theoretical nuclear and particle physics; computational physics.

Professor of the Practice

Craig, David, Ph.D., University of California, Santa Barbara. Quantum Cosmology Mathematical Cosmology General Relativity Decoherence Quantum Computing Foundations of Quantum Mechanics Algebraic Structure of Generalized Quantum Theory.

Instructor

Bannon, David, M.S., University of California-Santa Cruz, 1987.

Coffin, Chris, M.A., Western Oregon University, 2002.

Hadley, Kathryn, Ph.D., University of Oregon, 2011. *Theoretical Physics.* Theoretical astrophysics, focusing on computational modeling of systems like protostellar disks.

Walsh, Kenneth, Ph.D., Oregon State University, 2010. *Computational Physics, Condensed Matter Physics.*

DEPARTMENTAL RESEARCH SPECIALTIES AND STAFF

Theoretical

Condensed Matter Physics. Electronic structure of solids; magnetism, metal clusters, and reduced dimensionality; aqueous interfaces and solutions; and density functional theory. Jansen, Roundy, Schneider.

Experimental

Astrophysics. Hydrodynamical numerical simulations of relativistic jets from short and long duration gamma-ray bursts, Monte Carlo radiation transfer in relativistic outflows, ab-initio quantum chemical calculation of cosmic dust and precursor molecules, dust formation in stellar explosions, soft sphere modeling of granular asteroid and planetesimal collisions. Lazzati.

Atomic, Molecular, & Optical Physics. Optoelectronic and photonic properties of organic materials; laser tweezers trapping of particles; optical spectroscopy of thin films; terahertz spectroscopy and ultrafast carrier dynamics in semiconductors using femtosecond lasers. Graham, Lee, McIntyre, Ostroverkhova.

Biophysics. Dissecting the motion, mechanism and regulation of novel biological motor proteins using high-sensitivity single-molecule light microscopy; developing novel superresolution microscopy methods; understanding the collective information processing of cells; and engineering and modeling collective invasion of tumor cells through both experiments and theory. Qiu, Sun.

Condensed Matter Physics. Electrical and thermal transport, magneto-transport and optical studies of novel thin films (organic and inorganic), 2-dimensional nanomaterials and 1-dimensional nanomaterials. Applications of new materials in photovoltaics, photodetectors, biosensors. Ultrafast electron dynamics in semiconductors. Development of scanning probe techniques. Graham, Lee, Minot, Ostroverkhova, Tate.

Particles and Fields. Neutrino research with the MINERvA neutrino cross section experiment at Fermilab and the DUNE long baseline neutrino oscillation experiment in South Dakota. Our group specializes in data analysis and large scale computing. Schellman.

Physics Education Research. Student understandings of upper division physics topics, learning progressions across math and physics, representational fluency, physics sense-making strategies, and active engagement teaching strategies. Home of the innovative Paradigms in Physics curriculum. Gire, Manogue, Roundy.

PORTLAND STATE UNIVERSITY

DEPARTMENT OF PHYSICS

Portland, Oregon 97207
http://www.pdx.edu/physics/

General University Information
President: Rahmat Shoureshi
Dean of Graduate School: Rossitza Wooster
University website: http://www.pdx.edu
School Type: Public
Setting: Urban
Total Faculty: 1,947
Total number of Students: 27,670
Total number of Graduate Students: 5,822

Department Information
Department Chairman: Prof. John L. Freeouf, Chair
Department Contact: Laurie Tull, Graduate Program
  Coordinator
  Total full-time faculty: 15
  Total number of full-time equivalent positions: 16
  Full-Time Graduate Students: 41
  Female Full-Time Graduate Students: 6
  First-Year Graduate Students: 6
  Female First-Year Students: 4

Department Address
P.O. Box 751
Portland, OR 97207
Phone: (503) 725-3812
E-mail: physics@pdx.edu
Website: http://www.pdx.edu/physics/

ADMISSIONS

Admission Contact Information
Address admission inquiries to: Department of Physics by e-mail
Phone: (503) 725-3812
E-mail: physicsgrad@pdx.edu
Admissions website: http://www.pdx.edu/physics/graduate-application-procedure

Application deadlines
Fall admission:
U.S. students: January 15   *Int'l. students*: January 15

Application fee
U.S. students: $67   *Int'l. students*: $67
Can't be waived.

Admissions information
For Fall of 2018:
  Number of applicants: 24
  Number admitted: 17
  Number enrolled: 6

Admission requirements
Bachelor's degree requirements: Bachelor's degree is required.
Minimum undergraduate GPA: 2.75

GRE requirements
The GRE is required.
  Quantitative score: 80
  Verbal score: 60
  Analytical score: 3.5

Mean GRE score range (25th–75th percentile): 50% - 70%
Actually based on percentage in year taken; should be above 60% of population.

Subjective GRE requirements
The Subjective GRE is not required.

TOEFL requirements
The TOEFL exam is required for students from non-English-speaking countries.
  PBT score: 550
  iBT score: 80
Minimum accepted Computer-based exam (CBT) score is 213. The internet-based TOEFL requirement (iBT) is a minimum score of 80 with minimum subscores of 18 each in reading and writing.

Other admissions information
Additional requirements: To increase chances of being accepted into the program the student should make make contact with their desired professor to determine if they can take on the student.
Undergraduate preparation assumed: Resnick and Halliday, Fundamentals of Physics; Tipler, Modern Physics; Fowles, Analytical Mechanics; Hecht, Modern Optics; Reif, Statistical Physics; Griffiths, Intro to Electrodynamics.

TUITION

Tuition year 2018–2019:
Tuition for in-state residents
  Full-time students: $12,588 annual
  Part-time students: $414 per credit
Tuition for out-of-state residents
  Full-time students: $18,420 annual
  Part-time students: $630 per credit
For annual estimates -Includes fees per credit/term incidental, Recreation Center building fee.
Credit hours per semester to be considered full-time: 9
Deferred tuition plan: No
Health insurance: Available at the cost of TBD per year.
Academic term: Quarter
Number of first-year students who received full tuition waivers: 4

Teaching Assistants, Research Assistants, and Fellowships
Number of first-year
  Teaching Assistants: 3
  Research Assistants: 1
Average stipend per academic year
  Teaching Assistant: $18,000
  Research Assistant: $18,000
The number of teaching assistantships is limited and they are awarded competitively.

FINANCIAL AID

Application deadlines
Fall admission:
U.S. students: December 1   *Int'l. students*: December 1
Spring admission:

U.S. students: December 1   *Int'l. students*: December 1

Loans

Loans are available for U.S. students.
Loans are available for international students.
GAPSFAS application required: No
FAFSA application required: Yes

For further information

Address financial aid inquiries to: Financial Aid Office.
Phone: (503) 725-3461
E-mail: askfa@pdx.edu
Financial aid website: http://www.pdx.edu/finaid/

HOUSING

Availability of on-campus housing

Single students: Yes
Married students: Yes

For further information

Address housing inquiries to: University Housing.
Phone: (503) 725-4375
E-mail: housing@pdx.edu
Housing aid website: http://www.pdx.edu/housing

Table A—Faculty, Enrollments, and Degrees Granted

| Research Specialty | 2018–19 Faculty | Enrollment Fall 2017 | | Number of Degrees Granted 2017–18 (2013–18) | | |
		Master's	Doctorate	Master's	Terminal Master's	Doctorate
Atmospheric Physics	3	1	2	–(2)	–	–
Atomic, Molecular, & Optical Physics	6	2	7	1(3)	–(1)	2(4)
Biophysics	3	3	4	1(5)	–(4)	–(4)
Condensed Matter Physics	5	1	4	2(6)	–(3)	1(4)
Materials Science	3	3	7	1(5)	–(4)	1(5)
Nanoscience and Technology	4	1	5	1(2)	–(1)	–(2)
Physics and other Science Education	1	–	1	–(1)	–	1(1)
Other	1	1	1	1(3)	1(3)	–
Total	–	12	31	7(27)	1(16)	5(20)
Full-time Grad. Stud.	–	12	31	–	–	–
First-year Grad. Stud.	–	–	1	–	–	–

GRADUATE DEGREE REQUIREMENTS

Master's: Program approval required. Forty-five quarter credit hours required. A GPA of 3.0/4.0 or better continuously is required. Thirty quarter credit hours must be taken in residence. A final oral examination is required..

Doctorate: Program approval required. A minimum GPA of 3.0/4.0 continuously. A minimum of 3 consecutive quarters in residence is required. Qualifying examinations and oral defense of dissertation is required..

Thesis: Master's thesis may be written in absentia.

SPECIAL EQUIPMENT, FACILITIES, OR PROGRAMS

In addition to individual laboratories having research equipment, the Center for Electron Microscopy (CEMN) has multiple state-of-the-art instruments for performing research. The department also hosts an NSF REU (Research Experience for Undergraduates) program focused on the education and use of advanced microscopy techniques in research.

Total External Sponsored Expenditures have averaged $1,049,256 over the past three full fiscal years. We show the breakdown for fiscal year 2014.

Table B—Separately Budgeted Research Expenditures by Source of Support

Source of Support	Departmental Research	Physics-related Research Outside Department
Federal government	$1,279,791	
State/local government	$24,964	
Non-profit organizations	$143,480	
Business and industry		
Other		
Total	$1,448,235	

Table C—Separately Budgeted Research Expenditures by Research Specialty

Research Specialty	No. of Grants	Expenditures ($)
Atmosphere, Space Physics, Cosmic Rays	3	$300,335
Atomic, Molecular, & Optical Physics	2	
Biophysics	2	$223,000
Materials Science, Metallurgy	8	$403,000
Nano Science and Technology	9	$376,903
Physics and other Science Education	3	$145,000
Total	27	$1,448,238

FACULTY

Professor

Bodegom, Erik, Ph.D., Catholic University, 1982. *Atomic, Molecular, & Optical Physics, Physics and other Science Education*. Complex systems; charge-coupled devices; imaging, solid state sensors; education.

Freeouf, John L., Ph.D., University of Chicago, 1973. Department Chair. *Nano Science and Technology*. Optical studies of semiconductors.

Könenkamp, Rolf, Ph.D., Tulane University, 1984. Solid-state physics; electron optics.

Khalil, M. Aslam Khan, Ph.D., University of Texas, 1976. *Climate/Atmospheric Science*. Atmospheric physics and chemistry; urban ozone chemistry and physics.

La Rosa, Andres H., Ph.D., North Carolina State University, 1996. Opto/ultrasonic near-field microscopy; optical MEMS.

Leung, Pui-Tak, Ph.D., State University of New York at Buffalo, 1982. *Atomic, Molecular, & Optical Physics, Theoretical Physics*. Atomic, optical, and surface physics.

Möck, Peter, Ph.D., Humboldt-University of Berlin, 1991. *Condensed Matter Physics, Crystallography, Materials Science, Metallurgy*. Electron microscopy; quantum dots; x-ray diffraction; crystallography at the nanometer length scale.

Mitchell, Drake C., Ph.D., University of Oregon, 1987. *Biophysics*. Membrane biophysics; signal transduction.

Sánchez, Erik J., Ph.D., Portland State University, 1999. *Atomic, Molecular, & Optical Physics, Computational Physics, Electromagnetism, Nano Science and Technology*. Microscopy; lasers; nanotechnology.

Solanki, Raj, Ph.D., Colorado State University, 1982. *Biophysics, Materials Science, Metallurgy, Nano Science and Technology*. Semiconductors; graphene; optoelectronic materials and materials characterization; electronic biosensors; 2D metal chacogenides (including topological insulators) and multivalent battery technology.

Widenhorn, Ralf, Ph.D., Portland State University, 2005. *Atomic, Molecular, & Optical Physics, Physics and other Science Education*. Physics education research; applications of physics in the biomedical field; solid state physics and digital image sensors; characterization of CCD and CMOS image sensors.

Associate Professor

Butenhoff, Chris, Ph.D., Portland State University, 2010. *Climate/Atmospheric Science, Computational Physics*. Atmospheric physics.

Nadeau, Jay L., Ph.D., University of Minnesota Twin Cities, 1996. Astrobiology; molecular biophysics; advanced microscopy; cell labeling; nanomaterials; photophysics; scintillation; fluorescence.

Rice, Andrew, Ph.D., University of California, Irvine, 2002. *Atmosphere, Space Physics, Cosmic Rays*. Atmospheric physics and chemistry.

Straton, Jack, Ph.D., University of Oregon, 1986. *Atomic, Molecular, & Optical Physics*. Quantum scattering theory; atomic theory; computational physics, nanometrology, quartic diode electron mirror design.

Emeritus

Abramson, Jonathan J., Ph.D., University of Rochester, 1975. *Biophysics*. Biophysics; rational drug design.

Smejtek, Pavel K., Ph.D., Czechoslovak Academy, 1965. *Biophysics*.

DEPARTMENTAL RESEARCH SPECIALTIES AND STAFF

Theoretical

Atomic, Molecular, & Optical Physics. Stopping power theory; sum rule calculations; near-field optics; surface effects. Leung, Sánchez, Straton.

Climate/Atmospheric Science. Climate modeling; atmospheric dispersion and chemistry; global emissions inventories of greenhouse gases. Butenhoff, Khalil, Rice.

Computational Physics. Computing nanoarchitectures. Sánchez.

Electromagnetism. Modeling of electromagnetic fields. Leung, Sánchez.

Nano Science and Technology. Molecular fluorescence; metallic nanoparticles and plasmonics. Freeouf, Könenkamp, La Rosa, Sánchez, Solanki.

Experimental

Atmosphere, Space Physics, Cosmic Rays. Global change science; design of field experimentation; instrumental analysis of air and water samples. Butenhoff, Khalil, Rice.

Atomic, Molecular, & Optical Physics. AFM; STM; charge-coupled devices. Bodegom, La Rosa, Sánchez, Widenhorn.

Biophysics. Membrane structure/function; calorimetry; biosensors; nanoparticles for anti-cancer applications; photophysics of quantum dots; time-resolved spectroscopy; microscopy in extreme environments, including the Arctic, Antarctic, and in space. Mitchell, Nadeau, Solanki.

Condensed Matter Physics. AFM; STM; quantum dots; crystallographic identification of compounds. Freeouf, La Rosa, Möck, Sánchez, Solanki.

Materials Science, Metallurgy. Electronic device physics. Freeouf, Könenkamp, Solanki.

Nano Science and Technology. Carbon nanotubes and nanoclusters; graphene; biosensors; nanometrology; nanoelectronics. Freeouf, Möck, Sánchez, Solanki.

Optics. Electron optics; near-field optics; biological imaging; electron microscopy. Freeouf, Könenkamp, La Rosa, Möck, Sánchez.

Physics and other Science Education. Improved general physics for life sciences. Bodegom, Widenhorn.

View additional information about this department at www.gradschoolshopper.com. Check out the "Why Choose Us?" section, find out more about the department's culture and get links to social media networks.

UNIVERSITY OF OREGON

DEPARTMENT OF PHYSICS

Eugene, Oregon 97403-1274
http://physics.uoregon.edu

General University Information
President: Michael H. Schill
Dean of Graduate School: Janet Woodruff-Borden
University website: http://www.uoregon.edu
School Type: Public
Setting: Urban
Total Faculty: 2,041
Total Graduate Faculty: 782
Total number of Students: 22,980
Total number of Graduate Students: 3,629

Department Information
Department Chairman: Prof. Richard Taylor, Head
Department Contact: Jodi Myers, Education Programs
  Manager
  Total full-time faculty: 38
  Total number of full-time equivalent positions: 38
  Full-Time Graduate Students: 92
  Female Full-Time Graduate Students: 17
  First-Year Graduate Students: 12
  Female First-Year Students: 2
  Total Post Doctorates: 15

Department Address
1371 E. 13th Avenue
120 Willamette Hall
Eugene, OR 97403-1274
Phone: (541) 346-4751
Fax: (541) 346-5861
E-mail: physgradinfo@uoregon.edu
Website: http://physics.uoregon.edu

ADMISSIONS

Admission Contact Information
Address admission inquiries to: Department of Physics, Graduate
  Selection Committee, 120 Willamette Hall, 1371 E. 13th Ave-
  nue, Eugene, OR 97403-1274
Phone: (541) 346-4751
E-mail: physgradinfo@uoregon.edu
Admissions website: http://atomoptics-nas.uoregon.edu/~dsteck/
  application/

Application deadlines
Fall admission:
U.S. students: January 15   *Int'l. students*: January 15

Application fee
U.S. students: $70   *Int'l. students*: $90

Admissions information
For Fall of 2018:
  Number of applicants: 188
  Number admitted: 53
  Number enrolled: 12

Admission requirements
Bachelor's degree requirements: A Bachelor's degree in Physics
  or a related subject is required.
Minimum undergraduate GPA: 3.0

GRE requirements
The GRE is required.
  Mean GRE score range (25th–75th percentile): 60th-87th
  No minimum acceptable General GRE score for admission is
  specified.

Subjective GRE requirements
The Subjective GRE is required.
  Mean Advanced GRE score range (25th–75th percentile):
  45th-77th
No minimum acceptable Physics GRE score for admission is
  specified.

TOEFL requirements
The TOEFL exam is required for students from non-English-
  speaking countries.
  PBT score: 600
  iBT score: 88

Other admissions information
Undergraduate preparation assumed: Familiarity with material
  at a level found in the following text books is assumed: Classical Mechanics, Chow; Analytical Mechanics: Electricity and
  Magnetism, Griffiths; Introduction to Electrodynamics; Statistical and Thermal Physics, Schroeder; Introduction to Thermal Physics; Modern Physics, Griffiths; Introduction to Quantum Mechanics, Griffiths.

TUITION

Tuition year 2018–19:
Tuition for in-state residents
  Full-time students: $16,602 annual
Graduate students typically have Graduate Employee (GE) con-
  tracts. Each GE receives a tuition waiver for 9-16 credit
  hours per term. For current information, see http://
  gradschool.uoregon.edu/gtf/salary-benefits
Credit hours per semester to be considered full-time: 9
Deferred tuition plan: Yes
Health insurance: Yes, 5% of premium.
Other academic fees: GEs have access to GE-specific insurance
  during each term of appointment. For current info, see http://
  gradschool.uoregon.edu/node/163
Academic term: Quarter
Number of first-year students who received full tuition waivers: 12

Teaching Assistants, Research Assistants, and Fellowships
Number of first-year
  Teaching Assistants: 12
  Fellowship students: 1
Average stipend per academic year
  Teaching Assistant: $18,203
  Research Assistant: $18,203
  Fellowship student: $18,000

FINANCIAL AID

Application deadlines
Fall admission:
U.S. students: March 1   *Int'l. students*: March 1

Loans

Loans are available for U.S. students.
Loans are available for international students.
GAPSFAS application required: No
FAFSA application required: Yes

For further information

Address financial aid inquiries to: Office of Financial Aid & Scholarships, 1278 University of Oregon Eugene, OR 97403-1278.
Phone: (541) 346-3221
E-mail: financialaid@uoregon.edu
Financial aid website: http://financialaid.uoregon.edu/

HOUSING

Availability of on-campus housing

Single students: Yes
Married students: Yes

For further information

Address housing inquiries to: University Housing, 1220 University of Oregon, Eugene, OR 97403-1220.
Phone: (541) 346-4277
E-mail: housing@uoregon.edu
Housing aid website: http://housing.uoregon.edu/

Table A—Faculty, Enrollments, and Degrees Granted

Research Specialty	2017–18 Faculty	Enrollment Fall 2017		Number of Degrees Granted 2017–18		
		Master's	Doctorate	Master's	Terminal Master's	Doctorate
Applied Physics	–	23	–	–	30	–
Astrophysics	5	–	4	–	–	–
Atomic, Molecular, & Optical Physics	10	–	26	–	1	5
Biophysics	3	–	16	2	–	2
Condensed Matter Physics	7	–	28	1	–	2
Geophysics	1	–	1	–	–	–
Particles and Fields	11	–	20	1	–	2
Non-specialized	1	–	–	–	–	–
Total	38	23	95	4	31	11
Full-time Grad. Stud.	–	23	95	–	–	–
First-year Grad. Stud.	–	23	25	–	–	–

GRADUATE DEGREE REQUIREMENTS

Master's: Forty-five credit hours of graduate-level courses, including 32 credits of physics and at least 24 credits of University of Oregon-graded courses, are required. These must include at least one three-term sequence in physics at the 600 level and an approved sequence in mathematics. A maximum of 15 hours of credits earned in another accredited graduate school with a grade of B or better may be counted. A minimum GPA of 3.0 must be maintained. Command of a foreign language is recommended but not required. A master's final examination, a thesis, or a certain course requirement has to be satisfactorily completed. The department offers an Applied Physics Master's Program that leads to a professional M.S. degree. This degree is an alternative to the research-based Ph.D. and is more oriented toward the needs of industrial physicists than the traditional master's degree. This program includes an internship component. The Applied Physics Master's Program is offered through the University of Oregon Materials Science Institute (see http://internship.uoregon.edu).

Doctorate: Students generally must complete core graduate courses in mechanics, statistical physics, electromagnetic theory, and quantum mechanics, although they can be excused based on previous study. In addition, students must take a total of six other one-quarter courses, chosen from the following areas: condensed matter physics; nuclear and particle physics; atomic physics and molecular physics; astronomy and early universe physics; experimental and theoretical techniques; and interdisciplinary. An oral comprehensive examination and a thesis are required. Proficiency in a foreign language is recommended but not required. Three years work beyond the bachelor's degree is required, of which three consecutive terms must be on the Eugene, Oregon campus.

Thesis: Thesis may be written in absentia.

SPECIAL EQUIPMENT, FACILITIES, OR PROGRAMS

The University of Oregon has several interdisciplinary institutes in which many physics faculty members participate.

The Materials Science Institute (MSI;http://materialscience.uoregon.edu/) not only focuses much of its efforts on the creation and study of new materials and devices but also addresses more abstract questions in experiment and theory. The MSI has a wide range of fabrication and characterization capabilities located in both individual laboratories and common facilities. An important mission of the MSI is education, and in this connection, it promotes integrated research between various departments and conducts Summer Industrial Internship programs in semiconductor processing, polymer technology, and, with the Oregon Center for Optical, Molecular & Quantum Science (OMQ), optics and photonics. The MSI is a founding member and partner of the Oregon Nanoscience and Microtechnologies Institute (http://www.onami.us/).

The OMQ (http://oco.uoregon.edu/) promotes and facilitates research and education in the sciences at the University of Oregon whenever optical science is involved in an essential manner in either its fundamental aspects or its technological applications. The OMQ has a broad range of state-of-the-art lasers and spectroscopy equipment located in individual laboratories and also in common facilities.

The Institute of Theoretical Science (http://pages.uoregon.edu/its/index.shtml) is a center for theoretical research in overlapping areas of physics, chemistry, and mathematics. It provides an environment in which theorists can share common themes and mathematical approaches.

The Institute of Molecular Biology (http://molbio.uoregon.edu/) comprises biologists, chemists, and physicists pursuing a molecular-level understanding of living systems. It runs a weekly seminar series and operates common facilities to assist with imaging, cell culture, and analytic characterization.

The Center for High Energy Physics (http://pages.uoregon.edu/chep/) supports experimental and theoretical high-energy physics research activities at the University of Oregon and at various external laboratories, including CERN, Fermilab, the SLAC National Accelerator Laboratory, and LIGO.

The Pine Mountain Observatory (http://pmo-sun.uoregon.edu/) houses several telescopes and is equipped with charge-coupled device cameras for remote data collection.

The Center for Advanced Materials Characterization at Oregon (http://www.camcor.uoregon.edu/) houses capital-intensive equipment for microanalysis, surface analysis, electron microscopy, semiconductor device fabrication, as well as traditional chemical characterization for users from inside and outside the university. The staff members who run the facilities are experienced in sample preparation, data collection, and data analysis.

The Shared Laser Facility (SLF) is a multi-disciplinary laboratory available to the university community and others by arrangement. Faculty members may either set up long-term experiments in the SLF or use shared equipment for short-term experiments. SLF personnel also provide expertise in setting up experiments in user laboratories.

The Technical Services Administration maintains professional and student machine shops and an electronics shop.

Table B—Separately Budgeted Research Expenditures by Source of Support

Source of Support	Departmental Research	Physics-related Research Outside Department
Federal government	$4,449,371	
State/local government	$176,292	
Non-profit organizations		
Business and industry	$463,961	
Other	$12,106	
Total	$5,101,730	

Table C—Separately Budgeted Research Expenditures by Research Specialty

Research Specialty	No. of Grants	Expenditures ($)
Astrophysics	2	$16,939
Biophysics	7	$463,984
Condensed Matter Physics	13	$564,705
Energy Sources & Environment	8	$159,392
Optics	29	$1,758,326
Particles and Fields	22	$1,913,693
Physics and other Science Education	9	$224,692
Total	90	$5,101,731

FACULTY

Professor

Belitz, Dietrich, Ph.D., University of Munich, 1982. Director of Institute of Theoretical Physics (ITS). *Condensed Matter Physics, Theoretical Physics.* Many-body theory; quantum phase transitions.

Bothun, Gregory D., Ph.D., University of Washington, 1981. *Astrophysics, Energy Sources & Environment.* Astronomy; properties of galaxies; observational cosmology; sustainable energy.

Brau, James E., Ph.D., Massachusetts Institute of Technology, 1978. *High Energy Physics, Particles and Fields.* Experimental elementary particle physics; electroweak symmetry breaking (ATLAS and ILC); gravitational radiation (LIGO).

Deutsch, Miriam, Ph.D., Hebrew University, 1996. *Optics.* Quantum optics; photonics.

Frey, Raymond E., Ph.D., University of California, Riverside, 1984. Department Head. *Astrophysics, High Energy Physics, Particles and Fields, Relativity & Gravitation.* Gravitational-wave astrophysics (LIGO); astrophysics of gamma-ray bursts and other transient phenomenon; detector development.

Haydock, Roger, Ph.D., University of Cambridge, 1972. *Solid State Physics.* Solid-state theory; electronic structure and processes at surfaces; computational physics; quantum chaos.

Imamura, James N., Ph.D., Indiana University, 1981. *Astrophysics.* Astrophysics; accretion disks; dense fluids; X-ray timing observations.

Kevan, Stephen D., Ph.D., University of California, Berkeley, 1980. *Solid State Physics.* Experimental solid-state physics; thin-film and surface physics; magnetism.

Kribs, Graham, Ph.D., University of Michigan, 1998. *High Energy Physics, Particles and Fields, Theoretical Physics.* Theoretical high-energy physics; effective field theory of models beyond the standard model; particle astrophysics; early universe cosmology.

Parthasarathy, Raghuveer, Ph.D., University of Chicago, 2002. *Biophysics, Condensed Matter Physics.* Experimental solid state and biophysics; material properties of biological membranes; mechanism of protein organization; advanced microscopy techniques.

Raymer, Michael G., Ph.D., University of Colorado, 1979. *Optics.* Quantum optics; quantum information; quantum control; semiconductor optical physics; non-linear optics.

Schombert, James, Ph.D., Yale University, 1984. *Astrophysics.* Astronomy; galaxy surveys; evolution and properties of galaxies.

Strom, David, Ph.D., University of Wisconsin-Madison, 1986. *High Energy Physics, Particles and Fields.* Experimental elementary particle physics; new physics with tau decays in proton-proton collisions; detectors and electronics for linear colliders; precision electroweak measurements; instrumentation for the detection of gravity waves; ATLAS; LIGO.

Taylor, Richard, Ph.D., University of Nottingham, 1988. Director of Materials Science Institute. *Biophysics, Condensed Matter Physics.* Experimental solid-state physics; nanoelectronics; retinal implants; solar cells; visual science of fractals.

Toner, John, Ph.D., Harvard University, 1981. *Condensed Matter Physics, Theoretical Physics.* Condensed matter theory; flocking; liquid crystal and superconducting glasses; novel phases of Josephson junction arrays; quantum whistling; supersolids.

Torrence, Eric, Ph.D., Massachusetts Institute of Technology, 1997. Director of Center for High Energy Physics (UOCHEP). *High Energy Physics, Particles and Fields.* Experimental high-energy physics.

van Enk, Steven, Ph.D., Leiden University, 1992. *Optics, Theoretical Physics.* Theoretical optical physics; quantum communication; entanglement; coherence and decoherence.

Wang, Hailin, Ph.D., University of Michigan, 1990. *Condensed Matter Physics, Optics.* Quantum optics; optical properties of semiconductor nanostruture.

Associate Professor

Chang, Spencer, Ph.D., Harvard University, 2004. *High Energy Physics, Theoretical Physics.* Theoretical high-energy physics; beyond the standard model physics; electroweak symmetry breaking; dark matter; cosmology.

Corwin, Eric, Ph.D., University of Chicago, 2007. *Biophysics, Condensed Matter Physics.* Experimental soft condensed matter and biophysics; atomic force microscopy of single molecule proteins; structure and dynamics of jammed athermal packings.

Gregory, Stephen, Ph.D., University of Waterloo, 1975. *Solid State Physics.* Experimental condensed matter; tunneling microscopy and spectroscopy; molecular electronics.

Majewski, Stephanie, Ph.D., Stanford University, 2007. *High Energy Physics, Particles and Fields.* Experimental particle physics.

McMorran, Benjamin, Ph.D., University of Arizona, 2009. *Condensed Matter Physics, Optics.* Experimental condensed matter; optical physics; free electron physics and interferometry; matter wave optics; electron microscopy; magnetic materials.

Nöckel, Jens, Ph.D., Yale University, 1997. *Optics, Theoretical Physics.* Optical physics; quantum chaos and semiclassical physics in microactivity optics; optical and transport properties of mesoscopic systems.

Smith, Brian, Ph.D., University of Oregon, 2007. *Optics*. Quantum optics, quantum information science and technology, and optics.

Steck, Daniel, Ph.D., University of Texas, 2001. *Optics*. Experimental and theoretical optical physics; quantum and atom optics; quantum non-linear dynamical systems; laser cooling and trapping atoms.

Assistant Professor

Alemán, Benjamín, Ph.D., The University of California, Berkeley, 2011. *Condensed Matter Physics*. Physics and synthesis of low-dimensional systems; nanoelectromechanical systems, solid-state defect centers and qubits; quantum and nanoscale-based sensing and microscopy; photonics; microfluids.

Allcock, David, Ph.D., University of Oxford, 2012. *Atomic, Molecular, & Optical Physics*. Ion trapping; quantum computing; hybrid quantum systems.

Cohen, Tim, Ph.D., University of Michigan, 2011. *High Energy Physics, Theoretical Physics*. Particle physics and cosmology beyond the standard model.

Farr, Benjamin, Ph.D., Northwestern University, 2014. *Astrophysics*. Gravitational wave astronomy and astrophysics.

Jeanty, Laura, Ph.D., Harvard University, 2013. *High Energy Physics, Particles and Fields*. Experimental particle physics.

Paulose, Jayson, Ph.D., Harvar, 2013. *Condensed Matter Physics, Theoretical Physics*.

Ursell, Tristan, Ph.D., California Institute of Technology, 2009. *Biophysics*. We use tools from microscopy, mechanics, computational modeling, and statistical physics to understand how cells move and invade, how cells die, and how cells engage in collective behavior that benefits the group over the individual, in a variety of natural and medically relevant settings.

Yu, Tien-Tien, Ph.D., University of Wisconsin, Madison, 2008. *High Energy Physics, Particles and Fields, Theoretical Physics*. Theoretical high-energy physics.

Research Professor

Wineland, David, Ph.D., Harvard University, 1970. 2012 Nobel Prize in Physics for the manipulation and measurement of individual quantum systems. *Other*. High-resolution atomic spectroscopy, quantum information, and quantum-limited metrology.

Instructor

Livelybrooks, Dean, Ph.D., University of Oregon, 1990. Tenured Senior Instructor Director of Graduate Studies. *Geophysics*. Science education and outreach; magnetotellurics; dynamic margin model constraints.

Lecturer

Boggs, Bryan, Ph.D., University of Oregon, 2012. *Optics*. Optical properties of semiconductors; ultra-fast fiberlasers; fiber optic-based rotation sensing.

Fisher, Scott, Ph.D., University of Florida, 2001. Astronomy Lecturer and Outreach Coordinator; Director of Undergraduate Studies; Director of Pine Mountain Observatory. *Astronomy*. Monitoring variable sources; infrared astronomy; observatory facilities management.

DEPARTMENTAL RESEARCH SPECIALTIES AND STAFF

Theoretical

Astrophysics. Astrophysical flows; accretion disks; dense fluids; X-ray timing observations. Imamura.

Condensed Matter Physics. Metal insulator transitions; localization; phases in complex fluids; quantum critical phenomena. Belitz, Haydock, Toner.

High Energy Physics. Electroweak symmetry breaking; dark matter; cosmology; early universe physics; particle astrophysics. Chang, Cohen, Jeanty, Kribs, Yu.

Optics. Quantum optics; quantum information and nanophotonics. Nöckel, Steck, van Enk.

Solid State Physics. Haydock.

Experimental

Astrophysics. Properties of galaxies; observational cosmology; evolution and properties of galaxies; gravitational waves. Bothun, Farr, Frey, Imamura, Schombert.

Biophysics. X-ray crystallography of proteins; membrane biophysics; biomolecule mechanics. Corwin, Parthasarathy, Taylor, Toner, Ursell.

Condensed Matter Physics. Phonon and electron transport in low-dimensional systems; electronic properties of amorphous semiconductors; surface physics. Corwin, Deutsch, Gregory, Kevan, McMorran, Parthasarathy, Taylor, Wang.

High Energy Physics. Experimental elementary particle physics; electroweak symmetry breaking (ATLAS and ILC); gravitational radiation (LIGO). Brau, Frey, Jeanty, Majewski, Strom, Torrence.

Optics. Quantum optics and quantum information; cold atoms; plasmonics. Deutsch, Gregory, McMorran, Raymer, Smith, Steck, Wang, Wineland.

Solid State Physics. Photovoltaic materials; magnetism and magnetic materials; thin-film physics, plasmonics; optical properties of semiconductors. Alemán, Deutsch, Gregory, Kevan, McMorran, Taylor, Wang.

View additional information about this department at www.gradschoolshopper.com. Check out the "Why Choose Us?" section, find out more about the department's culture and get links to social media networks.

BRYN MAWR COLLEGE

DEPARTMENT OF PHYSICS

Bryn Mawr, Pennsylvania 19010-2899
http://www.brynmawr.edu/physics

General University Information
President: Kimberly Wright Cassidy
Dean of Graduate School: Sharon J. Nieter Burgmayer
University website: http://www.brynmawr.edu/
School Type: Private
Setting: Suburban
Total Faculty: 152
Total number of Students: 1,708
Total number of Graduate Students: 253

Department Information
Department Chairman: Prof. Michael Noel, Chair
Department Contact: David Schaffner, Assistant Professor
  Total full-time faculty: 6
  Total number of full-time equivalent positions: 6
  Full-Time Graduate Students: 6
  Female Full-Time Graduate Students: 2
  First-Year Graduate Students: 2
  Female First-Year Students: 1

Department Address
101 North Merion Avenue
Bryn Mawr, PA 19010-2899
Phone: (610) 526-5358
Fax: (610) 526-7469
E-mail: dschaffner@brynmawr.edu
Website: http://www.brynmawr.edu/physics

ADMISSIONS

Admission Contact Information
Address admission inquiries to: Dean of Graduate Studies, Bryn
  Mawr College, 101 N Merion Ave, Bryn Mawr, PA 19010-2899
Phone: (610) 526-5072
E-mail: gsas@brynmawr.edu
Admissions website: http://www.brynmawr.edu/gsas/
  Admissions/

Application deadlines
Fall admission:
U.S. students: January 1   *Int'l. students*: January 1

Application fee
U.S. students: $50   *Int'l. students*: $50

Admissions information
For Fall of 2017:
  Number of applicants: 15
  Number admitted: 3

Admission requirements
Bachelor's degree requirements: A Bachelor's degree in Physics
  or a closely related field is required.

GRE requirements
The GRE is required.

Subjective GRE requirements
The Subjective GRE is required.

TOEFL requirements
The TOEFL exam is required for students from non-English-
  speaking countries.
  PBT score: 600
  iBT score: 100

Other admissions information
Additional requirements: Students from non-English-speaking
  countries are required to demonstrate proficiency in English
  via the TOEFL or IELTS examination; minimum IELTS
  score 7.

TUITION

Tuition year 2017–18:
  Full-time students: $29,080 annual
  Part-time students: $7,010 per credit
One academic unit: $7,010 and one unit of supervised work:
  $1,130. Full load is two or more units/semester and four or
  more units/year.
Deferred tuition plan: No
Health insurance: Available.
Other academic fees: Financial support package includes stipend,
  tuition waiver, and a health insurance subsidy of $4,576 per
  year.
Academic term: Semester

Teaching Assistants, Research Assistants, and Fellowships
  Average stipend per academic year
  Teaching Assistant: $27,250
  Research Assistant: $27,250
  Fellowship student: $27,250

FINANCIAL AID

Application deadlines
Fall admission:
U.S. students: January 1   *Int'l. students*: January 1

Loans
Loans are available for U.S. students.
Loans are not available for international students.
GAPSFAS application required: Yes
FAFSA application required: Yes

For further information
Address financial aid inquiries to: Financial Aid Office, Bryn
  Mawr College, 101 N. Merion Ave, Bryn Mawr, PA 19010.
Phone: (610) 526-5245
E-mail: finaid@brynmawr.edu
Financial aid website: http://www.brynmawr.edu/financialaid/

HOUSING

Availability of on-campus housing
  Single students: No
  Married students: No

For further information

Address housing inquiries to: Angie Sheets, Director of Residential Life, Bryn Mawr College, 101 N. Merion Ave, Bryn Mawr, PA 19010.

Phone: (610) 526-7334

E-mail: asheets@brynmawr.edu

Housing aid website: http://www.brynmawr.edu/residentiallife/

Table A—Faculty, Enrollments, and Degrees Granted

Research Specialty	2017–18 Faculty	Enrollment Fall 2017		Number of Degrees Granted 2016–17 (2008–17)		
		Master's	Doctorate	Master's	Terminal Master's	Doctorate
Astrophysics	1	–	1	–	–	–
Atomic, Molecular, & Optical Physics	1	–	1	–	–(1)	1(2)
Biophysics	–	–	–	–	–	–(1)
Chemical Physics	–	–	–	–(1)	–	–
Condensed Matter Physics	1	–	2	–	–	–
Cosmology & String Theory	1	–	–	–	–	–(1)
High Energy Physics	–	–	–	–(1)	–(1)	–
Plasma and Fusion	1	–	1	–	–	–
Non-specialized	–	–	–	–	–	–
Total	**5**	**–**	**5**	**–(2)**	**–(2)**	**1(4)**
Full-time Grad. Stud.	–	–	5	–	–	–
First-year Grad. Stud.	–	–	–	–	–	–

GRADUATE DEGREE REQUIREMENTS

Master's: At least six units of work with satisfactory performance, including at least one full year in residence; master's thesis and oral examination are required.

Doctorate: At least 12 units of work with satisfactory performance, including at least three full years in residence; written and oral preliminary examinations are required; dissertation and oral examination are required.

Thesis: Thesis may be written in absentia.

SPECIAL EQUIPMENT, FACILITIES, OR PROGRAMS

Cooperative agreements with the University of Pennsylvania and Drexel University allow Bryn Mawr graduate students to pursue work in special field areas not available at Bryn Mawr. State-of-the-art laboratory facilities include an atomic force microscope, electrochemical deposition system, AJA sputtering thin film deposition system, class 1000 soft-curtain clean room, vibrating sample magnetometer, X-ray diffractometer, various tunable pulsed and CW laser systems, two ultra-high vacuum systems for laser cooling and trapping, a beowulf cluster, and a machine and instrument shop. Students have access to user facilities at national laboratories, including the Advanced Photon Source (APS) at Argonne National Laboratory, the Center for Functional Nanomaterials (CFN) at Brookhaven National Laboratory, and the Basic Plasma Science Facility at UCLA including the Large Plasma Device (LAPD). The Collier Science Library offers extensive information technology and library resources. The college and the department offer computing facilities for data acquisition, modeling, and data analysis, as well as high-speed computer links to the national and international physics communities.

Table B—Separately Budgeted Research Expenditures by Source of Support

Source of Support	Departmental Research	Physics-related Research Outside Department
Federal government	$354,633	$192,000
State/local government		
Non-profit organizations		
Business and industry		
Other	$25,000	
Total	**$379,633**	**$192,000**

Table C—Separately Budgeted Research Expenditures by Research Specialty

Research Specialty	No. of Grants	Expenditures ($)
Astrophysics	1	$10,000
Atomic, Molecular, & Optical Physics	1	$67,716
Condensed Matter Physics	2	$236,917
Plasma and Fusion	3	$257,000
Total	**7**	**$571,633**

FACULTY

Professor

Noel, Michael W., Ph.D., University of Rochester, 1996. *Atomic, Molecular, & Optical Physics*. Ultra-cold Rydberg atoms.

Associate Professor

Cheng, Xuemei May, Ph.D., Johns Hopkins University, 2006. *Condensed Matter Physics, Nano Science and Technology*. Nanomaterials, spintronics, and spin dynamics in nanomagnetic materials.

Schulz, Michael B., Ph.D., Stanford University, 2002. *Cosmology & String Theory*. Theoretical physics with a focus on string theory.

Assistant Professor

Daniel, Kathryne, Ph.D., Johns Hopkins University, 2015. *Astrophysics*. Theoretical explorations of the evolution of disk galaxies through internal processes.

Schaffner, David, Ph.D., University of California, Los Angeles, 2013. *Plasma and Fusion*. Plasma physics, turbulence, transport, fusion energy, and space physics.

Lecturer

Matlin, Mark D., Ph.D., University of Maryland, 1991. Laboratory Coordinator. *Relativity & Gravitation*. General relativity.

DEPARTMENTAL RESEARCH SPECIALTIES AND STAFF

Theoretical

Cosmology & String Theory. String theory and its applications to quantum field theory, cosmology, and particle physics. Schulz.

Galaxy Evolution & Dynamics.. Evolution of galaxies through internal dynamical processes. Use analytic arguments and simulations to explore the orbital response to non-axisymmetric structures in the disk, like spiral arms, a bar, giant molecular clouds, or dark matter substructure. Resonant response, the nature of transient spiral structure, and the emergence of major structural components of the galaxy. Orbital stability and chaos. Kinematic heating. Daniel.

Experimental

Atomic, Molecular, & Optical Physics. Resonant energy transfer in ultra-cold samples of highly excited atoms using laser cooling and trapping techniques to prepare and manipulate the atomic sample and study the extremely long-range many-body interactions that result when the atoms are excited to weakly bound states. Noel.

Condensed Matter Physics. Fabrication, characterization, and application of nanoscale materials, including templated electrochemical deposition of nanoscaled materials for energy and medical applications, time-resolved photoemission electron microscopy imaging of spin dynamics in magnetic nanostructures, and X-ray magnetic circular dichroism study of multiferroic materials. Synchrotron X-ray-based experiments are carried out at the Advanced Photon Source at Argonne National Laboratory. Cheng.

Plasma and Fusion. Study of magnetohydrodynamic (MHD) turbulence in a laboratory plasma device. Analysis of fluctu-

ations in magnetic field, fluid flows, density, and temperature of plasma is conducted using a wide variety of time-series and statistical techniques including spectral decomposition, wavelets, probability distribution functions, temporal and spatial correlations, conditional averaging, and permutation entropy/statistical complexity. Goals include understanding the mechanisms involved in energy transfer and energy dissipation in MHD turbulence and making comparisons to simulations and satellite observations of heliospheric turbulence (such as that found in the solar wind and magnetosheath). Studies of turbulent suppression and transport mechanisms in edge plasma relevant to magnetic confinement fusion are carried out on the Large Plasma Device (LAPD), an NSF User Facility at the University of California, Los Angeles. Schaffner.

CARNEGIE MELLON UNIVERSITY

DEPARTMENT OF PHYSICS

Pittsburgh, Pennsylvania 15213
http://www.cmu.edu/physics

General University Information
President: Dr. Farnam Jahanian
Dean of Graduate School: Professor Rebecca Doerge
University website: http://www.cmu.edu
School Type: Private
Setting: Urban
Total Faculty: 1,391
Total Graduate Faculty: 1,391
Total number of Students: 14,528
Total number of Graduate Students: 7,582

Department Information
Department Chairman: Prof. Scott Dodelson, Head
Department Contact: Heather Corcoran, Student Programs
  Coordinator
  Total full-time faculty: 32
  Total number of full-time equivalent positions: 31
  Full-Time Graduate Students: 87
  Female Full-Time Graduate Students: 21
  First-Year Graduate Students: 16
  Female First-Year Students: 4
  Total Post Doctorates: 19

Department Address
5000 Forbes Avenue
Pittsburgh, PA 15213
Phone: (412) 268-2849
Fax: (412) 681-0648
E-mail: physgrad@andrew.cmu.edu
Website: http://www.cmu.edu/physics

ADMISSIONS

Admission Contact Information
Address admission inquiries to: Graduate Studies, Department
  of Physics, Carnegie Mellon University, Pittsburgh, PA 15213
Phone: (412) 268-2849
E-mail: physgrad@andrew.cmu.edu
Admissions website: http://www.cmu.edu/physics/graduate-
  program/admission.html

Application deadlines
Fall admission:
U.S. students: December 15   *Int'l. students*: December 15

Application fee
There is no application fee required.

Admissions information
For Fall of 2017:
  Number of applicants: 302
  Number admitted: 59
  Number enrolled: 16

Admission requirements
Bachelor's degree requirements: A bachelor's degree in Physics
  or related field is required.

GRE requirements
The GRE is required.

Subjective GRE requirements
The Subjective GRE is required.

TOEFL requirements
The TOEFL exam is required for students from non-English-
  speaking countries.
TOEFL OR IELTS is required

Other admissions information
Additional requirements: No minimum scores are specified.
Undergraduate preparation assumed: A typical student will have
  completed intermediate courses in mechanics (Marion), electricity and magnetism (Griffiths or Wangsness), modern
  physics (Eisberg and Resnick), wave mechanics (Townsend),
  thermodynamics and statistical mechanics (Reif or Swendsen), and modern physics laboratory (Melissinos).

TUITION
Tuition year 2017–18:
  Full-time students: $44,500 annual
  Part-time students: $600 per credit
Credit hours per semester to be considered full-time: 36
Deferred tuition plan: No
Health insurance: Available at the cost of $2340 per year.
Other academic fees: $852/year (paid for by the department).
Academic term: Semester
Number of first-year students who received full tuition waivers: 14

Teaching Assistants, Research Assistants, and Fellowships
Number of first-year
  Teaching Assistants: 14
Average stipend per academic year
  Teaching Assistant: $29,400
  Research Assistant: $29,400
  Fellowship student: $29,400

FINANCIAL AID

Loans
Loans are not available for U.S. students.
Loans are not available for international students.
GAPSFAS application required: No
FAFSA application required: No

HOUSING

Availability of on-campus housing
Single students: No
Married students: No

For further information

Phone: 412-268-2139
E-mail: plaid@andrew.cmu.edu
Housing aid website: http://www.cmu.edu/housing/graduate-students/index.html

Table A—Faculty, Enrollments, and Degrees Granted

Research Specialty	2017–18 Faculty	Enrollment Fall 2017 Master's	Enrollment Fall 2017 Doctorate	Number of Degrees Granted 2017–18 (2010–18) Master's	Number of Degrees Granted 2017–18 (2010–18) Terminal Master's	Number of Degrees Granted 2017–18 (2010–18) Doctorate
Applied Physics	7	–	–	–	–	–(8)
Astrophysics	11	–	15	–	–	4(14)
Biophysics	5	–	10	–	–	3(14)
Computational Physics	10	–	–	–	–	–
Condensed Matter Physics	8	–	17	–	–	6(17)
Nuclear Physics	6	–	9	–	–	2(8)
Particles and Fields	6	–	6	–	–	3(10)
Quantum Foundations	–	–	1	–	–	–(3)
Statistical & Thermal Physics	–	–	–	–	–	–(2)
Non-specialized	–	–	29	13(87)	–	–
Total	–	–	87	13(87)	–	18(76)
Full-time Grad. Stud.	–	–	87	–	–	–
First-year Grad. Stud.	–	–	16	–	–	–

GRADUATE DEGREE REQUIREMENTS

Master's: Thirty-two semester hours (96 units) of course work with grade average of B or above are required. There are no thesis or language requirements. One year of residence is required.

Doctorate: Satisfactory performance in an approved program. Additional course requirements will depend on level of preparation. Comprehensive oral research qualifying examination, annual research reviews, thesis, and final thesis defense are required. One year of residence as a full-time student is required. There is a teaching requirement for the Ph.D. degree.

Thesis: Thesis may be written in absentia.

SPECIAL EQUIPMENT, FACILITIES, OR PROGRAMS

The McWilliams Center for Cosmology brings together astrophysicists, particle physicists, computer scientists, and statisticians to advance our understanding of the dark matter and dark energy that dominate the universe. Observational astrophysics is performed using a variety of space-based and ground-based telescopes. Computation for astrophysics is performed on the largest NSF and NASA facilities and using the McWilliams Center 2000 core cluster. Instrumentation for several internationally deployed radio telescopes is developed in laboratories within the center.

The department maintains facilities for condensed matter and biological physics research, including apparatus for X-ray diffraction and reflection, laser spectroscopies, calorimetry, low-temperature magnetic and electrical transport measurements, optical characterization of interfaces, scanning tunneling and atomic force microscopies, low-energy electron microscopy, and sample preparation. Scattering experiments are performed at an in-house X-ray facility, including fixed tube and rotating anode sources as well as at national synchrotron and neutron facilities. Computation facilities for these groups include five multicore, multinode, high-performance clusters. Collaborations with other departments provide access to additional facilities, including clean-room and nanofabrication facilities, electron microscopies, optical microscopies, magnetic measurements, and fluids and interface characterization.

High-energy research is performed by faculty using facilities at the Fermi National Accelerator Laboratory (Chicago, Illinois), CERN (Geneva, Switzerland), IHEP (Beijing, China), and KEK (Tsukuba, Japan). A data analysis facility is maintained on campus, as are laboratories for small projects to develop detection systems.

The nuclear physics group has its own machine shop and machinist, allowing design, construction and testing of large detectors on campus. These are used in our experiments at the Thomas Jefferson National Accelerator Facility (JLab) in Virginia, KATRIN in Germany and Coherent at Oak Ridge. Present work uses the recent 12Gev JLab energy upgrade and includes the GlueX exotic meson search and the Hall A parity violation program and SBS spectometer. Our efforts in neutrino physics are currently focused on the KATRIN experiment in Germany and we have recently joined an effort at Oak Ridge to measure neutrino scattering (Coherent). The group maintains a 1000-core computer cluster for computational studies and data analysis.

Departmental facilities include machine shops, numerous computer clusters, and a stock room. The University Computing Center operates an extensive system of networked scientific workstations and microcomputers with central file servers for research and educational applications. Access to a Cray XT3 MPP supercomputer as well as sets of SMP machines are available through the Pittsburgh Supercomputing Center. The Physics Department is located in Wean Hall, which also houses the science and engineering library.

Table B—Separately Budgeted Research Expenditures by Source of Support

Source of Support	Departmental Research	Physics-related Research Outside Department
Federal government	$6,123,587	$230,800
State/local government		
Non-profit organizations		
Business and industry		
Other	$2,106,155	
Total	$8,229,742	$230,800

Table C—Separately Budgeted Research Expenditures by Research Specialty

Research Specialty	No. of Grants	Expenditures ($)
Astrophysics	35	$1,933,096
Biophysics	17	$1,194,116
Condensed Matter Physics	48	$2,043,979
Nuclear Physics	16	$1,802,900
Particles and Fields	7	$950,233
Quantum Foundations	1	$81,625
Statistical & Thermal Physics	3	$223,793
Total	127	$8,229,742

FACULTY

Professor

Briere, Roy A., Ph.D., University of Chicago, 1995. *Particles and Fields.* Experimental high-energy physics; Belle II at KEK; BESIII at IHEP (Beijing).

Croft, Rupert, Ph.D., University of Oxford, 1995. *Astrophysics.* Theoretical astrophysics/cosmology; simulations of the evolution of the universe.

Deserno, Markus, Ph.D., University of Mainz, 2000. *Biophysics.* Theoretical condensed matter and biophysics; membrane structure and properties.

Di Matteo, Tiziana, Ph.D., University of Cambridge, 1998. *Astrophysics.* Theoretical astrophysics/cosmology; cosmological simulations.

Dodelson, Scott, Ph.D., Columbia University, 1988. Department Head. *Astrophysics.* Theoretical and observational cosmology; fundamental physics from cosmic surveys.

Feenstra, Randall M., Ph.D., California Institute of Technology, 1982. *Condensed Matter Physics.* Experimental condensed matter physics; semiconductor surfaces.

Franklin, Gregg B., Ph.D., Massachusetts Institute of Technology, 1980. *Nuclear Physics.* Experimental medium energy/nuclear physics; nucleon form factors, structure functions and neutrino physics.

Garoff, Stephen, Ph.D., Harvard University, 1977. *Condensed Matter Physics.* Experimental condensed matter physics; surfaces and interfaces.

Gilman, Frederick, Ph.D., Princeton University, 1965. *Particles and Fields.* Theoretical elementary particle physics; CP violation, heavy quarks, and leptons.

Lösche, Mathias, Ph.D., Technical U. of Munich, 1986. *Biophysics.* Experimental biological physics; molecular and membrane biophysics.

Majetich, Sara A., Ph.D., University of Georgia, 1987. *Condensed Matter Physics.* Experimental condensed matter physics; semiconductor and magnetic nanoparticles.

Meyer, Curtis A., Ph.D., University of California, Berkeley, 1987. Associate Dean of Mellon College of Science. *Nuclear Physics.* Experimental medium-energy/nuclear physics; meson spectroscopy; search for gluonic excitations with GlueX at JLab.

Morningstar, Colin J., Ph.D., University of Toronto, 1991. *Nuclear Physics.* Theoretical nuclear physics and Lattice QCD; nonperturbative phenomena in quantum field theories; meson and baryon spectroscopies.

Paulini, Manfred, Ph.D., University of Erlangen, 1993. *Particles and Fields.* Experimental high-energy physics; CMS at CERN.

Peterson, Jeffrey B., Ph.D., University of California, Berkeley, 1985. *Astrophysics.* Experimental astrophysics; observational cosmology.

Quinn, Brian P., Ph.D., Massachusetts Institute of Technology, 1984. *Nuclear Physics.* Experimental medium energy/nuclear physics; nucleon form factors; parity-violating electron scattering and nucleon structure functions.

Rothstein, Ira Z., Ph.D., University of Maryland, College Park, 1992. *Particles and Fields.* Theoretical particle physics and cosmology; LHC theory; gravity waves.

Schumacher, Reinhard A., Ph.D., Massachusetts Institute of Technology, 1983. *Nuclear Physics.* Experimental medium energy/nuclear physics; photo-and electro-production of hadrons; GlueX and CLAS at JLab.

Widom, Michael, Ph.D., University of Chicago, 1983. *Condensed Matter Physics.* Theoretical condensed matter physics; metal alloys; crystallography; biophysics.

Associate Professor

Kahniashvili, Tina, Ph.D., Space Research Institute, Moscow, 1988. *Astrophysics.* Theoretical cosmology/astrophysics; Theory of gravity; studying physical processes in the early universe.

Mandelbaum, Rachel, Ph.D., Princeton University, 2006. *Astrophysics.* Observational astrophysics/cosmology; lensing studies of galaxies and large-scale structure.

Trac, Hy, Ph.D., University of Toronto, 2004. *Astrophysics.* Theoretical astrophysics/cosmology; evolution of the dark matter, baryons, and stars.

Xiao, Di, Ph.D., University of Texas, Austin, 2007. *Condensed Matter Physics.* Theoretical condensed matter physics; quantum transport; Berry phase.

Assistant Professor

Alison, John, Ph.D., University of Pennsylvania, 2012. CMS at CERN. *Particles and Fields.* Experimental high-energy physics.

Heinrich, Frank, Ph.D., University of Leipzig, 2005. *Biophysics.* Experimental biological physics; neutron scattering.

Hunt, Benjamin, Ph.D., Cornell University, 2009. Experimental condensed matter physics; graphene heterostructures.

Katoch, Jyoti, Ph.D., University of Central Florida, 2014. *Condensed Matter Physics.* Experimental condensed matter physics; 2D materials and nanoARPES.

Koposov, Sergey, Ph.D., University of Heidelberg, 2009. *Astrophysics.* Observational astrophysics/cosmology; dark matter; galaxy evolution; near-field cosmology.

Parno, Diana, Ph.D., Carnegie Mellon University, 2011. *Nuclear Physics.* Experimental nuclear physics; parity violation; fundamental symmetries; neutrino physics.

Penco, Riccardo, Ph.D., Syracuse University, 2012. *Particles and Fields.* Theoretical particle physics, condensed matter, and cosmology; effective field theory.

Singh, Simran, Ph.D., University of Central Florida, 2014. *Condensed Matter Physics.* Experimental condensed matter physics; 2D materials and spintronics.

Walker, Matthew, Ph.D., University of Michigan, 2007. *Astrophysics.* Observational astrophysics/cosmology; dark matter; galactic dynamics; near-field cosmology.

Emeritus

Berger, Luc, Ph.D., University of Lausanne, 1960. *Condensed Matter Physics.* Experimental and theoretical condensed matter physics; studies of metallic ferromagnets.

Engler, Arnold, Ph.D., University of Berne, 1953. *Particles and Fields.* Experimental high-energy physics; colliding beams techniques.

Ferguson, Thomas A., Ph.D., University of California, Los Angeles, 1978. *Particles and Fields.* Experimental high-energy physics; CMS at CERN.

Fetkovich, John G., Ph.D., Carnegie Mellon University, 1959. Special Assistant to the President for Academic Affairs.

Griffiths, Robert B., Ph.D., Stanford University, 1962. *Quantum Foundations.* Theoretical physics; foundations of quantum mechanics.

Holman, Richard F., Ph.D., Johns Hopkins University, 1982. *Particles and Fields.* Theoretical particle physics and cosmology; inflation; dark energy.

Kisslinger, Leonard S., Ph.D., Indiana University, 1956. *Nuclear Physics.* Theoretical nuclear and particle physics; nonperturbative QCD.

Kraemer, Robert W., Ph.D., Johns Hopkins University, 1962. *Particles and Fields.* Experimental high-energy physics; colliding beams techniques.

Levine, Michael J., Ph.D., California Institute of Technology, 1963. *Particles and Fields.* Theoretical elementary particle physics.

Li, Ling-Fong, Ph.D., University of Pennsylvania, 1970. *Particles and Fields.* Theoretical elementary particle physics; unified theories of particle interactions.

Nagle, John F., Ph.D., Yale University, 1965. *Biophysics*. Experimental and theoretical biological physics; statistical mechanics of phase transitions; biomembranes.

Russ, James S., Ph.D., Princeton University, 1966. *Particles and Fields*. Experimental high-energy physics; CDF at Fermilab; CMS at CERN.

Schumacher, Robert T., Ph.D., University of Illinois, 1955. Musical acoustics; magnetic resonance in solids.

Sekerka, Robert F., Ph.D., Harvard University, 1965. *Condensed Matter Physics*. Theoretical condensed matter physics; problems in materials science.

Suter, Robert M., Ph.D., Clark University, 1978. *Condensed Matter Physics*. Experimental condensed matter physics; X-ray and neutron scattering studies.

Swendsen, Robert H., Ph.D., University of Pennsylvania, 1971. *Condensed Matter Physics*. Theoretical condensed matter physics; computer simulations; statistical mechanics of phase transitions and biological molecules.

Tristram-Nagle, Stephanie, Ph.D., University of California, Berkeley, 1981. *Biophysics*. Experimental biophysics; membrane biophysics.

Vander Ven, Ned S., Ph.D., Princeton University, 1962. *Condensed Matter Physics*. Experimental condensed matter physics; electron and nuclear spin resonance in solids.

Vogel, Helmut, Ph.D., University of Erlangen, 1979. *Particles and Fields*. Experimental high-energy physics; CMS at CERN.

Faculty by Courtesy

Anna, Shelley, Ph.D., Harvard University, 2000. Dynamic of soft matter; fluid mechanics.

Greve, David, Ph.D., Lehigh University, 1979. Physics and development of novel sensors.

Islam, Mohammad, Ph.D., Lehigh University, 2000. Structure, dynamics, and self-assembly of soft matter; properties of nanoscale structures.

Marom, Noa, Ph.D., Weizmnn Institute of Science, 2010. Computational materials science.

McHenry, Michael, Ph.D., Massachusetts Institute of Technology, 1988. Magnetic properties of materials.

Rollett, Anthony, Ph.D., Drexel University, 1987. Microstructure of polycrystalline materials.

Skowronski, Marek, Ph.D., Warsaw University, 1982. *Solid State Physics*. electronic materials, nanoscale devices.

Viswanathan, Venkat, Ph.D., Stanford, 2013. Materials physics for novel energy conversion and storage.

Zhu, Jian-Gang, Ph.D., University of California, San Diego, 1983. Magnetic data storage technologies.

DEPARTMENTAL RESEARCH SPECIALTIES AND STAFF

Theoretical

Astrophysics. The largest scale simulations of the structure formation of the universe yet performed; the formation and evolution of galaxies, and their associated supermassive black holes; the nature of dark matter and dark energy; the cosmology-particle physics interface; early universe/inflationary physics; gravitational waves. Croft, Di Matteo, Dodelson, Kahniashvili, Penco, Rothstein, Trac.

Biophysics. Theoretical and computational studies of biomembranes and proteins; elastic continuum theory and differential geometry of lipid membranes; statistical mechanics and coarse-grained simulation studies of biophysical systems; structure of viruses and nucleic acids. Deserno, Nagle, Widom.

Computational Physics. There is a broad range of computational activity within each of the research groups, including simulations in cosmology, biophysics, and Lattice QCD; tight connections with statistics and machine learning; and pipeline development for analyses. Croft, Deserno, Di Matteo, Dodelson, Koposov, Levine, Mandelbaum, Marom, Meyer, Morningstar, Paulini, Rollett, Suter, Swendsen, Trac, Walker, Widom, Xiao.

Condensed Matter Physics. Topological insulators and Berry phases; Monte Carlo studies of complex fluids, biological molecules, disordered solids and phase transitions; modeling of quasicrystals, ferromagnets, incommensurate phases, and quantum transport. Marom, Nagle, Penco, Rollett, Rothstein, Swendsen, Widom, Xiao, Zhu.

Nuclear Physics. Strong and weak nuclear force; formation of hadrons, confinement, exotic forms of matter; Markov-chain and Monte Carlo computation of QCD; lattice gauge theory; QCD sum rules. Kisslinger, Morningstar.

Particles and Fields. Quantum gauge field theories and their applications to experiments; weak interaction phenomenology; CP violation; heavy quark physics; LHC phenomenology; effective field theories. Gilman, Penco, Rothstein.

Quantum Foundations. Reformulation of quantum theory using consistent histories and decoherence and application of quantum mechanics in computing. Griffiths.

Experimental

Astrophysics. Astrophysics research is integrated within the Bruce and Astrid McWilliams Center for Cosmology, which brings together physicists, computer scientists, and statisticians to advance our understanding of dark matter and dark energy. Institutional member of the Sloan Digital Sky Survey and the Large Synoptic Survey Telescope collaborations. Individuals participate in a number of other ongoing observational cosmology experiments, including those in 21-cm cosmology, development of radio and optical telescopes for intensity mapping, studies of weak lensing and large-scale structure, early evolution and formation of galaxies, and dark matter via detection and dynamics of dwarf galaxies (near-field cosmology). Dodelson, Koposov, Mandelbaum, Peterson, Walker.

Biophysics. Structure and function of biomembranes; neutron and X-ray scattering investigations of lipid bilayers and their interactions with peptides and proteins; biofluid mechanics of lung airways; biopolymer dynamics. Garoff, Heinrich, Lösche, Nagle, Tristram-Nagle.

Condensed Matter Physics. Properties and applications of nanoparticles and nanostructures; structure of thin organic and metal solid films; structure and properties of liquid/solid interfaces; wetting of fluids on solids; structure of semiconductor and metal surfaces; structure and properties of graphene; materials; graphene heterostructures; low-temperature transport measurements under high magnetic fields; influence of surface properties on semiconductor devices; magnetic films for data storage; X-ray scattering from thin films and surfaces; X-ray microscopy for characterization of grain structure and growth in metals; microfluidics; interfacial fluid mechanics; properties and application of nanotubes and nanorods; many of these activities are performed in active collaboration with other departments, institutes, and centers in the science and engineering colleges. Anna, Feenstra, Garoff, Greve, Hunt, Islam, Katoch, Majetich, McHenry, Singh, Skowronski, Suter, Viswanathan, Zhu.

Nuclear Physics. Strong QCD; the spectrum of excited baryons; gluonic excitations of mesons and quark confinement using GlueX at JLab; form factors and structure functions of the proton and neutron; parity-violating eletron scattering and compton polarimetry in ItallA at JLab; neutrino mass limits at KATRIN; coherent scattering at the Spallation Neutron Source. Franklin, Meyer, Parno, Quinn, Reinhard Schumacher.

Particles and Fields. Operation, data analysis, and R&D for detector upgrade of the CMS experiment at the LHC collider at CERN; search for physics beyond the standard model in the form of supersymmetry and heavy non-standard quarks; study of heavy quark production and decay properties; studies of the properties of charm quarks using the BESIII experiment in Beijing, China; high-precision studies of heavy quark systems at Belle II. Alison, Briere, Paulini, Russ, Vogel.

View additional information about this department at www.gradschoolshopper.com. Check out the "Why Choose Us?" section, find out more about the department's culture and get links to social media networks.

DREXEL UNIVERSITY

DEPARTMENT OF PHYSICS

Philadelphia, Pennsylvania 19104
http://www.drexel.edu/physics

General University Information
President: John A. Fry
Dean of Graduate School: Elisabeth Van Bockstaele
University website: http://www.drexel.edu
School Type: Private
Setting: Urban
Total Faculty: 2,489
Total number of Students: 24,190
Total number of Graduate Students: 8,692

Department Information
Department Chairman: Prof. Stephen L.W. McMillan, Head
Department Contact: Prof. Michael Vogeley, Associate
   Department Head for Graduate Studies
   Total full-time faculty: 20
   Total number of full-time equivalent positions: 20
   Full-Time Graduate Students: 43
   Female Full-Time Graduate Students: 10
   First-Year Graduate Students: 5
   Total Post Doctorates: 3

Department Address
3141 Chestnut Street
Philadelphia, PA 19104
Phone: (215) 895-2708
Fax: (215) 895-5934
E-mail: physics@drexel.edu
Website: http://www.drexel.edu/physics

ADMISSIONS

Admission Contact Information
Address admission inquiries to: Office of Graduate Admissions,
   Main Building, Room 212, 3141 Chestnut Street, Philadel-
   phia, PA 19104
Phone: 1-800-2-DREXEL
E-mail: enroll@drexel.edu
Admissions website: http://www.drexel.edu/grad/programs/coas/
   physics/

Application deadlines
Fall admission:
U.S. students: January 1   *Int'l. students*: January 1

Application fee
U.S. students: $65   *Int'l. students*: $65

Admissions information
For Fall of 2018:
   Number of applicants: 65
   Number admitted: 21
   Number enrolled: 8

Admission requirements
Bachelor's degree requirements: Bachelor's degree in an ap-
   proved program is required.
Minimum undergraduate GPA: 3.0

GRE requirements
The GRE is required.
   Quantitative score: 150
   Verbal score: 150
   Analytical score: 3.5

Subjective GRE requirements
The Subjective GRE is required.
GRE Physics Subject Test is required for Ph.D. applicants to be
   considered for assistantships (no minimum score).

TOEFL requirements
The TOEFL exam is required for students from non-English-
   speaking countries.
   PBT score: 600
   iBT score: 100
IELTS scores may be submitted in lieu of TOEFL scores - minimum band score 7.0. TOEFL or IELTS scores below these
   levels may be considered, but may require an interview.

Other admissions information
Additional requirements: An essay, a resume, and two letters of
   recommendations are required for all applicants.
   Teaching assistants educated in non-English-speaking countries must complete a special English program.
Undergraduate preparation assumed: Advanced undergraduate
   coursework in classical mechanics, electromagnetism, statistical physics, and quantum mechanics. Mathematics coursework in differential equations and linear algebra.

TUITION

Tuition year 2017–18:
   Full-time students: $1,297 per credit
   Part-time students: $1,297 per credit
Average cost per course: $3,891.
Credit hours per semester to be considered full-time: 9
Deferred tuition plan: No
Health insurance: Available
Other academic fees: Health insurance is covered by Drexel for
   full-time PhD program students with assistantships.
Academic term: Quarter
Number of first-year students who received full tuition waivers: 9

Teaching Assistants, Research Assistants, and Fellowships
   Number of first-year
      Teaching Assistants: 7
      Research Assistants: 1
   Average stipend per academic year
      Teaching Assistant: $23,500
      Research Assistant: $27,000
      Fellowship student: $5,000
All admitted full-time PhD students receive full support. Support is normally provided over a twelve-month period to all
   eligible students and includes full tuition, fees, and health insurance. Admitted students are automatically considered for
   other graduate school fellowships that range from $2,500 to
   $5,000 of additional support per year. Fellowships are
   awarded based on academic merit at the time of acceptance
   to the program.

FINANCIAL AID

Application deadlines

Fall admission:
U.S. students: September 1   *Int'l. students*: September 1

Loans

Loans are available for U.S. students.
Loans are not available for international students.
GAPSFAS application required: No
FAFSA application required: Yes

For further information

Address financial aid inquiries to: Student Financial Services, 3141 Chestnut Street, Main Building, Room 106, Philadelphia, PA 19104.
Phone: (215) 895-1600
Financial aid website: http://www.drexel.edu/grad/financing/

HOUSING

Availability of on-campus housing

Single students: Yes
Married students: No
Childcare Assistance: No

For further information

Address housing inquiries to: Office of University Housing, 101 N. 34th Street, Philadelphia, PA 19104.
Phone: (215) 895-6155
E-mail: housing@drexel.edu
Housing aid website: http://www.drexel.edu/campusservices/ universityHousing/graduate-housing/

Table A—Faculty, Enrollments, and Degrees Granted

Research Specialty	2017–18 Faculty	Enrollment Fall 2017–18		Number of Degrees Granted AY 2017–18 (2013–18)		
		Master's	Doctorate	Master's	Terminal Master's	Doctorate
Astrophysics	4	–	16	3(14)	–(2)	4(12)
Biophysics	4	–	8	1(7)	–(3)	2(8)
Condensed Matter Physics	3	–	9	5(9)	–	1(3)
Nonlinear Dynamics and Complex Systems	–	–	–	–	–(1)	–(1)
Particles and Fields	4	–	11	2(7)	–	2(4)
Physics and other Science Education	1	–	2	–	–	–
Non-specialized	–	–	–	–(1)	–(3)	–
Other	1	–	–	–	–	–
Total	17	1	43	11(38)	–(9)	9(28)
Full-time Grad. Stud.	–	–	40	–	–	–
First-year Grad. Stud.	–	–	8	–	–	–

GRADUATE DEGREE REQUIREMENTS

Master's: The requirement for the Master's degree is 45 quarter credits. The student is required to maintain at least a 3.0 GPA. There are no thesis or foreign language requirement for the M.S. degree. There is no specific residence requirement for the M.S. degree. There are no examinations required for the M.S. degree.

Doctorate: In addition to required graduate-level coursework in physics, the successful Ph.D. candidate must: (a) pass the Ph.D. candidacy examination; and (b) perform original re-search, write a satisfactory thesis describing that research and defend the thesis in an oral examination. There is no foreign language requirement.

Thesis: Thesis may be written in absentia.

SPECIAL EQUIPMENT, FACILITIES, OR PROGRAMS

Astrophysics Facilities:

● The Numerical Astrophysics Facility emphasizes theoretical and numerical studies of stars, star formation, planetary systems, star clusters, galaxy distributions, cosmological modeling, gravitational lensing, and the early universe. The facility employs a high-performance Graphics Processing Unit (GPU) compute cluster, each node containing two 6-core, 2.7 GHz Intel Xeon CPUs and 96 Gbytes of RAM, accelerated by 4–6 Nvidia Fermi/ Titan GPUs, and connected by QDR infiniband, affording computational speeds of up to 50 trillion floating point operations per second.

● The Joseph R. Lynch Observatory houses a 16-inch Mead Schmidt-Cassegrain telescope equipped with an SBIG CCD camera.

● Drexel was a member of the original Sloan Digital Sky Survey (SDSS) collaboration; faculty and students remain active in analyzing data from the SDSS. Drexel is an institutional member of the Large Synoptic Survey Telescope (LSST), currently under construction in Chile; faculty and students are developing LSST-related machine learning tools and analyzing simulated LSST data to prepare for "first light" in 2022.

Biophysics Facilities:

● Bio-manipulation and microscopy laboratories. Four optical tables and six research grade microscopes are configured to perform microscopic spectroscopy and manipulation on solutions and individual cells. A spatial light modulator allows spatial patterns to be encoded on samples and explored; all microscopes are temperature controlled with state of the art cameras, including a 2,000 frame per second high speed system. Each optical table is also equipped with high power lasers for photolysis or fluorescence spectroscopy. Microfluidic attachments are present on one table, and in an adjacent laboratory, a small microfluidic fabrication facility has been established.

● Experimental biophysics lab for studies of proteins and biomimetic lipids, including a fluorescence spectrometer.

● The Computational Biophysics facility also includes: (i) a Beowulf cluster with 46 dual Quad-core hyperthreaded Xeon CPU (736 cores) and 12Gb of RAM nodes plus a master with 1Tb of storage and 24Gb of RAM, (ii) a Beowulf cluster with 44 dual-core Xeon CPU (344 cores),(iii) a dual Quad-core hyperthreaded Xeon CPU workstation with 24Gb RAM and 3Tb disk with two Tesla C2050 GPU CUDA-accelerated graphics card, (iv) a dual Quad-core hyperthreaded Xeon CPU workstation with 8Gb RAM and 4Tb disk with an NVIDIA N280 GPU CUDA-accelerated graphics card, (v) a quad 8-core hyperthreaded Xeon CPU workstation with 128Gb RAM and 16Tb total disk, (vi) a 72Tb file server with 12Gb RAM, (vii) a 96Tb quad 6-core file server with 64Gb RAM, (viii) and several Linux workstations connected through a gigabit network.

Condensed Matter Facilities:

● The Ultrafast Electron Diffraction laboratory investigates structural dynamics in nanoscale materials at timescales that are fundamental to materials science and condensed matter physics. The techniques are based on exciting matter with light and probing the response of the lattice with electrons. The research interests of the lab are in a range of phenomena and systems including phase transformations induced by strong laser excitation, phase transformations in strongly correlated systems, generation and detection of coherent lattice vibrations, and characterization of materials properties of graphene, few-layer-graphene, ultra-thin graphite & nanocrystalline diamond.

● Research in the Energy Materials Research Laboratory is devoted to atomic scale investigations of materials for energy. As the size of the system shrinks, conventional bulk thermodynamics becomes irrelevant and we enter the realm of mesoscopic physics. The equilibrium behavior of small systems is governed by the prevailing number of surface atoms that behave differently from the bulk ones. The electronic properties are also subject to reduced number of available electronic states. We take advantage of different scanning probe microscopy and spectroscopy techniques to elucidate the local electronic properties of materials that are relevant to solving energy problems. This laboratory research is funded by grants from NSF and DOE.

● The Ultra-low Temperature Laboratory includes a dilution refrigerator, 3He and 4He cryostats and microwave sources to study quantum phenomena in nano and microscale devices, superconducting qubits, nanostructures and quantum fluids and solids.

● The Mesoscale Materials Laboratory investigates light-matter interactions and the extent and effects of ordering of lattice, charge and spin degrees of freedom on electronic phases and functional properties in solids, with an emphasis on bulk and epitaxial film complex oxides. Facilities include instrumentation for pulsed laser deposition of epitaxial complex oxide films, atomic layer deposition, variable-temperature characterization of carrier transport (DC to 20 GHz), and a laser spectroscopy lab enabling high-resolution Raman scattering spectroscopy at temperatures to 1.5 K and under magnetic field to 7 T.

Particle Physics Facilities:

● The Drexel particle physics group contributes to neutrino oscillation experiments at different baselines, including the DUNE long baseline experiment hosted by Fermilab, the Double Chooz experiment in France, and the PROSPECT short baseline experiment at Oak Ridge National Laboratory.

● We are also active in the IceCube neutrino telescope located at the geographic South Pole, the EXO-200 experiment located in NM, and the PICO dark matter experiment located at SNO-LAB in Canada.

● The Bubble Chamber Laboratory develops superheated-liquid detectors for rare-interaction searches.

Laboratory for High-Performance Computational Physics:

● In addition to the department computing cluster (15 linux workstations), high-performance computing resources include a dual-processor server with two Xeon E5-2650 processors (16 cores), 128 GB of RAM, and two Xeon Phi P5110 co-processor cards (480 cores). Department researchers also have access to a cluster of 18 Dell PowerEdge C6145 servers (AMD Opteron 6378 Piledriver CPU's, 64 cores/server, 256 GB RAM/server) with a total of 1152 cores and 4.5TB RAM.

FACULTY

Professor

DiNardo, N. John, Ph.D., University of Pennsylvania, 1982. Studies of surfaces and interfacial phenomena in solids.

Ferrone, Frank, Ph.D., Princeton University, 1974. *Biophysics*. Experimental and theoretical protein dynamics, kinetics of biological self-assembly, including sickle cell and Alzheimer's disease, sickle cell testing and diagnostic devices.

Goldberg, David M., Ph.D., Princeton University, 2000. Associate Department Head for Undergraduate Studies. *Astro-*

physics. Theoretical and computational cosmology, extragalactic astrophysics, gravitational lensing.

Karapetrov, Goran, Ph.D., Oregon State University, 1996. *Condensed Matter Physics, Nano Science and Technology*. Experimental solid state physics, scanning probe microscopy, nanoscale catalysis, mesoscopic superconductivity.

Lane, Charles E., Ph.D., California Institute of Technology, 1987. *Particles and Fields*. Experimental tests of invariance principles and conservation laws, neutrino oscillations and properties.

McMillan, Stephen L. W., Ph.D., Harvard University, 1983. Department Head. *Astrophysics*. Stellar dynamics, large-scale computations of stellar systems, and high-performance special-purpose computers.

Richards, Gordon, Ph.D., University of Chicago, 2000. *Astrophysics*. Quasars, active galactic nuclei, supermassive black holes, galaxy evolution, sky surveys, infrared/X-ray/radio astronomy.

Tyagi, Somdev, Ph.D., Brigham Young University, 1976. Associate Head of Non-Major Studies in Physics. *Condensed Matter Physics*. Nanobiophysics, Raman spectroscopy, magnetic materials.

Vogeley, Michael S., Ph.D., Harvard University, 1993. Associate Department Head for Graduate Studies. *Astrophysics*. Large-scale structure and cosmology; galaxy formation and evolution; statistical analysis of large data sets; active galactic nuclei.

Yuan, Jian-Min, Ph.D., University of Chicago, 1973. *Biophysics*. Protein folding, signal transduction pathways, computational biophysics, nonlinear dynamics and chaos in atomic and molecular systems, protein folding.

Associate Professor

Brewe, Eric, Ph.D., Arizona State University, 2002. *Physics and other Science Education*. Physics Education Research, Introductory course reform, Network analysis in learning, Neuromechanisms of learning.

Cruz Cruz, Luis, Ph.D., Massachusetts Institute of Technology, 1994. *Biophysics*. Computational studies of confinement effects on the folding of amyloidogenic proteins, spatial correlations of neurons in the brain, firing dynamics of neuronal networks, fluid flow through porous media.

Dolinski, Michelle J., Ph.D., University of California, Berkeley, 2008. *Particles and Fields*. Neutrino physics, rare nuclear decays, cryogenic detector technologies.

Urbanc, Brigita, Ph.D., University of Ljubljana, 1994. *Biophysics*. Computational and experimental biophysics of protein folding and assembly, relevant to Alzheimer's and Parkinson's disease; discrete molecular dynamics of coarsegrained protein and lipid models.

Assistant Professor

Harb, Maher, Ph.D., University of Toronto, 2009. *Condensed Matter Physics, Solid State Physics*. Solid state physics, ultrafast electron diffraction, time-resolved X-ray diffraction, ultrafast lasers, nanofabrication, nano/microfluidics, instrument development, vacuum technologies.

Kurahashi Neilson, Naoko, Ph.D., Stanford University, 2010. *Particles and Fields*. Neutrino physics, high energy astroparticle physics.

Neilson, Russell, Ph.D., Stanford University, 2012. *Particles and Fields*. Dark matter, neutrino physics.

Teaching Assistant Professor

Aprelev, Alexey, Ph.D., St. Petersburg University, 1995. *Biophysics*. Experimental biophysics.

Kratzer, Rachael M., Ph.D., Drexel University, 2014. *Astrophysics*. Quasars, active galactic nuclei.

Love, Christina, Ph.D., Temple University, 2013. *Physics and other Science Education*. Educational Methods and Technology, STEM Education, Science Literacy and Outreach, Particle Physics, Astrophysics.

Affiliate Professor

Spanier, Jonathan, Ph.D., Columbia University, 2001. *Condensed Matter Physics, Nano Science and Technology, Solid State Physics*. Light-matter interactions in electronic materials, including ferroelectric semiconductors, complex oxide thin film science; laser spectroscopy, including Raman scattering.

Visiting Research Professor

Mac Low, Mordecai-Mark, Ph.D., University of Colorado, 1989. *Astrophysics*. Structure of the interstellar medium and molecular clouds; blast waves; star formation; circumstellar nebulae; planetary impacts; computational gas dynamics; magnetohydrodynamics.

Novosad, Valentyn, Ph.D., Institute for Low Temperature Physics & Engineering, 1998. *Solid State Physics*. Experimental solid state physics, scanning probe microscopy, nanomagnetism, mesoscopic superconductivity.

Posdoctoral Research Associate

Insler, Jonathan, Ph.D., University of Rochester, 2011. *Particles and Fields*. Neutrino physics.

Richman, Michael D., Ph.D., University of Maryland, 2015. *Particles and Fields*. IceCube, Astroparticle, Neutrino, Machine Learning.

Yen, Yung-Ruey, Ph.D., University of Maryland, 2013. *Particles and Fields*. Neutrino Physics, Rare Nuclear Decays, Cryogenic Detector Technologies.

DEPARTMENTAL RESEARCH SPECIALTIES AND STAFF

Theoretical

Astrophysics. Large-scale structure and cosmology; gravitational lensing; numerical simulation of dense stellar systems; high-performance computing. Goldberg, Mac Low, McMillan, Vogeley.

Biophysics. Protein folding and self-assembly; neurodegenerative diseases; systems biology and bionetwork. Cruz Cruz, Urbanc, Yuan.

Experimental

Astrophysics. Large-scale structure and cosmology; galactic and extragalactic astronomy; galaxy surveys (Sloan Digital Sky Survey, Large Synoptic Survey Telescope); active galactic nuclei/quasars; black holes; dynamics of star clusters and galactic nuclei. Goldberg, Richards, Vogeley.

Biophysics. Experimental protein dynamics, kinetics of biological self-assembly, including sickle cell and Alzheimer's disease, sickle cell testing and diagnostic devices. Protein folding and assembly relevant to Alzheimer's and Parkinson's disease; discrete molecular dynamics of coarse-grained protein and lipid models. Aprelev, Ferrone, Urbanc.

Condensed Matter Physics. Experimental solid-state physics; scanning probe microscopy; nanoscale catalysis; mesoscopic superconductivity; ultrafast electron diffraction; time-resolved X-ray diffraction; ultrafast lasers; nanofabrication; nano/microfluidics; instrument development; vacuum technologies. Harb, Karapetrov, Novosad, Spanier, Tyagi.

Particles and Fields. Neutrino physics, rare nuclear decays, cryogenic detector technologies; high energy astro-particle physics; dark matter; experimental tests of invariance principles and conservation laws, neutrino oscillations and properties. Dolinski, Insler, Kurahashi Neilson, Lane, Neilson, Richman, Yen.

Physics Education Research. Active learning classrooms and reformed pedagogical practices, student networks and physics learning, instructional transformation, and Modeling Instruction. Brewe.

View additional information about this department at www.gradschoolshopper.com. Check out the "Why Choose Us?" section, find out more about the department's culture and get links to social media networks.

LEHIGH UNIVERSITY

DEPARTMENT OF PHYSICS

Bethlehem, Pennsylvania 18015
http://www.physics.lehigh.edu

General University Information
President: John D. Simon
Dean of Graduate School: Donald E. Hall
University website: http://www.lehigh.edu
School Type: Private
Setting: Suburban
Total Faculty: 520
Total Graduate Faculty: 520
Total number of Students: 7,020
Total number of Graduate Students: 1,940

Department Information
Department Chairman: Prof. Volkmar Dierolf, Chair
Department Contact: Marina Long, Physics Graduate
  Coordinator
  Total full-time faculty: 17
  Total number of full-time equivalent positions: 17
  Full-Time Graduate Students: 42
  Female Full-Time Graduate Students: 16
  First-Year Graduate Students: 9
  Female First-Year Students: 3
  Total Post Doctorates: 6

Department Address
16 Memorial Drive, East
Bethlehem, PA 18015
Phone: (610) 758-3931
Fax: (610) 758-5730
E-mail: physics@lehigh.edu
Website: http://www.physics.lehigh.edu

ADMISSIONS

Admission Contact Information
Address admission inquiries to: Graduate Admissions Officer,
  Lehigh University, Department of Physics, 16 Memorial
  Drive, East, Bethlehem, PA 18015
Phone: (610) 758-3931
E-mail: physics@lehigh.edu
Admissions website: http://physics.cas2.lehigh.edu/how-apply-0

Application deadlines
Fall admission:
U.S. students: January 15   *Int'l. students*: January 15

Application fee
U.S. students: $75   *Int'l. students*: $75
Review of graduate applications begins around January 15th of
  each year.

Admissions information
For Fall of 2018:
  Number of applicants: 111
  Number admitted: 26
  Number enrolled: 9

Admission requirements
Bachelor's degree requirements: Bachelor's degree in physics
  or a related field is required.
Minimum undergraduate GPA: 3.0

GRE requirements
The GRE is required.

Subjective GRE requirements
The Subjective GRE is recommended.

TOEFL requirements
The TOEFL exam is required for students from non-English-
  speaking countries.
  iBT score: 85

Other admissions information
Undergraduate preparation assumed: Intermediate mechanics,
  electricity and magnetism, atomic and quantum physics, thermodynamics, and laboratory experience. Mathematics
  through partial differential equations. Able students with inadequate preparation may take a limited number of remedial
  courses after enrollment.

TUITION

Tuition year 2018–19:
  Full-time students: $1,500 per credit
  Part-time students: $1,500 per credit
Tuition waivers are part of each RA/TA/GA support package.
Credit hours per semester to be considered full-time: 9
Deferred tuition plan: Yes
Health insurance: Available at the cost of $1918 per year.
Academic term: Semester
Number of first-year students who received full tuition waivers: 9

Teaching Assistants, Research Assistants, and Fellowships
Number of first-year
  Teaching Assistants: 9
Average stipend per academic year
  Teaching Assistant: $28,800
  Research Assistant: $28,800
  Fellowship student: $28,800
  Numbers in this section refer to 12-month salaries, effective
  in Fall 2018.

FINANCIAL AID

Application deadlines
Fall admission:
U.S. students: January 15   *Int'l. students*: January 15

Loans
Loans are not available for U.S. students.
Loans are not available for international students.
GAPSFAS application required: No
FAFSA application required: No

For further information
Address financial aid inquiries to: Graduate Admissions Officer,
  Lehigh University, Dept. of Physics, 16 Memorial Drive,
  East, Bethlehem, PA 18015.
Phone: (610) 758-3931
E-mail: physics@lehigh.edu
Financial aid website: http://cas.cas2.lehigh.edu/content/
  financial-aid-0

HOUSING

Availability of on-campus housing
Single students: Yes
Married students: Yes
Childcare Assistance: Yes

For further information
Address housing inquiries to: Residence Services Office, Lehigh University, Rathbone Hall, 63 University Drive, Bethlehem, PA 18015.
Phone: (610) 758-3500
E-mail: inrsd@lehigh.edu
Housing aid website: http://financeadmin.lehigh.edu/content/residential-services

Table A—Faculty, Enrollments, and Degrees Granted

Research Specialty	2017–18 Faculty	Enrollment Fall 2017		Number of Degrees Granted 2017–18 (2013–18)		
		Master's	Doctorate	Master's	Terminal Master's	Doctorate
Astrophysics	2	–	6	1(6)	–(1)	1(2)
Atomic, Molecular, & Optical Physics	2	1	2	1(2)	–	–(4)
Biophysics	3	–	11	1(8)	–(1)	1(5)
Condensed Matter Physics	4	1	7	1(10)	–(2)	2(14)
Cosmology & String Theory	1	–	3	–(2)	–	–
High Energy Physics	1	–	4	1(3)	–	–
Nano Science and Technology	–	–	1	1(1)	–	–(4)
Optics	1	–	1	–	–	–
Plasma and Fusion	1	–	–	–	–	–
Polymer Physics/Science	–	–	–	–	–	–
Statistical & Thermal Physics	–	–	5	–(5)	–	2(4)
Non-specialized	2	–	–	–	–	–
Total	17	2	40	6(37)	–(4)	6(33)
Full-time Grad. Stud.	–	2	40	–	–	–
First-year Grad. Stud.	–	2	5	–	–	–

GRADUATE DEGREE REQUIREMENTS

Master's: Thirty credit hours required, including a research project. No minimum grade point average, but more than four grades below B cause a student to become ineligible for further graduate work. All work for M.S. must be done in residence at Lehigh. No foreign language requirement and no requirement for comprehensive/qualifying examination or thesis.

Doctorate: Nine credits of coursework beyond M.S. required, but Ph.D. programs usually include 20 or more credits beyond M.S. Minimum time requirement of two years with at least one year in residence. Qualifying examination, general examination, and thesis defense required. No departmental or university language requirements.

Other Degrees: The additional interdepartmental areas of research include materials science, surface science, photonics, and geophysics.

Thesis: Thesis may be written in absentia.

SPECIAL EQUIPMENT, FACILITIES, OR PROGRAMS

Research facilities are housed in the Sherman Fairchild Center for the Physical Sciences, containing the Lewis Laboratory, the Sherman Fairchild Laboratory for Solid State Studies, and a large connecting research wing. Well-equipped laboratory facilities are available for experimental investigations in research areas at the frontiers of physics. Instruments used for experimental studies include a wide variety of laser systems ranging from femtosecond and picosecond pulsed lasers to stabilized single-mode cw Ti-sapphire and dye lasers. There is also a Fourier-transform spectrometer, cryogenic equipment that achieves temperatures as low as 0.05 K, and magnetic fields up to 9 Tesla, a facility for luminescence microscopy, and a laser-tweezers system for studies of complex fluids. The Fairchild Laboratory also contains a processing laboratory where advanced Si devices can be fabricated and studied. All laboratories are well-furnished with electronic instrumentation for data acquisition and analysis.

Table B—Separately Budgeted Research Expenditures by Source of Support

Source of Support	Departmental Research	Physics-related Research Outside Department
Federal government	$1,104,800	$205,900
State/local government	$15,600	
Non-profit organizations		
Business and industry	$93,800	$28,400
Other	$971,000	
Total	$2,185,200	$234,300

Table C—Separately Budgeted Research Expenditures by Research Specialty

Research Specialty	No. of Grants	Expenditures ($)
Astronomy	3	$170,600
Atomic, Molecular, & Optical Physics	–	$106,400
Biophysics	2	$548,400
Condensed Matter Physics	11	$653,000
Cosmology & String Theory	1	$140,000
High Energy Physics	1	$173,000
Nano Science and Technology	1	$83,800
Optics	1	$92,000
Plasma and Fusion	4	$416,700
Statistical & Thermal Physics	–	$35,600
Total	24	$2,419,500

FACULTY

Professor

Biaggio, Ivan, Ph.D., ETH-Zurich, 1993. *Condensed Matter Physics, Optics*. Experiment.

DeLeo, Gary G., Ph.D., University of Connecticut, 1979. *Astrophysics, Physics and other Science Education*. Theory.

Dierolf, Volkmar, Ph.D., University of Utah, 1992. *Condensed Matter Physics, Optics*. Experiment.

Huennekens, John P., Ph.D., University of Colorado, 1982. *Atomic, Molecular, & Optical Physics*. Experiment.

Kim, Yong W., Ph.D., University of Michigan, 1968. *Atomic, Molecular, & Optical Physics, Fluids, Rheology, Plasma and Fusion, Statistical & Thermal Physics*. Experiment.

Ou-Yang, H. Daniel, Ph.D., University of California, Los Angeles, 1985. *Biophysics, Polymer Physics/Science*. Experiment.

Rickman, Jeffrey M., Ph.D., Carnegie Mellon University, 1989. *Condensed Matter Physics*. Theory.

Stavola, Michael J., Ph.D., University of Rochester, 1980. *Condensed Matter Physics*. Experiment.

Toulouse, Jean, Ph.D., Columbia University, 1981. *Condensed Matter Physics, Optics*. Experiment.

Vavylonis, Dimitrius, Ph.D., Columbia University, 2000. *Biophysics*. Theory.

Associate Professor

Licini, Jerome C., Ph.D., Massachusetts Institute of Technology, 1987. *Condensed Matter Physics, Physics and other Science Education*. Experiment.

McSwain, M. Virginia, Ph.D., Georgia State University, 2004. *Astronomy, Astrophysics*. Experimental/Observational.

Assistant Professor

Cremonini, Sera, Ph.D., Brown University, 2006. *Cosmology & String Theory, High Energy Physics*. Theory.

Honerkamp-Smith, Aurelia, Ph.D., University of Washington, 2010. *Biophysics*. Experiment.

Pepper, Joshua A., Ph.D., Ohio State University, 2007. *Astronomy, Astrophysics*. Theoretical and Observational.

Reed, Rosi J., Ph.D., University of California, Davis, 2011. *Accelerator, High Energy Physics*. Experiment.

Sommer, Ariel T., Ph.D., Massachusetts Institute of Technology, 2013. *Atomic, Molecular, & Optical Physics*. Experiment.

Professor Emeritus

Fowler, W. Beall, Ph.D., University of Rochester, 1963. *Condensed Matter Physics*. Theory.

Gunton, James D., Ph.D., Stanford University, 1967. *Biophysics, Condensed Matter Physics, Statistical & Thermal Physics*. Theory.

Hickman, A. Peet, Ph.D., Rice University, 1973. *Atomic, Molecular, & Optical Physics*. Theory.

McCluskey, George E., Ph.D., University of Pennsylvania, 1965. *Astrophysics*. Theory.

Shaffer, Russell A., Ph.D., Johns Hopkins University, 1962. *Particles and Fields*. Theory.

Adjunct Professor

Glueckstein, Jon, Ph.D., University of Wisconsin-Madison, 1997. *Condensed Matter Physics*.

Loomis, John, M.S., University of Massachusetts, 1973. *Astronomy*.

Lucic, Dragan, M.S., University of Colorado, 1997.

Quinn, Paul, Ph.D., Lehigh University, 2001. *Statistical & Thermal Physics*.

Richter, Kara, Ph.D., Lehigh University, 2016. *Atomic, Molecular, & Optical Physics*.

Professor of the Practice

Cereghetti, Paola, Ph.D., Swiss Federal Institute of Technology, 2000. *Condensed Matter Physics*.

Visiting Professor

Cheng, Chio, Ph.D., University of Iowa, 1975. *Plasma and Fusion*.

Iolin, Eugene, Ph.D., Latvian Academy of Sciences, 1968. *Condensed Matter Physics, Optics*.

Li, Li, Ph.D., Chinese Academy of Sciences · Institute of Theoretical Physics, 2014. *Cosmology & String Theory*.

Liu, Xiaobin, M.S., Chinese Academy of Sciences, 2010. *Polymer Physics/Science*.

Rafiq, Tariq, Ph.D., Chalmers University of Technology, 2004. *Plasma and Fusion*.

Shanmuganathan, Prashanth, Ph.D., Kent State University, 2016. *Accelerator*.

DEPARTMENTAL RESEARCH SPECIALTIES AND STAFF

Theoretical

Astrophysics. Ultraviolet spectroscopy and gas dynamics of interacting binary systems; orbits of binary stars; N-body dynamics. DeLeo, McCluskey.

Atomic, Molecular, & Optical Physics. Charge exchange collisions; fine-structure changing collisions; optical processes in gases; molecular hyperfine spectroscopy. Hickman.

Biophysics. Physical and engineering principles involved in the assembly of actin proteins into filaments and larger scale structures. Statistical mechanics and soft matter physics applied to actin protein assemblies and the emergent collective properties Equilibrium and nonequilibrium properties of protein phase transitions. Gunton, Vavylonis.

Condensed Matter Physics. Electronic and vibrational properties of defects in semiconductors and insulators. Fowler, Gunton, Rickman.

Cosmology & String Theory. Quantum field theory and string theory, and their applications to theoretical cosmology, quantum gravity, particle theory, and strongly coupled gauge theories. Cremonini.

High Energy Physics. Fundamental aspects and phenomenological applications of string theory, gravitational descriptions of quantum field theory, gauge/string dualities. Cremonini.

Statistical & Thermal Physics. Pattern formation in nonlinear, nonequilibrium systems; kinetics of first-order phase transitions focusing on crystallization of globular proteins; cell-cell communication via calcium oscillations. Gunton.

Experimental

Accelerator. Use of the Solenoidal Tracker (STAR) detector at the Relativistic Heavy Ion Collider (RHIC), A Large Ion Collider Experiment (ALICE) at the Large Hadron Collider (LHC), and other accelerator experiments to understand quark gluon plasmas. Reed.

Astronomy. Observational studies to understand the formation and evolution of stars: young open clusters, binary stars, X-ray binaries and pulsars, the formation of disks in Be stars, and the origin of magnetic fields in massive stars. Lehigh has a significant amount of telescope access as a partner in the SMARTS Consortium (McSwain). Theoretical modeling for the discovery of transiting exoplanets. Operation of the KELT small-telescope transit survey. Variable- and eclipsing-binary star studies, and large astronomical surveys and developments in the field of astroinformatics (Pepper). McSwain, Pepper.

Atomic, Molecular, & Optical Physics. Collisional processes in atomic vapors including excitation transfer and "energy pooling" line-broadening, quenching, diffusion, resonance exchange, and velocity-changing collisions; molecular spectroscopy of bound singlet and triplet states of alkali diatomics, photodissociation, predissociation, and bound-free emission. Investigation of strongly correlated quantum systems using quantum optics and cold-atom experiments. Huennekens, Kim, Sommer.

Biophysics. Application of optical imaging, trapping, and manipulation for cell mechanics studies (Ou-Yang). Use of nanomaterials for optical imaging of cells; carbon nanotube nanotoxicity (Rotkin). A combination of fluorescence microscopy, lipid physical chemistry, and fluid mechanics is used to investigate the mechanical principles underlying the response of living cells to fluid flow (Honerkamp-Smith). Honerkamp-Smith, Ou-Yang.

Condensed Matter Physics. Charge transport in insulators and semiconductors; nonlinear optical spectroscopy (Biaggio); point defects in insulating materials with ferroelectric domain walls and other dopants; optical spectroscopy under application of hydrostatic pressure and magnetic fields; carrier localization in wide band gap semiconductors (Dierolf); quantum transport behavior of electrons; conduction in ultrasmall silicon MOSFETs and gallium-arsenide devices and carbon nanotubes at low temperature and high magnetic field (Licini); defects in semiconductors; defect complexes that contain light-element impurities such as H, C, O, and N; vibrational spectroscopy and uniaxial stress techniques to elucidate microscopic properties (Stavola); Raman and neutron scattering; dielectric and ultrasonic spectroscopies; collective vibrational dynamics of disordered ferroelectrics and glasses (Toulouse). Biaggio, Dierolf, Licini, Stavola, Toulouse.

Fluids, Rheology. Nonlinear dynamics in fluid systems; dynamics of small particle suspensions; light scattering loss spectroscopy; instabilities of interfaces. Kim.

High Energy Physics. Examination of the quark gluon plasma (QGP) created in heavy ion collisions by using particle jets and heavy flavor quarks as probes of the medium. Reed.

Optics. Multiple orders of light-matter interactions; time-resolved spectroscopy of second- and third-order nonlinear optical effects in organic and inorganic materials; optical frequency conversion and all-optical switching (Biaggio); fiber optics; nonlinear effects in optical fibers and waveguides (Dierolf, Toulouse). Biaggio, Dierolf, Toulouse.

Plasma and Fusion. Collisional and collisionless phenomena of very dense plasmas in or near a local thermodynamic equilibrium; anomalies in radiation transport properties; lowering of ionization potentials in dense plasmas; laser-produced plasmas. Kim.

Polymer Physics/Science. Soft condensed matter and complex fluids. Ou-Yang.

Statistical & Thermal Physics. Intrinsic fluctuations in fluids under external forcing such as Brownian motion; chaotic transitions; light scattering from fractals; 1/f-dynamics of granular avalanches. Kim.

View additional information about this department at www.gradschoolshopper.com. Check out the "Why Choose Us?" section, find out more about the department's culture and get links to social media networks.

PENNSYLVANIA STATE UNIVERSITY

DEPARTMENT OF PHYSICS

University Park, Pennsylvania 16802
http://www.phys.psu.edu

General University Information
President: Eric Barron
Dean of Graduate School: Regina Vasilatos-Younken
University website: http://www.psu.edu
School Type: Public
Setting: Suburban
Total Faculty: 3,393
Total number of Students: 46,610
Total number of Graduate Students: 6,297

Department Information
Department Chairman: Prof. Nitin Samarth, Head
Department Contact: Julianne R Mortimore, Graduate Program
  Coordinator
  Total full-time faculty: 48
  Total number of full-time equivalent positions: 40
  Full-Time Graduate Students: 150
  Female Full-Time Graduate Students: 28
  First-Year Graduate Students: 29
  Female First-Year Students: 7
  Total Post Doctorates: 32

Department Address
104 Davey Laboratory
University Park, PA 16802
Phone: (814) 863-0118
Fax: (814) 865-0978
E-mail: graduate-admissions@phys.psu.edu
Website: http://www.phys.psu.edu

ADMISSIONS

Admission Contact Information
Address admission inquiries to: The Pennsylvania State University, Department of Physics, 104 Davey Laboratory, University Park, PA 16802
Phone: (814) 865-7534
E-mail: graduate-admissions@phys.psu.edu
Admissions website: https://apply.phys.psu.edu

Application deadlines
Fall admission:
U.S. students: January 13   *Int'l. students*: January 13

Application fee
U.S. students: $65   *Int'l. students*: $65

Admissions information
For Fall of 2018:
  Number of applicants: 477
  Number admitted: 116
  Number enrolled: 29

Admission requirements
Bachelor's degree requirements: Bachelor's degree in Physics
  or a related field is required.
Minimum undergraduate GPA: 3.0

GRE requirements
The GRE is recommended but not required.
The minimum acceptable score required for admission is not
  fixed.

Subjective GRE requirements
The Subjective GRE is recommended.
The minimum acceptable score required for admission is not
  fixed.

TOEFL requirements
The TOEFL exam is required for students from non-English-
  speaking countries.
PBT score: 550
iBT score: 80

Other admissions information
Additional requirements: There are no minimum GRE scores. We
  review all applications using a holistic approach and the best-
  qualified applicants will be accepted up to the number of
  spaces available. For recent offers, the GRE Q boundary was
  165 for the 25% quartile and 170 for the 75% quartile; the
  GRE physics boundary was 830 for the 25% quartile and 950
  for the 75% quartile.
Undergraduate preparation assumed: Marion & Thornton, Classical Dynamics of Particles and Systems; Griffiths, Introduction to Electrodynamics; Griffiths, Introduction to Quantum Mechanics; Reif, Fundamentals of Statistical and
  Thermal Physics.

TUITION
Tuition year 2018–2019:
Tuition for in-state residents
  Full-time students: $22,976 annual
  Part-time students: $957 per credit
Tuition for out-of-state residents
  Full-time students: $38,466 annual
  Part-time students: $1,603 per credit
The Department of Physics admits graduate students with an as-
  sistantship or fellowship that fully covers tuition. There is no
  separate application for financial aid.
Credit hours per semester to be considered full-time: 9
Deferred tuition plan: No
Health insurance: Yes, $567.60.
Other academic fees: Thesis fees: M.S., $25; Ph.D., $95.
Academic term: Semester
Number of first-year students who received full tuition waivers: 28

Teaching Assistants, Research Assistants, and Fellowships
Number of first-year
  Teaching Assistants: 22
  Fellowship students: 6
Average stipend per academic year
  Teaching Assistant: $24,577
  Research Assistant: $29,565
  Fellowship student: $34,000
All students accepted into the program receive a full assistant-
  ship.

FINANCIAL AID

Application deadlines

Fall admission:

U.S. students: January 1   *Int'l. students*: January 1

Loans

Loans are not available for U.S. students.
Loans are not available for international students.

GAPSFAS application required: No
FAFSA application required: No

For further information

Address financial aid inquiries to: The Graduate School, Penn
   State University, 114 Kern Graduate Building, University
   Park, PA 16802.
Phone: (814) 865-1795
E-mail: gswww@psu.edu
Financial aid website: http://www.gradschool.psu.edu/graduate-
   funding/

HOUSING

Availability of on-campus housing

Single students: Yes
Married students: Yes

For further information

Address housing inquiries to: The Pennsylvania State University,
   The Assignment Office for Campus Residences, 201 Johnston
   Commons, University Park, PA 16802.
Phone: (814) 865-7501
E-mail: assignmentoffice@psu.edu
Housing aid website: http://housing.psu.edu/graduate-family-
   housing

Table A—Faculty, Enrollments, and Degrees Granted

Research Specialty	2017–18 Faculty	Enrollment Fall 2017 Master's	Enrollment Fall 2017 Doctorate	Number of Degrees Granted 2016–17 (2011–16) Master's	Number of Degrees Granted 2016–17 (2011–16) Terminal Master's	Number of Degrees Granted 2016–17 (2011–16) Doctorate
Astrophysics	1	–	3	–	–	–
Atomic, Molecular, & Optical Physics	6	–	17	–	2	–(7)
Biophysics	3	–	13	–	1	3(5)
Condensed Matter Physics	16	–	53	–	1(12)	5(56)
Particles and Fields	11	–	15	–	–	10(14)
Relativity & Gravitation	7	–	21	–	1(2)	3(17)
Total	49	–	121	–	5(14)	22(104)
Full-time Grad. Stud.	–	–	121	–	–	–
First-year Grad. Stud.	–	–	28	–	–	–

GRADUATE DEGREE REQUIREMENTS

Master's: Thirty credits (semester-equivalent), at least 18 of
which are at the graduate (not advanced undergraduate) level,
are required. A minimum 3.0 grade point average is required.
There is no residence or foreign language requirement. There
are no qualifying examinations. A thesis or research paper
may be submitted.

Doctorate: There is no fixed number of total credits; 21 graduate
course credits are specified, a minimum of 12 additional
course credits are required. An overall 3.0 grade point average
is at each milestone (to pass candidacy, to pass the comprehensive exam, and at the final thesis defense.) A minimum
of two semesters of residence after candidacy are required.

There is no foreign language requirement. Qualifying examination is taken during the first year and a comprehensive
examination usually during the second year. A thesis is required.
Other Degrees: M.Ed. is also available.
Thesis: Thesis may be written in absentia.

SPECIAL EQUIPMENT, FACILITIES, OR PROGRAMS

Members of the condensed matter faculty are in leadership positions of two large centers: the Center for Nanoscale Science,
an NSF Materials Research Science and Engineering Center
(MRSEC); and the Two Dimensional Crystal Consortium
(2DCC), a user facility site for the NSF Materials Innovation
Platform. The 2DCC has a unique multimodule facility located
in the physics department, targeting sophisticated epitaxial synthesis of thin films and their characterization using scanning tunneling microscopy and angle-resolved photoemission at cryogenic temperatures. The condensed-matter faculty is also
associated with the Materials Research Institute, which coordinates, administers, and supports state-of-the-art research, nanofabrication, and characterization facilities at Penn State. Faculty
members specializing in high-energy physics, particle astrophysics, and gravitational physics are members of large external
collaborations such as Auger, HAWC, Ice Cube, ISS-CREAM,
LIGO, LUX, Lz, Project 8, and STAR. Faculty specializing in
cosmology, gravitational physics, particles and fields, and particle astrophysics belong to the renowned Institute for Gravitation
and the Cosmos which is dedicated to the study of the most fundamental structure and constituents of the universe.

Table B—Separately Budgeted Research Expenditures by Source of Support

Source of Support	Departmental Research	Physics-related Research Outside Department
Federal government	$10,522,085	
State/local government		
Non-profit organizations	$1,322,223	
Business and industry	$130,500	
Other		
Total	$11,974,808	

Table C—Separately Budgeted Research Expenditures by Research Specialty

Research Specialty	No. of Grants	Expenditures ($)
Atomic, Molecular, & Optical Physics	12	$2,257,337
Biophysics	3	$120,313
Condensed Matter Physics	47	$7,023,641
High Energy Physics	28	$1,841,475
Relativity & Gravitation	8	$732,042
Total	98	$11,974,808

FACULTY

Distinguished University Professor

Albert, Reka, Ph.D., University of Notre Dame, 2001. Distinguished Professor of Physics and Biology. *Biophysics, Nonlinear Dynamics and Complex Systems, Systems Science/
   Engineering*. Statistical mechanics; network theory; systems
   biology.

Ashtekar, Abhay V., Ph.D., University of Chicago, 1974. Eberly
   Professor of Physics. Evan Pugh Professor. *Relativity & Gravitation*. Gravity; geometry; physics.

Crespi, Vincent, Ph.D., University of California, Berkeley, 1994. Distinguished Professor of Physics, Chemistry, Materials Science and Engineering. *Computational Physics, Condensed Matter Physics, Materials Science, Metallurgy, Nano Science and Technology.* Theory of superconducting; transport; electronic and structural/mechanical properties of novel materials.

Jain, Jainendra K., Ph.D., Stony Brook University, 1985. Erwin W. Mueller Professor; Evan Pugh Professor Infosys Visiting Chair Professor, IISc Bangalore. *Condensed Matter Physics, Statistical & Thermal Physics.* Low-dimensional systems; fractional quantum Hall effect; composite fermions; topological states; Luttinger liquids.

Strikman, Mark, Ph.D., Leningrad Nuclear Physics Institute, 1978. Distinguished Professor of Physics. *High Energy Physics, Particles and Fields.* High-energy quantum chromodynamics; hard processes with nuclei; microscopic nuclear structure.

Terrones, Mauricio, Ph.D., University of Sussex, 1998. Distinguished Professor of Physics, Chemistry, Materials Science & Engineering; Distinguished Professor (Shinsu University, Japan). *Applied Physics, Chemical Physics, Condensed Matter Physics, Materials Science, Metallurgy, Nano Science and Technology.* Production of nanomaterials; electron microscopy techniques for analysis; molecular simulations.

Chair Professor

Brandt, Niel, Ph.D., University of Cambridge, 1996. Verne M. Willaman Professor of Astronomy & Astrophysics. *Astronomy, Astrophysics.* Astrophysics. High-energy astrophysics; X-ray astronomy; cosmic surveys; active galactic nuclei; supermassive black holes.

Meszaros, Peter, Ph.D., University of California, Berkeley, 1972. Eberly Chair Professor of Astronomy & Astrophysics. *Astronomy, Astrophysics.* Gamma-ray bursts and related phenomena (stellar progenitor and host environment, the jet structure and collimation, the role of ultra-high ($>$ TeV) energy neutrinos, the implications of GeV-TeV photons in GRB and active galaxies, the production of gravitational waves in GRB, related neutron star problems.

Samarth, Nitin, Ph.D., Purdue University, 1986. George A. and Margaret M. Downsbrough Department Head. *Applied Physics, Condensed Matter Physics, Materials Science, Metallurgy, Nano Science and Technology, Solid State Physics, Surface Physics.* Spintronics; topological insulators; quantum information processing; semiconductor, superconductor, and magnetic nanostructures; magneto-optical studies of artificial spin ice.

Sathyaprakash, Bangalore, Ph.D., Indian Institute of Science, 1987. Elsbach Professor of Physics Professor of Astronomy and Astrophysics. *Astrophysics, Cosmology & String Theory, Relativity & Gravitation, Theoretical Physics.* Gravitational physics and cosmology.

Schiff, Steven, Ph.D., Duke University Medical Center, 1985. Director, Penn State Center for Neural Engineering; Brush Chair Professor of Engineering; Professor of Neurosurgery, Engineering Science and Mechanics, Physics. *Biophysics, Neuroscience/Neuro Physics.* Neural engineering; control theory.

Professor

Badding, John, Ph.D., University of California, Berkeley, 1989. Professor of Chemistry, Physics and Materials Science and Engineering. *Chemical Physics, Condensed Matter Physics, Materials Science, Metallurgy, Nano Science and Technology.* Materials chemistry and physics. Condensed matter physics. Carbon nanomaterials. Semiconductor nanomaterials. Photonics.

Bojowald, Martin, Ph.D., RWTH Aachen University, 2000. *Relativity & Gravitation.* Quantum gravity; classical and quantum cosmology; classical and quantum aspects of black holes; general aspects of quantization; Poisson geometry and non-commutative geometry.

Coutu, Stephane, Ph.D., California Institute of Technology, 1993. Professor of Physics, Astronomy and Astrophysics. *Atmosphere, Space Physics, Cosmic Rays, High Energy Physics, Particles and Fields.* Cosmic rays; high-energy physics; particles and fields.

Cowen, Douglas, Ph.D., University of Wisconsin-Madison, 1990. Professor of Physics, Astronomy and Astrophysics. *Astrophysics, High Energy Physics, Particles and Fields.* Astrophysics; particles and fields.

Fichthorn, Kristen A., Ph.D., University of Michigan, 1989. Professor of Chemical Engineering and Physics. *Computational Physics, Condensed Matter Physics, Nano Science and Technology, Statistical & Thermal Physics.* Statistical mechanics and computer simulation; surface physics; colloidal nanostructures; structural evolution of materials; computer simulation.

Günaydin, Murat, Ph.D., Yale University, 1973. *High Energy Physics, Particles and Fields.* Theoretical physics; superstrings; super-gravity; Kaluza-Klein theories.

Gibble, Kurt, Ph.D., University of Colorado JILA, 1990. *Atomic, Molecular, & Optical Physics.* Microwave and optical frequency atomic clocks; space-based atomic clocks; ultracold atom-atom scattering; ultra-stable lasers; laser cooling; precision measurements; experimental atomic physics.

Gopalan, Venkatraman, Ph.D., Cornell. Professor of Materials Science & Engineering and Physics. *Condensed Matter Physics, Materials Science, Metallurgy.* Ultrafast optics, nonlinear optics, spectroscopy; symmetry and group theory, minimum energy pathways; atomic resolution imaging, coherent diffractive imaging with Xrays and electrons.

Heppelmann, Steven F., Ph.D., University Minnesota, 1981. *High Energy Physics, Particles and Fields.* Experimental high-energy physics.

Larson, Daniel J., Ph.D., Harvard University, 1971. Former Dean, Eberly College of Science. *Atomic, Molecular, & Optical Physics.* Atomic physics; molecules; optical physics.

Li, Qi, Ph.D., Peking University, 1989. *Condensed Matter Physics.* Spintronics; multiferroic multilayer structures; superconductivity and strong correlated systems; magnetic nanostructures.

Liu, Ying, Ph.D., University of Minnesota, 1991. *Condensed Matter Physics.* Experimental condensed matter physics; unconventional superconductivity; topological quantum states of matter; nanophysics.

Mao, Zhiqiang, Ph.D., UST, 1992. *Condensed Matter Physics, Materials Science, Metallurgy.* Synthesis and properties of quantum materials, including topological materials, exotic superconductors, strongly correlated electron systems.

McEntaffer, Randall L., Ph.D., University of Colorado, 2007. Professor of Astronomy & Astrophysics and Physics. *Astronomy, Astrophysics.* Astronomical Instrumentation, Optics, Nanofabrication. X-ray spectrographs; diffraction grating fabrication; diffuse X-ray spectroscopy; empirical verification of optics.

Mostafa, Miguel, Ph.D., Universidad Nacional de Cuyo. Instituto Balseiro, 2001. *Astrophysics, High Energy Physics, Particles and Fields.* High-energy particle astrophysics, especially neutrino and gamma ray astronomy.

Rigol, Marcos, Ph.D., University of Stuttgart, 2004. *Atomic, Molecular, & Optical Physics, Condensed Matter Physics.* Statistical mechanics; strong correlations; non-equilibrium quantum dynamics; ultracold gases; magnetism; disorder; superconductivity physics.

Robinett, Richard W., Ph.D., University of Minnesota, 1981. Associate Department Head; Director of Undergraduate Studies; Director of Graduate Studies. *Quantum Foundations.* Mathematical physics; time-dependent quantum systems; pedagogical issues related to quantum mechanics.

Roiban, Radu, Ph.D., Stony Brook University, 2001. *High Energy Physics, Particles and Fields.* String theory; gauge theories; quantum field theory.

Sofo, Jorge, Ph.D., Inst. Balseriro, Bariloche, 1991. Professor of Physics, and Materials Science & Engineering. *Applied Physics, Atomic, Molecular, & Optical Physics, Chemical Physics, Computational Physics, Condensed Matter Physics, Energy Sources & Environment, Geophysics, Low Temperature Physics, Materials Science, Metallurgy, Nano Science and Technology, Statistical & Thermal Physics.* Theoretical and computational methods to link properties and structures of materials.

Weiss, David, Ph.D., Stanford University, 1993. Associate Department Head. *Atomic, Molecular, & Optical Physics.* Optical lattices; Bose-Einstein condensation; 1D gases; quantum computing; precision measurements; laser cooling.

Zhu, Jun, Ph.D., Columbia University, 2002. *Applied Physics, Condensed Matter Physics, Low Temperature Physics, Materials Science, Metallurgy, Nano Science and Technology.* Experimental condensed-matter physics; low-temperature transport and scanned probe experiments; mesoscopic and nanoscale systems.

Associate Professor

Bai, Lu, Ph.D., Cornell University, 2007. Assistant Professor of Biochemistry and Molecular Biology. *Biophysics, Optics, Statistical & Thermal Physics.* Single-molecule/single-cell fluorescence microscopy.

Engel-Herbert, Roman, Ph.D., Humboldt University. Associate Professor of Chemistry, Materials Science & Engineering, and Physics. *Condensed Matter Physics, Materials Science, Metallurgy.* Experimental condensed-matter physics; low-temperature transport; mesoscopic and nano scale systems.

Hanna, Chad, Ph.D., Louisiana State University, 2008. *Astronomy, Relativity & Gravitation.* Gravitational Physics. Gravitational waves; multi-messenger astrophysics; black holes; neutron stars; LIGO, data analysis; signal processing.

Hudson, Eric, Ph.D., University of California, Berkeley, 1999. *Condensed Matter Physics, Low Temperature Physics, Nano Science and Technology, Physics and other Science Education.* Scanning tunneling microscopy; high-temperature superconductors and other complex materials.

Jin, Dezhe, Ph.D., University of California, San Diego, 1999. *Biophysics, Neuroscience/Neuro Physics.* Theory of biological neural networks and computational models of neurobiological functions.

Liu, Chaoxing, Ph.D., Tsinghua University, 2009. *Condensed Matter Physics.* Theoretical condensed-matter physics; spintronics; topological insulators and superconductors; electronic and transport properties of low-dimensional systems.

Mocioiu, Irina, Ph.D., Stony Brook University, 2002. *Astrophysics, High Energy Physics, Particles and Fields.* High-energy physics and its connections to astrophysics and cosmology; neutrinos.

O'Hara, Kenneth, Ph.D., Duke University, 2000. *Atomic, Molecular, & Optical Physics.* Experimental atomic, molecular, and optical physics; condensed-matter physics.

Shandera, Sarah, Ph.D., Cornell University, 2006. *Cosmology & String Theory, Particles and Fields.* Theory of the very early universe.

Stasto, Anna, Ph.D., Institute of Nuclear Physics at Polish Academy of Science, 1999. *High Energy Physics, Particles and Fields.* Elementary particle physics; phenomenology of strong interactions; hadronic interactions at high energies.

Assistant Professor

Bianchi, Eugenio, Ph.D., Scuola Normale Superiore di Pisa, 2010. *Relativity & Gravitation, Theoretical Physics.* Gravitational Physics & Cosmology. Quantum gravity; entanglement; chaos; primordial universe; black holes.

Carmona Benitez, Maria del Carmen, Ph.D., University of Granada, 2009. *Astrophysics, Particles and Fields.* Dark matter (LUX and LZ); design and construction of noble liquid TPC detectors and their operation in the search for dark matter.

Chang, Cui-Zu, Ph.D., Tsinghua University, 2013. *Condensed Matter Physics.* Condensed Matter Physics, Materials Science, Low-Temperature Physics. Experimental condensed matter physics; molecular beam epitaxy, angle-resolved photoemission spectroscopy, low-temperature transport experiments; topological materials, quantum anomalous Hall effect, interface superconductivity.

de Viveiros, Luiz, Ph.D., Brown University, 2009. *Astrophysics, Particles and Fields.* Dark matter (LUX and LZ); measurements of the neutrino mass (PROJECT 8).

Murase, Kohta, Ph.D., Kyoto University, 2010. *Astrophysics, Atmosphere, Space Physics, Cosmic Rays, Particles and Fields, Relativity & Gravitation.* High-Energy Astrophysics; neutrinos, dark matter, cosmic rays, multi-messenger astroparticle physics, black holes and neutron stars.

Rechtsman, Mikael C., Ph.D., Princeton University, 2008. *Atomic, Molecular, & Optical Physics.* Theoretical and experimental aspects of nonlinear optics, condensed matter physics, topological insulators, topological photonics.

Professor Emeritus

Chan, Moses H. W., Ph.D., Cornell University, 1974. Evan Pugh Professor Emeritus. *Condensed Matter Physics, Low Temperature Physics.* Low-temperature physics; phase transitions in two- and three-dimensions; superfluid and liquid-vapor transitions in random media; low-temperature transport studies of superconducting nanowires.

Cole, Milton W., Ph.D., University of Chicago, 1970. Distinguished Professor Emeritus. *Condensed Matter Physics.* Theoretical surface physics; superfluids; statistical mechanics.

Collins, John, Ph.D., University of Cambridge, 1975. Distinguished Professor Emeritus. *Biophysics, Particles and Fields.* Quantum field theory; perturbative methods and factorization in QCD; renormalization theory; neuroscience.

DEPARTMENTAL RESEARCH SPECIALTIES AND STAFF

Theoretical

Astrophysics. Physics of gamma-ray bursts (GRBs), including long-lasting burst afterglows, relation to stellar progenitor and host environment, jet structure and collimation, the role of ultra-high ($> $ TeV) energy neutrinos, the implications of GeV-TeV photons in GRB and active galaxies, the production of gravitational waves in GRB, related neutron star problems, and GRB as tools for cosmology. Multi-messenger study of extreme astrophysical objects. Meszaros, Murase.

Atomic, Molecular, & Optical Physics. Nonequilibrium quantum dynamics; bosons and fermions in low dimensions; superfluidity and Bose-Einstein condensation; optical lattices; quantum criticality and precision measurements. Rigol.

Biophysics. Computational models for birdsong experiments; modeling of neural mechanisms by which high-level memories are coded; biophysically realistic models of rhythm generation, seizures, and Parkinson's disease; prototype feedback control systems; molecular-level interaction networks among genes and proteins; complex systems; statics and dynamics of ecological communities. Albert, Collins, Jin.

Condensed Matter Physics. Fractional quantum Hall effect and composite fermions; Abelian and non-Abelian anyons; 1D Luttinger liquid; strongly correlated systems; many-body phenomena and electron/spin transport in low-dimensional solids (nanowires, nanotubes, quantum dots, 2DEGs, and graphene); topological insulators and topological superconductors; semiconductor spintronics; superconductivity in 1D, 2D, and 3D systems; first-principles density functional theory; dynamical mean field theory; empirical interatomic potentials; photonic band structures; effective continuum theories (Landau-Ginzburg); phase transitions in quantum solids and quantum fluids; wetting transitions of thin films; ultraweak forces binding atoms to surfaces; superfluidity in films; quasi-one-dimensional fluids within nanotubes; theory of classical frustrated magnetic systems; materials design; materials informatics; structural energetics of periodic biological systems; electromechanical response of nanostructures. Cole, Crespi, Fichthorn, Jain, Chaoxing Liu, Rigol, Sofo.

Particles and Fields. Application of relativistic quantum theory to internal structure of subnuclear particles; quantum chromodynamics and quantum electrodynamics; quantum chromodynamics in nuclei and in ultra-high-energy hadronic collisions; collider and supercollider phenomenology; electroweak interactions; neutrino physics; supersymmetry; conformal field theory and applications for helicity amplitudes; M/Superstring theory; supergravity. Collins, Günaydin, Mocioiu, Murase, Robinett, Roiban, Shandera, Stasto, Strikman.

Relativity & Gravitation. Classical and quantum theories of gravitation; nonperturbative approaches to quantum field theory and quantum gravity, including loop quantum gravity; gravitational waves; astrophysical applications of general relativity; numerical relativity; mathematical physics; cosmology. Ashtekar, Bianchi, Bojowald, Hanna, Murase, Sathyaprakash, Shandera.

Experimental

Astrophysics. Observational studies of supermassive black holes, cosmological X-ray surveys, starburst galaxies, and normal galaxies using the Chandra X-ray Observatory, XMM-Newton, NuSTAR, the Sloan Digital Sky Survey, Large Synoptic Survey Telescope, and the Advanced Telescope for High Energy Astrophysics. Design, fabrication, testing, and implementation of X-ray spectrographs for high throughput, high resolving power astrophysical observations of supernova remnants and their environments. Brandt, McEntaffer.

Atomic, Molecular, & Optical Physics. Bose-Einstein condensation; degenerate Fermi gases; laser-cooled atomic clocks; nonlinear optics; topological photonics; laser cooling and trapping of atoms; tests of fundamental symmetries; quantum computation; quantum scattering of cold atoms; optical lattices. Gibble, Larson, O'Hara, Rechtsman, Weiss.

Biophysics. Neural organization of complex motor sequences; neural activity in functioning neural circuits. Bai, Schiff.

Condensed Matter Physics. Quantum and mesoscopic transport in low-dimensional solids such as 2D transition metal dichalcogenides, graphene, carbon nanotubes, metal nanowires, and semiconductor nanowires; superconductivity in nanowires; optical spectroscopy of carbon-based and semiconductor nanostructures; physics of spintronic devices; exotic superconductors; quantum transport in topological insulator thin films, heterostructures, and nanowires; low-temperature scanning tunneling microscopy; angle resolved photoemission spectroscopy; nanomagnetism. Badding, Chan, Chang, Gopalan, Hudson, Li, Ying Liu, Mao, Samarth, Terrones, Zhu.

Gravitational wave astronomy. Gravitational wave detection via the Laser Interferometric Gravitational Wave Observatory (LIGO). Studies of compact binary systems consisting of neutron stars and black holes. Hanna, Sathyaprakash.

Materials Science, Metallurgy. Synthesis of carbon-based nanostructures; molecular beam epitaxy of semiconductor, oxide and topological insulator heterostructures; pulsed laser deposition of complex oxide thin films; electrochemical synthesis of metallic, ferromagnetic, superconducting, and semiconducting nanowires. Chan, Chang, Gopalan, Hudson, Li, Ying Liu, Mao, Samarth, Terrones, Zhu.

Particles and Fields. Particle astrophysics: studies of the properties of quarks and gluons in hadronic interactions; studies of nuclear color transparency with hard hadronic elastic collisions; spin physics in polarized proton-proton collisions at RHIC; direct measurements of high-energy cosmic rays and cosmic antimatter particles; studies of the highest-energy cosmic rays; neutrino physics; neutrino astrophysics; gamma-ray astrophysics. Carmona Benitez, Coutu, Cowen, de Viveiros, Heppelmann, Mostafa.

View additional information about this department at www.gradschoolshopper.com. Check out the "Why Choose Us?" section, find out more about the department's culture and get links to social media networks.

UNIVERSITY OF PENNSYLVANIA

PHYSICS AND ASTRONOMY

Philadelphia, Pennsylvania 19104-6396
http://www.physics.upenn.edu

General University Information
President: Amy Gutmann
Dean of Graduate School: Eve Troutt Powell
University website: http://www.upenn.edu/
Setting: Urban
Total Faculty: 4,722
Total number of Students: 21,358
Total number of Graduate Students: 10,890

Department Information
Department Chairman: Prof. Mark Trodden, Chair
Department Contact: Millicent Minnick, Department
Administrator
Total full-time faculty: 40
Total number of full-time equivalent positions: 40
Full-Time Graduate Students: 103
Female Full-Time Graduate Students: 29
First-Year Graduate Students: 14
Female First-Year Students: 3
Total Post Doctorates: 53

Department Address
209 South 33rd Street
Philadelphia, PA 19104-6396
Phone: (215) 898-8141
Fax: (215) 898-2010
E-mail: mminnick@physics.upenn.edu
Website: http://www.physics.upenn.edu

ADMISSIONS

Admission Contact Information
Address admission inquiries to: Physics and Astronomy, David
Rittenhouse Lab, University of Pennsylvania, 209 S. 33rd
Street, Philadelphia, PA 19104-6396
Phone: (215) 898-3125
E-mail: admiss@physics.upenn.edu
Admissions website: http://www.physics.upenn.edu/graduate

Application deadlines
Fall admission:
U.S. students: December 14   *Int'l. students*: December 14

Application fee
U.S. students: $80   *Int'l. students*: $80
In payment of the application fee, international applicants should
send an international postal money order for the amount.
Checks drawn on a foreign bank will be returned and cause
a delay processing of the application will be delayed. Discover, MasterCard, and Visa are also accepted.

Admissions information
For Fall of 2018:
Number of applicants: 423
Number admitted: 43
Number enrolled: 18

Admission requirements
Bachelor's degree requirements: A Bachelor's degree in physics,
astronomy, or a related science is required. If the Bachelor's
degree is not in physics or astronomy, a strong physics minor
is necessary. Prior research experience is strongly encouraged.
The GRE general test is required. proficiency in English.

GRE requirements
The GRE is required.

Subjective GRE requirements
The Subjective GRE is required.
No minimum score is set.

TOEFL requirements
The TOEFL exam is required for students from non-English-
speaking countries.
PBT score: 400
iBT score: 100
We will accept IELTS in hard copy in lieu of TOEFL scores
6.5-7. They must be sent directly from IELTS to Penn.

TUITION

Tuition year 2018–2019:
Tuition for in-state residents
Full-time students: $38,044 annual
Tuition for out-of-state residents
Full-time students: $38,044 annual
PH.D. tuition is based on Fall/Spring and general fees.
Credit hours per semester to be considered full-time: 3
Deferred tuition plan: No
Health insurance: Yes, $4032.00.
Other academic fees: Health insurance is no cost to the student.
Academic term: Semester

Teaching Assistants, Research Assistants, and Fellowships
Number of first-year
Teaching Assistants: 18
Fellowship students: 18
Average stipend per academic year
Teaching Assistant: $30,176
Research Assistant: $30,176
Fellowship student: $30,176
Essentially all students are funded and receive an annual sti-
pend and tuition coverage provided they remain in good ac-
ademic standing. Additionally, all fully funded graduate stu-
dents in the School of Arts and Sciences receive health
insurance benefits. This is provided by a combination of de-
partmental support and research grants from individual professors.

FINANCIAL AID

Loans
Loans are not available for U.S. students.
Loans are not available for international students.
GAPSFAS application required: No
FAFSA application required: No

For further information
Address financial aid inquiries to: N/A.
Financial aid website: N/A

HOUSING

Availability of on-campus housing
Single students: Yes
Married students: Yes
Childcare Assistance: No

For further information
Address housing inquiries to: Website.
Phone: (215) 898-3547
Housing aid website: http://cms.business-services.upenn.edu/offcampusservices/

Table A—Faculty, Enrollments, and Degrees Granted

Research Specialty	2017–2018 Faculty	Enrollment Fall 2017		Number of Degrees Granted 2017–2018 (2014–2018)		
		Master's	Doctorate	Master's	Terminal Master's	Doctorate
Physics and Astronomy	–	–	–	–	–	–
Physics and Astronomy	39	17	106	17(40)	12(38)	9(73)
Total	–	17	106	17(40)	12(38)	9(73)
Full-time Grad. Stud.	–	–	106	–	–	–
First-year Grad. Stud.	–	–	13	–	–	–

GRADUATE DEGREE REQUIREMENTS

Master's: It is possible for a student to complete the requirements for a bachelor's and master's degree within four or five years. For students starting the study of physics and calculus at Penn this combined program requires careful planning and an intensive focus on physics. Even those with advanced placement in physics or mathematics will need to chart their course work carefully in order to be able to devote their fourth year to graduate courses in physics. Students wishing to pursue this option should speak to both the undergraduate chair and the graduate chair as soon as possible in their careers. as soon as possible in their undergraduate careers. (It is important that you apply for submatriculation before taking graduate courses in physics.).

Doctorate: A grade of B+ or higher in each of Math Methods (Physics 500), Electrodynamics (Physics 516) and Quantum I and II (Physics 531/532). Successful completion of 20 graduate-level courses (including no more than 11 course credits for research and reading courses). These courses must include the four courses in requirement 1, Statistical Mechanics (611), and one course outside the student's field of specialization. Students may receive credit for graduate courses taken at other institutions, though no more than 8 credits may be transferred. If the Graduate Chair determines that an equivalent graduate course has been taken, then the student must go to the current instructor for that course for a standardized evaluation of the instructor's design. If the instructor determines that the student knows the course material, then that course will be waived and, if appropriate, credit will be given. An Oral Candidacy Exam must be taken within 18 months of the successful completion of the four required courses in requirement 1.

Thesis: N/A.

SPECIAL EQUIPMENT, FACILITIES, OR PROGRAMS

The University of Pennsylvania Department of Physics and Astronomy has access to the new Singh Center for Nanotechnology, new high-bay space for assembly of telescopes and other large instruments, and a world-class electronics instrumentation group.

FACULTY

Professor

Balasubramanian, Vijay, Ph.D., Princeton University. *High Energy Physics, Neuroscience/Neuro Physics, Particles and Fields*. String Theory, Particle Physics, High Energy Physics, Neuroscience.

Bernstein, Gary, Ph.D., University of California, Berkeley, 1989. *Astrophysics*. Astrophysics, Weak Gravitational Lensing.

Cvetic, Mirjam, Ph.D., University of Maryland, College Park, 1984. *Particles and Fields*. Elementary Particle Physics.

Devlin, Mark, Ph.D., University of California at Berkeley, 1993. Experimental cosmology at millimeter and submillimeter wavelengths.

Drndic, Marija, Ph.D., Harvard University, 2000. *Condensed Matter Physics, Nano Science and Technology*. Exploration of mesoscopic and nanoscale structures in the areas of experimental condensed matter physics, nanoscience and nanotechnology.

Durian, Douglas, Ph.D., Cornell University, 1989. *Condensed Matter Physics*. Soft matter physics.

Fortune, H. Terry, Ph.D., Florida State Universtiy, 1967.

Gladney, Larry, Ph.D., Stanford University, 1985. *High Energy Physics*. Experimental high energy physics and cosmology.

Goulian, Mark, Ph.D., Harvard University, 1990. *Biophysics*.

Heiney, Paul A., Ph.D., Massachusetts Institute of Technology, 1982. *Condensed Matter Physics*.

Hollebeek, Robert, Ph.D., University of California, Berkeley, 1974. *High Energy Physics, Medical, Health Physics, Particles and Fields*.

Jain, Bhuvnesh, Ph.D., Massachusetts Institute of Technology, 1994. *Astrophysics*.

Johnson, Charles A.T., Ph.D., Harvard University, 1990. *Condensed Matter Physics*.

Kamien, Randall, Ph.D., Harvard University, 1992. *Condensed Matter Physics*.

Kane, Charles, Ph.D., Massachusetts Institute of Technology, 1989. *Condensed Matter Physics*.

Khoury, Justin, Ph.D., Princeton University, 2002. *Particles and Fields*.

Kikkawa, Jay, Ph.D., University of California, Santa Barbara, 1997. *Condensed Matter Physics*.

Klein, Joshua, Ph.D., Princeton University, 1994. *High Energy Physics*.

Kroll, I. Joseph, Ph.D., Harvard University, 1989. *High Energy Physics*.

Lande, Kenneth, Ph.D., Columbia University, 1958. *Condensed Matter Physics*.

Liu, Andrea, Ph.D., Cornell University, 1989. *Condensed Matter Physics*.

Lubensky, Tom, Ph.D., Harvard University, 1969. *Condensed Matter Physics*.

Mele, Eugene, Ph.D., Massachusetts Institute of Technology, 1978. *Condensed Matter. Physics*.

Nelson, Philip, Ph.D., Harvard University, 1984. *Biophysics*.

Ovrut, Burt, Ph.D., University of Chicago, 1978. *High Energy Physics*.

Sheth, Ravi, Ph.D., University of Cambridge, 1994. *Astrophysics*.

Trodden, Mark, Ph.D., Brown University, 1995. *Particles and Fields*.

Williams, Hugh H., Ph.D., Stanford University, 1972. *High Energy Physics.*

Yodh, Arjun, Ph.D., Harvard University, 1986. *Condensed Matter Physics.*

Associate Professor

Aguirre, James, Ph.D., University of Chicago, 2003.

Bernardi, Mariangela, Ph.D., Ludwig-Maximilians-Universitaet, Munich, Germany, 1999. *Astrophysics.* Early-type galaxies.

Lidz, Adam, Ph.D., Columbia University, 2004.

Lipeles, Elliot, Ph.D., California Institute of Technology, 2004.

Mauger, Chrispher M., Ph.D., State University of New York at Stony Brook, 2002. *High Energy Physics.*

Sako, Masao, Ph.D., Columbia University, 2001. *Astrophysics.*

Sweeney, Alison, Ph.D., Duke University, 2007. *Biophysics.*

Thomson, Evelyn, Ph.D., University of Glasgow, 1998. *High Energy Physics.*

Assistant Professor

Blake, Cullen, Ph.D., Harvard University, 2009.

Heckman, Johnathan, Ph.D., Harvard, 2009. *High Energy Physics.* Centers on theoretical high energy physics.

Katifori, Eleni, Ph.D., Harvard University, 2008. Topology, function and development of biological distribution networks, elasticity and mechanics of thin cells, pattern formation.

Sanderson, Robyn, Ph.D., Massachusetts Institute of Technology, 2011. The end-to-end connection between predictions from different particle models for the distribution of dark matter in galaxies and the observations of these galaxies that we can make today and in the future, particularly observations of the dynamics of stars in galaxy outskirts where dark matter should dominate.

Wu, Liang, Ph.D., Johns Hopkins, 2015. *Condensed Matter Physics.* Experimental condensed matter physicist with a strong interest in light-matter.

Zhen, Bo, Ph.D., MIT, 2014. *Condensed Matter Physics, Optics.* using tools in experimental nano-photonics to attack problems in condensed matter physics and quantum electrodynamics, with an eye on their practical applications.

DEPARTMENTAL RESEARCH SPECIALTIES AND STAFF

Theoretical

Astrophysics. Aguirre, Bernardi, Bernstein, Jain, Lidz, Sako, Sheth.

Condensed Matter Physics. Goulian, Heiney, Kamien, Kane, Katifori, Lande, Liu, Lubensky, Mele, Yodh.

Cosmology & String Theory. Aguirre, Bernardi, Blake, Jain, Khoury, Lidz, Sako, Sheth, Trodden.

Particles and Fields. Balasubramanian, Cvetic, Gladney, Heckman, Hollebeek, Ovrut.

Experimental

Astrophysics. Aguirre, Blake, Devlin.

Biophysics. Katifori, Nelson, Sweeney.

Condensed Matter Physics. Drndic, Durian, Johnson, Katifori, Kikkawa, Sweeney, Wu, Yodh, Zhen.

Particles and Fields. Gladney, Klein, Kroll, Lipeles, Mauger, Thomson, Williams, Yodh.

View additional information about this department at www.gradschoolshopper.com. Check out the "Why Choose Us?" section, find out more about the department's culture and get links to social media networks.

UNIVERSITY OF PITTSBURGH

DEPARTMENT OF PHYSICS AND ASTRONOMY

Pittsburgh, Pennsylvania 15260
http://www.physicsandastronomy.pitt.edu

General University Information
Chancellor: Patrick D. Gallagher
Dean of Graduate School: Kathleen Blee
University website: http://www.pitt.edu
School Type: Public
Setting: Urban
Total Faculty: 4,207
Total Graduate Faculty: 1,446
Total number of Students: 7,098
Total number of Graduate Students: 28,642

Department Information
Department Chairman: Prof. Arthur Kosowsky, Chair
Department Contact: Andrew Zentner, Director of Graduate
  Studies
  Total full-time faculty: 38
  Total number of full-time equivalent positions: 58
  Full-Time Graduate Students: 115
  Female Full-Time Graduate Students: 34
  First-Year Graduate Students: 21
  Female First-Year Students: 10
  Total Post Doctorates: 24

Department Address
3941 O'Hara Street
Room 100 Allen Hall
Pittsburgh, PA 15260
Phone: (412) 624-9000
Fax: (412) 624-9163
E-mail: pagrad@pitt.edu
Website: http://www.physicsandastronomy.pitt.edu

ADMISSIONS

Admission Contact Information
Address admission inquiries to: Admissions Coordinator, Department of Physics and Astronomy, 3941 O'Hara Street, Rm. 100 Allen Hall, University of Pittsburgh, Pittsburgh, PA 15260
Phone: (412) 624-9066
E-mail: pagrad@pitt.edu
Admissions website: http://www.physicsandastronomy.pitt.edu/graduate/how-apply

Application deadlines
Fall admission:
U.S. students: January 15   *Int'l. students*: January 15

Application fee
Int'l. students: $50
Application fee is waived for domestic students; Late applications and supporting materials are accepted on the basis of space availability. No online applications for fall term permitted beyond March 31st.

Admissions information
For Fall of 2018:
  Number of applicants: 311
  Number admitted: 85
  Number enrolled: 21

Admission requirements
Bachelor's degree requirements: Bachelor's degree in one of the physical sciences, mathematics, astronomy/astrophysics or engineering with relevant physics courses is required. Research experience is recommended but not required.

GRE requirements
The GRE is required.
A waiver of the GRE (general) may be granted in a very rare case involving a truly exceptional applicant. Since a thorough review of the application is made, we do not list minimum accepted GRE scores.

Subjective GRE requirements
The Subjective GRE is recommended.
University of Pittsburgh GRE school code is 2927; Department code for Physics and Astronomy is 0808

TOEFL requirements
The TOEFL exam is required for students from non-English-speaking countries.
iBT score: 90
For the TOEFL a required score of 90 (with at least a score of 22 in all of the four sections of speaking, reading, listening, writing. Alternatively, IELTS minimum score is 7, with at least a 6.5 score in each of its four sections. Exceptions have been made for applicants with one component below the minimum required. International students admitted to the University are required to take an English Language Proficiency Test during orientation if they scored below 100 on the TOEFL or Band 7 on the IELTS. Academic departments also may ask students with higher scores to take the test. Other exceptions are listed here: http://www.oafa.pitt.edu/TOEFL_exceptions.html

Other admissions information
Additional requirements: International Students visit http://www.ois.pitt.edu/.
Undergraduate preparation assumed: Minimum GPA for admission with full status is 3.0 on a 4.0 scale (refer to Department's Graduate website - information Frequently Asked Questions.

TUITION
Tuition year 2018–19:
Tuition for in-state residents
  Full-time students: $11,423 per semester
  Part-time students: $920 per credit
Tuition for out-of-state residents
  Full-time students: $19,368 per semester
  Part-time students: $1,583 per credit
Fees, not reflected in the tuition rates above, are per semester (term) and subject to change. Nine to 15 credits are covered under full tuition.
Deferred tuition plan: Yes

Health insurance: Yes, $0 if eligible graduate student academic appointment.

Other academic fees: Mandatory fees per term: Full-time $425. Part-time $270. Breakdown per term as follows: Wellness—$130 (full-time)/$65 (part-time), Activities—$30 (full-time)/$15 (part-time), Computing & Network Services—$175 (full-time)/$100 (part-time), Security, Safety & Transportation—$90 (full-time and part-tim

Academic term: Semester

Number of first-year students who received full tuition waivers: 19

Teaching Assistants, Research Assistants, and Fellowships

Number of first-year

Teaching Assistants: 7

Fellowship students: 13

Average stipend per academic year

Teaching Assistant: $28,365

Research Assistant: $28,365

Fellowship student: $30,000

All newly admitted doctoral students receive funding support in the form of TA, GSR, or Fellowship. Several students arrange to begin in preceding summer as GSR. Important to note that our fellowship offers exceed the number that show as accepting.

FINANCIAL AID

Application deadlines

Fall admission:

U.S. students: January 15   *Int'l. students*: January 15

Loans

Loans are available for U.S. students.

Loans are not available for international students.

GAPSFAS application required: No

FAFSA application required: No

For further information

Address financial aid inquiries to: In reference to loan information:, Financial Aid Office, 4227 Fifth Avenue, Alumni Hall, University of Pittsburgh, Pittsburgh, PA 15260. Otherwise, please see the link to the Department's Graduate Program on the Department's web site.

Phone: (412) 624-7488

E-mail: oafa@pitt.edu

Financial aid website: http://www.oafa.pitt.edu/fahome.aspx

HOUSING

Availability of on-campus housing

Single students: No

Married students: No

Childcare Assistance: Yes

For further information

Address housing inquiries to: (For Off Campus), Off-Campus Living, 204 Brakenridge Hall, Pittsburgh, PA 15213, (For On Campus), Panther Central, Litchfield Towers Lobby, 412-648-1100, pc@bc.pitt.edu.

Phone: (412) 624-6998

E-mail: ocl@bc.pitt.edu

Housing aid website: http://www.ocl.pitt.edu/

Table A—Faculty, Enrollments, and Degrees Granted

Research Specialty	2017–18 Faculty	Enrollment 2017 Mas-ter's	Enrollment 2017 Doc-torate	Number of Degrees Granted 2017–18 (2013–18) Mas-ter's	Number of Degrees Granted 2017–18 (2013–18) Terminal Master's	Number of Degrees Granted 2017–18 (2013–18) Doc-torate
Astrophysics	10	–	16	–	–	3(18)
Condensed Matter Physics	14	–	47	–	–	5(34)
Particles and Fields	15	–	22	–	–	3(22)
Physics and other Science Education	5	–	6	–	–	3(8)
Total	44	2	91	–(59)	–(10)	12(68)
Full-time Grad. Stud.	–	–	110	–	–	–
First-year Grad. Stud.	–	–	19	–	–	–

GRADUATE DEGREE REQUIREMENTS

Master's: Candidates for the M.S. degree must satisfy the preliminary evaluation, which requires the successful completion of at least one course in each of the following core subjects: Dynamical Systems, Statistical Mechanics and Thermodynamics, Electricity and Magnetism, and Quantum Mechanics, with a final examination score of at least 50% for courses at the graduate level or 75% for courses at the advanced undergraduate level. A minimum of 30 credits (3.0 GPA) is required for the MS for both the thesis and non-thesis option. M.S. candidates may elect one of three alternative options to earn the degree: (1) Submit a thesis and complete at least six courses. Four courses must be at the 2000-level each with a grade of B or better. Courses needed to accrue the necessary credit hours may include up to four 1300-level undergraduate classes and/or any number of 3000-level advanced graduate courses. (2) Submit no thesis and complete at least eight courses. Four courses must be at the 2000-level each with a grade of B or better. Courses needed to accrue the necessary credit hours may include no more than four 1300-level undergraduate classes and/or any number of 3000-level advanced graduate courses. (3) Submit no thesis and successfully complete at least six courses at the graduate level. In order to accrue the requisite 30 credits for graduation, the student may engage in Directed Study, directed Research, or take additional, approved courses at the 3000-level. There is no foreign language requirement.

Doctorate: Ph.D. students must successfully complete the following six graduate-level core courses: Dynamical Systems (one term), Statistical Mechanics and Thermodynamics (one term), Classical Electricity and Magnetism (one term), Mathematical Methods (one term), and Non-relativistic Quantum Mechanics (two terms). Exemptions from any of these courses may be granted if a student has successfully completed an equivalent course elsewhere. Students must complete these core courses with a grade point average of at least 3.00, which corresponds to a B average; they must also maintain a GPA of at least 3.00 in all of their graduate courses. To satisfy the Ph.D. Comprehensive Examination requirement, students must achieve a score of at least 60% on the final examination in each of the six core courses. This requirement must be fulfilled within the first two years unless an extension is granted. After passing the Ph.D. Comprehensive Examination, the student must find a research advisor and begin the process that leads to Admission to Candidacy and ultimately to the preparation and defense of a satisfactory dissertation. All Ph.D.

students are required to serve for two terms as a Teaching Assistant in introductory undergraduate laboratories or recitations. An exemption may be granted if a student has substantial prior teaching experience. A minimum of four advanced physics courses are required, exemptions may be given if evidence of this done at another institution. There is no foreign language requirement. There is a residence requirement of six full terms, with a total of 72 credit hours. Under some circumstances prior graduate work may be transferred from another institution. A PhD timeline is available at http://www.physicsandastronomy.pitt.edu/graduate/phd-program/phd-milestones.

Other Degrees: Interdisciplinary research programs may be arranged on a case-by-case basis. There have been Physics Doctorates awarded for work done in collaboration with the faculty members in the Chemistry Department, the Mathematics Department, the Materials Science Department, the Electrical and Chemical Engineering Departments, the Department of Biological Sciences, the Department of Computational Biology and the Department of Radiology in the School of Medicine, among others.

SPECIAL EQUIPMENT, FACILITIES, OR PROGRAMS

The Department of Physics and Astronomy is located on the University of Pittsburgh's main campus and housed in a complex of five interconnecting buildings, containing numerous cutting-edge research laboratories and educational facilities. The department also houses a number of cross-disciplinary centers including the PITTsburgh Particle physics, Astrophysics, and Cosmology Center (PITT PACC, the Discipline-Based Science Education Research Center (dB-SERC) and Pittsburgh Quantum Institute (PQI). The department also has access to a number of facilities including machine, electric, and glass shops, the Gertrude E. and John M. Peterson Institute of NanoScience and Engineering (PINSE), the Nano Fabrication and Characterization Facility (NFCF), the Center for Simulation and Modeling (SAM), and the Pittsburgh Supercomputing Center (PSC). Other local facilities include University of Pittsburgh's Allegheny Observatory (AO). Experiments in particle physics are carried out at national and international facilities such as Fermilab near Chicago (www.fnal.gov/), CERN in Switzerland (home.web.cern.ch/) and J–PARC in Japan (http://j-parc.jp/index-e.html). This includes, for example, the Large Hadron Collider ATLAS experiment at CERN and various neutrino experiments (MINOS (www-numi.fnal.gov/), MINERvA (minerva.fnal.gov/), and T2K (t2k-experiment.org/).

Observational programs in astrophysics and cosmology are conducted at national and international ground-based observatories such as, Kitt Peak and Mount Hopkins, in Arizona, Cerro Tololo in Chile, Mauna Kea in Hawaii, and Apache Point in New Mexico for collection of Sloan Digital Sky Survey data. Faculty also makes use of space-based telescopes, including the Hubble Space Telescope; the Chandra X-Ray Telescope; and the GALEX UV Telescope. University of Pittsburgh faculty are members of several current and/or future large-telescope consortia: the Sloan Digital Sky Survey (SDSS, www.sdss.org), the Atacama Cosmology Telescope (ACT, www.physics.princeton.edu/act/), the Panoramic Survey Telescope & Rapid Response System (Pan-STARRS, www.ps1sc.org), the Dark Energy Spectroscopic Instrument (DESI, desi.lbl.gov), and the Large Synoptic Survey Telescope (LSST, www.lsst.org). Many members of the department have significant leadership roles in these projects.

Table B—Separately Budgeted Research Expenditures by Source of Support

Source of Support	Departmental Research	Physics-related Research Outside Department
Federal government		$8,017,800.3
State/local government		
Non-profit organizations		$394,858.36
Business and industry		
Other	$99,595.11	
Total	**$99,595.11**	**$8,412,658.66**

Table C—Separately Budgeted Research Expenditures by Research Specialty

Research Specialty	No. of Grants	Expenditures ($)
Astrophysics	37	$1,045,209
Condensed Matter Physics	49	$5,259,849
Particles and Fields	21	$1,878,059
Other	2	$229,542
Total	**109**	**$8,412,659**

FACULTY

Professor

Boudreau, Joseph, Ph.D., University of Wisconsin-Madison, 1991. *High Energy Physics, Particles and Fields*. Experimental particle physics.

Boyanovsky, Daniel, Ph.D., University of California, Santa Barbara, 1982. *Cosmology & String Theory, Particles and Fields, Relativity & Gravitation, Statistical & Thermal Physics*. Theoretical condensed matter physics; particle astrophysics, astrophysics, and cosmology.

Coalson, Rob, Ph.D., Harvard University, 1984. *Chemical Physics*.

Dytman, Steven A., Ph.D., Carnegie Mellon University, 1978. *High Energy Physics, Particles and Fields*. Experimental particle physics; experimental neutrino physics.

Han, Tao, Ph.D., University of Wisconsin-Madison, 1990. Director of the PITTsburgh Particle physics, Astrophysics and Cosmology Center (PITT PACC). *Particles and Fields*. Theoretical particle physics.

Hillier, D. John, Ph.D., Australian National University, 1984. *Astrophysics, Computational Physics*. Theoretical and observational astrophysics.

Kosowsky, Arthur, Ph.D., University of Chicago, 1994. Professor and Department Chair. *Astrophysics, Cosmology & String Theory, Relativity & Gravitation*. Theoretical and experimental cosmology and astrophysics. Interim Chair of the Department.

Leibovich, Adam, Ph.D., California Institute of Technology, 1997. Associate Dean for Faculty Recruitment and Research Development. *High Energy Physics, Particles and Fields, Relativity & Gravitation*. Theoretical particle physics.

Levy, Jeremy, Ph.D., University of California, Santa Barbara, 1993. Director of the Pittsburgh Quantum Institute (PQI). *Applied Physics, Condensed Matter Physics, Low Temperature Physics, Materials Science, Metallurgy, Nano Science and Technology, Optics*. Experimental condensed matter physics; nanoscience; quantum information.

Liu, W. Vincent, Ph.D., University of Texas, Austin, 1999. *Condensed Matter Physics, Low Temperature Physics*. Theoretical condensed matter physics, cold atoms.

Mueller, James A., Ph.D., Cornell University, 1989. *High Energy Physics, Particles and Fields*. Experimental particle physics.

Naples, Donna, Ph.D., University of Maryland, 1993. *Particles and Fields*. Experimental neutrino physics.

Newman, Jeffrey, Ph.D., University of California, Berkeley, 2000. *Astronomy, Astrophysics, Cosmology & String Theory*. Extragalactic astronomy; observational cosmology.

Paolone, Vittorio, Ph.D., University of California, Davis, 1990. *Particles and Fields*. Experimental particle physics; experimental neutrino physics.

Petek, Hrvoje, Ph.D., University of California, Berkeley, 1985. *Atomic, Molecular, & Optical Physics, Chemical Physics, Condensed Matter Physics, Nano Science and Technology*. Experimental condensed matter/AMO physics; nanoscience; solid-state physics.

Roskies, Ralph Z., Ph.D., Princeton University, 1966. Co-Director of the Pittsburgh Supercomputing Center. *Computational Physics, High Energy Physics, Particles and Fields*. Theoretical particle physics; use of computers in theoretical physics.

Savinov, Vladimir, Ph.D., University of Minnesota, 1996. *High Energy Physics, Particles and Fields*. Experimental particle physics.

Singh, Chandralekha, Ph.D., University of California, Santa Barbara, 1993. Director of the Discipline-based Science Education Research Center (dB-SERC). *Physics and other Science Education*. Polymer physics; physics education research.

Snoke, David W., Ph.D., University of Illinois, 1990. *Applied Physics, Atomic, Molecular, & Optical Physics, Biophysics, Condensed Matter Physics, Low Temperature Physics, Nano Science and Technology, Optics, Statistical & Thermal Physics*. Experimental condensed matter physics; solid-state physics; nanoscience.

Swanson, Eric, Ph.D., University of Toronto, 1991. *Particles and Fields*. Theoretical particle physics.

Turnshek, David A., Ph.D., University of Arizona, 1981. Director of Allegheny Observatory. *Astronomy, Astrophysics*. Extragalactic astronomy; observational cosmology.

Wu, Xiao-Lun, Ph.D., Cornell University, 1987. *Biophysics*. Experimental condensed matter physics, experimental biological physics.

Xu, Yan, Ph.D., Stony Brook, 1990. *Biophysics*. Biophysics.

Yang, Judith, Ph.D., Cornell University, 1993. *Materials Science, Metallurgy*. Materials science and engineering.

Zentner, Andrew, Ph.D., Ohio State University, 2003. Director of the Graduate Program. *Astronomy, Astrophysics, Cosmology & String Theory, Particles and Fields, Relativity & Gravitation*. Theoretical cosmology.

Associate Professor

Badenes, Carles, Ph.D., Universitat Politecnicade de Catalunya, 2004. *Astronomy, Astrophysics, Cosmology & String Theory*. Type 1a supernovae; supernova remnants; large astronomical data bases; extragalactic astronomy; observational cosmology.

Devaty, Robert P., Ph.D., Cornell University, 1983. Chair of the Graduate Admissions Committee. *Condensed Matter Physics*. Solid-state physics; semiconductor physics.

Dutt, Gurudev, Ph.D., University of Michigan, 2004. *Condensed Matter Physics, Nano Science and Technology*. Quantum optics; quantum information.

Freitas, Ayres, Ph.D., University of Hamburg, 2002. *Cosmology & String Theory, High Energy Physics, Particles and Fields*. Theoretical particle physics.

Salman, Hanna, Ph.D., Weizmann Institute of Science, 2002. *Applied Physics, Biophysics, Condensed Matter Physics, Nonlinear Dynamics and Complex Systems, Statistical & Thermal Physics*. Experimental biological physics.

Wood-Vasey, Michael, Ph.D., University of California, Berkeley, 2004. Undergraduate Program Director. *Astronomy, Astrophysics, Cosmology & String Theory*. Extragalactic astronomy; observational cosmology.

Assistant Professor

Batell, Brian, Ph.D., University of Minnesota, 2008. *Particles and Fields, Relativity & Gravitation, Theoretical Physics*. Particle physics, astroparticle physics and cosmology.

Bezanson, Rachel, Ph.D., Yale University, 2013. *Astrophysics*.

Frolov, Sergey, Ph.D., University of Illinois, 2005. *Condensed Matter Physics, Nano Science and Technology*. Experimental condensed matter physics; quantum nanowires, Majorana fermions in nanowires, and nanowire quantum bits.

Hatridge, Michael, Ph.D., University of California, Berkeley, 2010. *Condensed Matter Physics*.

Hong, Tae Min, Ph.D., University of California, Santa Barbara, 2009. *Particles and Fields*. He is an experimental particle physicist interested in questions related to the fundamental forces of Nature and the basic building blocks of the Universe [1]. Professor Hong is currently studying proton-proton collisions produced by the Large Hadron Collider (LHC) at the European Organization for Nuclear Research (CERN) in Geneva, Switzerland. As a member of the ATLAS Collaboration of about 3000 physicists, his significant contributions are in the trigger system and the discovery of the Higgs boson.

Lee, Sangyeop, Ph.D., MIT. Mechanical Engineering and Material Science.

Mong, Roger, Ph.D., University of California, Berkeley, 2012. *Condensed Matter Physics, Low Temperature Physics, Quantum Foundations, Solid State Physics, Theoretical Physics*. Theoretical condensed matter.

Pekker, David, Ph.D., Illinois at Urbana-Champaign. *Atomic, Molecular, & Optical Physics, Computational Physics, Condensed Matter Physics*.

Purdy, Thomas, M.D./Ph.D., University of California, Berkeley. *Condensed Matter Physics*.

Emeritus

Cleland, Wilfred E., Ph.D., Yale University, 1964. *High Energy Physics, Particles and Fields*. Experimental particle physics.

Duncan, H. E. Anthony, Ph.D., Massachusetts Institute of Technology, 1975. *High Energy Physics, Particles and Fields*. Theoretical particle physics.

Engels, Eugene, Ph.D., Princeton University, 1962. *High Energy Physics*. Experimental particle physics.

Janis, Allen I., Ph.D., Syracuse University, 1957. *Relativity & Gravitation, Other*. History and philosophy of science.

Jasnow, David M., Ph.D., University of Illinois, 1969. *Biophysics, Condensed Matter Physics, Fluids, Rheology, Nonlinear Dynamics and Complex Systems, Polymer Physics/Science, Statistical & Thermal Physics*. Theory of phase transitions; statistical physics; biological physics.

Johnsen, Rainer, Ph.D., University of Kiel, 1966. *Atmosphere, Space Physics, Cosmic Rays, Atomic, Molecular, & Optical Physics, Chemical Physics, Fluids, Rheology, Plasma and Fusion*.

Koehler, Peter F. M., Ph.D., University of Rochester, 1967. Academic Assistant to the Dean, University Honors College. *High Energy Physics, Particles and Fields, Physics and other Science Education*. Experimental particle physics; physics education research.

Newman, Ezra T., Ph.D., Syracuse University, 1956. *Relativity & Gravitation*.

Pratt, Richard H., Ph.D., University of Chicago, 1959. *Atomic, Molecular, & Optical Physics*. Theoretical atomic physics.

Shepard, Paul, Ph.D., Princeton University, 1969. *High Energy Physics, Particles and Fields*. Experimental particle physics.

Vincent, C. Martin, Ph.D., University of the Witwatersrand, South Africa, 1966. *Nuclear Physics*.

Professor Emeritus

Maher, James V., Ph.D., Yale University, 1969. *Condensed Matter Physics, Statistical & Thermal Physics*. Experimental solid-state physics; critical phenomena; physics of fluids.

Schulte-Ladbeck, Regina, Ph.D., Heidelberg University, 1985. *Astronomy, Astrophysics, Cosmology & String Theory*. Extragalactic astronomy; observational cosmology.

Research Professor

Choyke, W. James, Ph.D., Ohio State University, 1952. *Condensed Matter Physics*. Experimental solid-state physics; defect states in semiconductors; large-band-gap spectroscopy.

Rao, Sandhya, Ph.D., University of Pittsburgh, 1994. *Astronomy, Astrophysics, Cosmology & String Theory*. Extragalactic astronomy, observational cosmology.

Winicour, Jefferey, Ph.D., Syracuse University, 1964. *Astrophysics, Relativity & Gravitation*. General relativity; numerical relativity.

Research Associate Professor

Niedermaier, Max, Ph.D., University of Hamburg. *Particles and Fields*.

Research Assistant Professor

Irvin, Patrick, Ph.D., University of Pittsburgh, 2009. *Condensed Matter Physics*. Experimental condensed matter physics.

Adjunct Professor

Cheng, Guanglei, Ph.D., University of Pittsburgh, 2011. *Condensed Matter Physics*. Experimental condensed matter physics.

Feng, Min, Ph.D., Chinese Academy of Sciences, 2005. *Condensed Matter Physics*. Experimental condensed matter physics.

Ishioka, Kunie, Ph.D., Kyoto University, 1994. *Condensed Matter Physics*.

Tan, Shijing, Ph.D., University of Science and Technology of China. *Condensed Matter Physics*.

Zhao, Jin, Ph.D., University of Science and Technology of China, 2003. *Condensed Matter Physics, Nano Science and Technology*.

Adjunct Assistant Professor

Cui, Xuefeng, Ph.D., Univ. of Science & Technology of China, 2009. *Condensed Matter Physics*.

Senior Lecturer

Clark, Russell, Ph.D., Louisiana State University, 1997. Lab Supervisor. *Physics and other Science Education*. Neutrino physics.

Lecturer

Broccio, Matteo, Ph.D., University of Messina, 2005. *Biophysics, Physics and other Science Education*. Physics education, experimental biophysics.

Good, Melanie, Ph.D., University of Pittsburgh, 2018. *Physics and other Science Education*.

Marshman, Emily, Ph.D., University of Pittsburgh, 2015. *Physics and other Science Education*.

Nero, David, Ph.D., University of Toledo, 2010. *Astronomy, Physics and other Science Education*.

Lab Personnel

Danko, Istvan, Ph.D., Vanderbilt University, 2001. *Particles and Fields*. Experimental neutrino physics.

DEPARTMENTAL RESEARCH SPECIALTIES AND STAFF

Theoretical

Astrophysics. Astrophysics and cosmology. Early universe physics; dark matter and dark energy; theoretical and numerical cosmology; model stellar atmospheres; massive stars; supernovae; gravitational lensing; general relativity and gravitation; numerical relativity; gravitational radiation; black hole physics; plasma physics. Boyanovsky, Hillier, Kosowsky, Ezra Newman, Winicour, Zentner.

Condensed Matter Physics. Phase transitions; disordered systems; nonequilibrium behavior; polymer physics; biological physics; atomic cold gases; superconductivity; topological insulators and superconductors, fractional quantum Hall; quantum kinetics, atomic, molecular, and optical physics. Boyanovsky, Coalson, Jasnow, Liu, Mong, Pekker, Zhao.

Particles and Fields. Gauge field theories; lattice calculations; nonperturbative effects; weak interaction models and phenomenology; heavy-quark physics; supersymmetry; QCD modeling; extra dimensions; baryogenesis. Batell, Boyanovsky, Duncan, Freitas, Han, Leibovich, Roskies, Swanson.

Experimental

Astrophysics. Astronomy, Astrophysics, and Cosmology. Local and distant galaxies; active galactic nuclei and quasars; studies of the interstellar medium, circumgalactic medium, and intergalactic medium using quasar absorption line systems; statistical analysis of the properties of galaxies; clustering and large-scale structure; dark matter and dark energy; cosmic microwave background; supernovae; massive stars; stellar atmospheres. Observations take place with ground-based telescopes around the world and with space telescopes. Badenes, Bezanson, Jeffrey Newman, Rao, Turnshek, Wood-Vasey.

Condensed Matter Physics. Nanoscience; quantum information; quantum optics; quantum states of matter; semiconductor physics; soft condensed matter physics; superconductivity and superfluidity; ultrafast optics; atomic, molecular, and optical physics; biological physics; turbulence. Experimental work takes place on campus in the individual laboratories of faculty members, at the Peterson Institute for Nanoscience and Engineering (PINSE), and at the Nano Fabrication and Characterization Facility (NFCF). Choyke, Devaty, Dutt, Feng, Frolov, Hatridge, Irvin, Johnsen, Levy, Maher, Petek, Salman, Snoke, Wu, Yang.

Particles and Fields. Particle Physics. Origin of mass and flavor; search for new symmetries of nature; neutrino physics; CP violation; heavy quarks; leptoquarks; supersymmetry; extra dimensions; baryogenesis. Studies take place at the Tevatron proton-antiproton collider, located at the Fermi National Accelerator Laboratory, and at the Large Hadron Collider ATLAS detector, located at CERN. Studies at the LHC may uncover the elusive Higgs boson as well as a spectrum of new particles arising from "supersymmetry." Studies of fundamental properties of neutrinos, such as oscillations, mass differences, and neutrino-nucleus interactions take place at a variety of locations. Boudreau, Cleland, Danko, Dytman, Hong, Mueller, Naples, Paolone, Savinov, Shepard.

Physics and other Science Education. Physics education research. Identification of sources of student difficulties in learning concepts in both introductory and advanced-level physics courses; design, implementation, and outcome assessment of changes in curricular offerings; pedagogical methods that are designed to reduce learning difficulties. Broccio, Clark, Danko, Koehler, Nero, Singh.

BROWN UNIVERSITY

DEPARTMENT OF PHYSICS

Providence, Rhode Island 02912
http://www.brown.edu/academics/physics/

General University Information
President: Christina Hull Paxson
Dean of Graduate School: Andrew G. Campbell
University website: http://brown.edu
School Type: Private
Setting: Urban
Total Faculty: 1,424
Total Graduate Faculty: 1,424
Total number of Students: 8,848
Total number of Graduate Students: 2,094

Department Information
Department Chairman: Prof. Gang Xiao, Chair
Department Contact: Mary Ellen Woycik, Student Affairs & Programs Manager
  Total full-time faculty: 28
  Total number of full-time equivalent positions: 28
  Full-Time Graduate Students: 124
  Female Full-Time Graduate Students: 27
  First-Year Graduate Students: 38
  Female First-Year Students: 10
  Total Post Doctorates: 16

Department Address
182 Hope Street
Providence, RI 02912
Phone: (401) 863-1434
Fax: (401) 863-2024
E-mail: mew@brown.edu
Website: http://www.brown.edu/academics/physics/

ADMISSIONS

Admission Contact Information
Address admission inquiries to: Graduate School: admission_graduate@brown.edu, Physics: physics@brown.edu
Phone: 401-863-2600
E-mail: admission_graduate@brown.edu
Admissions website: http://www.brown.edu/academics/gradschool/application-information

Application deadlines
Fall admission:
U.S. students: January 2   *Int'l. students*: January 2

Application fee
U.S. students: $75   *Int'l. students*: $75
The deadline listed is for the Ph.D. program. The ScM program has rolling admissions, with an academic year application deadline of May 1.

Admissions information
For Fall of 2018:
  Number of applicants: 319
  Number admitted: 45
  Number enrolled: 18

Admission requirements
Bachelor's degree requirements: Bachelor's degree in Physics or related field is required. Applicants are expected to have a strong background in physics or closely related subjects.

GRE requirements
The GRE is required.
For Ph.D. program, GRE General is required. For ScM program, GRE General is recommended.

Subjective GRE requirements
The Subjective GRE is recommended.
For both Ph.D. and ScM program, GRE subject is recommended.

TOEFL requirements
The TOEFL exam is required for students from non-English-speaking countries.
  PBT score: 577
  iBT score: 90
TOEFL is not required for one whose native language is not English but who has received a degree from a university in which English is the primary language of instruction. To update the application, a waiver must be obtained from the Graduate School. More information: https://www.brown.edu/academics/gradschool/application-information/international-applicants/language-proficiency-toefl-or-ielts

Other admissions information
Additional requirements: The Ph.D. program provides students with opportunities to perform independent research in some of the most current and dynamic areas of physics. Three letters of recommendation are required.
The ScM program is suitable as both a means for professional development and preparation for further graduate study. The program is designed to be completed in 4 semesters with 2 courses per semester as full-time enrollment. There is flexibility to allow for completion of the degree in two, or three semesters depending on a student's background. Two recommendation letters are required.
Undergraduate preparation assumed: Undergraduate requirements flexible to some extent; preference given for strong upper-class study in mechanics, E&M, wave theory, modern physics, and mathematics through partial differential equations. Purcell, Electricity and Magnetism; Schey, Div, Grad, Curl and All That; Feynman, The Feynman Lectures on Physics, Vol. II recommended; French and Taylor, An Introduction to Quantum Physics; Marion, Classical Electromagnetic Radiation; Gasiorowicz, Quantum Physics; Reif, Fundamentals of Statistical and Thermal Physics; French, Vibrations and Waves; Kibble, Classical Mechanics (2nd. ed. or later).

TUITION

Tuition year 2018–19:
  Full-time students: $54,320 annual
  Part-time students: $6,790 per credit
Average stipends listed below are for academic year 2018–19 and do not include summer funding. The Graduate School offers incoming doctoral students five years of guaranteed financial support, including stipend, tuition remission, health-

services fee, and health-insurance subsidy. More information on: http://www.brown.edu/academics/gradschool/financing-support/phd-funding All enrolled Physics Master's students are self-supported. The tuition for the Physics Master's program for AY2018–19 is $59,758 for all eight courses. Students are billed per course taken, typically 2 courses per semester. Domestic students may be eligible for federal direct student loans and other loans administered through the Office of Financial Aid. More information on: http://www.brown.edu/academics/gradschool/financing-support/masters-funding

Deferred tuition plan: Yes
Health insurance: Available
Other academic fees: $60 Activity Fee $64 Recreation Fee
Academic term: Semester
Number of first-year students who received full tuition waivers: 18

Teaching Assistants, Research Assistants, and Fellowships

Number of first-year
  Teaching Assistants: 18
  Fellowship students: 3
Average stipend per academic year
  Teaching Assistant: $25,635
  Research Assistant: $25,635
  Fellowship student: $25,635
All Ph.D. students are supported as fellows, TA's or RA's regardless of the number of students enrolled in any particular year. Average stipends listed are for AY18-19 and do not include guaranteed summer funding. Summer stipends range from $2,848 to 1/3 of the academic year stipend, depending on a number of factors.

FINANCIAL AID

Loans

Loans are available for U.S. students.
Loans are available for international students.
GAPSFAS application required: No
FAFSA application required: Yes

For further information

Address financial aid inquiries to: Office of Financial Aid, Brown University, Box #1827, Providence, RI 02912.
Phone: (401) 863-2721
E-mail: GS_Financial_Aid@brown.edu
Financial aid website: http://www.brown.edu/about/administration/financial-aid/contact-information

HOUSING

Availability of on-campus housing

Single students: Yes
Married students: Yes
Childcare Assistance: Yes

For further information

Address housing inquiries to: Off-Campus:, Office of Auxiliary Housing, Brown University, Box 1902, Providence, RI 02912,, On-campus:, Office of Residential Life, Box 1864, Brown University, Providence, RI 02912.
Phone: (401) 863-2541
E-mail: Ronni_Edmonds@brown.edu
Housing aid website: http://www.brown.edu/academics/gradschool/graduate/housing

Table A—Faculty, Enrollments, and Degrees Granted

Research Specialty	Faculty	Enrollment Fall 2017 Master's	Enrollment Fall 2017 Doctorate	Number of Degrees Granted 2017–18 (2013–17) Master's	Number of Degrees Granted 2017–18 (2013–17) Terminal Master's	Number of Degrees Granted 2017–18 (2013–17) Doctorate
Astrophysics	4	–	13	–	–	1(11)
Biophysics	3	–	6	–	–	1(10)
Condensed Matter Physics	10	–	25	–	–	5(27)
Particles and Fields	9	–	24	–	–	3(18)
Non-specialized	–	46	13	32(97)	16(34)	–
Other	–	–	2	–	–	–(1)
Total	26	46	83	32(97)	16(34)	10(67)
Full-time Grad. Stud.	–	46	83	–	–	–
First-year Grad. Stud.	–	28	11	–	–	–

GRADUATE DEGREE REQUIREMENTS

Master's: Approved sequence of eight semester courses. Of the eight required courses, four will be selected from the six core courses (PHYS2010, 2030, 2040, 2050, 2060, and 2140). Four additional credits at the 2000 level are required, selected with guidance based on a student's goals and interests. Because preparation of a master's thesis is highly recommended, as it forms an important pillar of the professional training, one of the eight required courses may be Research in Physics (PHYS2980, 2981).

Doctorate: Approved sequence of ten semester courses comprised of all six core courses (PHYS2010, 2030, 2040, 2050, 2060, 2140) and four advanced courses. Qualifying exam normally taken at start of second year in program. Preliminary exam completed by end of third year, marking advancement to candidacy.

Thesis: Preparation of a master's thesis is highly recommended for those enrolled in the ScM program. The Ph.D. written dissertation and oral defense is required.

SPECIAL EQUIPMENT, FACILITIES, OR PROGRAMS

(a) Brown is a member of Universities Research Association, Inc. (URA), part of the Fermilab Research Alliance, which operates the Fermi National Accelerator Laboratory (FNAL) in Batavia, Illinois, and other facilities. Brown physicists are involved in the D0 experiment at the 2 TeV Tevatron collider located at FNAL, as well as in the CMS experiment at the 14 TeV Large Hadron Collider (LHC) located at CERN, in Geneva, Switzerland. Brown leads experimental collaborations that operate rare particle search experiments at international underground laboratories at Gran Sasso, Italy, and Sanford Lab, Homestake Mine, South Dakota. Brown in involved with ground-based, balloon-borne, and satellite-based cosmology and astrophysics experiments. Researchers at Brown are collaborating on telescope projects in Arizona and Chile, and balloon flights launched from Texas and the Antarctic. Using equipment designed and built at Brown, as well as the National Laboratories, data are recorded in experimental runs and analyzed at Brown with extensive use of computer systems.

(b) The Physics Department is an active participant in Brown's Institute for Molecular and Nanoscale Innovation (IMNI), an umbrella organization that supports centers and collaborative research teams in targeted areas of the molecular and nanosciences. IMNI is a "polydisciplinary" venture, with 60 faculty participants representing nine departments across campus. IMNI serves as a focal point for interaction with industry, government, and affiliated hospitals.

(c) Physics is also associated with the Institute for Brian and Neural Systems and the Center for Biomedical Engineering at Brown.

(d) Extensive computer facilities are available. These include a variety of Windows and Linux/UNIX workstations within the department, all of which are connected via Ethernet. In addition, the department has several powerful Zinux clusters for dealing with problems needing large-scale computation. Several high-speed network links provide worldwide access to experimental facilities and enable extensive and efficient use of national super-computing centers. A department web server provides access to personal home pages of faculty, staff, and students as well as general departmental information.

Table B—Separately Budgeted Research Expenditures by Source of Support

Source of Support	Departmental Research	Physics-related Research Outside Department
Federal government	$3,821,700	
State/local government		
Non-profit organizations	$553,936	
Business and industry	$561,712	
Other	$4,343,025	
Total	**$9,280,373**	

Table C—Separately Budgeted Research Expenditures by Research Specialty

Research Specialty	No. of Grants	Expenditures ($)
Astrophysics	15	$1,975,139
Biophysics	3	$334,834
Condensed Matter Physics	14	$2,313,064
Particles and Fields	23	$4,597,444
Physics and other Science Education	1	$59,892
Total	**56**	**$9,280,373**

FACULTY

Chair Professor

Xiao, Gang, Ph.D., Johns Hopkins University, 1988. *Applied Physics, Condensed Matter Physics, Electromagnetism, Materials Science, Metallurgy, Nano Science and Technology, Solid State Physics, Surface Physics.*

Professor

Alexander, Stephon, Ph.D., Brown University, 2000.

Cutts, David, Ph.D., University of California, Berkeley, 1968. *Particles and Fields.*

Dell'Antonio, Ian P., Ph.D., Harvard University, 1995. *Astronomy, Astrophysics, Cosmology & String Theory, Relativity & Gravitation.*

Feldman, Dmitri, Ph.D., Landau Institute for Theoretical Physics, 1998. *Condensed Matter Physics, Solid State Physics, Statistical & Thermal Physics, Theoretical Physics.*

Gaitskell, Richard, Ph.D., University of Oxford, 1993. *Astrophysics, Cosmology & String Theory, High Energy Physics.*

Gates, Sylvester J., Ph.D., Massachusetts Imstitute of Technology, 1977. *High Energy Physics.*

Heintz, Ulrich, Ph.D., Stony Brook University, 1991. *High Energy Physics.* Elementary Particle Physics.

Jevicki, Antal, Ph.D., City University of New York, 1976. Quantum Field Theory (String Theory, Quantum Gravity, Black Holes, Non-perturbative and Collective Phenomena).

Kosterlitz, J. Michael, Ph.D., University of Oxford, 1969. 2016 Nobel Laureate. *Condensed Matter Physics, Statistical & Thermal Physics.*

Landsberg, Greg L., Ph.D., Stony Brook University, 1994. *Particles and Fields.*

Ling, Xinsheng, Ph.D., University of Connecticut, 1992. *Biophysics, Condensed Matter Physics, Nano Science and Technology, Solid State Physics, Statistical & Thermal Physics.*

Lowe, David A., Ph.D., Princeton University, 1993. *Cosmology & String Theory, High Energy Physics, Particles and Fields, Relativity & Gravitation, Theoretical Physics.*

Marston, J. Bradley, Ph.D., Princeton University, 1989. *Climate/Atmospheric Science, Computational Physics, Condensed Matter Physics, Fluids, Rheology, Nonlinear Dynamics and Complex Systems, Theoretical Physics.*

Mitrovic, Vesna, Ph.D., Northwestern University, 2001. *Applied Physics, Computational Physics, Condensed Matter Physics, Engineering Physics/Science, Low Temperature Physics, Medical, Health Physics, Polymer Physics/Science, Solid State Physics.*

Narain, Meenakshi, Ph.D., Stony Brook University, 1991. *Computational Physics, High Energy Physics, Particles and Fields.*

Pelcovits, Robert A., Ph.D., Harvard University, 1978. *Condensed Matter Physics.*

Spradlin, Marcus, Ph.D., Harvard University, 2001. *High Energy Physics, Particles and Fields, Theoretical Physics.*

Tan, Chung-I, Ph.D., University of California, Berkeley, 1968. *Theoretical Physics.*

Tang, Jay X., Ph.D., Brandeis University, 1995. *Biophysics, Condensed Matter Physics, Fluids, Rheology, Mechanics, Physics and other Science Education, Polymer Physics/Science, Statistical & Thermal Physics.*

Tucker, Gregory S., Ph.D., Princeton University, 1991. *Astronomy, Astrophysics.*

Valles, James M., Ph.D., University of Massachusetts, 1988. *Biophysics, Condensed Matter Physics, Low Temperature Physics, Solid State Physics.*

Volovich, Anastasia, Ph.D., Harvard University, 2002. *Theoretical Physics.*

Associate Professor

Koushiappas, Savvas, Ph.D., Ohio State University, 2004. *Astrophysics, Cosmology & String Theory, High Energy Physics, Particles and Fields, Relativity & Gravitation, Theoretical Physics.*

Stein, Derek, Ph.D., Harvard University, 2003. *Applied Physics, Biophysics, Condensed Matter Physics, Fluids, Rheology, Nano Science and Technology, Polymer Physics/Science, Other.*

Assistant Professor

Fan, JiJi, Ph.D., Yale University, 2009. *High Energy Physics, Particles and Fields, Theoretical Physics.*

Plumb, Kemp, Ph.D., University of Toronto, 2014. *Condensed Matter Physics.*

Pober, Jonathan C., Ph.D., University of California, Berkeley, 2013. *Astronomy, Astrophysics.*

DEPARTMENTAL RESEARCH SPECIALTIES AND STAFF

Theoretical

Astrophysics and Cosmology. Cosmological models for structure formation and particle-physics predictions of the nature of the dark matter are analyzed. Computational and analytic tools are used to predict the distribution of matter on sub- and super-galaxy scales and to aid in the design of the next generation of cosmological experiments. Alexander, Dell'Antonio, Gaitskell, Koushiappas, Pober.

Physics of Condensed Matter. Research problems currently under investigation include interference and interaction in mesoscopic systems, including the quantum Hall effect, quantum wires, and quantum phase transitions; strongly correlated electrons in layered materials; development of a non-equilibrium statistical mechanics of planetary climates; non-equilibrium transport in nanostructures; modeling actinide complexes in aqueous solution; liquid crystal physics and its interface with biology; dynamics of biopolymers in nanochannels; strain relaxation and dynamics of heteroepitaxial nanostructures; microscopic theories of friction; out of equilibrium systems in the presence of weak stochastic noise; ultra-fast dynamics in liquids. Feldman, Kosterlitz, Marston, Pelcovits, Plumb.

Physics of Elementary Particles. Current activities include studies in quantum field theory; quantum chromodynamics; gauge/gravity duality; non-perturbative methods in field theory; solitons; monopoles; spontaneous symmetry breaking; lattice field theories; renormalization group; field theoretic approaches to condensed matter; gauge theories of weak and electromagnetic interactions; grand unification theory and phenomenology; phenomenology of scattering and production processes; the quantum theory of gravitation; supersymmetry; supergravity; superstrings; cosmology; Beyond Standard Model phenomenology including supersymmetry phenomenology; Higgs physics; collider physics; dark matter models; and detection. Fan, Gates, Jevicki, Lowe, Spradlin, Tan, Volovich.

Experimental

Astrophysics and Cosmology. The origins and evolution of the universe are being measured. We are carrying out measurements of the Cosmic Microwave Background from satellite, balloon-borne and ground-based missions to understand the early Universe. We are also using the highly redshifted 21 cm line of neutral hydrogen to map out the three-dimensional structure and evolution of the universe through the epochs of reionization and first star-formation. This work is done using dedicated low-frequency radio interferometers in South Africa and Western Australia. Wide-field optical and near-infrared surveys are being carried out with telescopes in Arizona and Chile to map out the gravitational lensing signal and measure the shear correlation function and the growth of clustering over cosmic time to measure the evolution of the dark energy equation of state. Studies of mass substructure from gravitational lensing maps of clusters of galaxies taken with HST and ground-based telescopes are being used to measure the clustering properties of dark matter. Investigations using the next generation of wide-field survey instruments to map the galaxy group and cluster distribution out to high redshift are being planned. Studies of the galaxy interaction and star formation properties through optical photometry, spectroscopy, NIR photometry, and radio spectral line observations are being carried out. We are also pursuing the direct detection of dark matter using large detectors located in un-

derground laboratories. Direct detection is at the cusp of astrophysics, cosmology and particle physics. The discovery of Weakly Interacting Massive Particles would have a major impact on all these fields. Work focuses on the world-leading LUX experiment, and the future LZ experiment, both based at Sanford Laboratory in the US. Work also continues in studying and developing new technologies for the. Alexander, Dell'Antonio, Gaitskell, Koushiappas, Pober, Tucker.

Biological Physics. Research problems currently under investigation include: the development of single-molecule sequencing technology for DNA and for proteins using nanopores and mass spectrometry; studies of polymer physics, electrokinetics, and fluid dynamics using nanopores and nanofluidic chips; electronic DNA barcode sequencing; biomechanics and rheology of protein networks regulated by physical mechanisms; biophysical mechanism of bacterial swimming, swarming and adhesion; biomechanics and force sensing in soft matter, including live cells. Ling, Stein, Tang, Valles.

Condensed Matter Physics. Research interests include: superconductivity; electron correlation effects in disordered metals and nanostructures; spintronic effects in nanostructures and devices (for example, magnetic quantum tunneling and giant spin Hall effect); spin-logics and magnetic memories; strongly correlated electronic systems in epitaxial or low dimensional systems; high performance magnetic materials with enhanced spin polarization, induced magnetic anisotropies, or large spin-orbit coupling; quantum wires and dots; topological insulators and solids; electronic and magnetic processes probed by NMR; magnetic resonance studies of exotic quantum phases of matter and superconductivity in high magnetic field; spin manipulation in systems where spin is not a good quantum number; studies of ultrasonic and thermal properties of solids using picosecond laser pulses; nano-photonics. Ling, Mitrovic, Plumb, Stein, Tang, Valles, Xiao.

Physics of Elementary Particles. The properties of elementary particles and their interactions are being investigated, with current effort focused on the study of proton-proton collisions at the highest available energy with the CMS experiment at the Large Hadron Collider at CERN and proton-antiproton collisions at the previous energy frontier facility: the DO experiment at Fermilab Tevatron accelerator. The CMS program is focused on searches for new particles, forces, and properties of space-time, beyond the predictions of the Standard Model of particle physics. That includes searches for supersymmetry and other heavy partners of the known particles, extra spatial dimensions, and new forces. In addition to this avenue to discovery, the CMS and DO programs include precision measurements of the properties of electroweak and strong interactions, in particular measurement of the top-quark properties. An important component of the current DO and near-future CMS program is the search for the last missing piece of the Standard Model-the Higgs boson. High-performance LHC Computing Grid networking and video conferencing facilities provide tight links between Brown, CERN, and Fermilab. Local computer cluster connected to the Grid allows for massive parallel computing support of the D0 and CMS physics program. Cutts, Heintz, Landsberg, Narain.

CLEMSON UNIVERSITY

DEPARTMENT OF PHYSICS AND ASTRONOMY

Clemson, South Carolina 29634-0978
http://www.clemson.edu/ces/physics-astro/

General University Information
President: James P. Clements
Dean of Graduate School: Jason W. Osborne
University website: http://www.clemson.edu
School Type: Public
Setting: Suburban
Total Faculty: 1,264
Total number of Students: 23,406
Total number of Graduate Students: 4,807

Department Information
Department Chairman: Prof. Sean Brittain, Chair
Department Contact: Risé Sheriff, Office Manager
  Total full-time faculty: 32
  Total number of full-time equivalent positions: 32
  Full-Time Graduate Students: 58
  Female Full-Time Graduate Students: 17
  First-Year Graduate Students: 15
  Female First-Year Students: 6
  Total Post Doctorates: 7

Department Address
118 Kinard Laboratory
Clemson, SC 29634-0978
Phone: (864) 656-3416
Fax: (864) 656-0805
E-mail: risem@clemson.edu
Website: http://www.clemson.edu/ces/physics-astro/

ADMISSIONS

Admission Contact Information
Address admission inquiries to: Dr. Jens Oberheide, Chair, Graduate Admissions Committee, Department of Physics and Astronomy
Phone: (864) 656-3416
E-mail: joberhe@clemson.edu
Admissions website: http://www.grad.clemson.edu/prospectiveStudents.php

Application deadlines
Fall admission:
U.S. students: January 15   *Int'l. students*: January 15

Application fee
U.S. students: $80   *Int'l. students*: $90
All students should apply directly to the Graduate School for a special self-managed application package. We do not generally offer spring admission.

Admissions information
For Fall of 2018:
  Number of applicants: 82
  Number admitted: 38
  Number enrolled: 20

Admission requirements
Bachelor's degree requirements: Bachelor's degree is required.
Minimum undergraduate GPA: 3.0

GRE requirements
The GRE is required.
No minimum scores set

Subjective GRE requirements
The Subjective GRE is not required.

TOEFL requirements
The TOEFL exam is required for students from non-English-speaking countries.
  PBT score: 570
  iBT score: 90

Other admissions information
Additional requirements: Usual preparation is undergraduate major in physics. Students from other fields will have an opportunity to make up deficiencies.
Undergraduate preparation assumed: Courses are based upon texts such as Hecht, Optics; Griffiths, Introduction to Electrodynamics; Marion and Thornton, Mechanics, Eisberg; Modern Physics, Stowe, Introduction to Statistical Mechanics and Thermodynamics; Griffiths and Townsend, Quantum Physics. Included with these standard areas of study should be an advanced undergraduate laboratory in experimental physics, mathematics including differential equations, complex variable, Fourier analysis, and operational mathematics. Some knowledge of computer programming including standard methods using Mathematica, Maple, MatLab, etc., will also be helpful.

TUITION
Tuition year 2017–2018:
Tuition for in-state residents
  Full-time students: $4,413 per semester
  Part-time students: $612 per credit
Tuition for out-of-state residents
  Full-time students: $9,212 per semester
  Part-time students: $1,223 per credit
Credit hours per semester to be considered full-time: 12
Deferred tuition plan: Yes
Health insurance: Available at the cost of 611.00 per year.
Other academic fees: Graduate assistantship fees are $1122.00 per semester (fall and spring).
Academic term: Semester
Number of first-year students who received full tuition waivers: 15

Teaching Assistants, Research Assistants, and Fellowships
Number of first-year
  Teaching Assistants: 15
Average stipend per academic year
  Teaching Assistant: $20,000
  Research Assistant: $23,000
  Fellowship student: $24,000
  TA stipend raised to $22,000 for 2018–19.

FINANCIAL AID

Application deadlines
Fall admission:
U.S. students: April 1   *Int'l. students*: April 1

Loans

Loans are available for U.S. students.

Loans are not available for international students.

GAPSFAS application required: No

FAFSA application required: Yes

For further information

Address financial aid inquiries to: Clemson University, Financial Aid Counselor, G-01 Sikes Hall, Box 345123, Clemson, SC 29634.

Phone: (864) 656-2280

E-mail: finaid@clemson.edu

Financial aid website: http://www.clemson.edu/financial-aid/index.html

HOUSING

Availability of on-campus housing

Single students: Yes

Married students: No

Childcare Assistance: No

For further information

Address housing inquiries to: University Housing, 200 Mell Hall, Box 344075, Clemson, SC 29634-4075.

Phone: (864) 656-2295

E-mail: housinginfo-l@clemon.edu

Housing aid website: http://www.clemson.edu/campus-life/housing/

Table A—Faculty, Enrollments, and Degrees Granted

Research Specialty	2017–18 Faculty	Enrollment Fall 2017–18 Master's	Enrollment Fall 2017–18 Doctorate	Number of Degrees Granted 2017–18 (2013–17) Master's	Number of Degrees Granted 2017–18 (2013–17) Terminal Master's	Number of Degrees Granted 2017–18 (2013–17) Doctorate
Astrophysics	6	1	10	1(16)	1(12)	–(7)
Atmosphere, Space Physics, Cosmic Rays	6	–	5	–(3)	–(3)	–(1)
Atomic, Molecular, & Optical Physics	3	–	6	–(2)	–	1(2)
Biophysics	4	–	10	1(3)	–(3)	3(8)
Condensed Matter Physics	8	–	17	1(6)	–(6)	5(11)
Quantum Foundations	1	–	2	–(2)	–(1)	–(1)
Non-specialized	–	–	6	–	–	–
Total	32	1	57	3(32)	1(25)	9(30)
Full-time Grad. Stud.	–	1	57	–	–	–
First-year Grad. Stud.	–	–	15	–	–	–

GRADUATE DEGREE REQUIREMENTS

Master's: Thirty semester credits of coursework are required, including six credits of thesis research with an oral defense. For non-thesis degrees, 36 credits are needed. A grade point average of 3.0 is required. There are no foreign language requirements.

Doctorate: A core of six graduate physics courses is required, except for students who have a M.S. degree in physics. All students complete four advanced graduate courses related to their areas of research. Students must pass a set of Ph.D. qualifying examinations and a dissertation topic defense. Original research culminates in a dissertation that is defended before a faculty advisory committee. A 3.0 grade point average is required. There is no foreign language requirement.

Thesis: Thesis may be written in absentia.

SPECIAL EQUIPMENT, FACILITIES, OR PROGRAMS

The department is housed in the four-story 64,000 sq. ft. physics and astronomy building. A fully equipped research/instrument laboratory and computing facilities is available, along with a state-of-the-art planetarium. Office space is provided for graduate students. Extensive research facilities include an electron beam ion trap facility for highly charged ion beam production; an atomic molecular and optical physics laboratory; a scanning tunneling microscope nanomaterial processing laboratory with electric arc discharge, pulsed laser vaporization, and CVD synthesis capabilities; bulk and thin film thermoelectric materials growth facilities; Raman scattering, infrared/visible spectroscopy, electron microscopy, atomic force microscopy, and electrical transport measurements are used extensively for characterizing carbon nanotubes, nanodiamond, semiconducting oxide nanobelts, and nanowires. Access is also available to the SARA and Super Lotis telescopes.

Table B—Separately Budgeted Research Expenditures by Source of Support

Source of Support	Departmental Research	Physics-related Research Outside Department
Federal government	$3,622,098	
State/local government		
Non-profit organizations		
Business and industry		
Other	$246,950	
Total	$3,869,048	

Table C—Separately Budgeted Research Expenditures by Research Specialty

Research Specialty	No. of Grants	Expenditures ($)
Astrophysics	15	$375,360
Atmosphere, Space Physics, Cosmic Rays	21	$686,511
Atomic, Molecular, & Optical Physics	5	$1,199,683
Biophysics	8	$640,606
Condensed Matter Physics	14	$966,888
Total	63	$3,869,048

FACULTY

Professor

Alexov, Emil, Ph.D., Sofia University, 1990. *Biophysics, Computational Physics*. Developing methods for modeling electrostatics in biological systems (DelPhi package); predicting effects of nsSNP on human health.

Daw, Murray S., Ph.D., California Institute of Technology, 1981. *Condensed Matter Physics, Solid State Physics, Theoretical Physics*. Solid-state theory, structure and dynamics of defects in solids.

Hartmann, Dieter H., Ph.D., University of California, Santa Cruz, 1989. *Astronomy, Astrophysics*. Gamma-ray astronomy, nucleosynthesis, galactic structure.

King, J. R., Ph.D., University of Hawaii, 1993. *Astronomy, Astrophysics*. Stellar abundances, stellar atmospheres, galactic populations, high-resolution spectroscopy.

Larsen, M. F., Ph.D., Cornell University, 1979. Atmosphere, space physics.

Leising, Mark D., Ph.D., Rice University, 1987. Department Chair. *Astronomy, Astrophysics*. Gamma-ray astronomy, supernovae.

Marinescu, D. C., Ph.D., Purdue University, 1996. *Condensed Matter Physics, Theoretical Physics.* Condensed-matter theory.

Meriwether, J. W., Ph.D., University of Maryland, 1970. *Optics.* Atmosphere, space physics, optics.

Meyer, Bradley S., Ph.D., University of Chicago, 1989. *Astronomy, Astrophysics, Theoretical Physics.* Nuclear astrophysics, supernova theory, cosmology.

Rao, Apparao M., Ph.D., University of Kentucky, 1989. *Condensed Matter Physics, Nano Science and Technology, Solid State Physics.* Condensed-matter physics, nanomaterial synthesis, mechanical properties, chem-bio sensing, solid-state spectroscopy.

Associate Professor

Brittain, Sean, Ph.D., University of Notre Dame, 2004. *Astronomy, Astrophysics.* Astrophysics, planet formation, circumstellar disks, spectroscopy.

He, Jian, Ph.D., University of Tennessee, 2004. *Condensed Matter Physics.* Condensed-matter physics, single crystal growth and characterizations, functional nanocomposite materials.

Lehmacher, Gerald, Ph.D., University of Bonn, 1993. Atmosphere, space physics, Atmospheric physics, turbulence in the mesosphere and lower thermosphere, suborbital rocket instrumentation.

Oberheide, Jens, Ph.D., Wuppertal University, 2000. *Climate/Atmospheric Science.* Atmosphere, space physics, Atmospheric and geospace physics, climate and weather of the sun-earth system.

Sosolik, Chad E., Ph.D., Cornell University, 2001. *Condensed Matter Physics, Physics of Beams, Solid State Physics.* Experimental surface and highly charged ion beam physics.

Assistant Professor

Ajello, Marco, Ph.D., Max Planck Institute for Extraterrestrial Physics, 2007. *Astronomy, Astrophysics.*

Alper, Joshua D., Ph.D., MIT, 2010. *Biophysics.* Biophysics, the mechanics of molecular motors.

Ding, Feng, Ph.D., Boston University, 2004. *Biophysics, Computational Physics.* Multi-scale modeling of biomolecules and molecular complexes, Understanding the interface between nanomaterials and biology, and designing functional biomolecules, including proteins and RNA.

Gao, Jianbo, Ph.D., UC Berkeley. The research of UPD group focuses on development of next generation technologies based on quantum materials and use unique ultrafast photocurrent spectroscopy approaches to understand fundamental device photophysics dynamics. UPD research includes three main areas: Fundamental quantum physics: we use ultrafast photocurrent spectroscopy (UPS) and ultrafast electroluminescence spectroscopy (UES) to understand ultrafast photophysics in situ devices. Novel quantum devices: semi-transparent single-photon emitter (quantum dot LED); single-photon detector (infrared ultrafast photodetector); solar cells, and thin film transistors. New quantum materials: Quantum materials synthesis and novel property characterization.

Kaeppler, Stephen R., Ph.D., University of Iowa, 2013. *Atmosphere, Space Physics, Cosmic Rays.* Experimental ionospheric physics and data analysis: ionospheric and auroral electrodynamics, rocket-based hardware development, incoherent scatter radar data analysis, and high frequency (HF) remote sensing of the bottom side ionosphere and software defined radio (SDR) hardware development.

Lu, Xian, Ph.D., University of Illinois, Urbana-Champaign, 2011. *Atmosphere, Space Physics, Cosmic Rays.* Observational study and numerical modeling of the atmospheric dynamics and space weather, atmospheric gravity waves, planetary waves and tides.

Marler, Joan P., Ph.D., University of California, San Diego, 2005. *Atomic, Molecular, & Optical Physics.* Experimental low-temperature atomic and molecular ion physics, laser trapping and cooling, cold chemistry.

Sanabria, Hugo, Ph.D., University of Houston, 2005. *Biophysics.* The focus of my research is to understand how biomolecules interact, store and transfer information. We try to answer what are the principles underlying the relation between structure and dynamics of biomolecules, and how these relate to their biological function. We address this by using state-of-the-art single-molecule fluorescence spectroscopy.

Takacs, Endre, Ph.D., University of Debrecen, 1992. *Atomic, Molecular, & Optical Physics.* X-Ray Spectroscopy - highly charged ions, high energy radiation, biomedical physics.

Tewari, Sumanta, Ph.D., University of California, Los Angeles, 2003. *Condensed Matter Physics, Theoretical Physics.* Condensed-matter theory, topological quantum computation, high-temperature superconductivity, cold atomic physics in optical traps and lattices.

Research Assistant Professor

Podila, Ramakrishna, Ph.D., Clemson University, 2011. *Condensed Matter Physics, Materials Science, Metallurgy, Nano Science and Technology.* Nanomaterial synthesis and characterization, energy storage, nonlinear optics, nanobiophysics, and nanomedicine. Dr. Podila has published more than 45 peer-reviewed articles in high-impact journals including Nature Scientific Reports, Advanced Materials, Advanced Functional Materials, Nano Letters, and ACS Nano.

Lecturer

Brown, Jason, Ph.D., Clemson University, 1999. *Physics and other Science Education.*

Pope, Amy, Ph.D., Clemson University, 2002. *Condensed Matter Physics, Physics and other Science Education.* Condensed-matter physics, physics education.

Puneet, Pooja, Ph.D., Clemson University, 2013.

The, Lih-Sin, Ph.D., University of Arizona, 1989. *Astronomy, Astrophysics, Physics and other Science Education.* Gamma-ray astronomy, supernova remnants, stellar nucleosynthesis.

DEPARTMENTAL RESEARCH SPECIALTIES AND STAFF

Theoretical

Astrophysics. Nucleosynthesis; space astrophysics; stellar atmospheres; cosmic rays; gamma-ray bursts; supernova theory; origin of solar system; stellar evolution; cosmology. Brittain, Hartmann, King, Leising, Meyer, The.

Atmosphere, Space Physics, Cosmic Rays. Atmospheric wave dynamics, propagation, and interaction with chemical and airglow processes; ionospheric electrodynamics: plasma; climate and weather of the sun-earth system. Kaeppler, Larsen, Lehmacher, Lu, Meriwether, Oberheide.

Biophysics. DNA repair mechanisms; quantum biology. Alexov, Ding, Podila.

Computational Physics. Computational biophysics and bioinformatics; developing methods for modeling electrostatics in biological systems (DelPhi package); understanding the effects of missense mutations causing mental disorders and intellectual disability; predicting protein-protein interactions and 3D structures of the protein-protein complexes; computer simulations of protein-protein interactions modeling the role of conformation changes, pH, and salt concentration on biological function. Alexov, Daw, Ding, Lu, Marinescu, Meyer, Tewari.

Condensed Matter Physics. Surface phenomena, including scattering; anharmonic effects in crystal lattices; magnetic, optic, and transport properties of semiconductor mesoscopic structures (quantum wells and superlattices); broken symmetry states; charge and spin density waves; non-equilibrium superconductivity; topological computation; high-temperature superconductivity; cold atomic physics in optical traps and lattices. Daw, He, Marinescu, Rao, Sosolik, Tewari.

Quantum Foundations. Foundations of quantum mechanics and astrophysics; cosmology; black holes. Daw.

Experimental

Astronomy. Gamma-ray astronomy; observational astronomy; stellar evolution; stellar atmospheres; circumstellar evolution; planet formation; stellar accretia; abundance determinations; galactic chemical evolution; star clusters; close binary star systems. Ajello, Brittain, Hartmann, King, Leising, Meyer, The.

Atmosphere, Space Physics, Cosmic Rays. Rocket, radar, and spacecraft studies of ionospheric dynamics, electrodynamics, and plasma physics; studies of atmospheric dynamics and composition with LIDAR and Fabry-Perot systems; sounding rocket instrumentation, density, temperature, and turbulence in the mesosphere and lower thermosphere; satellite data analysis of vertical coupling processes. Kaeppler, Larsen, Lehmacher, Meriwether.

Atomic, Molecular, & Optical Physics. Experimental low-temperature atomic and molecular ion physics; laser trapping and cooling; cold chemistry; physics with highly charged ions. Marler, Sosolik, Takacs.

Biophysics. Biomedical optical imaging; fluorescence tomography; optical spectroscopy; microwave imaging; ultrasound tomography; bioluminescence tomography; X-ray tomosynthesis; spectroscopy; DNA repair mechanisms; structure of biological molecules; biological effects of radiation damage; mechanisms of carcinogenesis; mechanisms for single-event effects in microelectronics; microdosimetry using microelectronic technology; structural biology of RNA; biomolecular structure function relationships; NMR spectroscopy; fluorescence spectroscopy; single-molecule biophysics; nanoscience. Alper, Podila, Rao, Sanabria.

Condensed Matter Physics. Thermoelectric materials and applied physics; thermophysical properties of novel materials, including investigations of low-temperature heat capacity and thermal transport; investigations of thermal, magnetic, and electronic transport properties of exotic systems, low-dimensional conductors, strongly electron correlated materials, and phase transition materials; high-temperature thermophysical properties of novel materials; synthesis of thermoelectric nanomaterials and composite thermoelectrics. He, Podila, Puneet, Rao, Sosolik.

Condensed Matter Physics. Atomic and molecular beam interactions at surfaces; formation and characterization of surface nanostructures with an energetic beam and scanning tunneling microscope. Gao, He, Podila, Puneet, Rao, Sosolik, Tewari.

Nano Science and Technology. Synthesis of nanostructured materials using electric arc discharge, pulsed laser vaporization, neutron scattering, and CVD methods; optical characterization of novel materials by Raman scattering, infrared/visible, and fluorescence spectroscopy; mechanical properties of one-dimensional materials and chem-bio sensing using harmonic detection of resonance technique; superconducting nanotubes. Podila, Rao.

View additional information about this department at www.gradschoolshopper.com. Check out the "Why Choose Us?" section, find out more about the department's culture and get links to social media networks.

UNIVERSITY OF SOUTH DAKOTA

PHYSICS

Vermillion, South Dakota 57069
www.usd.edu/physics

General University Information
President: Sheila Gestring
Dean of Graduate School: Dr. Ranjit Koodali
University website: http://www.usd.edu/
School Type: Public
Setting: Rural

Department Information
Department Chairman: Prof. Yongchen Sun, Chair
Department Contact: Joel Sander, Assistant Professor
　Total full-time faculty: 12
　Total number of full-time equivalent positions: 8
　Full-Time Graduate Students: 18
　Female Full-Time Graduate Students: 0
　First-Year Graduate Students: 6
　Female First-Year Students: 1
　Total Post Doctorates: 3

Department Address
414 E. Clark Street
Vermillion, SD 57069
Phone: (605) 677-3966
E-mail: physics@usd.edu
Website: www.usd.edu/physics

ADMISSIONS

Admission Contact Information
Address admission inquiries to: Graduate School, McKusick Room 211, University of South Dakota, 414 E. Clark St., Vermillion, SD 57069
Phone: 1-800-233-7937
E-mail: grad@usd.edu
Admissions website: www.usd.edu/graduate-school/future-students.cfm

Application deadlines
Fall admission:
U.S. students: February 1　　*Int'l. students*: February 1

Application fee
U.S. students: $35　　*Int'l. students*: $35

Admissions information
For Fall of 2018:
　Number of applicants: 21
　Number admitted: 8
　Number enrolled: 4

Admission requirements
Bachelor's degree requirements: B.S. or B.A. in Physics or related fields.
Minimum undergraduate GPA: 3.0

GRE requirements
The GRE is required.

Subjective GRE requirements
The Subjective GRE is required.
Physics GRE is required for Ph.D. applicants only.

TOEFL requirements
The TOEFL exam is required for students from non-English-speaking countries.
　PBT score: 550
　iBT score: 79
For score requirements of other tests, see Graduate School website.

TUITION

Tuition year 2018–2019:
Tuition for in-state residents
　Full-time students: $326.05 per credit
Tuition for out-of-state residents
　Full-time students: $626.85 per credit
Resident graduate assistants pay fifty-three percent (53%) of the resident graduate tuition rate and nonresident graduate assistants pay sixty-three percent (63%) of the resident graduate tuition rate.
Credit hours per semester to be considered full-time: 9
Other academic fees: Additional fees of $123.40 per credit hour are charged for all physics graduate courses.
Academic term: Semester
Number of first-year students who received partial tuition waivers: 4

Teaching Assistants, Research Assistants, and Fellowships
　Number of first-year
　　Teaching Assistants: 2
　　Research Assistants: 4
　Average stipend per academic year
　　Teaching Assistant: $20,000
　　Research Assistant: $20,000
　Nine-month stipend, summer support available, PhD stipends ($24K for nine months) are higher than MS stipends

FINANCIAL AID

Application deadlines
Fall admission:
U.S. students: April 1　　*Int'l. students*: April 1

Loans
Loans are available for U.S. students.
Loans are not available for international students.
GAPSFAS application required: No
FAFSA application required: Yes

For further information
Address financial aid inquiries to: Office of Financial Aid, Belbas Center, University of South Dakota, 414 E. Clark St., Vermillion, SD 57069.
Phone: 605-677-5446
Financial aid website: www.usd.edu/finaid

HOUSING

Availability of on-campus housing
　Single students: Yes
　Married students: No

For further information

Address housing inquiries to: Office of Student Life/Housing, Muenster University Center 219, University of South Dakota, 414 E. Clark St., Vermillion, SD 57069.
Phone: 605 677 5666
E-mail: housing@usd.edu
Housing aid website: www.usd.edu/campus-life/student-services/university-housing/

Table A—Faculty, Enrollments, and Degrees Granted

Research Specialty	2016–17 Faculty	Enrollment Fall 2018		Number of Degrees Granted 2017–2018		
		Master's	Doctorate	Master's	Terminal Master's	Doctorate
Nuclear Physics	8	8	10	2	–	1
Total	–	–	–	2	–	–
Full-time Grad. Stud.	–	8	10	–	–	–
First-year Grad. Stud.	–	3	4	–	–	–

SPECIAL EQUIPMENT, FACILITIES, OR PROGRAMS

Our faculty are involved in several world-leading efforts to learn about matter. Graduate students have the opportunity to be involved in the following experiments:

- LUX/LZ, an experiment searching for dark matter at SURF
- The Majorana Demonstrator, searching for neutrinoless double beta decay and dark matter at SURF
- SuperCDMS, searching for dark matter at the Soudan Mine in Minnesota and at SNOLAB in Canada
- EXO-200/nEXO, searching for neutrinoless double beta decay at WIPP in New Mexico
- DUNE, a long baseline neutrino experiment
- CUBED, a state-wide collaboration to develop technologies for underground experiments

Our department is also involved in a world-wide effort to develop germanium detectors for the next generation of underground experiments as well as for industrial application. USD has a unique facility for growing germanium crystals and fabricating detectors.

FACULTY

Professor
Mei, Dongming, Ph.D., University of Alabama, 2003. *Astrophysics, Nuclear Physics*. Nuclear physics; astrophysics.

Associate Professor
Sun, Yongchen, Ph.D., Montana State University, 1993. *Condensed Matter Physics, Optics*. Laser spectroscopy; condensed matter physics.

Assistant Professor
Liu, Jing, Ph.D., Max Planck Insitute, 2009. *Nuclear Physics, Particles and Fields*. Nuclear physics; astrophysics.
MacLellan, Ryan, Ph.D., Queens University, 2009. *Astrophysics, Nuclear Physics, Particles and Fields*. Nuclear physics; astrophysics.
Sander, Joel, Ph.D., University of California, Santa Barbara, 2007. *Astrophysics, Particles and Fields*. Particle physics; astrophysics.
Shoemaker, Ian, Ph.D., UCLA, 2010. *Astrophysics, Theoretical Physics*. Theoretical physics, neutrino physics, dark matter.
Xu, Wenqin, Ph.D., UCLA, 2012. *Particles and Fields*. neutrino physics.

Professor Emeritus
Keller, Christina, Ph.D., North Dakota State University, 1988. *Condensed Matter Physics*. Condensed matter physics.

Research Assistant Professor
Wang, Guojian, Ph.D., Fujian Institute of Research on the Structure of Matter, Chinese Academy of Sciences, 2008. *Condensed Matter Physics, Crystallography*. High purity Germanium crystal growth and characterization; HP-Ge detector fabrication. Czochralski, Top seeded solution and Bridgman methods for growing laser crystals.

View additional information about this department at www.gradschoolshopper.com. Check out the "Why Choose Us?" section, find out more about the department's culture and get links to social media networks.

UNIVERSITY OF TENNESSEE, KNOXVILLE

DEPARTMENT OF PHYSICS AND ASTRONOMY

Knoxville, Tennessee 37996-1200
http://www.phys.utk.edu

General University Information
President: Dr. Joe DiPietro
Dean of Graduate School: Dixie Thompson
University website: http://www.utk.edu
School Type: Public
Setting: Urban
Total Faculty: 1,567
Total number of Students: 28,321
Total number of Graduate Students: 6,004

Department Information
Department Chairman: Dr. Hanno Weitering, Head
Department Contact: Chrisanne Romeo, Administrative
  Assistant, Graduate Program
  Total full-time faculty: 33
  Total number of full-time equivalent positions: 28
  Full-Time Graduate Students: 123
  Female Full-Time Graduate Students: 8
  First-Year Graduate Students: 22
  Female First-Year Students: 1
  Total Post Doctorates: 27

Department Address
1408 Circle Drive
401 Nielsen Physics Building
Knoxville, TN 37996-1200
Phone: (865) 974-3342
Fax: (865) 974-7843
E-mail: physics@utk.edu
Website: http://www.phys.utk.edu

ADMISSIONS

Admission Contact Information
Address admission inquiries to: Graduate School, University of
  Tennessee, 111 Student Services Building, Knoxville, TN
  37996-0211
Phone: (865) 974-2475
E-mail: gradschool@utk.edu
Admissions website: http://gradschool.utk.edu/

Application deadlines
Fall admission:
U.S. students: August 1   *Int'l. students*: February 1
Spring admission:
U.S. students: December 1   *Int'l. students*: June 15

Application fee
U.S. students: $60   *Int'l. students*: $60

Admissions information
For Fall of 2017:
  Number of applicants: 144
  Number admitted: 78
  Number enrolled: 22

Admission requirements
Bachelor's degree requirements: Bachelor's degree in Physics,
  mathematics, or engineering is required.
Minimum undergraduate GPA: 3.0

GRE requirements
  The GRE is not required.

Subjective GRE requirements
The Subjective GRE is recommended.
Subject GRE required for financial support.

TOEFL requirements
The TOEFL exam is required for students from non-English-
  speaking countries.
  PBT score: 550
  iBT score: 80
For financial consideration, speaking score must be greater than
  20 or an International English Language Testing System
  (IELTS) score of 6.5.

Other admissions information
Additional requirements: A minimum undergraduate GPA of 3.0
  for international students.
Undergraduate preparation assumed: Griffiths, Introduction to
  Electrodynamics; Marion and Thornton, Classical Dynamics;
  Griffiths, Introduction to Quantum Mechanics or equivalent.

TUITION

Tuition year 2017–2018:
Tuition for in-state residents
  Full-time students: $6,417 per semester
  Part-time students: $3,690 per semester
Tuition for out-of-state residents
  Full-time students: $15,626 per semester
  Part-time students: $6,066 per semester
Credit hours per semester to be considered full-time: 9
Deferred tuition plan: No
Health insurance: Yes, $1752.00.
Other academic fees: Technology
Academic term: Semester
Number of first-year students who received full tuition waivers: 21

Teaching Assistants, Research Assistants, and Fellowships
  Number of first-year
    Teaching Assistants: 21
  Average stipend per academic year
    Teaching Assistant: $21,500

FINANCIAL AID

Application deadlines
Fall admission:
U.S. students: August 1   *Int'l. students*: February 1
Spring admission:
U.S. students: December 1   *Int'l. students*: June 15

Loans
Loans are available for U.S. students.
Loans are not available for international students.
GAPSFAS application required: No
FAFSA application required: Yes

For further information

Address financial aid inquiries to: Financial Aid Office, 115 Student Services Building, University of Tennessee, Knoxville, TN 37996-0210.

Phone: 865-974-3131

E-mail: finaid@utk.edu

Financial aid website: http://gradschool.utk.edu/gradfund.shtml

HOUSING

Availability of on-campus housing

Single students: Yes

Married students: No

For further information

Address housing inquiries to: University Housing, 405 Student Services Building and UT Rental Property, 472 South Stadium Hall, Knoxville, TN 37996.

Phone: 865-974-2426

E-mail: housing@utk.edu

Housing aid website: http://uthousing.utk.edu/tnliving/current/housing-options.shtml

Table A—Faculty, Enrollments, and Degrees Granted

Research Specialty	2017–2018 Faculty	Enrollment 2017–2018 Master's	Enrollment 2017–2018 Doctorate	Number of Degrees Granted 2017–2018 (2016–2017) Master's	Number of Degrees Granted 2017–2018 (2016–2017) Terminal Master's	Number of Degrees Granted 2017–2018 (2016–2017) Doctorate
Astrophysics	3	–	10	–	1	–(1)
Atomic, Molecular, & Optical Physics	–	–	1	–	–	–(2)
Biophysics	2	–	2	1(1)	–(1)	–
Chemical Physics	1	–	3	–	–	–
Condensed Matter Physics	8	–	19	–	1	3(1)
High Energy Physics	3	–	11	–	–(2)	1(3)
Nuclear Physics	9	2	18	1(1)	–(1)	3
Particles and Fields	2	1	10	–	1	1
Theoretical Physics	3	–	19	–	–(1)	3(1)
Non-specialized	3	–	28	–	–	–
Total	33	3	121	2(2)	3(5)	9(8)
Full-time Grad. Stud.	–	3	121	–	–	–
First-year Grad. Stud.	–	–	22	–	–	–

GRADUATE DEGREE REQUIREMENTS

Master's: Thesis Option The course requirements include 24 hours of physics courses, of which at least 12 hours are taken from PHYS 506, PHYS 513-PHYS 514, PHYS 521-PHYS 522, PHYS 531, PHYS 541, PHYS 571, PHYS 573. Each candidate must present an acceptable thesis, 6 hours of PHYS 500, and pass an oral examination on course material and thesis. Geophysics concentration. The department offers an MS thesis program with a concentration in geophysics. Program requirements are 12 hours from PHYS 506, PHYS 513-PHYS 514, PHYS 521-PHYS 522, PHYS 531, PHYS 541, PHYS 571, PHYS 573; a minimum of 12 additional hours in geology, geophysics, and/or physics, as approved by the student's committee; and the presentation of an acceptable thesis, 6 hours of PHYS 500, and the passing of an oral examination on course material and thesis. Project Option The course requirements include a minimum of 30 hours of graduate credit in courses composed of PHYS 513-PHYS 514; 9 hours from PHYS 411-PHYS 412, PHYS 421, PHYS 431-PHYS 432, PHYS 461, PHYS 507, PHYS 508, PHYS 521-PHYS 522, PHYS 531, PHYS 541, PHYS 555, PHYS 571, PHYS 573

(at least 6 hours above the 500-level); 6 hours from PHYS 593, PHYS 594 for a Project in Lieu of Thesis; and 6 additional hours which may come from physics or from a single minor field outside of the Physics Department, such as computer science, mathematics, engineering, chemistry, biology, education, business, or law. The candidate must pass an oral examination on course material and on the project representing the culmination of an original research project completed by the student. A written report must be approved and accepted by the Physics Graduate Committee and the department head. An electronic version of the written report must also be submitted to the permanent electronic archive of the Physics Department available on the Internet. Non-Thesis Option Students seeking the non-thesis option must apply to the Director of the Graduate program for permission to enroll under this program. The requirements are the satisfactory completion of 30 hours of course work composed of 18 hours from PHYS 506, PHYS 513-PHYS 514, PHYS 521-PHYS 522, PHYS 531, PHYS 541, PHYS 571, PHYS 573; 6 additional hours from physics or a minor field; and 6 hours from other courses numbered above 400 (preferably of advanced laboratory nature.) At least 20 hours must be taken at the 500-level or above. In addition, the candidate must pass a written examination administered by his/her committee.

Doctorate: All students are expected to take the graduate core curriculum in physics consisting of PHYS 521-PHYS 522 (Quantum Mechanics), PHYS 531 (Classical Mechanics), PHYS 541 (Electromagnetism), PHYS 551 (Statistical Mechanics), and PHYS 571 (Mathematical Methods). Students concentrating in chemical physics may substitute CHEM 572 for PHYS 551 and should complete at least 6 hours from CHEM 530, CHEM 570, CHEM 571, CHEM 573, CHEM 595, CHEM 630, CHEM 670, and CHEM 690. Students concentrating in energy science and engineering should complete ESE 511, ESE 512 (Introduction to Energy Science and Technology (3 + 3 credits), at least 3 hours from the Knowledge Breadth Curriculum (a list of courses is available from the Graduate Program Director) and 3 credit hours (1+1+1) of topical seminars in the focus area of CIRE. Students must take either i) a minimum of 15 hours of 600-level courses with 6 of these hours in their concentration area, or ii) a minimum of 12 hours of 600-level courses with 6 of these hours in their concentration area and a minimum of 3 hours of 500-level courses described in a list available from the Director of the Graduate Program and approved by the student's Doctoral Committee. Among the 600-level courses, PHYS 601-PHYS 602 are normally required of students concentrating in atomic physics; PHYS 621-PHYS 622 of students in nuclear physics; PHYS 626-PHYS 627 of students in elementary particle physics (and/or PHYS 611-PHYS 612 for students concentrating in theoretical elementary particle physics); PHYS 615-PHYS 616 of students in astrophysics and cosmology; and PHYS 671-PHYS 672 of students in condensed matter and surface physics. Students concentrating in nanomaterials must take a minimum 15 hours of 600-level courses, of which at least 6 hours are offered by the department and at least 6 hours are from a list of courses offered by several departments which are appropriate for a concentration in nanomaterials. This list is available from the Director of the Graduate Program. In addition to the departmental core curriculum listed above, they must take additional courses at the 400- through 500-level, with at least 6 hours offered by the department and 6 hours from the list. Students concentrating in energy science and engineering must take a minimum of 15 hours of 600-level courses, of which at least 6 hours are offered by the department and at least 6 hours are from a list of courses offered by several departments which are appropriate for a concentration in energy science and engineering. This list is available from the Graduate Program Director. To be admitted to PhD candidacy, students must fulfill all general requirements of the Graduate Council; pass the qualifying examination; have at least a 3.0 GPA on the graduate core curriculum in physics; form a doctoral committee; and pass the comprehensive examination. The qualifying examination is designed to test the student's general knowledge of the fundamentals of physics. The performance needed to pass this examination corresponds to a mature command of the material typically included in the undergraduate physics major curriculum. The qualifying examination should be passed after the student's first year of study. Based on the student's performance on the qualifying examinations, the course work, the GRE scores, and optional research participation, the faculty will decide if the student will be allowed to continue in the PhD program. Students are required to find a research advisor and form a doctoral committee before the end of the second year of study. This committee is responsible for advising the student and monitoring his/her progress toward the doctoral degree. The comprehensive examination is designed to test the student on specific knowledge and skills in the areas essential to the student's research program; on capability to successfully complete the doctoral dissertation; and on general knowledge of the graduate core curriculum. The most essential component of this examination is the presentation and defense of an original research proposal. The comprehensive examination must be passed before the end of the third year of study. It contains both a written and an oral component and is conducted by the student's doctoral committee and an additional faculty member appointed by the department head. The dissertation topic will be chosen with reference to one of the fields in which research facilities can be made available either at the University of Tennessee laboratories in Knoxville; the University of Tennessee Space Institute at Tullahoma, Tennessee; the Oak Ridge National Laboratory, Oak Ridge, Tennessee; or at other research facilities used by the university faculty. Energy Science and Engineering Concentration This concentration is offered in collaboration with the Center for Interdisciplinary Research and Graduate Education (CIRE). The CIRE is a joint effort between University of Tennessee colleges and the Oak Ridge National Laboratory. The students who wish to pursue this concentration will normally have completed the ESE Core for CIRE students, and 1 hour of CIRE seminar.

SPECIAL EQUIPMENT, FACILITIES, OR PROGRAMS

Special experimental facilities include semiconductor- and oxide molecular beam epitaxy growth facilities, various ultrahigh vacuum systems with provisions for photoelectron spectroscopy (UV and X-ray), time-of-flight mass spectrometry, ultrahigh-resolution scanning tunneling microscopy, QPlus atomic force microscopy, low-energy electron diffraction, reflection high-energy electron diffraction, secondary ion mass spectrometry, angle-resolved photo electron spectroscopy, pump and probe photo emission. Other facilities include optical floating zone furnaces; SQUID magnetometers; physical properties measurement systems; 15 crucible furnaces; a large computer-controlled, high-resolution molecular spectrometer; computer-controlled nuclear data analysis systems; scintillator detector test facility; and a complete biophysics laboratory.

The department has fully staffed instrument- and electronics shops. Research facilities are also available at Oak Ridge National Laboratory in astrophysics, nuclear, and condensed matter physics.

A Ph.D. program in Chemical Physics is conducted jointly with the Department of Chemistry. The department also conducts a resident Ph.D. program in physics at the University of Tennessee Space Institute in Tullahoma. Facilities there support research in atomic and molecular physics, laser physics, chemical physics, quantum optics, infrared spectroscopy, and laser scattering. A cooperative arrangement permits research appointments for selected students at the nearby Air Force Arnold Engineering Development Center research operation.

Table B—Separately Budgeted Research Expenditures by Source of Support

Source of Support	Departmental Research	Physics-related Research Outside Department
Federal government	$9,863,303	
State/local government	$1,586,375	
Non-profit organizations		
Business and industry		
Other	$1,000,828	
Total	$12,450,506	

Table C—Separately Budgeted Research Expenditures by Research Specialty

Research Specialty	No. of Grants	Expenditures ($)
Astrophysics	7	$ 495,937
Atomic, Molecular, & Optical Physics	1	$ 57,312
Biophysics	3	$ 398,073
Condensed Matter Physics	31	$ 2,420,266
Nuclear Physics	23	$ 7,230,438
Particles and Fields	15	$ 1,848,481
Total	80	$12,450,507

FACULTY

Distinguished University Professor

Dagotto, Elbio, Ph.D., Bariloche, 1985. UTK/ORNL Distinguished Scientist. *Condensed Matter Physics.* Theoretical condensed matter physics.

Chair Professor

Batista, Cristian, Ph.D., Instituto Balseiro Universidad Nacional de Cuyo, 1996. Willis Lincoln Chair of Excellence. *Condensed Matter Physics, Theoretical Physics.*

Professor

Breinig, Marianne, Ph.D., University of Oregon, 1979. Associate Department Head. *Atomic, Molecular, & Optical Physics, Physics and other Science Education.* Physics education.

Efremenko, Yuri, Ph.D., ITEP, Moscow, Russia, 1989. *Particles and Fields.* Experimental high-energy physics.

Eguiluz, Adolfo, Ph.D., Brown University, 1976. *Condensed Matter Physics.* Theoretical condensed matter physics.

Elston, Stuart, Ph.D., University of Massachusetts, 1975. *Atomic, Molecular, & Optical Physics, Physics and other Science Education.* Physics education.

Fitzsimmons, Michael, Ph.D., Cornell University, 1988. Material Science & Engineering.

Greene, Geoffrey L., Ph.D., Harvard University, 1977. UTK/ORNL Joint Faculty. *Nuclear Physics.* Experimental nuclear physics.

Grzywacz, Robert, Ph.D., University of Warsaw, 1997. Director, UTK/ORNL Joint Institute for Nuclear Physics and Applications. *Nuclear Physics.* Experimental nuclear physics.

Grzywacz-Jones, Kate, Ph.D., University of Surrey, 2000. Associate Department Head. *Nuclear Physics*. Experimental nuclear physics.

Guidry, Michael W., Ph.D., University of Tennessee, 1974. *Astrophysics*. Computational and theoretical astrophysics.

Handler, Thomas, Ph.D., Rutgers University, 1974. *Particles and Fields*. Experimental high-energy physics.

Hix, Raph W., Ph.D., Harvard University, 1995. Group leader, Physics Division, ORNL, Joint Faculty. *Astrophysics, Nuclear Physics*. Computational and theoretical nuclear astrophysics.

Kamyshkov, Yuri, Ph.D., University of Moscow, 1970. *High Energy Physics*. Experimental High Energy Physics.

Mezzacappa, Anthony, Ph.D., University of Texas, Austin, 1988. Director, UTK/ORNL Joint Institute for Computational Sciences. Computational and theoretical astrophysics.

Moreo, Adriana, Ph.D., Bariloche, 1985. UTK/ORNL Joint Faculty. *Condensed Matter Physics*. Theoretical condensed matter physics.

Papenbrock, Thomas, Ph.D., Max-Planck Institute, 1996. UTK/ORNL Joint Faculty. *Nuclear Physics*. Theoretical nuclear physics.

Read, Kenneth F., Ph.D., Cornell University, 1987. UTK/ORNL Joint Faculty. *Nuclear Physics*. Experimental nuclear physics.

Riedinger, Leo L., Ph.D., Vanderbilt University, 1969. Director, Bredesen Center. *Nuclear Physics*. Experimental nuclear physics.

Siopsis, George, Ph.D., California Institute of Technology, 1987. Director of Governor's School for Science & Engineering. *Particles and Fields, Quantum Foundations*. High-energy physics; quantum information.

Sorensen, Soren, Ph.D., Niels Bohr Institute, 1981. *Nuclear Physics*. Experimental nuclear physics.

Spanier, Stefan M., Ph.D., University Mainz, 1994. *Particles and Fields*. Experimental high-energy physics.

Weitering, Harm H., Ph.D., University of Groningen, 1991. Department Head; Associate Director, UTK/ORNL Joint Institute for Advanced Materials; UTK/ORNL Joint Faculty. *Condensed Matter Physics, Solid State Physics, Surface Physics*. Experimental condensed matter physics.

Associate Professor

Mannella, Norman, Ph.D., University of California, Davis, 2003. *Condensed Matter Physics*. Experimental condensed matter.

Mannik, Jaan, Ph.D., Stony Brook University, 2003. *Biophysics*. Experimental biophysics.

Nattrass, Christine, Ph.D., Yale University, 2009. *Nuclear Physics*. Experimental nuclear physics.

Parigger, Christian, Ph.D., University of Otago, 1986. *Atomic, Molecular, & Optical Physics*. Atomic physics; laser spectroscopy; laser-induced breakdown spectroscopy; UT - Space Institute, Tullahoma, TN.

Zhou, Haidong, Ph.D., University of Texas at Austin, 2005. *Condensed Matter Physics*. Experimental condensed matter physics.

Assistant Professor

Fomin, Nadia, Ph.D., University of Virginia, 2007. *Nuclear Physics*. Fundamental neutron physics.

Gollapinni, Sowjanya, Ph.D., Wayne State, 2012. *High Energy Physics*. High Energy Physics.

Johnston, Steven, Ph.D., University of Waterloo, 2010. *Condensed Matter Physics*. Theoretical condensed matter physics.

Lavrentovich, Maxim, Ph.D., Harvard University, 2014. *Biophysics*. Biophysics.

Liu, Jian, Ph.D., University of Arkansas, 2012. *Condensed Matter Physics*. Experimental condensed matter physics.

Madurga Flores, Miguel, Ph.D., University Autonoma of Madrid, 2009. *Nuclear Physics*. Low Energy Nuclear Physics.

Platter, Lucas J., Ph.D., Bonn, 2005. Joint Faculty ORNL. *Nuclear Physics, Theoretical Physics*. Theoretical Nuclear Physics.

Steiner, Andrew W., Ph.D., Stony Brook, 2002. Joint Faculty ORNL. *Nuclear Physics, Theoretical Physics*. Theoretical Nuclear Physics.

Professor Emeritus

Bingham, Carroll R., Ph.D., University of Tennessee, 1965. Experimental nuclear physics.

Bugg, William M., Ph.D., University of Tennessee, 1959. Experimental high-energy physics.

Compton, Robert N., Ph.D., University of Tennessee, 1964. *Atomic, Molecular, & Optical Physics, Chemical Physics*. Experimental chemical physics.

Macek, Joseph H., Ph.D., Rensselaer Polytechnic Institute, 1964. *Atomic, Molecular, & Optical Physics*. Theoretical atomic physics.

Quinn, John J., Ph.D., University of Maryland, 1958. *Condensed Matter Physics*. Theoretical solid-state physics.

Shih, Chia C., Ph.D., Cornell University, 1967. Theoretical elementary particle and atomic physics; experimental medical physics.

Thompson, James R., Ph.D., Duke University, 1969. Experimental condensed matter physics.

Research Associate Professor

Loizides, Constantinos A., Ph.D., University of Frankfurt, 2001. *Theoretical Physics*. Theoretical Particle Physics.

Research Assistant Professor

Cunqueiro Mendez, Leticia, Ph.D., University of Santiago de Compostela, 2000. *Theoretical Physics*. Theoretical Particle Physics.

Lentz, Eric, Ph.D., University of Oklahoma, 2000. *Astrophysics*. Astrophysics.

Lindsay, Sean S., Ph.D., Astronomy, 2012. *Astronomy*. Computationally modeling the optical properties of cosmic crystalline silicates.

Adjunct Professor

Datskos, Panos, Ph.D., University of Tennessee, 1988. Staff scientist ORNL. *Condensed Matter Physics*. Condensed matter physics.

Dean, David, Ph.D., Vanderbilt University, 1991. Director, Physics Division, ORNL. *Nuclear Physics*. Theoretical nuclear physics.

Gabriel, Tony A., Ph.D., University of Tennessee, 1969. Staff scientist ORNL. *High Energy Physics, Particles and Fields*. High-energy physics.

Galindo-Uribarri, Alfredo, Ph.D., University of Toronto, 1991. ORNL staff scientist. *Nuclear Physics*.

Garrett, William R., Ph.D., University of Alabama, 1963. *Atomic, Molecular, & Optical Physics, Chemical Physics*.

Mandrus, David G., Ph.D., Stony Brook University, 1992. *Condensed Matter Physics, Materials Science, Metallurgy*. experimental condensed matter physics.

Musfeldt, Janice, Ph.D., University of Florida, 1992. *Chemical Physics*.

Nagler, Stephen, Ph.D., University of Toronto, 1982. Staff scientist ORNL. *Condensed Matter Physics*. experimental condensed matter physics; neutron scattering.

Passian, Ali, Ph.D., University of Tennessee, 2000. Staff scientist ORNL. *Condensed Matter Physics*.

Sokolov, Alexei, Ph.D., Russian Academy of Sciences, 1986. *Condensed Matter Physics*. Soft condensed matter.

Stone, Jirina, Ph.D., Charles University, Prague, 1975. *Astrophysics, Nuclear Physics.*

Adjunct Assistant Professor
Hagen, Gaute, Ph.D., University of Bergen, Norway. *Nuclear Physics.* Theoretical nuclear physics.

Laboratory Director
Cheney, Christine P., Ph.D., Vanderbilt University, 2001. *Condensed Matter Physics.* Laser spectroscopy.

Joint Appointment
Aczel, Adam, Ph.D., McMaster University, 2010. *Condensed Matter Physics, Physics and other Science Education.* Neutron Sciences.

Budiardja, Reuben, Ph.D., University of Tennessee, 2010. *Astrophysics.* Computational Astrophysics.

Christianson, Andrew, Ph.D., Colorado State, 2003. UTK/ORNL Joint Faculty. *Condensed Matter Physics.* Complex oxides.

Cormier, Thomas M., Ph.D., Massachusetts Institute of Technology, 1974. *Nuclear Physics.*

Cousineau, Sarah M., Ph.D., Indiana University, 2003. UTK/ORNL Joint Faculty. *Accelerator, Nuclear Physics.* Accelerator physics.

Endeve, Eirik, Ph.D., University of Oslo, 2003. UTK/ORNL Joint Faculty. *Astrophysics.* Computational and theoretical astrophysics.

Fernández-Baca, Jaime, Ph.D., University of Maryland, 1986. UTK/ORNL Joint Faculty. *Condensed Matter Physics.* Neutron scattering of complex materials.

Fishman, Randy S., Ph.D., Brown University, 1980. UTK/ORNL Joint Faculty. *Condensed Matter Physics, Theoretical Physics.* Theoretical condensed matter physics.

He, Lilin, Ph.D., Clemson University, 2008. *Polymer Physics/Science.* Neutron and X-ray Scattering.

Katsaras, John, Ph.D., University of Guelph, 1991. UTK/ORNL Joint Faculty. *Biophysics.* Soft condensed matter and biophysics.

Maceira, Monica, Ph.D., Penn State, 2006. *Geophysics.*

Maier, Thomas A., Ph.D., University of Regensburg, 2001. *Condensed Matter Physics.*

Messer, O.E. Bronson, Ph.D., University of Tennessee, 2000. *Astrophysics, Theoretical Physics.*

Pooser, Raphael, Ph.D., Unversity of Virgina, 2007. UTK/ORNL Joint Faculty. *Computational Physics.* Quantum information science; quantum optics.

Qi, Bing, Ph.D., Dalian University of Techology, 1996. *Optics.*

Tennant, David A., Ph.D., Oxford University, 1994. *Condensed Matter Physics.* Experimental Condensed Matter Physics.

Tong, Xin (Tony), Ph.D., Indiana, 2008. Joint Faculty Assistant Professor. *Condensed Matter Physics.* Neutron Physics.

Ward, Thomas Zack, Ph.D., University of Tennessee, 2008. UTK/ORNL Joint Faculty. *Condensed Matter Physics.* Experimental condensed matter physics.

Yoon, Mina, Ph.D., Michigan State, 2004. Joint Faculty Associate Professor. *Condensed Matter Physics.* Nanophase Materials Sciences.

DEPARTMENTAL RESEARCH SPECIALTIES AND STAFF

Theoretical
Biophysics. Information flow in cellular systems. Lavrentovich, Mannik.

Computational astrophysics. Core collapse supernovae; novae; computational modeling; nuclear astrophysics. Endeve, Guidry, Hix, Mezzacappa.

Condensed Matter Physics. Strongly correlated electron systems; colossal magnetoresistance; high Tc superconductivity; transport properties; nanostructures; many-body excitations; thin film growth; surface physics; quantum magnetism. Batista, Dagotto, Eguiluz, Johnston, Mannella, Moreo, Weitering, Zhou.

High Energy Physics. Neutrino physics; neutron oscillations; CP-violation in the heavy quark sector; strings and quantum gravity. Efremenko, Gollapinni, Handler, Siopsis, Spanier.

Nuclear Physics. Nuclear structure far from stability and at high spins; hot and dense nuclear matter; quark-gluon plasma; neutron physics; nuclear structure; many body problems; physics of open systems; nuclear astrophysics, quantum chaos and random matrices. Grzywacz, Grzywacz-Jones, Madurga Flores, Nattrass, Papenbrock, Platter, Sorensen, Steiner.

Physics and other Science Education. Breinig, Elston.

Experimental
Accelerator. Accelerator physics studies utilizing the ORNL Spallation Neutron Source. Cousineau.

Biophysics. Nanotechnology-based probes to interrogate single molecules/molecular complexes within living cells. Lavrentovich, Mannik.

Condensed Matter Physics. Neutron scattering; high Tc superconductivity; magnetism and lattice effects in colossal magnetoresistance; physics of novel materials and complex electron systems; low-dimensional materials; nanostructures; surface and interface physics; x-ray spectroscopy; thin-film materials. Christianson, Fernández-Baca, Katsaras, Mandrus, Mannella, Nagler, Passian, Sokolov, Ward, Weitering, Zhou.

High Energy Physics. CP violation measurements; meson spectroscopy; electron neutrino detection; neutrino oscillation. Efremenko, Gabriel, Handler, Kamyshkov, Spanier.

Nuclear Physics. Decay spectroscopy; experimental nuclear astrophysics; gamma-ray spectroscopy; relativistic heavy-ion physics; hot and dense nuclear matter; neutron physics. Fomin, Galindo-Uribarri, Greene, Grzywacz, Grzywacz-Jones, Madurga Flores, Nattrass, Platter, Read, Riedinger, Sorensen.

View additional information about this department at www.gradschoolshopper.com. Check out the "Why Choose Us?" section, find out more about the department's culture and get links to social media networks.

VANDERBILT UNIVERSITY

DEPARTMENT OF PHYSICS AND ASTRONOMY

Nashville, Tennessee 37240-1807
http://as.vanderbilt.edu/physics/

General University Information

Chancellor: Nicholas S. Zeppos
Dean of Graduate School: Mark Wallace
University website: http://www.vanderbilt.edu/
School Type: Private
Setting: Urban
Total Faculty: 4,313
Total Graduate Faculty: 972
Total number of Students: 12,587
Total number of Graduate Students: 5,716

Department Information

Department Chairman: Prof. M. Shane Hutson, Chair
Department Contact: M. Shane Hutson, Professor & Chair
   Total full-time faculty: 27
   Total number of full-time equivalent positions: 27
   Full-Time Graduate Students: 65
   Female Full-Time Graduate Students: 18
   First-Year Graduate Students: 13
   Female First-Year Students: 1
   Total Post Doctorates: 20

Department Address

6301 Stevenson Center
PMB# 401807
Nashville, TN 37240-1807
Phone: (615) 322-2828
Fax: (615) 343-7263
E-mail: physics-astronomy@vanderbilt.edu
Website: http://as.vanderbilt.edu/physics/

ADMISSIONS

Admission Contact Information

Address admission inquiries to: Director of Graduate Studies,
   Physics & Astronomy Department, 6301 Stevenson Center
   Vanderbilt University, Nashville, TN 37240
Phone: (615) 322-2828
E-mail: physics-astronomy@vanderbilt.edu
Admissions website: http://as.vanderbilt.edu/physics/graduate/

Application deadlines

Fall admission:
U.S. students: January 1   *Int'l. students*: January 1

Application fee

U.S. students: $95   *Int'l. students*: $95
To request consideration for an application fee waiver, please
   see: https://gradschool.vanderbilt.edu/admissions/application/
   index.php

Admissions information

For Fall of 2018:
   Number of applicants: 201
   Number admitted: 23
   Number enrolled: 13

Admission requirements

Bachelor's degree requirements: Bachelor's degree in Physics
   is required.
Minimum undergraduate GPA: 3.0

GRE requirements

The GRE is required.
   Mean GRE score range (25th–75th percentile): 145-160(Q),
   144-155(V), 3-4(A)
There is no GRE cut-off score for admission.

Subjective GRE requirements

The Subjective GRE is required.
   Mean Advanced GRE score range (25th–75th percentile): 580-
   850
For the Physics Subject test.

TOEFL requirements

The TOEFL exam is required for students from non-English-
   speaking countries.
   PBT score: 570
   iBT score: 88

Other admissions information

Undergraduate preparation assumed: Content equivalent to
   Resnick and Halliday, Physics; Eisberg and Resnick, Quantum Physics of Atoms, Molecules, Solids, Nuclei, and Particles; Reitz, Milford, Christy, Foundations of Electromagnetic Theory; Zemansky,Heat and Thermodynamics; Reif,
   Fundamentals of Statistical and Thermal Physics; Symon,
   Mechanics; Saxon, Elementary Quantum Mechanics.

TUITION

Tuition year 2018–19:
   Full-time students: $1,910 per credit
   Part-time students: $1,910 per credit
Credit hours per semester to be considered full-time: 9
Deferred tuition plan: Yes
Health insurance: Available at the cost of $3253 per year.
Other academic fees: $457 for annual student activities fee and
   recreation center fee; $100 one-time transcript fee for all new
   students.
Academic term: Semester
Number of first-year students who received full tuition waivers: 13

Teaching Assistants, Research Assistants, and Fellowships

Number of first-year
   Teaching Assistants: 9
   Research Assistants: 3
Average stipend per academic year
   Teaching Assistant: $30,000
   Research Assistant: $30,000
   Fellowship student: $5,000
University Fellowships are awarded competitively based on
   academic merit or to under-represented minority graduate stu-
   dents, as there are several types. They are typically for up
   to 3 years, and are in addition to the $30K stipend for all
   TA and RA's. Many external fellowships are also available
   and students are highly encouraged to apply for them.

FINANCIAL AID

Loans

Loans are available for U.S. students.
Loans are not available for international students.
GAPSFAS application required: No
FAFSA application required: Yes

For further information

Address financial aid inquiries to: Office of Student Financial
Aid and Undergraduate Scholarships, 2309 West End Avenue,
Nashville, TN 37203-1725.
Phone: (615) 322-3591
E-mail: finaid@vanderbilt.edu
Financial aid website: http://www.vanderbilt.edu/financialaid/

HOUSING

Availability of on-campus housing

Single students: No
Married students: No
Childcare Assistance: No

For further information

Address housing inquiries to: Office of Housing and Residential
Education, Vanderbilt University, VU #351677, Station B,
Nashville, TN 37235.
Phone: (615) 322-2591
E-mail: resed@vanderbilt.edu
Housing aid website: http://www.vanderbilt.edu/ResEd/main/

Table A—Faculty, Enrollments, and Degrees Granted

Research Specialty	2017–18 Faculty	Enrollment Fall 2018 Master's	Enrollment Fall 2018 Doctorate	Number of Degrees Granted 2017–18 (2010–17) Master's	Number of Degrees Granted 2017–18 (2010–17) Terminal Master's	Number of Degrees Granted 2017–18 (2010–17) Doctorate
Astrophysics	4	–	24	1(13)	–	1(27)
Atomic, Molecular, & Optical Physics	2	–	6	3(5)	–	1(8)
Biophysics	4	–	4	1(10)	–	–(8)
Condensed Matter Physics	3	–	8	–(10)	–	1(7)
Medical, Health Physics	1	8	2	–(10)	4	–(15)
Nuclear Physics	5	–	12	–(3)	–	1(10)
Particles and Fields	7	–	9	1(2)	1	4(16)
Non-specialized	–	–	–	–(2)	–	–
Total	26	8	65	6(47)	5	8(91)
Full-time Grad. Stud.	–	8	65	–	–	–
First-year Grad. Stud.	–	–	13	–	–	–

GRADUATE DEGREE REQUIREMENTS

Master's: Students in Physics and Astrophysics are only admitted for doctoral studies, but a Master's degree can be
earned along the way. M.S. in Physics: 30 semester-hours of
coursework plus research thesis. A "B" average is required.
There is no foreign language requirement and no comprehensive examination. M.A. is awarded without thesis on the basis
of 42 hours of coursework, Ph.D.-qualifying examination, and
some research experience. M.S. in health physics is awarded
based on 30 hours of course work and a research thesis.

Doctorate: Ph.D. in Physics & Ph.D. In Astrophysics: 72
semester-hours of coursework is required, up to 44 of which
can be research. A "B" average is required in formal coursework. Completion of core coursework and oral qualifying examination in the fourth semester of studies. Publication of

original research in refereed journal(s) is required. Dissertation in physics or astrophysics is required. One year of residency is required.

Other Degrees: Separate, but related degree programs are avail-
able to earn a Masters in Medical Physics, Masters in Health
Physics, or interdisciplinary Ph.D. in Materials Science or
Chemical and Physical Biology. Interdisciplinary work is en-
couraged and is tailored to fit the needs of the individual stu-
dent. Masters of Science at Fisk University with a Ph.D. at
Vanderbilt University is also available through the Fisk-
Vanderbilt Masters-to-PhD Bridge Program.

Thesis: Thesis or dissertation based on original published research is required.

SPECIAL EQUIPMENT, FACILITIES, OR PROGRAMS

The Nanofabrication Laboratory, a collaborative activity with the
School of Engineering, has a focused ion beam, state-of-the-art
pulsed laser thin film deposition system, atomic-force microscope, and a variety of diagnostics for studying nanometer-scale
structures and materials. This laboratory is a centerpiece of the
Vanderbilt Institute of Nanoscale Science and Engineering.

Vanderbilt University is a member of the University Radioactive
Ion Beam (UNIRIB) Consortium at Oak Ridge National Laboratory. The Joint Institute for Heavy-Ion Research at Oak Ridge,
Tennessee, is operated by Vanderbilt University, the University
of Tennessee, and Oak Ridge National Laboratory to support research with radioactive beams and sponsors a visitor's program
that brings distinguished scientists for research and lecturing.

Members of the nuclear structure physics group have additional
cooperative research programs at Argonne National Laboratory,
Lawrence Berkeley Laboratory, Idaho National Engineering Laboratory, the Joint Institute for Nuclear Research in Russia, the
Universities of Frankfurt, Tsinghua, and Bucharest, and access
to a number of supercomputers around the country.

The Vanderbilt Relativistic Heavy Ion (RHI) nuclear group has
made major hardware and software contributions to the PHENIX
experiment at RHIC (Brookhaven National Laboratory) and hosts
a key computing facility for the heavy-ion program of the CMS
experiment at CERN, Switzerland. The RHI group studies nuclear matter under extreme conditions of temperature and energy
density and searches for exotic new states of matter.

The Atomic, Molecular, Optical and Surface (AMOS) groups
study the dynamics of surface and interface processes under a
wide variety of conditions and has collaborators in the Department of Chemistry and in the School of Engineering. The AMOS
resources include femosecond Ti-Sapphire lasers, OPAs, linear
and ring dye lasers, excimer and excimer-pumped lasers, frequency doublers, ultrafast tunable lasers, low-energy ion electron
and atomic beam sources, 300 kV ion implanter, and visible and
vacuum-ultraviolet spectrometers. Members of the group are involved in cooperative research programs at the Max-Planck-
Institute in Garching, the Synchrotron Radiation Center in Madison, Wisconsin, and Universities in Vienna, Berlin, and Krakow.

Members of the biological physics group investigate cellular
electric, magnetic, and mechanical phenomena. Included in the
laboratories are a magnetic imaging facility with high-resolution
SQUID magnetometers and microscopes, scanning stages and
magnetic shields, numerous video fluorescence microscopes, and
a confocal microscope with a coupled laser microsurgery system.
Studies under way are examining the nonlinear electrodynamics
of cardiac tissue, intracellular and paracrine signaling in cellular
biosystems, coupling among genetics, morphologic change and
the mechanics of soft condensed matter, and nanoparticle and
nanocluster labeling and spectroscopy. The Project to Instrument
and Control the Single Cell is developing tools and techniques

for cellular biophysics and wide-bandwidth metabolic measurements. The group, in conjunction with the Vanderbilt Institute for Integrative Biosystems Research and Educations (VIBRE), operates the BioMEMS Fabrication Facility that includes three class-100 clean rooms for photolithography, soft lithography, biomicrofluidics, e-beam and ion-etch fabrication of metal microelectrode arrays, and extensive cellular biophysics instrumentation. The group uses infrared, visible, and ultraviolet spectroscopic techniques for investigating the dynamics of biopolymers and laser-tissue interactions.

The high-energy physics group at Vanderbilt University leads detector development and maintenance projects at the CMS detector at CERN, and hosts a major compute facility at Vanderbilt. The group made significant contributions to the discovery of the Higgs boson, and is active in searches of physics beyond the standard model.

The astronomy group actively uses national and international ground-based and space-platform observatories. Vanderbilt is a partner in SMARTS (Small and Medium Aperture Research Telescope System) that operates telescopes at the Cerro Tololo Inter-American Observatory in Chile. Vanderbilt is a member of the Sloan Digital Sky Survey (SDSS) III. Vanderbilt University is a charter member of the Extreme Universe Space Observatory (EUSO) Consortium, formed of three U.S. universities, two national laboratories, and seven European nations. The energy, direction, and composition of nature's most energetic particles will be measured.

The Department has exceptionally good research computing facilities at the Advanced Computing Center for Research and Education (ACCRE). The facility is one of the top university supercomputing resources in the United States. There is also a wide variety of modern computational facilities within each of the research groups. Vanderbilt University is a participant in the Internet II network and is thus involved in developing and using the next-generation network.

The materials and nanoscience physics group focuses on the growth and analysis of thin films with enhanced electronic and optical properties. Resources include a 2.0 MeV Van de Graaff accelerator, 4 Kelvin optical cryostate, a 300 KeV accelerator for ion-scattering analysis and ion implantation, an Si-based molecular beam epitaxy (MBE) system, a combined focused ion beam-pulsed laser deposition system for nanostructure fabrication, and various apparatuses for growth, automated nanocrystalline thin film deposition system, annealing, and film measurement. Members of the group collaborate with Oak Ridge National Laboratory, the Engineering School, and other centers for materials science in an extensive interdisciplinary program.

The theoretical condensed matter physics group and the nuclear theory group have joint research activities with Oak Ridge National Laboratory, where the computational facilities include several massively parallel computers.

Table B—Separately Budgeted Research Expenditures by Source of Support

Source of Support	Departmental Research	Physics-related Research Outside Department
Federal government	$7,562,375	
State/local government		
Non-profit organizations		
Business and industry	$483,494	
Other		
Total	$8,045,869	

Table C—Separately Budgeted Research Expenditures by Research Specialty

Research Specialty	No. of Grants	Expenditures ($)
Astronomy	16	$1,348,670
Biophysics	15	$2,811,263
Condensed Matter & Optical Physics	17	$1,448,235
Nuclear Physics	4	$1,983,872
Particles and Fields	6	$453,829
Total	58	$8,045,869

FACULTY

Distinguished University Professor

Gore, John C., Ph.D., University of London, 1976. Development and application of imaging; magnetic resonance imaging and spectroscopic techniques.

Pantelides, Sokrates T., Ph.D., University of Illinois, 1973. Theoretical physics; semiconductor physics; first principles atomic-scale dynamics; mesoscopic dynamics in complex solids; interactions of light with matter.

Wikswo, John P., Ph.D., Stanford University, 1975. Biological physics; biomedical engineering; cardiac and cellular electrophysiology; cellular instrumentation and control; complex matter; electromagnetism; nondestructive evaluation, nonlinear dynamics, and non-equilibrium behavior; SQUID magnetometry.

Chair Professor

Greene, Senta V., Ph.D., Yale University, 1992. *Nuclear Physics.* Experimental nuclear physics; relativistic heavy ion collisions.

Haglund, Richard F., Ph.D., University of North Carolina, 1975. Experimental physics; nanoscale nonlinear optics and phase transitions; laser modification of surfaces and films; free-electron laser applications including polymer thin film deposition and biomolecular mass spectroscopy.

Hamilton, Joseph H., Ph.D., Indiana University, 1958. Experimental nuclear physics; nuclear structure and reactions with heavy ions; fission processes.

Stassun, Keivan, Ph.D., University of Wisconsin-Madison, 2000. Observations and modeling of star formation; science pedagogy; diversity issues.

Professor

Ernst, David J., Ph.D., Massachusetts Institute of Technology, 1970. Nuclear theory; intermediate-energy nuclear reactions; neutrino oscillation phenomenology; hadronic structure.

Hutson, M. Shane, Ph.D., University of Virginia, 2000. Experimental biophysics; cell- and tissue-level mechanics in morphogenesis; laser-tissue interactions.

Johns, Will, Ph.D., University of Colorado Boulder, 1995. Experimental physics; high-energy physics.

Kephart, Thomas W., Ph.D., Northeastern University, 1981. Theoretical physics; elementary particles; field theory; cosmology.

Scherrer, Robert J., Ph.D., University of Chicago, 1986. Theoretical astrophysics: physics of the early universe and the large-scale structure of the universe, including studies of primordial nucleosynthesis, dark energy, the cosmic microwave background, and particle physics.

Sheldon, Paul D., Ph.D., University of California, Berkeley, 1986. Experimental physics; high-energy particles.

Tolk, Norman H., Ph.D., Columbia University, 1966. Experimental physics; inelastic interactions with surfaces; particle-solid interactions; quantum-mechanical phase-interference effects; free-electron laser applications.

Umar, Sait A., Ph.D., Yale University, 1985. Theoretical computational physics; nuclear theory; heavy-ion nuclear and atomic physics; models of supernovae.

Varga, Kalman, Ph.D., University of Debrecen, 1996. Theoretical and computational research on multiscale modeling of materials.

Velkovska, Julia, Ph.D., Stony Brook University, 1997. Experimental physics; relativistic heavy ion collisions.

Weiler, Thomas J., Ph.D., University of Wisconsin-Madison, 1976. Theoretical physics; elementary particles; high-energy astrophysics; cosmology.

Weintraub, David A., Ph.D., University of California, Los Angeles, 1989. Observational X-ray infrared and submillimeter astronomy; pre-main-sequence stars.

Associate Professor

Berlind, Andreas, Ph.D., Ohio State University, 2001. Large-scale structure and galaxy formation; ultrahigh cosmic energy cosmic rays.

Csorna, Steven E., Ph.D., Columbia University, 1974. Experimental physics; high-energy particles; detector research and development.

Holley-Bockelmann, Kelly, Ph.D., University of Michigan, 1999. Galaxy dynamics; N-body simulations; supermassive black holes; gravitational waves.

Xu, Yaqiong, Ph.D., Rice University, 2006. Experimental condensed-matter physics; interactions between single-walled carbon nanotubes and DNA.

Assistant Professor

Gurrola, Alfredo, Ph.D., Texas A&M, 2011. Experimental high-energy physics; particle physics.

Holmes, William, Ph.D., Indiana University, 2010. Theoretical biological physics; mathematical modeling of biological processes.

Rericha, Erin, Ph.D., University of Texas, 2004. Experimental biological physics; effect of cellular environments on cell migration.

Verweij, Marta, Ph.D., Utrecht University, 2013. Experimental nuclear physics; relativistic heavy ion collisions.

Professor Emeritus

Ramayya, Akunuri V., Ph.D., Indiana University, 1964. Experimental nuclear physics; nuclear structure and reactions with heavy ions; fission processes.

Research Professor

O'Dell, Robert C., Ph.D., University of Wisconsin-Madison, 1962. Optical imaging and spectroscopy; protoplanetary disks; planetary nebula.

Webster, Medford S., Ph.D., University of Washington, 1959. Experimental physics; high-energy physics and astrophysics; photon JETS; high-energy neutrinos.

Research Associate Professor

Hmelo, Anthony B., Ph.D., Stony Brook University, 1987. Materials physics; surface and thin films science; low-dimensional materials.

Research Assistant Professor

Gabella, William E., Ph.D., University of Colorado, 1991. Experimental optical physics.

Krzyzanowska, Halina T., Ph.D., Maria Curie-Sklodowska University, 2001. Experimental atomic, molecular and optical physics.

Stroud, Dina, Ph.D., Vanderbilt University, 2001. Executive Director, Fisk-Vanderbilt Masters-to-PhD Bridge Program. Cardiac repolarization; cardiac function and formation.

Tackett, Alan, Ph.D., Wake Forest University, 1998. Research computing systems administration.

Senior Lecturer

Charnock, Forrest, Ph.D., Wake Forest University, 1999. Fundamental electronic, magnetic and optical properties of a variety of dielectric and semi-conducting materials.

Dutta, Sourish, Ph.D., Case Western Reserve University, 2007. Dark energy, dark matter, modified gravity, the growth of structure, big bang nucleosynthesis, alternative cosmological models and topological defects.

Grundstrom, Erika D., Ph.D., Georgia State University, 2007. Massive star research using spectroscopy.

Velkovsky, Momchil, Ph.D., Stony Brook University, 1997. Experimental biological physics; particles and fields; cosmology.

DEPARTMENTAL RESEARCH SPECIALTIES AND STAFF

Theoretical

Astronomy. Large-scale structure; galactic dynamics; black holes; gravitational waves; cosmology. Berlind, Holley-Bockelmann, Scherrer.

Biophysics. Mathematical modeling of biological systems and processes; early organismal development; decision-making. Holmes.

Condensed Matter Physics. Equilibrium atomic configurations and atomic-scale dynamics of bulk defects, surfaces, and interfaces; growth process; grain boundary dynamics; interaction of radiation with materials; many-body effects in nanostructures; ultrafast dynamics of strongly correlated systems. Pantelides, Varga.

Cosmology & String Theory. Dark matter; dark energy; primordial nucleosynthesis; physics of the early universe. Kephart, Scherrer, Velkovsky, Weiler.

High Energy Physics. Electroweak symmetry breaking; supersymmetry; unification of forces; super-strings; cosmology and particle astrophysics; highest-energy cosmic rays; particle and dark matter phenomenology. Kephart, Weiler.

Nuclear Physics. Nuclear structure; intermediate-energy and high-energy nuclear reactions; hadronic structure; supernovae modeling; neutron oscillation, phenomenology. Ernst, Umar.

Experimental

Astronomy. Star formation; proto-planetary disks; planetary nebula; exoplanet detection (TESS); observational x-ray, visible, infrared and sub-millimeter wave astrophysics. Grundstrom, O'Dell, Stassun, Weintraub.

Atomic, Molecular, & Optical Physics. Interactions of ions, atoms, electrons, and synchrotron and laser photons with surfaces, interfaces, and thin films, with emphasis on electronic processes; carrier and spin dynamics; damage processes; desorption induced by electronic transitions; quantum interference effects; modification of surface electronic structure. Gabella, Gore, Haglund, Tolk.

Biophysics. Action potential propagation, shock response, and nonlinear dynamics in excitable system such as cardiac and smooth muscle; magnetic imaging of bioelectric currents, magnetic markers, and remanent geomagnetism; laser-tissue interactions; cellular development; differentiation morphogenesis; fluorescence imaging; instrumenting and controlling single cells; membrane transporters and channels. Gore, Hutson, Rericha, Stroud, Wikswo.

Condensed Matter Physics. Growth and characterization of nanostructures; electrophoretic deposition; magnetic and luminescent nanocrystals; carbon nanotubes; graphene. Haglund, Hmelo, Pantelides, Tolk, Xu.

High Energy Physics. CMS experiment at CERN. Greene, Johns, Sheldon, Velkovska.

Nuclear Physics. Nuclear structure; Coulomb excitation; fission processes; in-beam gamma-ray spectroscopy of heavy-ion reactions; isotope separator and recoil mass spectrometer work to study nuclei far from line of stability; behavior of nuclear matter at extreme temperatures; relativistic heavy ion physics at RHIC and CERN; the search for the quark gluon plasma and the colored glass condensate. Greene, Hamilton, Ramayya, Velkovska.

View additional information about this department at www.gradschoolshopper.com. Check out the "Why Choose Us?" section, find out more about the department's culture and get links to social media networks.

BAYLOR UNIVERSITY

DEPARTMENT OF PHYSICS

Waco, Texas 76798
http://www.baylor.edu/physics/

General University Information
President: Linda A. Livingstone
Dean of Graduate School: Larry Lyon
University website: http://www.baylor.edu/
School Type: Private
Setting: Suburban
Total Faculty: 1,103
Total Graduate Faculty: 843
Total number of Students: 17,059
Total number of Graduate Students: 2,743

Department Information
Department Chairman: Prof. Dwight Russell, Chair
Department Contact: Dwight Russell, Intermin Chairman
  Total full-time faculty: 17
  Total number of full-time equivalent positions: 21
  Full-Time Graduate Students: 45
  Female Full-Time Graduate Students: 6
  First-Year Graduate Students: 9
  Female First-Year Students: 2
  Total Post Doctorates: 5

Department Address
One Bear Place, #97316
Waco, TX 76798
Phone: (254) 710-2511
Fax: (254) 710-3878
E-mail: Marian_Nunn-Graves@baylor.edu
Website: http://www.baylor.edu/physics/

ADMISSIONS

Admission Contact Information
Address admission inquiries to: Graduate Admissions Office
Phone: (254) 710-3588
E-mail: gerald_cleaver@baylor.edu
Admissions website: http://www.baylor.edu/graduate/index.php?id=42273

Application deadlines
Fall admission:
U.S. students: February 1   *Int'l. students*: February 1

Application fee
U.S. students: $50   *Int'l. students*: $50

Admissions information
For Fall of 2018:
  Number of applicants: 54
  Number admitted: 9
  Number enrolled: 9

Admission requirements
Bachelor's degree requirements: Bachelor's degree in Physics is required.
Minimum undergraduate GPA: 3.0

GRE requirements
The GRE is required.

A minimum acceptable score of 1,000 is required on the verbal plus quantitative portions of the General Test.

Subjective GRE requirements
The Subjective GRE is required.

TOEFL requirements
The TOEFL exam is required for students from non-English-speaking countries.
  PBT score: 550
Minimum score of 800 on the TOEFL or the equivalent 6.5 on the IELTS.

Other admissions information
Undergraduate preparation assumed: Thirty-two semester hours of undergraduate physics, including 8 semester hours at senior level; 18 semester hours of undergraduate math, including differential equations.

TUITION

Tuition year 2018–19:
  Full-time students: $1,716 per credit
  Part-time students: $1,716 per credit
Full tuition remission (elimination) comes with each Teaching Assistantship (TA) or Research Assistantship (RA), in addition to an annual TA/RA salary of at least $22,100.
Credit hours per semester to be considered full-time: 6
Deferred tuition plan: No
Health insurance: Yes, $606.00.
Other academic fees: $181 up to 12 credit hrs Student Service Fees/semester. $50 Lab Fee.
Academic term: Semester
Number of first-year students who received full tuition waivers: 9

Teaching Assistants, Research Assistants, and Fellowships
Number of first-year
  Teaching Assistants: 9
  Fellowship students: 9
Average stipend per academic year
  Teaching Assistant: $22,100
  Research Assistant: $22,100
  Fellowship student: $5,000
All Baylor Physics graduate students are offered an RAship or a TAship with their admission. Over 90% of Baylor Physics graduate students also receive a Fellowship (a.k.a. Enhancement) in addition to their base TA/RA annual salary of $22,100 and their full tuition remission. Fellowships are available from $1000 per year to $10,000 per year.

FINANCIAL AID

Application deadlines
Fall admission:
U.S. students: February 1   *Int'l. students*: February 1

Loans
Loans are not available for U.S. students.
Loans are not available for international students.
GAPSFAS application required: No
FAFSA application required: No

For further information

Address financial aid inquiries to: Dr. Gerald Cleaver, Department of Physics, One Bear Place no. 97316, Waco, TX 76798-7316.

Phone: (254) 710-2283

E-mail: gerald_cleaver@baylor.edu

Financial aid website: http://www.baylor.edu/physics/

HOUSING

Availability of on-campus housing

Single students: Yes

Married students: Yes

For further information

Address housing inquiries to: Campus Living and Learning, Baylor University, One Bear Place no. 97076, Waco, TX 76798-7076.

Phone: (254) 710-1766

E-mail: living_learning@baylor.edu

Housing aid website: http://www.baylor.edu/graduate/current students/index.php?id=98874

Table A—Faculty, Enrollments, and Degrees Granted

Research Specialty	2017–18 Faculty	Enrollment Fall 2018		Number of Degrees Granted 2015–18 (2008–18)		
		Master's	Doctorate	Master's	Terminal Master's	Doctorate
Astronomy	2	–	–	–	–	–
Atmosphere, Space Physics, Cosmic Rays	2	–	6	1(6)	–	3(7)
Atomic, Molecular, & Optical Physics	1	–	1	–(2)	–	2(2)
Condensed Matter Physics	2	–	1	–(1)	–	2(3)
Cosmology & String Theory	2	–	13	3(5)	–	4(13)
Nonlinear Dynamics and Complex Systems	1	–	–	–(1)	–	–
Optics	1	–	3	–	–	1(1)
Particles and Fields	4	–	10	–(2)	–	2(10)
Non-specialized	–	–	11	–(2)	–	–
Total	**15**	**–**	**45**	**4(19)**	**–**	**14(36)**
Full-time Grad. Stud.	–	–	45	–	–	–
First-year Grad. Stud.	–	–	9	–	–	–

GRADUATE DEGREE REQUIREMENTS

Master's: Thirty semester hours with thesis; 36 semester hours without thesis; minimum GPA of 3.0; residence requirements: two full semesters or three full summers; comprehensive oral examination required for thesis and nonthesis degree; thesis requirements: under supervision of thesis director and three graduate faculty members. Completed draft of research thesis must meet approval of all committee members.

Doctorate: Seventy-eight semester hours with dissertation; minimum GPA of 3.0; residence requirements: at least two consecutive semesters (summer does not count as a full semester); preliminary (qualifying) examination: 12 hours written examination covering quantum mechanics, classical mechanics, electricity and magnetism, mathematical physics, statistical mechanics; and other topics (must be taken prior to admission to candidacy for Ph.D.); final oral exam: given after all course, research, and dissertation requirements have been fulfilled; dissertation requirements: covers program of original research, the results of which reveal scholarly competence and are publishable in AIP journals or equivalent.

Thesis: Thesis may be written in absentia.

SPECIAL EQUIPMENT, FACILITIES, OR PROGRAMS

Scanning tunneling microscope (STM) system. Metalorganic chemical vapor deposition (MOCVD) system. Equipment for X-ray diffraction studies. Surface analysis system (XSAM 800) allowing for the characterization of surface and atomic electronic structure(s) using ARXPS, ISS, AES, AM, and LEED. Hypervelocity accelerator laboratory including dust particle accelerator, light gas gun accelerators, laser gas cell accelerator system and laser hypervelocity impact simulation system, 2 GEC RF/DC Reference Cells used for complex (dusty) plasma and colloidal plasma physics, and an inductively coupled plasma generator (IPG). Low-field MRI. Spectra Nd:YAG laser, optical parametric oscillator FTIR spectrometer.

Table B—Separately Budgeted Research Expenditures by Source of Support

Source of Support	Departmental Research	Physics-related Research Outside Department
Federal government	$599,675	
State/local government		
Non-profit organizations	$140,629	
Business and industry		
Other		
Total	**$740,304**	

Table C—Separately Budgeted Research Expenditures by Research Specialty

Research Specialty	No. of Grants	Expenditures ($)
Atmosphere, Space Physics, Cosmic Rays	3	$106,405
Condensed Matter Physics	7	$242,554
Cosmology & String Theory	4	$101,805
Particles and Fields	5	$273,140
Physics and other Science Education	1	$16,400
Total	**20**	**$740,304**

FACULTY

Professor

Benesh, Gregory A., Ph.D., Northwestern University, 1980. *Condensed Matter Physics, Surface Physics*. Theoretical condensed matter physics.

Cleaver, Gerald, Ph.D., California Institute of Technology, 1993. Graduate Program Director. *Cosmology & String Theory, Particles and Fields*. Superstring/M theory. Quantum Gravity.

Dittmann, Jay R., Ph.D., Duke University, 1998. *Particles and Fields*. Experimental high-energy particle physics.

Hyde, Truell, Ph.D., Baylor University, 1988. *Astrophysics, Plasma and Fusion*. Theoretical and experimental space physics.

Lee, Howard, Ph.D., Max Planck Institute for the Sciences of Light, 2012. *Optics*.

Matthews, Lorin, Ph.D., Baylor University, 1998. *Atmosphere, Space Physics, Cosmic Rays, Plasma and Fusion*. Theoretical and experimental space physics.

Wang, Anzhong, Ph.D., University of Ioannina, 1991. *Cosmology & String Theory, Relativity & Gravitation*. Theoretical gravity and cosmology.

Ward, Bennie, Ph.D., Princeton University, 1973. *Cosmology & String Theory, Particles and Fields*. Theoretical particle physics and quantum general relativity.

Wilcox, Walter M., Ph.D., University of California, Los Angeles, 1981. *Particles and Fields*. Theoretical elementary particle physics.

Associate Professor

Ariyasinghe, Wickramasinghe, Ph.D., Baylor University, 1987. *Atomic, Molecular, & Optical Physics*. Experimental atomic, molecular, and solid-state physics.

Olafsen, Jeffrey, Ph.D., Duke University, 1994. *Nonlinear Dynamics and Complex Systems*. Experimental nonlinear dynamics.

Park, Kenneth, Ph.D., University of Rochester, 1993. *Condensed Matter Physics, Surface Physics*. Experimental surface physics.

Russell, Dwight, Ph.D., Vanderbilt University, 1986. *Condensed Matter Physics, Surface Physics*. Experimental surface physics.

Zhang, Zhenrong, Ph.D., Chinese Academy of Sciences, 2002. *Condensed Matter Physics, Surface Physics*. Experimental condensed matter physics.

Assistant Professor

Hatakeyama, Kenichi, Ph.D., Rockefeller University, 2003. *Particles and Fields*. Experimental high-energy particle physics.

Research Professor

Scully, Marlan, Ph.D., Yale, 1965. Distinguished Research Academician of Science and Engineering. *Atomic, Molecular, & Optical Physics, Biophysics, Optics*. Quantum Optics, especially Raman spectroscopy.

Lecturer

Castanheira Endl, Barbara, Ph.D., Fed Univ of Rio Grande Do Sul. *Astronomy*. Astronomy.

Kinslow, Linda, Ph.D., Baylor University, 1979. *Theoretical Physics*. Many-body theory.

Vasut, John, Ph.D., Baylor University, 2001. *Atmosphere, Space Physics, Cosmic Rays, Plasma and Fusion*. Theoretical dusty plasmas.

DEPARTMENTAL RESEARCH SPECIALTIES AND STAFF

Theoretical

Atmosphere, Space Physics, Cosmic Rays. Charging processes and dust dynamics in space (planetary rings, cometary comas, interplanetary/interstellar dust, protostellar/protoplanetary clouds) and laboratory environments. Hyde, Matthews.

Condensed Matter Physics. Embedding problems; electronic structure of surfaces; surface energies, magnetism, and catalysis. Benesh.

Cosmology & String Theory. Cleaver, Wang.

Particles and Fields. Ward, Wilcox.

Experimental

Atmosphere, Space Physics, Cosmic Rays. Hypervelocity impact phenomena as related to orbital debris and fusion devices, dusty plasmas, laser physics, shock physics, in situ instrumentation. Hyde, Matthews.

Atomic, Molecular, & Optical Physics. Heavy-ion-induced Auger electron studies, chemical binding effects on Auger electrons and energy-loss mechanisms, intermediate and high-energy electron scattering. Ariyasinghe.

Condensed Matter Physics. Surface atomic and electronic structure of transition metals and compounds, adsorbate-induced surface modifications, atomically resolved imaging of surface catalytic reactions on model catalytic systems, material characterization under ultrahigh vacuum. Park, Russell, Zhang.

Condensed Matter Physics. Optical and electronic properties of III-V semiconductors; infrared semiconductor lasers.

Nonlinear Dynamics and Complex Systems. Chemical, granular, and soft condensed matter physics; insect biomechanics; dissipative and dynamical systems. Olafsen.

Particles and Fields. Studies of high-energy hadron collisions with the CDF experiment at the Fermi National Accelerator Laboratory and the CMS experiment at CERN. Dittmann, Hatakeyama.

View additional information about this department at www.gradschoolshopper.com. Check out the "Why Choose Us?" section, find out more about the department's culture and get links to social media networks.

RICE UNIVERSITY

APPLIED PHYSICS GRADUATE PROGRAM

Houston, Texas 77005
https://appliedphysics.rice.edu/

General University Information
President: David Leebron
Dean of Graduate School: Seiichi Matsuda
University website: http://www.rice.edu
School Type: Private
Setting: Urban
Total Faculty: 800
Total Graduate Faculty: 500
Total number of Students: 6,740
Total number of Graduate Students: 2,861

Department Information
Department Chairman: Dr. Kevin Kelly, Chair
Department Contact: Carol Lively, Administrator
  Total full-time faculty: 112
  Total number of full-time equivalent positions: 112
  Full-Time Graduate Students: 70
  Female Full-Time Graduate Students: 12
  First-Year Graduate Students: 10
  Female First-Year Students: 4
  Total Post Doctorates: 4

Department Address
6100 Main St
300 Space Science, MS-100
Houston, TX 77005
Phone: 713-348-3566
Fax: 713-348-5320
E-mail: sciapp@rice.edu
Website: https://appliedphysics.rice.edu/

ADMISSIONS

Admission Contact Information
Address admission inquiries to: Applied Physics Graduate Program, Rice University, 6100 Main St, MS-100, Houston, TX 77005
Phone: 713-348-3566
E-mail: sciapp@rice.edu
Admissions website: https://sci.rice.edu/applying

Application deadlines
Fall admission:
U.S. students: January 15   *Int'l. students*: January 15

Application fee
U.S. students: $85   *Int'l. students*: $85
University Fee Waivers: - Vietnam Education Fellowship (VEF) - Nankai University Hundred Young Teachers Program - McNair Scholar Program - Fulbright Scholar Program - Institute for Recruitment of Teachers (IRT) - The National GEM Consortium (GEM) - Gulf Coast Undergraduate Research Symposium (GCURS)

Admissions information
For Fall of 2018:
  Number of applicants: 74
  Number admitted: 25
  Number enrolled: 9

Admission requirements
Bachelor's degree requirements: Average admitted students obtain a 3.63 GPA (on a 4 point scale).
Minimum undergraduate GPA: 3.0

GRE requirements
The GRE is required.
There is no minimum for any section of the GRE exam. Those scores are evaluated in combination with all other aspects of the candidate's application. Average GRE scores for admitted Applied Physics students are in the range of V157 and Q164.

Subjective GRE requirements
The Subjective GRE is not required.
The GRE Physics subject exam is not required. If applicants have taken the Physics subject test, then scores should be indicated on the application.

TOEFL requirements
The TOEFL exam is required for students from non-English-speaking countries.
  PBT score: 600
  iBT score: 90
Students who have obtained an undergraduate degree from an English-speaking university may have the TOEFL requirement waived. Students may also take the IELTS in lieu of the TOEFL. The IELTS minimum accepted score is 7. The average TOEFL iBT score for admitted international students is 100, and the average IELTS score is 7.5.

Other admissions information
Undergraduate preparation assumed: Students are expected to have an adequate background in their chosen undergraduate science or engineering discipline to successfully complete graduate-level courses in those topics.

TUITION

Tuition year 2018–19:
  Full-time students: $23,300 per semester
Part-time students are not accepted into the Applied Physics Graduate Program.
Credit hours per semester to be considered full-time: 9
Deferred tuition plan: No
Health insurance: Available at the cost of $893 per year.
Other academic fees: A tuition waiver is provided for all students receiving the minimum stipend required per semester ($8,000).
Academic term: Semester
Number of first-year students who received full tuition waivers: 9

Teaching Assistants, Research Assistants, and Fellowships
  Average stipend per academic year
    Fellowship student: $31,000

FINANCIAL AID

Application deadlines
Fall admission:
U.S. students: May 15   *Int'l. students*: May 15

Loans

Loans are available for U.S. students.
Loans are available for international students.
GAPSFAS application required: No
FAFSA application required: Yes

For further information

Address financial aid inquiries to: Office of Financial Aid, Rice University, PO Box 1892, MS-12, Houston, TX 77251-1892.
Phone: 713-348-4958
E-mail: fina@rice.edu
Financial aid website: http://financialaid.rice.edu

HOUSING

Availability of on-campus housing

Single students: No
Married students: No

For further information

Address housing inquiries to: Rice Graduate Apartments, ATTN: Manager, 1515 Bissonnet St, Houston, TX 77005.
Phone: 713-348-5440
E-mail: gradapts@rice.edu
Housing aid website: http://campushousing.rice.edu/

GRADUATE DEGREE REQUIREMENTS

Master's: Students admitted to our Ph.D. program with a bachelor's degree are required to earn the thesis M.S. within the program before proceeding to the Ph.D. A total of 9 academic courses is required, with a GPA of 3.0 or better, and research hours. Students are expected to achieve the MS within 3 year.

Doctorate: Students admitted to the PhD. program are required to complete 90 hours of credit for coursework and research, beyond the bachelor's degree. Four semesters of full-time study at Rice are also required.

Thesis: The MS is written in lieu of any qualifying exams or preliminaries.

FACULTY

DEPARTMENTAL RESEARCH SPECIALTIES AND STAFF

Theoretical

Biomedical Optics.
Carbon Nanotube Technology.
Computational Imaging.
Graphene and 2D Systems.
Heavy Fermion Superconductors.
Metamaterial Lenses.
Modeling Quantum Criticality.
Motor Protein Dynamics.
Nanocatalysts for Clean Energy.
Nanodevices for Neuroscience.
Nanoparticle-Based Theranostics.
Plasmonic Nanostructures.
Polymer Photovoltaics.
Superresolution Microscopy.
Terahertz Spectroscopy.
Topological Insulators.
Translational Medical Devices.
Ultracold Atoms and Plasmas.

Experimental

Biomedical Optics.
Carbon Nanotube Fibers.
Computational Imaging.
Graphene and 2D Systems.
Heavy Fermion Superconductors.
Metamaterial Lenses.
Modeling Quantum Criticality.
Motor Protein Dynamics.
Nanocatalysts for Clean Energy.
Nanodevices for Neuroscience.
Nanoparticle-Based Theranostics.
Plasmonic Nanostructures.
Polymer Photovoltaics.
Superresolution Microscopy.
Terahertz Spectroscopy.
Topological Insulators.
Translational Medical Devices.
Ultracold Atoms and Plasmas.

View additional information about this department at www.gradschoolshopper.com. Check out the "Why Choose Us?" section, find out more about the department's culture and get links to social media networks.

RICE UNIVERSITY

DEPARTMENT OF PHYSICS AND ASTRONOMY

Houston, Texas 77005
http://www.physics.rice.edu/

General University Information
President: David W. Leebron
Dean of Graduate School: Seiichi Matsuda
University website: http://www.rice.edu/
School Type: Private
Setting: Urban
Total Faculty: 865
Total Graduate Faculty: 545
Total number of Students: 6,904
Total number of Graduate Students: 2,934

Department Information
Department Chairman: Prof. Douglas Natelson, Chair
Department Contact: Stanley Dodds, Associate Chair
  Total full-time faculty: 50
  Total number of full-time equivalent positions: 46
  Full-Time Graduate Students: 95
  Female Full-Time Graduate Students: 20
  First-Year Graduate Students: 21
  Female First-Year Students: 5
  Total Post Doctorates: 17

Department Address
201 Brockman Hall
6100 Main St
Houston, TX 77005
Phone: (713) 348-4938
Fax: (713) 348-4150
E-mail: physics@rice.edu
Website: http://www.physics.rice.edu/

ADMISSIONS

Admission Contact Information
Address admission inquiries to: Graduate Admissions, Department of Physics and Astronomy, MS61, Rice University, P.O. Box 1892, Houston, TX 77251-1892
Phone: (713) 348-4938
E-mail: physgrad@rice.edu
Admissions website: https://physgradapps.rice.edu/

Application deadlines
Fall admission:
U.S. students: January 1   *Int'l. students*: January 1

Application fee
U.S. students: $85   *Int'l. students*: $85
see department website for admission requirements and other admission information: http://www.physics.rice.edu/Content.aspx?id=58

Admissions information
For Fall of 2018:
  Number of applicants: 249
  Number admitted: 60
  Number enrolled: 19

Admission requirements
Bachelor's degree requirements: Bachelor's degree in physics or closely related field is normally required.
Minimum undergraduate GPA: 3.0

GRE requirements
The GRE is required.

Subjective GRE requirements
The Subjective GRE is required.

TOEFL requirements
The TOEFL exam is required for students from non-English-speaking countries.
  PBT score: 600
  iBT score: 90
For students who choose to take the IELTS in lieu of TOEFL, the minimum score is 7. The TOEFL and the IELTS may be waived for an international student who received a degree from an institution in which English is the official language of communication. Contact the department for more information.

Other admissions information
Undergraduate preparation assumed: Typical preparation includes advanced undergraduate courses in mechanics, electricity and magnetism, quantum mechanics, and statistical physics. Mathematics at least through partial differential equations and complex analysis and one year of advanced undergraduate laboratory.

TUITION

Tuition year 2018–2019:
  Full-time students: $46,600 annual
Credit hours per semester to be considered full-time: 9
Deferred tuition plan: Yes
Health insurance: Yes, $878 (after subsidy).
Other academic fees: $583 - Miscellaneous Annual Fees
Academic term: Semester
Number of first-year students who received full tuition waivers: 19

Teaching Assistants, Research Assistants, and Fellowships
Number of first-year
  Fellowship students: 19
Average stipend per academic year
  Research Assistant: $31,000
  Fellowship student: $31,000
  $31,000 year (12-month stipend)

FINANCIAL AID

Application deadlines
Fall admission:
U.S. students: January 1   *Int'l. students*: January 1

Loans
Loans are available for U.S. students.
Loans are not available for international students.
GAPSFAS application required: No
FAFSA application required: No

For further information

Address financial aid inquiries to: Graduate Admissions, Department of Physics and Astronomy, MS61, Rice University, P.O. Box 1892, Houston, TX 77251-1892.
Phone: (713) 348-4938
E-mail: physgrad@rice.edu
Financial aid website: http://physics.rice.edu/Content .aspx?id=59

HOUSING

Availability of on-campus housing

Single students: Yes
Married students: Yes
Childcare Assistance: Yes

For further information

Address housing inquiries to: Two housing options:, Rice Graduate Apartments, Attn: Manager, 1515 Bissonnet St., Houston, TX 77005, Rice Village Apartments, Attn: Manager, 2410 Shakespeare St., Houston, TX 77030.
Phone: 713-348-4723
E-mail: gradapts@rice.edu
Housing aid website: http://campushousing.rice.edu/graduate-housing/

Table A—Faculty, Enrollments, and Degrees Granted

Research Specialty	2017–18 Faculty	Enrollment Fall 2017 Master's	Enrollment Fall 2017 Doctorate	Number of Degrees Granted 2017–18 (2013–18) Master's	Number of Degrees Granted 2017–18 (2013–18) Terminal Master's	Number of Degrees Granted 2017–18 (2013–18) Doctorate
Astrophysics	9	–	8	2(6)	–(1)	2(9)
Atmosphere, Space Physics, Cosmic Rays	6	–	8	1(6)	–(2)	–(4)
Atomic, Molecular, & Optical Physics	5	–	24	3(17)	1(2)	2(13)
Biophysics	7	–	18	4(18)	–(3)	6(15)
Condensed Matter Physics	11	–	31	5(32)	–(4)	5(26)
Particles and Fields	6	–	6	1(7)	–(2)	3(8)
Total	**44**	**–**	**95**	**16(86)**	**1(14)**	**18(75)**
Full-time Grad. Stud.	–	–	95	–	–	–
First-year Grad. Stud.	–	–	21	–	–	–

GRADUATE DEGREE REQUIREMENTS

Master's: Although students are not normally admitted to a Master of Science (MS) degree program, graduate students may earn the MS as they work towards the PhD.

Doctorate: To be eligible for the PhD degree, graduate students must demonstrate to the department their knowledge in the discipline and the ability to engage in advanced research. This normally is accomplished by: successfully completing required coursework for the MS; presenting a research progress report and proposal to a faculty committee; and passing an oral candidacy exam. Students must complete a total of 60 credit hours of approved graduate-level study at Rice and produce a research thesis under the direction of a departmental faculty member. At least two years of graduate study are required for the PhD.

Table B—Separately Budgeted Research Expenditures by Source of Support

Source of Support	Departmental Research	Physics-related Research Outside Department
Federal government	$9,262,171	
State/local government	$157,448	
Non-profit organizations	$1,737,757	
Business and industry	$55,554	
Other	$79,428	
Total	**$11,292,358**	

Table C—Separately Budgeted Research Expenditures by Research Specialty

Research Specialty	No. of Grants	Expenditures ($)
Astrophysics	16	$459,692
Atmosphere, Space Physics, Cosmic Rays	32	$1,598,617
Atomic, Molecular, & Optical Physics	22	$1,841,358
Biophysics	14	$900,788
Condensed Matter Physics	41	$3,534,570
High Energy Physics	10	$649,598
Particles and Fields	31	$2,307,735
Total	**166**	**$11,292,358**

FACULTY

Professor

Alexander, David, Ph.D., University of Glasgow, 1989. Director, Rice Space Institute. *Astrophysics, Heliophysics and Space Weather, Planetary Science, Solar Physics*. Solar Physics, Space Exploration, star-planet interactions.

Baring, Matthew G., Ph.D., University of Cambridge, 1989. *Astrophysics*. Theoretical high-energy astrophysics of compact objects.

Chan, Anthony A., Ph.D., Princeton University, 1991. *Atmosphere, Space Physics, Cosmic Rays, Heliophysics and Space Weather*. Theoretical plasma physics with emphasis on basic plasma physics and space plasmas.

Dai, Pengcheng, Ph.D., University of Missouri-Columbia, 1993. *Condensed Matter Physics*. Experimental condensed matter physics of correlated electron materials.

Deem, Michael W., Ph.D., University of California, Berkeley, 1994. *Biophysics, Statistical & Thermal Physics*. Immune response to multi-strain viruses and vaccine. Physical theories of pathogen evolution. Newton's laws of biology.

Du, Rui-Rui, Ph.D., University of Illinois, 1990. *Condensed Matter Physics*. Experimental condensed matter, nanophysics.

Dunning, F. Barry, Ph.D., University College, 1969. *Atomic, Molecular, & Optical Physics*. Experimental Atomic, Molecular, and Optical Physics, Nonlinear Dynamics, Chemical Physics.

Hafner, Jason H., Ph.D., Rice University, 1998. Associate chair for the undergraduate program. *Biophysics, Nano Science and Technology*. Biophysics, Nanoscience.

Halas, Naomi J., Ph.D., Bryn Mawr College, 1986. *Condensed Matter Physics, Nano Science and Technology, Optics*. Design and fabrication of optically responsive nanostructures, nanophotonics, plasmonics.

Hartigan, Patrick M., Ph.D., University of Arizona, 1987. *Astronomy, Astrophysics*. Star Formation, Stellar Jets, Laboratory Astrophysics, Nebulae.

Huang, Huey W., Ph.D., Cornell University, 1967. *Biophysics, Statistical & Thermal Physics*. Statistical Physics, X-ray, Neutron, and Optical Spectroscopies on Membrane Physics.

Hulet, Randall G., Ph.D., Massachusetts Institute of Technology, 1984. *Atomic, Molecular, & Optical Physics*. Experimental atomic physics with ultracold atoms; Bose-Einstein condensation; Fermi superfluidity; Simulation of condensed matter with ultracold atoms confined to optical lattices.

Johns-Krull, Christopher M., Ph.D., University of California, Berkeley, 1994. *Astronomy, Planetary Science*. Star formation and early stellar evolution. Solar and stellar magnetic activity. Extra-solar planets.

Killian, Thomas C., Ph.D., Massachusetts Institute of Technology, 1999. Associate chair for the graduate program, Associate Dean of Natural Sciences. *Atomic, Molecular, & Optical Physics, Plasma and Fusion*. Atomic Physics, Plasma Physics, and Biophysics. Strongly interacting quantum degenerate atomic gases and ultracold plasmas, Rydberg atoms in dense gases, and electro-magnetic characterization and control of biological structures.

Kono, Junichiro, Ph.D., State University of New York at Buffalo, 1995. *Condensed Matter Physics, Nano Science and Technology, Optics*. Nonlinear, ultrafast, and quantum optics in solids ; Optics and photonics of low-dimensional materials; Physics and applications of terahertz phenomena; High magnetic field phenomena in condensed matter.

Levy, Eugene H., Ph.D., University of Chicago, 1971. *Astrophysics, Atmosphere, Space Physics, Cosmic Rays, Geophysics, Planetary Science*. Astrophysics & Space Physics; Planetary Geophysics.

Liang, Edison P., Ph.D., University of California, Berkeley, 1971. *Astrophysics, Plasma and Fusion*. High Energy Density Physics, High Energy Astrophysics, Laser Plasma Interactions and Applications, Antimatter Creation, Inertial Fusion Energy, Fluid Dynamics.

Morosan, Emilia, Ph.D., Iowa State University, 2005. *Condensed Matter Physics*. Synthesis and characterization of novel electronic and magnetic materials. Strongly correlated electron systems, heavy fermions, local moment and itinerant electron magnetism, superconductivity, charge density wave transitions.

Natelson, Dougas, Ph.D., Stanford University, 1998. Department Chair. *Condensed Matter Physics, Nano Science and Technology*. Experimental Condensed Matter Physics, nanotechnology, nanostructures, nanoelectronics, organic electronics, strongly correlated materials, plasmonics.

Nordlander, Peter, Ph.D., Chalmers University of Technology, 1985. *Condensed Matter Physics, Nano Science and Technology, Optics*. Condensed Matter Theory, Electronic and Optical Properties of Nanoparticles, Electron Transfer and Transport in Nanostructures, Nanooptics, Nanophotonics, Plasmonics.

Onuchic, Jose N., Ph.D., California Institute of Technology, 1987. *Biophysics, Computational Physics*. Theoretical molecular biophysics.

Padley, B. Paul, Ph.D., University of Toronto, 1987. *Accelerator, High Energy Physics, Particles and Fields*. Experimental Elementary Particle Physics.

Pu, Han, Ph.D., University of Rochester, 1999. *Atomic, Molecular, & Optical Physics*. Theoretical Atomic, Molecular and Optical Physics Ultra-Cold atomic physics.

Reiff, Patricia H., Ph.D., Rice University, 1975. *Atmosphere, Space Physics, Cosmic Rays, Heliophysics and Space Weather*. Space Plasma Physics: Magnetospheric Physics, Aurorae, Solar Wind/Magnetosphere/Ionosphere Interactions; Space Weather.

Roberts, Jabus B., Ph.D., University of Pennsylvania, 1969. *High Energy Physics, Particles and Fields*. Experimental Elementary and Nuclear Physics.

Scuseria, Gustavo E., Ph.D., University of Buenos Aires, 1983. *Chemical Physics, Computational Physics, Condensed Matter Physics, Nano Science and Technology*. Theoretical chemistry, ab initio computational quantum chemistry, density functional theory, development of new methods for molecular electronic structure, and applications to materials and nanostructures.

Si, Qimiao, Ph.D., University of Chicago, 1991. *Condensed Matter Physics*. Theoretical Condensed matter physics, specializing in strongly correlated electron systems.

Toffoletto, Frank R., Ph.D., Rice University, 1987. *Computational Physics, Heliophysics and Space Weather*. Magnetospheric Physics, Computational Space Plasma Physics.

Wolynes, Peter, Ph.D., Harvard University, 1976. *Biophysics, Computational Physics, Condensed Matter Physics*. Theoretical chemical physics; protein folding and function; glasses and stochastic cell biology.

Associate Professor

Bradshaw, Stephen J., Ph.D., University of Cambridge, 2004. *Astrophysics, Computational Physics, Solar Physics*. Astrophysics of the Sun; Plasma physics; Numerical modeling.

Dodds, Stanley A., Ph.D., Cornell University, 1975. Associate chair.

Ecklund, Karl M., Ph.D., Stanford University, 1996. *Accelerator, High Energy Physics, Particles and Fields*. Experimental High-Energy Particle Physics.

Geurts, Frank, Ph.D., Universiteit Utrecht, 1998. *Accelerator, High Energy Physics, Nuclear Physics, Particles and Fields*. Relativistic Heavy-Ion Physics.

Kiang, Ching-Hwa, Ph.D., California Institute of Technology, 1995. *Biophysics*. Molecular biophysics.

Li, Wei, Ph.D., Massachusetts Institute of Technology, 2009. *Accelerator, Nuclear Physics, Particles and Fields*. Relativistic Heavy Ion Physics; High-Density QCD Proton-Proton Physics.

Nevidomskyy, Andriy, Ph.D., University of Cambridge, 2005. *Condensed Matter Physics*. Strong electron correlations in d- and f-electron systems; Emergent phenomena in correlated electron systems.

Assistant Professor

Amin, Mustafa, Ph.D., Stanford University, 2008. *Astrophysics, Cosmology & String Theory, Particles and Fields, Relativity & Gravitation*. Early universe: inflation, reheating after inflation. Late universe: dark matter & dark energy, large scale structure.

Foster, Matthew S., Ph.D., University of California, Santa Barbara, 2006. *Condensed Matter Physics*. Theoretical condensed matter physics: effects of disorder and interactions in low-dimensional systems; Anderson localization and metal-insulator transitions; Dirac materials; Non-equilibrium quantum dynamics; Topological materials physics; nonequilibrium dynamics.

Hazzard, Kaden, Ph.D., Cornell University, 2010. *Atomic, Molecular, & Optical Physics*. Theoretical Atomic, Molecular and Optical Physics. Ultracold atoms and molecules. Strongly correlated phases. Nonequilibrium dynamics. Quantum resources for metrology, communication, and computation.

Isella, Andrea, Ph.D., Universita degli Studi di Milano, 2006. *Astronomy, Astrophysics, Planetary Science*. Galactic astronomy and astrophysics. Planetary formation.

Tunnell, Christopher, Ph.D., Oxford University, 2013. *Astrophysics, Computational Physics*. Data analysis for dark matter searches, XENON collaboration.

Yi, Ming, Ph.D., Stanford, 2014. *Condensed Matter Physics*. Tuning and driving properties of quantum materials, photoemission spectroscopy, x-ray scattering.

Research Associate Professor

Sazykin, Stanislav, Ph.D., Utah State University, 2000. *Atmosphere, Space Physics, Cosmic Rays, Computational Physics, Heliophysics and Space Weather*. Physics of space plasmas: dynamics of the terrestrial ionosphere and magnetosphere, numerical modeling of planetary magnetospheres. Space weather.

Smith, Ian A., Ph.D., Washington University, 1990. *Astrophysics*. Multiwavelength observations and theory of gamma-ray bursters, supernovae, galactic and extragalactic black holes, radio pulsars, soft gamma-ray repeaters, and very high energy gamma-ray sources.

Yepes, Pablo, Ph.D., University of Santiago de Compostela, 1988. *Accelerator, High Energy Physics, Medical, Health Physics, Nuclear Physics, Particles and Fields*. Particle Physics, Nuclear Physics, Medical Physics, Proton Therapy.

Research Assistant Professor

Chaguine, Petr, Ph.D., Institute for High Energy Physics, 1990. *Astrophysics, High Energy Physics*. Particle Astrophysics, High Energy Physics, High Energy Density Physics. Dark matter search experiments.

DEPARTMENTAL RESEARCH SPECIALTIES AND STAFF

Theoretical

Astrophysics. High-energy electromagnetic processes; dense and/or intensely magnetized plasmas; accretion disk phenomena; gamma-ray bursters; radiative shock waves; photodissociation regions. Amin, Baring, Hartigan, Isella, Johns-Krull, Levy, Liang, Smith.

Atmosphere, Space Physics, Cosmic Rays. Magnetospheric structure and dynamics, both terrestial and planetary; electromagnetic wave-particle interactions. Alexander, Baring, Bradshaw, Chan, Sazykin, Toffoletto.

Atomic, Molecular, & Optical Physics. Degenerate quantum gases; atom optics; quantum optics. Hazzard, Pu.

Biophysics. Molecular biophysics; statistical mechanics and bioinformatics. Deem, Onuchic, Wolynes.

Condensed Matter Physics. Strongly correlated electron systems in high-temperature superconductors and mesoscopic structures; non-Fermi liquid behavior in various systems; particle-surface interactions. Foster, Nevidomskyy, Nordlander, Scuseria, Si.

Particles and Fields. Early universe: inflation, reheating after inflation. Late universe: dark matter & dark energy, large scale structure. Amin.

Experimental

Astrophysics. Multiwavelength imagery and spectroscopy of astrophysical plasmas, particularly HII regions, nebulae, and star-forming regions; gamma-ray bursters and pulsars; formation of planetary systems; accretion disks; young stars; stellar-exoplanet interactions; stellar jets; laboratory astrophysics; the chemistry of gaseous nebulae; solar corona; solar-terrestrial interactions; dark matter searches (XENON). Hartigan, Isella, Johns-Krull, Levy, Tunnell.

Atmosphere, Space Physics, Cosmic Rays. Mission planning and data analysis for earth and planetary plasma probes. Alexander, Bradshaw, Reiff.

Atomic, Molecular, & Optical Physics. Quantum gases and Bose-Einstein condensation; use of Rydberg atoms to probe chaotic dynamics, ion-surface interactions, and electron-molecule interactions. Dunning, Hulet, Killian.

Biophysics. Studies of membrane ion channels; nanoscale probes; biological macromolecular assemblies; photothermal techniques. Hafner, Huang, Kiang.

Condensed Matter Physics. Electrical transport in lithographically and chemically formed nanostructures; novel electronic materials; controlling quantum materials. Dai, Du, Halas, Kono, Morosan, Natelson, Yi.

Particles and Fields. Detector development, hardware, and software, for RHIC and CMS; study of quark-gluon plasma at RHIC, XENON dark-matter search. Chaguine, Ecklund, Geurts, Li, Padley, Roberts, Yepes.

View additional information about this department at www.gradschoolshopper.com. Check out the "Why Choose Us?" section, find out more about the department's culture and get links to social media networks.

SOUTHERN METHODIST UNIVERSITY

DEPARTMENT OF PHYSICS

Dallas, Texas 75275-0175
http://www.physics.smu.edu

General University Information
President: R. Gerald Turner
Dean of Graduate School: James E. Quick
University website: http://www.smu.edu
School Type: Private
Setting: Urban
Total Faculty: 758
Total number of Students: 11,789
Total number of Graduate Students: 5,337

Department Information
Department Chairman: Prof. Ryszard Stroynowski, Chair
Department Contact: Lacey Breaux, Administrative Assistant
  Total full-time faculty: 19
  Total number of full-time equivalent positions: 19
  Full-Time Graduate Students: 17
  Female Full-Time Graduate Students: 1
  First-Year Graduate Students: 3
  Total Post Doctorates: 5

Department Address
PO Box 750175
Dallas, TX 75275-0175
Phone: (214) 768-2495
Fax: (214) 768-4095
E-mail: Physics@mail.smu.edu
Website: http://www.physics.smu.edu

ADMISSIONS

Admission Contact Information
Address admission inquiries to: Dr. Pavel Nadolsky
Phone: (214) 768-4345
E-mail: smugrad@smu.edu
Admissions website: http://smu.edu/graduate

Application deadlines
Fall admission:
U.S. students: May 1   *Int'l. students*: May 1

Application fee
U.S. students: $75   *Int'l. students*: $75
Note that the priority deadline for Ph.D. applicants is December
  15. Applications received after this date may or may not be
  considered for funding.

Admissions information
For Fall of 2018:
  Number of applicants: 15
  Number admitted: 4
  Number enrolled: 3

Admission requirements
Bachelor's degree requirements: Bachelor's degree in physics
  or a related field.
Minimum undergraduate GPA: 3.0

GRE requirements
The GRE is required.

Subjective GRE requirements
The Subjective GRE is required.

TOEFL requirements
The TOEFL exam is required for students from non-English-
  speaking countries.
  iBT score: 80
The TOEFL is required for international students who do not
  qualify for a waiver. See http://www.smu.edu/graduate/
  ProspectiveStudents/International-Students for further details.
  IELTS minimum score is 6.5.

Other admissions information
Undergraduate preparation assumed: Serway, Physics; Marion
  and Thornton, Classical Dynamics; Griffiths, Introduction to
  Electrodynamics; Reif, Fundamentals of Statistical and Thermal Physics; Gasiorowicz, Quantum Physics; Bevington,
  Data Reduction and Error Analysis; Arfken/Weber, Mathematical Methods for Physicists.

TUITION

Tuition year 2017–2018:
  Full-time students: $1,704 per credit
  Part-time students: $1,704 per credit
Tuition is generally waived for students in Ph.D. program.
Credit hours per semester to be considered full-time: 9
Deferred tuition plan: No
Health insurance: Available at the cost of $2,800 per year.
Other academic fees: There is a fee per semester hour in addition
  to the tuition. This is also generally waived for students in
  the Ph.D. program.
Academic term: Semester
Number of first-year students who received full tuition waivers: 3

Teaching Assistants, Research Assistants, and Fellowships
Number of first-year
  Teaching Assistants: 3
  Fellowship students: 1
Average stipend per academic year
  Teaching Assistant: $26,400
  Research Assistant: $27,600
  Fellowship student: $37,600

FINANCIAL AID

Loans
Loans are not available for U.S. students.
Loans are not available for international students.
GAPSFAS application required: No
FAFSA application required: No

For further information
Address financial aid inquiries to:
Phone: (214) 768-3417
E-mail: Enrol_serv@smu.edu
Financial aid website: https://www.smu.edu/Enrollment
  Services/FinancialAid

HOUSING

Availability of on-campus housing
Single students: Yes
Married students: Yes

For further information
Address housing inquiries to: Residence Life & Student Housing, Southern Methodist University, PO Box 750215, Dallas Texas 75275-0215.
Phone: 214-768-2407
E-mail: housing@smu.edu
Housing aid website: http://smu.edu/housing

Table A—Faculty, Enrollments, and Degrees Granted

Research Specialty	2018–2019 Faculty	Enrollment 2017–2018 Mas-ter's	Enrollment 2017–2018 Doc-torate	Number of Degrees Granted 2017–2018 (2015–2018) Mas-ter's	Number of Degrees Granted 2017–2018 (2015–2018) Terminal Master's	Number of Degrees Granted 2017–2018 (2015–2018) Doc-torate
Astrophysics	3	–	4	–(1)	–(3)	1(2)
High Energy Physics	14	–	14	3(6)	–	2(8)
Total	17	–	18	3(7)	–(3)	3(10)
Full-time Grad. Stud.	–	–	18	–	–	–
First-year Grad. Stud.	–	–	4	–	–	–

GRADUATE DEGREE REQUIREMENTS

Master's: Students seeking the M.S. degree in physics must complete either 33 semester hours of approved graduate course work or 30 semester hours of courses including a research thesis. Every M.S. degree program must contain at least 18 semester hours of graduate courses in physics, including a prescribed sequence of three courses. Students must also pass a comprehensive exam or, if applicable, defend their thesis.

Doctorate: Students seeking the Ph.D. in Physics must complete eight core courses, four elective graduate courses in Physics, and at least 48 credit hours of graduate courses in total. To advance to Ph.D. candidacy, students must pass a comprehensive qualifying exam in the form of a four-part written exam, which must be completed prior to the end of their fifth semester.

SPECIAL EQUIPMENT, FACILITIES, OR PROGRAMS

The department maintains a fast signal processing opto-electronics laboratory that is used for R&D for the ATLAS detector, as well as collaborative projects with local hi-tech companies. In addition, the department is home to a materials screening facility (LUMINA) that serves high-sensitivity, low-background experiments in dark matter and neutrinoless double beta decay. Students participating in research use the facilities provided by national research laboratories: Fermilab, Argonne National Laboratory, Brookhaven National Laboratory, and the LHC (Large Hadron Collider) at CERN-the European Center for Particle Physics. SMU faculty members participate actively in the following experiments and collaborations: ATLAS, DESI, NOVA, SuperCDMS, eBubble, and CTEQ.

Table C—Separately Budgeted Research Expenditures by Research Specialty

Research Specialty	No. of Grants	Expenditures ($)
Dark Matter Direct Detection	1	
Stellar Astrophysics	1	
Collider Physics	1	
Total	3	

FACULTY

Professor
Coan, Thomas E., Ph.D., University of California, Berkeley, 1989. *High Energy Physics, Particles and Fields*. Experimental high-energy physics.

Kehoe, Robert L. P., Ph.D., University of Notre Dame, 1997. *Astrophysics, High Energy Physics, Particles and Fields*. Experimental high-energy physics.

Olness, Fredrick I., Ph.D., University of Wisconsin-Madison, 1985. *High Energy Physics, Particles and Fields, Theoretical Physics*. Particle theory and phenomenology.

Stroynowski, Ryszard, Ph.D., University of Geneva, Switzerland, 1973. *High Energy Physics, Particles and Fields*. Experimental high-energy physics.

Ye, Jingbo, Ph.D., Swiss Federal Institute of Technology, 1992. *High Energy Physics, Particles and Fields*. Experimental high-energy physics.

Associate Professor
Cooley, Jodi, Ph.D., University of Wisconsin-Madison, 2003. *Astrophysics, High Energy Physics, Low Temperature Physics, Particles and Fields*. Experimental astrophysics.

Nadolsky, Pavel, Ph.D., Michigan State University, 2001. *Particles and Fields, Theoretical Physics*. Theoretical high-energy physics.

Sekula, Stephen, Ph.D., University of Wisconsin-Madison, 2004. *High Energy Physics, Particles and Fields*. Experimental high-energy physics.

Vega, Roberto, Ph.D., University of Texas, 1988. *Particles and Fields, Theoretical Physics*. Particle theory and phenomenology.

Assistant Professor
Deiana, Allison McCarn, Ph.D., University of Illinois Urbana-Champaign, 2013. *High Energy Physics, Particles and Fields*. Experimental high-energy physics.

Meyers, Joel, Ph.D., University of Texas, 2012. *Astrophysics, Theoretical Physics*. Cosmic microwave background, gravitational waves, and cosmology.

Research Associate Professor
Liu, Chonghan, M.S., University of Texas at Arlington, 2003. *Applied Physics, Electrical Engineering, High Energy Physics*. Experimental high-energy physics.

Liu, Tiankuan, Ph.D., University of Science and Technology of China, 1998. *Applied Physics, Electrical Engineering, Nuclear Physics*. Nuclear physics.

Research Assistant Professor
Gong, Datao, Ph.D., University of Science and Technology of China, 1999. *Applied Physics, Electrical Engineering, High Energy Physics*. Particle physics.

Xiang, Annie Chu, Ph.D., Department of Electrical and Computer Engineering, Rice University, 2002. *Applied Physics, Computer Science, Electrical Engineering*. Fiber optics communication.

Adjunct Professor
Cotton, John, M.S., Southern Methodist University, 1991. *Astronomy*. Astronomy.

Fattaruso, John, Ph.D., University of California, Berkeley, 1986. Distinguished Member of the Technical Staff, Texas Instruments (retired). *Computational Physics*.

Senior Lecturer

Dalley, Simon, Ph.D., University of Southampton, 1991. *Particles and Fields, Theoretical Physics*. Theoretical elementary particle physics.

Scalise, Randall J., Ph.D., Pennsylvania State University, 1994. *Particles and Fields, Theoretical Physics*. Theoretical elementary particle physics.

Lecturer

Balakishiyeva, Durdana, Ph.D., Syracuse University, 2006. *Astrophysics, Low Temperature Physics*. Experimental Astrophysics.

DEPARTMENTAL RESEARCH SPECIALTIES AND STAFF

Theoretical

Cosmic Microwave Background and Cosmology. Early cosmic history from structure of the cosmic microwave background, including the influence of gravitational waves on the early cosmos. Meyers.

Particle Physics. QCD structure functions; heavy quark approximation; Monte Carlo simulations; Higgs production and scattering backgrounds; Lattice Gauge Theory.

Experimental

Astrophysics. Dark Matter Search (Super CDMS). Cooley.

Experimental Particle Physics. Participation in ATLAS experiment at CERN, eBubble (BNL), DO (FNAL), NOVA (FNAL), BaBar (SLAC) and LBNE (FNAL). Coan, Gong, Kehoe, Chonghan Liu, Tiankuan Liu, Nadolsky, Olness, Sekula, Stroynowski, Ye.

Stellar Astrophysics and Cosmic History. The DESI program will collect the light spectrum of tens of millions of stellar objects with the goal of understanding the large-scale structure of the cosmos and its origins in the evolution of the universe. Kehoe.

View additional information about this department at www.gradschoolshopper.com. Check out the "Why Choose Us?" section, find out more about the department's culture and get links to social media networks.

TEXAS CHRISTIAN UNIVERSITY

DEPARTMENT OF PHYSICS AND ASTRONOMY

Fort Worth, Texas 76129
http://www.phys.tcu.edu

General University Information
Chancellor: Victor Boschini
Dean of Graduate School: Phil Hartman
University website: http://www.tcu.edu/
School Type: Private
Setting: Urban
Total Faculty: 674
Total Graduate Faculty: 409
Total number of Students: 10,489
Total number of Graduate Students: 1,478

Department Information
Department Chairman: Dr. Yuri Strzhemechny, Chair
Department Contact: Marilyn Yates, Administrative Assistant
  Total full-time faculty: 9
  Total number of full-time equivalent positions: 9
  Full-Time Graduate Students: 17
  Female Full-Time Graduate Students: 7
  First-Year Graduate Students: 3
  Total Post Doctorates: 2

Department Address
TCU Box 298840
Fort Worth, TX 76129
Phone: (817) 257-7375
Fax: (817) 257-7742
E-mail: physics@tcu.edu
Website: http://www.phys.tcu.edu

ADMISSIONS

Admission Contact Information
Address admission inquiries to: Department of Physics & Astronomy, Texas Christian University, TCU Box 298840, Fort Worth, TX 76129
Phone: (817) 257-7375
E-mail: physics@tcu.edu
Admissions website: http://www.phys.tcu.edu

Application deadlines
Fall admission:
U.S. students: February 1   *Int'l. students*: February 1
Spring admission:
U.S. students: October 1   *Int'l. students*: October 1

Application fee
U.S. students: $60   *Int'l. students*: $60

Admissions information
For Fall of 2017:
  Number of applicants: 22
  Number admitted: 9
  Number enrolled: 7

Admission requirements
Bachelor's degree requirements: A Bachelor's degree in Physics is required.
Minimum undergraduate GPA: 3.0

GRE requirements
The GRE is required.
  Quantitative score: 150
  Verbal score: 150
Quantitative + Verbal = 300 minimum

Subjective GRE requirements
The Subjective GRE is not required.

TOEFL requirements
The TOEFL exam is required for students from non-English-speaking countries.
  PBT score: 550
  iBT score: 80
Minimum IELTS score of 6.5 is required.

Other admissions information
Undergraduate preparation assumed: A B.A. or B.S. with a physics major or 24 semester hour equivalent, including intermediate or advanced undergraduate courses in mechanics, electricity and magnetism, atomic and nuclear or modern physics, or their equivalents is needed. Twelve semester hours must be of junior or senior level. Mathematics through differential equations and a course in general chemistry are required.

TUITION

Tuition year 2018–2019:
  Full-time students: $1,480 per credit
Credit hours per semester to be considered full-time: 6
Deferred tuition plan: Yes
Health insurance: Available at the cost of $1,950 per year.
Academic term: Semester

Teaching Assistants, Research Assistants, and Fellowships
Number of first-year
  Fellowship students: 1
Average stipend per academic year
  Teaching Assistant: $20,500
  Research Assistant: $23,000
  Fellowship student: $22,000
TCU will cover 3/4 cost of the student health care insurance for those students receiving the required amount of aid.

FINANCIAL AID

Application deadlines
Fall admission:
U.S. students: February 1   *Int'l. students*: February 1
Spring admission:
U.S. students: October 1   *Int'l. students*: October 1

Loans
Loans are available for U.S. students.
Loans are not available for international students.
GAPSFAS application required: No
FAFSA application required: No

For further information

Address financial aid inquiries to: Department of Physics & Astronomy, Texas Christian University, TCU Box 298840, Fort Worth, TX 76129.

Phone: (817) 257-7375

E-mail: physics@tcu.edu

Financial aid website: http://www.phys.tcu.edu

HOUSING

Availability of on-campus housing

Single students: Yes

Married students: Yes

For further information

Address housing inquiries to: Housing and Residential Living Office.

Phone: 817-257-7865

Housing aid website: http://www.rlh.tcu.edu/

Table A—Faculty, Enrollments, and Degrees Granted

Research Specialty	2017–18 Faculty	Enrollment Spring 2018 Master's	Enrollment Spring 2018 Doctorate	Number of Degrees Granted 2017–2018 (2013–2018) Master's	Number of Degrees Granted 2017–2018 (2013–2018) Terminal Master's	Number of Degrees Granted 2017–2018 (2013–2018) Doctorate
Astronomy	2	–	6	1(1)	–	1(2)
Atomic, Molecular, & Optical Physics	1	–	1	–	–	–(1)
Biophysics	3	–	10	1(3)	–(4)	3(5)
Nano Science and Technology	1	–	1	–(1)	–(1)	–(3)
Statistical & Thermal Physics	–	–	–	–(2)	–	–(3)
Total	8	–	18	2(7)	–(5)	4(14)
Full-time Grad. Stud.	–	–	18	–	–	–
First-year Grad. Stud.	–	–	3	–	–	–

GRADUATE DEGREE REQUIREMENTS

Master's: The M.S. degree requires 30 approved semester hours with a thesis or 36 semester hours without a thesis. Course requirements for the degree are: Quantum Mechanics I & II, three courses from Classical Mechanics, Electrodynamics I & II, Solid State Physics or Statistical Physics, plus a minimum of six additional semester hours in Physics. An oral examination over coursework and thesis, if any, is required.

Doctorate: The Ph.D. degree is available on a physics, astrophysics, or biophysics track. An M.B.A. degree may also be earned in combination with the Ph.D. Course work: The following core of courses are required and are normally completed during the first four semesters of graduate study. The core courses must be completed with an average grade of 2.75 (out of 4.0) or better. Physics Track: Quantum Mechanics I & II; 12 semester hours selected from Classical Mechanics, Statistical Physics, Solid State Physics, or Electrodynamics I or II, and 9 semester hours of Research Problems in Physics. Additional coursework may be required to ensure adequate preparation for the specified courses. Astrophysics Track: Astrophysics, Quantum Mechanics I, Electrodynamics I; 12 semester hours selected from Quantum Mechanics II, Classical Mechanics, Statistical Physics or Electrodynamics II; and nine semester hours of Research Problems in Astronomy. Students may also be required to take Advanced Topics in Astrophysics to ensure an adequate background for their dissertation research. Biophysics Track: Quantum Mechanics I and II; 12 semester hours selected from Non-linear Dynamics with Ap-

plications, Optical Spectroscopy and Fluorescence, Electrodynamics I and II, Statistical Physics; and nine semester hours of Research Problems in Biophysics. Students may be required to take one or more additional courses from Topics in Biophysics, Experimental Methods in Biochemistry and Biophysics or Advanced Topics in Biophysics to ensure an adequate background for their dissertation research. Each full-time student is required to participate in graduate seminars. The course requirements for any course other than research problems may also be met by satisfactory performance on a written examination or by transfer of credit in an equivalent course from another institution. Pre-dissertation examination: This examination is normally taken during the fourth semester of graduate study, and consists of three parts: first, a written report submitted to the advisory committee on a research project either completed or proposed for a dissertation; second, a colloquium based on the written research report; and third, an oral examination over the research report given by the advisory committee and faculty. Successful completion of the pre-dissertation examination and the required core work constitute admission to candidacy for the Ph.D. degree. Unsuccessful completion of the pre-dissertation examination may result in the student being advised to complete the requirements for a Master of Science degree. Dissertation: Completion of a dissertation consisting of an original research project directed by a faculty member at TCU. A final oral examination in defense of the dissertation is required and a paper based on the dissertation research must be submitted for publication in an appropriate scientific journal. Teaching Requirements: Each full-time graduate student pursuing a degree in physics is required to participate in the undergraduate teaching function of the department. The faculty are committed to effective teaching and believe that experience in the teaching of physics is an integral part of graduate education. This requirement is met by assisting in undergraduate laboratories, giving laboratory instructions, grading papers, conducting problems sessions, or offering tutorial help. No more than eight hours per week. The Ph.D. in Physics is also available with an M.B.A. option. Students entering the Ph.D. program with a B.S. degree are normally expected to compete the Ph.D. requirements within five years. At the end of the fourth year of graduate studies, a candidate for the Ph.D. degree who has demonstrated sufficient progress in dissertation research may apply for the M.B.A. option. During the fifth year the student is expected to continue with the dissertation on a reduced scale, and, if on Departmental Teaching Assistantship, to perform designated departmental teaching duties. Students entering the Ph.D. program with advanced standing (M.S. degree or more) can request an accelerated program. In addition to the coursework, qualifying examinations, and dissertation requirements specified above for the Ph.D. degree in Physics or Astrophysics, students electing to take the M.B.A. option will take 18 hours of M.B.A. coursework during two consecutive semesters as outlined in the TCU Graduate Studies Bulletin. Students are required to attend the Team Building and Skills workshop conducted by the School of Business. Students are assessed a fee for the workshop. The results of the GRE will be accepted in lieu of the GMAT. Students who wish to continue their studies in the program after their first year of business courses and pursue the M.B.A. degree will be required to complete such additional coursework as required of other M.B.A. students and as outlined in the TCU Graduate Studies Bulletin. The maximum term of fellowship or assistantship support through the Department of Physics is five years for the Ph.D. Degree or the Ph.D. with M.B.A. Option. Support for M.B.A. courses from the TCU Physics Department fellowships or assistantship is limited to 18 hours. Financial support for the additional 24 hours required for completion of the

M.B.A. degree is the student's responsibility. However, students are eligible to apply for financial aid from the School of Business.

SPECIAL EQUIPMENT, FACILITIES, OR PROGRAMS

The physics and astronomy research facilities are housed in spacious, well-equipped laboratories with specialized equipment, including TEM and SEM (transmission and scanning electron microscopes); FTIR (Fourier transform) spectrometers; closed-cycle cryogenic refrigerators operating below 10 K; multiple state-of-the-art spectrometers and laser lines (continuous wave and pulsed); a confocal microscope and a fluorescence microscope with hyperspectral imaging; time-resolved spectroscopy setup; a positron lifetime apparatus.

Table B—Separately Budgeted Research Expenditures by Source of Support

Source of Support	Departmental Research	Physics-related Research Outside Department
Federal government	$324,900	
State/local government		
Non-profit organizations		
Business and industry		
Other		
Total	**$324,900**	

FACULTY

Professor

Gryczynski, Z. K., Ph.D., University of Gdansk, 1986. *Biophysics, Medical, Health Physics, Nano Science and Technology, Optics.* Fluorescence.

Rittby, Magnus, Ph.D., University of Stockholm, 1985. Senior Associate Dean. *Atomic, Molecular, & Optical Physics, Computational Physics.*

Associate Professor

Frinchaboy, Peter, Ph.D., University of Virginia, 2006. Graduate Program Director, REU Director. *Astronomy, Astrophysics.* Galactic evolution, star clusters, chemical abundances.

Strzhemechny, Yuri, Ph.D., City University of New York, 2000. Department Chairman. *Atomic, Molecular, & Optical Physics, Condensed Matter Physics, Materials Science, Metallurgy, Nano Science and Technology, Optics.* Surface science; optical spectroscopy.

Assistant Professor

Barger, Kat A., Ph.D., Wisconsin-Madison, 2012. Social Media Supervisor. *Astronomy, Astrophysics.* Galaxy evolution.

Dobrovolny, Hana M., Ph.D., Duke University, 2008. Webmaster. *Biophysics.* Modeling influenza and drug treatments.

Naumov, Anton, Ph.D., Rice University, 2011. *Biophysics, Nano Science and Technology.*

Instructor

Ingram, Douglas, Ph.D., University of Washington, 1996. *Astronomy.*

DEPARTMENTAL RESEARCH SPECIALTIES AND STAFF

Theoretical

Nonlinear Dynamics and Complex Systems.
Statistical & Thermal Physics.

Experimental

Astronomy. Barger, Frinchaboy, Ingram.
Astrophysics. Molecular clusters in solids. Barger, Frinchaboy.
Atomic, Molecular, & Optical Physics. Rittby, Strzhemechny.
Biophysics. Dobrovolny, Gryczynski, Naumov.
Nano Science and Technology. High-pressure materials science. Naumov, Strzhemechny.

View additional information about this department at www.gradschoolshopper.com. Check out the "Why Choose Us?" section, find out more about the department's culture and get links to social media networks.

TEXAS STATE UNIVERSITY-SAN MARCOS

DEPARTMENT OF PHYSICS

San Marcos, Texas 78666
http://www.txstate.edu/physics/

General University Information
President: Dr. Denise Trauth
Dean of Graduate School: Dr. Andrea Golato
University website: http://www.txstate.edu/
School Type: Public
Setting: Suburban
Total Faculty: 1,936
Total Graduate Faculty: 1,034
Total number of Students: 38,808
Total number of Graduate Students: 4,564

Department Information
Department Chairman: Prof. Mark Holtz, Chair
Department Contact: Dr. Edwin Piner, Graduate Advisor
　Total full-time faculty: 24
　Total number of full-time equivalent positions: 24
　Full-Time Graduate Students: 30
　Female Full-Time Graduate Students: 5
　First-Year Graduate Students: 3
　Female First-Year Students: 2
　Total Post Doctorates: 2

Department Address
601 University Drive
San Marcos, TX 78666
Phone: (512) 245-2131
E-mail: PhysicsGrad@txstate.edu
Website: http://www.txstate.edu/physics/

ADMISSIONS

Admission Contact Information
Address admission inquiries to: Graduate Program, Department
　of Physics, 601 University Dr., San Marcos, TX 78666
Phone: (512) 245-2131
E-mail: PhysicsGrad@txstate.edu
Admissions website: http://www.gradcollege.txstate.edu/

Application deadlines
Fall admission:
U.S. students: June 15　　　*Int'l. students*: June 1
Spring admission:
U.S. students: October 15　　*Int'l. students*: October 1

Application fee
U.S. students: $40　　　*Int'l. students*: $90
Students interested in an assistantship are encouraged to apply by April
　15. Priority deadline: Students interested in competing for a research
　fellowship award should apply by February 15.

Admissions information
For Fall of 2017:
　Number of applicants: 20
　Number admitted: 9

Admission requirements
Bachelor's degree requirements: Bachelor's degree is required
　in Physics or closely related discipline with a GPA of 3.0
　or higher in upper division undergraduate Physics courses.
Minimum undergraduate GPA: 3.0

GRE requirements
The GRE is recommended but not required.
GRE scores are not required for regular admission however it
　is recommended that all applicants take the GRE as the results
　can be used to support an applicant that is lacking in other
　areas such as GPA.

Subjective GRE requirements
The Subjective GRE is not required.

TOEFL requirements
The TOEFL exam is required for students from non-English-
　speaking countries.
iBT score: 78

Other admissions information
Additional requirements: B.S. in Physics or related fields.
Undergraduate preparation assumed: Junior or senior level Clas-
　sical Mechanics, Quantum Mechanics, Electrodynamics, and
　Mathematical Methods of Physics (or equivalent).

TUITION

Tuition year 2016–17:
Tuition for in-state residents
　Full-time students: $6,847.04 per semester
　Part-time students: $746.56 per credit
Tuition for out-of-state residents
　Full-time students: $7,582.04 per semester
　Part-time students: $1,161.56 per credit
Any student (international or domestic) on instructional or re-
　search assistantship is considered a state resident and is el-
　igible for in-state tuition.
Credit hours per semester to be considered full-time: 9
Deferred tuition plan: Yes
Health insurance: Available at the cost of $3,683 per year.
Academic term: Semester
Number of first-year students who received partial tuition waivers: 3

Teaching Assistants, Research Assistants, and Fellowships
　Number of first-year
　　Teaching Assistants: 2
　　Research Assistants: 1
　Average stipend per academic year
　　Teaching Assistant: $12,500
　　Research Assistant: $21,600
Assistantships are not guaranteed unless otherwise noted in
　program acceptance letter. Applicants may compete for an ad-
　ditional graduate fellowship in a University-wide competition
　upon application. Once enrolled, students are also eligible to
　compete for two University-wide scholarship programs.

FINANCIAL AID

Application deadlines
Fall admission:
U.S. students: March 1　　　*Int'l. students*: March 1
Spring admission:
U.S. students: March 1　　　*Int'l. students*: March 1

Loans

Loans are available for U.S. students.
Loans are available for international students.
GAPSFAS application required: No
FAFSA application required: Yes

For further information

Address financial aid inquiries to: Financial Aid and Scholarships, J. C. Kellam Building, Suite 240, Texas State University-San Marcos, 601 University Drive, San Marcos, Texas 78666–4602.
Phone: (512) 245-2315
E-mail: finaid@txstate.edu
Financial aid website: http://www.finaid.txstate.edu/

HOUSING

Availability of on-campus housing

Single students: Yes
Married students: Yes
Childcare Assistance: No

For further information

Address housing inquiries to: Housing and Residential Life, J.C. Kellam, Suite 320/380, 601 University Drive, San Marcos, TX 78666.
Phone: (512) 245-2382
E-mail: reslife@txstate.edu
Housing aid website: http://www.reslife.txstate.edu/

Table A—Faculty, Enrollments, and Degrees Granted

Research Specialty	2016–17 Faculty	Enrollment Spring 2017		Number of Degrees Granted 2017–18 (2013–17)		
		Master's	Doctorate	Master's	Terminal Master's	Doctorate
Astronomy	3	–	–	–	–	–
Atomic, Molecular, & Optical Physics	1	1	–	–	–(1)	–
Computational Physics	1	2	–	–	–(3)	–
Condensed Matter Physics	8	13	–	–	2(24)	–
Materials Science, Metallurgy	8	15	–	–	3(20)	–
Nano Science and Technology	3	6	–	–	2(5)	–
Physics Education Research	4	2	–	–	–	–
Non-specialized	–	2	–	–	–(3)	–
Total	24	30	–	–	7(33)	–
Full-time Grad. Stud.	–	30	–	–	–	–
First-year Grad. Stud.	–	9	–	–	–	–

GRADUATE DEGREE REQUIREMENTS

Master's: Course Work Master of Science (M.S.) in Physics Students can complete a 36-hour non-thesis program or a 30-hour thesis program. Both options include core physics courses and electives. The thesis option offers an especially strong opportunity for research in experimental condensed matter, nanotechnology and physics education research. The M.S. in physics educates students in advanced physics through a rigorous curriculum that includes cutting-edge, hands-on training. The M.S. in materials physics is a 35-hour program that requires preparation of a thesis and stresses experimental materials physics primarily related to the semiconductor and high-tech industries. The degree also requires a one-semester industry internship. There is no foreign language requirement.

Doctorate: Master degree graduates have the option to continue to an innovative, multidisciplinary Ph.D. program in Materials Science, Engineering and Commercialization offered at Texas State University. www.msec.txstate.edu.

Thesis: Thesis may be written in absentia.

SPECIAL EQUIPMENT, FACILITIES, OR PROGRAMS

Department Mission

The Department of Physics strives to provide an exciting, engaging and rigorous educational environment that stresses relevant research, classroom learning, and extensive training to prepare students for careers in industry, education, or further research. With an emphasis on graduate research, the department has an effective curriculum that provides high quality hands-on training in state-of-the-art research facilities. The department provides a meaningful educational experience facilitated by dedicated faculty who work closely with students. Most graduate students are supported as instructional or research assistants.

The Department of Physics has research concentrations in materials, education research, and historical astronomy.

The materials physics groups prepare M.S. graduates for professional employment, including the semiconductor and materials industry, or further graduate study in a doctoral program. Students working in experimental physics engage in fundamental and applied research for photovoltaics, nanoscience, III-nitride semiconductors, dilute magnetic materials, oxides, and other applied topics. Theoretical focus is on the study of the physical properties of materials through computational simulations with an emphasis on semiconductors and oxides. Students work in facilities under the Analysis Research Service Center (RSC), Cleanroom, and Advanced Functional Materials RSC. These facilities operate research-grade thin film sputtering, molecular beam epitaxy, metalorganic chemical vapor deposition (CVD), hot filament CVD, scanning electron microscopy, energy dispersive X-ray spectroscopy, micro-Raman and infrared spectroscopy, high-resolution X-ray diffraction/reflectivity, scanning probe microscopy (AFM and STM), magnetometry, resistivity, high temperature furnaces/ovens, ellipsometry, electric transport measurements, deep-level transient spectroscopy, impedance spectroscopy, and photoluminescence. Industrial internships are strongly encouraged in our program.

The physics education research (PER) group focuses on embodied and participationist models of learning, including gesture, conceptual metaphor, conceptual blending, communities of practice, relational discourse, and identity development. These research areas are pursued through qualitative analysis of video records of interactions between students, environment, and teachers; quantitative analysis of standard conceptual and attitudinal surveys; and hybrid analysis of student written and graphical artifacts. Graduate study in PER prepares students for careers in K-14 physics education, and further graduate study in a doctoral program in either physics or education.

A final research area consists of computational modeling of historical events in astronomy. The department maintains a small astronomical observatory (16″ reflector) for student use.

Texas State also offers a Ph.D. in Materials Science, Engineering, and Commercialization. This interdisciplinary program involves numerous physics faculty and their students.

Table B—Separately Budgeted Research Expenditures by Source of Support

Source of Support	Departmental Research	Physics-related Research Outside Department
Federal government	$360,000	
State/local government		$1,427,200
Non-profit organizations		
Business and industry		
Other		
Total	$360,000	$1,427,200

Table C—Separately Budgeted Research Expenditures by Research Specialty

Research Specialty	No. of Grants	Expenditures ($)
Condensed Matter Physics	7	$312,000
Physics Education Research	2	$36,000
Polymer Physics/Science	1	$12,000
Total	10	$360,000

FACULTY

Professor

Donnelly, David, Ph.D., University of California, Santa Barbara, 1990. Society of Physics Students Advisor. Associate Chair Department of Physics. Undergraduate Advisor. *Condensed Matter Physics, Physics and other Science Education*. Physics Education Research.

Holtz, Mark, Ph.D., Virginia Polytechnic Institute, 1987. University Chair Professor of Materials Science, Engineering, and Commercialization. *Atomic, Molecular, & Optical Physics, Condensed Matter Physics, Materials Science, Metallurgy, Nano Science and Technology, Solid State Physics*. Materials physics.

Myers, Tom, Ph.D., North Carolina State University, 1983. Associate Dean College of Science. *Condensed Matter Physics, Materials Science, Metallurgy, Optics*.

Olson, Donald W., Ph.D., University of California, Berkeley, 1975. *Astronomy, Astrophysics, Computational Physics, Relativity & Gravitation*. Astrophysics; general relativity; computational astronomy.

Piner, Edwin, Ph.D., North Carolina State University, 1998. Graduate Advisor. *Condensed Matter Physics, Materials Science, Metallurgy, Nano Science and Technology*. GaN Devices.

Associate Professor

Close, Hunter G., Ph.D., University of Washington, 2005. Undergraduate Program Director. *History & Philosophy of Physics/Science, Physics and other Science Education*. Body engagement with mathematical ideas in upper division physics; development of physics identity; improving attitudes about physics in physics courses.

Geerts, Wilhelmus J., Ph.D., University of Twente, Enschede, The Netherlands, 1992. *Applied Physics, Condensed Matter Physics, Materials Science, Metallurgy, Optics, Polymer Physics/Science, Systems Science/Engineering*. Nanostructured magnetic and semiconductor materials: electrical and optical characterization; instrumentation development; solar technology.

Theodoropoulou, Nikoleta, Ph.D., University of Florida, 2002. Graduate Program Director. *Applied Physics, Condensed Matter Physics, Materials Science, Metallurgy, Nano Science and Technology, Solid State Physics*. Spintronics/Magnetic Nanostructures/Oxide Interfaces.

Wistey, Mark, Ph.D., Stanford University, 2005.

Assistant Professor

Close, Eleanor, Ph.D., Seattle Pacific University, 2009. Learning Assistant Program Director. *Physics and other Science Education*. Implementation of learning assistants in introductory physics sequence.

Olmstead, Alice, Ph.D., University of Maryland, 2016. *Astronomy, Astrophysics, Physics and other Science Education*.

Rangelov, Blagoy, Ph.D., University of Toledo, 2012. *Astronomy, Astrophysics*.

Zakhidov, Alexander, Ph.D., Moscow State University, 2006. Graduate Admissions Advisor. *Materials Science, Metallurgy, Polymer Physics/Science*. Physics of organic semiconductors: Perovskite solar cells, OLEDS, organic transistors.

Senior Lecturer

Holtz, Susan, Ph.D., Virginia Poly Inst & State Univ, 1986. *Astronomy, Astrophysics, Physics and other Science Education*. Astronomy.

Palomino, Jennifer, Ph.D., University of Texas-Austin, 2012.

Scolfaro, Luisa, Ph.D., University of Sao Paulo, 1988. *Computational Physics, Condensed Matter Physics, Materials Science, Metallurgy*. First principles simulations of electronic structure of materials using density functional theory.

Lecturer

Bergeler, Elmar, Ph.D., Dresden University of Technology, 2009. *Physics and other Science Education*.

Lunk, Brandon, Ph.D., North Carolina State University, 2012. *Other*. Physics Education.

DEPARTMENTAL RESEARCH SPECIALTIES AND STAFF

Theoretical

Computational Physics. Theoretical focus is on the study of the physical properties of materials through computational simulations, either using first principles or approximation methods within the effective mass theory, with an emphasis on semiconductors and oxides. Scolfaro.

Physics Education Research. The physics education research (PER) group focuses on embodied and participationist models of learning, including gesture, conceptual metaphor, conceptual blending, communities of practice, relational discourse, and identity development. These research areas are pursued through qualitative analysis of video records of interactions between students, environment, and teachers; quantitative analysis of standard conceptual and attitudinal surveys; and hybrid analysis of student written and graphical artifacts. Graduate study in PER prepares students for careers in K-14 physics education, and further graduate study in a doctoral program in either physics or education. Eleanor Close, Hunter Close, Donnelly, Olmstead, Palomino.

Experimental

Adaptive Optics. The use of adaptive optics, including spatial light modulators, in Kerr microscopy and optical lithography is investigated. Geerts.

Condensed Matter Physics. Magnetic nanostructure/Spintronics/Oxide hetero-interfaces. Theodoropoulou.

Forensic Astronomy. Computational modeling of historical events in astronomy. Olmstead, Olson, Rangelov.

III-nitride semiconductors. MOCVD of GaN Devices grown on silicon substrates for high-power electronics and high-electron mobility transistors. Mark Holtz, Piner.

Materials Science, Metallurgy. We are focused on the development of novel III-V and II-VI materials for next generation semiconductor device and oxide-based multiferroic devices. We focus on detailed understanding of materials properties and their interaction with the electrical performance in devices. We partner with leading companies in all areas of manufacturing these devices in order to accelerate the process of innovation. Mark Holtz, Myers, Piner, Theodoropoulou, Zakhidov.

Micro mechanics. Study of MEMs device including the use of various etching technologies to create them.

Nano Science and Technology. 1. Optical properties of semiconductors, properties of III-Nitride based devices, heat transport at the nanoscale. 2. Properties of materials at the nanoscale and devices. 3. Organic light emitting diodes and transistors. 4. Properties of silicon nanoparticles. Mark Holtz, Theodoropoulou, Zakhidov.

Optical Materials Properties. The optical properties of bulk materials, thin films, and micro- and nanostructured materials are studied by Raman spectroscopy, ellipsometry, Magneto-Optical spectroscopy, FTIR, and photoluminescence experiments. Geerts, Mark Holtz.

Physics Education Research. The physics education research (PER) group focuses on embodied and participationist models of learning, including gesture, conceptual metaphor, conceptual blending, communities of practice, relational discourse, and identity development. These research areas are pursued through qualitative analysis of video records of interactions between students, environment, and teachers; quantitative analysis of standard conceptual and attitudinal surveys; and hybrid analysis of student written and graphical artifacts. Graduate study in PER prepares students for careers in K-14 physics education, and further graduate study in a doctoral program in either physics or education. Eleanor Close, Hunter Close, Donnelly, Olmstead, Palomino.

Physics of Organic Semiconductors. Science and Engineering of Organic Optoelectronic devices. Science and Engineering of Photovoltaic Materials and Devices. Zakhidov.

View additional information about this department at www.gradschoolshopper.com. Check out the "Why Choose Us?" section, find out more about the department's culture and get links to social media networks.

TEXAS TECH UNIVERSITY

DEPARTMENT OF PHYSICS & ASTRONOMY

Lubbock, Texas 79409
https://www.depts.ttu.edu/phas

General University Information
President: Lawrence Schovanec
Dean of Graduate School: Mark Sheridan
University website: http://www.ttu.edu/
School Type: Public
Setting: Urban
Total Faculty: 2,554
Total Graduate Faculty: 1,389
Total number of Students: 37,010
Total number of Graduate Students: 6,251

Department Information
Department Chairman: Prof. Nural Akchurin, Chair
Department Contact: Joyce Norton, Assistant Advisor
  Total full-time faculty: 21
  Full-Time Graduate Students: 47
  Female Full-Time Graduate Students: 0
  First-Year Graduate Students: 8
  Female First-Year Students: 1
  Total Post Doctorates: 10

Department Address
Box 41051
Lubbock, TX 79409
Phone: (806) 834-6355
Fax: (806) 742-1182
E-mail: joyce.norton@ttu.edu
Website: https://www.depts.ttu.edu/phas

ADMISSIONS

Admission Contact Information
Address admission inquiries to: Prof. Mahdi Sanati, Graduate Recruiter, Department of Physics & Astronomy
Phone: (806) 834-6169
E-mail: m.sanati@ttu.edu
Admissions website: https://www.depts.ttu.edu/phas/Academics/Graduate_Program/Prospective_Students/index.php

Application deadlines
Fall admission:
U.S. students: March 31   *Int'l. students*: January 15
Spring admission:
U.S. students: October 1   *Int'l. students*: June 15

Application fee
U.S. students: $60   *Int'l. students*: $60

Admissions information
For Fall of 2018:
  Number of applicants: 45
  Number admitted: 10
  Number enrolled: 10

Admission requirements
Bachelor's degree requirements: Bachelors degree in Physics is required for admission to the graduate programs in Physics. For students with a Bachelor's degree in a related field, undergraduate leveling may be required.
Minimum undergraduate GPA: 3.0

GRE requirements
The GRE is required.
  Quantitative score: 155
  Verbal score: 152
  Analytical score: 3.0
  Mean GRE score range (25th–75th percentile): 70%-85%

Subjective GRE requirements
The Subjective GRE is recommended.
  Minimum accepted Advanced GRE score: 712
  Mean Advanced GRE score range (25th–75th percentile): 65%-75%

TOEFL requirements
The TOEFL exam is required for students from non-English-speaking countries.
  PBT score: 550
  iBT score: 79

Other admissions information
Additional requirements: For the past several years, the average General GRE scores were verbal-152; quantitative-155; total-307. A minimum GRE total score of 307 is required to obtain financial support from the department.
The IELTS score of 6.5 or better is also accepted. All new foreign teaching assistants are required to pass an English workshop administered by the University.

TUITION
Tuition year 2018–19:
Tuition for in-state residents
  Full-time students: $9,197 annual
  Part-time students: $511 per credit
Tuition for out-of-state residents
  Full-time students: $17,920 annual
  Part-time students: $996 per credit
Health insurance cost is not included.
Credit hours per semester to be considered full-time: 9
Deferred tuition plan: Yes
Health insurance: Yes, $2,224.00.
Academic term: Semester
Number of first-year students who received partial tuition waivers: 10

Teaching Assistants, Research Assistants, and Fellowships
Number of first-year
  Teaching Assistants: 10
  Research Assistants: 1
  Fellowship students: 1
Average stipend per academic year
  Teaching Assistant: $15,531
  Research Assistant: $15,531
  Fellowship student: $15,531
Stipend is higher for students with M.S. degree and those who have passed the Ph.D. Qualifying Exam.

FINANCIAL AID

Application deadlines
Fall admission:

U.S. students: March 1   *Int'l. students*: March 1

Spring admission:

U.S. students: October 1   *Int'l. students*: October 1

Loans

Loans are available for U.S. students.

Loans are not available for international students.

GAPSFAS application required: Yes

FAFSA application required: Yes

For further information

Address financial aid inquiries to: Prof. Mahdi Sanati, Graduate Recruiter, Department of Physics & Astronomy.

Phone: (806) 834-6169

E-mail: m.sanati@ttu.edu

HOUSING

Availability of on-campus housing

Single students: Yes

Married students: No

Childcare Assistance: No

For further information

Address housing inquiries to: University Student Housing, Wiggins Complex, 3211 18th Street, Box 41141, Lubbock, TX 79409.

Phone: (806) 742-2661

E-mail: housing@ttu.edu

Housing aid website: http://housing.ttu.edu/

Table A—Faculty, Enrollments, and Degrees Granted

Research Specialty	2018–2019 Faculty	Enrollment Spring 2018 Master's	Enrollment Spring 2018 Doctorate	Number of Degrees Granted 2017–2018 (2016–2018) Master's	Number of Degrees Granted 2017–2018 (2016–2018) Terminal Master's	Number of Degrees Granted 2017–2018 (2016–2018) Doctorate
Astrophysics	5	2	9	4(6)	–	–
Atomic, Molecular, & Optical Physics	2	–	–	–	–	–
Biophysics	1	2	5	1(2)	–	1
Condensed Matter Physics	5	4	13	13(25)	–	3(5)
High Energy Physics	6	–	9	2(3)	–	1(2)
Physics and other Science Education	2	1	2	1(1)	–	–
Total	21	9	38	21(37)	–	5(7)
Full-time Grad. Stud.	–	9	38	–	–	–
First-year Grad. Stud.	–	4	6	–	–	–

GRADUATE DEGREE REQUIREMENTS

Master's: The M.S. with Thesis requires a minimum of 24 hours of graduate course work and 6 hours of thesis with a minimum GPA of 3.0. A thesis based on a research problem and a final oral exam over the research problem are required..

Doctorate: A minimum of 60 hours beyond the B.S. degree plus 12 hours of dissertation with a minimum GPA of 3.0. A minimum of 3 years of graduate study beyond the B.S. degree with 1 year of residence beyond the M.S. degree or equivalent is required. After completing the core courses, typically after one year, all candidates must pass the Prelim Qualifying Exam (a written and oral exam over the core curriculum). A dissertation on an original research project and an oral defense of the dissertation are required. Ph.D. degrees with either physics or applied physics options are offered..

Other Degrees: Dissertation may be written in absentia.

Table B—Separately Budgeted Research Expenditures by Source of Support

Source of Support	Departmental Research	Physics-related Research Outside Department
Federal government	$2,247,000	$2,000,000
State/local government		
Non-profit organizations		
Business and industry		
Other	$200,000	
Total	$2,447,000	$2,000,000

Table C—Separately Budgeted Research Expenditures by Research Specialty

Research Specialty	No. of Grants	Expenditures ($)
Astrophysics	18	$655,000
Biophysics	1	$246,000
Condensed Matter Physics	1	$866,000
Particles and Fields	5	$676,000
Total	25	$2,443,000

FACULTY

Distinguished University Professor

Estreicher, Stefan K., Ph.D., Zürich, 1982. Paul Whitfield Horn Professor. *Condensed Matter Physics*. Ab initio calculations, molecular dynamics, heat flow and defects in materials.

Wigmans, Richard, Ph.D., Vrije Universiteit Amsterdam, 1975. J.F. Bucy and O. Greer Bucy Chair in Physics. *High Energy Physics*. Experimental high-energy particle physics; particle detectors; calorimetry; astrophysics; cosmology.

Chair Professor

Akchurin, Nural, Ph.D., University of Iowa, 1990. Department Chair. *High Energy Physics*. Experimental particle physics at the LHC and particle detectors.

Professor

Duncan, Robert V., Ph.D., University of California, Santa Barbara, 1988. *Condensed Matter Physics*. Experimental low-temperature physics.

Grave de Peralta, Luis, Ph.D., Texas Tech University, 2000. *Electrical Engineering*. Bio-nano-photonics, nanotechnology, plasmonics, quantum optics, nanoscopy.

Huang, Juyang, Ph.D., State University of New York at Buffalo, 1987. *Biophysics*. Experimental and theoretical membrane biophysics; liposome technology; drug delivery; biochip; fluoresence microscopy; X-ray diffraction; Monte Carlo simulations.

Lee, Sung-Won, Ph.D., University of Glasgow, 2000. *High Energy Physics*. Experimental Particle Physics; precision measurements of Standard Model physics and searches for physics beyond the Standard Model at CERN LHC.

Maccarone, Thomas J., Ph.D., Yale University, 2001. Graduate Advisor. *Astrophysics*. X-ray binaries, globular clusters, binary stellar evolution.

Myles, Charles W., Ph.D., Washington University, 1973. Graduate Advisor. *Condensed Matter Physics*. Theoretical and computational materials physics, with emphasis on semiconductor materials. Clathrate materials and thermoelectrics. Electronic properties of defects, electronic banstructures, properties of semiconductor alloys. High electric field transport. Molecular Dynamics and Monte Carlo computer simulations.

Owen, Benjamin J., Ph.D., California Institute of Technology, 1998. *Astrophysics, Relativity & Gravitation.* Gravitational waves and relativistic astrophysics.

Romano, Joseph, Ph.D., Syracuse University, 1991. *Astrophysics.*

Associate Professor

Corsi, Alessandra, Ph.D., Sapienza University of Rome, 2007. *Astrophysics.* Gamma-ray bursts, Supernovae, LIGO data analysis.

Gibson, Thomas L., Ph.D., University of Oklahoma, 1982. Quantum collision theory; low-energy positron-molecule collisions; concurrent computational techniques; Monte Carlo simulations.

Glab, Wallace L., Ph.D., University of Illinois at Urbana-Champaign, 1984. Undergraduate advisor. Experimental atomic and molecular physics; laser spectroscopy of excited states of atoms and molecules; multiphoton ionization and photoelectron spectroscopy of small molecules.

Kunori, Suichi, Ph.D., Tohoku University, 1981. *High Energy Physics.* Experimental High Energy Physics.

Lamp, C. David, Ph.D., University of Missouri, Columbia, 1984. *Condensed Matter Physics, Physics and other Science Education.* Experimental solid state physics; uniaxial stress transient spectroscopy; semiconductor materials; materials science; physics education; science training for secondary school teachers.

Sanati, Mahdi, Ph.D., University of Cincinnati, 1999. Graduate Recruiter. *Condensed Matter Physics, Materials Science, Metallurgy.* Theoretical condensed matter physics; structural phase transformation in solids; solitons in physical systems.

Thacker, Beth A., Ph.D., Cornell University, 1990. *High Energy Physics.* Physics Education Research; assessment, modern and quantum physics, pedagogy.

Volobouev, Igor, Ph.D., Southern Methodist University, 1997. *High Energy Physics.* Jet reconstruction algorithms; Advanced data analysis techniques for HEP; CMS experiment at CERN.

Assistant Professor

Scaringi, Simone, Ph.D., University of Southampton, 2010. *Astrophysics.*

Whitbeck, Andrew, Ph.D., Johns Hopkins, 2013. *High Energy Physics.*

Professor Emeritus

Borst, Walter L., Ph.D., University of California, Berkeley, 1968.

Hatfield, Lynn L., Ph.D., Arkansas, 1966.

Lichti, Roger L., Ph.D., University of Illinois, 1972.

Thomas, Henry C., Ph.D., Vanderbilt University, 1950.

Research Professor

Lodhi, M. A. K., Ph.D., London, England, 1963. Nuclear and Particle Physics; Space Science; New and Renewable Energy.

Distinguished Adjunct Professor

Hussain, Fazle, Ph.D., Stanford University, 1969. *Fluids, Rheology.* Fluid mechanics.

Adjunct Professor

Bławdziewicz, Jerzy, Ph.D., University of Warsaw, 1986. *Biophysics.* Physics of soft matter and biophysics.

Cheng, Kwan Hon, Ph.D., University of Waterloo, 1983. Experimental biophysics; time-resolved fluorescence spectroscopy; membranes; nuclear magnetic resonance imaging; biochips.

Poirier, L. William, Ph.D., University of California, Berkeley, 1997. *Chemical Physics.* Theoretical and Computational Chemistry and Chemical Physics.

Quitevis, Edward L., Ph.D., Harvard University, 1981. Joint Professor. Ultrafast spectroscopy; nonlinear optics; photophysics; molecular aggregates; membranes and micelles; liquids. (Chemistry.).

Adjunct Associate Professor

Bernussi, Ayrton A., Ph.D., State University of Campinas, 1990. *Condensed Matter Physics, Nano Science and Technology.* Nanophotonics, Plasmonics, Sub-wavelength microscopy, and THz spectroscopy.

Fan, Zhaoyang, Ph.D., Northwestern University, 2001. *Materials Science, Metallurgy.* Wide bandgap semiconductors and Nanomaterials for energy applications.

Pal, Ranadip, Ph.D., Texas A&M University, 2007. *Electrical Engineering.* Bioinformatics and biophysics.

DEPARTMENTAL RESEARCH SPECIALTIES AND STAFF

Theoretical

Applied Physics. New and renewable energy sources; power conversion systems for space use. Photoconductive switch simulations. Duncan, Lodhi.

Astrophysics. Neutron star structure, oscillations, and microphysics. Owen, Romano.

Atomic, Molecular, & Optical Physics. Theory of vibration-rotation fine structure and intramolecular forces. Low-energy electron-molecule collisions; Computational techniques. Gibson, Glab.

Biophysics. Cell membranes; cholesterol domains; multibody interactions; anomalous diffusion; Monte Carlo and dynamic simulations. Huang.

Condensed Matter Physics. Defects in semiconductors, molecular dynamics and Monte Carlo simulations; breakdown in semiconductors; impurities and complexes in semiconductors; molecular orbital theory. Thermal conductivity of nano wires. High field transport, clathrates and thermoelectrics. Structural phase transformation in solids. Estreicher, Myles, Sanati.

Physics and other Science Education. Assessment, student understanding of Quantum Mechanics and Modern Physics, curriculum development, comparison of students taught traditionally and non-traditionally, science training for secondary school teachers. Lamp, Thacker.

Relativity & Gravitation. Gravitational wave emission, binary black holes. Owen.

Experimental

Astrophysics. The astrophysics group at Texas Tech has a variety of streams of research on extreme environment astrophysics. We pursue observations which are multi-wavelength (spanning the range from radio through TeV) and multi-messenger (with a strong level of participation in LIGO). We have strong efforts in supernovae, gamma-ray bursts, studies of compact objects, and studies of the lowest density stellar populations – ultrafaint dwarf galaxies – as well as the highest density stellar populations – globular clusters. Corsi, Maccarone, Owen, Scaringi.

Biophysics. Molecular spectroscopy of membranes; quantitative magnetic resonance imaging; membrane electrophysiology, Liposome technology; fluorescence microscopy; X-ray diffraction; drug delivery system; biochip conformal radiation dosimetry. Huang.

Condensed Matter Physics. Semiconductor materials, nanoscience; optical properties; Raman scattering. Photonics; Plasmonics. Bernussi, Fan, Grave de Peralta.

High Energy Physics. Compact Muon Solenoid (CMS)experiment at CERN; Advanced research and development in calorimetry and other particle detectors; Massive data analyses and development of novel algorithms for particle identification in collider experiments. Akchurin, Kunori, Lee, Volobouev, Whitbeck, Wigmans.

Nano Science and Technology. Bio-nano-photonics, nanotechnology, plasmonics, quantum optics, nanoscopy, wide band- gap semiconductors and nanomaterials for energy applications, sub-wavelength microscopy, and THz spectroscopy. Bernussi, Fan, Grave de Peralta.

View additional information about this department at www.gradschoolshopper.com. Check out the "Why Choose Us?" section, find out more about the department's culture and get links to social media networks.

UNIVERSITY OF TEXAS AT ARLINGTON

DEPARTMENT OF PHYSICS

Arlington, Texas 76019
http://www.uta.edu/physics

General University Information
President: Vistasp M. Karbhari
Dean of Graduate School: Raymond Jackson
University website: http://www.uta.edu/
School Type: Public
Setting: Urban
Total Faculty: 1,352
Total Graduate Faculty: 590
Total number of Students: 41,933
Total number of Graduate Students: 12,327

Department Information
Department Chairman: Prof. Alex Weiss, Chair
Department Contact: Stacey Cody, Administrative Assistant II
  Total full-time faculty: 28
  Total number of full-time equivalent positions: 34
  Full-Time Graduate Students: 57
  Female Full-Time Graduate Students: 15
  First-Year Graduate Students: 11
  Female First-Year Students: 3
  Total Post Doctorates: 11

Department Address
502 Yates Street
108 Science Hall
Arlington, TX 76019
Phone: (817) 272-2266
Fax: (817) 272-3637
E-mail: scody@uta.edu
Website: http://www.uta.edu/physics

ADMISSIONS

Admission Contact Information
Address admission inquiries to: Graduate Admissions, Box 19167, Arlington, TX 76019
Phone: (817) 272-2090
E-mail: zhang@uta.edu; huda@uta.edu
Admissions website: http://www.uta.edu/admissions/contact/index.php

Application deadlines
Fall admission:
U.S. students: June 15   *Int'l. students*: April 1
Spring admission:
U.S. students: October 15   *Int'l. students*: September 15

Application fee
U.S. students: $40   *Int'l. students*: $90
Student seeking an assistantship should apply by January 31 to ensure full consideration.

Admissions information
For Fall of 2017:
  Number of applicants: 90
  Number admitted: 13
  Number enrolled: 13

Admission requirements
Bachelor's degree requirements: Bachelor's degree in physics or in related fields with a minimum 3.0 GPA on a 4.0 scale is required.
Minimum undergraduate GPA: 3.0

GRE requirements
The GRE is required.
  Quantitative score: 150
  Verbal score: 144
  Mean GRE score range (25th–75th percentile): 310
Successful candidates for assistantships typically score >160 on the Quantitative and >305 total.

Subjective GRE requirements
The Subjective GRE is not required.

TOEFL requirements
The TOEFL exam is required for students from non-English-speaking countries.
  PBT score: 550
  iBT score: 79
An applicant whose native language is not English is not required to submit a TOEFL, TOEFL iBT, TSE or IELTS for admission purposes if her or she holds a bachelor's or master's degree from an accredited U. S. instituion.

Other admissions information
Undergraduate preparation assumed: Junior and senior physics at the level suggested by the following textbooks: Carter, Statistical Physics; Wangsness, Electromagnetic Fields; Gasiorowicz, Quantum Mechanics; Marion, Classical Dynamics of Particle Systems; Riley, Hobson and Bence, Mathematical Methods for Physics and Engineering.

TUITION

Tuition year 2018–19:
Tuition for in-state residents
  Full-time students: $4,305 per semester
Tuition for out-of-state residents
  Full-time students: $9,180 per semester
Teaching or research assistants employed half-time are charged the same rate as in-state residents. See Graduate Catalog for more detailed breakdown. The department pays $3549.00 of the tuition costs per semester for students with GTA or GRA (or about 80%). The department pays 100% of the tuition costs for students receiving GAANN fellowships.
Credit hours per semester to be considered full-time: 9
Deferred tuition plan: Yes
Health insurance: Available.
Academic term: Semester
Number of first-year students who received full tuition waivers: 9
Number of first-year students who received partial tuition waivers: 2

Teaching Assistants, Research Assistants, and Fellowships
Number of first-year
  Teaching Assistants: 9
  Research Assistants: 2
  Fellowship students: 4

Average stipend per academic year
Teaching Assistant: $18,000
Research Assistant: $18,000
Fellowship student: $18,000
Ph.D. students typically receive an additional $6000 for the Summer resulting in a total of $24,000. for the calendar year. The department pays $3549.00 of the tuition costs per semester for students with GTA or GRA (or about The department pays 100% of the tuition costs for students receiving GAANN fellowships.

FINANCIAL AID

Application deadlines
Fall admission:
U.S. students: February 1   *Int'l. students*: February 1
Spring admission:
U.S. students: November 1   *Int'l. students*: November 1

Loans
Loans are available for U.S. students.
Loans are not available for international students.
GAPSFAS application required: No
FAFSA application required: No

For further information
Address financial aid inquiries to: Office of Financial Aid and Scholarships, Davis Hall, RM 252, 701 S. Nedderman Dr. Box 19199 Arlington, TX 76019.
Phone: (817) 272-3561 FAX: (817) 272-3555
Financial aid website: http://www.uta.edu/fao/scholarships/deadline.php

HOUSING

Availability of on-campus housing
Single students: Yes
Married students: Yes

For further information
Address housing inquiries to: Housing Office, 210 University Center.
Phone: (817) 272-2791
E-mail: housing@uta.edu
Housing aid website: http://www.uta.edu/housing/index.php

Table A—Faculty, Enrollments, and Degrees Granted

Research Specialty	2017–18 Faculty	Enrollment Fall 2017 Mas-ter's	Enrollment Fall 2017 Doc-torate	Number of Degrees Granted 2017–18 (2014–18) Mas-ter's	Number of Degrees Granted 2017–18 (2014–18) Terminal Master's	Number of Degrees Granted 2017–18 (2014–18) Doc-torate
Astronomy	1	–	4	–	–	–(1)
Astrophysics	2	–	5	–	–	–(2)
Atmosphere, Space Physics, Cosmic Rays	2	–	6	–	–(1)	1(2)
Experiment	6	–	9	–	–(1)	–(3)
High Energy Physics	9	–	16	–(1)	1(4)	1(5)
Materials	2	–	6	–	–(1)	–(5)
Medical, Health Physics	3	–	5	–(1)	–(1)	–(2)
Nano Science and Technology	2	–	5	–	–	–(2)
Optics	1	–	3	–	–	–(1)
Physics and other Science Education	1	–	1	–	–	1(2)
Relativity & Gravitation	1	–	2	–	–	1(1)
Total	26	–	62	–(2)	–(8)	4(26)
Full-time Grad. Stud.	–	–	62	–	–	–
First-year Grad. Stud.	–	–	14	–	–	–

GRADUATE DEGREE REQUIREMENTS

Master's: The Master of Science in physics requires a minimum of 30 credit hours, of which 24 hours, including six hours of thesis, will be in physics, and six may be selected from physics, mathematics, chemistry, geology, biology or engineering as approved by the Graduate Advisor. The completion of this degree normally takes two years. Foreign language, comprehensive, and qualifying exams are not required. However, a grade point average of 3.0 (on a scale of 4.0 maximum) must be maintained for all work undertaken as a graduate student. The student must conduct research leading to a thesis which must be defended in an oral exam. Thesis may be written in absentia. Non-thesis option is also available.

Doctorate: For the completion of the degree, the student must 1) demonstrate competence in a minimum of 39 credit hours of core courses in physics, chosen under the guidance of the supervising committee, and approved in advance by the Graduate Studies Committee; 2) complete 9 credit hours of internship or six credit hours of research with a written report and three hours of Applied Physics course; 3) pass qualifying and comprehensive examinations; and 4) conduct research leading to a dissertation which must be defended in an oral exam. Dissertation may be written in absentia.

SPECIAL EQUIPMENT, FACILITIES, OR PROGRAMS

Students conduct experiments both at UTA and at national and international laboratories including the Fermi National Laboratory, CERN Large Hadron Collider, Brookhaven National Laboratory and the IceCube Neutrino Observatory. Detector develop center with multiple high purity liquid argon purifier and a Pico second timing test facility.

Condensed matter experimental facilities include Four-probe electrical conductivity measurement system with closed-cycle liquid helium cryostat, photoemission spectrometer, photoluminescence spectrometer with single molecule capability, positron annihilation induced Auger electron spectroscopy, Raman spectrometer, scanning Auger microbe, thin-film deposition systems, variable temperature vibrating sample magnetometers, scanning electron microscopy with polarization analysis (SEMPA), alternating gradient magnetometer (AGM), magnetic properties measurement system (MPMS), and arc melting furnace, thermal particle analyzer, rapid thermal processor (RTP) and high-energy physics detector construction facility.

Computational facilities at UTA include high-performance computing environment that combines multiple independent systems connected via a private high-speed network. The high-energy physics group of the physics department group has established a grid based super computing system with 9000 cores and 6.5 petabytes of storage to support data simulation and analysis from the ATLAS experiment at CERN.

Table B—Separately Budgeted Research Expenditures by Source of Support

Source of Support	Departmental Research	Physics-related Research Outside Department
Federal government	$7,200,000	
State/local government	$500,000	
Non-profit organizations		
Business and industry		
Other		
Total	$7,700,000	

Table C—Separately Budgeted Research Expenditures by Research Specialty

Research Specialty	No. of Grants	Expenditures ($)
Astrophysics	6	$500,000
Atmosphere, Space Physics, Cosmic Rays	6	$1,400,000
Condensed Matter Physics	8	$1,800,000
High Energy Physics	7	$4,000,000
Total	27	$7,700,000

FACULTY

Professor

Brandt, Andrew, Ph.D., University of California, Los Angeles, 1992. Associate Chair. *High Energy Physics.* Experimental high-energy physics.

Chen, Wei, Ph.D., Peking University, 1992. *Biophysics, Condensed Matter Physics.* Nanobiophysics.

Cuntz, Manfred, Ph.D., Heidelberg University, 1988. Coordinator of Astronomy Teaching Programs. *Astronomy, Astrophysics, Plasma and Fusion, Solar Physics.* Theoretical astrophysics; observational astronomy, astrobiology.

De, Kaushik, Ph.D., Brown University, 1988. Director of the Center of Excellence in High Energy Physics. *High Energy Physics.* Experimental high-energy physics.

Deng, Yue, Ph.D., University of Michigan, 2006. *Atmosphere, Space Physics, Cosmic Rays.* Space Physics.

Koymen, Ali R., Ph.D., University of Michigan, 1984. *Solid State Physics, Surface Physics.* Surface physics; surface magnetism; positron physics.

López, Ramón E., Ph.D., Rice University, 1986. *Climate/Atmospheric Science, Physics and other Science Education, Planetary Science, Plasma and Fusion.* Space physics; physics and science education.

Liu, Ping, Ph.D., University of Amsterdam, 1994. *Condensed Matter Physics.* Condensed matter physics; magnetic materials; nano-materials.

Musielak, Zdzislaw, Ph.D., University of Gdansk, Poland, 1980. *Astrophysics, Cosmology & String Theory, Mechanics, Particles and Fields, Planetary Science, Relativity & Gravitation, Solar Physics.* Theoretical astrophysics; cosmology; chaos and nonlinear physics.

Nygren, David R., Ph.D., University of Washington, 1967. *Biophysics, Cosmology & String Theory, High Energy Physics, Nuclear Physics, Particles and Fields.* High Energy Physics, Neutrino Physics, High Energy Physics Detector Development.

Sharma, Suresh C., Ph.D., Brandeis University, 1976. *Condensed Matter Physics, Optics, Surface Physics.* Positron physics; high-pressure physics; surface science; nano-materials.

Weiss, Alex, Ph.D., Brandeis University, 1983. Department Chair. *Condensed Matter Physics, Physics and other Science Education, Physics of Beams, Solid State Physics, Surface Physics.* Positron physics; surface physics.

White, Andrew P., Ph.D., University of London, 1972. *High Energy Physics.* Experimental high-energy physics.

Yu, Jaehoon, Ph.D., Stony Brook University, 1993. *High Energy Physics.* Experimental high-energy physics.

Zhang, Qiming, Ph.D., SISSA, Trieste, Italy, 1989. *Computational Physics, Condensed Matter Physics, Materials Science, Metallurgy.* Theoretical condensed matter.

Associate Professor

Farbin, Amir, Ph.D., University of Maryland, 2004. *High Energy Physics.* Experimental high-energy physics.

Huda, Muhammad, Ph.D., University of Texas, Arlington, 2004. *Chemical Physics, Computational Physics, Condensed Matter Physics, Materials Science, Metallurgy.* Condensed matter theory.

Jin, Mingwu, Ph.D., Illinois Institute of Technology, 2007. *Biophysics.* Image science; Biomedical applications including X-ray/emission tomography and magnetic resonance imaging; image reconstruction, processing and analysis for stationary and dynamic data; statistical data analysis.

Ngai, Joseph, Ph.D., University of Alberta, 2001. *Condensed Matter Physics, Materials Science, Metallurgy, Solid State Physics.* Experimental condensed matter physics.

Park, Sangwook, Ph.D., Purdue University, 1998. *Astronomy, Astrophysics.* Astrophysics.

Assistant Professor

Asaadi, Jonathan, Ph.D., Texas A & M University, 2012. *High Energy Physics.*

Chi, Yujie, Ph.D., Peking University, 2014. *Biophysics, Computational Physics, Medical, Health Physics.* Medical Physics Radiation Oncology.

Hadavand, Haleh, Ph.D., University of California, 2005. *High Energy Physics, Medical, Health Physics.* High energy physics.

Jones, Benjamin J.P., Ph.D., Massachusetts Institute of Technology, 2015. *High Energy Physics, Nuclear Physics, Particles and Fields.* Development of apparatus to detect Neutrinoless Double Beta Decay. Experimental Particle Physics.

Shahmoradi, Amir, Ph.D., The University of Texas Austin, 2015. *Astronomy, Computational Physics, Computer Science.* Data Science.

Welling, Daniel T., Ph.D., University of Michigan, 2009. *Atmosphere, Space Physics, Cosmic Rays, Computer Science, Solar Physics.* Space Physics, Modeling.

DEPARTMENTAL RESEARCH SPECIALTIES AND STAFF

Theoretical

Astrophysics. Cuntz, Musielak, Park.

Atmosphere, Space Physics, Cosmic Rays. Deng, López, Welling.

Biophysics. Chen, Chi, Jin, Shahmoradi, Yu.

Computational Physics. De, Deng, Huda, Jin, López, Shahmoradi, Welling, Zhang.

Condensed Matter Physics. Koymen, Liu, Ngai, Sharma, Weiss.

Cosmology & String Theory. Cuntz, Musielak, Park.

High Energy Physics. Asaadi, Brandt, De, Farbin, Hadavand, Nygren, White, Yu.

Surface Physics. Koymen, Ngai, Weiss.

Experimental

Medical, Health Physics. Chen, Chi, Jin, Nygren, Yu.

Optics. Sharma.

THE UNIVERSITY OF TEXAS AT AUSTIN

DEPARTMENT OF PHYSICS

Austin, Texas 78712
http://ph.utexas.edu

General University Information

President: Gregory L. Fenves
Dean of Graduate School: Marvin L. Hackert
University website: https://www.utexas.edu
School Type: Public
Setting: Urban
Total Faculty: 3,081
Total Graduate Faculty: 1,956
Total number of Students: 52,186
Total number of Graduate Students: 11,123

Department Information

Department Chairman: Prof. Jack Ritchie, Chair
Department Contact: Matthew F. Ervin, Graduate Program
   Administrator
   Total full-time faculty: 48
   Full-Time Graduate Students: 208
   Female Full-Time Graduate Students: 0
   First-Year Graduate Students: 37
   Female First-Year Students: 5
   Total Post Doctorates: 41

Department Address

2515 Speedway, C1600
Austin, TX 78712
Phone: (512) 471-1664
Fax: (512) 471-9637
E-mail: admissions@physics.utexas.edu
Website: http://ph.utexas.edu

ADMISSIONS

Admission Contact Information

Address admission inquiries to: Admissions Coordinator, Department of Physics, RLM 5.208, University of Texas at Austin, 2515 Speedway, C1600, Austin, TX 78712-1081
Phone: (512) 471-1664
E-mail: admissions@physics.utexas.edu
Admissions website: http://www.ph.utexas.edu/grad-admissions.php

Application deadlines

Fall admission:
U.S. students: December 1   *Int'l. students*: December 1
Spring admission:
U.S. students: October 1   *Int'l. students*: October 1

Application fee

U.S. students: $65   *Int'l. students*: $90

Admissions information

For Fall of 2018:
   Number of applicants: 311
   Number admitted: 67
   Number enrolled: 29

Admission requirements

Bachelor's degree requirements: Bachelor's degree is required.
Minimum undergraduate GPA: 3.0

GRE requirements

The GRE is required.

Subjective GRE requirements

The Subjective GRE is required.
No specific score is required, just sufficient comprehension.

TOEFL requirements

The TOEFL exam is required for students from non-English-speaking countries.
   PBT score: 550
   iBT score: 120

Other admissions information

Additional requirements: The GRE Physics Subject Test is required. The average GRE advanced score for 2011–12 admission was 819. The TOEFL is absolutely required for foreign applicants and cannot be waived, substituted, or delayed. Foreign students who accept teaching assistantships must pass an English language proficiency assessment before any appointment can be made.
Undergraduate preparation assumed: Mechanics at the level of Halliday, Resnick, and Krane, Physics, Vol. 1; electricity and magnetism at the level of Halliday, Resnick, and Krane, Physics, Vol. 2; thermodynamics at the level of Kittel and Kroemer, Thermal Physics; atomic physics at the level of Morrison, Estle, and Lane, Quantum States of Atoms, Molecules and Solids; quantum mechanics at the level of Morrison, Understanding More Quantum Physics.

TUITION

Tuition year 2016–2017:
Tuition for in-state residents
   Full-time students: $8,350 annual
Tuition for out-of-state residents
   Full-time students: $16,454 annual
All required fees included in the above amounts. Other fees may vary.
Credit hours per semester to be considered full-time: 9
Deferred tuition plan: Yes
Health insurance: Available
Academic term: Semester
Number of first-year students who received full tuition waivers: 37

Teaching Assistants, Research Assistants, and Fellowships

Number of first-year
   Teaching Assistants: 25
   Research Assistants: 4
   Fellowship students: 3
Average stipend per academic year
   Teaching Assistant: $27,000
   Research Assistant: $27,000
   Fellowship student: $27,000

FINANCIAL AID

Application deadlines

Fall admission:
U.S. students: December 1   *Int'l. students*: December 1

Loans

Loans are available for U.S. students.
Loans are available for international students.
GAPSFAS application required: No
FAFSA application required: No

For further information

Address financial aid inquiries to: Admissions Coordinator, Department of Physics, The University of Texas at Austin, RLM 5.208, Austin, TX 78712-1081.
E-mail: admissions@physics.utexas.edu

HOUSING

Availability of on-campus housing

Single students: Yes
Married students: No

For further information

Address housing inquiries to: Division of Housing and Food Service, P.O. Box 7666, The University of Texas at Austin, Austin, TX 78712-7666.
Phone: (512) 471-3136
Housing aid website: http://www.utexas.edu/student/housing/

Table A—Faculty, Enrollments, and Degrees Granted

Research Specialty	2017–2018 Faculty	Enrollment Fall 2018 Master's	Enrollment Fall 2018 Doctorate	Number of Degrees Granted 2017–18 (2013–17) Master's	Number of Degrees Granted 2017–18 (2013–17) Terminal Master's	Number of Degrees Granted 2017–18 (2013–17) Doctorate
Atomic, Molecular, & Optical Physics	8	16	33	–(1)	2(4)	4(22)
Biophysics	2	4	10	–(1)	–(2)	–(5)
Condensed Matter Physics	15	28	42	–(2)	1(1)	17(30)
Cosmology & String Theory	7	8	14	1	–(3)	2(17)
High Energy Physics	5	4	10	–	–(1)	1(6)
Nonlinear Dynamics	2	1	4	–	–	3(5)
Particles and Fields	2	–	–	–	–	–(2)
Plasma and Fusion	4	6	17	–(1)	–	3(20)
Relativistic Heavy Ion Physics	2	1	3	–	–	–(1)
Relativity & Gravitation	1	–	2	–	–	3(2)
Statistical & Thermal Physics	1	–	1	–	–(1)	–(2)
Non-specialized	–	–	–	–	–	–
Total	49	68	136	1(5)	3(12)	33(110)
Full-time Grad. Stud.	–	67	133	–	–	–
First-year Grad. Stud.	–	27	–	–	–	–

GRADUATE DEGREE REQUIREMENTS

Master's: Master of Arts: The time required for the degrees will average about one calendar year plus one semester for a student with a strong undergraduate background. Requirements include 30 semester hours with a "B" average. Eighteen to 24 semester hours, including the thesis, must be in the major program. The minor, which is obligatory, consists of a minimum of six hours in a supporting subject or subjects outside the major program. Each program must include at least 30 semester hours of graduate work, including the thesis. All completed work included in the degree program at the time of admission to candidacy must have been taken within the previous six years. The Master of Science in Applied Physics: This degree is designed to provide students with a broad background in physics and related fields, with an emphasis on those aspects of the science most used in an industrial setting. The required physics courses include PHY 380N, 387K, and 389K, a course in the physics of sensors, and a technical seminar. A thesis is also required. The supporting work must be in engineering, chemistry, or geological sciences.

Doctorate: A student must fulfill the following requirements to be admitted to candidacy for the Ph.D. degree in Physics: (1) fulfill the core course requirements described below; (2) show evidence of exposure to modern methods of experimental physics–this exposure may be gained in a senior-level laboratory course taken by the student as an undergraduate and approved by the graduate adviser and the chairman of the Graduate Studies Committee by previous participation in an experimental program or in Physics 380N; and (3) fulfill the oral examination requirement described below. Core courses: During the first two years of graduate studies, the student must take four core courses: Classical Mechanics (385K), Statistical Mechanics (385L), Electromagnetism I (387K) or Electromagnetism II (387L), and Quantum Mechanics I (389K) or Quantum Mechanics II (389L). The student must earn an official grade of at least "B" in each course and must maintain a grade point average of at least 3.30 in the four courses. The student may ask for the grade he or she earns in Physics 380N to be substituted for the grade in one of the core courses when the average is computed. A well-prepared student may seek to fulfill the core course requirement by earning satisfactory grades on the final examinations for some of these courses rather than by registering for them; in this case, the student does not receive graduate credit for these courses and the grade is not counted toward the required average. Oral qualifying examination: After satisfying the first two requirements above, and within 27 months of entering the program, the student must take an oral qualifying examination. The examination consists of a presentation before a committee of four physics faculty members, one of whom is a member of the Graduate Studies Subcommittee. The presentation is open to all interested parties. It is followed by a question-and-answer period restricted to the student and the committee. The questions during this session are directed to clarifying the presentation and determining whether the student has a solid grasp of the basic material needed for research in his or her specialization. The student passes the examination by obtaining a positive vote from at least three of the four faculty members on the oral qualifying committee. Each program of work for the doctoral degree must include at least four advanced courses in physics; a list of acceptable courses is maintained by the Graduate Studies Subcommittee. The program must also include three courses outside of the student's area of specialization; one of these must be an advanced physics course, another must be outside of the Department of Physics, and the third may be either an advanced physics course or a course outside of the Department of Physics. A dissertation is required of every candidate, followed by a final oral examination covering the dissertation and the general field of the dissertation.

SPECIAL EQUIPMENT, FACILITIES, OR PROGRAMS

Modern facilities for graduate study and research include a large-scale cryogenic laboratory; nuclear magnetic and electron paramagnetic resonance laboratories; extensive facilities for tunneling and force microscopy and nanostructure characterization, SQUID magnetometry, and electron spectroscopy; well-equipped laboratories in optical spectroscopy, quantum optics, femtosecond spectroscopy and diagnostics, and electron-atom and surface scattering; and facilities including a table-top 100-terawatt laser for strong-field physics studies for turbulent flow and nonlinear dynamics experiments and two petawatt lasers (one Ti-sapphire providing 30J in 30fs and another glass laser at 200J in 150fs).

Plasma physics experiments are conducted at the major national tokamaks in Boston and San Diego and on the local machine, the Helimak. Experiments in high-energy heavy ion nuclear and particle physics are conducted at large accelerator facilities such as Brookhaven National Laboratory (New York), Fermi National Laboratory (Illinois), and Germany's Deutsches Electron Synchrotron.

Theoretical work in plasma physics, condensed matter physics, acoustics, nonlinear dynamics, relativity, astrophysics, statistical mechanics, and particle theory is conducted within the Department of Physics.

Students have access to excellent computer and library facilities, including Ranger, the 10th fastest computer at 504 Tflops.

The Department maintains and staffs a machine shop, student workshop, low-temperature and high-vacuum shop, and an electronics design and fabrication shop.

Table B—Separately Budgeted Research Expenditures by Source of Support

Source of Support	Departmental Research	Physics-related Research Outside Department
Federal government	$13,018,485	
State/local government	$1,735,176	
Non-profit organizations	$1,086,944	
Business and industry	$84,398	
Other	$1,289,191	
Total	**$17,214,194**	

Table C—Separately Budgeted Research Expenditures by Research Specialty

Research Specialty	No. of Grants	Expenditures ($)
Atomic, Molecular, & Optical Physics	11	$1,405,050
Biophysics	8	$657,436
Condensed Matter Physics	51	$4,256,947
Cosmology & String Theory	9	$705,873
Nonlinear Dynamics	2	$290,047
Relativistic Heavy Ion Physics	5	$796,372
Particles and Fields	18	$1,800,824
High Energy Density Science	18	$3,133,129
Plasma and Fusion	27	$4,049,069
Statistical & Thermal Physics	3	$119,446
Total	**152**	**$17,214,193**

FACULTY

Professor

Chelikowsky, J., Ph.D., University of California, Berkeley, 1975. Director, Institute for Computational Engineering Sciences (ICES). *Condensed Matter Physics*. Solid-state physics; computational materials science.

Coker, W. R., Ph.D., University of Georgia, 1966. *Nuclear Physics*. Theoretical nuclear physics, with emphasis on scattering and reactions of hadrons and nuclei at medium energies.

de Lozanne, A. L., Ph.D., Stanford University, 1982. *Condensed Matter Physics*. Low-temperature vacuum-tunneling microscopy.

Demkov, A., Ph.D., University of Arizona, 1995. *Condensed Matter Physics*. Condensed-matter theory; physics of elec-tronic materials, surfaces, and interfaces; thin films and devices; novel materials; quantum transport.

Dicus, D. A., Ph.D., University of California, Los Angeles, 1968. *Particles and Fields*. Field theory of strong, weak, and electromagnetic interactions; astrophysical implications of the weak force.

Distler, J., Ph.D., Harvard University, 1987. *Cosmology & String Theory*. High-energy theory; mathematical physics; string theory.

Ditmire, T., Ph.D., University of California, Davis, 1995. Director, Texas Center for High-Intensity Laser Science. *Atomic, Molecular, & Optical Physics, Plasma and Fusion*. Intense ultrafast laser interactions.

Downer, M. C., Ph.D., Harvard University, 1983. *Atomic, Molecular, & Optical Physics, Condensed Matter Physics*. Atomic and molecular physics; atomic physics; femtosecond spectroscopy; condensed matter surfaces; high-field atomic and plasma physics.

Erskine, J. L., Ph.D., University of Washington, 1973. *Condensed Matter Physics*. Experimental solid-state physics; surface physics; magnetism.

Fink, M., Ph.D., Technische Hochschule Karlsruhe, 1966. *Atomic, Molecular, & Optical Physics*. Electron diffraction.

Fischler, W., Ph.D., Université Libre de Bruxelles, 1976. *Cosmology & String Theory, Relativity & Gravitation*. Theoretical physics; particle theory; invisible axion and supersymmetry.

Fitzpatrick, R., Ph.D., University of Sussex, 1988. Chair, Graduate Recruitment Committee. *Plasma and Fusion*. Magnetic reconnection and gross plasma instabilities in fusion, terrestrial, and astrophysical contexts.

Gentle, K. W., Ph.D., Massachusetts Institute of Technology, 1962. *Plasma and Fusion*. Experimental plasma physics.

Gleeson, A. M., Ph.D., University of Pennsylvania, 1965. *Acoustics, Particles and Fields, Physics and other Science Education*. Field theory of strong interactions and the physics of superdense matter.

Hazeltine, R., Ph.D., University of Michigan, 1968. *Plasma and Fusion*. Theoretical plasma physics.

Heinzen, D., Ph.D., Massachusetts Institute of Technology, 1988. *Atomic, Molecular, & Optical Physics*. Atomic and molecular physics; laser cooling and atom trapping; Bose-Einstein condensation.

Kaplunovsky, V., Ph.D., Tel Aviv University, 1983. *Cosmology & String Theory*. Particle theory; string phenomenology.

Keto, J. W., Ph.D., University of Wisconsin-Madison, 1972. Graduate Advisor. *Atomic, Molecular, & Optical Physics*. Reactions and radiative processes of excited atoms and molecules; laser spectroscopy high-power lasers.

Lang, K., Ph.D., University of Rochester, 1985. *High Energy Physics*. Rare decay of the K-meson.

MacDonald, A. H., Ph.D., University of Toronto, 1978. *Condensed Matter Physics*. Condensed-matter theory with emphasis on electron-electron interactions.

Marder, M. P., Ph.D., University of California, Santa Barbara, 1986. Co-Director of UTeach. *Condensed Matter Physics, Nonlinear Dynamics and Complex Systems, Physics and other Science Education*. Nonlinear dynamics; statistical physics of solids.

Markert, C., Ph.D., Johann Wolfgang Goethe Universität, 2001. *Nuclear Physics*. Nuclear physics; relativistic heavy-ion physics; the quark-gluon plasma (QGP) phase.

Markert, J. T., Ph.D., Cornell University, 1987. *Condensed Matter Physics, Physics and other Science Education*. Experimental condensed-matter physics; crystal growth; high-Tc materials; magnetic materials; magnetic resonance; magnetic microscopies.

Matzner, R. A., Ph.D., University of Maryland, 1967. *Relativity & Gravitation*. General relativity and cosmology; manifolds with little symmetry; kinetic theory; conservation laws in general relativity; black hole physics and gravitational radiation.

Morrison, P. J., Ph.D., University of California, San Diego, 1979. *Nonlinear Dynamics and Complex Systems, Plasma and Fusion*. Plasma physics.

Niu, Q., Ph.D., University of Washington, 1985. *Condensed Matter Physics*. Field theory of condensed matter; theory of superconductivity; mesoscopic physics; quantum transport and diffusion.

Orbach, Raymond L., Ph.D., University of California - Berkley, 1960. Cockrell Family Chair in Engineering #12, Fellow of the American Physical Society and the American Association for the Advancement of Science. *Energy Sources & Environment, Physics and other Science Education, Theoretical Physics*. Energy-related challenges.

Raizen, M., Ph.D., University of Texas, Austin, 1989. *Atomic, Molecular, & Optical Physics, Nonlinear Dynamics and Complex Systems*. Atomic, molecular, and optical physics; atom optics; quantum chaos.

Reichl, L. E., Ph.D., University of Denver, 1969. Director, Center for Complex Quantum Systems. *Statistical & Thermal Physics*. Nonequilibrium quantum statistical mechanics; Brownian motion; nonlinear dynamics.

Ritchie, J. L., Ph.D., University of Rochester, 1983. Department Chair Director, Center for Particles and Fields. *High Energy Physics*. High-energy/nuclear physics.

Schwitters, R. F., Ph.D., Massachusetts Institute of Technology, 1971. *High Energy Physics*. Experimental high-energy physics detector development and B-physics studies.

Shih, C. K., Ph.D., Stanford University, 1988. *Condensed Matter Physics*. Condensed matter; study of surface properties of microelectronic materials.

Sitz, G. O., Ph.D., Stanford University, 1987. Undergraduate Advisor. *Atomic, Molecular, & Optical Physics*. Experimental atomic and molecular physics; oriented molecules; surface scattering.

Tsoi, M., Ph.D., Universität Konstanz, 1998. *Condensed Matter Physics*. Experimental condensed-matter physics; nanostructures; spintronics.

Weinberg, S., Ph.D., Princeton University, 1957. Nobel Laureate; Director, The Weinberg Theory Group. *Cosmology & String Theory, Relativity & Gravitation*. Theoretical physics.

Associate Professor

Fiete, G. A., Ph.D., Harvard University, 2003. *Condensed Matter Physics*. Theory of quantum matter and correlated electrons at the nanoscale.

Florin, E.-L., Ph.D., Technische Universität Munchen, 1990. Chair, Graduate Welfare Committee. *Biophysics, Nonlinear Dynamics and Complex Systems*. Experimentalist, nonlinear dynamic; biophysics.

Hegelich, Bjorn, Ph.D., Ludwig-Maximilians-Universität München, 2002. *Atomic, Molecular, & Optical Physics, Plasma and Fusion*. Interaction of ultra-intense electromagnetic fields with matter; high-energy density physics; laser-particle acceleration.

Lai, Keji, Ph.D., Princeton University, 2006. *Condensed Matter Physics*. Experimental condensed matter physics; nanoscale electromagnetic imaging; complex oxides; nanomaterials; transport in low-dimensional systems.

Li, X., Ph.D., University of Michigan, 2003. *Atomic, Molecular, & Optical Physics, Condensed Matter Physics*. Experimental condensed-matter physics; femtosecond spectroscopy; phase-sensitive nonlinear optical interactions in semiconductors.

Paban, S., Ph.D., Universidad de Barcelona, 1988. Chair, Graduate Studies Committee. *Cosmology & String Theory*. Quantum mechanics; particle phenomenology; string theory.

Yao, Z., Ph.D., Harvard University, 1997. *Condensed Matter Physics, Physics and other Science Education, Statistical & Thermal Physics*. Nanostructures and mesoscopic physics; condensed-matter physics; experimental physics.

Assistant Professor

Alvarado, José, Ph.D., Massachusetts Institute of Technology, 2013. *Biophysics*. Soft matter; fluid mechanics; active matter.

Andeen, T., Ph.D., Northwestern University, 2008. *High Energy Physics*. Experimental searches for new particles and interactions and investigation of electroweak symmetry breaking; high-speed electronics development for new, large scale particle detectors.

Gordon, Vernita, Ph.D., Harvard University, 2003. *Biophysics*. Experimental biological physics; multicellular systems; the role of physics and spatial structure in developmental and evolutionary systems; biological physics and engineering of membranes.

Kilic, Can, Ph.D., Harvard University, 2006. *Particles and Fields*. Theoretical particle physics; extensions of the Standard Model; collider phenomenology; dark matter models and searches.

Onyisi, Peter, Ph.D., Cornell University, 2008. *High Energy Physics*. Experimental investigation of electroweak symmetry breaking and searches for new particles and interactions; computing with large datasets of structured data.

Potter, Andrew C., Ph.D., Massachusetts Institute of Technology, 2013. *Condensed Matter Physics*. Quantum materials, Topological phases of matter, Strongly correlated electron systems, Non-equilibrium quantum dynamics and many-body localization.

Zimmerman, Aaron, Ph.D.*Relativity & Gravitation*. General Relativity, black holes, gravitational waves, numerical relativity, strong gravity.

Professor Emeritus

Böhm, A., Ph.D., Universität Marburg, 1966. *High Energy Physics, Particles and Fields*. Particle phenomena in terms of algebraic and group-theoretical methods.

Bengtson, R. D., Ph.D., University of Maryland, 1968. *Plasma and Fusion*. Experimental plasma physics; atomic reactions in plasmas.

Berk, H. L., Ph.D., Princeton University, 1964. *Plasma and Fusion*. Theoretical plasma physics; computer simulation of plasmas.

Chiu, C. B., Ph.D., University of California, Berkeley, 1965. *Particles and Fields*. Theoretical particle physics, particularly in quantum chromodynamics; confinement problems; subquark and sublepton models; theories in hadron collisions.

de Wette, F. W., Ph.D., Universiteit Utrecht, 1959. *Condensed Matter Physics*. Theoretical study of structural, thermodynamics, and scattering properties of crystal surfaces.

Drummond, W. E., Ph.D., Stanford University, 1958. *Plasma and Fusion*. Theoretical plasma physics.

Frommhold, L. W., Ph.D., Universität Hamburg, 1959. *Atomic, Molecular, & Optical Physics*. Atomic and molecular physics.

Gavenda, J. D., Ph.D., Brown University, 1959. *Atomic, Molecular, & Optical Physics*. Study of properties of conduction electrons in metals using ultrasonic and electromagnetic waves.

Griffy, T. A., Ph.D., Rice University, 1961. *Condensed Matter Physics*. Theoretical medium-energy physics; underwater acoustics.

Horton, C. W., Ph.D., University of California, San Diego, 1967. *Plasma and Fusion*. Theoretical plasma physics.

Kleinman, L., Ph.D., University of California, Berkeley, 1960. *Condensed Matter Physics*. Solid-state theory; electronic structure of solids, surfaces, and clusters; chemisorption.

McCormick, W. D., Ph.D., Duke University, 1959. *Condensed Matter Physics*. Experimental low-temperature and solid-state physics; phase transitions in solids (critical phenomena); instabilities in nonequilibrium systems.

Moore, C. F., Ph.D., Florida State University, 1964. *Nuclear Physics*. Detection and measurement of the interactions and involvement of the nuclear continuum in scattering experiments; atomic interactions in highly ionized atoms.

Oakes, M. E., Ph.D., University of Florida, 1964. *Physics and other Science Education, Plasma and Fusion*. Theoretical and experimental studies of wave propagation in plasmas.

Riley, P. J., Ph.D., University of Alberta, 1962. *Nuclear Physics*. Experimental studies of the nucleon-nucleon interaction at medium energy; actions in decaying plasmas; environmental effects on spectra.

Schieve, W. C., Ph.D., Lehigh University, 1959. *Statistical & Thermal Physics*. Nonequilibrium statistical mechanics; quantum optics; stochastic processes.

Swift, J. B., Ph.D., University of Illinois, 1968. *Nonlinear Dynamics and Complex Systems*. Studies of nonlinear dynamics; phase transitions.

Swinney, H. L., Ph.D., Johns Hopkins University, 1968. *Nonlinear Dynamics and Complex Systems*. Equilibrium and nonequilibrium phase transitions; dynamics of nonlinear systems.

Thompson, J. C., Ph.D., Rice University, 1956. *Condensed Matter Physics*. Studies of electronic states in disordered systems (metallic and semiconducting) by galvanomagnetic parameters; optical properties; photoemission; the metal-nonmetal transition.

Udagawa, T., Ph.D., Tokyo University of Education, 1962. *Nuclear Physics, Physics and other Science Education*. Theoretical nuclear physics.

DEPARTMENTAL RESEARCH SPECIALTIES AND STAFF

Theoretical

Condensed Matter Physics. Ab initio electronic structure calculations of the physical, electronic, and magnetic (including noncolinear magnetic systems) properties of solids, surfaces, interfaces, and liquids; molecular dynamics calculations of properties of solids, liquids, and crack propagation; density functional theory; Berry phases in polarization theory and spinwave theory; block electrons in magnetic fields, quantum Hall effect; quantum theory of thin-film growth and surface diffusion; theory of mesoscopic phenomena, phonon calculations and lattice dynamics for high Tc superconductors; theory of atom surface interactions; physisorption; chemisorption. Chelikowsky, de Wette, Demkov, Fiete, Gavenda, Kleinman, MacDonald, Marder, McCormick, Niu, Swift, Thompson.

Nonlinear Dynamics. Dynamics of materials, especially fracture and dislocation dynamics; instabilities and turbulence in fluids, granular media, liquid crystals, and chemical reaction-diffusion systems; chaos in low-dimensional dynamical systems. Marder, McCormick, Morrison, Swift, Swinney.

Nuclear Physics. Scattering and reactions of hadrons and nuclei at medium energies; nuclear structure in the low-energy region using neutron-scattering techniques; nuclear structure and reaction mechanism. Coker, C. Markert, Moore, Riley, Udagawa.

Particles and Fields. Phenomenological studies of the properties of matter ranging from medium-energy physics; symmetries in elementary particle physics; field theory of strong interactions and the physics of superdense matter; quantum chromodynamics; confinement problems; subquark and sublepton models; supersymmetry; quantum optics, basic quantum field theory, and quantum mechanics; classical mechanics; particle phenomena in terms of algebraic and group-theoretical methods; electromagnetic interactions. Böhm, Chiu, Dicus, Gleeson.

Physics Education. Curriculum development and evaluation at the university level; science teacher preparation program; computer-based education. Chiu, Gleeson, Marder, Orbach.

Plasma and Fusion. Kinetic theory and transport theory; turbulent heating; collisionless shock waves; plasma turbulence; computer simulation of plasmas; stability theory controlled fusion; plasma dynamics. Berk, Drummond, Fitzpatrick, Hazeltine, Horton, Morrison, Oakes.

Relativity & Gravitation. Quantum theory of space time; techniques of quantization in curved space-time; string theory; path integration; stochastic processes; critical phenomena in gravitational collapse; computational relativity; cosmology; exact solutions in general relativity; conformal properties of space time; manifolds with little symmetry; kinetic theory; conservation laws in general relativity; black hole physics; black hole interactions; gravitational radiation; interaction of matter with gravitation. Fischler, Matzner, Schieve, Weinberg, Zimmerman.

Statistical & Thermal Physics. Nonequilibrium statistical physics; thermodynamic processes; nonequilibrium quantum statistical mechanics; quantum chaos; mesoscopic physics; nonlinear dynamics; complex systems theory; Brownian motion. Reichl, Schieve.

The Weinberg Theory Group. Research spans the range from studies of physics at the most fundamental level to exploration of phenomenologically relevant current issues in elementary particle physics. On the more fundamental level, the work continues in gravity and quantum cosmology, conformal field theories, superstring theories, and M theory, with special attention to the links between these topics and to the implication of superstring and M theory for effective field theories at accessible energies. Such theories offer the hope of uniting all forces including gravitation in a theory of superstrings. So far, it seems that these theories allow for the first time a satisfactory elimination of the infinities that have plagued all earlier quantum theories of gravitation. Distler, Fischler, Kaplunovsky, Kilic, Matzner, Paban, Weinberg, Zimmerman.

Experimental

Atomic, Molecular, & Optical Physics. Atom optics; quantum transport in optical lattices; quantum chaos with ultracold atoms; ultracold collisions; Bose-Einstein condensation; search for atomic electric dipole moment; state-resolved molecular-surface scattering and gas-surface dynamics; the Raman spectroscopy; electron diffraction; neutrino rest mass experiments; laser spectroscopy of nanoparticles; development of new materials; molecular collision and sonoluminescence; femtosecond spectroscopy; high-power lasers; wake-field accelerators; terawatt lasers; optical properties of nanostructured plasmas at high fields. Ditmire, Downer, Fink, Frommhold, Hegelich, Heinzen, Keto, Li, Raizen, Sitz.

Biophysics. Elastic properties of cells; motility of cells; bacterial competition; dynamics of swimming organisms; biofilms; spatial structures formed through intercellular interactions; adhesion phenomena; cell mechanics; cargo transport in cells; molecular motors (dynamics and regulation); membranes; assembly of biological complexes; diffusive and ballistic Brownian motion; biopolymers; characterization of single biomolecules; microtubule mechanics; yeast mechanics; membrane fusion; thermal noise imaging. Alvarado, Florin, Gordon.

Condensed Matter Physics. Surface and thin-film magnetism; dynamics of magnetization reversal; magnetic switching; Barkhansen noise; domain dynamics; magnetic and electronic effects in ultrathin-film multilayers and nanostructures; normal and superconducting properties of high-temperature superconductors; nonlinear optical response of solids; femtosecond spectroscopy of solid-state systems; nanostructure fabrication and characterization based on scanning tunneling microscopy; intrinsic phenomena at surfaces and interfaces studied by electron diffraction, spectroscopy, atom surface scattering, linear and nonlinear optical spectroscopy; scanning probe techniques, including near-field optical microscopy; thin-film nucleation and growth; cluster physics, mesoscopic phenomena in solids; materials synthesis including novel magnetic and superconducting materials; transport and magnetic characterization; strongly correlated electron systems; mechanical properties of materials including fracture. de Lozanne, Demkov, Downer, Erskine, Lai, Li, Marder, J. Markert, Shih, Tsoi, Yao.

High Energy Physics. Properties of elementary particles, particularly kaons, B-mesons, and neutrinos; rare decays of the kaons; tests of conservation laws and CP violation; B-meson decays; information on CP violation; neutrino oscillation measurements; information on neutrino mass; detector development; applications of particle detectors to medical imaging. Experiments are conducted at national and international accelerator laboratories. Andeen, Lang, Onyisi, Ritchie, Schwitters.

Nonlinear Dynamics and Complex Systems. Pattern formation and chaotic dynamics of diverse systems; planetary fluid dynamics (especially internal gravity waves in the oceans); viscous fingering; crack propagation in amorphous and crystalline solids; rupture in rubber; friction; control of atomic and molecular motion; trapping of different isotopes; trapping and cooling of macroscopic particles (microspheres); dynamics of Brownian motion; stretching and wrinkling of thin sheets and graphene; physics education research (people dynamics). See also, biophysics. Florin, Gordon, Marder, McCormick, Morrison, Raizen, Swinney.

Plasma and Fusion. Plasma turbulence and transport; plasma heating; plasma propulsion; plasma spectroscopy; plasma diagnostics; plasma processing; atomic reactions in plasmas. Bengtson, Ditmire, Downer, Gentle, Hegelich.

Relativistic Heavy Ion Physics. The research focuses on two experiments: (1) E896 (using the AGS at the Brookhaven National Laboratory), a definitive search for the short-lived HO di-baryon, a strangeness $=-2$, 6-quark object predicted by bag models. E896 also searches for other short-lived objects composed of strange hadrons that may be produced in high-energy nucleus-nucleus collisions. (2) STAR [Solenoidal Tracker at RHIC (Relativistic Heavy Ion Collider)] at the Brookhaven National Laboratory to study primordial matter at conditions of extreme temperature and pressure. Such matter is produced through central collisions of circulating beams of Au ions of momenta 100 GeV/c per nucleon (total center-of-momentum energy = 40 TeV). STAR searches for evidence of the formation of a quark-gluon plasma (a phase of nuclear matter in which quarks and gluons are not confined within nucleons or mesons) and for evidence of the restoration of the fundamental chiral symmetry of the strong interaction at high temperature. Both experiments explore the most fundamental physics and chemistry of nature as it may have existed during the early evolution of the Universe (about $10-7-10-6$ seconds after the Big Bang). C. Markert, Moore, Riley.

View additional information about this department at www.gradschoolshopper.com. Check out the "Why Choose Us?" section, find out more about the department's culture and get links to social media networks.

UNIVERSITY OF TEXAS AT DALLAS

PHYSICS DEPARTMENT

Richardson, Texas 75080-3021
http://www.utdallas.edu/physics/

General University Information
President: Richard Benson
Dean of Graduate School: Marion Underwood
University website: http://www.utdallas.edu/
School Type: Public
Setting: Suburban
Total Faculty: 1,150
Total Graduate Faculty: 600
Total number of Students: 29,000
Total number of Graduate Students: 9,000

Department Information
Department Chairman: Prof. Mark Lee, Head
Department Contact: Amanda Hunter, Graduate Program
  Coordinator; PHY 36
  Total full-time faculty: 27
  Total number of full-time equivalent positions: 27
  Full-Time Graduate Students: 82
  Female Full-Time Graduate Students: 12
  First-Year Graduate Students: 18
  Female First-Year Students: 4
  Total Post Doctorates: 12

ADMISSIONS

Admission Contact Information
Address admission inquiries to: Amanda Hunter, Graduate Program Administator, The University of Texas at Dallas, Dept. of Physics PHY36, 800 W. Campbell Rd., Richardson, TX 75080
Phone: (972) 883-2835
E-mail: amanda.hunter1@utdallas.edu
Admissions website: http://www.utdallas.edu/physics/prospective-students/

Application deadlines
Fall admission:
U.S. students: May 1   *Int'l. students*: May 1
Spring admission:
U.S. students: October 1   *Int'l. students*: October 1

Application fee
U.S. students: $50   *Int'l. students*: $100
Application fee may be deferred until acceptance and enrollment.

Admissions information
For Fall of 2018:
  Number of applicants: 78
  Number admitted: 32
  Number enrolled: 18

Admission requirements
Bachelor's degree requirements: Bachelor's degree in physics or a closely related field is required.
Minimum undergraduate GPA: 3.0

GRE requirements
The GRE is required.
  Quantitative score: 155
  Verbal score: 153
  Mean GRE score range (25th–75th percentile): 310-325

Subjective GRE requirements
The Subjective GRE is required.
  Minimum accepted Advanced GRE score: 650
  Mean Advanced GRE score range (25th–75th percentile): 690 - 860
Students applying for MS program do not need a GRE Physics score.

TOEFL requirements
The TOEFL exam is required for students from non-English-speaking countries.
  PBT score: 550
  iBT score: 80
Minimum iBT score of 80 is a University requirement that cannot be waived by the Physics Department.

Other admissions information
Undergraduate preparation assumed: The student applicant should have an undergraduate background that includes the following courses at the level indicated by texts referred to: mechanics at the level of Symon, Mechanics; electromagnetism at the level of Reitz and Milford, Foundations of Electromagnetic Theory; thermodynamics at the level of Kittel, Thermal Physics; quantum mechanics at the level of Griffiths, Introduction to Quantum Mechanics (chapters 1-4). Math preparation up through multivariable calculus, linear algebra, and differential equations.

TUITION

Tuition year 2018–19:
Tuition for in-state residents
  Full-time students: $6,961 per semester
  Part-time students: $1,547 per credit
Tuition for out-of-state residents
  Full-time students: $13,876 per semester
  Part-time students: $2,352 per credit
Tuition and fees are paid by the university for Teaching Assistants and Research Assistants. International students pay $100.00/semester as a fee.
Credit hours per semester to be considered full-time: 9
Deferred tuition plan: Yes
Health insurance: Available at the cost of $2,504 per year.
Other academic fees: International student orientation fee (one-time assessment)$50.00
Academic term: Semester
Number of first-year students who received full tuition waivers: 12

Teaching Assistants, Research Assistants, and Fellowships
Number of first-year
  Teaching Assistants: 12
Average stipend per academic year
  Teaching Assistant: $22,800
  Research Assistant: $22,800
  Fellowship student: $25,000
University Fellowships are open to US citizens and permanent residents on a competitive basis.

FINANCIAL AID

Application deadlines
Fall admission:
U.S. students: March 31   *Int'l. students*: March 15
Spring admission:
U.S. students: November 1   *Int'l. students*: September 1

Loans
Loans are available for U.S. students.
Loans are not available for international students.
GAPSFAS application required: No
FAFSA application required: Yes

For further information
Address financial aid inquiries to: Amanda Hunter, The University of Texas at Dallas, Dept. of Physics PHY36, 800 West Campbell Rd., Richardson, TX 75080.
Phone: (972) 883-2835
E-mail: amanda.hunter1@utdallas.edu
Financial aid website: http://www.utdallas.edu/student/finaid/

HOUSING

Availability of on-campus housing
Single students: Yes
Married students: Yes
Childcare Assistance: No

For further information
Address housing inquiries to: University Village, 2800 Waterview Pkwy, Richardson, TX 75080.
Phone: (972)-883-5561
E-mail: reslife@utdallas.edu
Housing aid website: http://www.utdallas.edu/admissions/graduate/housing-and-location/

Table A—Faculty, Enrollments, and Degrees Granted

Research Specialty	2018–19 Faculty	Enrollment Fall 2018 Master's	Enrollment Fall 2018 Doctorate	Number of Degrees Granted 2017–18 (2013–18) Master's	Number of Degrees Granted 2017–18 (2013–18) Terminal Master's	Number of Degrees Granted 2017–18 (2013–18) Doctorate
ATLAS/IHEP	2	–	2	–(3)	–(1)	–(2)
Carbon Nanotubes, Nanostructured Superconductors	1	1	1	–(8)	1(1)	–(4)
Device & Materials Physics	1	2	4	–(2)	–	1(3)
DNA electronics; NMR	2	–	7	–(2)	–	5(8)
Earth & Planetary Atmospheric Physics	5	–	6	2(8)	–(1)	5(9)
Experiment: Topological Insulators, 2DEGs	3	1	7	–	1	–(2)
Extragalactic, Black Holes	3	2	4	2(5)	–(1)	2(2)
Fast Laser Spectroscopy	1	–	3	–(4)	–(1)	–(2)
General Relativity	1	–	2	1(4)	–(1)	2(5)
Plasmas for Materials Synthesis	1	1	–	–(2)	–	–(1)
Remote Sensing	1	–	4	–(5)	–(1)	1(3)
Theory	4	–	4	2(3)	–(2)	–(4)
Total	**26**	**7**	**46**	**7(46)**	**2(9)**	**16(45)**
Full-time Grad. Stud.	52	16	66	–	–	–
First-year Grad. Stud.	17	2	12	–	–	–

GRADUATE DEGREE REQUIREMENTS

Master's: For the M.S., all students must complete at least 30 hours of graduate physics courses, including a 12-hour "core." The degree is completed either by six hours of research, including a thesis, or by six hours of additional graduate courses.

Doctorate: The Ph.D. students must complete the 24-hour core, a minimum of 3 elective courses, 1 from within his/her area of specialization and 2 selected from different areas within the department plus whatever his/her committee requires. A Ph.D. candidate must pass, in the first year, a written qualifying exam that is presented twice each academic year. Once a dissertation topic has been selected and a faculty committee formed, the student presents a dissertation proposal to his/her committee for approval, presents a seminar, and is given an oral examination on the dissertation topic and related subjects. The student must then complete an acceptable dissertation and present a seminar. A successful defense of the dissertation concludes the requirements for the Ph.D. degree.

Thesis: Thesis may be written in absentia.

SPECIAL EQUIPMENT, FACILITIES, OR PROGRAMS

UT Dallas Alan MacDiarmid NanoTech Institute

William B. Hanson Center for Space Sciences

Texas Analog Center of Excellence

Low-Temperature Center (Helium-4 and Dilution Refrigerator, High-field magnets, Physical Property Measurement System)

Table B—Separately Budgeted Research Expenditures by Source of Support

Source of Support	Departmental Research	Physics-related Research Outside Department
Federal government	$3,574,732	
State/local government		
Non-profit organizations	$203,029	
Business and industry	$54,227	
Other		
Total	**$3,831,988**	

Table C—Separately Budgeted Research Expenditures by Research Specialty

Research Specialty	No. of Grants	Expenditures ($)
Remote Sensing	3	$102,352
Gravitation, Cosmology, & Astrophysics	7	$312,833
Atmosphere, Space Physics, Cosmic Rays	25	$2,223,479
Biophysics	5	$163,395
Experiment and Theory	20	$798,721
High Energy Physics	2	$231,208
Total	**62**	**$3,831,988**

FACULTY

Chair Professor

Heelis, Roderick A., Ph.D., University of Sheffield, 1973. Director of the William B. Hanson Center for Space Sciences. Endowed chair. *Atmosphere, Space Physics, Cosmic Rays*. Plasma processes and electrodynamics in planetary atmospheres and ionospheres; space flight instrumentation.

Malina, Roger, Ph.D., UC Berkeley, 1979. *Applied Physics, Astronomy, Computational Physics, Optics, Other*. Instrumentation for astronomy and space physics; intersection of science and art.

Professor

Anderson, Phillip C., Ph.D., University of Texas, Dallas, 1990. Graduate Advisor. *Atmosphere, Space Physics, Cosmic Rays.* Ionospheric and magnetospheric electrodynamics; space weather; space environment effects on human systems, properties of materials.

Glosser, Robert, Ph.D., University of Chicago, 1967. *Condensed Matter Physics, Medical, Health Physics, Solid State Physics.* Optical properties of solids and biological materials; Raman, modulation, and fluorescence spectroscopies.

Goeckner, Matthew, Ph.D., UCLA. Associate Dean of Natural Sciences and Mathematics. *Applied Physics, Atomic, Molecular, & Optical Physics, Chemical Physics, Plasma and Fusion.* Plasma physics, plasma processing, atomic physics.

Ishak-Boushaki, Mustapha, Ph.D., Queen's University, 2002. *Astrophysics, Computational Physics, Cosmology & String Theory, Relativity & Gravitation.* Classical and modern cosmology; relativity; gravitational lensing (cosmic shear); cosmological models; computer algebra systems applied to relativity.

Izen, Joseph M., Ph.D., Harvard University, 1982. *High Energy Physics, Particles and Fields.* Elementary particles, charm, bottom, and τ decay, e+e−; collider experiments, high-energy physics computing.

Lee, Mark, Ph.D., Stanford University, 1991. Department Head. *Applied Physics, Condensed Matter Physics, Electromagnetism, Engineering Physics/Science, Low Temperature Physics, Nano Science and Technology, Solid State Physics.* Pure and applied condensed matter physics; science and engineering of novel electronic and optical materials; electronic and photonic device engineering.

Lou, Xinchou, Ph.D., State University of New York at Albany, 1989. *High Energy Physics, Particles and Fields.* Elementary particles physics; bottom and charm physics, e+e− colliders; offline software and distributed computing.

Zakhidov, Anvar, Ph.D., Institute of Spectroscopy, U.S.S.R. Academy of Sciences, 1981. Deputy Director of the Nano-Tech Institute. *Applied Physics, Condensed Matter Physics, Low Temperature Physics, Nano Science and Technology, Solid State Physics.* Nanotechnology; photonic crystals; carbon nanotubes; organic molecular crystals.

Zhang, Chuanwei, Ph.D., The University of Texas, Austin, 2005. Associate Department Head ; Graduate Program Head. *Atomic, Molecular, & Optical Physics, Computational Physics, Condensed Matter Physics, Low Temperature Physics, Materials Science, Metallurgy, Nano Science and Technology, Nonlinear Dynamics and Complex Systems, Solid State Physics, Theoretical Physics.* Topological superfluids, superconductors and insulators; ultra-cold atomic gases; quantum computation; graphene.

Associate Professor

Chen, Lunjin, Ph.D., University of California. Los Angeles, 2011. *Atmosphere, Space Physics, Cosmic Rays, Plasma and Fusion.* Magnetospheric physics, Interaction of electromagnetic waves and energetic charge particles in geospace plasma. Modeling of radiation belt dynamics Instability and propagation of plasma waves Applications of plasma waves.

Gartstein, Yuri, Ph.D., Institute for Spectroscopy, USSR Academy of Sciences, 1988. *Condensed Matter Physics, Nano Science and Technology, Solid State Physics, Theoretical Physics.* Condensed matter physics with emphasis on nanoscience; electronic, optical, and transport properties of organic materials.

King, Lindsay J., Ph.D., University of Manchester, 1995. *Astronomy, Astrophysics, Computational Physics, Cosmology & String Theory, Relativity & Gravitation.* Physical cosmology using tools such as gravitational lensing to understand dark matter and dark energy. Computational and theoretical work as well as observations with large telescopes.

Lary, David J., Ph.D., University of Cambridge, 1991. *Applied Physics, Atmosphere, Space Physics, Cosmic Rays, Computational Physics.* Computational and information systems to facilitate discovery and decision support in earth system science.

Malko, Anton V., Ph.D., New Mexico State/Los Alamos National Labs, 2002. Graduate Admissions Chair. *Applied Physics, Atomic, Molecular, & Optical Physics, Condensed Matter Physics, Nano Science and Technology, Optics.* Femtosecond laser spectroscopy of Nanomaterials such as semiconductor quantum dots, wires, and wells; photoluminescence spectroscopy and microscopy; quantum optics; photoluminescence spectroscopy of single nanoparticles; solid-state physics; laser physics.

Rodrigues, Fabiano, Ph.D., Cornell University, 2008. *Atmosphere, Space Physics, Cosmic Rays, Solar Physics.* Atmosphere, Space Physics; cosmic rays, radio remote sensing of the upper atmosphere/ionosphere, ionospheric electrodynamics and irregularities; space weather.

Slinker, Jason D., Ph.D., Cornell University, 2007. Undergraduate Program Head Society of Physics Students Advisor. *Applied Physics, Biophysics, Condensed Matter Physics, Nano Science and Technology.* Organic optoelectronic devices and laboratory assays. Devices include light emitting electrochemical cells and electrochemical biosensors with DNA-modified electrodes.

Assistant Professor

Kesden, Michael H., Ph.D., California Institute of Technology, 2005. *Astrophysics, Cosmology & String Theory, Relativity & Gravitation.* Theoretical astrophysics and relativity; binary black hole formation, evolution, and merger; gravitational wave emission and detection; stellar tidal disruption by supermassive black holes; astrophysical probes of dark-matter dynamics; gravitational lensing of the cosmic microwave background.

Kolodrubetz, Michael, Ph.D., Princeton University, 2012. *Condensed Matter Physics, Solid State Physics, Statistical & Thermal Physics, Theoretical Physics.* Theoretical condensed matter physics; topological states of matter.

Lumata, Lloyd L., Ph.D., Florida State University, 2008. *Biophysics, Medical, Health Physics.* Biomedical physics; biophysics; magnetic Resonance; nuclear magnetic resonance (NMR); electron paramagnetic resonance (EPR); magnetic resonance imaging (MRI); biomedical applications of dynamic nuclear polarization.

Lv, Bing, Ph.D., University of Houston, 2008. *Condensed Matter Physics, Low Temperature Physics, Materials Science, Metallurgy, Solid State Physics.* Experimental condensed matter physics; new materials; synthesis of solid state crystals; topological insulators and superconductors; novel thermoelectric materials.

Penev, Kaloyan, Ph.D., Harvard University, 2009. *Astronomy, Astrophysics.* Exoplanets.

Shi, Xiaoyan, Ph.D., Florida State University, 2011. *Condensed Matter Physics, Low Temperature Physics, Solid State Physics.* Experimental low temperature physics, 2D electron gases, quantum transport, spin Hall effect.

Stoneback, Russell, Ph.D., University of Texas at Dallas, 2008. *Atmosphere, Space Physics, Cosmic Rays, Climate/Atmospheric Science, Computational Physics.* Global and non-local forces that drive ionospheric and magnetospheric weather; Cube satellites; Computional analysis of large but sparse data sets.

Zhang, Fan, Ph.D., The University of Texas, Austin, 2011. *Condensed Matter Physics, Solid State Physics, Theoretical Physics*. Topological insulators and superconductors.

Professor Emeritus

Heikkila, Walter J., Ph.D., University of Toronto, 1954. *Atmosphere, Space Physics, Cosmic Rays, Plasma and Fusion, Solar Physics*. Magnetospheric physics; solar wind; auroral substorms.

Hoffman, John H., Ph.D., University of Minnesota, 1958. *Atmosphere, Space Physics, Cosmic Rays, Planetary Science*. Ionospheric composition; planetary atmospheres; mass spectroscopy; stratospheric cluster ion composition.

Rindler, Wolfgang, Ph.D., University of London, 1956. *Astrophysics, Cosmology & String Theory, Relativity & Gravitation*. Special and general relativity; cosmology; spinors.

Salamon, Myron, Ph.D., UC Berkeley, 1966. *Condensed Matter Physics, Low Temperature Physics, Optics, Solid State Physics*. Optical properties of highly correlated condensed matter systems.

Tinsley, Brian, Ph.D., University of Canterbury, 1963. *Atmosphere, Space Physics, Cosmic Rays*. Airglow; aurora; theoretical research in aeronomy; instrumentation for atmospheric spectroscopy.

Senior Lecturer

MacAlevey, Paul J., Ph.D., University of Texas, Dallas, 1996. *Physics and other Science Education, Relativity & Gravitation*.

Sun, Kuei, Ph.D., University of Illinois Urbana Champaign, 2012. *Condensed Matter Physics, Solid State Physics, Statistical & Thermal Physics, Theoretical Physics*. Theoretical condensed matter physics.

DEPARTMENTAL RESEARCH SPECIALTIES AND STAFF

Theoretical

Astrophysics. Extragalactic, Black Holes, Early Universe, Exoplanets. Ishak-Boushaki, Kesden, King, Penev, Rindler.

Computational Physics. Computational methods, Numerical simulations, Machine learning, Big data, Data analytics. Lary, Rodrigues, Stoneback.

Nano Science and Technology. Topological insulators and superconductors, Properties of organic materials, electronic structure by LCAO, highly correlated systems. Gartstein, Kolodrubetz, Sun, Chuanwei Zhang, Fan Zhang.

Relativity & Gravitation. Gravitational radiation; exact solutions of Einstein's field equations. Classical and modern cosmology; gravitational lensing (cosmic shear); cosmological models; computer algebra systems applied to relativity. Ishak-Boushaki, Kesden, MacAlevey, Rindler.

Remote Sensing for Atmospheric Physics. Computational and information systems to facilitate discovery and decision support in earth system science. Lary, Stoneback.

Experimental

Atmosphere, Space Physics, Cosmic Rays. Aeronomy; thermospheric, ionospheric and magnetospheric physics; planetary atmospheres. Instrumentation and data analysis for various satellites and deep space probes; microphysics of clouds, climate. Atmospheric electricity. Thermal properties of airless planetary regoliths, distribution of volatiles in the Martian crust, misconceptions in physics and astronomy education, space science and physics educational outreach programs. Anderson, Chen, Heelis, Heikkila, Lary, Rodrigues, Stoneback, Tinsley.

Atomic, Molecular, & Optical Physics. Optical properties of solids, fast spectroscopies, Raman spectroscopy. Glosser, Malko.

Biophysics. DNA electronics and electronic properties; advanced methods of NMR. Lumata, Slinker.

Condensed Matter Physics. Raman, photoluminescence, and modulation spectroscopy of solids. Unconventional superconductivity. Magnetism; disordered and nanoscale magnets. Femtosecond laser spectroscopy of materials, photoluminescence, absorption spectroscopy. Novel electronic and optical materials and electronic and photonic device engineering. Organic optoelectronic devices and laboratory assays. Light emitting electrochemical cells and electrochemical biosensors with DNA-modified electrodes. Topological insulators and superconductors. Quantum transport. Low-dimensional systems. Glosser, Lee, Lv, Malko, Shi, Slinker, Zakhidov.

Exoplanets. Search for new exoplanets. Penev.

High Energy Physics. Charm, bottom, and τ decays at e+e− colliders; simulation of fixed target detectors for b physics. Izen, Lou.

Low Temperature Physics. Experimental studies of unconventional superconductors, manganites, and layered magnetic materials. Low-temperature physics, neutron and X-ray scattering. Lee, Lv, Salamon, Shi, Zakhidov.

Nano Science and Technology. Quantum semiconductor nanostructure, optical properties. Glosser, Lee, Malko, Shi, Slinker, Zakhidov.

Optics. Quantum and nonlinear optics; single and multiphoton emission processes; ultrafast laser spectroscopy. Glosser, Malina, Malko.

View additional information about this department at www.gradschoolshopper.com. Check out the "Why Choose Us?" section, find out more about the department's culture and get links to social media networks.

UNIVERSITY OF UTAH

DEPARTMENT OF PHYSICS AND ASTRONOMY

Salt Lake City, Utah 84112-0830
http://www.physics.utah.edu

General University Information

President: Ruth Watkins
Dean of Graduate School: David Kieda
University website: http://www.utah.edu/
School Type: Public
Setting: Urban
Total Faculty: 4,155
Total Graduate Faculty: 1,656
Total number of Students: 31,860
Total number of Graduate Students: 8,071

Department Information

Department Chairman: Prof. Peter Trapa, Chair
Department Contact: Douglas Bergman, Director of Graduate
Studies
Total full-time faculty: 38
Total number of full-time equivalent positions: 38
Full-Time Graduate Students: 92
Female Full-Time Graduate Students: 27
First-Year Graduate Students: 14
Female First-Year Students: 3
Total Post Doctorates: 11

Department Address

115 South 1400 East #201
Salt Lake City, UT 84112-0830
Phone: (801) 585-5973
Fax: (801) 581-4801
E-mail: bergman@physics.utah.edu
Website: http://www.physics.utah.edu

ADMISSIONS

Admission Contact Information

Address admission inquiries to: Graduate Coordinator, Department of Physics and Astronomy, 115 South 1400 East #201, Salt Lake City, UT 84112-0830
Phone: (801) 581-6861
E-mail: admissions@physics.utah.edu
Admissions website: http://admissions.utah.edu/apply/graduate/

Application deadlines

Fall admission:
U.S. students: February 1   *Int'l. students*: February 1

Application fee

U.S. students: $55   *Int'l. students*: $75
http://www.physics.utah.edu

Admissions information

For Fall of 2017:
Number of applicants: 127
Number admitted: 14
Number enrolled: 14

Admission requirements

Bachelor's degree requirements: A Bachelor's degree in Physics is required or a Bachelor's degree in a closely related field (science or engineering) with a strong physics and math background.

Minimum undergraduate GPA: 3.0

GRE requirements

The GRE is recommended but not required.
There is no minimum required score.

Subjective GRE requirements

The Subjective GRE is required.
No minimum subject GRE score required.

TOEFL requirements

The TOEFL exam is required for students from non-English-speaking countries.
PBT score: 550
iBT score: 80
IELTS score of 6.5 or better is also accepted.

Other admissions information

Additional requirements: Bachelor's degree from an accredited school.
Undergraduate preparation assumed: Thornton & Marion, Classical Dynamics; Griffiths, Electricity and Magnetism; Griffiths, Quantum Mechanics; Tipler, Modern Physics.

TUITION

Tuition year 2015–16:
Tuition for in-state residents
   Full-time students: $4,421 per semester
   Part-time students: $1,489 per credit
Tuition for out-of-state residents
   Full-time students: $14,209 per semester
   Part-time students: $4,233 per credit
Tuition Waiver Benefits available to qualified students in good academic standing.
Credit hours per semester to be considered full-time: 9
Deferred tuition plan:
Health insurance: Yes, varies per semester.
Other academic fees: Mandatory University fees. Some laboratories require special fees.
Academic term: Semester
Number of first-year students who received full tuition waivers: 13

Teaching Assistants, Research Assistants, and Fellowships

Number of first-year
   Teaching Assistants: 13
Average stipend per academic year
   Teaching Assistant: $23,120
   Research Assistant: $24,990

FINANCIAL AID

Application deadlines

Fall admission:
U.S. students: February 1   *Int'l. students*: February 1

Loans

Loans are available for U.S. students.
Loans are not available for international students.
GAPSFAS application required: No
FAFSA application required: Yes

For further information

Address financial aid inquiries to: Financial Aid & Scholarships, 201 S. 1460 E., Salt Lake City, UT 84112.
Phone: (801) 581-6211
E-mail: financialaid@sa.utah.edu
Financial aid website: https://financialaid.utah.edu/index.php

HOUSING

Availability of on-campus housing

Single students: Yes
Married students: Yes
Childcare Assistance: No

For further information

Address housing inquiries to: Office of Residential Living, 5 Heritage Center, Salt Lake City, UT 84112-2036.
Phone: (801) 587-2002
E-mail: info@housing.utah.edu
Housing aid website: https://housing.utah.edu/housing-options/graduate-housing/

Table A—Faculty, Enrollments, and Degrees Granted

Research Specialty	2017–18 Faculty	Enrollment Fall 2017		Number of Degrees Granted 2016–17 (2003–10)		
		Master's	Doctorate	Master's	Terminal Master's	Doctorate
Acoustics	–	–	–	–(3)	–	–(1)
Applied Physics	–	–	–	–(3)	–	–(2)
Astronomy	6	–	4	–(18)	–	1
Astrophysics	4	–	20	–	–	–
Atmosphere, Space Physics, Cosmic Rays	4	1	7	–(1)	–	3(4)
Biophysics	3	1	2	–	–	1
Chemical Physics	1	–	1	–	–	–(1)
Condensed Matter Physics	11	–	43	3	2	4
Medical, Health Physics	9	–	1	1(6)	–	–(9)
Particles and Fields	3	–	3	–	–	–(1)
Physics and other Science Education	–	–	–	–(1)	–	–(5)
Polymer Physics/Science	–	–	–	–(2)	–	–
Relativity & Gravitation	1	–	1	–(17)	–	2(22)
Non-specialized	–	–	6	–	–	–
Total	38	2	90	2(69)	4	11(46)
Full-time Grad. Stud.	–	2	90	–	–	–
First-year Grad. Stud.	–	1	13	–	–	–

GRADUATE DEGREE REQUIREMENTS

Master's: Thirty graduate semester hours required with a 3.0 grade average in an approved program with satisfactory performance on Departmental Common Exam. Either thesis or non-thesis M.S. available. Master's of Instrumentation: 30 graduate semester hours with a 3.0 grade average. Nine to fifteen hours will be related to the instrumentation project. No language required. For admission, a Bachelor's degree in Engineering, Biology, Chemistry or some related field may be substituted for a degree in Physics.

Doctorate: Forty-five graduate semester hours required. Satisfactory performance on Departmental Common Exam or GRE Physics required for admission to Ph.D. program (no set minimum). Satisfactory performance (3.0 average) in an approved course program is required. Qualifying exam, dissertation and dissertation exam required. Teaching experience required, and one of last two years must be in residence. No language requirement.

Other Degrees: Interdisciplinary studies available in chemical physics, and a variety of other areas by special arrangement. The Ph.D. program in Medical Physics is an interdisciplined program in which complex medical and biological systems are studied using physics-based techniques and models. M.A. requirements are the same as M.S., except proficiency in one foreign language is required. M.Phil. requirements the same as Ph.D., except no dissertation required.

Thesis: Thesis may be written in absentia.

SPECIAL EQUIPMENT, FACILITIES, OR PROGRAMS

The Department maintains extensive facilities for teaching and research. The INSCC Building (Intermountain Network & Scientific Computation Center) houses seven state-of-the-art laser laboratories on the first floor run by several condensed matter and biophysics experimental groups.

The research of one group focuses on time-resolved and steady state (cw) investigations of photo-excitations in solids, particularly in semiconductors. A state-of-the-art Ti:sapphire laser gives time resolution of 10 fs. Current efforts in this femtosecond laboratory include pulse amplification with a Nd:YAG laser and the generation of continuum pulses from the near-infrared to the UV.

In the picosecond laboratory, two tunable synchronously pumped dye lasers are used for further photo-excitation studies. A 2D streak camera is used to measure the photoluminescence spectrum evolution with picosecond resolution. The laser laboratory has also been used to study optical non-linear spectra in electronic polymers, solids, and other semiconductors. This includes spectra of two-photon absorption, nonlinear refractive index and third harmonic generation. Light absorption is measured from the UV to the far IR using self-contained commercial instruments (Cary 17 DX and Bruker IFS88, both recently upgraded with modern electronics), operated either by researchers or as a service provided by members of the technical staff.

The single molecule spectroscopy group runs a low-temperature laser microscopy laboratory centering around a helium cryostat and a one-box femtosecond laser system with wide (680 nm-1080 nm) automated tunability. An FEI NovaNano Field emission Scanning Electron Microscope with 1.0 nm resolution (1.6 nm at 1 keV or low vacuum) is widely used for imaging. EDS analysis and e-beam lithography, a Leo 440i SEM is used for images requiring extremely large depth of field as well as for teaching. The Scanning Probe Microscopy Group has many scanning probe microscopes, including several atomic force microscopes, a scanning tunneling microscope, two near-field optical microscopes, a scanning capacitance microscope and an ultra-high vacuum AFM/STM system.

Several research groups within the department operate a variety of commercial and custom built electron and nuclear magnetic magnetic resonance spectrometers including a Bruker Elexsys E580 pulsed electron paramagnetic resonance facility and several electrically and optically detected magnetic resonance facilities.

Two new biophysics laboratories are under construction. The first laboratory is located in the INSCC building. The focus of the group is on single molecule studies of molecular motor activity and other protein interactions. Equipment includes (or will shortly include) a high-resolution optical microscope with optical trapping and fluorescence capabilities, as well as auxiliary biological research equipment (e.g. low-temperature refrigeration facilities and a Beckman TL-100 ultracentrifuge). The second biophysics laboratory is under construction in the James Fletcher

Building. This laboratory focuses on understanding the mechanism of enveloped virus budding using single molecule, fluorescence spectroscopy and high-resolution live cell imaging technologies. A new iMIC digital microscope would be installed that is capable of confocal, TIRF, live cell imaging and fluorescence correlation spectroscopy.

In addition, the Department operated a fully equipped Opto-Electronic Materials Laboratory for chemical synthesis (including organic semiconductors not commercially available), purification, growth of single crystals, vacuum/controlled atmosphere annealing, sample cutting and polishing, thin-film deposition via thermal evaporation of rf sputtering, as well as a wide variety of techniques for chemical and physical characterization. A low-temperature AFM/STM (5 Kelvin) from Omicron Nanotechnology should arrive by the end of 2010.

The Astronomy and Astrophysics Group consists of nine full-time faculty members who are leading research programs at world-class astronomical facilities. As full institutional members of the Third Sloan Digital Sky Survey, the astronomy research group pursues an active research program in the BOSS, APGEE and SEGUE surveys. The astronomy group also pursues observational research using facilities in Chile, Hawaii, and the southwestern United States. The astronomy group is a key member of the proposed BigBOSS Observatory, a stage IV baryon acoustic oscillation survey designed to elucidate the formation of galaxies in the early universe, and properties of dark energy and dark matter. The Department operates the 32″ Willard L. Eccles Observatory on Frisco Peak, Utah, approximately 200 miles from Salt Lake City. This high-altitude (9600 ft a.s.l.) observatory is being developed for IR spectroscopy and imaging surveys. The department operates a pair of 3-meter interferometric telescopes at StarBase Utah, approximately 35 miles west of Salt Lake City. The South Physics observatory on campus houses the department 14″ fully automated telescope and several others with CCD photometers, spectrometers and other accessories. The gamma-ray research group pursues astrophysics research with the Very Energetic Radiation Imaging Telescope Array System (VERITAS) located near Tucson, Arizona. Its four 10-m telescopes make stereoscopic measurements of TeV gamma-rays from black holes, supernova remnants, pulsars and active galactic nuclei. Faculty members also pursue cosmic ray and gamma-ray research at the High-Altitude Water Cherenkov (HAWC) observatory, located on Sierra Negra, Mexico. The University of Utah is the host institution for the Telescope Array (TA) and Telescope Array Low-Energy Extension (TALE) projects, located 125 miles from Salt Lake City in the west-central Utah desert. Its ground array has more than 500 scintillation detectors covering 750 square kilometers, accompanied by three air-fluorescence detectors. Both TA and TALE are designed to study the highest-energy particles known, and both experiments make extensive use of the air-fluorescence technique first successfully employed at Utah by the Fly's Eye Experiment (1976-1991) here at University of Utah, Degree programs in astronomy are currently offered.

The department has a robust wired and wireless local network designed with growth and flexibility in mind. The local network is integrated into a cutting edge university network dedicated to providing premier Internet services. Core user and computational services are provided by a dozen Sun Fire and Sun Enterprise servers accompanied by several powerful Linux and Windows servers. Data storage and backup are provided by a growing storage area network (SAN) currently totaling roughly one terabyte of disk and ten terabytes of tape storage. We provide access to a large suite of programs for departmental use including Maple, Matlab, Mathematica, LabVIEW, Microsoft software and educational software. In addition, the University provides deeply discounted prices on hundreds of software titles through their office of software licensing. There are numerous open access terminals, desktops and printers in the department library, study areas, and the five open computer laboratories. Individual workstations are a mixture of Windows, Linux, Macintosh and UNIX. The department also supports several research groups that have various computational computers and multiple terabyte size data arrays, usually based on UNIX type architectures. Research groups also have access to large computational clusters through the University's Center for High-Performance Computing (CHPC), totaling well over 1500 processors in various clusters.

Research is also supported by a professional Research Machine Shop, as well as a Student Shop, the latter open to all faculty, staff, and students who have completed a training course. Both shops are equipped with state-of-the-art CNC lathes and mills, as well as cutting, drilling and welding equipment. The well-equipped wood shop allows fabrication of non-magnetic supports and shipping containers. The ample stockroom saves time and effort in procuring both common and hard-to-find materials and supplies.

Table B—Separately Budgeted Research Expenditures by Source of Support

Source of Support	Departmental Research	Physics-related Research Outside Department
Federal government	$5,724,000	
State/local government		
Non-profit organizations	$50,000	
Business and industry	$117,000	
Other	$176,000	
Total	$6,067,000	

Table C—Separately Budgeted Research Expenditures by Research Specialty

Research Specialty	No. of Grants	Expenditures ($)
Applied Physics	3	$141,000
Astronomy	17	$1,275,000
Astrophysics	8	$564,000
Atmosphere, Space Physics, Cosmic Rays	7	$1,639,000
Biophysics	6	$303,000
Computational Physics	1	$30,000
Computer Science	2	$266,000
Condensed Matter Physics	15	$1,236,000
Cosmology & String Theory	1	$117,000
High Energy Physics	7	$131,000
Nano Science and Technology	5	$169,000
Nonlinear Dynamics and Complex Systems	1	$105,000
Theoretical Physics	1	$91,000
Total	74	$6,067,000

FACULTY

Distinguished University Professor

Sokolsky, Pierre V., Ph.D., University of Illinois, 1973. Dean, College of Science. *Astrophysics, Atmosphere, Space Physics, Cosmic Rays, Plasma and Fusion.* Cosmic rays; high-energy physics.

Vardeny, Zeev V., Ph.D., Technion, Israel, 1979. *Atomic, Molecular, & Optical Physics, Biophysics, Condensed Matter Physics, Energy Sources & Environment, Materials Science, Metallurgy, Nano Science and Technology, Optics.* Experimental condensed matter.

Wu, Yong-Shi, Ph.D., Chinese Academy of Sciences, 1965. *Astrophysics, Condensed Matter Physics, Particles and Fields.* High-energy theory.

Professor

Ailion, David C., Ph.D., University of Illinois, 1964. *Atomic, Molecular, & Optical Physics, Biophysics, Condensed Matter Physics, Medical, Health Physics*. Experimental condensed matter.

Boehme, Christoph, Ph.D., University of Marburg, 2003. Associate Chair. *Applied Physics, Chemical Physics, Condensed Matter Physics, Materials Science, Metallurgy, Nano Science and Technology*. Experimental Condensed Matter Physics.

Bromley, Benjamin C., Ph.D., Dartmouth College, 1994. *Astronomy, Astrophysics, Relativity & Gravitation*. Theoretical astrophysics.

Cassiday, George L., Ph.D., Cornell University, 1968. *Astronomy, Astrophysics, Atmosphere, Space Physics, Cosmic Rays*. Cosmic rays.

DeFord, John W., Ph.D., University of Illinois, 1962. *Physics and other Science Education*. Physics education.

DeTar, Carleton E., Ph.D., University of California, Berkeley, 1970. *Astrophysics, Particles and Fields*. Elementary particle theory.

Gondolo, Paolo, Ph.D., University of California, Los Angeles, 1991. *Astronomy, Astrophysics, Particles and Fields*. Cosmology; dark matter.

Harris, Frank E., Ph.D., University of California, Berkeley, 1954. *Chemical Physics*. Chemical physics.

Jui, Charles C., Ph.D., Stanford University, 1992. *Atmosphere, Space Physics, Cosmic Rays, History & Philosophy of Physics/Science, Plasma and Fusion*. Cosmic rays.

Kieda, David B., Ph.D., University of Pennsylvania, 1989. Department Chair. *Astronomy, Astrophysics, Atmosphere, Space Physics, Cosmic Rays*. Experimental high-energy astrophysics.

Mishchenko, Eugene, Ph.D., Landau Institute for Theoretical Physics, Moscow, 1998. *Condensed Matter Physics*. Theoretical condensed matter.

Raikh, Mikhail, Ph.D., Ioffe Physico Technical Institute, 1981. *Condensed Matter Physics*. Theoretical condensed matter.

Springer, Wayne R., Ph.D., University of Maryland, 1991. *Astronomy, Astrophysics, Atmosphere, Space Physics, Cosmic Rays, Computer Science, Particles and Fields, Plasma and Fusion*. Experimental astrophysics.

Starykh, Oleg, Ph.D., Russian Academy of Science, 1991. *Condensed Matter Physics*. Theoretical condensed matter.

Symko, Orest G., Ph.D., University of Oxford, 1967. *Acoustics, Low Temperature Physics*. Thermoacoustics.

Williams, Clayton C., Ph.D., Stanford University, 1984. *Atomic, Molecular, & Optical Physics, Condensed Matter Physics, Electrical Engineering, Nano Science and Technology, Optics*. Experimental condensed matter.

Associate Professor

Belz, John, Ph.D., Temple University, 1993. *Astrophysics, Atmosphere, Space Physics, Cosmic Rays*. Cosmic rays.

Bergman, Douglas, Ph.D., Yale University, 1997. *Astrophysics, Atmosphere, Space Physics, Cosmic Rays, High Energy Physics*. Cosmic rays; high-energy physics.

Dawson, Kyle, Ph.D., University of California, Berkeley, 2004. Astronomy and astrophysics. *Astronomy, Astrophysics*.

Deemyad, Shanti, Ph.D., Washington University, St. Louis, 2004. *Condensed Matter Physics, Low Temperature Physics*. Experimental condensed matter.

Gerton, Jordan, Ph.D., Rice University, 2001. Director for the Center of Science and Math Education. *Biophysics, Condensed Matter Physics, Medical, Health Physics, Nano Science and Technology, Optics*. Experimental condensed matter.

LeBohec, Stephan, Ph.D., Paris XI University, 1992. *Astronomy, Astrophysics, Particles and Fields*. Experimental high-energy astrophysics.

Pesin, Dmytro, Ph.D., University of Washington, 2009. *Condensed Matter Physics*. Theoretical condensed matter.

Rogachev, Andrey, Ph.D., Nagoya University, 2000. *Condensed Matter Physics, Nano Science and Technology, Optics*. Experimental condensed matter physics.

Saffarian, Saveez, Ph.D., Washington University, St. Louis, 2003. *Biophysics*. Biophysics.

Sandick, Pearl, Ph.D., University of Minnesota, 2008. *Astrophysics, Particles and Fields*. Theoretical high energy astrophysics.

Seth, Anil, Ph.D., University of Washington, 2006. *Astronomy, Astrophysics*. Astronomy and astrophysics.

Zheng, Zheng, Ph.D., Ohio State University, 2004. *Astronomy, Astrophysics*. Astronomy and astrophysics.

Assistant Professor

Deshpande, Vikram V., Ph.D., California Institute of Technology, 2008. *Applied Physics, Condensed Matter Physics*. Synthesis, nanofabrication, and combined electrical, mechanical, and optical measurements of ultra-high-quality graphene and carbon nanotube devices.

Ivans, Inese, Ph.D., University of Texas, Austin, 2002. *Astronomy*. Astronomy.

Li, Yan (Sarah), Ph.D., University of California, Riverside, 2010. *Condensed Matter Physics, Materials Science, Metallurgy*. Spin noise spectroscopy of electrons and holes in semiconductor quantum dots.

Vershinin, Michael, Ph.D., University of Illinois, 2004. *Biophysics*. Biophysics.

Wik, Daniel R., Ph.D., University of Virginia, 2010. *Astronomy, Astrophysics*. Astronomy and astrophysics.

Zasowski, Gail, Ph.D., University of Virginia, 2012. *Astronomy, Astrophysics*. Astronomy and astrophysics.

Zhao, Yue, Ph.D., Rutgers University, 2012. *High Energy Physics, Theoretical Physics*.

Emeritus

Rudolph, Sidney, Ph.D., University of Utah, 1986. Physics education.

Thomson, Gordon B., Ph.D., Harvard University, 1972. Jack W. Keuffel Chair. *Astrophysics, Atmosphere, Space Physics, Cosmic Rays*. Cosmic rays.

Professor Emeritus

Efros, Alexei L., Ph.D., Ioffe Physico Technical Institute, 1972. *Condensed Matter Physics*. Theoretical condensed matter.

Kuchar, Karel V., Ph.D., Charles University in Prague, 1966. *Relativity & Gravitation*. Relativity.

Mattis, Daniel C., Ph.D., University of Illinois, 1957. *Condensed Matter Physics*. Theoretical condensed matter.

Ohlsen, William D., Ph.D., Cornell University, 1961. *Condensed Matter Physics*. Experimental condensed matter.

Price, Richard, Ph.D., California Institute of Technology, 1971. *Relativity & Gravitation*.

Sutherland, T. Bill, Ph.D., Stony Brook University, 1968. *Condensed Matter Physics*. Theoretical condensed matter.

Taylor, P. Craig, Ph.D., Brown University, 1969. *Condensed Matter Physics*. Experimental condensed matter.

Williams, George A., Ph.D., University of Illinois, 1956. *Condensed Matter Physics*. Experimental condensed matter.

Research Professor

Lupton, John M., Ph.D., University of Durham, London, 2001. *Atomic, Molecular, & Optical Physics, Condensed Matter*

Physics, Materials Science, Metallurgy, Nano Science and Technology. Experimental condensed matter.

Matthews, John N., Ph.D., Rutgers University, 1995. *Astrophysics, Atmosphere, Space Physics, Cosmic Rays.* Cosmic rays.

Worlock, John M., Ph.D., Cornell University, 1962. *Condensed Matter Physics.* Condensed matter.

Research Associate Professor

AbuZayyad, Tareq, Ph.D., University of Utah, 2000. *Astrophysics, Atmosphere, Space Physics, Cosmic Rays, Plasma and Fusion.* Cosmic rays.

Brownstein, Joel R., Ph.D., University of Waterloo, 2009. *Astronomy.* Galaxy evolution; BOSS; lensing.

Laicher, Gernot, Ph.D., University of Utah, 1994. *Atomic, Molecular, & Optical Physics, Condensed Matter Physics, Medical, Health Physics.* Experimental condensed matter.

Research Assistant Professor

Malissa, Hans, Ph.D., Johannes Kepler University Linz, 2007. *Condensed Matter Physics.*

Teaching Professor

Ingebretsen, Richard J., Ph.D., University of Utah, 1989. MD. *Medical, Health Physics, Physics and other Science Education.* Physics education, medical physics.

Teaching Associate Professor

Buehler, Tabitha C., Ph.D., Brigham Young University, 2011. *Astronomy.* Astronomy.

Pantziris, Anthony, Ph.D., Brown University, 1987. *Physics and other Science Education.* Physics education.

Stone, Christopher, Ph.D., University of Utah, 1992. *Physics and other Science Education.* Physics education.

Teaching Assistant Professor

De Grandi, Claudia, Ph.D., Boston University, 2011. *Condensed Matter Physics, Solid State Physics, Theoretical Physics, Other.* Physics Education Research.

Nyawelo, Tino S., Ph.D., National Institute for Nuclear Physics and High Energy Physics, 2004. *Astrophysics, High Energy Physics, Particles and Fields, Theoretical Physics.* Teaching education.

Adjunct Faculty

Bartl, Michael, Ph.D., Karl-Franzens-University, Graz, Austria, 2000. *Chemical Physics, Nano Science and Technology.*

Blair, Steven, Ph.D., University of Colorado Boulder, 1998. *Electrical Engineering, Nano Science and Technology.* Nanophotonics.

Chubukov, Andrey, Ph.D., Moscow State University, 1985. *Condensed Matter Physics.* Condensed matter.

Ehrenfreund, Eitan, Ph.D., Hebrew University, 1970. *Condensed Matter Physics.* Experimental condensed matter.

Facelli, Julio C., Ph.D., University of Buenos Aires, Argentina, 1981. *Atomic, Molecular, & Optical Physics, Computer Science.* Nuclear magnetic resonance.

Huentemeyer, Petra, Ph.D., University of Hamburg, 2001. *Astrophysics.* High-energy astrophysics.

Jeong, Eun-Kee, Ph.D., Washington University, St. Louis, 1991. *Medical, Health Physics.* MRI.

Johnson, Christopher R., Ph.D., University of Utah, 1989. *Applied Mathematics, Computer Science.* Physics.

Liu, Feng, Ph.D., Virginia Commonwealth University, 1990. *Chemical Physics, Materials Science, Metallurgy.*

McCamey, Dane, Ph.D., University of New South Wales, Sydney, 2007. *Condensed Matter Physics.* Experimental condensed matter.

Nahata, Ajay, Ph.D., Columbia University, 1997. *Electrical Engineering, Nano Science and Technology, Optics.*

Parker, Dennis, Ph.D., University of Utah, 1978. *Biophysics, Medical, Health Physics.* Medical biophysics; computing.

Saam, Brian T., Ph.D., Princeton University, 1995. Associate Dean, College of Science. *Atomic, Molecular, & Optical Physics, Biophysics, Condensed Matter Physics, Medical, Health Physics.* Experimental atomic/molecular.

Scarpulla, Michael, Ph.D., University of California, Berkeley, 2006. *Electrical Engineering, Materials Science, Metallurgy.*

Shahbazyan, Tigran, Ph.D., University of Utah, 1995. *Condensed Matter Physics.* Theoretical condensed matter.

Shapiro, Boris, Ph.D., USSR Academy of Science, 1970. *Condensed Matter Physics.* Theoretical condensed matter.

Sun, Dali, Ph.D., Institute of Physics, Chinese Academy of Sciences, 2009. *Condensed Matter Physics.*

DEPARTMENTAL RESEARCH SPECIALTIES AND STAFF

Theoretical

Astronomy. Bromley, Dawson, Gondolo, Ivans, Pantziris, Seth, Springer, Wik, Zasowski, Zheng.

Astrophysics. Belz, Bergman, Bromley, Brownstein, Dawson, DeTar, Gondolo, Ivans, Pantziris, Price, Sandick, Seth, Wik, Zheng.

Atmosphere, Space Physics, Cosmic Rays. AbuZayyad, Belz, Bergman, Huentemeyer, Jui, Kieda, LeBohec, Matthews, Sokolsky, Springer.

Chemical Physics. Bartl, Boehme, Harris, Lupton, Malissa.

Condensed Matter Physics. Bartl, Boehme, Efros, Ehrenfreund, LeBohec, Liu, Mishchenko, Pesin, Raikh, Saam, Shapiro, Starykh, Sun, Sutherland, Worlock, Wu.

Particles and Fields. DeTar, Gondolo, Sandick, Wu.

Plasma and Fusion.

Relativity & Gravitation. Bromley, Price.

Experimental

Acoustics. Symko.

Astronomy. Dawson, Ivans, Kieda, Seth.

Astrophysics. AbuZayyad, Belz, Bergman, Cassiday, Jui, Kieda, LeBohec, Matthews, Seth, Sokolsky, Springer.

Biophysics. Gerton, Saffarian, Vershinin.

Condensed Matter Physics. Ailion, Boehme, Deemyad, Deshpande, Gerton, Jeong, Laicher, Liu, Rogachev, Saam, Sun, Taylor, Vardeny, Clayton Williams.

Low Temperature Physics. Boehme, Deemyad, Deshpande, Li, Vardeny.

Materials Science, Metallurgy. Boehme, Liu, Sun, Vardeny, Clayton Williams.

Medical, Health Physics. Ailion, Gerton, Ingebretsen, Jeong, Laicher, Parker, Saam.

Nano Science and Technology. Bartl, Boehme, Deemyad, Deshpande, Gerton, Nahata, Rogachev, Scarpulla, Sun, Taylor, Vardeny, Clayton Williams.

Optics. Boehme, Gerton, Rogachev, Saam, Sun, Vardeny, Clayton Williams.

Particles and Fields. Bergman, Sokolsky, Springer.

UTAH STATE UNIVERSITY

DEPARTMENT OF PHYSICS

Logan, Utah 84322-4415
http://physics.usu.edu

General University Information
President: Noelle Cockett
Dean of Graduate School: Mark R. McLellan
University website: http://www.usu.edu
School Type: Public
Setting: Rural
Total Faculty: 800
Total number of Students: 19,000
Total number of Graduate Students: 3,061

Department Information
Department Chairman: Prof. Jan J. Sojka, Head
Department Contact: Karalee Ransom, Academic Advisor
  Total full-time faculty: 20
  Total number of full-time equivalent positions: 18
  Full-Time Graduate Students: 26
  Female Full-Time Graduate Students: 4
  First-Year Graduate Students: 5
  Female First-Year Students: 1 4

Department Address
Department of Physics
Utah State University
Logan, UT 84322-4415
Phone: (435) 797-2857
Fax: (435) 797-2492
E-mail: physics@usu.edu
Website: http://physics.usu.edu

ADMISSIONS

Admission Contact Information
Address admission inquiries to: Karalee Ransom, Department of
  Physics, 4415 Old Main Hill, Logan, UT 84322-4415
Phone: (435) 797-4021
E-mail: karalee.ransom@usu.edu
Admissions website: http://physics.usu.edu/students/graduate-
  program

Application deadlines
Fall admission:
U.S. students: January 15   *Int'l. students*: January 15

Application fee
U.S. students: $55   *Int'l. students*: $55
Official applications can be found on the School of Graduate
  Studies website: http://usu.edu/graduateschool.

Admissions information
For Fall of 2018:
  Number of applicants: 40
  Number admitted: 10
  Number enrolled: 5

Admission requirements
Bachelor's degree requirements: Physics degree or equivalent.
Minimum undergraduate GPA: 3.0

GRE requirements
The GRE is required.
  Quantitative score: 150
  Verbal score: 149
  Analytical score: 3.5
  Mean GRE score range (25th–75th percentile): 40%
Minimum is 40th percentile.

Subjective GRE requirements
The Subjective GRE is recommended.
No minimum score.

TOEFL requirements
The TOEFL exam is required for students from non-English-
  speaking countries.
  PBT score: 550
  iBT score: 79

TUITION

Tuition year 2018–19:
Tuition for in-state residents
  Full-time students: $3,138.72 per semester
  Part-time students: $2,321.43 per semester
Tuition for out-of-state residents
  Full-time students: $9,793.05 per semester
  Part-time students: $7,054.74 per semester
Amounts shown are for tuition and fees. Full time was deter-
  mined by a 9-credit semester. Part time was determined by
  a 6-credit semester.
Credit hours per semester to be considered full-time: 9
Deferred tuition plan: Yes
Health insurance: Available at the cost of $438 per year.
Other academic fees: International students pay a $100 per se-
  mester student fee. Health insurance is mandatory for all grad-
  uate students working as either a TA or an RA. The insurance
  is available through the University and is paid by both the
  student ($438 per academic year) and the Department ($1755
  per academic year.
Academic term: Semester
Number of first-year students who received full tuition waivers: 5

Teaching Assistants, Research Assistants, and Fellowships
Number of first-year
  Teaching Assistants: 5
  Research Assistants: 1
Average stipend per academic year
  Teaching Assistant: $15,000
  Research Assistant: $18,000
  Fellowship student: $20,000

FINANCIAL AID

Application deadlines
Fall admission:
U.S. students: June 30
Spring admission:
U.S. students: June 30

Loans
Loans are available for U.S. students.
Loans are not available for international students.
GAPSFAS application required: Yes
FAFSA application required: Yes

For further information

Address financial aid inquiries to: USU Financial Aid Office, 1800 Old Main Hill, Logan, UT 84322-1800.
Phone: (435) 797-0173
E-mail: finaid@usu.edu
Financial aid website: http://www.usu.edu/financialaid/

HOUSING

Availability of on-campus housing

Single students: Yes
Married students: Yes
Childcare Assistance: No

For further information

Address housing inquiries to: USU Housing and Residence Life, 8600 Old Main Hill, Logan, UT 84322-8600.
Phone: (800) 863-1085
E-mail: info@housing.usu.edu
Housing aid website: http://usu.edu/housing

Table A—Faculty, Enrollments, and Degrees Granted

| Research Specialty | 2016–2017 Faculty | Enrollment Fall 2016 | | Number of Degrees Granted 2016–17 (2012–17) | | |
		Master's	Doctorate	Master's	Terminal Master's	Doctorate
Atmosphere, Space Physics, Cosmic Rays	8	–	–	–	–	–
Condensed Matter Physics	3	–	–	–	–	–
Nano Science and Technology	1	–	–	–	–	–
Nonlinear Dynamics and Complex Systems	2	–	–	–	–	–
Particles and Fields	4	–	–	–	–	–
Plasma and Fusion	2	–	–	–	–	–
Total	20	–	–	–	–	–
Full-time Grad. Stud.	–	–	–	–	–	–
First-year Grad. Stud.	–	–	–	–	–	–

GRADUATE DEGREE REQUIREMENTS

Master's: Required coursework. Thesis.
Doctorate: Required coursework. Qualification decision made after first year. Candidacy exam in the third year. Dissertation.

Table B—Separately Budgeted Research Expenditures by Source of Support

Source of Support	Departmental Research	Physics-related Research Outside Department
Federal government	$700,834	$1,095,745
State/local government		
Non-profit organizations		
Business and industry		
Other		
Total	$700,834	$1,095,745

Table C—Separately Budgeted Research Expenditures by Research Specialty

Research Specialty	No. of Grants	Expenditures ($)
Atmosphere, Space Physics, Cosmic Rays	30	$1,095,745
Condensed Matter Physics	3	$300,834
Nonlinear Dynamics and Complex Systems	2	$150,000
Plasma and Fusion	3	$250,000
Mathematical Physics and Computer Algegra	1	$360,000
Total	39	$2,156,579

FACULTY

Professor

Dennison, J. R., Ph.D., Virginia Polytechnic Institute and State University (Virginia Tech), 1985. *Materials Science, Metallurgy, Solid State Physics, Surface Physics.* Solid-state and surface physics.

Edwards, Boyd, Ph.D., Stanford University, 1985. *Applied Physics.* Applied Physics.

Fejer, Bela, Ph.D., Cornell University, 1974. *Atmosphere, Space Physics, Cosmic Rays, Geophysics.* Space plasma physics.

Hagan, Maura, Boston College, 1987. Dean of the College of Science. *Atmosphere, Space Physics, Cosmic Rays.* Atmospheric physics.

Held, Eric D., Ph.D., University of Wisconsin-Madison, 1999. *Plasma and Fusion.* Computational plasma physics.

Peak, David, Ph.D., University at Albany, 1969. *Biophysics, Nonlinear Dynamics and Complex Systems.* Complex materials and dynamics.

Scherliess, Ludger, Ph.D., Utah State University, 1997. *Atmosphere, Space Physics, Cosmic Rays, Geophysics.* Space physics.

Schunk, Robert W., Ph.D., Yale University, 1970. *Atmosphere, Space Physics, Cosmic Rays, Geophysics.* Space plasma physics.

Shen, T. C., Ph.D., University of Maryland, 1985. *Nano Science and Technology, Solid State Physics.* Surface science.

Sojka, Jan J., Ph.D., University College London, 1976. *Atmosphere, Space Physics, Cosmic Rays, Geophysics.* Space plasma physics.

Taylor, Michael, Ph.D., University of Southampton, 1986. *Atmosphere, Space Physics, Cosmic Rays, Geophysics.* Atmospheric physics.

Torre, Charles, Ph.D., University of North Carolina, 1985. Associate Department Head. *Applied Mathematics, Particles and Fields, Relativity & Gravitation, Theoretical Physics.* Gravitational physics; field theory; mathematical physics; computer algebra.

Wickwar, Vincent, Ph.D., Rice University, 1971. *Atmosphere, Space Physics, Cosmic Rays, Optics.* Atmospheric physics.

Associate Professor

Riffe, D. Mark, Ph.D., Cornell University, 1989. *Condensed Matter Physics, Surface Physics.* Optical studies of surfaces.

Wheeler, James T., Ph.D., University of Chicago, 1986. *Particles and Fields.* Gravitational and unified gauge theories of the conformal group.

Assistant Professor

Rodriguez, Maria, Ph.D., Universidad de Barcelona, 2007. *Astrophysics, High Energy Physics, Particles and Fields, Relativity & Gravitation, Theoretical Physics.* Black Holes, Gravitation, Relativistic Astrophysics, Mathematical Physics.

Varela, Oscar, Ph.D., Universidad de Valencia, 2006. *Cosmology & String Theory, High Energy Physics, Particles and*

Fields, Relativity & Gravitation, Theoretical Physics. String Theory, Gravitation, Supergravity, Mathematical Physics.

Yuan, Titus, Ph.D., Colorado State University, 2004. *Atmosphere, Space Physics, Cosmic Rays, Optics.* Lidar.

Professor Emeritus

Edwards, W. Farrell, Ph.D., California Institute of Technology, 1960. *Atmosphere, Space Physics, Cosmic Rays, Electromagnetism, Geophysics, Plasma and Fusion, Theoretical Physics.* Electromagnetic theory.

Research Professor

Ji, Jeong-Young, Ph.D.*Plasma and Fusion.* Plasma Physics.

Research Associate Professor

Zhu, Lie, Ph.D., University of Alaska, 1990. *Atmosphere, Space Physics, Cosmic Rays, Geophysics.* Space plasma physics.

Senior Lecturer

Triplett, Tonya, M.S., Utah State University, 2003. *Physics and other Science Education.* Physics education.

DEPARTMENTAL RESEARCH SPECIALTIES AND STAFF

Theoretical

Atmosphere, Space Physics, Cosmic Rays. W. Edwards, Fejer, Hagan, Scherliess, Schunk, Sojka, Taylor, Zhu.

Computational Physics. Held, Ji.

Condensed Matter Physics. Riffe.

Field Theory. Classical and quantum field theory; relativity and gravitation; mathematical physics. Rodriguez, Torre, Varela, Wheeler.

High Energy Physics. String theory, supergravity. Varela.

Mathematical Physics. Differential geometry; computer algebra; mathematical physics. Torre.

Nonlinear Dynamics and Complex Systems. Peak.

Physics and other Science Education. Triplett.

Plasma and Fusion. W. Edwards, Held, Ji.

Relativity & Gravitation. Mathematical relativity, computer algebra approaches to gravitation and field theory, black holes, relativistic astrophysics. Rodriguez, Torre, Varela.

Experimental

Atmosphere, Space Physics, Cosmic Rays. Taylor, Wickwar, Yuan.

Condensed Matter Physics. Dennison, Riffe, Shen.

View additional information about this department at www.gradschoolshopper.com. Check out the "Why Choose Us?" section, find out more about the department's culture and get links to social media networks.

UNIVERSITY OF VERMONT

DEPARTMENT OF PHYSICS

Burlington, Vermont 05405-0125
http://www.uvm.edu/physics

General University Information
President: E. Thomas Sullivan
Dean of Graduate School: Cynthia Forehand, Ph.D.
University website: http://www.uvm.edu
School Type: Public
Setting: Urban
Total Faculty: 1,600
Total Graduate Faculty: 643
Total number of Students: 13,340
Total number of Graduate Students: 1,517

Department Information
Department Chairman: Prof. Jun-Ru Wu, Chair
Department Contact: Denise M. Fontaine, Department
  Administrative Coordinator
Total full-time faculty: 13
Total number of full-time equivalent positions: 14
Full-Time Graduate Students: 15
Female Full-Time Graduate Students: 4
First-Year Graduate Students: 3
Female First-Year Students: 1
Total Post Doctorates: 2

Department Address
82 University Place
STEM Discovery Hall, RM W203
Burlington, VT 05405-0125
Phone: (802) 656-2664
Fax: (802) 656-0817
E-mail: physics@uvm.edu
Website: http://www.uvm.edu/physics

ADMISSIONS

Admission Contact Information
Address admission inquiries to: Department of Physics, University of Vermont, STEM Discovery Hall, W203, 82 University Place, Burlington, VT 05405-0125
Phone: (802) 656-2644
E-mail: physics@uvm.edu
Admissions website: http://www.uvm.edu/~gradcoll/?Page=Admissions.html&SM=Prospectivemenu.html

Application deadlines
Fall admission:
U.S. students: March 1   *Int'l. students*: March 1
Spring admission:
U.S. students: November 15   *Int'l. students*: November 15

Application fee
U.S. students: $65   *Int'l. students*: $65
Online

Admissions information
For Fall of 2018:
  Number of applicants: 29
  Number admitted: 11
  Number enrolled: 5

Admission requirements
Bachelor's degree requirements: Bachelor's degree in Physics is required.
Minimum undergraduate GPA: 3.0

GRE requirements
The GRE is required.
The GRE is required. The minimum acceptable score suggested for admission is not specified. The minimum acceptable score for admission is dependent upon the applicant's overall record.

Subjective GRE requirements
The Subjective GRE is not required.
The GRE Physics is not required.

TOEFL requirements
The TOEFL exam is required for students from non-English-speaking countries.
  PBT score: 577
  iBT score: 90
For student funded, an internet-based score of 100 is required, and a paper-based score of 600 is required.

Other admissions information
Additional requirements: The General GRE cannot be waived. The Advanced GRE can be waived in special cases. No minimum acceptable score is specified. The average GRE internet-based scores for 2017–2018 admissions were as follows: verbal, 153.0; quantitative, 159.0; analytical writing, 3.5.
Undergraduate preparation assumed: Taylor, Classical Mechanics; Griffiths, Introduction to Electrodynamics; Kittel and Kroemer, Thermal Physics; Griffiths, Introduction to Quantum Mechanics.

TUITION

Tuition year 2017–18:
Tuition for in-state residents
  Full-time students: $664 per credit
Tuition for out-of-state residents
  Full-time students: $1,674 per credit
Credit hours per semester to be considered full-time: 10
Deferred tuition plan: No
Health insurance: Available at the cost of $1,347 per year.
Other academic fees: $10 comp fees per credit. $7 graduate student senate fee
Academic term: Semester

Teaching Assistants, Research Assistants, and Fellowships
Number of first-year
  Teaching Assistants: 1
  Teaching Assistant: $16,125 (M.S.) $19,950 (Ph.D, MATS)
  Research Assistant: $16,125 (M.S.) $19,950 (Ph.D, MATS)

FINANCIAL AID

Application deadlines
Fall admission:
U.S. students: March 1   *Int'l. students*: March 1

Spring admission:
U.S. students: November 15   *Int'l. students*: November 15

Loans

Loans are available for U.S. students.
Loans are available for international students.
GAPSFAS application required: No
FAFSA application required: Yes

For further information

Address financial aid inquiries to: Student Financial Services, 223 Waterman Building, 85 South Prospect Street, Burlington, VT 05405.
Phone: (802) 656-5700
E-mail: sfs@uvm.edu
Financial aid website: http://www.uvm.edu/~stdfinsv/

HOUSING

Availability of on-campus housing

Single students: Yes
Married students: Yes

For further information

Address housing inquiries to: Office of Family Housing, Fort Ethan Allen, 36 Catamount Lane, Colchester, VT 05446.
Phone: (802) 656-3434
E-mail: reslife@uvm.edu
Housing aid website: https://reslife.uvm.edu/content/apartments_and_family_housing/contact_afh

Table A—Faculty, Enrollments, and Degrees Granted

Research Specialty	2017–18 Faculty	Enrollment Fall 2017		Number of Degrees Granted 2017–18 (2007–17)		
		Master's	Doctorate	Master's	Terminal Master's	Doctorate
Acoustics	1	–	–	–	–(2)	–
Astronomy	3	–	–	–(2)	–	–
Astrophysics	–	1	–	–	–	–
Biophysics	2	–	–	–(2)	–(5)	–
Condensed Matter Physics	8	1	–	1(2)	–(12)	–
History & Philosophy of Physics/Science	–	–	–	–	–(2)	–
Low Temperature Physics	–	–	–	–	–	–
Materials Science, Metallurgy	–	–	13	–	–(2)	2(14)
Optics	–	–	–	–	–	–
Polymer Physics/Science	–	–	–	–	–	–
Total	14	2	13	1(6)	–(23)	–(14)
Full-time Grad. Stud.	–	2	13	–	–	–
First-year Grad. Stud.	–	1	2	–	–	–

GRADUATE DEGREE REQUIREMENTS

Master's: A minimum of 30 semester hours of graduate credit is required. Of the 30 hours, 21 must be completed in residence. At least six must be in thesis research and nine in other courses numbered above 300 (graduate students only). No more than 15 hours of thesis research may be included in the degree program. The candidate must pass a written and oral comprehensive examination, as well as an oral examination on the thesis. The graduate student must maintain a B average. There are no foreign language requirements.

Doctorate: For Ph.D. in Physics: a minimum of 75 credits, including 6 core graduate courses completed with a grade B

or better. All of these courses must be completed with a grade B or better within the first two years of graduate study. To accommodate the needs of the specific subfields in physics such as astrophysics, biological physics, condensed-matter physics and materials physics, three elective courses (nine credits) have to be chosen to fulfill the breadth requirement with a grade of B or higher. Elective courses must be completed within the first three years of the program, as the fourth year (and beyond if needed) should be dedicated to progress towards the Ph.D. dissertation. In addition, at least 20 credits of Doctoral Dissertation Research is required for Ph.D. students engaged in dissertation research, and at least 3 credits of Teaching College Physics is required. At the start of their second semester at UVM, students are expected to sit for the written part of the Comprehensive Exam which covers classical mechanics, quantum mechanics, electricity and magnetism, as well as thermal physics and mathematical physics. Students are given two opportunities to pass the comprehensive exam. In addition to the written portion, there is also an oral portion that consists of a Ph.D. dissertation proposal given after the start of a dissertation research project.

Other Degrees: For the Materials Science Program, Master's of Science and the Doctor of Philosophy degrees are offered in this interdisciplinary program. The faculty are drawn from the departments of Chemistry, Electrical Engineering, Mechanical Engineering, and Physics. The program is committed to educating the students in the application of basic sciences and engineering to promote understanding of the properties of materials, their development and applications, and to perform advanced and stimulating research in these areas. (The research program pursued in Materials Science at the University of Vermont has two areas of specialization: Electronic Materials and Bio/Polymeric Materials.) Each student must meet the general requirements or admissions as described at http://www.uvm.edu/matsci. Students in the program are sponsored by the participating department that best reflects the student's background and interest. The degree of Doctor of Philosophy requires a minimum of 75 credit hours earned in courses and in dissertation research of which a minimum of 51 hours must be earned in residence.

Thesis: Thesis may be written in absentia.

SPECIAL EQUIPMENT, FACILITIES, OR PROGRAMS

Research is concentrated in areas of astrophysics, biological physics, polymer physics, materials science, and condensed matter physics. Collaboration is feasible with other departments of science, engineering, and medicine on this geographically small campus. There is especially close cooperation with the School of Engineering, the College of Medicine, and the Department of Chemistry. The department shares a building with the Department of Chemistry.

Table B—Separately Budgeted Research Expenditures by Source of Support

Source of Support	Departmental Research	Physics-related Research Outside Department
Federal government	$1,511,409	
State/local government		
Non-profit organizations		
Business and industry	$104,631	
Other		
Total	$1,616,040	

Table C—Separately Budgeted Research Expenditures by Research Specialty

Research Specialty	No. of Grants	Expenditures ($)
Condensed Matter Physics	1	$1,616,040
Total	1	$1,616,040

FACULTY

Professor

Clougherty, Dennis P., Ph.D., Massachusetts Institute of Technology, 1989. *Atomic, Molecular, & Optical Physics, Condensed Matter Physics, Theoretical Physics.* Theoretical condensed matter physics.

Headrick, Randall, Ph.D., University of Pennsylvania, 1988. Interim Chair. *Condensed Matter Physics, Nano Science and Technology.* Materials science. Molecular beam epitaxy; X-ray scattering surface processing.

Rankin, Joanna M., Ph.D., University of Iowa, 1970. *Astronomy, Astrophysics.* Radio astrophysics; history of science.

Wu, Jun-Ru, Ph.D., University of California, Los Angeles, 1985. Chair. *Acoustics, Biophysics, Condensed Matter Physics, Medical, Health Physics.* Experimental condensed matter physics and ultrasound.

Associate Professor

Del Maestro, Adrian, Ph.D., Harvard University, 2008. *Computational Physics, Condensed Matter Physics.* Theoretical condensed matter physics.

Furis, Madalina, Ph.D., State University of New York at Buffalo, 2004. *Condensed Matter Physics, Nano Science and Technology, Optics.* Materials science; ultrafast spectroscopy, time-resolved photoluminescence.

Kotov, Valeri, Ph.D., Clarkson University, 1996. *Condensed Matter Physics, Theoretical Physics.* Theoretical condensed matter physics.

Yang, Jie, Ph.D., Princeton University, 1987. *Biophysics.* Experimental biophysics; atomic force microscopy.

Assistant Professor

Vanegas, Juan, Ph.D., University of California, 2011. *Biophysics.* Biophysics.

White, Matthew S., Ph.D., University of Colorado, Boulder, 2009. *Applied Physics, Nano Science and Technology.* Experimental condensed/materials physics.

Emeritus

Arns, Robert G., Ph.D., University of Michigan, 1960. *History & Philosophy of Physics/Science, Nuclear Physics.* History of science.

Smith, David Y., Ph.D., University of Rochester, 1962. *Condensed Matter Physics, Optics.* Optical and X-ray properties of matter.

Spartalian, Kevork, Ph.D., Carnegie Mellon University, 1974. *Biophysics, Physics and other Science Education.* Mössbauer spectroscopy; biological physics; physics education.

Adjunct Professor

Ohanian, Hans C., Ph.D., Princeton University, 1968. *Relativity & Gravitation.* Relativity.

Senior Lecturer

Pepe, Jason, M.S., University of Vermont, 2003. Physics education.

Sanders, Malcolm, Ph.D., Yale University, 1984. *Nonlinear Dynamics and Complex Systems.* Applied physics; nonlinear systems; chaos.

Lecturer

Perry, John, Ph.D., University of Rochester, 1992. *Astrophysics.* Astrophysics.

DEPARTMENTAL RESEARCH SPECIALTIES AND STAFF

Theoretical

Biophysics. Physical mechanisms for biological effects of ultrasound. Wu.

Condensed Matter Physics. Electronic and transport properties of metals, random alloys, and liquid metals; lattice dynamics; order-disorder phase transitions in alloys; superconductivity; superfluidity; strongly correlated electron systems; electronic properties of graphene; ultracold atom-surface scattering; Berry-phase effects in condensed matter systems. Clougherty, Del Maestro, Kotov.

Experimental

Acoustics. Physical mechanisms for biological effects of ultrasound. Wu.

Astrophysics. Pulsar radio-frequency emission; pulsars as probes of the interstellar medium. Rankin.

Biophysics. Spectroscopy of proteins and nucleic acids and the use of biomolecules in nanotechnological applications. Vanegas.

Condensed Matter Physics. Spin-polarized magneto-optical spectroscopy studies of nitride semiconductors; the time-resolved spectroscopy of nitride emitters and semiconductor nanocrystals; magneto-optical Kerr rotation spectroscopy of ferromagnetic nanostructures. Furis, White.

Materials Science, Metallurgy. Kinetics of thin-film growth and etching; real-time X-ray and electron diffraction studies of materials growth and surface evolution. Furis, Headrick, White.

View additional information about this department at www.gradschoolshopper.com. Check out the "Why Choose Us?" section, find out more about the department's culture and get links to social media networks.

COLLEGE OF WILLIAM AND MARY

DEPARTMENT OF PHYSICS

Williamsburg, Virginia 23187-8795
http://www.wm.edu/as/physics

General University Information

President: W. Taylor Reveley III
Dean of Graduate School: Virginia J. Torczon
University website: http://www.wm.edu/
School Type: Public
Setting: Suburban
Total Faculty: 664
Total Graduate Faculty: n/a
Total number of Students: 8,740
Total number of Graduate Students: 2,455

Department Information

Department Chairman: Prof. Christopher D. Carone, Chair
Department Contact: Paula C. Perry, Coordinator, Physics Graduate Program
 Total full-time faculty: 30
 Total number of full-time equivalent positions: 28
 Full-Time Graduate Students: 63
 Female Full-Time Graduate Students: 12
 First-Year Graduate Students: 7
 Female First-Year Students: 2
 Total Post Doctorates: 8

Department Address

P. O. Box 8795
Williamsburg, VA 23187-8795
Phone: (757) 221-3502
Fax: (757) 221-3540
E-mail: phys_grad_adm@wm.edu
Website: http://www.wm.edu/as/physics

ADMISSIONS

Admission Contact Information

Address admission inquiries to: Graduate Admissions Chair, Department of Physics, College of William and Mary, P. O. Box 8795, Williamsburg, Virginia 23187-8795
Phone: (757) 221-3502
E-mail: phys_grad_adm@wm.edu
Admissions website: http://www.wm.edu/as/physics

Application deadlines

Fall admission:
U.S. students: January 15   *Int'l. students*: January 15

Application fee

U.S. students: $45   *Int'l. students*: $45

Admissions information

For Fall of 2018:
 Number of applicants: 59
 Number admitted: 18
 Number enrolled: 8

Admission requirements

Bachelor's degree requirements: A bachelor's degree in Physics or a related field is required.
Minimum undergraduate GPA: 3.0

GRE requirements

The GRE is required.
No minimum acceptable score for admissions is specified.

Subjective GRE requirements

The Subjective GRE is required.
No minimum acceptable score for admissions is specified.

TOEFL requirements

The TOEFL exam is required for students from non-English-speaking countries.
No minimum acceptable score for admissions is specified.

Other admissions information

Undergraduate preparation assumed: Marion and Thornton, Mechanics; Griffiths, Quantum Physics; Griffiths, Electricity and Magnetism; Kittel and Kroemer, Thermal Physics.

TUITION

Tuition year 2018–19:
Tuition for in-state residents
 Full-time students: $15,760 annual
 Part-time students: $560 per credit
Tuition for out-of-state residents
 Full-time students: $33,354 annual
 Part-time students: $1,325 per credit
A graduate assistantship includes a full tuition and fee waiver.
Credit hours per semester to be considered full-time: 9
Deferred tuition plan: No
Health insurance: Yes, paid by dept.
Other academic fees: Tuition and fees are paid by the department.
Academic term: Semester
Number of first-year students who received full tuition waivers: 7
Number of first-year students who received partial tuition waivers: 7

Teaching Assistants, Research Assistants, and Fellowships

Number of first-year
 Teaching Assistants: 7
 Fellowship students: 3
Average stipend per academic year
 Teaching Assistant: $26,000
 Research Assistant: $26,000
 Fellowship student: $31,000
A graduate assistantship is a 12-month appointment of $26,000 that includes a full tuition waiver, fees, and health insurance at no cost to the student.

FINANCIAL AID

Loans

Loans are available for U.S. students.
Loans are available for international students.
GAPSFAS application required: No
FAFSA application required: No

For further information

Address financial aid inquiries to: Graduate Admissions Chair, Department of Physics, P. O. Box 8795, College of William and Mary, Williamsburg, Virginia 23187-8795.

Phone: (757) 221-3502
E-mail: phys_grad_adm@wm.edu

HOUSING

Availability of on-campus housing
Single students: Yes
Married students: No
Childcare Assistance: No

For further information
Address housing inquiries to: Office of Residence Life.
Phone: (757) 221-4314
E-mail: living@wm.edu
Housing aid website: http://www.wm.edu/offices/residencelife

Table A—Faculty, Enrollments, and Degrees Granted

Research Specialty	2018–19 Faculty	Enrollment Fall 2017 Master's	Enrollment Fall 2017 Doctorate	Number of Degrees Granted 2016–17 (2012–17) Master's	Number of Degrees Granted 2016–17 (2012–17) Terminal Master's	Number of Degrees Granted 2016–17 (2012–17) Doctorate
Applied Physics	1	–	1	–(2)	–(1)	–
Atomic, Molecular, & Optical Physics	5	–	5	2(6)	1(1)	3(9)
Biophysics	–	–	1	–(1)	–	–(2)
Computational Physics	8	–	3	–(4)	–	1(1)
Condensed Matter Physics	6	–	18	4(16)	2(3)	7(12)
High Energy Physics	6	–	9	1(8)	1(2)	2(8)
Nonlinear Dynamics and Complex Systems	3	–	2	–(3)	–(1)	1(2)
Nuclear Physics	15	–	24	6(20)	–(1)	2(12)
Physics of Beams	2	–	–	–	–	–
Plasma and Fusion	3	–	–	–(1)	–	–(1)
Total	35	–	63	13(61)	4(9)	16(47)
Full-time Grad. Stud.	–	–	63	–	–	–
First-year Grad. Stud.	–	–	7	–	–	–

GRADUATE DEGREE REQUIREMENTS

Master's: For the M.S. degree, the requirements are taking the Ph.D. qualifying exam and 32 satisfactory credits of graduate work with a B average. A student progressing toward the Ph.D. degree will usually satisfy the M.S. requirements en route. At least one semester must be spent in residence, and a minimum of one semester of teaching is required for all candidates. There are no foreign language or thesis requirements.

Doctorate: For the Ph.D., required courses include Classical Mechanics, Mathematical Physics, Quantum Mechanics I and II, Classical Electricity and Magnetism I and II, Quantum Field Theory I, and Statistical Physics and Thermodynamics. In addition, two semesters of Colloquium and Teaching Physics, at least one elective from inside and at least one outside the student's field of study may be required. The candidate must, in addition to passing the qualifying exam, demonstrate a mastery of the material in the first- and second-year courses, by either doing well in these courses or individual examinations. A student must maintain a B average for all course work. The research must be a significant original contribution. The dissertation must be approved by the candidate's faculty committee and must be successfully defended in a public oral examination. A Ph.D. candidate must teach a minimum of two semesters. There are no foreign language requirements.

Other Degrees: Ph.D. with Concentration in Computational Science.

Thesis: Thesis may be written in absentia.

SPECIAL EQUIPMENT, FACILITIES, OR PROGRAMS

The Department is housed in the William Small Physical Laboratory, which contains its own library, machine shop, makerspace, and other support facilities in addition to research and teaching laboratories, classrooms, and offices. Small was entirely renovated in 2011, and the research space in the department was doubled by adding two new wings to the building. The Physics Department has many high-performance computing clusters and access to supercomputers through national and international networks. Extensive computational resources are available through the Center for Piezoelectric Design and the nuclear/particle group. The high field solid state Nuclear Magnetic Resonance Laboratory houses a number of NMR machines, including a 17 T magnet. A 12-GeV continuous electron beam accelerator facility, Thomas Jefferson National Accelerator Facility (JLAB), and Applied Research Center (ARC) is located in nearby Newport News.

Faculty and graduate students are engaged in experiments at Fermilab (Batavia, Illinois), The Jefferson Lab (Newport News, Virginia), NASA (Langley, Virginia), Mainz Institute for Theoretical Physics and Mainz Institute for Nuclear Physics (Mainz, Germany), TRIUMF (Vancouver, British Columbia, Canada), Ash River Neutrino Laboratory (Ash River, Minnesota), Sanford Underground Laboratory (Lead, South Dakota), Daya Bay (China), CERN (Geneva, Switzerland), ORNL (Oak Ridge, Tennessee), and Joint Institute for Nuclear Research (Dubna, Russia).

The Small Hall Makerspace gives students access to professional design tools and staff support for use of 3D scanners, 3D printers, laser cutters, CNC machining equipment, controls and electronics, to aid in development from research products to commercial prototypes. The Physics Department is a partner institution in the Physics Innovation and Entrepreneurship network of the American Physical Society.

Table B—Separately Budgeted Research Expenditures by Source of Support

Source of Support	Departmental Research	Physics-related Research Outside Department
Federal government	$4,142,343	
State/local government	$1,078,327	
Non-profit organizations	$213,922	
Business and industry		
Other		
Total	$5,434,592	

Table C—Separately Budgeted Research Expenditures by Research Specialty

Research Specialty	No. of Grants	Expenditures ($)
Atomic, Molecular, & Optical Physics	5	$644,452
Chemical Physics	4	$246,900
Condensed Matter Physics	16	$1,043,393
Energy Sources & Environment	4	$112,305
High Energy Physics	7	$644,452
Medical, Health Physics	1	$50,098
Plasma, Fusion, and Nonlinear Dynamics	2	$90,874
Nuclear Physics	30	$1,767,292
Other	8	$1,081,360
Total	77	$5,681,126

FACULTY

Professor

Armstrong, David S., Ph.D., University of British Columbia, 1989. *Nuclear Physics, Particles and Fields*. Electroweak interactions; electron scattering; parity violation; muon capture; experiment.

Averett, Todd D., Ph.D., University of Virginia, 1995. *Atomic, Molecular, & Optical Physics, Nuclear Physics*. Nucleon structure; polarized nuclear targets; spin exchange optical pumping; experiment.

Carlson, Carl E., Ph.D., Columbia University, 1968. *Nuclear Physics, Particles and Fields*. Theory.

Carone, Christopher D., Ph.D., Harvard University, 1994. Department Chair. *Cosmology & String Theory, High Energy Physics, Particles and Fields, Theoretical Physics*. Theory of elementary particles; theory.

Cooke, William E., Ph.D., Massachusetts Institute of Technology, 1976. *Atomic, Molecular, & Optical Physics, Energy Sources & Environment*. Experiment.

Erlich, Joshua, Ph.D., Massachusetts Institute of Technology, 1999. *Cosmology & String Theory, High Energy Physics, Particles and Fields, Theoretical Physics*. Theory.

Griffioen, Keith A., Ph.D., Stanford University, 1984. *Nuclear Physics, Particles and Fields*. Nucleon structure; dark matter searches; experiment.

Hoatson, Gina L., Ph.D., University of East Anglia, 1980. *Chemical Physics, Condensed Matter Physics*. Solid-state NMR spectroscopy; experiment.

Kordosky, Michael A., Ph.D., University of Texas, Austin, 2004. *High Energy Physics, Particles and Fields*. Experiment.

Krakauer, Henry, Ph.D., Brandeis University, 1975. *Chemical Physics, Computational Physics, Condensed Matter Physics, Solid State Physics*. Electronic properties of materials; quantum many-body simulations. Theory.

Lukaszew, R. Alejandra, Ph.D., Wayne State University, 1996. *Condensed Matter Physics, Electromagnetism, Nano Science and Technology, Optics, Solid State Physics, Surface Physics*. Thin films and nanostructures; experiment.

Manos, Dennis M., Ph.D., Ohio State University, 1976. Vice Provost for Research and Graduate/Professional Studies. *Applied Physics, Biophysics, Nano Science and Technology, Plasma and Fusion, Surface Physics*. Experiment.

McKeown, Robert D., Ph.D., Princeton University, 1979. Deputy Director for Science at the Thomas Jefferson National Accelerator Facility (JLAB). *Nuclear Physics, Particles and Fields*. Electron scattering and reactor neutrinos; experiment.

Nelson, Jeffrey K., Ph.D., University of Minnesota, 1994. Director of Graduate Studies. *High Energy Physics, Particles and Fields*. Neutrino oscillations; neutrino scattering; experiment.

Novikova, Irina, Ph.D., Texas A&M University, 2003. *Atomic, Molecular, & Optical Physics, Optics*. Quantum optics; experiment.

Orginos, Konstantinos N., Ph.D., Brown University, 1998. *Applied Mathematics, Computational Physics, Nuclear Physics, Particles and Fields, Theoretical Physics*. Hadron structure; lattice QCD; nuclear physics; algorithms; theory.

Qiu, Jianqei, Ph.D., Columbia, 1987. Associate Director for Theoretical and Computational Physics; Theory Center Director at the Thomas Jefferson National Accelerator Facility (JLAB). *Nuclear Physics*. Quantum Chromodynamics (QCD) and its applications in high-energy particle and nuclear physics, in particular, in theoretical and phenomenological study of the strong force; Theory.

Sher, Marc T., Ph.D., University of Colorado, 1980. *Cosmology & String Theory, High Energy Physics, Particles and Fields, Theoretical Physics*. Theory.

Tracy, Eugene R., Ph.D., University of Maryland, 1984. *Nonlinear Dynamics and Complex Systems, Plasma and Fusion*. Phase space methods in plasma wave theory; nonlinear modeling and time series analysis; theory.

Vahala, George M., Ph.D., University of Iowa, 1972. *Computational Physics, Nonlinear Dynamics and Complex Systems, Plasma and Fusion*. Lattice Boltzmann; quantum lattice algorithms; theory.

Vahle, Patricia L., Ph.D., University of Texas, Austin, 2004. *High Energy Physics, Particles and Fields*. Neutrino oscillations; development of future neutrino facilities; experiment.

Zhang, Shiwei, Ph.D., Cornell University, 1993. *Computational Physics, Condensed Matter Physics, Solid State Physics*. Quantum many-body simulations; strongly correlated systems; Theory.

Associate Professor

Aubin, Seth A. M., Ph.D., Stony Brook University, 2003. *Atomic, Molecular, & Optical Physics*. Ultracold quantum gases; precision measurements; laser cooling and trapping; experiment.

Mikhailov, Eugeniy E., Ph.D., Texas A&M University, 2003. *Atomic, Molecular, & Optical Physics*. Quantum optics; experiment.

Qazilbash, M. Mumtaz, Ph.D., University of Maryland, College Park, 2004. *Condensed Matter Physics, Low Temperature Physics, Nano Science and Technology, Optics, Solid State Physics*. Infrared and optical spectroscopy; near-field infrared nanospectroscopy; metal-insulator transitions; structural instabilities; superconducting and density-wave transitions; experiment.

Rossi, Enrico, Ph.D., University of Texas, Austin, 2005. *Condensed Matter Physics, Nano Science and Technology, Solid State Physics, Theoretical Physics*. Electronic properties of materials; graphene; two-dimensional electron systems; strongly correlated electron systems; theory.

Assistant Professor

Deconinck, Wouter, Ph.D., University of Michigan, 2008. *Nuclear Physics, Particles and Fields*. Parity; parity violation; electron scattering; fundamental symmetries; Jefferson Laboratory; physics innovation and entrepreneurship; experiment.

Dudek, Jozef J., D.Phil., Oxford, 2004. *Nuclear Physics*. hadronic; nuclear; theory.

Stevens, Justin R., Ph.D., Indiana University, 2012. *Nuclear Physics*. Hadron spectroscopy and structure; experiment.

Emeritus

Champion, Roy L., Ph.D., University of Florida, 1966. *Atomic, Molecular, & Optical Physics*. Experiment.

Eckhause, Morton, Ph.D., Carnegie Mellon University, 1962. *Nuclear Physics, Particles and Fields*. Experiment.

Gross, Franz L., Ph.D., Princeton University, 1963. *Nuclear Physics, Particles and Fields*. Theory.

Kossler, William J., Ph.D., Princeton University, 1964. *Condensed Matter Physics, Nuclear Physics, Physics of Beams*. Experiment.

McKnight, John L., Ph.D., Yale University, 1957. *History & Philosophy of Physics/Science*. Foundations of quantum theory.

Perdrisat, Charles F., Ph.D., Swiss Federal Institute of Technology, 1961. *High Energy Physics, Nuclear Physics, Particles and Fields*. Measurements of the proton structure from elastic electron scattering; experiment.

Petzinger, Kenneth G., Ph.D., University of Pennsylvania, 1971. *Condensed Matter Physics*. Theory.

Remler, Edward A., Ph.D., University of North Carolina, 1963. *Nuclear Physics, Particles and Fields*. Theory.

Schone, Harlan E., Ph.D., University of California, Berkeley, 1960. *Condensed Matter Physics.* Experiment.

von Baeyer, Hans C., Ph.D., Vanderbilt University, 1964. *Particles and Fields, Theoretical Physics.* Theory; public understanding of science.

Walecka, J. Dirk, Ph.D., Massachusetts Institute of Technology, 1958. *High Energy Physics, Nuclear Physics, Particles and Fields.* Theory.

Welsh, Robert E., Ph.D., Pennsylvania State University, 1960. *Nuclear Physics, Particles and Fields.* Experiment.

Adjunct Professor

Bosted, Peter, Ph.D., Massachusetts Institute of Technology, 1980. *Nuclear Physics.* Experiment.

Buck, Warren W., Ph.D., William & Mary, 1976. Theory.

Delos, John B., Ph.D., Massachusetts Institute of Technology, 1970. *Atomic, Molecular, & Optical Physics, Chemical Physics, Medical, Health Physics, Nonlinear Dynamics and Complex Systems, Theoretical Physics.* Chaos; theory.

Melnitchouk, Wally, Ph.D., University of Adelaide, 1993. *Nuclear Physics, Particles and Fields.* Theory.

Richards, David, Ph.D., University of Cambridge, 1984. *Computational Physics, Nuclear Physics, Particles and Fields.* Theory.

Venkataraman, Malathy D., Ph.D., University of Kerala, 1968. *Chemical Physics.* Spectroscopy.

Adjunct Assistant Professor

Walker-Loud, André P., Ph.D., University of Washington-Seattle, 2006. *Astrophysics, Computational Physics, Nuclear Physics, Particles and Fields, Theoretical Physics.* Nonperturbative QCD; implications of the standard model; theory.

Lecturer / Lab Supervisor

Hanni, Hani, Ph.D., Tennessee, 2000. Director of Teaching Laboratories. *Physics and other Science Education.*

DEPARTMENTAL RESEARCH SPECIALTIES AND STAFF

Theoretical

Condensed Matter Physics. Electronic properties of materials; surface physics; high-temperature superconductivity; ferroelectrics; ultra-cold atoms; graphene; two-dimensional systems; strongly correlated electron systems; electron-phonon dynamics; computational physics. Krakauer, Rossi, Zhang.

High Energy Physics. Electroweak phenomenology and symmetry breaking; extensions of the standard model; supersymmetry, grand unification and extra dimensions; string theory; cosmology. Carone, Erlich, Sher.

Medical, Health Physics. Heart rates and respiration of infants in neonatal intensive care units. Delos.

Nonlinear Dynamics and Complex Systems. Order and chaos in classical and quantum systems; atoms in strong fields; atomic and molecular collisions. Delos, Tracy, Vahala.

Nuclear Physics. Perturbative and nonperturbative QCD; lattice gauge theory; effective field theories for hadrons. Carlson, Dudek, Melnitchouk, Orginos, Qiu, Richards, Walker-Loud.

Particles and Fields. Electroweak phenomenology and symmetry breaking; extensions of the standard model; supersymmetry, grand unification and extra dimensions; string theory; cosmology. Carone, Erlich, Sher, Walker-Loud.

Plasma and Fusion. Magnetohydrodynamics; kinetic theory; turbulence; numerical simulation of plasmas; applications to fusion; nonlinear dynamics and chaotic signal process; ocean waves; developing type II quantum computer algorithms for MHD; supercomputers are used at DoE-NERSC, DoD-NAVO, DoD-ERDC, and Earth Simulator (Japan). Tracy, Vahala.

Experimental

Atomic, Molecular, & Optical Physics. Atomic, Molecular, & Optical Physics. Ultracold quantum gases (Bose-Einstein condensates and degenerate Fermi gases), slow and stored light, quantum properties of light, atom-based non-classical light generation, precision measurements (time, fields, and fundamental symmetries), the study of biological systems using AMO techniques, intense laser-matter interactions. Aubin, Cooke, Mikhailov, Novikova.

Condensed Matter Physics. Infrared and optical spectroscopy; near-field infrared nanospectroscopy; phase transitions (metal-insulator, structural, magnetic, superconducting, and density wave); nuclear magnetic resonance; piezoelectrics and high dielectric microwave ceramics; thin films (metallic, magnetic, superconducting for SRF applications, correlated-electron-materials) and nanostructures; electron-phonon dynamics; plasmonics and magneto-plasmonics. Hoatson, Lukaszew, Qazilbash.

High Energy Physics. Experiments at Fermilab, Daya Bay, Ash River, SURF, and CERN; neutrino masses and mixing; CP violation in neutrinos; neutrino interactions on nucleons and nuclei; structure of the weak current; reactor and long baseline neutrino oscillation experiments. Kordosky, McKeown, Nelson, Vahle.

Nuclear Physics. Intermediate energy experiments at Jefferson Laboratory and other facilities; measurements of the structure of nucleons and nuclei via electromagnetic and electroweak interactions; precision tests of the standard model and dark matter searches with electron scattering; hadron spectroscopy; hyperpolarized nuclear targets. Armstrong, Averett, Bosted, Deconinck, Griffioen, Kordosky, McKeown, Perdrisat, Stevens.

Particles and Fields. Experiments at Fermilab, Daya Bay, Ash River; neutrino masses and mixing; CP violation in neutrinos; neutrino interactions on nucleons and nuclei; structure of the weak current; reactor and long baseline neutrino oscillation experiments. Kordosky, Nelson, Vahle.

Physics of Beams. Particle accelerator physics; relativistic electron beams; synchrotron radiation; free-electron lasers; relativistic electrodynamics; superconducting RF cavity surface physics; design and optimization of future accelerator facilities. Lukaszew, Nelson.

View additional information about this department at www.gradschoolshopper.com. Check out the "Why Choose Us?" section, find out more about the department's culture and get links to social media networks.

GEORGE MASON UNIVERSITY

PHYSICS & ASTRONOMY

Fairfax, Virginia 22030–4444
http://physics.gmu.edu

General University Information
President: Angel Cabrera
Dean of Graduate School: Peggy Agouris
University website: http://www.gmu.edu/
School Type: Public
Setting: Suburban
Total Faculty: 1,331
Total number of Students: 34,112
Total number of Graduate Students: 12,365

Department Information
Department Chairman: Prof. Paul So, Chair
Department Contact: Stephanie Kuhta, Academic
 Administrative Specialist
 Total full-time faculty: 51
 Total number of full-time equivalent positions: 32
 Full-Time Graduate Students: 54
 Female Full-Time Graduate Students: 0
 First-Year Graduate Students: 13
 Female First-Year Students: 2
 Total Post Doctorates: 5

Department Address
4400 University Drive, MSN: 3F3
Fairfax, VA 22030–4444
Phone: 703-993-1280
Fax: 703-993-1269
E-mail: physics@gmu.edu
Website: http://physics.gmu.edu

ADMISSIONS

Admission Contact Information
Address admission inquiries to: Office of Admissions, Physics
 PhD, George Mason University, 4400 University Drive, Fair-
 fax, Virginia, 22030
Phone: (703) 993-3430
E-mail: cosgrad@gmu.edu
Admissions website: http://admissions.gmu.edu/grad/

Application deadlines
Fall admission:
U.S. students: January 15 *Int'l. students*: January 15
Spring admission:
U.S. students: October 31 *Int'l. students*: October 31

Application fee
U.S. students: $75 *Int'l. students*: $75
Priority deadlines for applicants requesting financial support are
 Feb. 15th/Feb 1st (domestic/international). If financial support
 is not requested, applicants will be considered if application
 is completed 6 weeks before the start of the desired enrollment
 semester.

Admissions information
For Fall of 2017:
 Number of applicants: 46
 Number admitted: 20
 Number enrolled: 6

Admission requirements
Bachelor's degree requirements: Bachelor's degree in physics
 or a related discipline.
Minimum undergraduate GPA: 3.0

GRE requirements
The GRE is required.
GRE General is required for the PhD and recommended for MS
 applicants.

Subjective GRE requirements
The Subjective GRE is recommended.

TOEFL requirements
The TOEFL exam is required for students from non-English-
 speaking countries.
 PBT score: 570
 iBT score: 88
Minimum of 20 points in each section required for iBT

Other admissions information
Undergraduate preparation assumed: A Junior/Senior level
 course in each of: Classical Mechanics, Electricity and Magnetism, Statistical Mechanics, and Quantum Mechanics.

TUITION

Tuition year 2017–2018:
Tuition for in-state residents
 Full-time students: $595 per credit
Tuition for out-of-state residents
 Full-time students: $1,416 per credit
Credit hours per semester to be considered full-time: 9
Deferred tuition plan: No
Health insurance: Available
Other academic fees: Some courses have a $40 fee
Academic term: Semester
Number of first-year students who received full tuition waivers: 7
Number of first-year students who received partial tuition waivers: 1

Teaching Assistants, Research Assistants, and Fellowships
Number of first-year
 Teaching Assistants: 3
 Research Assistants: 2
 Fellowship students: 2
Average stipend per academic year
 Teaching Assistant: $20,000
 Research Assistant: $20,000
 Fellowship student: $22,000

FINANCIAL AID

Loans
Loans are available for U.S. students.
Loans are not available for international students.
GAPSFAS application required: Yes
FAFSA application required: Yes

644

For further information

Address financial aid inquiries to: Office of Student Financial Aid, George Mason University, 4400 University Drive, MS 3B5, Fairfax, VA 22030–4444.

Phone: (703) 993-2353

E-mail: latienza@gmu.edu

Financial aid website: http://financialaid.gmu.edu/

HOUSING

Availability of on-campus housing

Single students: Yes

Married students: Yes

For further information

Address housing inquiries to: Housing & Residence Life, George Mason University, 4400 University Drive, MS 3F6, Fairfax, Virginia, 22030–4444.

Phone: (703) 993-2720

E-mail: housing@gmu.edu

Housing aid website: http://housing.gmu.edu/

Table A—Faculty, Enrollments, and Degrees Granted

Research Specialty	2017–2018 Faculty	Enrollment Fall 2017 Master's	Enrollment Fall 2017 Doctorate	Number of Degrees Granted 2015–2018 Master's	Number of Degrees Granted 2015–2018 Terminal Master's	Number of Degrees Granted 2015–2018 Doctorate
Astrophysics	8	–	–	–	–	–
Atomic, Molecular, & Optical Physics	2	–	–	–	–	–
Biophysics	5	–	–	–	–	–
Condensed Matter Physics	8	–	–	–	–	–
Heliophysics and Space Weather	7	–	–	–	–	–
High Energy Physics	1	–	–	–	–	–
Mechanics	4	–	–	–	–	–
Nonlinear Dynamics and Complex Systems	4	–	–	–	–	–
Nuclear Physics	2	–	–	–	–	–
Particles and Fields	2	–	–	–	–	–
Physics and other Science Education	3	–	–	–	–	–
Non-specialized	–	–	–	–	–	–
Total	46	30	48	–	–	–
Full-time Grad. Stud.	–	15	32	–	–	–
First-year Grad. Stud.	–	12	12	–	–	–

GRADUATE DEGREE REQUIREMENTS

Master's: The MS degree program has three emphases: (1) Standard, (2) Engineering Physics, and (3) Applied and Engineering Physics. Each requires 30 credits. For students with a previously earned master's degree, the required 30 credits may be reduced by up to 12 credits.

Doctorate: The PhD degree program has two concentrations: Standard and Engineering Physics. Both require 72 credits: (1) 12 credits of core courses; (2) 6 credits of Required Electives; (3) 3 credits of Seminar; (4) 27 credits of General Electives (including preliminary research and directed reading and research credits); and (5) 24 credits of Dissertation Research. For students with a previously earned master's degree, the required 72 credits may be reduced by up to 30 credits.

SPECIAL EQUIPMENT, FACILITIES, OR PROGRAMS

An observatory, high-performance computing facilities, and access to major national laboratories located in the Washington DC metropolitan region.

Table B—Separately Budgeted Research Expenditures by Source of Support

Source of Support	Departmental Research	Physics-related Research Outside Department
Federal government		
State/local government		
Non-profit organizations		
Business and industry		
Other		$3,400,000
Total		$3,400,000

FACULTY

Professor

Barreto, Ernest, Ph.D., University of Maryland, College Park, 1996. *Biophysics, Nonlinear Dynamics and Complex Systems*. Non-linear dynamics, neuroscience.

Becker, Peter, Ph.D., University of Colorado, 1987. *Astronomy, Astrophysics, Computational Physics*. Astrophysics, computational sciences and informatics.

Kan, Cing-Dao, Ph.D., University of Maryland, 1990. *Engineering Physics/Science, Mechanics*. Computational Solid Mechanics.

Lohner, Rainald, Ph.D., University of Wales, 1985. *Computational Physics, Fluids, Rheology, Mechanics*. Computational fluid mechanics.

Mishin, Yuri, Ph.D., Moscow Institute of Steel and Alloys, 1985. *Computational Physics, Condensed Matter Physics, Solid State Physics, Statistical & Thermal Physics, Surface Physics*. Computational materials science, solid state.

Rubin, Philip, Ph.D., University of California, Los Angeles (UCLA), 1989. *High Energy Physics, Particles and Fields*. Particle physics, physics education.

Satija, Indu, Ph.D., Columbia University, 1983. *Condensed Matter Physics, Nonlinear Dynamics and Complex Systems*. Nonlinear dynamics, condensed matter.

Satyapal, Shobita, Ph.D., University of Rochester, 1995. *Astronomy, Astrophysics*. Astrophysics, infrared astronomy.

Sauer, Karen, Ph.D., Princeton University, 1998. *Atomic, Molecular, & Optical Physics*. Atomic and molecular physics, and magnetic resonance.

So, Paul, Ph.D., University of Maryland, College Park, 1995. *Biophysics, Nonlinear Dynamics and Complex Systems*. Nonlinear dynamics, neuroscience.

Summers, Michael E., Ph.D., California Institute of Technology, 1985. *Astronomy, Astrophysics, Climate/Atmospheric Science*. Planetary sciences, atmospheric physics, astrobiology.

Trefil, James, Ph.D., Stanford University, 1966. *Theoretical physics, science education.*

Yang, Chi, Ph.D., Shanghai Jiao Tong University, 1988. *Engineering Physics/Science, Fluids, Rheology, Mechanics*. Computational fluid dynamics.

Zhang, Jie, Ph.D., University of Maryland, 1999. *Heliophysics and Space Weather*. Space Weather.

Associate Professor

Camelli, Fernando E., Ph.D., George Mason University, 2002. *Climate/Atmospheric Science, Computational Physics, Fluids, Rheology*. Computational fluid mechanics.

Cressman, J. Robert, Ph.D., University of Pittsburgh, 1997. *Biophysics*. Experimental biophysics.
Marzougui, Dhafer, Ph.D., George Washington University. *Mechanics*. Computational solid mechanics.
Nikolic, Predrag, Ph.D., Massachusetts Institute of Technology, 2004. *Condensed Matter Physics*. Condensed matter theory.
Rosenberg, Jessica, Ph.D., University of Massachusetts, 2000. *Astronomy*. Astronomy.
Sheng, Howard, Ph.D., Chinese Academy of Sciences. *Computational Physics, Materials Science, Metallurgy*. Materials science.
Tian, Ming, Ph.D., Nankai University, 1984. *Computational Physics, Optics, Quantum Foundations*. Quantum computing; quantum optics.
Weigel, Robert, Ph.D., University of Texas, Austin, 2000. *Computational Physics, Heliophysics and Space Weather, Physics and other Science Education, Other*. Space Weather, magnetospheric physics, computational physics.
Weingartner, Joseph, Ph.D., Princeton University, 1999. *Astrophysics*. Theoretical astrophysics, cosmic dust.
Zhao, Erhai, Ph.D., Fudan University, 2005. *Condensed Matter Physics*. Condensed matter theory.

Assistant Professor

Plavchan, Peter, Ph.D., UCLA, 2006. *Astronomy, Astrophysics, Planetary Science*. Exoplanets.
Vora, Patrick, Ph.D., University of Pennsylvania, 2010. *Condensed Matter Physics*. Experimental condensed matter physics.
Yigit, Erdal, Ph.D., University College London, 2009. *Climate/Atmospheric Science, Heliophysics and Space Weather*. Space Weather.

Professor Emeritus

Ehrlich, Robert, Ph.D., Columbia University, 1964. *Climate/Atmospheric Science, Particles and Fields, Physics and other Science Education*. Particle physics, physics education, climate change.
Ellsworth, Robert, Ph.D., University of Rochester, 1966. *Atmosphere, Space Physics, Cosmic Rays, Particles and Fields*. Particle physics, cosmic rays.
Lieb, B. Joseph, Ph.D., College of William and Mary, 1971. *Atmosphere, Space Physics, Cosmic Rays, Nuclear Physics, Planetary Science*. Nuclear physics, planetary physics, atmospheric physics.

Research Professor

Bilitza, Dieter, Ph.D., Albert-Ludwigs University, 1984. *Climate/Atmospheric Science, Heliophysics and Space Weather*. Ionospheric physics.
Duxbury, Thomas, M.S., Purdue University, 1966. *Heliophysics and Space Weather*. Space sciences.
Mariska, John T., Ph.D., Harvard, 1977. *Solar Physics*.
Meier, Robert, Ph.D., University of Pittsburgh, 1966. *Atmosphere, Space Physics, Cosmic Rays, Climate/Atmospheric Science*. Upper atmospheric and ionospheric physics, remote sensing.
Odstrcil, Dusan, Ph.D., Comenius University in Bratislava, 1978. *Solar Physics*. Solar physics.
Poland, Arthur, Ph.D., Indiana University, 1968. *Astrophysics, Heliophysics and Space Weather*. Solar physics, astrophysics, space weather.

Research Associate Professor

Gliozzi, Mario, Ph.D., Torino University. *Astrophysics*. Astrophysics.
Hunt, Lucas, Ph.D., West Virginia University. *Astronomy, Astrophysics*.

Research Assistant Professor

Huang, Fuxin, Ph.D., George Mason University, 2013. *Computational Physics, Fluids, Rheology*. Fluid Dynamics.
Purja Pun, Ganga, Ph.D., George Mason University, 2011. *Computational Physics, Materials Science, Metallurgy*. Computational materials science.
Secrest, Nathan, Ph.D., George Mason University, 2014. *Astronomy, Astrophysics*. Astrophysics, infrared astronomy.

Teaching Associate Professor

Djordjevi, Branislav R., Ph.D., Michigan State University, 1996. Physics education. *Physics and other Science Education*.
Ericson, Rebecca, M.S., Creighton University, 1975. *Astronomy, Physics and other Science Education*. Astronomy education.
Geller, Harold A., Ph.D., George Mason University, 2005. *Astronomy, Physics and other Science Education*. Education, observational astronomy, astrobiology.
Oerter, Robert, Ph.D., University of Maryland, College Park, 1989. *Particles and Fields, Other*. Particle physics, string theory.
Wyczalkowski, Ania, Ph.D., University of Maryland, College Park, 1998. *Condensed Matter Physics, Fluids, Rheology*. Condensed matter, critical phenomena in fluids.

Posdoctoral Research Associate

Prescott, David, Ph.D., George Mason University, 2005. *Atomic, Molecular, & Optical Physics*. Atomic and molecular physics, and magnetic resonance.

DEPARTMENTAL RESEARCH SPECIALTIES AND STAFF

Theoretical

Astrophysics. Becker, Geller, Gliozzi, Plavchan, Rosenberg, Satyapal, Summers, Weingartner.
Biophysics. Barreto, Cressman, So.
Condensed Matter Physics. Mishin, Nikolic, Purja Pun, Satija, Sheng, Zhao.
Heliophysics and Space Weather. Bilitza, Duxbury, Meier, Poland, Weigel, Yigit, Zhang.
Mechanics. Kan, Lohner, Marzougui, Yang.
Neuroscience/Neuro Physics. Barreto, Cressman, So.
Nonlinear Dynamics and Complex Systems. Barreto, Cressman, Satija, So.
Nuclear Physics. Lieb.
Particles and Fields. Ehrlich, Oerter.
Physics and other Science Education. Ehrlich, Ericson, Geller, Trefil, Wyczalkowski.

Experimental

Atomic, Molecular, & Optical Physics. Sauer, Tian.
Biophysics. Cressman.
Condensed Matter Physics. Vora.
High Energy Physics. Ellsworth, Rubin.
Neuroscience/Neuro Physics. Cressman.
Nonlinear Dynamics and Complex Systems. Cressman.

UNIVERSITY OF VIRGINIA

DEPARTMENT OF PHYSICS

Charlottesville, Virginia 22904-4714
http://www.phys.virginia.edu/

General University Information
President: James E. Ryan
Dean of Graduate School: Ian Baucom
University website: http://www.virginia.edu/
School Type: Public
Total Faculty: 3,014
Total number of Students: 22,805
Total number of Graduate Students: 6,771

Department Information
Department Chairman: Prof. Joseph Poon, Chair
Department Contact: Beth Guyton, Assistant to the Chair
  Total full-time faculty: 33
  Full-Time Graduate Students: 98
  Female Full-Time Graduate Students: 16
  First-Year Graduate Students: 16
  Female First-Year Students: 3
  Total Post Doctorates: 9

Department Address
382 McCormick Road
Charlottesville, VA 22904-4714
Phone: (434) 924-6791
E-mail: grad-info-request@physics.virginia.edu
Website: http://www.phys.virginia.edu/

ADMISSIONS

Admission Contact Information
Address admission inquiries to: Graduate Admissions Advisor,
  382 McCormick Road, PO Box 400714, Charlottesville, VA
  22904-4714
Phone: (434) 924-3781
E-mail: Grad-Info-Request@physics.virginia.edu
Admissions website: http://gsas.virginia.edu/admission/require-
  ments

Application deadlines
Fall admission:
U.S. students: December 15   *Int'l. students*: December 15

Application fee
U.S. students: $85   *Int'l. students*: $85

Admissions information
For Fall of 2018:
  Number of applicants: 171
  Number admitted: 59
  Number enrolled: 11

Admission requirements
Bachelor's degree requirements: Bachelor's degree is required.
  There is no set minimum GPA.

GRE requirements
The GRE is required.
  Quantitative score: 750

Verbal score: 500
Analytical score: 4.0

Subjective GRE requirements
The Subjective GRE is required.
  Mean Advanced GRE score range (25th–75th percentile): N/A
There is no set minimum GRE Physics score.

TOEFL requirements
The TOEFL exam is required for students from non-English-
  speaking countries.
  PBT score: 600
  iBT score: 90
Minimum of 22 in speaking, 22 in writing and 23 in listening

Other admissions information
Undergraduate preparation assumed: Marion and Thornton,
  Classical Dynamics of Particles and Systems (mechanics);
  Kittel, Thermal Physics (statistical physics); Fermi, Thermodynamics (statistical physics); Marion, Classical Electromagnetic Radiation (electromagnetism); Gasioriowicz, Quantum Physics (quantum mechanics).

TUITION

Tuition year 2018–19:
Tuition for in-state residents
  Full-time students: $18,222 annual
Tuition for out-of-state residents
  Full-time students: $29,400 annual
Please note that the tuition amount includes fees. Also, tuition
  fees reduce substantially after the 3rd year of the Ph.D. pro-
  gram.
Credit hours per semester to be considered full-time: 12
Deferred tuition plan: Yes
Health insurance: Available at the cost of $2,690 per year.
Other academic fees: $50 per semester international fee applied
  to all international students.

Teaching Assistants, Research Assistants, and Fellowships
  Average stipend per academic year
    Teaching Assistant: $20,000
    Research Assistant: $20,000
    Fellowship student: $20,000
  An additional $5,600 is available in the summer for students
  working as RA's.

FINANCIAL AID

Application deadlines
Fall admission:
U.S. students: December 15   *Int'l. students*: December 15

Loans
Loans are available for U.S. students.
Loans are not available for international students.
GAPSFAS application required: No
FAFSA application required: No

For further information

Address financial aid inquiries to: Graduate Admissions Advisor.
E-mail: phys-grad-info@virginia.edu
Financial aid website: http://sfs.virginia.edu/

HOUSING

Availability of on-campus housing

Single students: Yes
Married students: Yes

For further information

Address housing inquiries to: Housing & Residence Life, Gibbons House, 425 Tree House Drive, Charlottesville, VA 22904.
Phone: 434-924-3736
E-mail: housing@virginia.edu
Housing aid website: http://www.virginia.edu/housing/grad.php

Table A—Faculty, Enrollments, and Degrees Granted

Research Specialty	2017–18 Faculty	Enrollment Fall 2017 Master's	Enrollment Fall 2017 Doctorate	Number of Degrees Granted 2017–18 (2013–18) Master's	Number of Degrees Granted 2017–18 (2013–18) Terminal Master's	Number of Degrees Granted 2017–18 (2013–18) Doctorate
Astrophysics	1	–	–	–	–	–
Atomic, Molecular, & Optical Physics	7	1	17	–(2)	1(4)	3(16)
Chemical Physics	1	–	–	–	–	–
Condensed Matter Physics	13	–	20	–	–(1)	5(18)
Medical, Health Physics	2	–	1	–	–	–(2)
Nuclear Physics	10	1	20	1(3)	–	3(13)
Particles and Fields	7	–	13	–	–(1)	1(13)
Non-specialized	–	1	35	–	1(6)	–
Total	42	3	106	–(5)	8(32)	11(61)
Full-time Grad. Stud.	–	2	96	–	–	–
First-year Grad. Stud.	–	1	13	–	–	–

GRADUATE DEGREE REQUIREMENTS

Master's: Twenty-four graduate credits in approved program with satisfactory performance, thesis, and thesis exam; no language requirement.

Doctorate: Fifty-four graduate credits required; satisfactory performance in an approved course program is required; comprehensive exam, dissertation, and dissertation exam; two semesters residency required; no language required.

Other Degrees: A Ph.D. in Biophysics is available through an interdisciplinary program associated with the physics department and other science departments of the University.

Thesis: Thesis may be written in absentia.

SPECIAL EQUIPMENT, FACILITIES, OR PROGRAMS

Department facilities include machine and electronics shops, a physics library, and extensive computing resources. Most on-site research is carried out in the J. W. Beams Laboratory building, with additional facilities on campus for work in laser science, materials science, nanoscale fabrication, and particle detector development. The department is active at many off-site facilities as well, including major particle accelerators, neutron sources, and synchrotron sources in the United States and abroad.

Table B—Separately Budgeted Research Expenditures by Source of Support

Source of Support	Departmental Research	Physics-related Research Outside Department
Federal government	$7,610,450.9	
State/local government	$723,182.93	
Non-profit organizations	$894,104.32	
Business and industry	$118,134.05	
Other		
Total	$9,345,872.2	

Table C—Separately Budgeted Research Expenditures by Research Specialty

Research Specialty	No. of Grants	Expenditures ($)
Atomic, Molecular, & Optical Physics	–	$1,570,331.27
Condensed Matter Physics	–	$1,725,278.59
Nuclear Physics	–	$2,497,193.05
Particles and Fields	–	$1,998,994.94
Other	–	$1,554,074.35
Total	–	$9,345,872.2

FACULTY

Professor

Arnold, Peter B., Ph.D., Stanford University, 1986. Theoretical particle physics.

Bloomfield, Louis A., Ph.D., Stanford University, 1983. Experimental atomic and solid-state physics.

Cates, Gordon D., Ph.D., Yale University, 1987. Experimental nuclear and atomic physics.

Cox, Bradley B., Ph.D., Duke University, 1967. Experimental high-energy particle physics.

Dukes, Edmond C., Ph.D., University of Michigan, 1984. Experimental elementary particle physics.

Hirosky, Robert J., Ph.D., University of Rochester, 1994. Experimental particle physics.

Hung, Pham Q., Ph.D., University of California, Los Angeles, 1978. Theoretical particle physics; cosmology.

Jones, Robert R., Ph.D., University of Virginia, 1990. Experimental atomic molecular and optical physics.

Lee, Seung-Hun, Ph.D., Johns Hopkins University, 1996. Experimental condensed matter physics.

Lehmann, Kevin, Ph.D., Harvard University, 1983. Experimental chemical physics; experimental atomic, molecular, and optical physics.

Liyanage, Nilanga, Ph.D., Massachusetts Institute of Technology, 1999. Experimental nuclear and particle physics.

Louca, Despina A., Ph.D., University of Pennsylvania, 1997. Experimental condensed matter.

Norum, Blaine E., Ph.D., Massachusetts Institute of Technology, 1979. Experimental nuclear and particle physics.

Pfister, Olivier, Ph.D., University of Paris-North, 1993. Experimental atomic, molecular, and optical physics.

Počanić, Dinko, Ph.D., Zagreb, 1981. Experimental intermediate-energy nuclear and particle physics.

Poon, S. Joseph, Ph.D., California Institute of Technology, 1978. Experimental solid-state physics; nanostructured materials; quasicrystals; thermoelectric compounds.

Associate Professor

Baeßler, Stefan, Ph.D., University of Heidelberg, 1996. Experimental nuclear and particle physics.

Group, R. Craig, Ph.D., University of Florida, 2006. Experimental high energy physics.

Klich, Israel, Ph.D., Israel Institute of Technology, 2004. Theoretical condensed matter; theoretical mathematical physics.

Kolomeisky, Eugene B., Ph.D., Academy of Sciences of the USSR, Moscow, 1988. Theoretical condensed matter.

Neu, Christopher, Ph.D., Ohio State University, 2003. Experimental high-energy physics.

Paschke, Kent D., Ph.D., Carnegie Mellon University, 2001. Experimental nuclear and particle physics.

Sackett, Charles A., Ph.D., Rice University, 1998. Experimental atomic, molecular, and optical physics.

Shivaram, Bellave S., Ph.D., Northwestern University, 1984. Experimental solid state physics.

Vaman, Diana, Ph.D., Stony Brook University, 2001. Theoretical nuclear and particle physics.

Yoon, Jongsoo, Ph.D., Pennsylvania State University, 1997. Experimental condensed matter physics.

Zheng, Xiaochao, Ph.D., Massachusetts Institute of Technology, 2002. Experimental nuclear and particle physics.

Assistant Professor

Chatterjee, Utpal, Ph.D., University of Illinois at Chicago, 2007. Experimental condensed matter physics.

Chern, Gia-Wei, Ph.D., Johns Hopkins University, 2008. *Theoretical Physics.* Theoretical condensed matter physics.

Schauss, Peter, Ph.D., Max-Planck Institute of Quantum Optics and Ludwig-Maximilians-Universitat Munchen, 2015. *Atomic, Molecular, & Optical Physics, Condensed Matter Physics, Optics.* Ultra cold atoms; Quantum computing and simulation.

Teo, Jeffrey, Ph.D., University of Pennsylvania, 2011. Theoretical condensed matter.

Vucelja, Marija, Ph.D., Weizmann Institute of Science, 2010. *Theoretical Physics.* Theoretical biophysics, Soft condensed matter, and computational physics.

Yagi, Kent, Ph.D., Kyoto University, 2012. Theoretical gravitational waves.

Emeritus

Celli, Vittorio, Ph.D., Pavia, 1958. Theoretical solid-state physics; surface studies.

Deaver, Bascom S., Ph.D., Stanford University, 1962. Experimental solid state physics: superconducting devices.

Fowler, Michael, Ph.D., St. John's College, Cambridge University, 1962. Theoretical physics; field theory and solid-state theory; physics education.

Gallagher, Thomas F., Ph.D., Harvard University, 1971. Collisions and spectroscopy of atoms and molecules.

Hess, George B., Ph.D., Stanford University, 1967.

Minehart, Ralph C., Ph.D., Harvard University, 1962. Experimental nuclear and particle physics.

Ritter, Rogers C., Ph.D., University of Tennessee, 1961. Gravitation; precision measurements; medical physics.

Ruvalds, John, Ph.D., University of Oregon, 1967. Theoretical solid-state physics.

Schnatterly, Stephen, Ph.D., University of Illinois, 1965. Experimental solid-state physics; soft x-ray and inelastic electron scattering spectroscopy of solids, atoms, and molecules.

Thacker, Harry B., Ph.D., University of California, Los Angeles, 1973. Elementary particle physics; quantum field theory.

Weber, Hans J., Ph.D., University of Frankfurt, 1965. Theoretical nuclear and particle physics.

Research Professor

Day, Donal B., Ph.D., University of Virginia, 1979. Experimental nuclear and particle physics.

Gillies, George T., Ph.D., University of Virginia, 1980. Engineering physics.

Lindgren, Richard A., Ph.D., Yale University, 1969. Experimental nuclear and particle physics, physics education.

Williams, Mark B., Ph.D., University of Virginia, 1990. Medical physics.

Research Associate Professor

Liuti, Simonetta, Ph.D., Universitád: Roma, 1989. Theoretical nuclear and particle physics.

Affiliate Professor

Herbst, Eric, Ph.D., Harvard University, 1972. Theoretical chemical physics.

DEPARTMENTAL RESEARCH SPECIALTIES AND STAFF

Theoretical

Astrophysics. Theoretical studies to address unsolved problems in fundamental physics using astrophysical compact objects, such as black holes and neutron stars, that form after gravitational collapse of massive stars. Their extremely strong gravitational field allows us to test whether General Relativity is correct in the regime that is inaccessible from table-top or Solar System experiments. Their large number of population allows us to carry out high precision cosmology. Neutron star's remarkably high density allows us to determine the correct equation of state (relation between pressure and density) for nuclear matter. Yagi.

Condensed Matter Physics. Field theoretic models for solid state systems; many-body physics in ultracold atomic gases; quantum Hall effect; Bethe Ansatz systems; topological quantum computation; phase transitions and renormalization group methods in statistical physics; Bose-Einstein condensation; theory of macroscopic quantum phenomena; pattern formation; nonperturbative statistical mechanics. Chern, Klich, Kolomeisky, Teo, Vucelja.

High Energy Physics. Theoretical studies of high-energy physics, including properties of quantum chromodynamics; lattice gauge theory; string/gauge duality; high-temperature field theory; electroweak interactions; grand unified theories; supersymmetry; neutrino physics including models of neutrino masses; dark matter; dark energy; cosmology. Arnold, Hung, Thacker, Vaman.

Nuclear Physics. Lattice gauge theory; inclusive and exclusive deep inelastic electron and neutrino scattering on nucleons and nuclei; the spin composition of quarks and gluons within hadrons; the role of QCD in hadronic structure. Liuti, Vaman.

Experimental

Atomic, Molecular, & Optical Physics. Laser manipulation and spectroscopy of atoms, ions, small molecules, and clusters, including Bose-Einstein condensation in dilute vapors; atom interferometry; quantum optics; quantum information; optical interferometry; dipole-dipole interactions between cold Rydberg atoms; ultracold plasmas; observation and control of electronic wavepackets in Rydberg atoms using microwave, THz, and optical fields; dynamics of atoms and molecules in intense femtosecond laser pulses; high-order harmonic generation in gases; spectroscopy of single and doubly excited Rydberg atoms; studies of magnetic properties of clusters; photodetachment and photoionization; development of new techniques in laser spectroscopy; noble gas hyper polarization via spin exchange with optically pumped alkali atoms, optical control of chemical processes; cavity ring-down spectroscopy; spectroscopy using helium nano-droplet isolation; investigation of highly excited vibrational states; microwave-optical double resonance. Cates, Gallagher, Jones, Lehmann, Pfister, Sackett.

Condensed Matter Physics. The experimental condensed matter physics groups at UVa explore the structural, electronic, magnetic, and superconducting properties of different types of amorphous and crystalline solids including thin films. The groups are equipped with state-of-the-art equipment. Activities include the synthesis and characterization of amorphous alloys, quantum magnets, frustrated spin systems, multiferroics, high temperature superconductors, and strongly correlated systems. Several groups perform research at national and international neutron and synchrotron facilities. There are joint research programs with the Engineering School. Facilities accessible to the groups include photolithography lab and x-ray diffraction and electron microscopes, as well as national labs where high magnetic fields sources are available. Celli, Chatterjee, Lee, Louca, Poon, Shivaram, Yoon.

High Energy Physics. The experimental group participates in major research collaborations at the world's leading particle accelerators in the United States and in Europe where we are able to study the most fundamental interactions of matter to elicit the inner workings of the natural world. The group is housed in its own building a short walk from the main physics building. This superb laboratory has an electronics lab, mechanical shop, a large assembly area, and powerful computing capabilities. Cox, Dukes, Group, Hirosky, Neu.

Nuclear Physics. The Physics Department and the Institute of Nuclear and Particle Physics support some of the leading research groups in this basic area of physics. Faculty members are the spokesmen for experiments that test fundamental aspects of nucleon and nuclear structure. These include experiments at the Stanford Linear Accelerator Center (SLAC) on the origin of the nucleon's spin, the details of the charge distribution of the neutron at Thomas Jefferson National Accelerator Facility (TJNAF), and a precision measurement of pion beta decay at the Paul Scherrer Institute (PSI). At SLAC the inelastic scattering of polarized electrons from polarized nucleon targets allows a detailed investigation of the spin structures of the nucleon. These measurements provide the best determination of how the quarks and gluons contribute to the fundamental spin of the nucleon. There is active research and development of high-power polarized targets, using high-field superconducting magnets, low-temperature refrigerators, and high-frequency microwaves. Electron paramagnetic resonance characterization of these targets is proceeding together with theoretical and computational modeling of local hyperfine interactions that contribute to dynamic nuclear polarization. At TJNAF an extensive series of experiments has been approved, including a measurement of the electric charge form factor of the neutron. The experimental measurements are complemented by strong theoretical support in the Department. This theoretical effort involves work in relativistic chiral quark models; spontaneous chiral symmetry breaking; quantum theories based on light-front formalism; and perturbative quantum chromodynamics (QCD) phenomenology, including studies of power corrections to the nucleon/nuclear structure functions, quark-hadron duality and low Bjorken x physics. Baeßler, Cates, Day, Liyanage, Norum, Paschke, Počanić, Zheng.

VIRGINIA COMMONWEALTH UNIVERSITY

DEPARTMENT OF PHYSICS

Richmond, Virginia 23284-2000
http://www.vcu.edu/hasweb/phy

General University Information
President: Michael Rao
Dean of Graduate School: F. Douglas Boudinot
University website: http://www.vcu.edu
School Type: Public
Setting: Urban
Total Faculty: 2,338
Total Graduate Faculty: Not available
Total number of Students: 31,036
Total number of Graduate Students: 5,283

Department Information
Department Chairman: Dr. Shiv Khanna, Chair
Department Contact: Dr. Shiv Khanna, Chair
  Total full-time faculty: 20
  Total number of full-time equivalent positions: 20
  Full-Time Graduate Students: 14
  Female Full-Time Graduate Students: 1
  First-Year Graduate Students: 7
  Total Post Doctorates: 10

Department Address
701 West Grace Street (Laurel Street Entrance)
P. O. Box 842000
Richmond, VA 23284-2000
Phone: (804) 828-1818 (C) 1820
Fax: (804) 828-7073
E-mail: snkhanna@vcu.edu
Website: http://www.vcu.edu/hasweb/phy

ADMISSIONS

Admission Contact Information
Address admission inquiries to: Virginia Commonwealth University, Graduate Admissions, P.O. Box 843051, Richmond, VA 23284-3051
Phone: (804) 828-6916
E-mail: vcu-grad@vcu.edu
Admissions website: https://graduate.vcu.edu/

Application deadlines
Fall admission:
U.S. students: May 1   *Int'l. students*: May 1
Spring admission:
U.S. students: December 1   *Int'l. students*: December 1

Application fee
U.S. students: $70   *Int'l. students*: $70
https://www.vcu.edu/admissions/apply/graduate/#tabs-192416

Admissions information
For Fall of 2017:
  Number of applicants: 11
  Number admitted: 8
  Number enrolled: 8

Admission requirements
Bachelor's degree requirements: A Bachelor's degree in Physics or Engineering is recommended.
Minimum undergraduate GPA: 3.0

GRE requirements
The GRE is required.
  Quantitative score: 150
  Verbal score: 150
  Analytical score: 3.5

Subjective GRE requirements
The Subjective GRE is not required.

TOEFL requirements
The TOEFL exam is required for students from non-English-speaking countries.
  PBT score: 550
  iBT score: 90

Other admissions information
Undergraduate preparation assumed: A typical student will have completed intermediate and/or advanced courses using Classical Mechanics, Marion and Thornton; Electricity and Magnetism, Reitz, Milford and Christy; and Modern Physics, Eisberg and Resnick. Deficiencies in advanced courses may be made up while a graduate student.

TUITION

Tuition year 2018–2019:
Tuition for in-state residents
  Full-time students: $7,248 per semester
  Part-time students: $768 per credit
Tuition for out-of-state residents
  Full-time students: $13,985 per semester
  Part-time students: $1,508 per credit
Fees included. Housing and meal plan not included.
Credit hours per semester to be considered full-time: 9
Deferred tuition plan: Yes
Health insurance: Not available.
Academic term: Semester
Number of first-year students who received full tuition waivers: 5

Teaching Assistants, Research Assistants, and Fellowships
Number of first-year
  Teaching Assistants: 4
Average stipend per academic year
  Teaching Assistant: $18,000
  Research Assistant: $25,000

FINANCIAL AID

Application deadlines
Fall admission:
U.S. students: March 1

Loans
Loans are available for U.S. students.
Loans are available for international students.
GAPSFAS application required: No
FAFSA application required: Yes

For further information

Address financial aid inquiries to: Financial Aid, 1015 Floyd Avenue, Richmond, VA 23284-3026.
Phone: (804) 828-6669
Financial aid website: https://finaid.vcu.edu/

HOUSING

Availability of on-campus housing

Single students: Yes
Married students: No
Childcare Assistance: No

For further information

Address housing inquiries to: Residential Life & Housing, 301 West Cary Street, Richmond, VA 23284.
Phone: (804) 828-7666
E-mail: vcuhousing@vcu.edu
Housing aid website: http://www.housing.vcu.edu/

Table A—Faculty, Enrollments, and Degrees Granted

| Research Specialty | 2017–2018 Faculty | Enrollment Fall 2017 | | Number of Degrees Granted 2017–18 (2013–18) | | |
		Master's	Doctorate	Master's	Terminal Master's	Doctorate
Applied Physics	20	13	–	3(22)	–	–
Nano Science and Technology	7	–	14	–	–	6(15)
Total	27	13	14	3(22)	–	6(15)
Full-time Grad. Stud.	–	10	13	–	–	–
First-year Grad. Stud.	–	6	3	–	–	–

GRADUATE DEGREE REQUIREMENTS

Master's: Completion of 30 approved graduate credits with at least 15 credits of didactic or laboratory coursework and successful completion of a master's thesis. Each student will choose an advisor during the first semester and propose a plan of study to fulfill the student's individual career goals.
Thesis: Thesis may not be written in absentia.

SPECIAL EQUIPMENT, FACILITIES, OR PROGRAMS

The department has facilities for surface and material physics research, including an atomic force microscope and equipment for Raman and photoluminescence. Other analytical equipment (SEM, XPS, TEM) is available in a shared facility.

Table B—Separately Budgeted Research Expenditures by Source of Support

Source of Support	Departmental Research	Physics-related Research Outside Department
Federal government	$1,310,000	
State/local government		
Non-profit organizations		
Business and industry	$48,500	
Other		
Total	$1,358,500	

Table C—Separately Budgeted Research Expenditures by Research Specialty

Research Specialty	No. of Grants	Expenditures ($)
Condensed Matter Physics	13	$1,358,500
Total	13	$1,358,500

FACULTY

Distinguished University Professor

Jena, Purusottam, Ph.D., University of California, Riverside, 1970. *Atomic, Molecular, & Optical Physics, Chemical Physics, Condensed Matter Physics, Energy Sources & Environment, Materials Science, Metallurgy, Nano Science and Technology, Solid State Physics, Surface Physics, Theoretical Physics.* Electronic structure theory of metals and alloys, semiconductors, intermetallics, and insulators; atomic clusters and cluster assembled materials.

Chair Professor

Khanna, Shiv N., Ph.D., University of Delhi, 1976. Commonwealth Professor. *Chemical Physics, Condensed Matter Physics, Materials Science, Metallurgy, Nano Science and Technology, Solid State Physics.* Theoretical solid-state physics; electronic structure and magnetic properties of amorphous metals, small atomic clusters, and cluster assembled materials.

Associate Professor

Bertino, Massimo F., Ph.D., MPI-Germany, 1996. *Chemical Physics, Condensed Matter Physics, Nano Science and Technology.* Production of nanostructures by photo-lithographic methods.

Bishop, Marilyn F., Ph.D., University of California, Irvine, 1976. *Acoustics, Biophysics, Chemical Physics, Condensed Matter Physics, Medical, Health Physics, Nano Science and Technology, Optics, Solid State Physics, Statistical & Thermal Physics.* Charge density waves; superconductivity; semiconductors, biophysics.

Demchenko, Denis, Ph.D., South Dakota School of Mines & Technology, 2002. *Condensed Matter Physics, Nano Science and Technology, Solid State Physics.* Theoretical and computational nanoscience; electronic structure theory of semiconductor nanocrystals, defects in semiconductors.

Gowdy, Robert H., Ph.D., Yale University, 1968. Department Associate Chair. *Applied Mathematics, Astrophysics, Relativity & Gravitation.* General relativity and cosmology.

Reed, Jason C., Ph.D., New York University, 2007. *Biophysics, Medical, Health Physics, Nano Science and Technology.* Applications of nanotechnology to biological systems: Cell-mass measurements by interference Microscopy; Gene expression profiling on Atomic Force Microscopy.

Reiner, Joseph, Ph.D., Stony Brook University, 2003. *Chemical Physics, Condensed Matter Physics, Nano Science and Technology.* Single-molecule biophysics nanopores; fluorescence; optical tweezers.

Reshchikov, Michael A., Ph.D., Ioffe Physical-Technical Institute, 1989. *Condensed Matter Physics, Nano Science and Technology, Solid State Physics, Surface Physics.* Defects in semiconductors; photoluminescence.

Ye, Dexian, Ph.D., Rensselaer Polytechnic Institute, 2006. *Chemical Physics, Condensed Matter Physics, Nano Science and Technology.* Fabrication and characterization of nanostructured surfaces.

Assistant Professor

Foster, Kerwin C., Ph.D., Florida State University, 2002. *Condensed Matter Physics.*

Prok, Yelena, Ph.D., University of Virginia, 2004. *Nuclear Physics*. Spin structure of the proton.

Reveles, J. Ulises, Ph.D., Cinvestav, Mexico City, 2004. *Chemical Physics, Condensed Matter Physics, Nano Science and Technology*. Theoretical solid-state physics; electronic structure and magnetic properties of amorphous metals, small atomic clusters, and cluster assembled materials.

Instructor

Capuano, Carissa, D.Phil., The College of William & Mary, 2012. *Nuclear Physics*.

Duraisamy, Murugeswaran, Ph.D., University of Cincinnati, Ohio, 2009. *Theoretical Physics*. Phenomenology with particular emphasis on the physics beyond the Standard Model.

McMullen, J. Thomas, Ph.D., Queen's College, 1968. *Acoustics, Biophysics, Chemical Physics, Condensed Matter Physics, Medical, Health Physics, Nano Science and Technology, Optics, Solid State Physics, Statistical & Thermal Physics*. Charge density waves; superconductivity; semiconductors, biophysics.

Skrobiszewski, John L., M.S., Virginia Commonwealth University, 2003. *Condensed Matter Physics, Nano Science and Technology*.

Steck, Amanda M., M.S., University of Nebraska - Lincoln, 2014. Physics Lab Coordinator. *High Energy Physics*.

Wickramarachchi, Samanthi J., Ph.D., Western Michigan University, 2015. *Condensed Matter Physics, Physics of Beams*.

Woodworth, Patrick H., M.S., Virginia Commonwealth University, 2007. *Condensed Matter Physics, Nano Science and Technology*. Semiconductor surface studies.

DEPARTMENTAL RESEARCH SPECIALTIES AND STAFF

Theoretical

Acoustics. Bishop, McMullen.

Atomic, Molecular, & Optical Physics.

Biophysics. Bishop, McMullen, Reed, Reiner.

Chemical Physics. Properties of metal clusters and cluster-assembled materials. Bertino, Bishop, Jena, Khanna, McMullen, Reveles, Ye.

Energy Sources & Environment. Jena.

Materials Science, Metallurgy. Bertino, Jena, Khanna.

Nano Science and Technology. Electronic structure of defects and defect complexes; electronic and magnetic properties of multilayer thin films, dilute magnetic semiconductors, metal oxides, and hydrogen storage materials in bulk and nanostructured forms; transport theory for simple metals and charge density waves; electronic, structural, and elastic properties of semiconductors; nanostructures and nanoscale photovoltaics. Bertino, Bishop, Demchenko, Jena, Khanna, McMullen, Reiner, Reshchikov, Reveles, Skrobiszewski, Woodworth, Ye.

Optics. Bishop, McMullen, Reiner.

Relativity & Gravitation. Dynamical structure of gravitational theories; gravitational waves; exact solutions of Einstein's equations; quantum gravity. Gowdy.

Solid State Physics. Bishop, Demchenko, Jena, Khanna, McMullen, Reshchikov.

Statistical & Thermal Physics. Bishop, McMullen.

Surface Physics. Jena, Reshchikov.

Theoretical Physics. Demchenko, Duraisamy, Gowdy, Jena, Khanna.

Experimental

Condensed Matter Physics. Growth and characterization of semiconductor and metal systems using scanning probe microscopy techniques, modulation spectroscopy, Raman, and photoluminescence; photo-lithographic fabrication of nanocomposites for structural and energetic applications; directed self-assembly of nanostructures. Bertino, Bishop, Demchenko, Foster, Jena, Khanna, McMullen, Reiner, Reshchikov, Reveles, Skrobiszewski, Woodworth, Ye.

Nuclear Physics. Capuano, Prok.

VIRGINIA TECH

DEPARTMENT OF PHYSICS

Blacksburg, Virginia 24061
http://www.phys.vt.edu

General University Information
President: Timothy Sands
Dean of Graduate School: Karen DePauw
University website: http://www.vt.edu/
School Type: Public
Setting: Rural
Total Faculty: 4,265
Total number of Students: 34,440
Total number of Graduate Students: 6,746

Department Information
Department Chairman: Prof. Mark L. Pitt, Chair
Department Contact: Mark L. Pitt, Department Chair
  Total full-time faculty: 35
  Full-Time Graduate Students: 85
  Female Full-Time Graduate Students: 14
  First-Year Graduate Students: 19
  Total Post Doctorates: 17

Department Address
Robeson Hall (MC 0435)
850 West Campus Drive
Blacksburg, VA 24061
Phone: (540) 231-6544
Fax: (540) 231-7511
E-mail: info@phys.vt.edu
Website: http://www.phys.vt.edu

ADMISSIONS

Admission Contact Information
Address admission inquiries to: Graduate Program Coordinator,
  Physics Department
Phone: (540) 231-8728
E-mail: gradphys@vt.edu
Admissions website: http://www.phys.vt.edu

Application deadlines
Fall admission:
U.S. students: January 5   *Int'l. students*: January 5

Application fee
U.S. students: $75   *Int'l. students*: $75

Admissions information
For Fall of 2018:
  Number of applicants: 101
  Number admitted: 47
  Number enrolled: 18

Admission requirements
Bachelor's degree requirements: Bachelor's degree in Physics
  with a minimum undergraduate GPA of 3.0 in physics/math
  during the last two years of undergraduate study or, if the
  Bachelor's degree is in a subject other than physics, 18 semester hours in intermediate mechanics, electromagnetism, and
  quantum mechanics, excluding general physics, are required.
Minimum undergraduate GPA: 3.0

GRE requirements
The GRE is required.

Subjective GRE requirements
The Subjective GRE is required.

TOEFL requirements
The TOEFL exam is required for students from non-English-
  speaking countries.
  PBT score: 550
  iBT score: 90
TOEFL scores of 20 or greater in Listening, Writing, Speaking,
  and Reading subsections are required.

Other admissions information
*Undergraduate preparation assumed: Undergraduate prepara-
  tion assumed:* Thornton, Marion, *Classical Mechanics*; Reitz,
  Milford, and Christy, *Foundations of Electromagnetic Theory*; Griffiths, *Electrodynamics*; Hecht, *Optics*; Kittel, Kroemer, *Thermal Physics*; Griffiths, *Quantum Mechanics*; Liboff, *Quantum Mechanics*.

TUITION

Tuition year 2018–19:
Tuition for in-state residents
  Full-time students: $6,742.5 per semester
  Part-time students: $2,218.5 per semester
Tuition for out-of-state residents
  Full-time students: $13,500 per semester
  Part-time students: $4,470.75 per semester
Tuition for part-time is for three credit hours. Assistantships
  come with proportional tuition waivers.
Credit hours per semester to be considered full-time: 9
Deferred tuition plan: No
Health insurance: Yes, 90% subsidy of University negotiated
  plan.
Other academic fees: In-state residents, $1,012 ($550.00, part-
  time/three credits) per semester. Out-of-state residents:
  $1,314.50 ($701.00, part-time/three credits) per semester.
Academic term: Semester
Number of first-year students who received full tuition waivers: 18

Teaching Assistants, Research Assistants, and Fellowships
Number of first-year
  Teaching Assistants: 18
Average stipend per academic year
  Teaching Assistant: $16,857
  Research Assistant: $16,857
All assistantships come with tuition waivers.

FINANCIAL AID

Application deadlines
Fall admission:
U.S. students: January 5   *Int'l. students*: January 5

Loans

Loans are not available for U.S. students.
Loans are not available for international students.
GAPSFAS application required: No
FAFSA application required: No

For further information

Address financial aid inquiries to: Graduate Program Coordinator, Physics Department.
E-mail: gradphys@vt.edu
Financial aid website: http://www.finaid.vt.edu/

HOUSING

Availability of on-campus housing

Single students: Yes
Married students: No
Childcare Assistance: No

For further information

Address housing inquiries to: Housing Residence and Life, 144 New Hall West, Blacksburg, VA 24061-0428.
Phone: (540) 231-6205
Housing aid website: http://www.housing.vt.edu

Table A—Faculty, Enrollments, and Degrees Granted

Research Specialty	2018–19 Faculty	Enrollment Fall 2018 Master's	Enrollment Fall 2018 Doctorate	Number of Degrees Granted 2017–18 (2008–18) Master's	Number of Degrees Granted 2017–18 (2008–18) Terminal Master's	Number of Degrees Granted 2017–18 (2008–18) Doctorate
Astrophysics	4	–	4	–(1)	1(3)	–(5)
Biophysics	4	–	1	–(2)	–	–(2)
Condensed Matter Physics	15	–	42	2(28)	–(8)	5(52)
Medical, Health Physics	4	–	–	–	–	–
Nuclear Physics	5	–	9	1(7)	1(3)	2(17)
Particles and Fields	8	–	9	–(7)	–(2)	–(8)
Non-specialized	–	3	16	–	3(10)	–
Total	–	3	81	3(45)	3(20)	7(79)
Full-time Grad. Stud.	–	3	81	–	–	–
First-year Grad. Stud.	–	2	16	–	–	–

GRADUATE DEGREE REQUIREMENTS

Master's: Both thesis and non-thesis options are available. A written thesis must be submitted and defended at an oral final examination. For the non-thesis option, 32 hours of coursework are required. An oral final examination must be passed. For both options, a minimum 3.0 grade point average must be maintained. There is no foreign language requirement.

Doctorate: A Ph.D. candidate must pass an oral qualifying and preliminary examination covering classical mechanics, electromagnetism, and non-relativistic quantum mechanics. The preliminary examination covers the proposed thesis research. Ninety hours total (minimum) must be completed, including coursework (32 hours minimum) and research while maintaining a minimum 3.0 grade point average. A written dissertation is required and must be defended at an oral final examination.

SPECIAL EQUIPMENT, FACILITIES, OR PROGRAMS

The faculty in Virginia Tech's Physics Department conducts research in astronomical, mathematical, medical, nuclear, elementary particle, and condensed-matter physics. Medical and neuroscience research is conducted at sites in Arlington and Roanoke, Virginia. Much of the research activity in astronomy and experimental nuclear and particle physics utilizes off-campus facilities, while most of the instrumentation and data analysis are performed on-campus. These facilities include Brookhaven National Laboratory, Daya Bay, Fermilab, KEK, LANL, ORNL, TJNAF, NRAO, Gran Sasso, and the nearby Kimballton Underground Research Facility (KURF). Telescopes used by the astronomy group include the Hubble Space Telescope, the Very Large Telescope, the Chandra X-ray satellite, the Spitzer IR satellite, and the XMM-Newton X-ray satellite.

Experimental facilities in condensed-matter physics include low-temperature facilities and variable-temperature high-magnetic-field magneto-transport systems, low-temperature optical systems, pulsed near- and mid-infrared lasers, visible-ultraviolet lasers, spectrometers, confocal microscopy and related optical characterization facilities, nanofabrication systems, thin-film materials deposition systems, materials synthesis, room-temperature and low-temperature scanning tunneling microscopy, and various other microscopy systems. More analytical and nanofabrication systems (e.g., X-ray, Auger, TEM, AFM, SIMS, SQUID, and FIB) are housed in on-campus facilities. Research is also performed off-campus, for example, at the National High Magnetic Field Laboratory.

Housed in Robeson Hall is the University's Center for Neutrino Physics (CNP). Many theorists are members of the University Center for Statistical Mechanics, Mathematical Physics, and Theoretical Chemistry, composed of faculty from the Departments of Chemistry, Physics, and Mathematics.

The Department of Physics is also home to the Center for Soft Matter and Biophysics at Virginia Tech. This interdisciplinary research Center was established in February 2016, and is administered by the Department of Physics in the College of Science. Its mission is to advance the rapidly growing research areas of soft matter and biological physics. Special attention will be extended to how these developments can address many of the most significant problems currently facing society, for example effective drug design and delivery, next generation materials, programmable biology, and models for human disease.

Virginia Tech University computing offers multiple high-performance computing systems. The Physics Department has two dedicated clusters and a distributed collection of about 200 limited-availability nodes, all running Linux. Access to supercomputers is available through national and international networks.

The Physics Department operates a professional machine shop, a computer shop, and a student shop.

Table B—Separately Budgeted Research Expenditures by Source of Support

Source of Support	Departmental Research	Physics-related Research Outside Department
Federal government	$2,696,221.71	
State/local government	$171,667.68	
Non-profit organizations	$110,664.14	
Business and industry	$221,853.26	
Other	$36.15	
Total	$3,200,442.94	

FACULTY

Professor

Arav, Nahum, Ph.D., University of Colorado, Boulder, 1994 Astrophysics.

Chang, Lay Nam, Ph.D., University of California, Berkeley, 1967. Theoretical particle physics.

Heflin, James R., Ph.D., University of Pennsylvania, 1990. Associate Dean for Research and Graduate Studies, College of Science. Experimental condensed matter physics; biophysics.

Heremans, Jean J., Ph.D., Princeton University, 1994. Experimental condensed matter physics.

Huber, Patrick, Ph.D., Technische Universität München, 2003. Theoretical particle physics.

Link, Jonathan M., Ph.D., University of California, Davis, 2001. Experimental nuclear and particle physics.

Minic, Djordje, Ph.D., University of Texas, Austin, 1993. Theoretical particles physics.

Montague, Read P., Ph.D., University of Alabama, 1988. Neuroscience; medical physics; biophysics.

Mun, Seong K., Ph.D., SUNY, Albany, 1979. Neuroscience; medical physics.

Piilonen, Leo E., Ph.D., Princeton University, 1985. Experimental nuclear and particle physics.

Pitt, Mark, Ph.D., Princeton University, 1992. Chair of the Department of Physics. Experimental nuclear and particle physics.

Pleimling, Michel J.F., Ph.D., Universität des Saarlandes, 1996. Director of the Academy of Integrated Sciences for the College of Science. Theoretical condensed matter physics.

Sharpe, Eric R., Ph.D., Princeton University, 1998. Theoretical particle physics.

Simonetti, John H., Ph.D., Cornell University, 1985. Astrophysics.

Täuber, Uwe C., Ph.D., Technische Universität München, 1992. Theoretical condensed matter physics.

Vogelaar, R. Bruce, Ph.D., California Institute of Technology, 1989. William E. Hassinger, Jr. Senior Faculty Fellow in Physics. Experimental nuclear and particle physics.

Associate Professor

Economou, Sophia, Ph.D., University of California at San Diego, 2006. Condensed matter theoretical physics.

Khodaparast, Giti A., Ph.D., University of Oklahoma, 2001. Experimental condensed matter physics; biophysics.

Mariani, Camillo, Ph.D., University of Rome, 2008. Experimental nuclear and particle physics.

Park, Kyungwha, Ph.D., Princeton University, 2000. Theoretical condensed matter physics.

Robinson, Hans D., Ph.D., Boston University, 2000. Experimental condensed matter physics.

Scarola, Vito W., Ph.D., Pennsylvania State University, 2002. Theoretical condensed matter physics.

Soghomonian, Victoria, Ph.D., Syracuse University, 1995. Experimental condensed matter physics.

Takeuchi, Tatsu, Ph.D., Yale University, 1989. Theoretical particle physics.

Assistant Professor

Anderson, Lara B., Ph.D., Oxford University, 2008. Theoretical particle physics.

Ashkar, Rana, Ph.D., Indiana University, 2012. *Biophysics, Condensed Matter Physics*. Experimental condensed matter physics.

Barnes, Edwin, Ph.D., University of California at San Diego, 2006. Condensed matter theoretical physics.

Cheng, Shengfeng, Ph.D., Johns Hopkins University, 2010. Experimental condensed matter physics.

Emori, Satoru, Ph.D., Massachusetts Institute of Technology, 2013. *Condensed Matter Physics, Nano Science and Technology*. Experimental condensed matter physics.

Gray, James, Ph.D., University of Sussex, 2001. Theoretical particle physics.

Horiuchi, Shunsaku, Ph.D., University of Tokyo, 2009. Astroparticle physics.

Nguyen, Vinh, Ph.D., University of Amsterdam, Zeeman Intstitute, 2004. Experimental condensed matter physics.

O'Donnell, Thomas M., Ph.D., University of California- Berkeley, 2011. *High Energy Physics, Nuclear Physics*. Experimental Particle Physics.

Tao, Chenggang, Ph.D., University of Maryland, 2007. Experimental condensed matter physics.

Research Faculty

Özcan, Alpay, Ph.D., Washington University, St. Louis, 2000. Neuroscience; medical physics.

Wong, Kenneth, Ph.D., University of California, Berkeley/San Francisco, 2002. Neuroscience; medical physics.

DEPARTMENTAL RESEARCH SPECIALTIES AND STAFF

Theoretical

Condensed Matter/Statistical Physics. Theoretical investigations of a wide range of systems, both in thermal equilibrium and driven far from equilibrium, are being carried out using both analytical techniques and computational approaches. Research interests include phase transitions, critical phenomena, electronic, transport, and optical properties of a variety of physical systems. Examples include universal properties and scaling behavior in magnetic systems, topological matter, structural phase transitions, boson localization, driven diffusive systems, branching, and annihilating random walks, vortex transport and flux pinning in superconductors, chemical reactions, population dynamics, and percolation problems. Research is also carried out on electronic, transport, and optical properties of materials, interfaces, semiconductor heterostructures, molecular devices, biological systems, and ultracold quantum gases. Analytical approaches include classical Landau-Ginzburg theory as well as modern techniques such as coherent-state path-integrals and field theoretic renormalization group analysis are used to study problems in quantum mechanics; molecular dynamics; dynamical systems; equilibrium and non-equilibrium statistical mechanics. Computational approaches include numerical solutions of Master and Langevin equations, Monte Carlo simulations of model systems and first-principle approaches for ground state and transport problems within density functional theory. Collaborations with numerous members in other departmTheoretical investigations of a wide range of systems, both in thermal equilibrium and driven far from equilibrium, are being carried out using both analytical techniques and computational approaches. Research interests include phase transitions, critical phenomena, electronic, transport, and optical properties of a variety of physical systems and quantum information science. Examples include univ. Barnes, Cheng, Economou, Park, Pleimling, Scarola, Täuber.

Particles and Fields. Analysis of high-energy particle physics phenomenology and precision tests within and beyond the standard model framework. One special focus is neutrino phenomenology in close collaboration with the Center for Neutrino Physics and includes internationally well-known efforts like the development of the GLoBES software package. Neutrinos are also investigated in astrophysical settings. Also in connection to astrophysics is the study of the nature of dark matter using neutrino, gamma-ray, and other cosmic messengers. Another special focus is on string theory and M theory, especially string compactifications, supersymmetric field theories, and mathematical aspects of string theory. Research is also carried out on QCD and other gauge theories, supersymmetric, and otherwise, in three and four dimensions. Anderson, Chang, Gray, Horiuchi, Huber, Minic, Sharpe, Takeuchi.

Experimental

Astrophysics. The group at Virginia Tech is active in extragalactic astronomy and studies of radio transients. Current extragalactic research is concerned with measuring stellar and supermassive black hole mass assembly history in galaxies from multiwavelength surveys and the observation and interpretation of mass outflow from active galactic nuclei (AGNs). This work has impact on studies of the formation of galaxies and galaxy clusters and the way these structures trace the underlying dark matter distribution. Searches for radio transients are under way in collaboration with searches for gravity wave signals (e.g., by LIGO, the Laser Interferometer Gravitational Wave Observatory). This work has impact on the study of high-energy or explosive astrophysical events (e.g., supernovae, mergers of compact objects, and the explosion of primordial black holes) and implications for work at the frontier of fundamental physics (e.g., the existence of gravitational radiation and extra-spatial dimensions). Research facilities currently used include the Hubble Space Telescope, the Herschel Space Observatory, the Spitzer Space Telescope, the Chandra X-Ray Observatory, the Very Large Telescope, the Long Wavelength Array (LWA), and the Eight-meter-wavelength Transient Array (ETA). Arav, Horiuchi, Simonetti.

Biophysics. Topics include biosensors using ionic self-assembled multilayers on fiber gratings; targeted delivery of functionalized nanoparticles using laser techniques in nanomedicine; nanoscale structure and dynamics of biomimetic lipid membranes, topologically tunable membranes for biosensing and biosorting applications, tailoring structural and dynamical hierarchy in polymeric systems for reliable designs of advanced functional materials; and voltametric chemical detection methods for subsecond measurements of neurotransmitters in the human brain during active decision-making. Experimental approaches include near-infrared laser techniques, self-assembly techniques, optical characterization, voltametric methods, temporally resolved fluorescence microscopy, x-ray and neutron scattering, ps-ns spectroscopy, imaging, MD simulations, and molecular biology techniques. Ashkar, Heflin, Khodaparast, Montague.

Condensed Matter Physics. Research includes semiconductors, heterostructures, oxides, magnetic materials, polymers, self-assembled nanostructures, lithographic nanostructures, metallic nanoparticles, biological systems, new quantum states of matter, and quantum mesoscopic systems, using nonlinear optics, terahertz science, ultrafast dynamics, transport, scanning probes, and low-temperature physics techniques. Topics addressed include nonlinear optical response in self-assembled organic materials; optoelectronic applications and photovoltaics of semiconducting polymers; hierarchical structure and dynamics of soft materials; plasmonic enhancement of nonlinear optical and photovoltaic effects; spintronics; mesoscopic physics, spin physics, and quantum physics of metals, semimetals and semiconductors; magnetization dynamics in complex oxides; quantum transport, low-temperature physics, and magnetic properties; quantum and spin coherence effects in the solid state; quantum information processing architectures; nanoscience and nanofabrication techniques; energy storage and conversion; gigahertz and terahertz spectroscopy of biological systems; ultrafast dynamics of quantum systems; and nanometer-thick materials with robust spin-driven physics, with potential room-temperature applications in computing and communications technologies. Ashkar, Cheng, Emori, Heflin, Heremans, Khodaparast, Nguyen, Robinson, Soghomonian, Tao.

Neuroscience and Medical Physics. Topics include computational models of cognitive functions to gain insight into healthy and injured brain cognition and the characterization of cognitive phenotypes, both supported by magnetic resonance imaging; the use of medical physics to study sleep; the transitions between wake and sleep states in the brainstem; the interplay between sleep and stress on brain networks; multisource-multimodal data analysis methods, including but not limited to medical imaging and bioinformatics, with initial focus on prostate cancer and multiple sclerosis; development of new diffusion magnetic resonance imaging methods for assessment of brain white matter integrity; development of mobile health systems for military medics development of open source electronic health record architectures. Experimental efforts use functional magnetic resonance imaging, positron emission tomography, and electroencephalography. A study of interacting subjects uses new models of social exchange and uses the new technique of hyperscanning. Özcan, Montague, Mun, Wong.

Nuclear and Particle Physics. Much of our research in this area explores the properties of neutrinos, the primary focus of the Department's Center for Neutrino Physics. Current experimental activities include measurement of neutrino mixing angles with the Daya Bay reactor neutrino experiment in China and with liquid-argon-based accelerator neutrino detectors, including the Short Baseline Neutrino Program at Fermilab and CERN's ProtoDUNE SP. Faculty are involved in solar neutrino studies with Borexino and in searches for neutrinoless double beta decay with CUORE, both at Gran Sasso Underground lab in Italy. The department manages the Kimballton Underground Research Facility (KURF), a nearby low-background laboratory (1,700-foot depth), which supports VT and external experiments. Future experiments are in development to constrain sterile neutrinos and fundamental neutrino parameters (CHANDLER, NULAT, DUNE). Heavy-flavor physics (b and c quarks and tau leptons) is studied to probe CP violation and other phenomena at the Belle and Belle II experiments at KEK in Japan. Electron scattering experiments (e-Ar, QWEAK and MOLLER) are carried out at Jefferson Laboratory (Newport News, VA) to understand neutrino interactions in matter and to test the standard model using parity-violating scattering experiments. The department has laboratory space and machine/electronic shop support for significant equipment contributions to our experiments. Link, Mariani, O'Donnell, Piilonen, Pitt, Vogelaar.

UNIVERSITY OF WASHINGTON

DEPARTMENT OF ASTRONOMY

Seattle, Washington 98195-1580
http://depts.washington.edu/astron

General University Information
President: Dr. Ana Mari Cauce
Dean of Graduate School: Dr. Rebecca Aenerud
University website: http://www.washington.edu/
School Type: Public
Setting: Urban
Total Faculty: 4,350
Total number of Students: 46,700
Total number of Graduate Students: 14,800

Department Information
Department Chairman: Prof. Julianne Dalcanton, Chair
Department Contact: Main Office, Astronomy
  Total full-time faculty: 18
  Total number of full-time equivalent positions: 12
  Full-Time Graduate Students: 28
  Female Full-Time Graduate Students: 13
  First-Year Graduate Students: 4
  Female First-Year Students: 3
  Total Post Doctorates: 18

Department Address
Box 351580
Seattle, WA 98195-1580
Phone: (206) 543-2888
Fax: (206) 685-0403
E-mail: office@astro.washington.edu
Website: http://depts.washington.edu/astron

ADMISSIONS

Admission Contact Information
Address admission inquiries to: Graduate Program Advisor, Department of Astronomy, Box 351580, Seattle, WA 98195
Phone: (206) 543-2888
E-mail: astrgrad@uw.edu
Admissions website: http://depts.washington.edu/astron/academics/graduate-admissions/

Application deadlines
Fall admission:
U.S. students: December 15   *Int'l. students*: December 15

Application fee
U.S. students: $85   *Int'l. students*: $85

Admissions information
For Fall of 2018:
  Number of applicants: 352
  Number admitted: 16
  Number enrolled: 9

Admission requirements
Bachelor's degree requirements: A Bachelor's degree in Astronomy, Physics, Mathematics, or other field related to Astronomy is required.
Minimum undergraduate GPA: 3.0

GRE requirements
The GRE is required.

Subjective GRE requirements
The Subjective GRE is not required.
Physics GRE will only be considered if the applicant explains how the physics score provides information about physics ability that is not already clear from their transcript and other elements of the application.

TOEFL requirements
The TOEFL exam is required for students from non-English-speaking countries.
  PBT score: 580
  iBT score: 92

Other admissions information
Undergraduate preparation assumed: Undergraduate preparation assumed allows for a range of backgrounds of incoming graduate students. However, the equivalent of an undergraduate physics program is typical.

TUITION

Tuition year 2017–18:
Tuition for in-state residents
  Full-time students: $5,530 per quarter
  Part-time students: $820 per credit
Tuition for out-of-state residents
  Full-time students: $9,627 per quarter
  Part-time students: $1,406 per credit
For students with teaching or research assistant appointments (TAs or RAs), tuition/fees are reduced to about $1,200 annually. Students with appointments that meet minimum qualifications receive a non-resident tuition waiver in addition to in-state tuition paid by grant/state funding. Students are still responsible for a portion of tuition/fees that cannot be covered.
Credit hours per semester to be considered full-time: 10
Deferred tuition plan: No
Health insurance: Available.
Academic term: Quarter
Number of first-year students who received full tuition waivers: 4

Teaching Assistants, Research Assistants, and Fellowships
  Number of first-year
    Teaching Assistants: 6
  Average stipend per academic year
    Teaching Assistant: $32,000
    Research Assistant: $32,000
    Fellowship student: $35,000

FINANCIAL AID

Loans
Loans are available for U.S. students.
Loans are not available for international students.
GAPSFAS application required: No
FAFSA application required: No

For further information

Address financial aid inquiries to: Office of Student Financial Aid.
Phone: (206) 543-6101
E-mail: osfa@u.washington.edu
Financial aid website: http://www.washington.edu/students/osfa

HOUSING

Availability of on-campus housing

Single students: Yes
Married students: Yes

For further information

Address housing inquiries to: Housing Office.
Phone: (206) 543-4059
Housing aid website: http://hfs.washington.edu

Table A—Faculty, Enrollments, and Degrees Granted

Research Specialty	2017–18 Faculty	Enrollment Fall 2017		Number of Degrees Granted 2017–18		
		Master's	Doctorate	Master's	Terminal Master's	Doctorate
Astronomy	29	–	28	7	–	3
Total	29	–	28	7	–	3
Full-time Grad. Stud.	–	–	28	–	–	–
First-year Grad. Stud.	–	–	4	–	–	–

GRADUATE DEGREE REQUIREMENTS

Master's: Thesis not required. Students must pass 7 of the 8 core Astronomy classes w/ minimum 2.7 GPA per class and 3.0 minimum average GPA.

Doctorate: Admission Requirements: Entering students are expected to have a strong background in physics and mathematics. Graduation Requirements: A minimum of 10 approved courses with no more than 3 from outside Astronomy. Satisfactory completion of the departmental research qualifying examination. Master's degree in astronomy or equivalent knowledge; at least three quarters of teaching experience in astronomy; dissertation and final examination. Students interested in work in theoretical astrophysics may take additional courses in physics and mathematics. Students working on other topics may take certain courses in related fields, such as astrobiology, astronautics, atmospheric sciences, geophysics, or computer science.

Thesis: Doctoral thesis may be written in absentia.

SPECIAL EQUIPMENT, FACILITIES, OR PROGRAMS

The Department owns, in consortium with several other universities, a 3.5-meter telescope at Apache Point, NM, and receives 25% of the observing time on this facility. It is operated largely remotely over the internet and used heavily for graduate student dissertation research. UW is also a participant in the Sloan Digital Sky Survey, a project making a digital photometric and spectroscopic map of 25% of the celestial sphere, using a special purpose 2.5-meter telescope also on Apache Point. The Department is a founding member of the future Large Synoptic Survey Telescope. The Department also operates a 0.8-meter telescope in the Cascade Mountains of Washington, for the use of its students. Additional facilities in Seattle include an electron microscopy laboratory for analysis of cosmic dust particles and laboratories for developing astronomical telescopes and instrumentation. Members of the faculty are on teams that supplied instrumentation for the Hubble Space Telescope. Faculty and students are also extensive users of other national ground- and space-based observatories at a variety of wavelengths, and of national supercomputing facilities. The Department operates a large network of Linux workstations in support of all of these efforts.

FACULTY

Professor

Agol, Eric, Ph.D., University of California, Santa Barbara, 1997. *Astronomy, Astrophysics*. Relativistic astrophysics and gravity; black holes; active galaxies; accretion disks; extrasolar planets.

Anderson, Scott, Ph.D., University of Washington, 1985. *Astronomy*. Quasars; compact binaries; high-energy phenomena.

Connolly, Andrew, Ph.D., University of London, 1993. *Astronomy*. Formation and evolution of galaxies; cosmology; astronomical surveys.

Dalcanton, Julianne, Ph.D., Princeton University, 1995. Department Chair. *Astronomy*. Galaxy evolution and formation; cosmology; galactic dynamics.

Hawley, Suzanne, Ph.D., University of Texas, 1989. Divisional Dean of Natural Sciences. *Astronomy*. Low-mass stars; variable stars; star clusters; dwarf galaxies; galactic structure.

Ivezic, Zeljko, Ph.D., University of Kentucky, 1995. *Astronomy*. Deep sky surveys; quasars; stellar populations; asteroids; origin of interstellar dust.

Meadows, Victoria, Ph.D., University of Sydney, 1994. *Astronomy*. Planetary atmospheres; astrobiology.

Quinn, Tom, Ph.D., Princeton University, 1986. *Astronomy, Astrophysics*. Astrophysical dynamics on a wide range of scales, from asteroids to clusters of galaxies; solar system studies.

Associate Professor

Juric, Mario, Ph.D., Princeton, 2006. *Astronomy*. Large astronomical surveys; data intensive studies; Galactic structure, formation, and evolution; minor bodies of the Solar System.

Assistant Professor

Levesque, Emily, Ph.D., University of Hawaii, 2010. *Astronomy*. Evolution of massive stars; supernovae; gamma-ray bursters.

McQuinn, Matthew, Ph.D., Harvard, 2009. *Astrophysics*. Theoretical modeling of the intergalactic medium, galaxy formation and cosmology.

Tuttle, Sarah, Ph.D., Columbia University, 2010. *Astronomy, Astrophysics*. Instrumental astrophysics. Observations of nearby galaxies. Observing faint & diffuse matter. Integral field spectroscopy techniques. Novel materials for astronomical gratings and filters, as well as approaches to bring polarimetry (and spectropolarimetry) to small telescopes.

Werk, Jessica, Ph.D., University of Michigan, 2010. *Astronomy*. Role of gaseous components of galaxies in galaxy formation and evolution; optical and ultraviolet spectroscopy.

Professor Emeritus

Balick, Bruce B., Ph.D., Cornell University, 1971. *Astronomy*. Planetary nebulae and late stages of stellar evolution; gas dynamics; active nuclei and their impact on galactic structure.

Brownlee, Donald E., Ph.D., University of Washington, 1971. *Astronomy*. Interplanetary dust; comet physics; meteoritics; origin of the solar system.

Hodge, Paul, Ph.D., Harvard University, 1960. *Astronomy*. Galaxies; the Magellanic clouds.

King, Ivan, Ph.D., Harvard University, 1952. *Astronomy, Astrophysics*. Stellar populations; star clusters; structure and dynamics of globular clusters.

Lutz, Julie, Ph.D., University of Illinois, 1972. *Astronomy*. Planetary nebulae and symbiotic stars; astronomy education.

Sullivan, Woodruff T., Ph.D., University of Maryland, 1971. *Astronomy, History & Philosophy of Physics/Science*. Astrobiology; galaxies; clusters of galaxies; distance scale; history of radio astronomy.

Szkody, Paula, Ph.D., University of Washington, 1975. *Astronomy*. Cataclysmic variables; white dwarfs.

Wallerstein, George, Ph.D., California Institute of Technology, 1958. *Astronomy*. Spectra of variable stars; chemical composition of stellar atmospheres; interstellar lines.

Research Associate Professor

Becker, Andrew, Ph.D., University of Washington, 2000. *Astronomy*. Time domain science; techniques of massive survey astronomy; data mining.

Research Assistant Professor

Barnes, Rory, Ph.D., University of Washington, 2004. *Astrophysics*. Exoplanets; orbital dynamics; planet formation, astrobiology.

Williams, Benjamin, Ph.D., University of Washington, 2002. *Astronomy*. Nearby galaxies; galaxy evolution; galactic x-ray sources.

Adjunct Professor

Morales, Miguel, Ph.D., University of California, Santa Cruz, 2002. *Astronomy, Astrophysics, Electromagnetism*. Epoch of reionization; cosmology; radio astronomy surveys and instrumentation; radio transients.

Rosenberg, Leslie, Ph.D., Stanford University, 1985. *Astrophysics, Nuclear Physics, Particles and Fields*. Searches for axionic dark matter; surveys of dark matter and energy in the universe; novel particle and nuclear instrumentation; ultra-low-noise electromagnetic amplification.

Affiliate Professor

DeBattista, Victor, Ph.D., Rutgers University, 1998. *Astronomy, Astrophysics*. Cosmology; computational astrophysics.

Hughes Clark, Joanne, Ph.D., University of London, 1989. *Astronomy*. Observational astronomy; astrophysics of dwarf galaxies and globular clusters.

Linnell, Albert, Ph.D., Harvard University, 1950. *Astronomy, Astrophysics*. Modeling of accretion disks; cataclysmic variables.

Murphy, Thomas, Ph.D., California Institute of Technology, 2000. *Astrophysics, Relativity & Gravitation*. Solar system tests of general relativity; energy and the environment.

Senior Lecturer

Laws, Christopher, Ph.D., University of Washington, 2004. *Astronomy*. Extrasolar planetary systems; stellar evolution; chemical evolution.

Smith, Toby, Ph.D., University of Washington, 1995. *Astronomy*. Terrestrial impact craters; meteoritics.

Lecturer

Fraser, Oliver, Ph.D., University of Washington, 2008. *Astronomy*. Variable stars; teaching methods.

Silvestri, Nicole, Ph.D., Florida Institue of Technology, 2002. *Astronomy*. Low-mass stars, white dwarfs.

DEPARTMENTAL RESEARCH SPECIALTIES AND STAFF

Theoretical

Astrophysics. *Active galaxies and quasars: nuclear properties; accretion; lensing; high-energy phenomena. *Astrobiology and planetary studies: extrasolar planet detection and characterization; planetary atmospheres. *Clusters of stars: evolution; structure. *Compact objects: degenerate stars; black holes. *Computational astrophysics: N-body simulations. *Cosmology: intergalactic medium; large-scale structure formation and evolution; cosmological parameters; dark matter and dark energy. *Galactic nebulae: H II regions and planetary nebulae. *Galaxies: structure and dynamics; formation and evolution; dark matter; internal motions. *Stars: chemical composition; magnetic activity and flares; low-mass stars and brown dwarfs; massive stars. Agol, Balick, Barnes, Dalcanton, King, Linnell, McQuinn, Meadows, Quinn, Tuttle, Werk.

Experimental

Astronomy. *Active galaxies and quasars: nuclear properties; accretion; luminosity functions and evolution; absorption lines; lensing; BL Lacs and other radio sources; high-energy phenomena. *Astrobiology and planetary studies: extrasolar planet detection and characterization; planetary atmospheres; asteroids and comets; meteorites. *Clusters of stars: evolution; abundance determinations; statistical properties. *Compact objects: degenerate stars; black holes; cataclysmic variables and other compact binaries; gamma-ray bursts; supernovae. *Cosmology: intergalactic medium; large-scale structure formation and evolution; cosmological parameters; dark matter and dark energy. *Galactic nebulae: hot and cool components in the interstellar medium: H II regions and planetary nebulae. *Galaxies: structure and dynamics; formation and evolution; dark matter; gaseous and stellar content; internal motions; extragalactic distance scale; clusters of galaxies; properties of star-forming regions. *Stars: chemical composition; magnetic activity and flares; circumstellar material; variable stars; low-mass stars and brown dwarfs; massive stars. *Survey science: data mining; imaging, spectroscopic, and time-domain astronomical surveys. Agol, Anderson, Balick, Brownlee, Connolly, Dalcanton, Hawley, Hodge, Ivezic, Juric, King, Levesque, Lutz, Meadows, Morales, Sullivan, Szkody, Wallerstein, Werk, Williams.

View additional information about this department at www.gradschoolshopper.com. Check out the "Why Choose Us?" section, find out more about the department's culture and get links to social media networks.

UNIVERSITY OF WASHINGTON

DEPARTMENT OF PHYSICS

Seattle, Washington 98195
http://www.phys.washington.edu

General University Information
President: Ana Mari Cauce
Dean of Graduate School: Rebecca Aanerud
University website: http://www.washington.edu/
School Type: Public
Setting: Urban
Total Faculty: 4,350
Total number of Students: 56,819
Total number of Graduate Students: 15,987

Department Information
Department Chairman: Prof. Blayne Heckel, Chair
Department Contact: Front desk, Receptionist
  Total full-time faculty: 57
  Total number of full-time equivalent positions: 43
  Full-Time Graduate Students: 164
  Female Full-Time Graduate Students: 36
  First-Year Graduate Students: 29
  Female First-Year Students: 11
  Total Post Doctorates: 36

Department Address
3910 15th Ave. NE
Seattle, WA 98195
Phone: (206) 543-2771
Fax: (206) 685-0635
E-mail: physrecp@uw.edu
Website: http://www.phys.washington.edu

ADMISSIONS

Admission Contact Information
Address admission inquiries to: Graduate Program Assistant, Department of Physics, University of Washington Box 351560, Seattle, WA 98195-1560
Phone: (206) 543-2488
E-mail: grad@phys.washington.edu
Admissions website: http://www.phys.washington.edu/phd_admissions.htm

Application deadlines
Fall admission:
U.S. students: January 5   *Int'l. students*: January 5

Application fee
U.S. students: $85   *Int'l. students*: $85

Admissions information
For Fall of 2018:
  Number of applicants: 570
  Number admitted: 103
  Number enrolled: 29

Admission requirements
Bachelor's degree requirements: Bachelor's degree in Physics is required.
Minimum undergraduate GPA: 3.0

GRE requirements
The GRE is required.
No minimum score is set

Subjective GRE requirements
The Subjective GRE is required.
No minimum score is set

TOEFL requirements
The TOEFL exam is required for students from non-English-speaking countries.
  PBT score: 500
  iBT score: 80
For additional details regarding http://grad.uw.edu/admissions/understanding-the-application-process/international-applicant-faqs/english-proficiency-tests/

Other admissions information
Undergraduate preparation assumed: Undergraduate courses in quantum mechanics, electricity and magnetism, classical mechanics, statistical mechanics, and mathematical physics and one senior-level survey course.

TUITION

Tuition year 2017–18:
Tuition for in-state residents
  Full-time students: $15,207 annual
Tuition for out-of-state residents
  Full-time students: $27,255 annual
This tuition rate is for the academic year (9 months). Students holding assistantships of half-time or more receive a tuition waiver.
Credit hours per semester to be considered full-time: 10
Deferred tuition plan: No
Health insurance: Available
Other academic fees: Approximately $360/quarter student fees.
Academic term: Quarter
Number of first-year students who received full tuition waivers: 29

Teaching Assistants, Research Assistants, and Fellowships
  Number of first-year
    Teaching Assistants: 22
    Research Assistants: 2
    Fellowship students: 5
  Average stipend per academic year
    Teaching Assistant: $20,655
    Research Assistant: $20,655

FINANCIAL AID

Application deadlines
Fall admission:
U.S. students: February 15

Loans
Loans are available for U.S. students.
Loans are available for international students.
GAPSFAS application required: No
FAFSA application required: No

For further information

Address financial aid inquiries to: Office of Student Financial
Aid, University of Washington, Box 355880, Seattle, WA
98195-5880.
Phone: (206) 543-6101
E-mail: osfa@u.washington.edu
Financial aid website: http://www.washington.edu/students/osfa

HOUSING

Availability of on-campus housing

Single students: Yes
Married students: Yes
Childcare Assistance: Yes

For further information

Address housing inquiries to: Student Services Office, Housing
and Food Services, University of Washington, 301 Schmitz
Hall, Box 355842, Seattle, WA 98195–5842.
Phone: (206) 543-4059
E-mail: hfsinfo@u.washington.edu
Housing aid website: http://hfs.washington.edu

Table A—Faculty, Enrollments, and Degrees Granted

Research Specialty	2017–18 Faculty	Enrollment Fall 2018		Number of Degrees Granted 2017–18		
		Master's	Doctorate	Master's	Terminal Master's	Doctorate
Applied Physics	–	–	–	–	–	–
Astrophysics	6	–	–	–	–	–
Atomic, Molecular, & Optical Physics	6	–	–	–	–	–
Biophysics	10	–	–	–	–	–
Condensed Matter Physics	20	–	–	–	–	–
High Energy Physics	8	–	–	–	–	–
Nuclear Physics	22	–	–	–	–	–
Particles and Fields	5	–	–	–	–	–
Physics and other Science Education	3	–	–	–	–	–
Non-specialized	–	–	–	–	–	–
Total	78	40	164	7	1	18
Full-time Grad. Stud.	–	–	164	–	–	–
First-year Grad. Stud.	–	10	29	–	–	–

GRADUATE DEGREE REQUIREMENTS

Master's: Minimum of 36 approved credits are required, 18 of
which must in courses numbered 500 or above, including a
minimum of three credits in Physics 600 research. At least
18 credits must be in graded courses. No thesis is required.
No foreign language is required. Students must pass qualifying examination (Ph.D. program). Must submit project report and pass a final oral examination (evening master's degree program). A minimum of three full-time quarters of
residency are required. Part-time quarters may be accumu-
lated to meet this requirement. A grade point average of 3.0
is required.

Doctorate: Grade point average above 3.0 is required. A sequence of required courses must be taken. Master's Review
Exam, General examination, and a Final examination, which
is usually a defense of the dissertation, are required. Eighteen
graded credits at the University of Washington are required.
A minimum of three academic years of resident study are required. A minimum of 27 credits of dissertation over period
of at least three quarters and some teaching experience are

required. There is no language examination required. Students
must be registered for the quarter that they receive their degree.
Thesis: Thesis may be written in absentia.

SPECIAL EQUIPMENT, FACILITIES, OR PROGRAMS

At our Center for Experimental Nuclear Physics and Astrophysics, an FN tandem Van de Graaff accelerator can be used
with negative-ion injection to reach energies of 18 MeV for protons and higher energies for heavier ions. For nuclear astrophysics experiments with a terminal ion source, the proton (or
helium ion) beam energy can be as low as 100 keV, with currents
up to 30 microamps. The Center includes active research programs in neutrino physics and muon physics.

Our High-Energy Laboratory maintains facilities for the preparation and analysis of experiments performed at off-campus accelerators. We have a 3He dilution refrigerator for extremely low-
temperature research, a laser facility for generating tunable
optical radiation at precisely controlled frequencies, and an extended X-ray absorption fine structure (XAFS) facility for determining the atomic structure of condensed matter.

Facilities for research into nanostructure include two atomic force
microscopes, one at room temperature and the other at low temperature in extra-high vacuum, and a 14-Tesla superconducting
magnet.

The Department also houses the Institute for Nuclear Theory
(INT), a national facility funded by the Department of Energy
to host visitor programs for the exploration of current topics in
nuclear theory. The INT is closely integrated with the Physics
Department both physically and intellectually, with INT senior
fellows supervising thesis research in physics and INT seminars
frequently attended by members of the Physics Department.

Computing facilities include numerous modern workstations and
server machines plus access to both University mainframes and
national supercomputing centers. Since 1994, the Department has
been located in a recently constructed building with state-of-
the-art facilities for instruction and research.

Table B—Separately Budgeted Research Expenditures by Source of Support

Source of Support	Departmental Research	Physics-related Research Outside Department
Federal government	$17,099,147	
State/local government	$2,532,674	
Non-profit organizations	$348,622	
Business and industry		
Other	$134,889	
Total	$20,115,332	

Table C—Separately Budgeted Research Expenditures by Research Specialty

Research Specialty	No. of Grants	Expenditures ($)
Atomic, Molecular, & Optical Physics	11	$3,222,572
Condensed Matter Physics	13	$3,504,245
Nuclear Physics	14	$6,191,931
Particles and Fields	6	$2,578,204
Physics and other Science Education	5	$592,933
Relativity & Gravitation	7	$1,683,658
Total	56	$17,773,543

FACULTY

Professor

Andreev, Anton, Ph.D., Massachusetts Institute of Technology, 1996. *Condensed Matter Physics*. Theoretical condensed-matter physics.

Beane, Silas, Ph.D., University of Texas, Austin, 1994. *Computational Physics, Nuclear Physics*. Theoretical nuclear physics.

Bulgac, Aurel, Ph.D., Leningrad Nuclear Physics Institute, 1977. *Nuclear Physics*. Theoretical nuclear physics.

Cobden, David H., Ph.D., University of Cambridge, 1991. *Condensed Matter Physics*. Experimental condensed-matter physics; nanodevice physics.

den Nijs, Marcel, Ph.D., Radboud University Nijmegen, 1979. *Condensed Matter Physics, Statistical & Thermal Physics*. Theoretical condensed-matter physics; statistical physics; neural science.

Garcia, Alejandro, Ph.D., University of Washington, 1991. *Nuclear Physics*. Experimental nuclear physics.

Goussiou, Anna, Ph.D., University of Wisconsin-Madison, 1995. *Particles and Fields*. Experimental particle physics.

Gundlach, Jens, Ph.D., University of Washington, 1990. *Biophysics, Nuclear Physics*. Experimental nuclear physics and biophysics.

Heckel, Blayne, Ph.D., Harvard University, 1981. Chairman Physics Department. *Atomic, Molecular, & Optical Physics*. Experimental atomic physics.

Heron, Paula, Ph.D., University of Western Ontario, 1995. *Physics and other Science Education*. Physics education.

Hertzog, David W., Ph.D., William & Mary, 1983. Director CENPA. *Astrophysics, Nuclear Physics*. Experimental nuclear physics; astrophysics.

Kaplan, David B., Ph.D., Harvard University, 1985. *Nuclear Physics*. Theoretical nuclear physics.

Karch, Andreas, Ph.D., Humbold University, 1998. *Particles and Fields*. Theoretical particle physics.

Lubatti, Henry J., University of California, Berkeley, 1966. *Particles and Fields*. Experimental elementary particle physics.

McDermott, Lillian C., Ph.D., Columbia University, 1959. *Physics and other Science Education*. Physics education.

McLerran, Larry, Ph.D., University of Washington, 1971. Director of INT. *Nuclear Physics, Theoretical Physics*. Hot and dense matter, high energy nuclear physics.

Miller, Gerald A., Ph.D., Massachusetts Institute of Technology, 1972. *Nuclear Physics*. Theoretical nuclear physics.

Nelson, Ann E., Ph.D., Harvard University, 1984. *Particles and Fields*. Theoretical particle physics.

Olmstead, Marjorie A., Ph.D., University of California, Berkeley, 1985. *Condensed Matter Physics, Nano Science and Technology*. Experimental condensed matter physics; nanotechnology.

Reddy, Sanjay, Ph.D., Massachusetts Institute of Technology, 1998. Theoretical nuclear physics; astrophysics.

Rosenberg, Leslie, Ph.D., Stanford University, 1985. *Astrophysics*. Experimental astrophysics.

Savage, Martin J., Ph.D., California Institute of Technology, 1990. *Computational Physics, Nuclear Physics*. Theoretical nuclear physics.

Seidler, Gerald T., Ph.D., University of Chicago, 1993. *Condensed Matter Physics*. Experimental condensed matter physics.

Shaffer, Peter S., Ph.D., University of Washington, 1993. *Physics and other Science Education*. Physics education.

Sharpe, Stephen R., Ph.D., University of California, Berkeley, 1983. *Particles and Fields*. Theoretical elementary particle physics.

Spivak, Boris, Ph.D., Leningrad Politecknical Institute, 1978. *Condensed Matter Physics*. Theoretical condensed matter physics.

Watts, Gordon T., Ph.D., University of Rochester, 1994. *Particles and Fields*. Experimental elementary particle physics.

Yaffe, Laurence G., Ph.D., Princeton University, 1980. *Particles and Fields*. Theoretical elementary particle physics.

Associate Professor

Blinov, Boris B., Ph.D., University of Michigan, 2000. *Atomic, Molecular, & Optical Physics*. Experimental atomic physics; quantum information.

Fu, Kai-Mei C., Ph.D., Stanford University, 2007. *Condensed Matter Physics*. Condensed matter experiment; single-impurity optoelectronics.

Gupta, Subhadeep, Ph.D., Massachusetts Institute of Technology, 2003. *Atomic, Molecular, & Optical Physics*. Experimental atomic physics.

Morales, Miguel F., Ph.D., University of California, Santa Cruz, 1992. *Astrophysics, Cosmology & String Theory*. Experimental astrophysics; cosmology.

Wiggins, Paul A., Ph.D., California Institute of Technology, 2005. *Biophysics*. Biophysics.

Xu, Xiaodong, Ph.D., University of Michigan, 2008. *Condensed Matter Physics*. Experimental condensed matter physics; nanoscale optoelectronics.

Assistant Professor

Chavarravia, Alvarro, Ph.D., Princeton, 2012. Neutrino Physics.

Chu, Jiun-Haw, Ph.D., Stanford University. Experimental condensed matter.

Detwiler, Jason, Ph.D., Stanford University, 2005. Neutrino physics.

Fidkowski, Lucasz, Ph.D., Stanford University, 2007. *Condensed Matter Physics*. The role of symmetry and topology in condensed matter systems.

Gray, Rybka, Ph.D., Massachusetts Institute of Technology, 2007. Experimental astrophysics.

Hsu, Shih-Chieh, Ph.D., University of California, San Diego, 2008. High-energy physics.

Rybka, Gray, Ph.D., MIT, 2007. *Astrophysics, Nuclear Physics*.

White Brahmia, Suzanne, Ph.D., Rutgers, 2014. *Physics and other Science Education*. Physics education.

Emeritus

Adelberger, Eric G., Ph.D., California Institute of Technology, 1967. *Nuclear Physics, Relativity & Gravitation*. Experimental nuclear physics; gravitation.

Baker, Marshall, Ph.D., Harvard University, 1958. *Particles and Fields*. Theoretical elementary particle physics.

Bardeen, James M., Ph.D., California Institute of Technology, 1965. *Astrophysics, Relativity & Gravitation*. Theoretical astrophysics and relativity.

Bertsch, George F., Ph.D., Princeton University, 1965. *Nuclear Physics*. Theoretical physics; quantum many-body physics with application to nuclei.

Boulware, David G., Ph.D., Harvard University, 1962. *Astrophysics, Particles and Fields, Relativity & Gravitation*. Theoretical physics; astrophysics; relativity; elementary particles.

Boynton, Paul E., Ph.D., Princeton University, 1967. *Astronomy, Astrophysics, Relativity & Gravitation*. Astronomy; astrophysics; gravitation.

Brown, Lowell S., Ph.D., Harvard University, 1961. *Particles and Fields*. Theoretical elementary particle physics.

Burnett, Thompson H., Ph.D., University of California, San Diego, 1968. *Particles and Fields*. Experimental elementary particle physics.

Chaloupka, Vladimir, Ph.D., University of Geneva, 1975. *Particles and Fields*. Experimental elementary particle physics.

Cook, Victor, Ph.D., University of California, Berkeley, 1962. *Particles and Fields*. Experimental elementary particle physics.

Cramer, John G., Ph.D., Rice University, 1961. *Nuclear Physics*. Experimental nuclear physics.

Ellis, Stephen D., Ph.D., California Institute of Technology, 1971. *Particles and Fields*. Theoretical elementary particle physics.

Forston, E. Norval, Ph.D., Harvard University, 1963. *Atomic, Molecular, & Optical Physics*. Experimental atomic physics.

Halpern, Isaac, Ph.D., Massachusetts Institute of Technology, 1948.

Haxton, Wick C., Ph.D., Stanford University, 1976. *Nuclear Physics, Particles and Fields*. Theoretical nuclear physics.

Ingalls, Robert L., Ph.D., Carnegie Mellon University, 1962. *Condensed Matter Physics*. Experimental condensed matter physics.

Rehr, John J., Ph.D., Cornell University, 1972. *Condensed Matter Physics*. Theoretical condensed matter physics.

Robertson, R. G. Hamish, Ph.D., McMaster University, 1971. *Nuclear Physics*. Experimental nuclear physics; neutrino physics.

Rothberg, Joseph E., Ph.D., Columbia University, 1963. *Particles and Fields*. Experimental elementary particle physics.

Schick, Michael, Ph.D., Stanford University, 1967. *Biophysics, Condensed Matter Physics, Statistical & Thermal Physics*. Theoretical statistical physics and biophysics.

Snover, Kurt A., Ph.D., Stanford University, 1969. *Nuclear Physics*. Experimental nuclear physics.

Sorensen, Larry B., Ph.D., University of Illinois, 1979. *Condensed Matter Physics*. Experimental condensed matter physics; neural science.

Storm, Derek W., Ph.D., University of Washington, 1970. *Nuclear Physics*. Experimental nuclear physics.

Trainor, Thomas A., Ph.D., University of North Carolina, 1973. *Nuclear Physics*. Experimental nuclear physics.

Van Dyck, Robert S., Ph.D., University of California, Berkeley, 1971. *Atomic, Molecular, & Optical Physics*. Experimental atomic physics.

Vilches, Oscar E., Ph.D., Universidad Nacional de Cuyo, Argentina, 1966. *Condensed Matter Physics, Low Temperature Physics*. Experimental low-temperature physics.

Weitkamp, William G., Ph.D., University of Wisconsin-Madison, 1965. *Nuclear Physics*. Experimental nuclear physics.

Wilkes, Richard J., Ph.D., University of Wisconsin-Madison, 1974. *High Energy Physics*. Experimental high-energy physics; space science.

Williams, Robert W., Ph.D., Massachusetts Institute of Technology, 1948. *High Energy Physics*.

Research Professor

Doe, Peter J., Ph.D., Durham University, 1977. *Nuclear Physics*. Experimental nuclear physics.

Kammel, Peter, Ph.D., University of Vienna, 1982. *Nuclear Physics*. Nuclear physics.

Research Assistant Professor

Enomoto, Sanshiro, Ph.D., Tohoku University, 2005. *Nuclear Physics*.

Lin, Huey-Wen, Ph.D., Columbia University, 2006. *Nuclear Physics*. Nuclear theory.

Adjunct Professor

Agol, Eric, Ph.D., University of California, Santa Barbara, 1997. *Astrophysics*. Theoretical astrophysics.

Baker, David, Ph.D., University of California, Berkeley, 1989. *Biophysics*. Computational biological physics; protein folding.

Buck, Warren W., Ph.D., College of William and Mary, 1976. *Nuclear Physics, Particles and Fields*. Theoretical nuclear and elementary particle physics.

Campbell, Charles, Ph.D., University of Texas, Austin, 1979. *Chemical Physics*. Chemical physics.

Dalcanton, Julianne, Ph.D., Princeton University, 1995. *Astrophysics*. Astrophysics.

Drobny, Gary, Ph.D., University of California, Berkeley, 1981. Biophysical chemistry.

Dunham, Scott T., Ph.D., Stanford University, 1985. Modeling and simulation of microfabrication processes and device behavior.

Fairhall, Adrienne, Ph.D., Weizmann Institute of Science, 1998. *Biophysics*. Theoretical neuroscience.

Ginger, David S., Ph.D., University of Cambridge, 2001. *Chemical Physics, Condensed Matter Physics*. Experimental nanophysics.

Hawley, Suzanne L., Ph.D., University of Texas, Austin, 1989. *Astrophysics*. Theoretical astrophysics.

Holzworth, Robert, Ph.D., University of California, Berkeley, 1977. *Geophysics*. Geophysics.

Jarboe, Thomas R., Ph.D., University of California, Berkeley, 1974. *Plasma and Fusion*. Plasma physics.

Keller, Sarah L., Ph.D., Princeton University, 1995. *Biophysics*. Biophysics.

Kinehan, Paul E., Ph.D., University of Pittsburgh, 1994. *Biophysics, Engineering Physics/Science*. Biophysics.

Krishnan, Kannon M., Ph.D., University of California, Berkeley, 1984. *Condensed Matter Physics, Materials Science, Metallurgy*. Material science.

Kutz, Jose N., Ph.D., Northwestern University, 1990. *Applied Mathematics*. Dynamical systems; nonlinear differential equations; bifurcation theory.

Lin, Lih, Ph.D., University of California, Los Angeles, 1996. *Condensed Matter Physics, Engineering Physics/Science, Nano Science and Technology*. Nanoscale photonic devices.

Ohuchi, Fumio, Ph.D., University of Florida, 1981. *Materials Science, Metallurgy, Nano Science and Technology*. Materials and surface science.

Quinn, Thomas R., Ph.D., Princeton University, 1986. *Astrophysics*. Astrophysics.

Rieke, Frederick M., Ph.D., University of California, Berkeley, 1991. *Biophysics*. Neural science; vision sensory signal processing and computation.

Thompson, LuAnne, Ph.D., Massachusetts Institute of Technology, 1990. *Marine Science/Oceanography*. Oceanography.

Winglee, Robert, Ph.D., University of Sydney, 1985. *Geophysics*. Geophysics.

Affiliate Professor

Alberg, Mary A., Ph.D., University of Washington, 1974. *Nuclear Physics*. Theoretical nuclear physics.

Balantekin, A. Baha, Ph.D., Yale University, 1982. *Nuclear Physics*. Theoretical nuclear physics.

Barrett, Bruce R., Ph.D., Stanford University, 1967. *Nuclear Physics*. Nuclear many-body theory.

Bichsel, Hans, Ph.D., University of Basel, 1951. *Nuclear Physics*. Experimental nuclear physics.

Bowles, Thomas J., Ph.D., Princeton University, 1978. *Nuclear Physics*. Experimental nuclear physics.

Cleveland, Bruce T., Ph.D., Johns Hopkins University, 1970. Experimental neutrino physics.

Elliot, Steven R., Ph.D., University of California, Irvine, 1987. *Nuclear Physics*. Experimental nuclear physics.

Friedman, William A., Ph.D., Massachusetts Institute of Technology, 1966. *Nuclear Physics*. Nuclear physics.

Habig, Alec T., Ph.D., Indiana University, 1996. *Astrophysics, Nuclear Physics*.

Hoyle, Charles D., Ph.D., University of Washington, 2001. *Relativity & Gravitation*. Laboratory tests of gravity.

Levanyuk, Arkady, Ph.D., Moskow University, 1977. *Condensed Matter Physics*.

Magierski, Piotr A., Ph.D., Warsaw University of Technology, 1995. *Nuclear Physics*. Theoretical nuclear physics.

Mandula, Jeffrey E., Ph.D., Harvard University, 1966. *Particles and Fields*. Theoretical particle physics.

Nordtvedt, Kenneth, Ph.D., Stanford University, 1964. *Relativity & Gravitation*. General relativity.

Raschke, Markus B., Ph.D., Max-Planck Institute for Quantum Optics and Technology University, Munich, 1999. *Nano Science and Technology*. Chemistry and nanoparticles.

Riedel, Eberhard K., Ph.D., München, 1966. *Condensed Matter Physics, Statistical & Thermal Physics*. Theoretical condensed matter and statistical physics.

Strassler, Matthew, Ph.D., Stanford University, 1993. *Particles and Fields*. Quantum field theory; string theory; particle physics.

Stubbs, Christopher W., Ph.D., University of Washington, 1988. *Cosmology & String Theory*. Experimental and observational cosmology.

Van Bibber, Karl, Ph.D., Massachusetts Institute of Technology, 1976. *High Energy Physics*. High-energy physics.

van Kolck, Ubirijara, Ph.D., University of Texas, Austin, 1993. *Nuclear Physics*. Theoretical nuclear physics.

Wettlaufer, John S., Ph.D., University of Washington, 1991. Ice physics. Affiliate Assistant Professor

Miller, Michael L., Ph.D., Yale University, 2004. *Nuclear Physics, Particles and Fields*. Experimental nuclear and particle physics.

Affiliate Assistant Professor

Mueller, Peter, Ph.D., Johannes Gutenberg University, 2003.

Lecturer

Tolich, Nikolai, Ph.D., Stanford University, 2005. *Nuclear Physics*. Experimental nuclear physics.

DEPARTMENTAL RESEARCH SPECIALTIES AND STAFF

Theoretical

Astrophysics. Agol, Bardeen, Nelson, Quinn, Reddy.

Biophysics. David Baker, den Nijs, Fairhall, Schick.

Condensed Matter Physics. Andreev, den Nijs, Dunham, Fidkowski, Rehr, Schick, Spivak.

Nuclear Physics. Beane, Bertsch, Bulgac, Haxton, Kaplan, Huey-Wen Lin, McLerran, Gerald Miller, Reddy, Savage.

Particles and Fields. Marshall Baker, Ellis, Kaplan, Karch, Nelson, Sharpe, Thompson, Yaffe.

Experimental

Astrophysics. Adelberger, Gundlach, Heckel, Morales, Rosenberg, Wilkes.

Atomic, Molecular, & Optical Physics. Blinov, Forston, Gupta, Heckel, Kutz, Van Dyck.

Biophysics. Gundlach, Keller, Huey-Wen Lin, Rieke, Sorensen, Wiggins.

Condensed Matter Physics. Campbell, Chu, Cobden, Fu, Ginger, Keller, Ohuchi, Olmstead, Seidler, Sorensen, Vilches, Xu.

High Energy Physics. Goussiou, Hsu, Lubatti, Rosenberg, Watts.

Nuclear Physics. Adelberger, Doe, Garcia, Gundlach, Heckel, Hertzog, Kammel, Robertson, Rosenberg, Rybka, Tolich, Trainor.

Physics and other Science Education. Heron, McDermott, Shaffer, White Brahmia.

Relativity & Gravitation. Adelberger, Gundlach, Heckel.

View additional information about this department at www.gradschoolshopper.com. Check out the "Why Choose Us?" section, find out more about the department's culture and get links to social media networks.

WEST VIRGINIA UNIVERSITY

DEPARTMENT OF PHYSICS AND ASTRONOMY

Morgantown, West Virginia 26506
http://physics.wvu.edu/

General University Information
President: E. Gordon Gee
Dean of Graduate School: Greg Dunaway
University website: http://www.wvu.edu
School Type: Public
Setting: Urban
Total Faculty: 2,034
Total Graduate Faculty: 1,100
Total number of Students: 28,409
Total number of Graduate Students: 5,905

Department Information
Department Chairman: Prof. Earl E. Scime, Chair
Department Contact: Earl E. Scime, Chair
  Total full-time faculty: 28
  Total number of full-time equivalent positions: 28
  Full-Time Graduate Students: 74
  Female Full-Time Graduate Students: 12
  First-Year Graduate Students: 14
  Female First-Year Students: 2
  Total Post Doctorates: 14

Department Address
135 Willey Street
P.O. Box 6315
Morgantown, WV 26506
Phone: (304) 293-3422
Fax: (304) 293-5727
E-mail: Earl.Scime@mail.wvu.edu
Website: http://physics.wvu.edu/

ADMISSIONS

Admission Contact Information
Address admission inquiries to: Admissions Committee, Department of Physics and Astronomy, P.O. Box 6315, Morgantown, WV 26506
Phone: (304) 293-3422
E-mail: physics@wvu.edu
Admissions website: http://physics.wvu.edu/grad/apply

Application deadlines
Fall admission:
U.S. students: January 15   *Int'l. students*: January 15

Application fee
U.S. students: $60
A personal statement and CV are required.

Admissions information
For Fall of 2018:
  Number of applicants: 161
  Number admitted: 35
  Number enrolled: 12

Admission requirements
Bachelor's degree requirements: A bachelor's degree in Physics, Astronomy, or a related field is required.
Minimum undergraduate GPA: 3.0

GRE requirements
The GRE is required.
No minimum score set.

Subjective GRE requirements
The Subjective GRE is not required.

TOEFL requirements
The TOEFL exam is required for students from non-English-speaking countries.
  PBT score: 550
  iBT score: 79
The minimum accepted computer-based exam (CBT) score is 213. The minimum accepted IELTS score is 6.5.

Other admissions information
Additional requirements: No minimum score is specified.
Undergraduate preparation assumed: Intermediate mechanics, electricity and magnetism, atomic and quantum physics, thermodynamics, and mathematics through partial differential equations. Typical physics texts include Davis (mechanics), Wangsness (electricity and magnetism), McIntyre (quantum mechanics), and Sears and Salinger (thermodynamics).

TUITION

Tuition year 2018–19:
Tuition for in-state residents
  Full-time students: $5,373 per semester
  Part-time students: $597 per credit
Tuition for out-of-state residents
  Full-time students: $13,563 per semester
  Part-time students: $1,507 per credit
Costs include University tuition, University fees, and College tuition.
Credit hours per semester to be considered full-time: 9
Deferred tuition plan: Yes
Health insurance: Yes, $1,824.00.
Other academic fees: Fees are included in tuition numbers cited above.
Academic term: Semester
Number of first-year students who received full tuition waivers: 12

Teaching Assistants, Research Assistants, and Fellowships
Number of first-year
  Teaching Assistants: 12
Average stipend per academic year
  Teaching Assistant: $24,000
  Research Assistant: $24,000
  Fellowship student: $28,000
Teaching assistantships guaranteed to all incoming first year students. Fellowships in specific fields are available; contact faculty or go to http://graduateeducation.wvu.edu/funding-and-cost/fellowships-and-scholarships

FINANCIAL AID

Application deadlines
Fall admission:
U.S. students: January 15   *Int'l. students*: February 15

Loans

Loans are available for U.S. students.

Loans are not available for international students.

GAPSFAS application required: No

FAFSA application required: Yes

For further information

Address financial aid inquiries to: Graduate Program Committee Department of Physics and Astronomy, West Virginia University, Morgantown, WV 26506-6315.

Phone: (304) 293-3422

E-mail: earl.scime@mail.wvu.edu

Financial aid website: http://grad.wvu.edu/financial_assistance

HOUSING

Availability of on-campus housing

Single students: Yes

Married students: Yes

Childcare Assistance: No

For further information

Address housing inquiries to: University Apartments, PO Box 6430, Morgantown, WV 26505.

Phone: (304) 293-5840 or (304) 293-054e

E-mail: wvumedcenterapt@mail.wvu.edu

Housing aid website: http://housing.wvu.edu/graduate_student_faculty_and_staff_housing

Table A—Faculty, Enrollments, and Degrees Granted

Research Specialty	2017–18 Faculty	Enrollment Fall 2018 Master's	Enrollment Fall 2018 Doctorate	Number of Degrees Granted 2017–18 (2008–17) Master's	Number of Degrees Granted 2017–18 (2008–17) Terminal Master's	Number of Degrees Granted 2017–18 (2008–17) Doctorate
Astrophysics	6	–	27	3(20)	–	2(17)
Condensed Matter Physics	13	–	27	4(30)	–(4)	2(41)
Fluids, Rheology	–	–	–	–(2)	–	–(2)
Medical, Health Physics	–	–	–	–(2)	–	–
Neuroscience/Neuro Physics	1	–	1	–	–	–(1)
Physics and other Science Education	4	–	2	1(1)	–	1(1)
Plasma and Fusion	4	–	18	1(19)	–(1)	2(17)
Statistical & Thermal Physics	–	–	–	–(1)	–	–(1)
Total	28	–	75	8(70)	–(5)	7(76)
Full-time Grad. Stud.	–	–	75	–	–	–
First-year Grad. Stud.	–	–	12	–	–	–

GRADUATE DEGREE REQUIREMENTS

Master's: Approved courses with a minimum GPA of 3.0 is required. There is no residence or language requirement. For a degree with thesis, 24 credits are required. For a degree without a thesis, 30 credits are required.

Doctorate: A minimum of 36 hours of course work in an approved program with a minimum GPA of 3.0 are required. A written comprehensive exam, oral research exam, dissertation, and oral dissertation defense are required.

Thesis: Thesis may be written in absentia.

SPECIAL EQUIPMENT, FACILITIES, OR PROGRAMS

The department and associated instrument and electronics shops are housed in White Hall, a six-story building located on the downtown campus. The building renovation was completed in 2011 and houses a 60-seat planetarium, a roof-top observatory, a small radio telescope, and 23 state-of-the-art research laboratories.

The plasma facilities include a triple plasma source, a Q-machine for generating space-like plasmas and waves, two helicon plasma sources, a space simulation chamber, a plasma processing test facility, four laser facilities dedicated to plasma diagnosis, and a magnetic reconnection experiment.

The condensed matter physics facilities include molecular beam epitaxy (MBE) growth facilities, pulsed laser deposition magnetic resonance laboratory (EPR, ENDOR), SQUID magnetometer with magneto-resistance probe, QD PPMS system, rotating anode X-ray source, an atomic force microscope, Hall effect apparatus, ARPES, a 4 mK STM, an optical spectrophotometer, an FTIR spectrophotometer, a high-temperature graphite furnace, ultrasonic, thermogravimetry, and differential scanning calorimetry; characterization capabilities for thermoluminescence, optical absorption, photoreflectance, photoconductance, and photoluminescence of materials, two-dimensional Fourier transform spectroscopy, second harmonic generation system for interface studies, and a sputtering system for thin-film deposition.

Laser facilities include four cw argon ion lasers, three dye lasers, three tunable diode lasers, three cw and Q-switched Nd:YAG lasers, and three femtosecond lasers.

Departmental computing facilities include two dedicated cluster facilities for development of new computational resources and two large computer clusters. Cooperative research programs with National Energy Technology Laboratory and Pittsburgh Supercomputing Center are possible. University-wide shared research facilities that include sophisticated materials characterization and device fabrication tools, as well as high-performance computing, are available (http://sharedresearchfacilities.wvu.edu). A nanotechnology program focusing on bionanotechnology (NanoSAFE, https://research.wvu.edu/researchers/nanosafe) engages students in interdisciplinary research. A comprehensive astrophysics program, teaming with the National Radio Astronomy Observatory in Green Bank, WV, gives students the opportunity to work with a wide array of world-class researchers in the field (http://astro.wvu.edu).

Table B—Separately Budgeted Research Expenditures by Source of Support

Source of Support	Departmental Research	Physics-related Research Outside Department
Federal government	$5,665,759	
State/local government	$12,956	
Non-profit organizations	$388,993	
Business and industry		
Other	$338	
Total	$6,068,046	

Table C—Separately Budgeted Research Expenditures by Research Specialty

Research Specialty	No. of Grants	Expenditures ($)
Astrophysics	28	$2,757,688
Condensed Matter Physics	23	$1,492,081
Physics and other Science Education	9	$776,806
Plasma and Fusion	19	$1,041,471
Total	79	$6,068,046

FACULTY

Distinguished University Professor

Li, Lian, Ph.D., Arizona State University, 1995. Robert L. Carroll Chair of Physics. *Condensed Matter Physics, Solid State Physics, Theoretical Physics.* Condensed Matter.

McLaughlin, Maura A., Ph.D., Cornell University, 2001. Eberly Family Distinguished Professor of Physics and Astronomy. *Astronomy, Astrophysics.* Radio astronomy; astrophysics.

Scime, Earl E., Ph.D., University of Wisconsin-Madison, 1992. Oleg Jefimenko Professor of Physics and Astronomy, Chair of Physics and Astronomy. *Applied Physics, Atmosphere, Space Physics, Cosmic Rays, Plasma and Fusion.* Experimental plasma physics.

Seehra, Mohindar S., Ph.D., University of Rochester, 1969. Eberly Family Distinguished Professor. *Applied Physics, Condensed Matter Physics.* Solid state experiment; X-ray scattering; applied physics; magnetism.

Professor

Abdul-Razzaq, Wathiq, Ph.D., University of Illinois at Chicago, 1986. *Condensed Matter Physics, Physics and other Science Education.* Experimental solid state; magnetism of nanoparticles; particulate matter in the environment.

Cassak, Paul, Ph.D., University of Maryland, 2006. *Plasma and Fusion.* Theoretical plasma physics.

Golubovic, Leonardo, Ph.D., University of Belgrade, 1987. *Condensed Matter Physics, Statistical & Thermal Physics.* Condensed matter theory and statistical physics.

Johnson, Matthew B., Ph.D., California Institute of Technology, 1989. *Condensed Matter Physics, Nano Science and Technology.* Condensed Matter.

Koepke, Mark E., Ph.D., University of Maryland, 1984. *Atmosphere, Space Physics, Cosmic Rays, Plasma and Fusion.* Experimental plasma physics; nonlinear dynamics.

Lewis, James, Ph.D., Arizona State University, 1996. *Chemical Physics, Condensed Matter Physics, Materials Science, Metallurgy.* Computational physics.

Lorimer, Duncan R., Ph.D., University of Manchester, 1994. *Astronomy, Astrophysics.* Radio astronomy; astrophysics.

Murphy, Sheena, Ph.D., Cornell University, 1991. Associate VP for Research Development. *Low Temperature Physics.* Low Temperature Physics.

Stewart, Gay, Ph.D., University of Illinois, 1994. Eberly Professor of STEM Education, Flexible Education Research Network (FERN) initiative leader. *Physics and other Science Education.* STEM education, graduate student training.

Associate Professor

Anderson, Loren, Ph.D., Boston University, 2009. *Astronomy, Astrophysics.* Observational astrophysics.

Bristow, Alan, Ph.D., University of Sheffield, 2003. *Condensed Matter Physics, Optics.* Experimental condensed matter physics; optics.

Cen, Cheng, Ph.D., University of Pittsburgh, 2010. *Applied Physics, Condensed Matter Physics, Materials Science, Metallurgy, Nano Science and Technology.* Novel complex oxide-based material systems.

Holcomb, Mikel, Ph.D., University of California - Berkeley, 2009. *Condensed Matter Physics, Materials Science, Metallurgy, Nano Science and Technology, Optics, Solid State Physics, Surface Physics.* Multiferroic materials and interfaces.

Pisano, Daniel J., Ph.D., University of Wisconsin-Madison, 2001. *Astronomy, Astrophysics.* Radio astronomy; astrophysics.

Romero, Aldo H., Ph.D., University of California, San Diego, 1998. *Computational Physics, Condensed Matter Physics, Nano Science and Technology, Theoretical Physics.*

Stanescu, Tudor, Ph.D., University of Illinois at Urbana-Champaign, 2002. *Condensed Matter Physics.* Theoretical condensed matter physics.

Stewart, John, Ph.D., University of Illinois, Urbana-Champaign, 1994. *Physics and other Science Education.* Physics Education Research.

Assistant Professor

Burke-Spolaor, Sarah, Ph.D., Swinburne University of Technology, 2011. *Astronomy, Astrophysics.* Astrophysics.

Flagg, Edward, Ph.D., University of Texas-Austin, 2008. *Nano Science and Technology, Optics, Quantum Foundations.* Quantum optics.

Lee, Joonhee, Ph.D., Seoul National University, 2010. *Nano Science and Technology, Neuroscience/Neuro Physics.* Qualitative Neuroscience.

McWilliams, Sean, Ph.D., University of Maryland, 2008. General relativity. *Astronomy, Astrophysics.* Gravitational wave theory.

Tu, Weichao, Ph.D., University of Colorado at Boulder, 2011. *Engineering Physics/Science.* Theoretical and numerical space plasma physics.

Emeritus

Halliburton, Larry E., Ph.D., University of Missouri, Columbia, 1971. *Applied Physics, Condensed Matter Physics, Materials Science, Metallurgy, Optics.* Optical and magnetic properties of point defects.

Pavlovic, Arthur S., Ph.D., Pennsylvania State University, 1966. *Condensed Matter Physics.* Solid state physics experiments.

Treat, Richard P., Ph.D., University of California, Riverside, 1967. Quantum field theory.

Weldon, H. Arthur, Ph.D., Massachusetts Institute of Technology, 1974. *Particles and Fields.* Particle theory.

Research Assistant Professor

Fang, Fang, Ph.D., University of Michigan, 2012. *Solar Physics.* Numerical Modeling on Solar and Stellar Physics.

Kobelski, Adam, Ph.D., Montana State University, 2014. *Astronomy, Astrophysics, Plasma and Fusion.* Radio signatures of solar coronal activity, including radio burst activity related to photospheric magnetic flux emergence. Using radio observations of non-solar sources passing behind the solar corona to better understand coronal turbulence, the extended coronal magnetic field, and the solar wind. Observational signatures of the instigation of magnetic reconnection, with emphasis on constraining the heating of Active Regions by modeling X-ray and EUV observations of micro flares as bundles of independent strands.

Ma, Yanjun, Ph.D., University of Pittsburgh, 2013. *Condensed Matter Physics.* Condensed Matter.

Prestage, Richard M., Ph.D., University of Edinburgh, 1985. *Astronomy, Astrophysics.* Radio astronomy.

Schulze, Felix J., Ph.D., Ruhr-University Bochum, Germany, 2009. *Low Temperature Physics, Plasma and Fusion.* Plasma Physics.

Wang, Qiang, Ph.D., University of Colorado Boulder, 2011. *Condensed Matter Physics.* Condensed Matter.

Teaching Associate Professor

Miller, Paul, Ph.D., West Virginia University, 2009. *Physics and other Science Education, Plasma and Fusion.* Physics education.

Teaching Assistant Professor

Williamson, Kathryn, Ph.D., Montana State University, 2013. *Physics and other Science Education.* Physics Education.

Adjunct Professor

Ganguli, Gurudas, Ph.D., Boston College, 1980. *Plasma and Fusion.* Plasma physics theory.

Lockman, Felix J., Ph.D., University of Massachusetts, 1979. *Astronomy, Astrophysics.* Galactic and extragalactic radio astronomy.

O'Neil, K., Ph.D., University of Oregon, 1997. Extragalactic radio astronomy.

Raylman, Raymond R., Ph.D., University of Michigan, 1991. *Medical, Health Physics, Nuclear Physics.* Medical physics; radiology; imaging.

Adjunct Associate Professor

Frayer, D., Ph.D., University of Virginia, 1996. *Astronomy, Astrophysics.* Extragalactic astronomy.

Adjunct Assistant Professor

Bandura, Kevin, Ph.D., Carnegie Mellon University, 2011. *Astronomy, Cosmology & String Theory.* Radio Astronomy.

Bates, Samuel D., Ph.D., The University of Manchester, 2011. *Astronomy.*

Biloiu, Costel, Ph.D., Bucharest University, 1999. Principal Scientist, Varian Semiconductor Equipment, Applied Materials. *Plasma and Fusion.*

Etienne, Zach B., Ph.D., University of Illinois, 2009. *Astronomy, Astrophysics.* Gravitational Wave Theory.

Lynch, Ryan S., Ph.D., University of Virginia, 2011. *Astronomy.* Radio astronomy.

Affiliate Assistant Professor

Zhang, Fan, Ph.D., California Institute of Technology, 2013. *Astrophysics.* General relativity.

DEPARTMENTAL RESEARCH SPECIALTIES AND STAFF

Theoretical

Applied Physics. Photocatalytic materials, new materials by design. Lewis, Romero.

Astrophysics. Interstellar medium; galactic structure; stellar evolution; compact objects; general relativity; pulsars. Anderson, Bandura, Burke-Spolaor, Kobelski, Lockman, Lorimer, Lynch, McLaughlin, McWilliams, O'Neil, Pisano, Prestage.

Condensed Matter Physics. Surface and interface phenomena; lattice stability and relaxation; molecular dynamics; properties of disordered materials; biomaterials; complex fluids and membranes; fracture; transport in random media; thin-film growth; optical properties of materials. Golubovic, Lewis, Romero, Seehra, Stanescu.

Plasma and Fusion. Plasma instabilities; simulations applicable to space and laboratory plasmas; low-temperature plasmas; fusion diagnostics; space plasma instrumentation; space plasma modeling and data analysis. Cassak, Fang, Ganguli, Kobelski, Koepke, Schulze, Scime.

Statistical & Thermal Physics. Fractals; percolation theory; chaos; phase transitions and critical phenomena; nonequilibrium growth and pattern formation. Golubovic, Tu.

Experimental

Applied Physics. Preparation and characterization of nanoparticles; iron-based catalysts; properties of air-borne particulate matter; coal-based high-purity carbons and carbon fibers; electrochemical detection of Hg and other trace metals using boron-doped diamond films; visible and UV light emitters and sensors; nonlinear optical and photorefractive materials. Bristow, Flagg.

Astrophysics. Radio astronomy; X-ray astronomy; pulsars; tests of strong-field gravity; digital signal processing; computational astrophysics. Anderson, Bandura, Burke-Spolaor, Etienne, Frayer, Kobelski, Lockman, Lorimer, McLaughlin, McWilliams, O'Neil, Pisano.

Biophysics. Optogenetic devices, implantable neural sensors, neural signal processing. Lee.

Condensed Matter Physics. Electronic structure and magnetic properties of artificially grown surfaces and superlattices and nanoscale particles; spin transport; properties of magnetic ions and clusters; elementary excitations in antiferromagnets; magnetic susceptibility; magnetostriction; electrical, structural, and electro-optic properties of semiconductors; optical and magnetic resonance characterization of point defects. Bristow, Cen, Flagg, Golubovic, Holcomb, Johnson, Li, Murphy, Seehra, Wang.

Materials Science, Metallurgy. X-ray scattering from disordered systems; Auger and X-ray photoelectron spectroscopy deposition physics; molecular beam epitaxy; properties of monolayer and multilayer thin films; optical properties of quantum-confined systems and semiconductors. Holcomb, Seehra.

Nano Science and Technology. Nanostructured materials; nano toxicology; biological sensors; nanomagnetism; quantum dots. Bristow, Cen, Flagg, Holcomb, Johnson, Seehra, Stanescu, Wang.

Physics and other Science Education. K-12 teacher training; development of GTA training programs; curriculum development. Abdul-Razzaq, Miller, Gay Stewart, John Stewart, Williamson.

Plasma and Fusion. Plasma waves and instabilities; nonlinear interactions; turbulence and chaos; space plasma instrument design; space plasma data analysis and instrument (sensor) development; magnetic reconnection; plasma processing. Biloiu, Kobelski, Koepke, Schulze, Scime.

View additional information about this department at www.gradschoolshopper.com. Check out the "Why Choose Us?" section, find out more about the department's culture and get links to social media networks.

UNIVERSITY OF WISCONSIN, MADISON

DEPARTMENT OF ASTRONOMY

Madison, Wisconsin 53706-1582
http://www.astro.wisc.edu

General University Information
President: University of Wisconsin System: Raymond W. Cross
Dean of Graduate School: William J. Karpus
University website: http://www.wisc.edu
School Type: Public
Setting: Urban
Total Faculty: 2,205
Total Graduate Faculty: 2,205
Total number of Students: 43,820
Total number of Graduate Students: 8,952

Department Information
Department Chairman: Prof. Sebastian Heinz, Chair
Department Contact: Sharon Pittman, Graduate Program
  Coordinator
  Total full-time faculty: 11
  Total number of full-time equivalent positions: 11
  Full-Time Graduate Students: 23
  Female Full-Time Graduate Students: 8
  First-Year Graduate Students: 7
  Female First-Year Students: 1
  Total Post Doctorates: 5

Department Address
475 North Charter Street
Madison, WI 53706-1582
Phone: (608) 262-3071
Fax: (608) 263-6386
E-mail: grading@astro.wisc.edu
Website: http://www.astro.wisc.edu

ADMISSIONS

Admission Contact Information
Address admission inquiries to: Graduate Coordinator, Department of Astronomy, 475 N. Charter Street, Madison, WI 53706
Phone: (608) 890-3775
E-mail: gradinq@astro.wisc.edu
Admissions website: http://www.astro.wisc.edu

Application deadlines
Fall admission:
U.S. students: December 15   *Int'l. students*: December 15

Application fee
U.S. students: $75   *Int'l. students*: $75
Application is submitted online through the UW Graduate School at https://grad.wisc.edu/apply/

Admissions information
For Fall of 2018:
  Number of applicants: 158
  Number admitted: 16
  Number enrolled: 7

Admission requirements
Bachelor's degree requirements: Applicants must have undergraduate preparation that includes at least three years of college physics and mathematics through differential equations.

GRE requirements
The GRE is required.

Subjective GRE requirements
The Subjective GRE is not required.

TOEFL requirements
The TOEFL exam is required for students from non-English-speaking countries.
  PBT score: 600
  iBT score: 100

Other admissions information
Additional requirements: Applicants are judged on the basis of their previous academic record, letters of recommendation, personal statement, research plans, and Graduate Record Examination (GRE) scores.
Undergraduate preparation assumed: Applicants must have undergraduate preparation that includes at least three years of college physics and mathematics through differential equations.

TUITION
Tuition year 2018 - 2019:
Tuition for in-state residents
  Full-time students: $5,993.88
Tuition for out-of-state residents
  Full-time students: $12,657.32
Assistantships and fellowships provide tuition remission.
Credit hours per semester to be considered full-time: 8
Deferred tuition plan: Yes
Health insurance: Available at the cost of $546 per year.
Other academic fees: None
Academic term: Semester
Number of first-year students who received full tuition waivers: 7

Teaching Assistants, Research Assistants, and Fellowships
Number of first-year
  Research Assistants: 7
  Fellowship students: 1
Average stipend per academic year
  Teaching Assistant: $16,148
  Research Assistant: $24,730
  Fellowship student: $24,730
Ph.D. students perform TA duties during their second year in the program. (TA's are supplemented to the RA rate.)

FINANCIAL AID

Application deadlines
Fall admission:
U.S. students: December 15   *Int'l. students*: December 15

Loans
Loans are available for U.S. students.
Loans are not available for international students.
GAPSFAS application required: No
FAFSA application required: No

For further information

Address financial aid inquiries to: Graduate Coordinator, Department of Astronomy, 475 N. Charter Street, Madison, Wi 53706.
Phone: (608) 890-3775
E-mail: grading@astro.wisc.edu
Financial aid website: http://grad.wisc.edu/studentfunding/types

HOUSING

Availability of on-campus housing
Single students: Yes
Married students: Yes

For further information

Address housing inquiries to: University Apartments Office, University Apartments Community Center, 611 Eagle Heights, Madison WI 53705.
Phone: (608) 262-3407
E-mail: leasing@housing.wisc.edu
Housing aid website: http://www.housing.wisc.edu/index.htm

Table A—Faculty, Enrollments, and Degrees Granted

Research Specialty	Fall 2017–18 Faculty	Enrollment Fall 2017–18 Master's	Enrollment Fall 2017–18 Doctorate	Number of Degrees Granted 2017–18 (2017–18) Master's	Number of Degrees Granted 2017–18 (2017–18) Terminal Master's	Number of Degrees Granted 2017–18 (2017–18) Doctorate
Astronomy	11	–	26	4(4)	2(2)	8(8)
Total	11	–	26	4(4)	2(2)	8(8)
Full-time Grad. Stud.	–	–	26	–	–	–
First-year Grad. Stud.	–	–	3	–	–	–

GRADUATE DEGREE REQUIREMENTS

Doctorate: In their first 4 semesters, students both engage in research and complete their required coursework. They take written and oral preliminary exams in their second academic year. Doctoral candidates submit a written dissertation proposal and make an oral presentation to the faculty by the end of their third academic year. A written dissertation must be submitted and successfully defended before a faculty committee within five years after passing the preliminary examination.
Thesis: Theses may be written in absentia.

SPECIAL EQUIPMENT, FACILITIES, OR PROGRAMS

Astronomy at Wisconsin combines strong traditions in observational, instrumental, and theoretical research.

The Astronomy Department has a 18% share in the WIYN 3.5-m Telescope, an advanced technology optical telescope on Kitt Peak in Arizona, and a 9% share in the nearby WIYN 0.9-m telescope, which is optimized for wide-field optical imaging.

UW-Madison has 15% share in the Southern African Large Telescope (SALT), an 11-m spectroscopic telescope. SALT's Robert Stobie Spectrograph (RSS) was designed and built in our department. A near-infrared addition to this spectrograph is currently under construction in our instrumentation labs.

UW-Madison is a full institutional member in the Sloan Digital Sky Survey-IV (SDSS-IV) and collaborative international project to study cosmology and galaxy evolution using large spectroscopic surveys.

The Wisconsin H-Alpha Mapper (WHAM) is a remotely operated observatory in Cerro Tololo, Chile dedicated to studies of the diffuse interstellar medium.

The Astronomy Department also manages Washburn Observatory, a historic 15.6-inch refractor on campus used for public observing.

The department is home to Washburn Astronomical Laboratories, an instrumentation design and fabrication center. They have designed and built instruments and critical components for WIYN, SALT, and SDSS-IV, and supported stand-alone experiments on the ground (e.g., WHAM) and in sub-orbital modes (rocket and balloons).

The department hosts several research computing clusters and makes use of campus-wide resources such as the Center for High Throughput Computing and the Advanced Computing Initiative.

Table B—Separately Budgeted Research Expenditures by Source of Support

Source of Support	Departmental Research	Physics-related Research Outside Department
Federal government	$8,649,839	$5,260,000
State/local government		
Non-profit organizations	$395,195	
Business and industry		
Other		
Total	$9,045,034	$5,260,000

Table C—Separately Budgeted Research Expenditures by Research Specialty

Research Specialty	No. of Grants	Expenditures ($)
Astronomy	60	$13,819,850
Total	60	$13,819,850

FACULTY

Professor

Barger, Amy, Ph.D., University of Cambridge, 1997. *Astronomy*. Observational cosmology; distant galaxies and supermassive black holes; star formation and accretion histories of the universe.

Bershady, Matthew A., Ph.D., University of Chicago, 1994. *Astronomy*. Galaxy kinematics; stellar populations; galaxy and quasar evolution; optical and IR spectra and instrumentation.

Heinz, Sebastian, Ph.D., University of Colorado, 2000. *Astronomy*. Relativistic jets; black holes; AGN; X-ray binaries; galaxy clusters; gamma-ray bursts; interstellar and intergalactic medium; numerical methods.

Lazarian, Alex, Ph.D., University of Cambridge, 1995. *Astronomy, Astrophysics*. Theoretical astrophysics, in particular plasma processes, properties of magnetic turbulence, and techniques of its observational studies; magnetic reconnection; cosmic ray physics; star formation; physics of dusty plasmas; physics of microwave foregrounds; techniques for observational studies of astrophysical magnetic fields.

Mathieu, Robert D., Ph.D., University of California, Berkeley, 1983. Department Chair. *Astronomy*. Observational study of star formation, binary stars, and open star clusters; high-resolution optical and infrared spectroscopy; optical, infrared, and sub-mm imaging and photometry.

Stanimirovic, Snezana, Ph.D., University of Western Sydney Nepean, 1999. Undergraduate Advisor. *Astronomy*. Galactic disk/halos; dust properties in low-metallicity environments; physics of the ISM; radio techniques and applications.

Wilcots, Eric M., Ph.D., University of Washington, 1992. *Astronomy*. Studies of the structure and evolution of galaxies through 21-cm HI, optical, and infrared observations; extended gas around galaxies; distribution and kinematics of the interstellar medium in nearby galaxies; structure and evolution of classical HII regions.

Zweibel, Ellen, Ph.D., Princeton University, 1977. *Astronomy, Astrophysics*. Theoretical plasma astrophysics; generation and evolution of astrophysical magnetic fields; interstellar astrophysics; star formation; stellar physics.

Associate Professor

Townsend, Richard, Ph.D., University College, London, 1997. Graduate Committee Chair. *Astronomy, Astrophysics*. Stellar astrophysics; magnetic fields; stellar winds; massive stars.

Tremonti, Christy, Ph.D., Johns Hopkins University, 2003. *Astronomy*. Galaxy and AGN co-evolution; galactic chemical evolution.

Assistant Professor

D'Onghia, Elena, Ph.D., University of Milan, 2003. *Astronomy, Astrophysics*. Cosmology: nature of dark matter, large-scale structure formation, dynamics, and galaxy formation.

Emeritus

Cassinelli, Joseph P., Ph.D., Washington University, 1970. *Astronomy*. Structure of stellar winds; high-resolution X-ray observations; effects of rotation and magnetic fields on the circumstellar envelopes of hot stars.

Churchwell, Edward B., Ph.D., Indiana University, 1970. *Astronomy*. Star formation; hot molecular cores; UC HII regions; atomic abundances; radio and infrared astronomy.

Gallagher, John S., Ph.D., University of Wisconsin-Madison, 1972. *Astronomy*. Multi-wavelength observational investigations of evolutionary processes in galaxies; stellar populations; classical novae.

Nordsieck, Kenneth H., Ph.D., University of California, Santa Cruz, 1972. *Astronomy*. Stellar and extragalactic optical/ultraviolet spectropolarimetry; ground-based instrument control; space astronomy.

Reynolds, Ronald J., Ph.D., University of Wisconsin-Madison, 1971. *Astronomy*. High-resolution spectroscopy of diffuse sources; development of high-throughput spectrometers; physics of the interstellar medium.

Savage, Blair D., Ph.D., Princeton University, 1968. *Astronomy*. Physical properties of the interstellar medium; gas in galactic halos and the intergalactic medium; high-resolution ultraviolet spectroscopy.

Whitney, Barbara, Ph.D., University of Wisconsin-Madison, 1989. *Astronomy*. Radiative transfer models of planets, forming stars, and galaxies; infrared surveys of our galaxy and the Magellanic Clouds.

Senior Scientist

Haffner, Matt, Ph.D., University of Wisconsin-Madison, 1999. *Astronomy*. Milky Way structure and dynamics; physics of the interstellar medium; extended galactic halos; diffuse emission-line spectroscopy; remote observing.

Orio, Marina, Ph.D., University of Technion, Haifa, Israel, 1987. *Astronomy, Astrophysics*. Stellar evolution and compact objects, particularly close binary stars; classical and recurrent novae; supersoft X-ray sources; cataclysmic variables; low-mass X-ray binaries, ionization nebulae.

Percival, Jeffrey, Ph.D., University of Wisconsin-Madison, 1979. *Astronomy*. Instrument control software; telescope control systems; guidance and navigation for suborbital rockets.

Wakker, Bastiaan, Ph.D., Gronigen University, 1990. *Astronomy*. High-velocity clouds and low-redshift intergalactic medium.

DEPARTMENTAL RESEARCH SPECIALTIES AND STAFF

Theoretical

Extragalactic astronomy and cosmology. Barger, Bershady, D'Onghia, Gallagher, Tremonti, Wilcots.

Instrumentation. Bershady, Nordsieck, Percival, Reynolds.

Interstellar and intergalactic media. Haffner, Heinz, Reynolds, Savage, Stanimirovic, Wakker.

Plasma astrophysics and magnetic fields.. Cassinelli, Lazarian, Nordsieck, Zweibel.

Stellar star formation, young stars. Cassinelli, Churchwell, Mathieu, Nordsieck, Orio, Townsend.

View additional information about this department at www.gradschoolshopper.com. Check out the "Why Choose Us?" section, find out more about the department's culture and get links to social media networks.

UNIVERSITY OF WISCONSIN

MEDICAL PHYSICS

Madison, Wisconsin 53705
http://medphysics.wisc.edu

General University Information
Chancellor: Rebecca M. Blank
Dean of Graduate School: William Karpus
University website: http://wisc.edu
School Type: Public
Setting: Suburban
Total Faculty: 2,220
Total Graduate Faculty: 2,220
Total number of Students: 43,820
Total number of Graduate Students: 8,952

Department Information
Department Chairman: Prof. Edward F. Jackson, Chair
Department Contact: Carol Aspinwall, Educational Programs Coordinator
   Total full-time faculty: 28
   Total number of full-time equivalent positions: 28
   Full-Time Graduate Students: 73
   Female Full-Time Graduate Students: 21
   First-Year Graduate Students: 14
   Female First-Year Students: 6
   Total Post Doctorates: 3

Department Address
1111 Highland Ave, 1005 WIMR
Madison, WI 53705
Phone: (608) 265-6504
Fax: (608) 262-2413
E-mail: carol.aspinwall@wisc.edu
Website: http://medphysics.wisc.edu

ADMISSIONS

Admission Contact Information
Address admission inquiries to: Graduate Admissions, UW-Madison, Medical Physics, 1111 Highland Avenue, 1005 WIMR, Madison, WI 53705-2275
Phone: (608) 265-6504
E-mail: admissions@medphysics.wisc.edu
Admissions website: https://www.medphysics.wisc.edu/graduate/admissions/

Application deadlines
Fall admission:
U.S. students: December 1   *Int'l. students*: November 15

Application fee
U.S. students: $75   *Int'l. students*: $81
Application is submitted online through the UW Graduate School at https://www.gradsch.wisc.edu/eapp/eapp.pl

Admissions information
For Fall of 2018:
   Number of applicants: 79
   Number admitted: 32
   Number enrolled: 21

Admission requirements
Bachelor's degree requirements: Degree in physics or related field with at least a minor in physics. The mean GPA of our last entering class was 3.62/4.00.
Minimum undergraduate GPA: 3.0

GRE requirements
The GRE is required.
   Quantitative score: 163
   Verbal score: 158
   Analytical score: 4.0
   Mean GRE score range (25th–75th percentile): 75
The GRE scores listed are the average scores of the Fall 2018 incoming class.

Subjective GRE requirements
The Subjective GRE is recommended.
   Minimum accepted Advanced GRE score: 743
   Mean Advanced GRE score range (25th–75th percentile): 57
The Physics subject GRE is the average of the four incoming students who took it.

TOEFL requirements
The TOEFL exam is required for students from non-English-speaking countries.
   PBT score: 600
   iBT score: 100

Other admissions information
Additional requirements: Applicants are judged on the basis of their previous academic record, letters of recommendation, personal statement, research plans and Graduate Record Examination (GRE) scores.
Undergraduate preparation assumed: At least three upper level physics courses required of a physics major (or equivalent), including modern physics.

TUITION

Tuition year 2018–2019:
Tuition for in-state residents
   Full-time students: $5,993.88 per semester
Tuition for out-of-state residents
   Full-time students: $12,657.32 per semester
Tuition listed is based on 2017–2018 rates. 2018–2019 rates have not been released at this time of submission.
Credit hours per semester to be considered full-time: 8
Deferred tuition plan: No
Health insurance: Available at the cost of $2,136 per year.
Academic term: Semester
Number of first-year students who received full tuition waivers: 14

Teaching Assistants, Research Assistants, and Fellowships
Number of first-year
   Research Assistants: 14
   Fellowship students: 2
Average stipend per academic year
   Teaching Assistant: $17,118
   Research Assistant: $19,125
   Fellowship student: $19,125

Every attempt is made to have the assistantships and fellowships be an annual appointment (not academic).

FINANCIAL AID

Application deadlines
Fall admission:

U.S. students: December 1   *Int'l. students*: November 15

Loans
Loans are available for U.S. students.
Loans are not available for international students.
GAPSFAS application required: No
FAFSA application required: Yes

For further information
Address financial aid inquiries to: Office of Student Financial Aid, 333 East Campus Mall #9701, Madison, WI 53715-1382.
Phone: (608) 262-3060
E-mail: finaid@finaid.wisc.edu
Financial aid website: https://finaid.wisc.edu/

HOUSING

Availability of on-campus housing
Single students: Yes
Married students: Yes
Childcare Assistance: Yes

For further information
Address housing inquiries to: Division of University Housing, 625 Babcock Drive, Madison, WI 53706-1213.
Phone: (608) 262-2522
E-mail: info@housing.wisc.edu
Housing aid website: https://www.housing.wisc.edu/

Table A—Faculty, Enrollments, and Degrees Granted

Research Specialty	2017–18 Faculty	Enrollment Fall 2017		Number of Degrees Granted 2016–17 (2010–2017)		
		Master's	Doctorate	Master's	Terminal Master's	Doctorate
Medical, Health Physics	28	2	73	4(100)	–(22)	19(102)
Total	28	2	73	29(100)	3(25)	19(102)
Full-time Grad. Stud.	–	–	73	–	–	–
First-year Grad. Stud.	–	–	14	–	–	–

GRADUATE DEGREE REQUIREMENTS

Master's: Candidates must complete "core" courses: Medical Physics 501, 563, 566, 567, 569, 573, 578 and 701 if completing the CAMPEP Track. Either anatomy or physiology must also be taken, if completing the CAMPEP Track, and 4 credits (two graded and two pass/fail) of Journal Club (Medical Physics 990). Minimum number of: 30. The vast majority of students complete a MS degree en route to the PhD degree. The number of students pursuing a terminal MS degree in our department is relatively small.

Doctorate: Completion of the core and elective course requirements as defined for the master's degree is required. Completion of an Oral PhD Qualifier Exam is required at end of second spring semester following matriculation. A PhD Preliminary Exam must be completed by the end of the third year of enrollment. A dissertation is required and a PhD Dissertation Exam must be successfully completed. Minimum number of credits: 51.

SPECIAL EQUIPMENT, FACILITIES, OR PROGRAMS

The Department of Medical Physics is housed in the Wisconsin Institutes for Medical Research Tower I (WIMR I), which opened in 2008. Located on Level 1 of WIMR I are translational imaging facilities, including a 1.5T GE Signa HDxt MR system, a 3.0T GE Discovery MR750 system, a DNP hyperpolarization system, a GE Discovery CT750 scanner, an angiography research and development suite, and an RF ablation facility. These translational facilities are all part of the WIMR Imaging Services facility, which facilitates the reception, preparation, and scanning of ambulatory patients for both clinical research protocol and patient care applications. Additional facilities on this floor include a CT Physics research laboratory, an Imaging Analysis Core facility (IMAC), a large wet lab for MR and ultrasound phantom development and basic physics measurements, a smaller ultrasound phantom laboratory, an electronics lab (with a shielded a RF facility), three ultrasound physics and imaging laboratories, a biomagnetism laboratory, and a radiation therapy Treatment Planning System Laboratory (with 3 Varian Eclipse, 3 Philips Pinnacle, 3 TomoTherapy HDA VoLO, 1 CyberKnife, and 2 Oncentra Brachy workstations, all dedicated for education and research).

On the Basement Level of WIMR I are the Medical Radiation Research Center (MRRC) and Accredited Dosimetry Calibration Lab (ADCL), a cyclotron facility (GE PETtrace) and associated radiochemistry and detector laboratories, a GMP Radiopharmaceutical Production Facility (RPF), a radiation therapy physics lab, a primary computing cluster facility, and a machine shop. Among the extensive resources in the MRRC is a Varian 21EX linear accelerator dedicated to research and education. Also on this floor is the Small Animal Imaging Facility (SAIF), with 4.7T MR (with DNP hyperpolarization system), Siemens microCAT-II, Inveon microPET/CT, IVIS Spectrum optical, and Visualsonics Vevo 2100/LAZR high resolution ultrasound and photoacoustic imaging systems. Additionally, this floor of WIMR I houses a next generation image-guided radiation therapy system, a 3.0T GE Discovery PET/MR system, a GE 710 PET/CT system, a GE VCT PET/CT system, and a small reading room. The two PET/CT systems and the PET/MR system are used for both clinical and research purposes.

The UW Hospital and Clinics (UWHC) is located immediately adjacent to these WIMR facilities as are the American Family Children's Hospital and the Veteran's Administration Hospital. The Waisman Center, described below, is across the street from the WIMR towers.

The Waisman Laboratory for Brain Imaging and Behavior houses a 3T GE Discovery MR750 scanner, a Siemens HR+ PET scanner, a Concord Microsystems microPET, a National Electrostatics Corporation 7 MeV tandem accelerator and associated radiochemistry laboratory, and a 256-channel EEG system. The Waisman Center is internationally known for its efforts to advance our knowledge of human development, developmental disabilities, and neurodegenerative diseases.

Another facility at which some of our faculty and graduate students perform their research is the Laboratory for Optical and Computer Instrumentation (LOCI), which is a biophotonics instrumentation laboratory located approximately 0.5 miles from the WIMR towers. The focus of this facility is the development of optical and computational techniques and instrumentation for imaging living specimens. Students working in LOCI are involved in projects focused on bridging the scales from microscopy (LOCI) to in vivo imaging (WIMR).

Finally, some of our faculty and graduate students have their offices and labs in the Discovery Building, which is located near the center of the UW-Madison campus. This building houses a public-private partnership between UW-Madison (Wisconsin Institutes for Discovery, or WID) and the Morgridge Institute for Research (MIR). This unique facility provides public education opportunities and focuses on the study of biosciences across the lifespan, inspires collaboration across disciplines, and sparks public interest in science. It houses numerous advanced laboratories, including an advanced microfabrication laboratory, a medical devices laboratory, and the Center for High-Throughput Computing.

In addition to the translational and clinical imaging systems located in WIMR I, the adjacent UWHC (and associated Research Park and Digestive Health facilities) have a total of 8 CT scanners, 15 CR/DR systems, 14 angiography systems, 29 fluoroscopy systems, 5 mobile radiography units, 7 mammography systems (including tomo systems), 2 stereotactic mammography units, 2 DXA bone densitometry systems, 2 dental x-ray units, 18 ultrasound systems, 8 MR scanners (5 1.5T and 3 3.0T), and 5 gamma cameras and SPECT/CT systems. The adjacent American Family Children's Hospital (AFCH) has additional imaging facilities, including 2 CR/DR systems, 1 angiography system, 3 fluoroscopy systems, 1 3.0T MR scanner, and 1 PET/CT scanner. Graduate students have access to all of these imaging facilities, although the majority of graduate student imaging research is performed on imaging systems in the WIMR I facilities and those in the Waisman Center.

With regard to radiation oncology equipment and research, in addition to the Treatment Planning System Laboratory, Varian 21EX linear accelerator in the MRRC/ADCL, and next generation image-guided radiation therapy facilities described in Section 6.1, above, the UWHC radiation oncology facilities include two Varian 21EX linacs, two Varian TrueBeam linacs, two TomoTherapy HDA systems, and a MR-guided ViewRay system. The facilities also include a Siemens Edge Dual Energy CT Simulation system and a BodyTom Portable CT scanner.

Table B—Separately Budgeted Research Expenditures by Source of Support

Source of Support	Departmental Research	Physics-related Research Outside Department
Federal government	$4,555,458	
State/local government	$73,509	
Non-profit organizations	$725,419	
Business and industry	$222,216	
Other	$932,911	
Total	$6,509,513	

Table C—Separately Budgeted Research Expenditures by Research Specialty

Research Specialty	No. of Grants	Expenditures ($)
Medical, Health Physics	50	$6,509,513
Total	50	$6,509,513

FACULTY

Chair Professor

Jackson, Edward F., Ph.D., University of Texas Health Science Center - Houston, 1990. Department Chair and Director of the Graduate Program. *Computational Physics, Medical, Health Physics*. Quantitative imaging biomarkers; Functional magnetic resonance imaging applications in treatment assessment; Multi-parametric and multi-modality imaging biomarker applications.

Professor

Alexander, Andrew L., Ph.D., University of Arizona-Tucson, 1994. Director of MR Physics, Waisman Laboratory for Brain Imaging and Behavior. *Biophysics, Medical, Health Physics, Neuroscience/Neuro Physics*. The use of Magnetic Resonance Imaging (MRI) for mapping and measuring the functional and structural organization of the human brain.

Bayouth, John E., Ph.D., University of Texas Health Science Center, M.D. Anderson Cancer Center, 1993. *Medical, Health Physics*. MRI guided radiation therapy, 4D radiation therapy, small animal radiation therapy.

Block, Walter F., Ph.D., Stanford University, 1998. *Applied Mathematics, Computer Science, Electrical Engineering, Medical, Health Physics*. theory of magnetic resonance imaging acquisition theory of magnetic resonance reconstruction image-guided surgery. brain mapping breast cancer detection and therapeutic monitoring magnetic resonance imaging of the musculoskeletal system.

Campagnola, Paul J., Ph.D., Yale University, 1992. *Medical, Health Physics*. Biophotonics, tissue imaging, breast and ovarian cancer, connective tissue disorders, nanofabrication, cancer cell biology, tissue engineering.

Chen, Guang-Hong, Ph.D., University of Utah, 2000. Editorial Board Member, Medical Physics, Journal of Engineering Charter Member, BMIT Study Section Fellow of American Institute of Medical and Biomedical Engineering (AIMBE) Director of X-ray and CT Research Scientific Program Committee Member of SPIE Medical Imaging, Fully 3D Meeting, and CT Meeting Scientific Program Co-Director (2016) and Director (2017)-Imaging Track, AAPM Annual Meeting. *Applied Mathematics, Applied Physics, Atomic, Molecular, & Optical Physics, Biophysics, Computational Physics, Electrical Engineering, Electromagnetism, Engineering Physics/ Science, High Energy Physics, Low Temperature Physics, Medical, Health Physics, Nano Science and Technology, Nonlinear Dynamics and Complex Systems, Nuclear Physics, Optics, Particles and Fields, Physics and other Science Education, Solid State Physics, Statistical & Thermal Physics, Systems Science/Engineering, Theoretical Physics*Dr. Guang-Hong Chen is a tenured Full Professor of Medical Physics and Radiology at the University of Wisconsin-Madison. His current interests cover a variety of topics in medical imaging and medical physics, including digital image representation theories, sparse encoding schemes for medical images, medical image reconstruction methods, image artifact correction algorithms, task-based image evaluation methods, and hardware/software engineering developments to provide acquisition systems achieving low radiation dose, high spatial resolution, high temporal resolution, and multi-contrast x-ray.

Christian, Bradley T., Ph.D., University of Wisconsin-Madison, 1994. *Accelerator, Medical, Health Physics*. PET Neuroimaging Molecular Imaging Neurodevelopment Alzheimer's Disease.

DeJesus, Onofre T., Ph.D., Ph.D Virginia Tech, 1980. *Medical, Health Physics, Neuroscience/Neuro Physics*. Nuclear Medicine Positron Emission Tomography (PET) Radiochemistry Radiopharmaceutical Chemistry Neuroreceptor Imaging Cancer Imaging Agents.

DeWerd, Larry A., Ph.D., University of Wisconsin-Madison, 1970. *Medical, Health Physics, Solid State Physics*. Radiation metrology, including calibration of inoization chambers, radiation dosimetry in diagnostic radiology and radiotherapy, quality assurance in radiology and radiotherapy, luminescence for dosimetry (TLD).

Fain, Sean B., Ph.D., Mayo Graduate School, 2000. Director of Image Analysis Core, CTSA, School of Medicine and Public Health, Director of Lung Imaging Research, Department of

Radiology. *Medical, Health Physics*. Magnetic Resonance Imaging; Quantitative Imaging; X-ray CT and Dose Reduction.

Grist, Thomas M., Medical College of Wisconsin, 1985. Professor (Tenure) and Chair, Department of Radiology. *Medical, Health Physics, Other*. Interested in the development and application of advanced magnetic resonance imaging techniques for diagnosis and therapy of human disease, primarily for the evaluation of cardiovascular disorders.

Hall, Timothy J., Ph.D., University of Wisconsin-Madison, 1988. Vice Chair for Faculty, Program Director for the Radiological Sciences Training Program. *Acoustics, Applied Mathematics, Applied Physics, Engineering Physics/Science, Medical, Health Physics, Systems Science/Engineering*. From 1988 to 2002, he was in the Radiology Department at the University of Kansas Medical Center, where he worked on measurements of acoustic scattering in tissues, metrics of observer performance in ultrasound imaging, and developed elasticity imaging methods and phantoms for elasticity imaging. In 2003, he returned to the University of Wisconsin-Madison, where he is a Professor in the Medical Physics Department. His research interests continue to center on developing new image formation strategies based on acoustic wave propagation and tissue viscoelasticity, the development of methods for system performance evaluation, and quantitative biomarker development.

Henderson, Douglass L., Ph.D., University of Wisconsin-Madison, 1987. *Nuclear Engineering, Other*. Reactor physics, radiation transport, fusion reactor technology, nuclear waste, brachytherapy treatment planning.

Jeraj, Robert, Ph.D., University of Ljubljana, 1999. *Applied Physics, Computational Physics, Medical, Health Physics, Particles and Fields*. Molecular imaging, Oncology, Modeling, Clinical trials.

Korosec, Frank R., Ph.D., University of Wisconsin-Madison, 1991. *Medical, Health Physics*. Time-resolved MRI, dynamic contrast-enhanced breast MRI, MR angiography, rapid imaging.

Meyerand, M. Beth, Ph.D., Medical College of Wisconsin, 1996. *Applied Mathematics, Computational Physics, Engineering Physics/Science, Medical, Health Physics, Neuroscience/ Neuro Physics, Physics and other Science Education, Systems Science/Engineering*. Magnetic Resonance Imaging (MRI).

Peppler, Walter W., Ph.D., University of Wisconsin-Madison, 1981. *Medical, Health Physics*. Diagnostic Imaging, X-ray Imaging.

Reeder, Scott B., M.D./Ph.D., Johns Hopkins University, 1999. *Engineering Physics/Science, Medical, Health Physics*. MR physics, particularly in cardiovascular imaging, as well as chemical shift based water-fat MRI methods for quantification of iron and fat.

Thomadsen, Bruce R., Ph.D., University of Wisconsin-Madison, 1989. Professor, Director, Center of the Assessment of Radiological Sciences, Patient Safety Organization. *Medical, Health Physics, Systems Science/Engineering*. Radionuclide Therapy Clinical Quality and Patient Safety Robotics. Brachytherapy Physics Image-based localization.

Varghese, Tomy, Ph.D., University of Kentucky, 1995. *Acoustics, Applied Mathematics, Electrical Engineering, Medical, Health Physics, Statistical & Thermal Physics*. Ultrasound Imaging, Elastography, Biomedical Signal and Image Processing, Elasticity Imaging, Cardiovascular Imaging, Quantitative Ultrasound, Vascular Imaging.

Wakai, Ronald T., Ph.D., University of Illinois-Urbana, 1987. *Medical, Health Physics*. Biomagnetism, magnetocardiography, magnetoencephalography, SQUIDs, fetal monitoring, signal processing.

Associate Professor

Bednarz, Bryan P., Ph.D., Rensselaer Polytechnic Institute, 2008. *Biophysics, Engineering Physics/Science, Medical, Health Physics, Nuclear Engineering*. Monte Carlo methods, proton therapy, radiation protection.

Birn, Rasmus, Ph.D., Medical College of Wisconsin, 2000. *Medical, Health Physics*. My current research interests are: 1) to increase the accuracy, specificity, interpretability, and usefulness of MRI measures of functional connections in the brain, and 2) to determine the changes in functional connectivity during brain development. In addition, I am interested in determining the alterations in brain connectivity that relate to various mental disorders, particularly as they emerge during development. My previous research has focused on the characterizing various sources of noise, improving methods to map connections between brain areas, the development of new imaging strategies and the application of post-processing techniques to reduce artifacts resulting from task-induced subject motion, and understanding the dynamics of the blood oxygenation level dependent (BOLD) fMRI signal. Advancements in these areas are essential for the improved application of fMRI to clinical studies and basic neuroscience research.

Brace, Chris L., Ph.D., University of Wisconsin-Madison, 2005. *Medical, Health Physics*. Image-guided interventional oncology, thermal therapies such as radiofrequency and microwave ablation, medical imaging, and applications of electromagnetics in medicine.

Cai, Weibo, Ph.D., University of California - San Diego, 2004. *Engineering Physics/Science, Medical, Health Physics, Nano Science and Technology, Optics*. Research of the Cai Group is focused on three areas: 1) development of multimodality molecular imaging agents; 2) molecular therapy of cancer; and 3) nanotechnology and its biomedical applications.

Cho, Steve Y., New York University, 1995. *Medical, Health Physics*. Dr. Steve Y. Cho, M.D. is an Associate Professor (CHS) in the Nuclear Medicine Section of the Department of Radiology. He is engaged in translational molecular imaging research as Director of the Translational Imaging Research Core at the University of Wisconsin Carbone Comprehensive Cancer Center, Director of the new cGMP Radiopharmaceutical Production Facility, and Associate Director of the UW PET Center. His research interest involves translational imaging, with a focus on development of novel and existing PET radiopharmaceuticals to improve clinical management and therapy development for cancer and infection.

Emborg, Marina, M.D./Ph.D., Universidad de Buenos Aires, 1993. *Medical, Health Physics, Neuroscience/Neuro Physics*. Animal models, Neurorepair, Neuroprotection, Target validation.

Nagle, Scott K., M.D./Ph.D., University of Chicago, 2002. Radiologist in cardiovascular and thoracic sections. *Medical, Health Physics*. Dr. Nagle focuses his research on translational pulmonary MRI, focussing in particular on proton-based methods of imaging lung structure and function using ultrashort echo time and dynamic contrast-enhanced perfusion methods. In particular, he is applying these methods to cystic fibrosis in order to track disease severity and response to therapy. Other active projects include the use of pulmonary MR angiography for detection of pulmonary embolism, time-resolved ultrashort echo time methods, and pulmonary perfusion MRI methodology.

Ranallo, Frank N., Ph.D., University of Wisconsin-Madison, 1993. *Medical, Health Physics*. The development of improved protocols for CT imaging that optimize image quality and reduce patient dose. These protocols will now be licensed to General Electric for use on their CT scanners by the University of Wisconsin. The evaluation and optimization of image quality and dosimetry in CT and other forms of medical imaging. The clinical use of dual energy CT including the imaging of uric acid in gout patients, the imaging of patients with implants in musculoskeletal imaging, and the imaging of patients with clips and other metal inferring objects in neuro vascular studies.

Skala, Melissa C., Ph.D., Duke University, 2007. *Biophysics, Optics.* My lab develops and applies novel optical imaging techniques to provide personalized treatment options to patients, streamline drug development, and monitor dynamic in vivo changes in tissue structure and function to answer questions in basic science. My research program seeks to impact patient care, drug development and assessment, fundamental discovery, and new technology development in photonics. The majority of my work has focused on cancer, with additional investigations in vascular diseases and collaborative work spanning multiple disciplines.

Smilowitz, Jennifer B., Ph.D., University of Wisconsin-Madison, 2002. *Medical, Health Physics.* Tomotherapy, treatment planning, quality assurance.

Vetter, John R., Ph.D., University of Wisconsin-Madison, 1990. Associate Director of Imaging Physics Residency Program, Director of Radiological Physics Services. *Medical, Health Physics.* Image reconstruction in computed tomography and tomosynthesis, radiation dosimetry in mammographic imaging, radiation safety.

Weichert, Jamey P., Ph.D., University of Michigan, 1985. *Medical, Health Physics.* My lab is focused on the development of new targeted CT, MRI, optical and PET imaging agents as well as therapeutic anticancer agents. These diapeutic agents are conceptualized via a biochemical approach whereby compounds known to be stored or synthesized by the organ or tissue of interest, including tumors, serve as the delivery platform for the imaging or therapeutic moiety. A founding aim of my lab is to discover new agents, synthesize and evaluate them preclinically in small animal models and then translate promising agents to clinical evaluation and commercialization.

Wieben, Oliver, Ph.D., University of Wisconsin-Madison, 2002. *Applied Physics, Biophysics, Computational Physics, Electrical Engineering, Engineering Physics/Science, Fluids, Rheology, Medical, Health Physics.* MRI: Data Acquisition and Reconstruction, Accelerated MRI, Cardiovascular MRI: Methodology development and clinical translation, Flow-sensitive MRI, especially 4D Flow MRI, Realtime MRI / exercise MRI, Motion detection and correction in MRI, MRI of the placenta, MRI of the aging brain.

Assistant Professor

Bayliss, R. Adam, Ph.D., University of Wisconsin-Madison, 2006. *Medical, Health Physics.* Research interests include Stereotactic radiosurgery, hyprofractionation, dose painting, inter and intrafraction motion variability and its effect on dose, and novel dosimetric methods applied to clinical cases.

Culberson, Wesley S., Ph.D., University of Wisconsin-Madison, 2006. UW ADCL director. *Accelerator, Applied Physics, Medical, Health Physics, Nuclear Engineering.* Radiation therapy, radiation dosimetry, metrology, radiobiology, nuclear physics, brachytherapy.

Engle, Jonathan W., Ph.D., University of Wisconsin-Madison, 2011. *Medical, Health Physics.* Novel radionuclide production and applications.

Hernando, Diego, Ph.D., University of Illinois at Urbana-Champaign, 2010. *Electrical Engineering, Medical, Health Physics.* My research focuses on the development and translational validation of quantitative MRI techniques. Specific areas of interest are diffusion MRI, as well as quantification

of fat and iron concentration in tissue. This multi-disciplinary research requires theoretical characterization and optimization of sampling schemes and parameter estimation techniques, phantom construction and validation, and clinical validation studies to assess the resulting techniques in patients.

Johnson, Kevin M., Ph.D., University of Wisconsin - Madison, 2008. *Applied Physics, Computer Science, Electrical Engineering, Medical, Health Physics.* MR pulse sequence development, non-Cartesian and non-Fourier imaging,Signal encoding and decoding, sampling theory, recovery from incomplete samples, Motion robust imaging, free breathing MRI, motion sensing, Macro and micro vascular remodeling, perfusion, flow, Improving the MRI experience for patients.

Li, Ke, Ph.D., University of Wisconsin-Madison, 2013. *Applied Physics, Medical, Health Physics.* Diagnostic CT imaging; cone beam CT imaging; X-ray phase contrast imaging; CT perfusion imaging; CT system instrumentation; CT image quality assessment.

Mitchell, Carol, Ph.D., University of Missouri-Kansas City, 2002. *Medical, Health Physics.* Carotid Plaque Strain Imaging, Plaque characterization (grayscale analyss) and relationship to plaque composition and vulnerability, Plaque volume and development of alogrithims to quantify 3D plaque volumes, 3D evaluation of carotid plaque, Carotid hemodynamics and the relationship to plaque formation, relationship of vulnerable plaque and/or flow limiting lesions to vascular dementia/cognitive decline.

Prabhakaran, Vivek, M.D./Ph.D., Stanford Medical School, 2001. *Medical, Health Physics, Neuroscience/Neuro Physics, Other.* The goal of my research program is to characterize brain plasticity changes in aging and in stroke patient populations as well as develop novel interventions toward recovery. Specifically my lab combines neuroimaging measures such as functional magnetic resonance imaging (fMRI), diffusion tensor imaging (DTI), and other advanced neuroimaging as well as behavioral measures to 1) identify prognostic factors that predict functional recovery, 2) identify adaptive and maladaptive networks that contribute to functional recovery, and 3) identify a critical time window for intervention in these patients. My lab in collaboration with Justin Williams' Lab and TCNL lab is developing Brain-Computer Interface technology respectively as a rehabilitation treatment for patients, which will lead to faster and more optimal level of recovery.

Speidel, Michael A., Ph.D., University of Wisconsin-Madison, 2003. Technical Director of the Cardiac Catheterization Laboratory of the University of Wisconsin Hospital and Clinics. *Medical, Health Physics.* X-ray Fluoroscopy, X-ray Angiography, Computed Tomography, Image-guided Interventions, Cardiac imaging.

Strigel, Roberta, University of Wisconsin-Madison, 2004. Breast Imaging Fellowship Director. *Medical, Health Physics.* Breast MRI, Simultaneous breast MR/PET.

Szczykutowicz, Timothy P., Ph.D., University of Wisconsin - Madison, 2012. Clinical CT physicist. *Medical, Health Physics.* clinical CT workflow, protocol optimization, dual energy CT, image quality metrics for CT.

Emeritus

DeLuca, Jr., Paul, Ph.D., University of Notre Dame, 1991. Emeritus Professor, Medical Physics, Radiology, Human Oncology, Biomedical Engineering, and Engineering Physics. *Medical, Health Physics.* Research interests have concentrated on fast neutron dosimetry including production of intense sources of fast neutrons, determination of elemental neutron kerma coefficients and applications of microdosimetry to radiation dosimetry.

Holden, James E., Ph.D., University of Pennsylvania, 1971. *Applied Mathematics, Medical, Health Physics, Neuroscience/*

Neuro Physics. Quantitative physiological and biochemical modeling and interpretation of PET data in brain and heart.

Mistretta, Charles A., Ph.D., Harvard University, 1968. National Advisory Counsil NIBIB National Academy of Engineering. *Medical, Health Physics*. Focus has been on angiography, first in X-ray, then in MR, most recently in intervention X-ray and diagnostic CT.

Nickles, R. Jerry, Ph.D., University of Wisconsin-Madison, 1968. *Medical, Health Physics*. Providing radiotracers (C-11 PIB, F-18 tau probes, Cu-61 ATSM, ...) for human research studies (1972 – present), providing radiotracers (several dozen cycloton-produced transition metals) for basic research with small animal imaging, basic radiochemical research to optimize the yields of cyclotron products.

Paliwal, Bhudatt R., Ph.D., University of Texas, Houston, 1973. *Medical, Health Physics*. My current research is dedicated to developing robust methods of image guidance in radiation therapy. My current emphasis is on real time MR applications utilizing a unique "MRIdian" delivery tool from viewRay Inc.

Zagzebski, James A., Ph.D., University of Wisconsin-Madison, 1972. *Acoustics, Medical, Health Physics*. Ultrasound imaging Quantitative ultrasound Tumor localization with ultrasound.

Research Faculty

Eliceiri, Kevin, Ph.D., University of Wisconsin-Madison. Director, Laboratory for Optical and Computational Instrumentation (LOCI). *Computational Physics, Optics*. Biophotonics, Optical Instrumentation, Correlative and Multiscale Imaging, Live Cell imaging, Breast and Prostate Cancer, Cancer Cell Biology, Stem Cell Biology, Neuroscience and NeuroEngineering, Imaging Processing, and Imaging Informatics.

DEPARTMENTAL RESEARCH SPECIALTIES AND STAFF

Theoretical

Biomagnetism. Biomagnetism is the study of magnetic fields produced naturally by the body. Like other types of magnetism, biomagnetism arises from electrical currents, such as ionic current generated by brain or heart activity, and from magnetic materials, such as iron compounds in the liver. Biomagnetism can provide important information about bodily function. The most active area of biomagnetism research is magnetoencephalography (MEG), a functional brain imaging technique. In addition to MEG, UW investigators are especially interested in fetal applications; i.e., detection of magnetic signals from the fetal heart and brain. Wakai.

Diagnostic X-Ray Imaging. Quantitative measurements of cardiac wall motion and myocardial perfusion using dual energy imaging; methods for evaluating the performance of X-ray imaging devices; advanced CT physics and applications, e.g., phase-contrast CT; advanced 4D digital subtraction angiography (DSA) and scanning beam techniques, etc. Chen, Li, Mistretta, Peppler, Ranallo, Speidel, Szczykutowicz, Vetter.

Magnetic Resonance Imaging and Spectroscopy. Functional MRI (fMRI) and diffusion tensor imaging techniques and applications, e.g., Alzheimer's disease and traumatic brain injury; 4D flow assessment and visualization; quantitative MR applications, e.g., phase-sensitive techniques for assessment of fat / water; early assessment of therapeutic intervention; image-guided treatment planning; small animal imaging facility; hyperpolarized agent developments and applications. Alexander, Birn, Block, Fain, Grist, Hernando, Jackson, Johnson, Korosec, Meyerand, Mistretta, Nagle, Prabhakaran, Reeder, Strigel, Wieben.

Nuclear Medicine, PET, Molecular Imaging. Advanced radionuclide production and applications (two cyclotrons, a GMP radiopharmaceutical facility); novel multifunctional probe development and applications; small animal imaging applications; clinical trial applications; early assessment of therapy; PET agent development and applications in Alzheimer's Disease, Parkinson's Disease, etc.; PET/MR and PET/CT applications. Cai, Cho, Christian, DeJesus, Emborg, Engle, Holden, Jeraj, Nickles, Weichert.

Optical Imaging. Development of advanced optical and image analysis approaches that can be use in multi-modality, multiscale imaging efforts of cancer and other biomedical studies. Cai, Campagnola, Eliceiri, Skala.

Radiation and Thermal Therapy. Treatment of cancer by radiation dose or thermal therapy delivery, especially using innovative beam delivery techniques, some of which were developed entirely by our faculty; image-guided treatment planning and treatment assessment; adaptive radiation therapy. Bayliss, Bayouth, Bednarz, Brace, Culberson, Engle, Jeraj, Paliwal, Smilowitz, Thomadsen, Weichert.

Radiation Dosimetry, Radiation Protection. Image processing science combined with sophisticated radiation field calculations applied to the field of dosimetry and radiation oncology; Monte Carlo simulations; radiation metrology. Bednarz, Culberson, DeLuca, Jr., DeWerd, Henderson.

Ultrasound Imaging. Development of quantitative acoustic imaging; ultrasound scatter measurement; mathematical modeling of gray scale image generation; B-mode image texture analysis; design of materials which mimic the acoustic and MR properties of tissues and the inclusion of these materials in geometries which simulate certain aspects of patients. Hall, Mitchell, Varghese, Zagzebski.

Experimental

Biomagnetism. Biomagnetism is the study of magnetic fields produced naturally by the body. Like other types of magnetism, biomagnetism arises from electrical currents, such as ionic current generated by brain or heart activity, and from magnetic materials, such as iron compounds in the liver. Biomagnetism can provide important information about bodily function. The most active area of biomagnetism research is magnetoencephalography (MEG), a functional brain imaging technique. In addition to MEG, UW investigators are especially interested in fetal applications; i.e., detection of magnetic signals from the fetal heart and brain. Wakai.

Diagnostic X-Ray Imaging. Quantitative measurements of cardiac wall motion and myocardial perfusion using dual energy imaging; methods for evaluating the performance of X-ray imaging devices; advanced CT physics and applications, e.g., phase-contrast CT; advanced 4D digital subtraction angiography (DSA) and scanning beam techniques, etc. Chen, Li, Mistretta, Peppler, Ranallo, Speidel, Szczykutowicz, Vetter.

Magnetic Resonance Imaging and Spectroscopy. Functional MRI (fMRI) and diffusion tensor imaging techniques and applications, e.g., Alzheimer's disease and traumatic brain injury; 4D flow assessment and visualization; quantitative MR applications, e.g., phase-sensitive techniques for assessment of fat / water; early assessment of therapeutic intervention; image-guided treatment planning; small animal imaging facility; hyperpolarized agent developments and applications. Alexander, Birn, Block, Fain, Grist, Hernando, Jackson, Johnson, Korosec, Meyerand, Mistretta, Nagle, Prabhakaran, Reeder, Strigel, Wieben.

Nuclear Medicine, PET, Molecular Imaging. Advanced radionuclide production and applications (two cyclotrons, a GMP radiopharmaceutical facility); novel multifunctional probe development and applications; small animal imaging applications; clinical trial applications; early assessment of therapy; PET agent development and applications in Alzheimer's Disease, Parkinson's Disease, etc.; PET/MR and PET/CT applications. Cai, Cho, Christian, DeJesus, Emborg, Engle, Holden, Nickles, Weichert.

Optical Imaging. Development of advanced optical and image analysis approaches that can be use in multi-modality, multi-scale imaging efforts of cancer and other biomedical studies. Cai, Campagnola, Eliceiri, Skala.

Radiation and Thermal Therapy. Treatment of cancer by radiation dose or thermal therapy delivery, especially using innovative beam delivery techniques, some of which were developed entirely by our faculty; image-guided treatment planning and treatment assessment; adaptive radiation therapy. Bayliss, Bayouth, Brace, Engle, Jeraj, Paliwal, Smilowitz, Thomadsen, Weichert.

Radiation Dosimetry, Radiation Protection. Image processing science combined with sophisticated radiation field calculations applied to the field of dosimetry and radiation oncology; Monte Carlo simulations; radiation metrology. Bednarz, Culberson, DeLuca, Jr., DeWerd, Engle, Henderson.

Ultrasound Imaging. Development of quantitative acoustic imaging; ultrasound scatter measurement; mathematical modeling of gray scale image generation; B-mode image texture analysis; design of materials which mimic the acoustic and MR properties of tissues and the inclusion of these materials in geometries which simulate certain aspects of patients. Hall, Mitchell, Varghese, Zagzebski.

View additional information about this department at www.gradschoolshopper.com. Check out the "Why Choose Us?" section, find out more about the department's culture and get links to social media networks.

UNIVERSITY OF WISCONSIN-MADISON

DEPARTMENT OF PHYSICS

Madison, Wisconsin 53706
http://physics.wisc.edu

General University Information
President: Ray Cross
Dean of Graduate School: William Karpus
University website: http://www.wisc.edu
School Type: Public
Setting: Urban
Total Faculty: 2,205
Total Graduate Faculty: 2,205
Total number of Students: 43,389
Total number of Graduate Students: 9,002

Department Information
Department Chairman: Prof. Sridhara Dasu, Chair
Department Contact: Graduate Student Coordinator, Graduate
  Student Coordinator
  Total full-time faculty: 44
  Total number of full-time equivalent positions: 45
  Full-Time Graduate Students: 188
  Female Full-Time Graduate Students: 25
  First-Year Graduate Students: 27
  Female First-Year Students: 9
  Total Post Doctorates: 80

Department Address
1150 University Avenue
Chamberlin Hall
Madison, WI 53706
Phone: (608) 262-9678
Fax: (608) 263-0800
E-mail: physgrad@physics.wisc.edu
Website: http://physics.wisc.edu

ADMISSIONS

Admission Contact Information
Address admission inquiries to: Graduate Coordinator, Department of Physics, 1150 University Avenue, University of Wisconsin-Madison, Madison, WI 53706
Phone: (608) 262-9678
E-mail: physgrad@physics.wisc.edu
Admissions website: http://physics.wisc.edu

Application deadlines
Fall admission:
U.S. students: December 15   *Int'l. students*: December 15

Application fee
U.S. students: $75   *Int'l. students*: $81

Admissions information
For Fall of 2018:
  Number of applicants: 426
  Number admitted: 110
  Number enrolled: 27

Admission requirements
Bachelor's degree requirements: A bachelor's degree in physics or related field is required.
Minimum undergraduate GPA: 3.0

GRE requirements
The GRE is required.

Subjective GRE requirements
The Subjective GRE is required.

TOEFL requirements
The TOEFL exam is required for students from non-English-speaking countries.
PBT score: 580
iBT score: 92

Other admissions information
Additional requirements: The average GRE scores for admissions were as follows: verbal, 580; quantitative, 780; total, 1395. The average GRE subject score for admissions was 794. All international students who are admitted as teaching assistants will be required to take and pass the SPEAK test when they arrive on campus, as well as participate in the six-week Summer Orientation Program before the fall semester for which they have been admitted. An admitted applicant may be required to take the English Placement exam on arrival and register for the recommended English as a second language (ESL) course.
Undergraduate preparation assumed: Classical mechanics; electromagnetic fields; electric circuits and elementary electronics; waves and optics; thermal physics; quantum physics; and laboratory experience in classical and atomic physics.

TUITION

Tuition year 2018–19:
Tuition for in-state residents
  Full-time students: $15,645 annual
Tuition for out-of-state residents
  Full-time students: $12,657 per semester
Segregated Fees are included in the tuition cost.
Credit hours per semester to be considered full-time: 8
Deferred tuition plan: No
Health insurance: Available at the cost of 1000 per year.
Academic term: Semester
Number of first-year students who received full tuition waivers: 27

Teaching Assistants, Research Assistants, and Fellowships
Number of first-year
  Teaching Assistants: 24
  Research Assistants: 2
  Fellowship students: 1
Average stipend per academic year
  Teaching Assistant: $20,000
  Research Assistant: $20,331
  Fellowship student: $24,090
Most TAs find summer RA appointments. RA and Fellow appointees are generally paid annually, not by the academic year.

FINANCIAL AID

Application deadlines
Fall admission:
U.S. students: December 15   *Int'l. students*: December 15

Loans

Loans are available for U.S. students.

Loans are not available for international students.

GAPSFAS application required: No

FAFSA application required: No

For further information

Address financial aid inquiries to: Office of Student Financial Aid, 333 E. Campus Mall, Madison, WI 53715.

Phone: (608) 262-3060

E-mail: finaid@finaid.wisc.edu

Financial aid website: http://finaid.wisc.edu

HOUSING

Availability of on-campus housing

Single students: Yes

Married students: Yes

Childcare Assistance: No

For further information

Housing aid website: http://www.housing.wisc.edu

Table A—Faculty, Enrollments, and Degrees Granted

Research Specialty	2015–16 Faculty	Enrollment Fall 2015		Number of Degrees Granted		
		Master's	Doctorate	Master's	Terminal Master's	Doctorate
Atmosphere, Space Physics, Cosmic Rays	2	–	–	–	–	–
Atomic, Molecular, & Optical Physics	5	–	–	–	–	–
Biophysics	1	–	–	–	–	–
Condensed Matter Physics	10	–	–	–	–	–
Cosmology & String Theory	3	–	–	–	–	–
Neutrino/Astro	4	–	–	–	–	–
Nuclear Physics	1	–	–	–	–	–
Particles and Fields	13	–	–	–	–	–
Plasma and Fusion	6	–	–	–	–	–
Total	45	–	–	–	–	–
Full-time Grad. Stud.	–	–	188	–	–	–
First-year Grad. Stud.	–	–	28	–	–	–

GRADUATE DEGREE REQUIREMENTS

Master's: To earn the M.S. degree in the Department of Physics, a student must satisfy the Department's minimum graduate-level credit requirement. The Physics Department requires at least 30 credits at the 500 level or above. Fifteen of the 30 credits must be earned from taking the physics core graduate courses, each passed with a grade of B or better. These courses are Physics 711 (Dynamics), 715 (Statistical Mechanics), 721 (Electrodynamics), 731 (Quantum Mechanics I), and 732 (Quantum Mechanics II). The remaining 15 credits may be earned through a combination of research (Physics 990) and coursework, to be determined by the advisor in consultation with the student. An overall 3.0 GPA must be maintained. A degree is awarded to a student who has (1) satisfied the graduate-level credit and course requirements, (2) passed the qualifying exam, and (3) completed a master's project, including a thesis.

Doctorate: The following are required for a doctorate degree: 1) a qualifying exam, 2) satisfying the Ph.D. graduate-level credit requirement, 3) satisfied the minor requirement, 4) pass-ing a preliminary exam, 5) completed required course work (711, 715, 721, 731, 732) with grades of B or better, and 6) a Ph.D. thesis.

Thesis: Thesis work may be done in absentia.

Table B—Separately Budgeted Research Expenditures by Source of Support

Source of Support	Departmental Research	Physics-related Research Outside Department
Federal government	$26,051,023	
State/local government		
Non-profit organizations		
Business and industry		
Other	$2,162,832	
Total	$28,213,855	

Table C—Separately Budgeted Research Expenditures by Research Specialty

Research Specialty	No. of Grants	Expenditures ($)
Atmosphere, Space Physics, Cosmic Rays	18	$2,688,462
Atomic, Molecular, & Optical Physics	19	$2,352,404
Condensed Matter Physics	27	$5,593,463
Nuclear Physics	8	$672,116
Particles and Fields	66	$9,514,138
Plasma and Fusion	15	$7,393,272
Total	153	$28,213,855

FACULTY

Professor

Balantekin, A. Baha, Ph.D., Yale University, 1982. *Nuclear Physics*. Theoretical physics at the interface of nuclear physics, particle physics, and astrophysics; mathematical physics; neutrino physics; astrophysics; fundamental symmetries; nuclear structure physics.

Barger, Vernon, Ph.D., Pennsylvania State University, 1963. Theory and phenomenology of elementary particle physics; neutrino physics; electroweak gauge models; heavy quarks; supersymmetry; cosmology.

Black, Kevin M., Ph.D., Boston University, 2005. *Particles and Fields*. Experimental High Energy Physics.

Boldyrev, S., Ph.D., Princeton University, 1999. *Plasma and Fusion*. Plasma theory.

Bose, Tulika, Ph.D., Columbia University, 2006. *Particles and Fields*. Experimental Particle Physics with CMS.

Carlsmith, Duncan L., Ph.D., University of Chicago, 1984. *High Energy Physics, Particles and Fields*. High energy and fundamental particle physics at the Tevatron and LHC.

Chung, Daniel J.H., Ph.D., University of Chicago, 1998. Theoretical cosmology; high energy physics; quantum field theory in curved space time.

Coppersmith, Susan N., Ph.D., Cornell University, 1983. *Biophysics, Condensed Matter Physics, Other*. Theoretical condensed matter physics; nonlinear dynamics; quantum computation and information; biomineralization.

Dasu, Sridhara R., Ph.D., University of Rochester, 1988. *High Energy Physics, Particles and Fields*. High energy physics; LHC; CMS; BaBar; SLAC National Accelerator Laboratory.

Egedal, Jan, Ph.D., Oxford University, 1998. *Plasma and Fusion*. Magnetic reconnection.

Eriksson, Mark, Ph.D., Harvard University, 1997. *Condensed Matter Physics, Nano Science and Technology, Other*. Condensed matter physics; nanoscience; semiconductor membranes; semiconductor nanostructures; quantum dots; quantum computing; thermoelectric materials.

Everett, Lisa, Ph.D., University of Pennsylvania, 1998. *Particles and Fields*. Theoretical elementary particle physics; superstring phenomenology; supersymmetry.

Forest, Cary B., Ph.D., Princeton University, 1992. *Plasma and Fusion, Other*. Experimental plasma physics; liquid metal magnetohydrodynamics with applications to astrophysics and magnetic confinement of fusion plasmas.

Gilbert, Pupa, Ph.D., First University of Rome "La Sapienza", 1987. *Biophysics*. Biophysics, specializing in biomineralization, nanobiology, and synchrotron spectromicroscopy.

Halzen, Francis, Ph.D., University of Louvain, 1969. *Astrophysics, Particles and Fields*. Theory and phenomenology of particle physics; particle astrophysics; neutrino astronomy.

Hanson, Kael, Ph.D., University of Michigan, 2000. *Astrophysics, Particles and Fields*. Experimental particle astrophysics; high energy neutrino astronomy; IceCube.

Hashimoto, Akikazu, Ph.D., Princeton University, 1997. *Particles and Fields*. String theory; black hole physics; quantum field theory; theoretical physics.

Herndon, M., Ph.D., University of Maryland, 1998. *High Energy Physics, Particles and Fields*. Fundamental particle physics involving high energy hadron collisions with the Collider Detector at Fermilab at the Tevatron and the CMS at LHC; research topics include rare decay of B hadrons, diboson physics, Higgs physics, and searches for fundamental new particles; detector and algorithm development involving muon triggers and tracking detectors.

Ioffe, Lev, Ph.D., Landau Institute for Theoretical Physics, 1985. *Condensed Matter Physics, Materials Science, Metallurgy, Quantum Foundations, Solid State Physics, Surface Physics*. Theoretical Condensed Matter Physics.

Joynt, R. J., Ph.D., University of Maryland, 1982. *Condensed Matter Physics*. Theory of superconductivity and heavy fermion systems; quantum Hall effect; magnetism; high-temperature superconductivity; quantum computing.

Karle, A., Ph.D., University of Munich, 1994. *Astronomy, Astrophysics, Atmosphere, Space Physics, Cosmic Rays, Particles and Fields*. Experimental particle astrophysics; high-energy neutrino astronomy; neutrino physics; cosmic rays.

Lagally, M. G., Ph.D., University of Wisconsin-Madison, 1968. *Materials Science, Metallurgy*. Surface physics; structure and disorder; electronic materials; thin-film growth.

Lawler, J. E., Ph.D., University of Wisconsin-Madison, 1978. *Astrophysics, Atomic, Molecular, & Optical Physics*. Experimental atomic physics; laser spectroscopy; gas discharges; laboratory astrophysics.

McCammon, D., Ph.D., University of Wisconsin-Madison, 1971. *Astrophysics*. Astrophysics; x-ray astronomy; interstellar and intergalactic medium; x-ray detectors.

McDermott, Robert, Ph.D., University of California, Berkeley, 2002. *Condensed Matter Physics*. Experimental condensed matter physics; quantum computing.

Onellion, Marshall, Ph.D., Rice University, 1984. *Condensed Matter Physics, Nano Science and Technology*. Experimental solid state, synchrotron radiation, and ultra-fast optical techniques; nanomaterials.

Rzchowski, Mark S., Ph.D., Stanford University, 1988. *Condensed Matter Physics, Materials Science, Metallurgy, Nano Science and Technology*. Experimental condensed matter physics; magnetic heterostructures and nanostructures; low-temperature scanning tunneling spectroscopy; superconductivity in novel materials; thin-film growth and fabrication.

Saffman, M., Ph.D., University of Colorado Boulder, 1994. *Atomic, Molecular, & Optical Physics, Optics*. Atomic physics; quantum computing with neutral atoms; quantum optics; entanglement; nonlinear optics; solitons; pattern formation.

Sarff, John S., Ph.D., University of Wisconsin-Madison, 1988. *Plasma and Fusion*. Plasma physics; magnetic confinement; instabilities and turbulence.

Shiu, Gary, Ph.D., Cornell University, 1998. *Particles and Fields*. String theory; theoretical physics; elementary particle physics; cosmology.

Terry, P. W., Ph.D., University of Texas, Austin, 1981. *Astrophysics, Plasma and Fusion*. Theory of turbulent plasmas and neutral fluids; plasma theory; anomalous transport and turbulence in fusion plasmas; plasma astrophysics.

Timbie, Peter T., Ph.D., Princeton University, 1985. *Astrophysics, Low Temperature Physics*. Observational astrophysics and cosmology; measurements of the 2.7 K cosmic microwave background radiation; 21-cm hydrogen tomography; microwave detectors; cryogenics.

Vavilov, Maxim, Ph.D., Cornell University, 2001. *Condensed Matter Physics, Nano Science and Technology*. Condensed matter theory; nanoscale- and low-dimensional systems.

Walker, T., Ph.D., Princeton University, 1988. *Atomic, Molecular, & Optical Physics, Low Temperature Physics*. Laser trapping of atoms; collisions between ultra-cold atoms; neutral atom quantum computing; spin-exchange optical pumping; biomagnetometry.

Wu, Sau Lan, Ph.D., Harvard University, 1970. *Electromagnetism, High Energy Physics, Particles and Fields*. High energy and elementary particle physics; weak, electromagnetic, and strong interactions; Higgs boson, CERN, Geneva, Switzerland.

Yavuz, Deniz, Ph.D., Stanford University, 2003. *Atomic, Molecular, & Optical Physics*. Experimental atomic, molecular, and optical physics.

Zweibel, Ellen, Ph.D., Princeton University, 1977. *Astronomy, Astrophysics*. Theoretical astrophysics; plasma astrophysics; origin and evolution of astrophysical magnetic fields.

Associate Professor

Bai, Yang, Ph.D., Yale University, 2007. *High Energy Physics, Particles and Fields*. Collider physics; dark matter; electroweak symmetry breaking; B physics; topological interactions.

Levchenko, Alex, Ph.D., Univeristy of Minnesota, 2009. *Condensed Matter Physics, Theoretical Physics*. Quantum kinetics, Mesoscopic effects, Nonequilibrium systems, Superconductivity.

Pan, Yibin, Ph.D., University of Wisconsin-Madison, 1991. *High Energy Physics, Particles and Fields*. High energy experimental particle physics.

Rebel, Brian, Ph.D., Indiana University, 2004. *Particles and Fields*. Experimental neutrino physics.

Assistant Professor

Bechtol, Keith, Ph.D., Stanford University, 1985. Detection of stellar substructures in the Galactic halo using wide-field optical surveys, including ultra-faint galaxies and stellar streams; spectroscopic follow-up to determine dark matter content; Indirect dark matter searches; ommissioning, science verification, and observing strategy for optical surveys.

Brar, Victor, Ph.D., UC Berkeley, 2010. *Condensed Matter Physics*.

Kolkowitz, Shimon, Ph.D., Harvard University, 2015. *Atomic, Molecular, & Optical Physics*.

Palladino, Kimberly, Ph.D., Ohio State University, 2009. *Particles and Fields*. LZ, LUX, dark matter.

Vandenbroucke, Justin, Ph.D., University of California, Berkeley, 2009. *Astrophysics, Atmosphere, Space Physics, Cosmic Rays*. Experimental particle astrophysics; cosmogenic neutrinos; cosmology; gamma-ray astronomy.

Emeritus

Anderson, L. W., Ph.D., Harvard University, 1960. Atomic and molecular physics; atomic collisions; lasers.

Bruch, Ludwig W., Ph.D., University of California, San Diego, 1964. *Chemical Physics, Condensed Matter Physics, Statistical & Thermal Physics*. Theoretical condensed matter; statistical and chemical physics.

Callen, J. D., Ph.D., Massachusetts Institute of Technology, 1968. Plasma physics; theory of confinement and heating of magnetically confined plasmas, primarily for controlled thermonuclear fusion.

Cox, Donald P., Ph.D., University of California, San Diego, 1970. Astrophysics and space physics; theoretical studies of interstellar matter; cosmic-ray acceleration.

Dexter, R. N., Ph.D., University of Wisconsin-Madison, 1955. Plasma physics; diagnostics of high-temperature plasma physics; fluctuation and turbulence studies.

Durand, Bernice, Ph.D., Iowa State University, 1971. Associate Vice Provost. Theoretical high energy physics; use of algebras in theoretical physics.

Durand, L., Ph.D., Yale University, 1957. Theoretical physics; elementary particle physics; electroweak interactions; scattering processes; mathematical physics; special functions and group theory.

Friedman, William A., Ph.D., Massachusetts Institute of Technology, 1966. Nuclear physics; nuclear theory, including reaction theory and collective effects in nuclear models; heavy-ion reactions.

Goebel, C. J., Ph.D., University of Chicago, 1954. Theoretical physics; quantum field theory, including high energy interactions, elementary particles, and dispersion theory; general relativity.

Haeberli, Willy, Ph.D., Basel, 1952. Nuclear physics; polarized particle physics; polarized ion sources; polarized gas targets; tests of fundamental symmetries in hadronic and weak interactions.

Himpsel, Franz J., Ph.D., University of Munich, 1977. *Condensed Matter Physics, Nano Science and Technology*. Experimental condensed matter physics; synchrotron radiation techniques; nanoscience.

Huber, David L., Ph.D., Harvard University, 1964. Condensed matter theory; magnetic and optical properties of solids.

Knutson, Lynn, Ph.D., University of Wisconsin-Madison, 1973. Nuclear physics with polarized particles; properties of few-nucleon systems; medium energy physics.

Lin, C. C., Ph.D., Harvard University, 1955. *Atomic, Molecular, & Optical Physics*. Atomic and molecular physics; atomic collisions.

Morse, R., Ph.D., University of Wisconsin-Madison, 1969. High energy particle astrophysics; gamma-ray and neutrino astronomy.

Olsson, M. G., Ph.D., University of Maryland, 1964. Theory and phenomenology of fundamental particle physics; nonperturbative quantum chromodynamics; quark confinement; chiral dynamics; B-meson.

Pondrom, L. G., Ph.D., University of Chicago, 1958. High energy and fundamental particle physics; hadronic interactions.

Prager, Stewart, Ph.D., Columbia University, 1975. Plasma physics; magnetic confinement; instabilities and turbulence.

Prepost, R., Ph.D., Columbia University, 1961. High energy and fundamental particle physics; weak and electromagnetic interactions.

Reeder, D. D., Ph.D., University of Wisconsin-Madison, 1966. High energy and fundamental particle physics; weak and electromagnetic interactions; electron-positron colliders; cosmic rays.

Roesler, F. L., Ph.D., University of Wisconsin-Madison, 1962. Astrophysics; aeronomy; optical spectroscopy; interference spectroscopy.

Scherb, Frank, Ph.D., Massachusetts Institute of Technology, 1958. Astrophysics and space physics; space plasma physics; high-resolution astrophysical spectroscopy.

Smith, Wesley H., Ph.D., University of California, Berkeley, 1981. *High Energy Physics, Particles and Fields*. High energy and fundamental experimental particle physics and collisions at LHC, CERN, Geneva, Switzerland.

Sprott, J. C., Ph.D., University of Wisconsin-Madison, 1969. Plasma physics; computational nonlinear dynamics; chaos; complex systems.

Webb, M. B., Ph.D., University of Wisconsin-Madison, 1956. Solid state physics; surface studies.

Winokur, Michael J., Ph.D., University of Michigan, 1985. *Condensed Matter Physics*. Condensed matter physics; structure of novel materials; phase transitions.

DEPARTMENTAL RESEARCH SPECIALTIES AND STAFF

Theoretical

Atomic, Molecular and Optical Theory. Scattering theory; electron-electron and electron-atom collisions; atomic collisions; molecular Rydberg states. Saffman, Walker.

Biophysics Theory. Modeling of a variety of complex biological systems. Coppersmith.

Condensed Matter Theory. Magnetism; optical properties; energy band structure; many-body problems; superconductivity; heavy fermion systems; quantum Hall effect; quantum algorithms; studies of decoherence; studies of novel experimental architectures. Bruch, Coppersmith, Ioffe, Joynt, Levchenko, Vavilov.

High Energy Theory. Quantum field theory; particle astrophysics; string theory; mathematical physics; phenomenology of particle physics; collider physics; standard model and extensions; cosmology. Bai, Balantekin, Barger, Chung, Bernice Durand, L. Durand, Everett, Halzen, Hashimoto, Shiu.

Materials Science, Metallurgy. Many-body problems; disordered systems; thin films. Brar, Lagally.

Neutrino and Astroparticle Theory. Early universe cosmology; dark matter and energy; baryogenesis; cosmic microwave background radiation; modified gravity; string cosmology; interstellar medium; supernova remnants; gas dynamics and radiation; cosmic-ray acceleration; neutrino and gamma-ray astronomy. Bai, Balantekin, Barger, Chung, Everett, Halzen, Shiu, Zweibel.

Nuclear Theory. Reaction theory; scattering theory; nuclear structure; many-body theory; symmetry principles; heavy ions and intermediate energies; high energy nuclear physics; nuclear astrophysics. Balantekin, Friedman.

Plasma Theory. Stability theory; plasma confinement; turbulence theory; anomalous transport; heating theory; computer simulation. Boldyrev, Terry, Zweibel.

Experimental

Atomic, Molecular, and Optical Experiment. Atomic collisions; lasers; atomic oscillator strengths; high-resolution spectroscopy; trapped atoms; weakly ionized plasmas; Rydberg atom flux qubit; semiconductoring architectures; very high-resolution studies of atomic, molecular, and astrophysical phenomena; spectral line-strength determinations. Kolkowitz, Lin, Saffman, Walker, Yavuz.

Biophysics Experiment. Photoelectron spectromicroscopy of biological systems; cancer therapy. Coppersmith, Gilbert.

Condensed Matter Experiment. Mesoscopic systems; scanning force microscopies; strongly correlated magnetic materials;

high-temperature superconductivity; magnetic nanostructures and heterostructures; structural properties of polymers; synchrotron radiation studies of strongly correlated systems. Anderson, Brar, Coppersmith, Dexter, Eriksson, Gilbert, Himpsel, Huber, Lagally, McDermott, Onellion, Rzchowski, Winokur.

High Energy Experiment. CMS; LZ/LUX; ATLAS; LBNE; weak, electromagnetic, and strong interactions; search for Higgs bosons and new physics phenomena; study of B-meson and neutrino oscillation physics; study of leptonic CV violation; dark matter searches; study of proton structure. Black, Bose, Dasu, Halzen, Hanson, Herndon, Karle, Palladino, Pan, Rebel, Smith, Vandenbroucke, Wu.

Neutrino and Astroparticle Experiment. X-ray, gamma-ray, and neutrino astronomy; solar neutrinos; dark matter searches; observational cosmology; cosmic background radiation and spectroscopy. Balantekin, Halzen, Karle, McCammon, Morse, Palladino, Timbie, Vandenbroucke.

Plasma Experiment. Toroidal confinement, instabilities, turbulence, and anomalous transport; reversed field pinch and tokamak. Boldyrev, Egedal, Forest, Sarff, Terry, Zweibel.

Quantum Computing. Coppersmith, Eriksson, Ioffe, Joynt, Levchenko, McDermott, Saffman, Vavilov.

View additional information about this department at www.gradschoolshopper.com. Check out the "Why Choose Us?" section, find out more about the department's culture and get links to social media networks.

UNIVERSITY OF WYOMING

DEPARTMENT OF PHYSICS AND ASTRONOMY

Laramie, Wyoming 82071–3905
http://www.uwyo.edu/physics

General University Information
President: Laurie Nichols
Dean of Graduate School: Jim Ahern
University website: http://www.uwyo.edu
School Type: Public
Setting: Rural
Total Faculty: 754
Total number of Students: 12,366
Total number of Graduate Students: 2,578

Department Information
Department Chairman: Prof. Jinke Tang, Head
Department Contact: Wenyong Wang and Hannah
    Jang-Condell, Directors of Graduate Studies
Total full-time faculty: 15
Total number of full-time equivalent positions: 15
Full-Time Graduate Students: 35
Female Full-Time Graduate Students: 11
First-Year Graduate Students: 8
Female First-Year Students: 3
Total Post Doctorates: 2

Department Address
1000 E University Avenue
Dept 3905
Laramie, WY 82071–3905
Phone: (307) 766-6150
Fax: (307) 766-2562
E-mail: physics@uwyo.edu
Website: http://www.uwyo.edu/physics

ADMISSIONS

Admission Contact Information
Address admission inquiries to: Director of Graduate Studies,
    University of Wyoming, Department of Physics and Astron-
    omy, 1000 E. University, Department 3905, Laramie, WY
    82071
Phone: (307) 766-6150
E-mail: physics@uwyo.edu
Admissions website: http://www.uwyo.edu/physics/graduate-
    program/

Application deadlines
Fall admission:
U.S. students: January 15   *Int'l. students*: January 15

Application fee
There is no application fee required.

Admissions information
For Fall of 2018:
    Number of applicants: 90
    Number admitted: 15
    Number enrolled: 9

Admission requirements
Bachelor's degree requirements: Bachelor's degree in Physics
    or Astronomy is required.
Minimum undergraduate GPA: 3.0

GRE requirements
The GRE is required.

Subjective GRE requirements
The Subjective GRE is recommended.

TOEFL requirements
The TOEFL exam is required for students from non-English-
    speaking countries.
    PBT score: 540
    iBT score: 76

Other admissions information
Undergraduate preparation assumed: Undergraduate preparation
    in physics and mathematics equivalent to that specified for
    a physics major.

TUITION

Tuition year 2017–18:
Tuition for in-state residents
    Full-time students: $7,119 annual
Tuition for out-of-state residents
    Full-time students: $18,639 annual
Credit hours per semester to be considered full-time: 9
Deferred tuition plan: Yes
Health insurance: Yes, $2044.00.
Academic term: Semester
Number of first-year students who received full tuition waivers: 9

Teaching Assistants, Research Assistants, and Fellowships
Number of first-year
    Teaching Assistants: 4
    Research Assistants: 2
    Fellowship students: 2
Average stipend per academic year
    Teaching Assistant: $16,785
    Research Assistant: $16,785
    Fellowship student: $20,000

FINANCIAL AID

Application deadlines
Fall admission:
U.S. students: September 26   *Int'l. students*: September 26
Spring admission:
U.S. students: January 9   *Int'l. students*: January 9

Loans
Loans are available for U.S. students.
Loans are not available for international students.
GAPSFAS application required: No
FAFSA application required: No

For further information
Address financial aid inquiries to: Student Financial Aid, Depart-
    ment 3335, 1000 E. University Avenue, Laramie, WY 82071.
Phone: (307) 766-2116
E-mail: finaid@uwyo.edu
Financial aid website: http://www.uwyo.edu/sfa/

HOUSING

Availability of on-campus housing
Single students: Yes
Married students: Yes
Childcare Assistance: Yes

For further information
Address housing inquiries to: Residence Life & Dining, Department 3394, 1000 E. University Avenue, Laramie, WY 82071.
Phone: (866) 653-0212
E-mail: reslife-dining@uwyo.edu
Housing aid website: http://www.uwyo.edu/reslife-dining/

Table A—Faculty, Enrollments, and Degrees Granted

Research Specialty	2018–19 Faculty	Enrollment Fall 2018 Master's	Enrollment Fall 2018 Doctorate	Number of Degrees Granted 2017–18 (2013–18) Master's	Number of Degrees Granted 2017–18 (2013–18) Terminal Master's	Number of Degrees Granted 2017–18 (2013–18) Doctorate
Astrophysics	6	–	18	3(10)	2(5)	1(6)
Biophysics	–	–	–	–	–	–
Condensed Matter Physics	6	3	14	2(12)	–(4)	2(10)
Physics and other Science Education	1	–	–	1(9)	1(9)	–
Plasma and Fusion	2	–	–	–	–	–
Total	15	3	32	6(31)	3(18)	3(16)
Full-time Grad. Stud.	–	3	32	–	–	–
First-year Grad. Stud.	–	1	7	–	–	–

GRADUATE DEGREE REQUIREMENTS

Master's: Thirty hours of graduate course work. Thesis planning, development, and production guided by the committee chair and graduate committee. A 3.0 GPA (on 4.0 scale) required.

Doctorate: Forty-two hours of course work at the graduate level, 30 hours of research. Dissertation planning, development, and production guided by the committee chair and graduate committee. A 3.0 GPA (on 4.0 scale) required. Comprehensive exam required.

SPECIAL EQUIPMENT, FACILITIES, OR PROGRAMS

The Wyoming Infrared Observatory's 2.3-meter (92-inch) telescope is located on Jelm Mountain about 25 miles southwest of Laramie, WY at an altitude of 9656 ft (2943 m). The Red Buttes Observatory's 0.4-meter (24-inch) telescope is located 9 miles south of town. Both telescopes are remote-capable. The NCAR-Wyoming Yellowstone Supercomputer is a 1.5-petaflops facility dedicated to interdisciplinary work in Earth system science. The Department has several state-of-the-art condensed matter physics research labs devoted to materials physics and nanotechnology, with a suite of advanced instrumentation.

Table B—Separately Budgeted Research Expenditures by Source of Support

Source of Support	Departmental Research	Physics-related Research Outside Department
Federal government	$7,250,000	
State/local government	$1,060,000	
Non-profit organizations	$385,000	
Business and industry		
Other		
Total	$8,695,000	

FACULTY

Professor

Brotherton, Michael, Ph.D., University of Texas, 1996. *Astrophysics*. Multiwavelength observations of quasars and active galaxies; quasar/galaxy mutual evolution.

Dahnovsky, Yuri, Ph.D., Russian Academy of Sciences, 1983. *Condensed Matter Physics*. Computational and theoretical physics: molecular electronic devices, solar cells, electronic properties of surfaces, nonequilibrium Green functions, photon-assisted tunneling and electron transfer reactions.

Dale, Daniel, Ph.D., Cornell University, 1998. *Astrophysics*. Ground- and space-based multiwavelength studies of galaxies; clusters of galaxies; observational cosmology.

Kobulnicky, Chip, Ph.D., University of Minnesota, 1997. *Astrophysics*. Chip is an observational astronomer, using ground-based and space-based telescopes at radio, infrared, optical, and X-ray wavelengths to study stars, star formation, the chemical composition of interstellar material, and the evolution of galaxies.

Michalak, Rudi, Ph.D., Physics, Ruhr-Universität Bochum, 1993. *Condensed Matter Physics*. Experimental condensed matter physics; nuclear magnetic resonance; science education.

Synakowski, Edmund, Ph.D., University of Texas at Austin, 1988. VP for Research & Economic Development. *Plasma and Fusion*. Plasma fusion science.

Tang, Jinke, Ph.D., Iowa State University, 1989. *Condensed Matter Physics*. Experimental condensed matter physics and materials science: spintronics and optoelectronics; magnetic semiconductors; half-metals; magnetic, optical, and thermoelectric properties of nanomaterials; tunneling magnetoresistance; thin films.

Thayer, David, Ph.D., Massachusetts Institute of Technology, 1983. *Plasma and Fusion*. Theoretical studies of plasmas, fusion, turbulence, nonlinear dynamics, global change, and quantum mechanics.

Associate Professor

Jang-Condell, Hannah, Ph.D., Harvard University, 2004. *Astrophysics*. Theoretical planetary formation.

Myers, Adam, Ph.D., Durham University, 2004. *Astronomy*. Quasars; cosmology.

Pierce, Michael, Ph.D., University of Hawaii, 1988. *Astrophysics*. Galaxies, clusters of galaxies, large-scale structure of the universe, observational cosmology, astronomical instrumentation.

Wang, Wenyong, Ph.D., Yale University, 2004. *Condensed Matter Physics*. Experimental condensed matter physics; nanotechnology.

Assistant Professor

Chien, TeYu, Ph.D., University of Tennessee. *Condensed Matter Physics, Nano Science and Technology*. Solar cell devices; complex oxides electronic devices.

Rice, William, Ph.D., Rice University, 2012. *Applied Physics, Condensed Matter Physics, Materials Science, Metallurgy*. Low-dimensional structures, carbon nanotubes, magnetoresistance, and electron spin resonance.

Tian, Jifa, Ph.D., University of Chinese Academy of Sciences & Institute of Physics CAS, 2009. *Condensed Matter Physics*. Quantum materials, quantum devices, and their applications in quantum engineering and nanotechnology, such as nanoelectronic, spintronic, and thermoelectric devices.

Lecturer

O'Malley, Conor, M.S., Rutgers, 2011. Science Education.

DEPARTMENTAL RESEARCH SPECIALTIES AND STAFF

Theoretical
Astrophysics. Jang-Condell.
Condensed Matter Physics. Dahnovsky.
Materials Science, Metallurgy. Dahnovsky.
Plasma and Fusion. Synakowski, Thayer.

Experimental
Astrophysics. Brotherton, Dale, Kobulnicky, Myers, Pierce.
Biophysics.
Condensed Matter Physics. Chien, Michalak, Rice, Tang, Tian, Wang.
Materials Science, Metallurgy. Chien, Michalak, Rice, Tang, Tian, Wang.
Nano Science and Technology. Chien, Rice, Tang, Tian, Wang.

View additional information about this department at www.gradschoolshopper.com. Check out the "Why Choose Us?" section, find out more about the department's culture and get links to social media networks.

PART II

INTERNATIONAL

Geographic Listing of Graduate Programs

FUDAN UNIVERSITY

DEPARTMENT OF PHYSICS

Shanghai, 200438, CHINA
http://www.physics.fudan.edu.cn/

General University Information

President: Ningsheng Xu (许宁生)
Dean of Graduate School: Renhe Zhang (张人禾)
University website: http://www.fudan.edu.cn/en/
School Type: Public
Setting: Urban
Total Faculty: 2,871
Total Graduate Faculty: 2,523
Total number of Students: 35,433
Total number of Graduate Students: 19,903

Department Information

Department Chairman: Prof. Jian Shen (沈健), Chair
Department Contact: E Xu (徐娥), Assistant to Chair
  Total full-time faculty: 90
  Total number of full-time equivalent positions: 122
  Full-Time Graduate Students: 389
  Female Full-Time Graduate Students: 0
  First-Year Graduate Students: 64
  Female First-Year Students: 20
  Total Post Doctorates: 40

Department Address

No.2005 Songhu Road
Shanghai, 200438
CHINA
Phone: 86-21-31242360
Fax: 86-21-31242363
E-mail: xue@fudan.edu.cn
Website: http://www.physics.fudan.edu.cn/

ADMISSIONS

Admission Contact Information

Address admission inquiries to: Graduate Admissions Working Group, Department of Physics, Fudan University, 2005 Songhu Road, Shanghai 200433, China
Phone: 86-021-31242364
E-mail: xhyan@fudan.edu.cn
Admissions website: http://phys.fudan.edu.cn/7522/list.htm

Application deadlines

Fall admission:
U.S. students: December 31   *Int'l. students*: January 31

Application fee

Int'l. students: RMB 800

Admissions information

For Fall of 2018:
  Number of applicants: 150
  Number admitted: 90
  Number enrolled: 90

Admission requirements

Bachelor's degree requirements: Must have Bachelor degree.
Minimum undergraduate GPA: 2.8

GRE requirements

  The GRE is not required.

Subjective GRE requirements

  The Subjective GRE is not required.

TOEFL requirements

  The TOEFL exam is not required for students from non-English-speaking countries.

TUITION

Tuition year 2018–19:
Tuition for in-state residents
  Full-time students: RMB 30,000 annual
Number of first-year students who received full tuition waivers: 5

Teaching Assistants, Research Assistants, and Fellowships

  Average stipend per academic year
    Teaching Assistant: RMB 20,000
    Research Assistant: RMB 30,000
    Fellowship student: RMB 8,000

For futher information

Address financial aid inquiries to: International Student Office, Fudan University.
Phone: +86-21-65642258
E-mail: isoadmission@fudan.edu.cn
Financial aid website: http://iso.fudan.edu.cn/en/

HOUSING

Availability of on-campus housing

  Single students: Yes
  Married students: Yes

For further information

Address housing inquiries to: International Student Office, Fudan University.
Phone: +86-21-65642258
E-mail: isoadmission@fudan.edu.cn
Housing aid website: http://iso.fudan.edu.cn/en/

Table A—Faculty, Enrollments, and Degrees Granted

Research Specialty	2017–18 Faculty	Enrollment Fall 2018		Number of Degrees Granted 2015–52 (2014–68)		
		Master's	Doctorate	Master's	Terminal Master's	Doctorate
Condensed Matter Physics	42	–	–	–	–	–
Optics	12	–	–	–	–	–
Theoretical Physics	30	–	–	–	–	–
Total	84	–	–	–	–	–
Full-time Grad. Stud.	–	–	–	–	–	–
First-year Grad. Stud.	–	–	–	–	–	–

GRADUATE DEGREE REQUIREMENTS

Master's: **Time to degree:** - 3 years. **Coursework requirements:** - Master's students shall earn 31 degree credits with a minimum of 17 coursework credits. **Other requirements:** - Comprehensive exam in the third semester. - Mid-term evaluation by the Graduate Steering Group in the fourth semester. - Publish at least one paper in a journal indexed by SCI.

Doctorate: **Time to degree** - 3 years with a master's degree. - 5 years without a master's degree. **Coursework requirements:** - Doctoral students with a master's shall earn 12 degree credits for coursework. - Doctoral students without a master's degree shall earn at least 26 credits for coursework. **Other requirements** - Qualifying exam. - Three-year doctoral program students must publish 2 papers in SCI-indexed journals, with a combined impact factor greater than 2. - Five-year doctoral program students must publish 3 papers in SCI-indexed journals, with a combined impact factor greater than 3.

SPECIAL EQUIPMENT, FACILITIES, OR PROGRAMS

The Department runs 3 key labs: the State Key Laboratory of Surface Physics, Key Laboratory of Computational Physical Sciences, and Key Laboratory of Micro-and Nano-Photonic Structures.

Sponsored by the State Planning Commission, the State Key Laboratory of Surface Physics (SKLSP), Fudan University was established in 1990. SKLSP is based on the multi-discipline intergradations of computational condensed matter physics, semiconductor surface and interface physics, semiconductor optoelectronic physics and ultra-thin magnetic film physics, majoring in the directions of semiconductor surface, interface and optoelectronic physics to contribute to the development of new generation information science and technology of China.

The laboratory is mainly engaged in research in the following four subjects:

1. the novel properties of surface and interface;

2. optical physics and application of surface and micro-structure;

3. theory and computational s of surface and interface;

4. interface problems related to the soft matter and bio-physics.

Each research activity is cooperatively carried out by several research groups.

SKLSP is equipped with a large number of sophisticated equipment, of which 26 are large-scale apparatuses. The Lab stresses and strengthens the cooperation among the research groups, and most of the large-scale instruments are opened to and shared with other research groups.

The Laboratory attaches great importance to the international and domestic academic collaboration and exchange. So far, many international and domestic cooperative programs have been carried out with universities and laboratories home and abroad by the programs of "Opening Project" and "Senior Visiting Scholar." Now SKLSP is making all efforts to reach its goal of contributing to the development of basic subjects in China.

FACULTY

Chair Professor

Feng, Donglai, (封东来) Ph.D., Stanford University, 2001. Fudan-Haoqing Chair Professor. *Condensed Matter Physics.* Experimental condensed matter physics; study complex quantum materials, including correlated systems, cuprate- and iron-based superconductors, charge/spin/orbital ordered systems, and oxide interfaces, etc. with synchrotron- and laser-based spectroscopy and scattering techniques.

Shen, Jian, (沈健) Ph.D., Max Planck Institute of Microstructure Physics, 1996. Department Chair. *Condensed Matter Physics.* Investigation of emerging phenomena at surface, in reduce dimensionality, and at nanometer scale; specific interest includes magnetism and electronic transport of nanostructured materials, and their underlying physical mechanism.

Professor

An, Zhenghua, (安正华) Ph.D., Shanghai Institute of Microsystem and Information Technology, Chinese Academy of Sciences, 2004. *Nano Science and Technology, Optics.* Nanofabrication; low dimensional semi-conductors; optoelectronics; nano-photonics; subwavelength metallic plasmonics.

Bambi, Cosimo, Ph.D., Ferrara University, 2007. *Astronomy, Astrophysics, Theoretical Physics.* Theoretical physics in the areas of gravity, cosmology, and high-energy astrophysics. The research focuses on the possibility of testing the Kerr-nature of astrophysical black hole candidates by studying the electromagnetic radiation emitted by the gas in the accretion disk.

Che, Jingguang, (车静光) Ph.D., Muenster University, 1992. *Computational Physics, Condensed Matter Physics, Solid State Physics, Surface Physics.* Computational models for predicting geometric and electronic structure evolution in surfaces and interfaces of metals and semiconductors.

Chen, Gang, (陈钢) Ph.D., University of California Santa Barbara, 2010. *Theoretical Physics.* Theoretical condensed matter physics. My research bridges several disciplines of condensed matter that includes, for examples, atomic-molecular-optical physics, quantum materials, topological and exotic phases of matter. Generally speaking, we are interested in quantum mechanical properties of condensed matter systems in experiments that have fundamental impact. The current research focuses on quantum materials, frustrated magnetism, spin liquids, topological phase of matter and various strongly correlation physics. Opportunities are always available for motivated students and postdocs.

Chen, Wei, (陈唯) Ph.D., Institute of Physics, Chinese Academy of Sciences, 2001. *Biophysics, Condensed Matter Physics.* Soft matter: collodial physics; biophysics: cell motility.

Chen, Yan, (陈焱) Ph.D., Nanjing University, 1998. *Condensed Matter Physics, Quantum Foundations, Theoretical Physics.* Theoretical studies on many body physics in complex quantum systems. In particular, electronic states in high temperature superconductors, exotic superfluidity in ultrcold atoms, quantum phase transitions and quantum entanglement.

Chen, Zhanghai, (陈张海) Ph.D., Shanghai Institute of Technical Physics, Chinese Academy of Sciences, 1997. *Condensed Matter Physics, Nano Science and Technology, Optics, Quantum Foundations, Solid State Physics.* Optical spectroscopy of condensed matters, including (1) light-matter coupling in semiconductor nano/micro-structures and (2) quantum chaos of electrons in solid-state environment.

Gao, Chunlei, (高春雷) Ph.D., Max Planck Institute of Microstructure Physics, 2006. *Condensed Matter Physics.* Surface magnetism. We use spin-polarized scanning tunneling microscopy to study the surface magnetic structure of various magnetic systems as well as utilize tunneling electrons as a local probe to study spin excitation and spin reversal on the atomic scale to reveal the relation between structure and electronic states and magnetism. Our research interest includes magnetic thin films and nanostructures, magnetic molecule, magnetic semiconductor and topological insulators.

Gong, Xingao, (龚新高) Ph.D., Institute of Solid State Physics, Chinese Academy of Sciences, 1993. *Computational Physics, Condensed Matter Physics, Nano Science and Technology.* Theoretical study of nano-particle and nano-structure; computational design of new energy materials; structure and dynamic properties of surfaces and intersurfaces; development of computational method on electron structure of complex systems.

Hao, Bailin, (郝柏林) Kharkov State University, 1963. Academician, Chinese Academy of Sciences. Academician, Third World Academy of Sciences. *Computational Physics, Theoretical Physics*. Prokaryote phylogeny and taxonomy based on their complete genomes, the composition vector (CVTree) approach; statistics, combinatorics, language theory and graph theory inspired by the study of K-tuples in symbolic sequences of biological origin.

Hou, Xiaoyuan, (侯晓远) Ph.D., Fudan University, 1987. *Condensed Matter Physics*. Organic functional device, organic semiconductor/metal interface interaction.

Huang, Jiping, (黄吉平) Ph.D., The Chinese University of Hong Kong, 2003. *Theoretical Physics*. Soft matter and econophysics.

Hung, Lingyan, (孔令欣) Ph.D., University of Cambridge, 2009. *Quantum Foundations, Relativity & Gravitation, Theoretical Physics*. The gauge/gravity correspondence and its applications in the understanding of quantum entanglement and quantum information. Field theoretic studies of the renormalization group flow and non-equilibrium dynamics, and their applications in condensed matter physics and cosmology. Topological phases of matter in condensed matter physics, their classification and phenomenology.

Ji, Minbiao, (季敏标) Ph.D., Stanford University, 2011. *Biophysics, Optics*. Nonlinear optical spectroscopy and microscopy. We utilize ultrafast spectroscopic techniques to study carrier dynamics in novel materials as well as characterize chiral molecules. We are also interested in using coherent Raman scattering microscopy to study various biological and biomedical problems, such as label-free delineation of tumor and lipid metabolism. Novel nonlinear optical imaging techniques can also be used to learn the physics in material and devices.

Jiang, Zuimin, (蒋最敏) Ph.D., University of Science and Technology of China, 1988. *Condensed Matter Physics*. Si molecular epitaxy and low-dimensional Si-based materials.

Jin, Xiaofeng, (金晓峰) Ph.D., Fudan University, 1989. *Condensed Matter Physics*. Experimental condensed matter physics; surface and ultrathin film magnetism, spin-dependent transport in low-dimensional systems.

Le, Yongkang, (乐永康) Ph.D., 德国Kaiserslautern大学博士, 2003. *Physics and other Science Education*. Fundamental Physics Laboratory.

Li, Shiyan, (李世燕) Ph.D., University of Science and Technology of China, 2002. *Condensed Matter Physics*. Ultra-low temperature properties of superconductors, magnets, and quantum critical systems.

Lin, Zhifang, (林志方) Ph.D., Fudan University, 1990. *Optics, Statistical & Thermal Physics, Theoretical Physics*. Optical micromanipulation, electromagnetic metamaterials.

Liu, Weitao, (刘韡韬) Ph.D., University of California, Berkeley, 2008. *Condensed Matter Physics, Optics, Surface Physics*. Nonlinear optics.

Liu, Xiaohan, (刘晓晗) Ph.D., Fudan University, 1999. *Condensed Matter Physics*. Optical properties of condensed matter, photonic crystals.

Lu, Fang, (陆昉) Ph.D., Fudan University, 1995. *Condensed Matter Physics*. Deep levels in semiconductor, electric properties low dimensional quantum structures, semiconductor solar cell.

Ma, Shihong, (马世红) Ph.D., Fudan University, 1995. *Optics*. Functional ultrathin films physics and device, surface nonlinear optics, organic functional materials, teaching study of physics experiment.

Ma, Yongli, (马永利) Ph.D., Fudan University, 1993. Theoretical condensed matter physics; ensemble theory in quantum statistics; matter waves; quantum condensation phenomena and superfluidity.

Qi, Yang, (戚扬) Ph.D., Harvard University, 2010. *Condensed Matter Physics, Theoretical Physics*. Condensed matter theories, including strongly correlated electron systems, topological orders, quantum phase transition, and numerical simulations.

Shen, Yuanrang, (沈元壤) Ph.D., Harvard University, 1963. *Condensed Matter Physics, Optics, Surface Physics*. Molecular physics, nonlinear optics, laser spectroscopy, liquid crystals, and surface sciences. More recently developed novel nonlinear optical techniques to probe surfaces and interfaces, which can provide molecular-level information about interfacial water structures and orientations and conformation of adsorbates. Other interests include thee study of ice and oxide interfaces, development of a sensisive nonlinear optical spectroscopic technique to probe molecular chirality, and optical spectroscopy of nanostructures composite structures, and exotic materials.

Sheng, Weidong, (盛卫东) Ph.D., Chinese Academy of Sciences, 1997. *Condensed Matter Physics*. Physics of low-dimensional structures: electronic structure, optical properties, and many-body effects.

Shi, Yu, (施郁) Ph.D., Nanjing University, 1994. *Quantum Foundations, Theoretical Physics*. Quantum entanglement and its uses in condensed matter physics and particle physics.

Tan, Yanwen, (谭砚文) Ph.D., Columbia University, 2007. *Biophysics*. Experimental biological physics; single-molecule spectroscopy.

Tao, Ruibao, (陶瑞宝) Ph.D., Fudan University, 1964. *Theoretical Physics*. Theory of Condensed Matters: current focus: (1) Quantum Spin systems and its dynamics, (2) Transport theory of change and spin in mesoscopic system. (3) Quantum evolution and manipul.

Tao, Zhensheng, (陶镇生) Ph.D., Michigan State University, 2014. *Condensed Matter Physics, Optics*. Experimental optics and condensed matter physics. Our main research interest lies in the field of ultrafast material dynamics induced by light-matter interaction (especially under the strong-field limit). We generate coherent light covering terahertz to EUV and soft X-ray wavelengths using table-top femtosecond lasers. Through optical and electron spectroscopies, we investigate material dynamics ranging from electron and spin dynamics on attosecond emtosecond timescales to structural dynamics on picosecond anosecond timescales. The purpose of our research is to understand the underlying physics behind the laser-induced non-equilibrium material dynamics and to investigate the exciting opportunities of manipulating material states using optical methods.

Tian, Chuanshan, (田传山) Ph.D., Fudan University, 2006. *Optics*. Characterization of material with (nonlinear) optical spectroscopy, exotic optical effects and processes, and chemical physics. Research topics include: (1) Molecular structure of water surface and interfaces: (2) Pre-melting of ice interfaces below freezing point; (3) Interfacial structure of photocatalytic metal oxides; (4) Microscopic process of catalytic cracking of hydrocarbon on metal surface.

Wan, Yidun, (万义顿) Ph.D., University of Waterloo & Perimeter Institute for Theoretical Physics, 2009. *Particles and Fields, Quantum Foundations, Theoretical Physics*. Interdisciplinary theoretical studies on Emergent Spacetime (Quantum Gravity) and Matter, Topological Orders, Quantum Computation and Quantum Information (Holographic Principle, Entanglement Entropy), Particle Physics. Experimental detection and realization of topological orders and emergent quantum spacetime using quantum simulators.

Wang, Jing, (王靖) Ph.D., Tsinghua University, 2011. *Theoretical Physics*. Theoretical condensed matter physics, focused on the theory of quantum electronic phenomena in condensed matter systems. My research combines theoretical studies with advanced computational approaches, and collaborates closely with experimental groups.

Wang, Xun, (王迅) Fudan University, 1960. *Condensed Matter Physics, Surface Physics*. Semiconductor physics.

Wang, Yihua, (王熠华) Ph.D., Harvard University, 2012. *Condensed Matter Physics*. Experimental condensed matter physics. We study complex quantum materials, including high temperature superconductors, topological insulators, correlated electron systems, and heterostructures of these systems.

Wei, Guanghong, (韦广红) Ph.D., Fudan University, 1998. *Biophysics, Condensed Matter Physics*. Computation study of peptide folding, misfolding, aggregation; and ordered nanostructure formation; peptide-membrane iteractions; protein-nanoparticle interactions.

Wu, Changqin, (吴长勤) Ph.D., Fudan University, 1987. *Theoretical Physics*. Charge/spin transport and photoelectric conversion in organic materials and devices; quantum charge/spin and heat transport through nano-structures; Orders, phase transitions, and excitations in 1D correlated systems.

Wu, Hua, (吴骅) Ph.D., Institute of Solid State Physics, Chinese Academy of Sciences, 1999. *Computational Physics, Condensed Matter Physics, Surface Physics*. Computational condensed matter physics, correlated oxides, magnetic semiconductor, surface and interface.

Wu, Ruqian, (武汝前) Ph.D., Institute of Physics, Chinese Academy of Science, 1989. *Computational Physics, Condensed Matter Physics*. State-of-the-art first principles density functional electronic structure calculations have achieved great success in many exciting fields in both explaining existing phenomena and, more importantly, in predicting the properties of new systems. In the new age of information technology and novel man-made materials, computational simulations based on quantum mechanical equations can provide unprecedented physical insights to guide search and design of new materials and devices with properties desired. Members of our group are working on several research directions, including magnetism, spintronics, solar materials, catalysis and nanoscience. We have established long-term active collaborations with many leading experimental groups in difference countries.

Wu, Saijun, (吴赛骏) Ph.D., Harvard University, 2007. *Optics*. Laser cooling and trapping: Novel techniques; new species; theoretical descriptions. Atom interferometer: new geometries; matter-wave dephasing and quantum chaos. Coherent control; diffractive imaging.

Wu, Shiwei, (吴施伟) Ph.D., University of California, 2007. Scanning probe microscopy and spectroscopy; surface science; nano optics; ultrafast dynamics; ultrafast dynamics; scientific instrumentation.

Wu, Yizheng, (吴义政) Ph.D., Fudan University, 2001. *Condensed Matter Physics*. Experimental condense matter physics; magnetism; spintronics.

Wu, Yongshi, (吴咏时) M.S., Peking University, 1965. Distinguished Professor, Department of Physics and Astronomy, University of Utah. *Condensed Matter Physics, Particles and Fields, Quantum Foundations, Statistical & Thermal Physics, Theoretical Physics*. Prof. Wu is interested in topological, geometric, and algebraic structures underlying the fundamental laws in physics that unifies all matter and forces in Nature, as well as emergent phenomena in fundamental physics and strongly correlated systems. His fields over quantum field theory, particle physics, statistical physics, String/M theory, topological matter and topological quantum computation, an emergent interdisciplinary research frontier of physics, mathematics and computer science.

Xiang, Hongjun, (向红军) Ph.D., University of Science and Technology of China, 2006. *Computational Physics, Condensed Matter Physics, Nano Science and Technology*. Computational condensed matter physics; multiferroics, nanomaterials, photovoltaic materials, development of new methods.

Xiao, Jiang, (肖江) Ph.D., Georgia Institute of Technology, 2006. *Condensed Matter Physics*. Theoretical condensed matter physics, spintronics, magnetism.

Xiao, Yanhong, (肖艳红) Ph.D., Harvard University, 2004. *Optics*. Experimental Atomic Molecular and Optical (AMO) physics: coherent interaction between atoms and light, precision spectroscopy, quantum memory, magnetometry, atomic frequency standards and quantum optics.

Xiu, Faxian, (修发贤) Ph.D., University of California, Riverside, 2007. *Condensed Matter Physics*. Study of novel topological thin films and nanostructures by molecular beam epitaxy and tube furnaces. Integration of magnetic materials with topological insulators for novel device functionalities. Exploration of high Curie temperature dilute magnetic semiconductors and their spintronic application.

Yan, Hugen, (晏湖根) Ph.D., Columbia University, 2010. *Nano Science and Technology, Optics*. Ourinterests consist of the study of novel low-dimensional materialsby optical spectroscopy techniques, with a major focus ongraphene photonics and plasmonics. Our expertise in versatileoptical techniques ranging from single nano-object Rayleighscattering, Raman scattering and time-resolved pump-probemeasurements to terahertz time-domain spectroscopy, FTIR basedbroad-band linear spectroscopy and magneto-optics, equips us topursue many exciting and far-reaching projects. In the pursuit ofboth fundamental understanding and manipulating of the optical response of the novel materials, our group in.

Yang, Xinju, (杨新菊) Ph.D., Fudan University, 1994. *Condensed Matter Physics*. Quantum structure fabrications and nanoscale electrical property studies.

Yang, Zhongqin, (杨中芹) Ph.D., Fudan University, 2000. *Condensed Matter Physics*. Theoretical Condensed Matter Physics (1) Quantum charge and spin transport in nanojunctions. (2) Electronic states of novel materials. (3) Effects of spin-out coupling.

Yin, Lifeng, (殷立峰) Ph.D., Fudan University, 2007. *Condensed Matter Physics*. Spintronics, Nanomagnetism, Complex Oxides under Spatial Confinement, Surface and Interface of Complex Oxides.

Yu, Yue, (虞跃) Ph.D., Zhejiang University, 1987. *Condensed Matter Physics, Quantum Foundations, Theoretical Physics*. Theoretical condensed matter physics and quantum field theory. Our main focus is on low-dimensional strongly correlated many body systems, including fractional quantum Hall effects, topological states of matter, quantum fractional statistics and topological quantum computation, quantum simulation of strongly correlated systems, high-energy systems and exactly solvable models by cold atoms.

Zhang, Tong, (张童) Ph.D., Institute of Physics, Chinese Academy of Sciences, 2010. *Condensed Matter Physics*. Experimental condensed matter physics. We study complex quantum materials, including correlated systems, cuprate and iron based superconductors, charge/spin/orbital ordered systems, and oxide interfaces etc. with synchrotron & laser-based spectroscopy and scattering techniques.

Zhang, Xinyi, (张新夷) Ph.D., Universite Pierre et Marie Curie, 1981. *Condensed Matter Physics*. Luminescence dynamics and novel materials. Synchrotron radiation applications.

Zhang, Yuanbo, (张远波) Ph.D., Columbia University, 2006. *Condensed Matter Physics*. Experimental condensed matter physics, particularly the electronic properties of graphene and other low-dimensional electron systems.

Zhao, Jun, (赵俊) Ph.D., University of Tennessee, 2010. Using various neutron and X-ray scattering techniques to study the strongly correlated electron systems. Specific interest includes high Tc superconductors, multiferroics, and other transition metal oxides.

Zhao, Li, (赵利) Ph.D., Harbin Institute of Technology, 1994. *Optics*. Black silicon, microstructured metal films.

Zheng, Changlin, (郑长林) Ph.D., Humboldt University of Berlin, 2009. *Condensed Matter Physics, Materials Science, Metallurgy, Optics, Surface Physics*. Developing and applying advanced electron microscopy techniques to solve problems in condensed matter physics and material science. TEM techniques: Aberration corrected TEM/STEM, scanning confocal electron microscopy (SCEM), EELS and EDX, DPC, electron holography and Lorentz microscopy, ptychography, coherent CBED, electron phase modulation and beam shaping (Bessel beam, Airy beam...).

Zhong, Zhengyang, (钟振扬) Ph.D., Institute of Physics, Chinese Academy of Sciences, 2001. *Condensed Matter Physics*. Controlled formation of varieties of nanostructures on Si substrates; exploration of the unique properties and the applications of Si-based nanostructures.

Zhou, Lei, (周磊) Ph.D., Fudan University, 1997. *Optics, Theoretical Physics*. Metamaterials, nanophotonics, magnetism.

Zhou, Luwei, (周鲁卫) Ph.D., Temple University, 1986. *Condensed Matter Physics*. Soft matter physics.

Zhu, Huangjun, (朱黄俊) Ph.D., National University of Singapor, 2012. *Quantum Foundations, Theoretical Physics*. Quantum information and quantum computation. Specific interests include quantum measurements, quantum tomography, quantum metrology, and state verification; blind and cloud quantum computation; quantum entanglement and nonlocal correlations; foundations of quantum physics; mathematical physics.

Zi, Jian, (资剑) Ph.D., Fudan University, 1991. *Condensed Matter Physics, Optics*. Photonic crystals, plasmonics, metamaterials, natural photonic structures and structural colors, liquid surface waves propagating in periodic structures.

Associate Professor

Cai, Qun, (蔡群) Ph.D., Fudan University, 1996. *Condensed Matter Physics, Surface Physics*. Surface and interface structured studied with scanning probe microsocpy; formation and properties of metal nano-structures on semiconductor surfaces; kinetics of surface atomic processes; ultrathin dielectric films on semiconductor surfaces.

Chen, Junyi, (陈骏逸) Fudan University, 1985. *Physics and other Science Education*. Physics and other Science Education.

Du, Side, (杜四德) Ph.D., Nanjing University, 1995. *Physics and other Science Education, Theoretical Physics*. Physics and other Science Education.

Huang, Xuguang, (黄旭光) Ph.D., Tsinghua University, 2008. *Particles and Fields, Theoretical Physics*. Phase structure of QCD at nite density and temperature, and physics related to heavy-ion collisions and neutron stars. Superfuidity in nuclear matter and cold Fermi atoms. Relativistic hydrodynamics.

Ji, Min, (冀敏) Henan Normal University, 1981. *Physics and other Science Education*. Physics and other Science Education.

Li, Wei, (李炜) Ph.D., Fudan University, 2013. *Condensed Matter Physics, Theoretical Physics*. Condensed matter physics, including theory, simulation, and thin films deposition. Recent studies focus on exploring exotic quantum states in artificial interface.

Li, Xiaopeng, (李晓鹏) Ph.D., University of Pittsburgh, 2013. *Atomic, Molecular, & Optical Physics, Theoretical Physics*. Theoretical Atomic, Molecular, and Optical physics. We perform theoretical research at the interface of quantum atomic, molecular and optical physics, condensed matter, and quantum information. The physical systems of our interest include long-range interacting atomic systems—dipolar gases and Rydberg atoms, atomic Bose-Fermi mixtures, laser-driven electrons and artificial neural networks. We aim for exotic quantum physics and ground-breaking quantum technologies.

Lv, Jinglin, (吕景林) Jilin Univeristy of Technology, 1983. *Physics and other Science Education*. Physics and other Science Education.

Marciano, Antonino, (Antonino Marciano) Ph.D., University of Rome, 2008. *Cosmology & String Theory, Quantum Foundations, Theoretical Physics*. Early cosmology, inflation, dark energy, quantum comsology and quantum gravity, quantum gravity phenomenology.

Nawata, Satoshi, (Satoshi Nawata) Ph.D., University of Wisconsin-Milwaukee, 2008. *Quantum Foundations, Theoretical Physics*. I am interested in mathematical structure hidden behind dynamics of M5-branes. Although the world-volume theory on M5-branes remains mysterious, it generates huge classes of quantum field theories in various dimensions. I would like to understand intriguing connections of supersymmetric gauge theories, topological quantum field theories, mathematical physics and string theory via dynamics of M5-branes.

Shi, Lei, (石磊) Ph.D., Fudan University, 2010. *Atomic, Molecular, & Optical Physics, Condensed Matter Physics, Optics*. Micro- and Nano- Photonics materials, Light-Matter Interaction.

Shu, Lei, (殳蕾) Ph.D., University of California, Riverside, 2008. Muon spin relaxation/rotation, quantum criticality; non-Fermi-liquid phenomena, magnetism and superconductivity in correlated electron system, high temperature superconductivity.

Tan, Peng, (谭鹏) Ph.D., Fudan University, 2010. *Condensed Matter Physics*. Develop a new method for bond order analysis and apply it to illustrate kinetic pathways in colloidal crystallization.

Xu, Jianjun, (徐建军) Ph.D., Fudan University, 1988. *Astronomy, Astrophysics, Physics and other Science Education*. Physics and other Science Education.

Xu, Xiaohua, (徐晓华) Ph.D., Nanjing University, 1996. *Physics and other Science Education*. Physics and other Science Education.

Zhou, Yang, (周洋) Ph.D., Institute of Theoretical Physics, Chinese Academy of Sciences, 2011. *High Energy Physics, Theoretical Physics*. Theoretic high energy physics. My current interests are non-perturbative aspects of quantum field theory in various dimensions and their applications in particle physics, string theory and condensed matter physics. My recent works include information-theoretic structure of quantum field theory and supersymmetric Rényi entropy/BPS hyperbolic black hole correspondence.

Zuo, Guanghong, (左光宏) Ph.D., Fudan University, 2010. *Biophysics, Theoretical Physics*. Biophysics, Theoretical Physics.

Assistant Professor

He, Qiong, (何琼) Ph.D., University Paris XI, 2008. *Atomic, Molecular, & Optical Physics, Optics*. Metamaterials and Plasmonics.

Lou, Jie, (娄捷) Ph.D., Boston University, 2009. *Theoretical Physics*. Theoretical condensed matter physics. We use unbiased numerical method to study strongly correlated system in condensed matter physics. We are interested in quantum magnets (frustrated/non-frustrated), quantum phase transitions and strongly correlated electronic systems. Methods we use includes quantum Monte Carlo, Multi-scale entanglement renormalization ansatz (MERA), and other tensor network based methods. We combine Grassman algebra and tensor network to study fermionic system unbiased.

Zhou, Shiyun, (周诗韵) Ph.D., Fudan University, 2014. *Physics and other Science Education.* Physics and other Science Education.

Adjunct Professor

Shen, Xuechu, (沈学础) M.A., Fudan University, 1958. *Nano Science and Technology.* Solid State Spectroscopy, methods and physics. Recently interested in electronic states and quantum interactions in nano-sized single quantum structures, such as wires and dot, also chaotic motion of electrons in solid state environment.

Yang, Fujia, (杨福家) Fudan University, 1958. *Atomic, Molecular, & Optical Physics, Nuclear Physics.* Atomic physics, beam physics.

DEPARTMENTAL RESEARCH SPECIALTIES AND STAFF

Theoretical

Condensed Matter Physics. Quantum spin system with spin-dependent scattering, low-dimensional correlated electron systems, wave propagation of photonic crystals and electromagnetic exotic materials, first-principles study of low-dimensional and nano structures, quantum information and computing, electronic transmission in nano-structure, ultracold atomic systems. Jingguang Che, Xingao Gong, Xiaoyuan Hou, Shiyan Li, Ruibao Tao, Zhensheng Tao, Xun Wang, Hongjun Xiang, Jiang Xiao, Zhongqin Yang, Xinyi Zhang.

Gravitation, Cosmology and Black Hole Physics. General relativity, black hole physics and cosmology, quantum physics and quantum information, specific media electromagnetic physics, soft matter theory. Cosimo Bambi, Yongshi Wu.

Partical Physics. Particle physics and field theory. Yu Shi, Yidun Wan, Yongshi Wu, Jiang Xiao, Zhongqin Yang, Yang Zhou, Huangjun Zhu.

Theoretical Physics. Cosimo Bambi, Gang Chen, Yan Chen, Bailin Hao, Jiping Huang, Xiaopeng Li, Zhifang Lin, Yongli Ma, Antonino Marciano, Satoshi Nawata, Weidong Sheng, Yu Shi, Ruibao Tao, Changqin Wu, Hua Wu, Yongshi Wu, Hongjun Xiang, Jiang Xiao, Zhongqin Yang, Yue Yu, Lei Zhou, Huangjun Zhu, Guanghong Zuo.

Experimental

Condensed Matter and Material Physics. Semiconductor surface and interface, semiconductor quantum dots and nano-structure, low-dimensional magnetism and spintronics, strongly correlated electron systems, photonic crystals and electromagnetic metamaterials, synchrotron radiation applications, organic light-emitting and solar cells. Qun Cai, Zhanghai Chen, Donglai Feng, Chunlei Gao, Xiaoyuan Hou, Zuimin Jiang, Xiaofeng Jin, Shiyan Li, Weitao Liu, Xiaohan Liu, Fang Lu, Jian Shen, Weidong Sheng, Lei Shu, Xun Wang, Yizheng Wu, Faxian Xiu, Lifeng Yin, Tong Zhang, Xinyi Zhang, Yuanbo Zhang, Jun Zhao, Zhengyang Zhong, Jian Zi.

Optics. Applications of quantum dots and nano-materials in biological systems, surface photophysics, femtosecond micro-machining and surface modification, nano-materials, study of ultrafast photophysical and nonlinear optical properties in new materials like organic materials and biological systems. Zhanghai Chen, Qiong He, Minbiao Ji, Zhifang Lin, Weitao Liu, Xiaohan Liu, Yuanrang Shen, Weidong Sheng, Lei Shi, Yanwen Tan, Zhensheng Tao, Chuanshan Tian, Saijun Wu, Shiwei Wu, Yanhong Xiao, Hugen Yan, Xinju Yang, Li Zhao, Lei Zhou, Jian Zi.

Physical Biology. Physical biology, bioinformatics and computational biology, economical physics. Wei Chen, Minbiao Ji, Peng Tan, Yanwen Tan, Guanghong Wei, Guanghong Zuo.

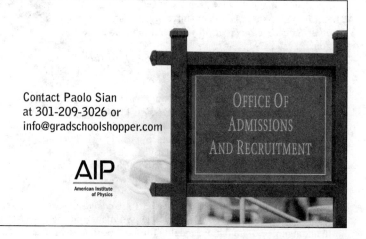

NATIONAL UNIVERSITY OF IRELAND GALWAY

SCHOOL OF PHYSICS

Galway, H91CF50
http://www.nuigalway.ie/physics/

General University Information
President: Ciarán Ó hÓgartaigh
Dean of Graduate School: Prof Donal Leech
University website: http://nuigalway.ie
School Type: Public
Setting: Urban
Total Faculty: 500
Total number of Students: 18,000

Department Information
Department Chairman: Dr. Gerard O'Connor, Head
Department Contact: Dr Mark Foley, Academic Director
  Female Full-Time Graduate Students: 0

Department Address
University Road
Galway, H91CF50
IRELAND
Phone: 0035391495383
E-mail: mark.foley@nuigalway.ie
Website: http://www.nuigalway.ie/physics/

ADMISSIONS

Admission Contact Information

Application deadlines
Fall admission:
U.S. students: July 1   *Int'l. students*: July 1

Admission requirements
Bachelor's degree requirements: Bachelor's degree in physics
  or a related field.

GRE requirements
The GRE is recommended but not required.

Subjective GRE requirements
The Subjective GRE is recommended.

TOEFL requirements
The TOEFL exam is recommended for students from non-
  English-speaking countries.

FINANCIAL AID

Loans
Loans are available for U.S. students.
Loans are available for international students.
GAPSFAS application required: No
FAFSA application required: Yes

Table A—Faculty, Enrollments, and Degrees Granted

Research Specialty	Faculty	Enrollment Fall 2017		Number of Degrees Granted		
		Master's	Doctorate	Master's	Terminal Master's	Doctorate
Astronomical Instrumentation and Technology	–	5	–	–	–	–
Key Enabling Technologies	–	5	–	–	–	–
Medical Physics	–	21	–	–	–	–
Occupational and Environmental Health and Safety	–	10	–	–	–	–
Total	–	–	–	–	–	–
Full-time Grad. Stud.	–	–	–	–	–	–
First-year Grad. Stud.	–	–	–	–	–	–

SPECIAL EQUIPMENT, FACILITIES, OR PROGRAMS

This MSc programme is designed to meet the demand for qualified medical physicists. It is primarily geared toward training for physicists in the application of radiation physics in medicine but maintains a reasonable exposure to key aspects of clinical engineering so that students receive a comprehensive knowledge of the application of the physical sciences and engineering to medicine.

The course is unique in that it is closely integrated with the University Hospital Galway.

The majority of lectures and course materials are delivered by hospital staff.

The course provides a unique opportunity to see the operation of a busy academic hospital.

September 2015: National University of Ireland Galway's MSc in Medical Physics is the first European MSc programme to be awarded accreditation from the Commission on Accreditation of Medical Physics Education Programmes (CAMPEP) and the second programme worldwide.

Appendix I
Geographic Listing of Departments
UNITED STATES

INTERNATIONAL

Appendix II
Alphabetical Listing of Departments

for Undergraduate Physics Students & their Mentors

Take charge of your career by using the resources and tools in
AIP's Career Toolbox
for Undergraduate Physics Students:

Identify and articulate your strengths	Craft a resume	Hone your interview skills
Write cover letters	Find jobs, research and internships	Network And more!

spsnational.org/career-resources